LAS	linear alkylate sulfonate	OTO	orthotolidine-oxalic acid
lb	pound(s)	oz	ounce(s)
LC	lethal concentration	pc	picocurie(s); 10^{-12} curie(s) $= 2.22$ dpm
LD	lethal dose		
		ppb	part(s) per billion; 10^9
μ	micron(s)	ppm	part(s) per million
μa	microampere(s)	psi	pound(s) per square inch
μc	microcurie(s)	pt	pint(s)
M	molar		
m	meter(s)	qt	quart(s)
me	milliequivalent(s)	rpm	revolution(s) per minute
mev	milliequivalent volt(s)	SCE	saturated calomel electrode
mg	milligram(s)		
mgd	million gallon(s) daily	SDI	sludge density index
min	minute(s)	Sec.	section(s)
ml	milliliter(s)	sec	second(s)
MLD	minimum lethal dose	sp gr	specific gravity
mm	millimeter(s)	sq cm	square centimeter(s)
MPN	most probable number(s)	sq ft	square foot (feet)
mv	millivolt(s)	sq in.	square inch(es)
mμ	millimicron(s)	sq mm	square millimeter(s)
		ST, $\mathbf{\mathcal{S}}$	standard taper
N	normal	SVI	sludge volume index
NBS	National Bureau of Standards	TL	tolerance limit
nc	nanocurie(s); 10^{-9} curies $= 1,000$ pc	TL$_m$	median tolerance limit
		T.O.	threshold odor number(s)
No.	number		
		USP	United States Pharma-copoeia
O.D.	outside diameter		
OII	odor intensity index unit(s)	v	volt(s)
OTA	orthotolidine-arsenite	w	watt(s)
OTM	orthotolidine-manganese sulfate	WPCF	Water Pollution Control Federation

Standard Methods

FOR THE EXAMINATION OF

Water and Wastewater

Including Bottom Sediments and Sludges

Prepared and Published Jointly by

AMERICAN PUBLIC HEALTH ASSOCIATION
AMERICAN WATER WORKS ASSOCIATION
WATER POLLUTION CONTROL FEDERATION

TWELFTH EDITION

Publication Office

AMERICAN PUBLIC HEALTH ASSOCIATION, INC.
1790 Broadway, New York, N.Y. 10019

Library of Congress Catalog Card Number 55-1979

PRINTED IN UNITED STATES OF AMERICA BY
BOYD PRINTING CO., INC., ALBANY, N.Y.

PREFACE TO THE TWELFTH EDITION

During the past 60 years, eleven editions of *Standard Methods* have been published following the first in 1905. 1965 marks the appearance of the 12th Edition, a culmination of all the previous volumes. During this period each new edition has encompassed significant developments and changes in methods for the examination of water and wastewater, with enlargement of the scope of each manual to include the pertinent methods required for analysis of the many types of water, wastewater and related materials encountered in the control of sanitation and water quality.

A brief historical review of the progress of *Standard Methods* over these 60 years is of interest.

A movement for "securing the adoption of more uniform and efficient methods of water analysis" led in the 1880's to the organization of a special committee of the Chemical Section of the American Association for the Advancement of Science. A report of this committee, published in 1889, was entitled: "A Method, in Part, for the Sanitary Examination of Water, and for the Statement of Results, Offered for General Adoption." * Five topics were covered: (1) "free" and "albuminoid" ammonia; (2) oxygen-consuming capacity; (3) total nitrogen as nitrates and nitrites; (4) nitrogen as nitrites; and (5) statement of results.

In 1895, members of the American Public Health Association, recognizing the need for standard methods in the bacteriologic examination of water, sponsored a convention of bacteriologists to discuss the problem. As a result, an APHA committee was appointed "to draw up procedures for the study of bacteria in a uniform manner and with special references to the differentiation of species." Submitted in 1897, † the procedures found wide acceptance.

In 1899, APHA appointed a Committee on Standard Methods of Water Analysis, charged with the extention of standard procedures to all methods involved in the analysis of water. The report of this committee, published in 1905, constituted the first edition of *Standard Methods* (then titled "Standard

---

* *J. Anal. Chem.* 3:398 (1889).
† *Proc. APHA* 23:56 (1897).

Methods of Water Analysis"). Physical, chemical, microscopic, and bacteriologic methods of water examination were included. In its letter of transmittal, the committee stated:

> The methods of analysis presented in this report as "Standard Methods" are believed to represent the best current practice of American water analysts, and to be generally applicable in connection with the ordinary problems of water purification, sewage disposal and sanitary investigations. Analysts working on widely different problems manifestly cannot use methods which are identical, and special problems obviously require the methods best adapted to them; but, while recognizing these facts, it yet remains true that sound progress in analytical work will advance in proportion to the general adoption of methods which are reliable, uniform and adequate.
>
> It is said by some that standard methods within the field of applied science tend to stifle investigations, and that they retard true progress. If such standards are used in the proper spirit, this ought not to be so. The committee strongly desires that every effort shall be continued to improve the techniques of water analysis and especially to compare current methods with those herein recommended, where different, so that the results obtained may be still more accurate and reliable than they are at present.

Revised and enlarged editions were published by APHA under the title "Standard Methods of Water Analysis" in 1912 (second edition), 1917 (third), 1920 (fourth), and 1923 (fifth). In 1925, the American Water Works Association joined APHA in publishing the sixth edition, which employed the more inclusive title, "Standard Methods for the Examination of Water and Sewage." Joint publication was continued in the seventh edition, dated 1933.

In 1935, the Water Pollution Control Federation (then the Federation of Sewage Works Associations) issued a committee report on "Standard Methods of Sewage Analysis." * With minor modifications, these methods were incorporated into the eighth edition (1936) of *Standard Methods*, which was thus the first to provide methods for the examination of "sewages, effluents, industrial wastes, grossly polluted waters, sludges, and muds." The ninth edition, appearing in 1946, likewise contained these methods, and, in the following year, the Federation became a full-fledged publishing partner. Since 1947, the work of the *Standard Methods* committees of the three associations—APHA, AWWA, and WPCF— has been coordinated by a Joint Editorial Board on which all three are represented.

The tenth edition, 1955, included specific methods for the examination of waterborne industrial wastes, and this was reflected by the new title: "Standard Methods for the Examination of Water, Sewage and Industrial Wastes."

---

* Sew. Works J. 7:444 (1935).

In order to describe more accurately and concisely the contents of the eleventh edition, the title was changed to "Standard Methods for the Examination of Water and Wastewater." This same title has been continued for this, the twelfth edition.

The Twelfth Edition

In preparing each new edition, the criteria for selecting the analytical procedures to be included have invariably been a major topic for discussion. Should *Standard Methods* include only comparatively simple procedures applicable to the control of treatment processes; or should it contain also techniques that are useful primarily for research and comparable investigations, and that may require complex costly equipment, as well as a high degree of skill and training on the part of the analyst?

An increasing number of larger larboratories have been placing greater reliance on instrumental methods. Concurrent with this trend this twelfth edition offers for the first time ultraviolet spectrophotometric, spectrographic, and gas chromatographic methods. Future editions will doubtless witness an extension of this emphasis.

The need for simple control methods for the operation of treatment facilities has not been overlooked. Accordingly, control procedures are given for each determination, along with the more complex techniques, where available. The distinguishing features, advantages, limitations, and applicability of alternative techniques for a determination are discussed under "selection of method" in each case. Careful study of the introductory material preceding most of the method descriptions will make possible the selection of the appropriate technique.

The twelfth edition continues the division into nine parts:

I—Physical and Chemical Examination of Natural and Treated Waters in the Absence of Gross Pollution

II—Methods for the Examination of Water and Wastewater for Radioactivity

III—Physical and Chemical Examination of Wastewater, Treatment Plant Effluents, and Polluted Waters

IV—Physical and Chemical Examination of Industrial Wastewaters

V—Physical and Chemical Examination of Sludge and Bottom Sediments in Wastewater Treatment Processes and in Polluted Rivers, Lakes and Estuaries

VI—Bioassay Methods for the Evaluation of Acute Toxicity of Industrial Wastewaters and Other Substances to Fish

VII—Routine Bacteriologic Examinations of Water to Determine Its Sanitary Quality

VIII—Methods for Detection and Isolation of Iron and Sulfur Bacteria

IX—Biologic Examination of Water, Wastewater Sludge, and Bottom Materials

"Tentative" methods for measuring gross alpha, gross beta, total strontium and strontium-90 radioactivity were continued in the previous (11th) edition. The adoption of radiation protection standards by the Federal Radiation Council and recommendations contained in the 1962 revisions of the Public Health Service Drinking Water Standards focused attention on the need of methods for radioactivity measurements.

Following a program of testing and evaluation, "tentative" methods were modified for gross beta, strontium-90, and a new "tentative" technique for total radium (by precipitation) was accepted. A "tentative" method was approved for the determination of radium-226 by radon measurement and the "tentative" methods for gross alpha and total strontium in the eleventh edition were retained. The principal change in the gross beta measurement was the adoption of cesium-137 as calibrating radionuclide and restricting the technique to the counting of thinly spread samples in efficient thin-window or internal proportional counters.

Three parts included first in the eleventh edition have been modified to conform to current knowledge and are continued in the twelfth edition—namely, Part II, Methods for the Examination of Water and Wastewater for Radioactivity; Part VI, Bioassay Methods for the Evaluation of Acute Toxicity of Industrial Wastewaters and Other Substances to Fish; and Part VIII, Methods for Detection and Isolation of Iron and Sulfur Bacteria.

Numerous changes have been made in Part I. Methods appearing for the first time in this edition include the silver diethyldithiocarbamate method for arsenic; the dithizone method for cadmium; the carbon chloroform extract method for organic contaminants; the iodometric, orthotolidine, and amperometric methods for chlorine dioxide; the orthotolidine method for the higher oxidation states of manganese; the ultraviolet spectrophotometric and polarographic methods for nitrate; the direct and distillation methods for selenium with diaminobenzidine reagent; the spectrographic and dithizone colorimetric method for silver; and the zincon colorimetric and polarographic methods for zinc. The flame photometric methods for potassium and sodium, the iodometric method for sulfite, and the introduction to Part I entitled *Industrial Water Supplies* have been completely revised. Important additions will be found in the potentiometric titration for low alkalinity in the alkalinity determination, the EDTA titrimetric method for calcium, the mercurimetric method for chloride, as well as the methods for iron, lead, nitrite, pH, specific conductance, and taste and odor. Advanced from tentative to standard status are the curcumin method for boron, the direct distillation step for fluoride, the SPADNS method for fluoride, and the brucine method for nitrate. Deleted from this edition are the heteropoly blue method for arsenic, the titrimetric method for potassium, and the monocolor dithizone method for zinc.

The following changes are worthy of notice in Part III. A mercurimetric method has replaced the Volhard method for chloride, while a diazotization method and a polarographic method have replaced the aluminum reduction method for nitrate. The determination of relative stability of sewage effluents has been deleted.

In Part IV a new polarographic scanning procedure for metals has been added. With known solutions for calibration curves the technique may be semi-quantitative for specific metals. A complete procedure for odor has been introduced indicating the tremendous complexity of this measurement. The new polarographic procedures for dissolved oxygen with solid metal electrodes are discussed along with the introduction to the dropping mercury electrode. A complete procedure for the solid metal electrodes should be ready for the next edition. A very significant improvement has been made in the chemical oxygen demand technique which eliminates the chloride ion error. The Gibbs method for phenol has been deleted.

In Part V, gas chromatography has been introduced for analyzing digester gases and column chromatography has been substituted for the separation and measurement of volatile acids in digesting mixtures.

The routine biological assay procedure of Part VI has been edited only.

Many suggestions have been received relative to the inclusion in the twelfth edition of a separate section covering methods applicable to the analysis of ocean and brackish waters. At the present time such methods have not been actively developed or studied and thus the establishment of such a section was deferred to be considered for a later edition. Modifications of established procedures for their application to saline water is emphasized in the introductory discussion of each of such techniques.

Recent investigations indicate that the portion of the coliform group which is present in the feces of warm-blooded animals generally include organisms which are capable of producing gas from lactose in a suitable culture medium at $44.5 \pm 0.5°C$. Both the multiple-tube dilution technique and the membrane filter procedure have been modified to include incubation of confirmatory tests at $35°C$ and $44.5°C$ to provide estimates of the density of both fecal and nonfecal organisms, as defined, in the sample under consideration. The investigations cited suggest that this differentiation will yield valuable information relative to the possible source of pollution in water, and especially the remoteness of this pollution, since the *nonfecal* members of the coliform group may be expected to survive longer than the *fecal* members, again as defined above, in the unfavorable environment provided by the water.

The twelfth edition retains the General Introduction with its important information concerning the proper execution of the procedures described in the various parts of the manual. The section dealing with the quality of the required chemical reagents has been expanded. The number of common acid and alkali concentrations has been maintained at a practical minimum. The bibliography has been updated and enlarged. The Joint Editorial Board strongly urges every reader to carefully study the General Introduction as well as the introduction to the various parts of the manual. Each introduction discusses vital matters of wide application within its specific province in order to minimize repetition throughout the succeeding text. The success of the analysis may well rest on the manner in which the recommendations in the various pertinent introductions are carried out. The same precaution holds true with respect to individual determinations. The complete discussion of each procedure embracing selection of method, sampling and storage, general discussion, and interference, should be read and fully understood before the preparation of the necessary reagents is undertaken.

The methods as included in each edition are the best available and generally accepted procedures for the analysis of water and wastewaters. They, therefore, are the recognized basis for the control and evaluation of research activities.

Obviously, many of the procedures are in need of more intensive investigation of their sensitivity, precision and accuracy, and general applicability. Such research is continually under way, as is evidenced by the improved techniques given in the 12th and, in fact, in all previous editions.

Status of Methods

As in its predecessor, all methods in the twelfth edition are "'standard" unless designated "tentative"; no other category is employed. Methods with "standard" status have been extensively studied and accepted as applicable within the limits of sensitivity, precision, and accuracy recorded. "Tentative" methods are those still under investigation which have not yet been fully evaluated or are not considered sufficiently specific at present to be designated "standard".

Many of the methods in this manual have been studied and checked through the Analytical Reference Service, Robert A. Taft Sanitary Engineering Center, U. S. Public Health Service, under the direction of Harry P. Kramer. Statistical evidence has thereby been obtained concerning the reliability and application of these techniques.

Technical progress makes advisable the establishment of a program to maintain *Standard Methods* abreast of advances in research and general practice. The Joint Editorial Board has developed the following procedure for effecting interim changes in methods between editions of the manual:

1. Any method given "tentative" status in the current edition may be elevated to "standard" by action of the Joint Editorial Board, based on adequate published data supporting such a change as submitted to the Board by the committee concerned with the part of the manual in which the method is included. Notification of such a change in status shall be accomplished by publication in the official journals of the three associations sponsoring *Standard Methods.*

2. No method having "standard" status may be deleted or reduced to "tentative" status during the interval between editions.

3. A new method may be adopted as "tentative" or "standard" by the Joint Editorial Board between editions, such action being based on adequate published data as submitted by the committee concerned with the part of the manual in which the method will be included. Upon adoption, the details of the method, together with a resume of the supporting data, shall be published in the official journal of any one of the three sponsoring associations, and reprints shall be made available at a nominal charge. Notice of such publication and of the availability of reprints shall appear in the official journals of the other two sponsors.

During the five-year period since the publication of the eleventh edition several methods have been added and others elevated from "tentative" status to "standard", thus demonstrating the continued progress in the study of methods and the value of those procedures for maintaining each edition in conformity to scientific advances.

Acknowledgments

For the major portion of the work in preparing and revising the methods in the twelfth edition, the Joint Editorial Board gives full credit to the *Standard Methods* committees of the three association sponsors. A list of the personnel of these committees, and their advisors, follows this preface.

The drawings of the biological organisms encountered in water and wastewaters were prepared by Mrs. A. L. Juneau, formerly Staff Artist, Department of Biology, University of Florida. The courtesy of the U. S. Public Health Service in permitting inclusion in the twelfth edition of the color plates of certain typical microorganisms is gratefully acknowledged, as is also the work of Dr. Mervin Palmer of the U.S.P.H.S. in preparing the key to these plates. These features should prove a valuable aid in the identification of such organisms occurring in water and wastewaters.

The Board expresses its appreciation to Berwyn F. Mattison, M.D., Executive Director, American Public Health Association; Raymond J. Faust, Executive Secretary, and Eric F. Johnson, Director of Publications, American Water Works Association; and Ralph E. Fuhrman, Dr. Eng., Secretary-Editor, Water Pollution Control Federation, for their continuous cooperation and helpful advice. George Kupchik, Dr. Eng., Director of Environmental Health, American Public Health Association, has capably handled the production details and the myriad of other tasks incidental to the preparation of another edition of *Standard Methods*.

Special recognition for his great services is due Herbert P. Orland, Editor of the twelfth edition, who has most efficiently carried out the editorial responsibilities upon which a completed volume depends.

AMERICAN WATER WORKS ASSOCIATION

Committee on Standard Methods for the Examination of Water and Wastewater

MICHAEL J. TARAS, *Chairman*
CLAYTON M. BACH
DWIGHT G. BALLINGER
E. ROBERT BAUMANN
ELWOOD L. BEAN
A. P. BLACK
RUSSELL F. CHRISTMAN
JESSE M. COHEN
JOSEPH J. CONNORS
JAMES N. DORNBUSH
DONALD T. DUKE
JOHN F. DYE
DARYL W. EBERT
JOSEPH F. ERDEI
RALPH F. FALKENTHAL
SAMUEL D. FAUST
JOSEPH G. FILICKY
RUSSELL E. FRAZIER
ROLAND L. GIUSTI
EUGENE GOLDMAN
ARNOLD E. GREENBERG
PAUL D. HANEY
SIDNEY A. HANNAH
LAUREL M. HENLEY
RICHARD R. HENDERSON
JAMES J. HICKEY
JOHN H. HUBBLE
ROBERT S. INGOLS
JOHN F. KEGEBEIN
HARRY P. KRAMER
ROBERT C. KRONER
RUSSELL W. LANE

THURSTON E. LARSON
HARRY F. LAUGHLIN
G. FRED LEE
LESTER L. LOUDEN
FRANZ J. MAIER
DELOSS M. MATHESON
FRANCIS M. MIDDLETON
ROBERT L. MORRIS
J. W. MURPHREY
REMO NAVONE
M. STARR NICOLS
MORRIS NUSSBAUM
JAMES E. O'BRIEN
HAROLD E. PEARSON
CHARLES I. PIERCE
RICHARD D. POMEROY
MERRILL L. RIEHL
WALTER C. RINGER, JR.
REED S. ROBERTSON
AARON A. ROSEN
JOHN R. ROSSUM
ROBERT W. SCHMIDT
KENNETH E. SHULL
MARVIN W. SKOUGSTAD
ROLF T. SKRINDE
OWEN SLETTEN
LEE STREICHER
WERNER STUMM
SIDNEY SUSSMAN
JAMES C. VAUGHN
PAUL J. WEAVER, JR.
FOYMAE KELSO WEST

JOHN FREDERICK WILKES

xi

WATER POLLUTION CONTROL FEDERATION

Committee on Standard Methods for the Examination of Water and Wastewater

ADVISORS

The valued assistance of the following, nonmembers of the various committees, is acknowledged by the Joint Editorial Board

CONTENTS

PART II
Methods for the Examination of Water and Wastewater for Radioactivity

PART III
Physical and Chemical Examination of Wastewater, Treatment Plant Effluents, and Polluted Waters

PART IV

Physical and Chemical Examination of Industrial Wastewaters

PART V

Physical and Chemical Examination of Sludge and Bottom Sediments in Wastewater Treatment Process and in Polluted Rivers, Lakes, and Estuaries

PART VI

Bioassay Methods for the Evaluation of Acute Toxicity of Industrial Wastewaters and Other Substances to Fish

PART VII

Routine Bacteriologic Examinations of Water to Determine Its Sanitary Quality

PART VIII

Methods for Detection and Isolation of Iron and Sulfur Bacteria

PART IX

Biologic Examination of Water, Wastewater Sludge, and Bottom Materials

TABLES

FIGURES

Plates

Color Plates

General Introduction

A. Laboratory Apparatus, Reagents, and Techniques

1. Containers

For general laboratory use, the most suitable material for containers is resistant borosilicate glass, commonly called "pyrex." * Special glasses are available with such characteristics as high resistance to alkali attack, low boron content, or exclusion of light. Stoppers, caps, and plugs should be chosen to resist the attack of material contained in the vessel. Cork stoppers wrapped with a relatively inert metal foil are suitable for many samples. Metal screw caps are a poor choice for any sample that will cause them to corrode readily. Glass stoppers are unsatisfactory for strongly alkaline liquids because of their tendency to stick fast. Rubber stoppers are excellent for alkaline liquids but very poor for organic solvents in which they swell or disintegrate. Teflon or silver plugs may be obtained for burets which are to be used for strongly alkaline liquids. For particular purposes, other materials such as porcelain, nickel, iron, platinum, stainless steel, and Vycor † can be employed to advantage.

It is recommended that samples be collected and stored in bottles made of pyrex, hard rubber, polyethylene, or other inert material.

For relatively short storage periods, or for constituents which are not affected by storage in soft glass, such as calcium, magnesium, sulfate, chloride, and perhaps others, the newer type of 2.5-liter acid bottle, "bell closure," is satisfactory. This type of closure holds a glass disc against the ground-glass surface of the bottle lip and insures adequate protection for the sample. If part of the sample is to be analyzed at a later date for silica, sodium, or some other substances which would be affected by prolonged storage in soft glass, it may be transferred to a small polyethylene bottle, while the remainder of the sample is left in the soft-glass bottle.

Sample bottles must be carefully cleaned before each use. Glass bottles may be rinsed with a chromic acid cleaning mixture, made by adding 1 liter of conc H_2SO_4 slowly, with stirring, to 35 ml saturated sodium dichromate solution, or with an alkaline permanganate solution followed by an oxalic acid solution. Rinsing with other concentrated acids may be used to remove inorganic matter. The newer detergents are excellent cleansers for many purposes; either detergents or conc HCl can be used for cleaning hard-rubber and polyethylene bottles. After having been cleaned, bottles must be rinsed thoroughly with tap water and then with distilled water.

For shipment, bottles may be packed in wooden, metal, plastic, or heavy fiberboard cases, with a separate compartment for each bottle. Boxes may be lined with corrugated fiber paper, felt, or other resilient material, or may be provided with spring-loaded corner strips, to prevent breakage. Lined wicker baskets may also be used.

---

* As used in this manual, "pyrex" refers not to a specific brand, but to the general type, such as that manufactured by Corning Glass Works (under the name "Pyrex"), or Kimble Glass Co., Division of Owens-Illinois ("Kimax"), or equivalent.

† A high-silica glass product of Corning Glass Works.

Samples stored in polyethylene bottles need no protection against breakage by impact or through freezing.

2. Distilled Water

Some of the colorimetric tests described in this manual are sufficiently sensitive to respond to even the minute traces of impurities which may be found in ordinary distilled water. In such cases, the use of double- or triple-distilled water may be required. The material of which the still is constructed may contribute impurities to the distillate. Most commercial stills, for example, are constructed in part of copper, and distilled water from them frequently contains 0.01 to 0.05 mg/1 Cu. For special purposes, water may be distilled from an all-glass apparatus, or from an apparatus in which the condenser is made of glass, fused quartz, silver, or block tin.

Ordinary distillation of water will not remove ammonia or carbon dioxide; in fact, distilled water is often supersaturated with carbon dioxide because of the decomposition of raw-water bicarbonates to carbonates in the boiler. Ammonia can be removed by distillation from acid solution or by passing the water through a column of mixed resins—see Part I, Nitrogen (Ammonia), Method A, Sec. 3.1. Carbon dioxide can be removed by distillation from a solution containing an excess of alkali hydroxide, by boiling for a few minutes, by vigorously aerating the water with a stream of inert gas for a sufficient period, or by passing the water through a column of strong anion-exchange resin in the hydroxide form. If ammonia and carbon dioxide are present at the same time, boiling and aerating are not effective.

If kept in glass containers, distilled water will slowly leach the more soluble materials from the glass and will increase in total dissolved solids.

Demineralized water from a mixed-bed ion exchanger is satisfactory for many applications in this manual. However, as ion exchange fails to remove such nonelectrolytes and colloids as plankton, nonionic organic materials, and dissolved air, it is not suitable for determinations where such constituents interfere.

A very-high-purity water, with less than 0.1 micromho/cm conductance, can be produced by passing ordinary distilled water through a mixed-bed exchanger—see Part I, Nitrogen (Ammonia), Method A, Sec. 3.1b—and discarding the effluent until the desired quality is obtained. A water prepared in this way is often satisfactory for use in the determination of trace cations and anions.

3. Reagents

It is to be understood that only the best quality of chemical reagents must be employed even though this injunction is not repeated in the description of a particular method. Chemicals for which the American Chemical Society has published specifications should always be ordered in the "ACS grade." Other chemicals should be ordered as "analytical reagent grade." Methods of checking the purity of reagents which are suspect will be found in books of reagent specifications.[21–23]

Unfortunately, many commercial dyes for which no "ACS grade" has been established fail to meet exacting analytical requirements, owing to variations in the color response of different lots. In such cases, dyes certified by the Biological Stain Commission may be satisfactory for chemical analysis.

Where neither the ACS grade nor the certified Biological Stain Commission dye is available, best results will be obtained by purifying the solid dye through recrystallization.

The following standard substances, each bottle of which is accompanied by a certificate of analysis, are issued by the National Bureau of Standards, Department of Commerce, Washington, D.C., for the purpose of standardizing analytical solutions:

Acidimetric:
84e —Acid potassium phthalate
350 —Benzoic acid

Oxidimetric:
40f —Sodium oxalate
83b —Arsenic trioxide
136a —Potassium dichromate

Buffer:
185b —Acid potassium phthalate
186 Ib —Potassium dihydrogen phosphate
186 IIb—Disodium hydrogen phosphate
187a —Borax
188 —Potassium hydrogen tartrate
189 —Potassium tetroxalate

Many hundreds of other standards issued by NBS are described in its Miscellaneous Publication 241.[24]

A successful dithizone test demands reagents of the highest purity. Chloroform and carbon tetrachloride are now commercially available in a grade declared to be suitable for the dithizone methods. Reagents of this quality should be selected preferentially for the several dithizone methods described in this manual.

The general availability of the water-soluble sodium salts of the common indicators at nominal cost has resulted in their predominant recommendation for indicator preparation in this edition.

When alcohol or ethyl alcohol is specified for the preparation of such solutions as phenolphthalein indicator, 95 per cent ethyl alcohol is the reagent of choice, with a similar grade of isopropyl alcohol a permissible alternate.

Certain organic reagents are somewhat unstable upon exposure to the atmosphere. In the event the stability of a chemical is limited or unknown, the purchase of small lots at frequent intervals is suggested.

Many of the chemical reagents prescribed in this book should be treated with the utmost care both in their original state and in the form of solutions. Chemical reagents bearing commercial labels with the words POISON, DANGER, CAUTION, FLAMMABLE, and comparable warnings should be handled with special discretion. In the interest of personal safety the analyst will be well repaid by a study of the manual published by the American Water Works Association [9] and the guide prepared by the Manufacturing Chemists' Association [7] concerning the hazards which may occur in the laboratory.

All anhydrous reagent chemicals required for the preparation of standard calibration solutions and titrants should be dried in an oven at 105° to 110°C for at least 1 to 2 hr and preferably overnight. After cooling to room temperature in an efficient desiccator, the proper amount should promptly be weighed for dissolution. Should a different drying temperature be necessary, a note to this effect is specified for the particular chemical. In the case of hydrated salts, milder drying in an efficient desiccator can be substituted for oven-drying.

4. Common Acid and Alkali Solutions

4.1. *Concentration units used:* Reagent concentrations are expressed in this manual in terms of normality, molarity, and additive volumes.

A *normal solution* contains one gram equivalent weight of solute per liter of solution.

A *molar solution* contains one gram molecular weight of solute per liter of solution.

In additive volumes $(a + b)$, the first number, a, refers to the volume of the concentrated reagent; the second number, b, refers to the volume of distilled water required for dilution. Thus, "$1 + 9$ HCl" denotes that 1 volume of concentrated HCl is to be diluted with 9 volumes of distilled water.

In order to make a solution of exact normality from a chemical which cannot be measured as a primary standard, a relatively concentrated stock solution may first be prepared, and then an exact dilution of this may be made to the desired strength. Another method is to make a solution of slightly stronger concentration than desired, standardize, and then make suitable adjustments in the concentration. Alternatively, the solution may be used as first standardized, with appropriate modification of the factor used in the calculation. This alternative procedure is especially useful in the case of a solution which slowly changes strength —for example, thiosulfate solution, which must be restandardized at frequent intervals. Often, however, adjustment to the exact normality specified is desirable when a laboratory runs a large number of determinations with one standard solution.

As long as the normality of a standard solution does not result in a titration volume so small as to preclude accurate measurement or so large as to cause abnormal dilution of the reaction mixture, and as long as the solution is properly standardized and the calculations are properly made, the determinations can be considered to be in accord with the instructions in this manual.

4.2. *Preparation and dilution of solutions:* If a solution of exact normality is to be prepared by dissolving a weighed amount of a primary standard or by dilution of a stronger solution, it is necessary that the solution be brought up to exact volume in a volumetric flask.

The stock and standard solutions prescribed for the colorimetric determinations in the chemical sections of this manual should also be accurately prepared in volumetric flasks. Where the concentration does not need to be exact, it is often easier to mix the concentrated solution or the solid with measured amounts of water, using graduated cylinders for these measurements. There is usually a significant change of volume when strong solutions are mixed, so that the total volume is less than the sum of the volumes used. For approximate dilutions, the volume changes are negligible when concentrations of $6N$ or less are diluted.

Very thorough and complete mixing is essential when making dilutions. One of the commonest sources of error in analyses using standard solutions diluted in volumetric flasks is failure to attain complete mixing.

4.3. *Storage of solutions:* Some standardized solutions alter slowly because of chemical or biologic changes. The practical life, required frequency of standardizations, or storage precautions will be indicated for such standards. Others, such as dilute hydrochloric acid, are nonreactive. Yet they, too, may change in strength as a result of evaporative processes. Such evaporation is not prevented by a glass stopper. Changes in temperature cause a bottle to "breathe," thus allowing some evaporation. Rarely should a standard be considered valid for more than a year unless it is restandardized, and it is valid for that length of time only if conditions are such that evaporation is minimal. If the bottle is often opened or if it is much less than half full, evaporation may be serious in a few months.

Where glass bottles are called for, these must be of chemically resistant glass. With standard solutions which do not react with rubber or neoprene, it is often advantageous to use stoppers of these materials, because they can, if properly fitted, prevent evaporation as long as the bottle is closed. Screw-cap bottles will also be found useful. If the cap has a gasket of a reasonably resistant material, permissible usage will be about the same as for rubber stoppers.

4.4. *Hydrochloric and sulfuric acid as alternatives:* Dilute standardized sulfuric and hydrochloric acids are called for in various procedures. Often these solutions are interchangeable. Where one is mentioned, the analyst may use the other if he is certain that the substitution will make no difference.

4.5. *Preparation:* Instructions in this manual usually describe the preparation of a liter of solution. A laboratory will frequently find it expedient to prepare a smaller or larger volume. The analyst should consider this and not limit the amount to 1 liter just because the instructions are so written. Sometimes the instructions call for the preparation of 100 ml; the solutions involved either have a short life or are used in small amounts, so that 1 liter would be an excessive amount for any ordinary laboratory. A safe general rule to follow in the preparation of solutions is to add the more concentrated acid or alkali to the water, with stirring, in a vessel which can withstand thermal shock, and then to dilute to the final volume after cooling to room temperature.

4.6. *Uniform acid concentrations:* An attempt has been made in the chemical sections to establish a uniform number of common acid and base concentrations which will serve for the adjustment of the acid and alkaline reaction of samples prior to color development or final titration. The following acid concentrations are recommended for general desk use: the concentrated reagent of commerce, $6N$, $1N$, $0.1N$, and $0.02N$. The preparation of these acid concentrations is presented in Table 1 for easy reference.

4.7. *Uniform sodium hydroxide concentrations:* The following sodium hydroxide concentrations are specified in Part I for general desk applications: $15N$, $6N$, $1N$, $0.1N$, and $0.02N$. The $15N$ sodium hydroxide can be prepared by cautiously dissolving 625 g of solid in 800 ml distilled water to form 1 liter of solution, or by dissolving 454 g in 650 ml distilled water. The solution can be clarified of sodium carbonate precipitate by keeping it at the boiling point for a few hours in a water bath or by letting the particles settle for a few days at room temperature. The following volumes of $15N$ sodium hydroxide can be diluted to 1 liter to form the indicated normalities: 400 ml for $6N$, 67 ml for $1N$, and 6.7 ml for $0.1N$.

As the solid sodium hydroxide absorbs water and carbon dioxide from the atmosphere, these impurities are always assumed to be present. In concentrated solutions, any carbon dioxide present is precipitated quantitatively as

TABLE 1—PREPARATION OF COMMON ACID CONCENTRATIONS USED IN THIS MANUAL *

Item	HCl	H$_2$SO$_4$	HNO$_3$
Specific gravity (20°/4° C) of ACS grade conc acid	1.174–1.189	1.834–1.836	1.409–1.418
Per cent of active ingredient in conc reagent	36–37	96–98	69–70
Normality of conc reagent	11–12	36	15–16
Volume (ml) of conc reagent to prepare 1 liter of:			
18N solution	—	500 (1+1)**	—
6N solution	500 (1+1)**	167 (1+5)**	380
1N solution	83 (1+11)**	28	64
0.1N solution	8.3	2.8	6.4
Volume (ml) of 6N reagent to prepare 1 liter of 0.1N solution	17	17	17
Volume (ml) of 1N reagent to prepare 1 liter of 0.02N solution	20	20	20

* All values approximate.
** The $a + b$ system of specifying preparatory volumes appears frequently throughout this manual and means that a volumes of the concentrated reagent are diluted with b volumes of distilled water to form the required solution.

sodium carbonate. Hence, a clarified concentrated solution may be diluted with carbon dioxide-free water to give carbon dioxide-free solutions of lower concentrations. The diluted solutions will become contaminated with carbon dioxide from the air if not properly protected. Where necessary, protection of sodium hydroxide solutions is usually afforded by attaching a tube of carbon dioxide-absorbing granular material,* preferably using at least 2 ft of rubber tubing to minimize vapor diffusion from the bottle. Attention must be given to replacement of the absorption tube before it becomes exhausted. It is desirable to arrange the bottle so that the solution is withdrawn by a siphon, thus avoiding opening of the bottle.

Sodium hydroxide solutions attack soft glass at rates which cause considerable contamination in a short time.

---

* Such as Caroxite (Fisher Scientific Company), Ascarite (A. H. Thomas Company), or equal.

Resistant glasses are affected more slowly, and dilute solutions may be kept for a limited period in bottles of these materials. Polyethylene bottles (preferably the rigid, heavy type) with polyethylene screw caps, or paraffin-coated bottles with rubber or neoprene stoppers, may also be used. Glass stoppers should never be used. Checks should be run periodically on solutions stored in polyethylene containers because carbon dioxide may pass through thin-walled bottles.

4.8. *Uniform ammonium hydroxide concentrations:* The following ammonium hydroxide concentrations meet the most common laboratory requirements: the concentrated ammonium hydroxide of commerce (which is approximately 15N), as well as the 5N, 3N and 0.2N concentrations. The last three normalities can be prepared by diluting the indicated volumes of concentrated ammonium hydroxide to 1 liter: 330 ml for 5N, 200 ml for 3N, and 13 ml for 0.2N.

5. Volumetric Glassware

Volumetric glassware may be calibrated either by the analyst who will use it or by some competent laboratory which can furnish certificates of accuracy. Volumetric glassware is calibrated either "to contain" (TC) or "to deliver" (TD). Glassware which is designed "to deliver" will do so with accuracy only when the inner surface is so scrupulously clean that water wets it immediately and forms a uniform film upon emptying. Pyrex glassware should be used whenever possible.

Approved quantitative techniques will yield the best results in the standard procedures. For this reason, the careful measurement of weights and volumes has been recommended in the preparation of standard solutions and calibration curves. Similar precautions should be observed in the measurement of sample volumes. Resort to volumetric pipets or burets is intended where the volume is designated to two decimal places (X.00 ml) in the text. Volumetric flasks are indicated for those cases where the volume is specified as "1,000 ml" rather than "1 liter," as well as where a volumetric flask is actually called for.

6. Nessler Tubes

Nessler tubes should be of the "tall" form (except when otherwise indicated), made of resistant glass, and selected from uniformly drawn tubing. The glass should be clear and colorless. The bottoms of the nessler tubes should be plane-parallel. When the tubes are filled with liquid and viewed from the top, using a light source beneath the tubes, there should be no dark spots nor any lenslike distortion of the transmitted light. The best quality of tube is manufactured by fusion-sealing a separately prepared, ground and polished circle of glass to the tube to form its bottom. The less expensive tubes are manufactured with integral bottoms, which cannot be made perfectly flat, but which appear to be satisfactory. The tops of the tubes should be flat, preferably fire polished, and smooth enough to permit cover slips to be cemented on for sealing. Nessler tubes provided with standard-taper clear-glass tops are commercially available. The graduation marks should completely encircle the tubes.

The 100-ml tubes should have a total length of approximately 375 mm. The inside diameter of such tubes should approximate 20 mm and the outside diameter 24 mm. The graduation mark on the tube should be as near to 300 mm above the inside of the bottom as possible. Tubes sold in sets should be of such uniformity that this distance does not vary more than 6 mm. (Sets are available commercially in which the maximum difference between tubes is not more than 2 mm.) A graduation mark also at 50 ml is permissible.

The 50-ml tubes should have a total length of about 300 mm. The inside diameter of the tubes should approximate 17 mm and the outside diameter 21 mm. The graduation mark on the tube should be as near 225 mm above the inside of the bottom as possible. Tubes sold in sets should be of such uniformity that this distance does not vary more than 6 mm. (Sets are available commercially in which the maximum difference between tubes is not more than 1.5 mm.) A graduation mark also at 25 ml is permissible.

Tubes for Jackson candle turbidimeters, in addition to conforming precisely to the measurements given in

Part I, Turbidity, should also conform to all the requirements as to quality, color of glass, and workmanship required for nessler tubes.

7. Colorimetric Equipment and Technique

Many of the procedures in this manual depend upon matching colors, either by eye or with a photometric instrument. In order to obtain the best possible results, the analyst should understand the principles and limitations of these methods, especially as the choice of instrument and of technique must be left to his discretion.

Both visual and photometric methods have their place in water analysis, and each has advantages. Tall-form nessler tubes provide a 30-cm light path, which is highly desirable when very faint colors are to be compared. Nessler tubes are inexpensive; their use does not require much training; they are not subject to mechanical or electrical failure; and, in general, they are entirely satisfactory for much of the routine work. Because they are portable and do not require a source of electric light, they can be used in the field. Photometric instruments are more versatile than nessler tubes; they are generally capable of superior accuracy if used intelligently; and they do not depend upon external lighting conditions or upon the analyst's eyesight. Therefore, results obtained with photometric instruments are less subject to personal bias and are more reproducible from one operator to another. Their use often allows corrections to be made for interfering color or turbidity. It is not necessary to prepare a complete set of standards for every single determination if a photometric instrument is used, but it is necessary to prepare such a set, or to maintain permanent standards, if nessler tubes are used for visual comparison.

Photometric methods are not, however, free from specific limitations. An analyst will recognize that something has gone wrong if he sees an off color or turbidity when making a visual comparison, but such a discrepancy may easily escape detection while making a photometric reading, for the instrument will always yield some sort of reading, whether meaningful or not. Filter photometers or spectrophotometers are subject to electrical and mechanical failure and sometimes to line voltage fluctuations. The photocells are subject to fatigue and to loss of sensitivity. Testing, maintaining, and repairing such instruments require specialized skills.

It must be emphasized that a photometer is not uniformly accurate over its entire scale. At very low transmittances, the scale is crowded in terms of concentration, so that a considerable change in the relative concentration of the substance sought will cause only a slight change in the position of the indicating dial or needle. At very high transmittances, slight differences between optical cells, the presence of condensed moisture, dust, bubbles, fingerprints, or a slight lack of reproducibility in positioning the cells can cause as great a change in readings as would a considerable relative change in concentration. The difficulties are minimized if readings fall in the middle range of the scale, and therefore the sample should be diluted or concentrated, or the light path varied by selecting cells of appropriate size, so that the middle range can be used. Some suggestions as to suitable ranges and light paths are offered under individual methods in this manual, but much reliance must necessarily be placed on the knowledge and judgment of the analyst. Most photometers are capable of their best performance if readings on samples fall in the range from approximately 10 per cent to 80 per cent transmittance (i.e., approximately 1 to 0.1 absorbance) with respect to a blank adjusted to read 100 per cent transmittance or 0 absorbance. The closer the readings approach 0 per cent or 100 per cent transmittance, the less accurate they can be expected to be. If it is impractical to use an optical cell with a sufficiently long light path, as in some commercial instruments, or to concentrate the sample or select a more sensitive color test, then it may actually be more accurate to compare very faint colors in nessler tubes than to attempt photometric readings close to 100 per cent transmittance.

In general, the best wavelength or filter to select is that which produces the largest spread of readings between a standard and a blank. This usually corresponds to a visual color for the light beam which is complementary to that of the solution; e.g., a green filter for a red solution, a violet filter for a yellow solution.

Although the employment of a photoelectric instrument makes unnecessary the preparation of a complete set of standards for every single set of samples to be analyzed, it is very necessary to prepare a reagent blank and at least one standard in the upper end of the optimum concentration range, along with every group of samples, in order to verify the constancy of the calibration curve. This precaution will reveal any unsuspected changes in the reagents, the instrument, or the technique. At regular intervals, or at any time results fall under suspicion, a complete set of

standards—at least five or six—should be prepared, spaced to cover the optimum concentration range, in order to check the calibration curve.

The utmost care should be exercised in the use of calibration curves supplied by the instrument manufacturer, or in the use of commercial permanent standards of colored liquids or glasses. The analyst must verify for himself the accuracy of the curves or permanent standards at frequent intervals by comparison with standards prepared in the laboratory, using the same set of reagents, the same instrument, and the same procedure used for analyzing samples. Even if permanent calibration curves or artificial standards have been accurately prepared by the manufacturer, they may not be valid under conditions of use. Permanent standards may be subject to fading or color alteration, and may also depend upon certain arbitrary lighting conditions. Standards and calibration curves may be incorrect owing to slight differences between reagents, instruments, or techniques at the manufacturer's laboratory and those at the analyst's laboratory.

If a photometer provides readings in terms of absorbance, it is convenient to plot calibration curves on rectangular graph paper; if readings are in terms of percentage transmittance, it is more convenient to plot calibration curves on semilogarithmic graph paper, with transmittance on the logarithmic scale and concentration on the linear scale. Usually, such graphs will be straight, or nearly straight, lines. Straight lines are easier to draw and read than strongly curved lines, and may be checked by verification of only a few points.

Photometric compensation can be used to correct for the interference caused by color or turbidity present in a sample, and also for impurities in the chemicals and distilled water used in the reagent blank, but not for those interfering substances which react with the color-developing reagents to produce a color. The principle involved is the additivity of absorbances.

If there is a significant reagent blank, but no color or turbidity in the sample, the necessary correction can be made by adding the color-developing reagents to distilled water and nulling the photometer with the resulting solution.

If there is color or turbidity or both in the sample, but a negligible reagent blank, correction can be made by carrying an additional aliquot of the sample through the procedure, with the exception that either: (a) one of the essential color-developing reagents is omitted; or, preferably, (b) the color is bleached out after it has been produced, but in such a way that the interfering color or turbidity is not bleached. The special blank is then used for nulling the photometer. Any significant change in volume produced by the addition or omission of reagents must be taken into account.

If color or turbidity or both are present in the sample, and if, in addition, the reagent blank is significant, then a slightly more complicated procedure is needed to correct for both interferences: The calibration curve should be prepared by setting the photometer to zero absorbance with plain distilled water and reading all the standards, including a zero standard or reagent blank, against the distilled water. If the graph is plotted in the recommended manner, and Beer's law holds, a straight line will be obtained; but if there is a measurable reagent blank, this line will not pass through the point of origin.

For each sample, a special blank must be prepared by either: (a) omitting a reagent, or (b) bleaching out the color as described above. Each special blank is then placed in the photometer in turn, the instrument is adjusted each time to read zero absorbance, and each regularly developed sample is read against its corresponding blank. The observed absorbances are then interpreted on the calibration graph. As before, any significant increase or decrease in volume caused by addition or omission of reagents must be considered in the calculations.

In visual color comparison with some instruments, compensation for color and turbidity can be made by the Walpole technique. The treated sample, after color development, is viewed through distilled water, while the color standard is viewed through an untreated sample. It is inconvenient to use the Walpole technique when viewing tall-form nessler tubes axially, because of the clumsy length.

Sometimes none of the preceding expedients will apply. In such an event, several approaches are available for the separation of turbidity from a sample. The nature of the sample, the size of the suspended matter, and the reasons for conducting the analysis will all combine to dictate the method for turbidity removal. The turbidity may be coagulated by the addition of zinc sulfate and an alkali, as is done in the direct nesslerization method for ammonia nitrogen. For samples of relatively coarse turbidity, centrifuging may suffice. In some instances, glass fiber filters, filter paper, or sintered-glass filters of fine porosity will serve the purpose. For very small particle sizes, the more recently developed cellulose acetate membrane filters may provide the required retentiveness. Used with discretion, each of these methods will yield satisfactory results in a suitable situation. However, it must be emphasized that no single universally ideal method of turbidity removal is available. Moreover, the analyst should perpetually be alert to adsorption losses possible with any flocculating or filtering procedure and an attendant alteration in the sample filtrate.

8. Other Methods of Analysis

The use of an instrumental method of analysis not specifically described in procedures in this manual is permissible, provided that the results so obtained are checked periodically, either against a standard method described in this manual or against a standard sample of undisputed composition. Identification of any such instrumental method used must be included in the laboratory report along with the analytical results.

8.1. *Flame photometry:* Flame photometry is used for the determination of sodium, potassium, lithium, and strontium. To some extent, it is also useful for the determination of calcium and other ions.

8.2. *Emission spectroscopy:* Arc-spark emission spectroscopy is becoming an important analytical tool for water analysis and is proving valuable both for trace analysis and for certain determinations not easily done by any other method. Considerable specialized training and experience with this technique are required to obtain satisfactory results, and frequently it is practical to obtain only semiquantitative results from such methods in water analysis. It should be noted that an arc-spark emission spectrograph is relatively expensive if used exclusively for routine water

testing, but its purchase is justified if it can be used as a general laboratory analytical instrument.

Among the advantages of arc-spark spectrographic analyses are: (a) the minute size of sample required; (b) the elimination of the necessity for bringing solids, such as precipitates and corrosion products, into solution; (c) the detection of all determinable elements present in a sample, whether specifically looked for or not; and (d) the unexcelled sensitivity for some elements. Among the disadvantages of spectrographic analyses are: (a) the high cost of first-class equipment; (b) the necessity for special training and experience; (c) the possible occurrence of severe interferences which must be taken into account if reasonable accuracy is to be achieved; and (d) the inability to distinguish between different valence states of an element, as, for instance, between chromic and chromate or ferric and ferrous.

Silver is the only element for which a spectrographic method is described in this manual. The following can also be determined spectrographically: aluminum, boron, chromium, copper, iron, lead, lithium, magnesium, manganese, nickel, silicon, strontium, and zinc. Among the elements for which there is no standard method in this manual but which are determinable by arc-spark spectrography are barium, cobalt, molybdenum, tin, titanium, vanadium, and a number of others.

8.3. *Polarography:* Polarographic methods for nitrate and zinc are described in the water section of this edition for the first time. Polarography is also suggested for scanning industrial wastes for all the various metal ions, especially where the possible interferences in the precise colorimetric procedures are unknown. The older polarographic method for dissolved oxygen remains from the past.

A method closely allied to polarography is amperometric titration, which is suitable for the determination of residual chlorine and other iodometric methods by titrimetry.

8.4. *Potentiometric titration:* Growing in acceptance for titrimetric work are electrical instruments called titrimeters or electrotitrators. If used discreetly, with a knowledge of their limitations, these instruments can be applied to many of the titrimetric determinations described, including those for acidity and the alkalinities. In addition, titrimetric precipitation reactions such as those for chloride, as well as titrimetric procedures based on complexometric and oxidation-reduction reactions, can be performed with these instruments. To be suitable for these extensive applications, an instrument must be equipped with all of the necessary special electrodes. Some recent electrotitrator models embody automatic features by which a titration is self-executing after the preliminary settings are made. In order to avoid spurious readings, the analyst is urged to check instrument operation against representative known samples in the same concentration range as the water under examination.

8.5. *Gas chromatography:* Some comparatively simple gas chromatographic equipment is available for limited procedures such as those described for sludge digester gas. Gas chromatography also shows strong promise for the determination of such organic materials as pesticides in the nanogram range. A number of methods for certain pesticides in water have been published in the literature. However, none of the methods has achieved sufficient acceptance to warrant a tentative status at this date and for this reason they have been omitted from this edition. The considerable work now under way in various laboratories suggests that this expensive and specialized instrumentation will probably be acquired by the larger organizations which can afford the sizeable financial outlay.

8.6. *Automated analytical instrumentation:* Automated analytical instrument systems are now available and in use to run individual samples at the rates of 10 to 60 samples per hour. The same instruments are also modified to be used as continuous monitoring systems for one to eight simultaneous analyses. The instruments are made up of a group of modules joined together in series by a tubing system. Each module performs the individual step required in the analytical procedure shown in the analytical methods described in this book.

The read-out system employs sensing elements with indicators, alarms and/or recorders. Sample clarification may be carried out continuously with a self-cleaning filter or dialyzer. For monitoring applications, automatic standardization-compensation electrically and chemically is done by a self-adjusting recorder when known chemical standards are sent periodically through the same analytical train. Several such instrument systems are presently available.

8.7. *Other newer methods of analysis:* Instrumentation and new methods of analysis are always under development. The analyst will find it to his advantage to keep abreast of current progress. Reviews of each branch of analytical chemistry are published regularly in *Analytical Chemistry*.[75]

9. Interferences

Many analytical procedures are subject to interference from substances which may be present in the sample. The more common and obvious interferences are known, and information about them has been included in the details of individual procedures. It is inevitable that the analyst will encounter interferences regarding which he is not forewarned. Such occurrences are unavoidable because of the diverse nature of waters and particularly of sewages and industrial wastes. Therefore, the analyst must be alert to the fact that hitherto untested ions, new treatment compounds, especially complexing agents, and new industrial wastes constitute an ever present threat to the accuracy of chemical analyses; and he must be on his guard at all times to detect the occurrence of such interferences.

Any sudden change in the analysis of a supply which has been of rather constant composition, any off color observed in a colorimetric test or during a titration, any unexpected turbidity, odor, or other laboratory finding is cause for suspicion. These phenomena may be due to a normal variation in the relative concentrations of the usual constituents, but they may also be caused by the introduction of an unforeseen interfering substance.

A few substances—such as chlorine, chlorine dioxide, alum, iron salts, silicates, copper sulfate, ammonium sulfate, and polyphosphates—are so widely used in water treatment that they deserve special mention as possible causes of interference. Of these, chlorine is probably the worst offender, in that it bleaches or alters the colors of many of the sensitive organic reagents which serve as titration indicators and as color developers for photometric methods. Among the methods which have proved effective in removing chlorine residuals are: the addition of minimal amounts of sulfite, thiosulfate, or arsenite; exposure to sunlight or an artificial ultraviolet source; and prolonged storage.

Whenever interference is encountered or suspected, and no specific recommendations are found in this manual for overcoming it, the analyst must endeavor to determine which, if any, technique suffices to eliminate the interference without adversely affecting the analysis itself. If two or more choices of procedure are offered, often one procedure will be less affected than another by the presence of the interfering substance. If different procedures yield considerably different results, it is likely that interference is present. Some interferences become less severe upon dilution, or upon use of smaller aliquots; any tendency of the results to increase or decrease in a consistent manner with extent of dilution indicates the likelihood of interference effects.

Interference may cause the analytical results to be either too high or too low, as a consequence of one of the following processes:

a. An interfering substance may react like the substance sought, and thus produce a high result: e.g., bromide will be titrated as though it were chloride.

b. An interfering substance may react with the substance sought and thus produce a low result: e.g., chloride will react with a portion of the nitrate in the presence of the sulfuric acid in the phenoldisulfonic acid method.

c. An interfering substance may combine with the analytical reagent and thus prevent it from reacting with the substance sought: e.g., chlorine will destroy many indicators and color-developing reagents.

Nearly every interference will fit one of these classes. For example, in a photometric method, turbidity may be considered as a "substance" which acts like the one being determined—i.e., it reduces the transmission of light. Occasionally, two or more interfering substances, if present simultaneously, may interact in a nonadditive fashion, either canceling or enhancing one another's effects.

The best way to minimize interference is to remove the interfering substance or to render it innocuous by one of these methods:

a. Either the substance sought or the interfering substance may be removed physically: e.g., fluoride and ammonia may be distilled off, leaving interferences behind; chloride may be converted to silver chloride and filtered off, leaving nitrate behind. The interferences may also be adsorbed on an ion-exchange resin, a process described more fully in Part I, Introduction, *B.*

b. The pH may be adjusted so that only the substance sought will react.

c. The sample may be oxidized or reduced to convert the interfering substance to a harmless form: e.g., chlorine may be reduced to chloride by adding thiosulfate.

d. The addition of a suitable agent may complex the interfering substance so that it is innocuous although still present: e.g., iron may be complexed with pyrophosphate to prevent it from interfering with the copper determination; copper may be complexed with cyanide or sulfide to prevent interference with the titrimetric hardness determination.

e. A combination of the first four techniques may be used: e.g., phenols are distilled from an acid solution to prevent amines from distilling; thiosulfate is used in the dithizone method for zinc to prevent most of the interfering metals from passing into the carbon tetrachloride layer.

f. Color and turbidity may sometimes be destroyed by wet or dry ashing, or removed by use of a flocculating agent. Some types of turbidity may be removed by filtration. These procedures, however, introduce the danger that the desired constituent will also be removed.

If none of these techniques is practical, several methods of compensation can be used:

a. If the color or turbidity initially present in the sample interferes in a photometric determination, it may be possible to use photometric compensation. The technique is described in Sec. 7 above. Examples of its use will be found in several procedures of analysis.

b. The concentration of interfering substances may be determined and then identical amounts may be added to the calibration standards. This involves much labor.

c. If the interference does not continue to increase as the concentration of interfering substance increases, but tends to level off, then a large excess of interfering substance may be added routinely to all samples and to all standards. This is called "swamping." For example, an excess of calcium is added in the photometric magnesium determination.

d. The presence in the chemical reagents of the substance sought may be accounted for by carrying out a blank determination.

10. Recovery

A qualitative estimate of the presence or absence of interfering substances in a particular determination may be made by means of a recovery procedure. Although this method does not enable the analyst to apply any correction factor to the results of an analysis, it does give him some basis for judging the applicability of a particular method of analysis to a particular sample. Furthermore, it enables the analyst to obtain information in this regard without an extensive investigation to determine exactly which substances can interfere in the method used. It also does away with the necessity of making separate determinations on the sample for the interfering substances themselves. A recovery may be performed at the same time as the determination itself. Of course, recoveries would not be run on a routine basis with samples whose general composition is known or when using a method whose applicability to the sample is well established. Recovery methods are to be regarded as tools to remove doubt about the applicability of a method to a sample.

In brief, the recovery procedure involves applying the analytical method to a reagent blank; to a series of known standards covering the expected range of concentration of the sample; to the sample itself, in at least duplicate run; and to the recovery samples, prepared by adding known quantities of the substance sought to separate portions of the sample itself, each portion equal to the size of sample taken for the run. The substance sought should be added in sufficient quantity to overcome the limits of error of the analytical method, but without causing the total in the sample to exceed the range of the known standards used.

The results are first corrected by subtracting the reagent blank from each of the other determined values. The resulting known standards are then graphically represented. From this graph the amount of sought substance in the sample alone is determined. This value is then subtracted from each of the determinations consisting of sample plus known added substance. The resulting amount of substance divided by the known amount originally added and multiplied by 100 gives the percentage recovery.

The procedure outlined above may be applied to a colorimetric, flame photometric, nephelometric, or fluorometric analysis. It may also be applied in a little more simple form to titrimetric, gravimetric, and other types of analyses.

Rigid rules concerning the percentage recoveries required for acceptance of results of analyses for a given sample and method cannot be stipulated. Recoveries of substances in the range of the sensitivity of the method may, of course, be very high or very low and approach a value nearer to 100 per cent recovery as the error of the method becomes small with respect to the magnitude of the amount of substance added. In general, intricate and exacting procedures for trace substances which have inherent errors due to their complexity may give recoveries that would be considered very poor and yet, from the practical viewpoint of usefulness of the result, may be quite acceptable. Poor results may reflect either interferences present in the sample or real inadequacy of the method of analysis in the range in which it is being used.

It must be stressed, however, that the judicious use of recovery methods for the evaluation of analytical procedures and their applicability to particular samples is an invaluable aid to the analyst in both routine and research investigations.

B. Expression of Results

1. Units

Analytical results may be expressed either as milligrams per liter (mg/1) or as parts per million (ppm). Assuming that 1 liter of water, sewage, or industrial waste weighs 1 kilogram, milligrams per liter is equivalent to parts per million.* When dealing with industrial wastes of high specific gravity, results should be expressed in milligrams per liter, with the specific gravity given. Only the significant figures (see Sec. 2 below) should be recorded.

If the concentrations are generally less than 1 mg/1, it may be more convenient to express the results in micrograms per liter (μg/1) or parts per billion (ppb), where billion is understood to be 10^9. If the concentration is greater than 10,000 mg/1, the results should be expressed in per cent, 1 per cent being equivalent to 10,000 mg/1.

For brines or wastes of high specific gravity, results obtained in mg/1 can be converted to ppm by the equation:

$$\text{ppm by weight*} = \frac{\text{mg/1}}{\text{sp gr}}$$

In reporting analyses of stream pollution or evaluation of plant operation and efficiencies, it is desirable to express the results on a weighted basis, including both the concentration and the volume of flow in cubic feet per second (cfs) or million gallons daily (mgd). These weighted results may be expressed as *quantity units* (QU) according to the practice of the US Public

Health Service, as *pounds per 24 hr,* or as *population equivalents* based on biochemical oxygen demand (BOD). Totals of the weighted units may be converted to the weighted average mg/1. The various units are calculated as follows:

$$QU_1 = (\text{mg/1}) \times (1,000\,\text{cfs})$$
$$QU_2 = (\text{mg/1}) \times (\text{mgd})$$
$$\text{lb/24 hr} = (\text{mg/1}) \times (\text{mgd}) \times 8.34$$
$$\text{lb/24 hr} = (\text{mg/1}) \times (\text{cfs}) \times 5.39$$

Population equivalent
$$= (\text{mg/1 5-day BOD}) \times (\text{mgd}) \times \frac{8.34}{0.17}$$

The inside back cover of this volume presents a table of factors which is useful for converting the concentrations of the common ions found in water from milligrams per liter to milliequivalents per liter, and vice versa. The term milliequivalent used in this table represents 0.001 of an equivalent weight. The equivalent weight, in turn, is defined as the weight of the ion (sum of the atomic weights of the atoms making up the ion) divided by the number of charges normally associated with the particular ion. The factors for converting results from mg/1 to me/1 were computed by dividing the ion charge by the weight of the ion. Conversely, the factors for converting results from me/1 to mg/1 were calculated by dividing the weight of the ion by the ion charge. This table is offered for the convenience of laboratories which report results in me/1 as well as mg/1.

2. Significant Figures

To avoid ambiguity in reporting results or in presenting directions for a procedure, it is the custom to use "significant figures." All of the digits in

---

* It should be noted that, in water analysis, "parts per million" is *always* understood to imply a weight/weight ratio, even though in practice a volume may be measured instead of a weight. By contrast, "per cent" may be either a volume/volume or a weight/weight ratio.

a reported result are expected to be known definitely, except for the last digit, which may be in doubt. Such a number is said to contain only significant figures. If more than a single doubtful digit is carried, the extra digit or digits are not significant. If an analytical result is reported as "75.6 mg/l," the analyst should be quite certain of the "75," but may be uncertain as to whether the ".6" should be .5 or .7, or even .4 or .8, because of unavoidable uncertainty in the analytical procedure. If the standard deviation were known from previous work to be ±2 mg/l, the analyst would have, or at least should have, rounded off the result to "76 mg/l" before reporting it. On the other hand, if the method were so good that a result of "75.61 mg/l" could have been conscientiously reported, then the analyst should not have rounded it off to 75.6.

A report should include only such figures as are justified by the accuracy of the work. The all too common practice of requiring that quantities listed in a column have the same number of figures to the right of the decimal point is justified in bookkeeping, but not in chemistry.

2.1. *Rounding off:* Rounding off is accomplished by dropping the digits which are not significant. If the digit 6, 7, 8, or 9 is dropped, then the preceding digit must be increased by one unit; if the digit 0, 1, 2, 3, or 4 is dropped, the preceding digit is not altered. If the digit 5 is dropped, the preceding digit is rounded off to the nearest even number: thus 2.25 becomes 2.2, and 2.35 becomes 2.4.

2.2. *Ambiguous zeros:* The digit 0 may either record a measured value of zero, or it may serve merely as a spacer to locate the decimal point. If the re-

sult of a sulfate determination is reported as 420 mg/l, the recipient of the report may be in doubt whether the zero is significant or not, because the zero cannot be deleted. If an analyst calculates a total-solids content of 1,146 mg/l, but realizes that the 4 is somewhat doubtful and that therefore the 6 has no significance, he will round off the answer to 1,150 mg/l and so report, but here, too, the recipient of the report will not know whether the zero is significant. Although the number could be expressed as a power of 10—e.g., 11.5×10^2 or 1.15×10^3—this form is not generally used as it would not be consistent with the normal expression of results and might also be confusing. In most other cases, there will be no doubt as to the sense in which the digit 0 is used. It is obvious that the zeros are significant in such numbers as 104, 40.08, and 0.0003. In a number written as 5.000, it is understood that all the zeros are significant, or else the number could have been rounded off to 5.00, 5.0, or 5, whichever was appropriate. Whenever the zero is ambiguous, it is advisable to accompany the result with an estimate of its uncertainty.

Sometimes significant zeros are dropped without good cause. If a buret is read as "23.60 ml," it should be so recorded, and not as "23.6 ml." The first number indicates that the analyst took the trouble to estimate the second decimal place; "23.6 ml" indicates that he read the buret rather carelessly.

2.3. *The plus-or-minus* (±) *notation:* If a calculation yields as a result "1,476 mg/l" with a standard deviation estimated as ±40 mg/l, it should be reported as 1,480 ± 40 mg/l. But if the standard deviation is estimated as ±100 mg/l, the answer should be rounded off still further and reported as $1,500 \pm 100$ mg/l. By this device, ambiguity is avoided and the recipient of the report can tell that the zeros are only spacers. Even if the problem of ambiguous zeros is not present, showing the standard deviation is helpful in that it provides an estimate of reliability.

2.4. *Calculations:* As a practical operating rule, the result of a calculation in which several numbers are multiplied or divided together should be rounded off to as few significant figures as are present in the factor with the fewest significant figures. Suppose that the following calculation must be made in order to obtain the result of an analysis:

$$\frac{56 \times 0.003462 \times 43.22}{1.684}$$

A ten-place desk calculator yields an answer of "4.975740996," but this number must be rounded off to a mere "5.0" because one of the measurements, 56, which entered into the calculation has only two significant figures. It was a waste of time to measure the other three factors to four significant figures because the "56" is "the weakest link in the chain" and limits the accuracy of the answer. If the other factors were measured to only three, instead of four, significant figures, the answer would not suffer and the labor would be less.

When adding or subtracting numbers, that number which has the fewest decimal places, not necessarily the fewest significant figures, puts the limit on the number of places that may justifiably be carried in the sum or difference. Thus the sum

$$
\begin{array}{r}
0.0072 \\
12.02 \\
4.0078 \\
25.9 \\
4,886 \\
\hline
4,927.9350
\end{array}
$$

must be rounded off to a mere "4,928," no decimals, because one of the addends, 4,886, has no decimal places. Notice that another addend, 25.9, has only three significant figures and yet it does not set a limit to the number of significant figures in the answer.

The preceding discussion is necessarily oversimplified, and the reader is referred to the bibliography for a more detailed discussion.

C. Precision and Accuracy

A clear distinction should be made between the terms "precision" and "accuracy" when applied to methods of analysis. *Precision* is a measure of the reproducibility of a method when repeated on a homogeneous sample under controlled conditions, regardless of whether or not the observed values are widely displaced from the true value as a result of systematic or constant errors present throughout the measurements.

Precision can be expressed by the standard deviation. *Accuracy* is a measure of the error of a method and may be expressed as a comparison of the amount of element or compound determined or recovered by the test method and the amount actually present. A method may have very high precision but recover only a part of the element being determined; or an analysis, although precise, may be in error because of poorly standardized solutions, inaccurate dilution techniques, inaccurate balance weights, or improperly calibrated equipment. On the other hand, a method may be accurate but lack precision because of low instrument sensitivity, variable rate of biologic activity, or other factors beyond the control of the analyst.

It is possible to determine both the precision and accuracy of a test method by analyzing samples to which known quantities of standard substances have been added. It is possible to determine the precision, but not the accuracy, of such methods as those for suspended solids, BOD, and numerous physical characteristics because of the unavailability of standard substances that can be added in known quantities on which percentage recovery can be based.

1. Statistical Approach

1.1. *Standard deviation (σ):* Experience has shown that, if a determination is repeated a large number of times under essentially the same conditions, the observed values, *x*, will be distributed at random about an average as a result of uncontrollable or experimental errors. If there are an infinite number of observations from a common universe of causes, a plot of the relative frequency against magnitude will produce a symmetrical bell-shaped curve known as the Gaussian or normal curve (Fig. 1). The shape of this curve is completely defined by two statistical parameters: (a) the mean or average, $\bar{x}$, of *n* observations; and (b) the standard deviation, σ, which fixes the width or spread of the curve on each side of the mean. The formula is:

$$\sigma = \pm \sqrt{\frac{\Sigma (x - \bar{x})^2}{n-1}}$$

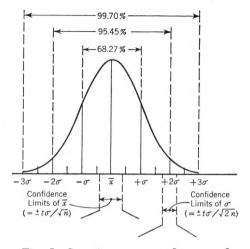

Fig. 1. **Gaussian or normal curve of frequencies**

The proportion of the total observations lying within any given range about the mean is related to the standard deviation. For example, 68.27 per cent of the observations lie between $\bar{x} \pm 1\,\sigma$; 95.45 per cent, between $\bar{x} \pm 2\,\sigma$; and 99.70 per cent, between $\bar{x} \pm 3\,\sigma$. These limits do not apply exactly for any finite sample from a normal population; the agreement with them may be expected to be better as the number of observations, *n*, increases.

1.2. *Application of standard deviation:* If the standard deviation, σ, for a particular analytical procedure has been determined from a large number of samples, and a set of *n* replicates on a sample gives a mean result $\bar{x}$, there is a 95 per cent chance that the true value of the mean for this sample lies within the values $\bar{x} \pm 1.96\,\sigma/\sqrt{n}$. This range is known as the 95 per cent confidence interval. It provides an estimate of the reliability of the mean, and may be used to forecast the number of replicates needed to secure suitable precision.

If the standard deviation is not known and is estimated from a single small * sample, or a few small samples, the 95 per cent confidence interval of the mean of n observations is given by the equation $\bar{x} \pm t\sigma/\sqrt{n}$, where t has the following value:

n	t
2	12.71
3	4.30
4	3.18
5	2.78
10	2.26
∞	1.96

The use of t compensates for the tendency of small samples to underestimate the variability.

1.3. *Range (R):* The difference between the smallest and largest of n observations is also closely related to the standard deviation. When the distribution of errors is normal in form, the range, R, of n observations exceeds the standard deviation times a factor d_n only in 5 per cent of the cases. Values for the factor d_n are:

n	d_n
2	2.77
3	3.32
4	3.63
5	3.86
6	4.03

As it is rather general practice to run replicate analyses, use of these limits is very convenient for detecting faulty technique, large sampling errors, or other assignable causes of variation.

1.4. *Rejection of experimental data:* Quite often in a series of observations one or more of the results deviate greatly from the mean whereas the other values are in close agreement with the mean value. The problem

---

* A "small sample" in statistical discussions means a small number of replicate determinations, n, and does not refer to the quantity used for a determination.

arises at this point as to rejection of the disagreeing values. Theoretically, no results should be rejected, since the presence of disagreeing results shows faulty techniques and therefore throws doubts on all of the results. Of course, the result of any test in which a known error has occurred is rejected immediately. For methods for the rejection of other experimental data, standard texts on analytical chemistry or statistical measurement should be consulted.

2. Graphical Representation of Data

Graphical representation of data is one of the simplest methods for showing the influence of one variable on another. Graphs are frequently desirable and advantageous in colorimetric analysis because they show any variation of one variable with respect to the other within specified limits.

2.1. *General:* Ordinary rectangular-coordinate paper is satisfactory for most purposes. Twenty lines per inch is recommended. Semilogarithmic paper is convenient when one of the coordinates is to be the logarithm of an observed variable.

The five rules listed by Worthing and Geffner [80] for choosing the coordinate scales are useful. Although these rules are not inflexible, they are satisfactory. When doubt arises common sense should prevail. The rules are:

a. The independent and dependent variables should be plotted on abscissa and ordinate in a manner which can be easily comprehended.

b. The scales should be chosen so that the value of either coordinate can be found quickly and easily.

c. The curve should cover as much of the graph paper as possible.

d. The scales should be chosen so

that the slope of the curve approaches unity as nearly as possible.

e. Other things being equal, the variables should be chosen to give a plot which will be as nearly a straight line as possible.

The title of a graph should adequately describe what the plot is intended to show. Legends should be presented on the graph to clarify possible ambiguities. Complete information on the conditions under which the data were obtained should be included in the legend.

2.2. *Method of least squares:* If sufficient points are available and the functional relationship between the two variables is well defined, a smooth curve can be drawn through the points. If the function is not well defined, as is frequently the case when using experimental data, the method of least squares is used to fit a straight line to the pattern.

Any straight line can be represented by the equation $x = my + b$. The slope of the line is represented by the constant m and the slope intercept (on the x axis) is represented by the constant b. The method of least squares has the advantage of giving a set of values for these constants not dependent upon the judgment of the investigator. Two equations besides the one for a straight line are involved in these calculations:

$$m = \frac{n\Sigma xy - \Sigma x \Sigma y}{n\Sigma y^2 - (\Sigma y)^2}$$

$$b = \frac{\Sigma y^2 \Sigma x - \Sigma y \Sigma xy}{n\Sigma y^2 - (\Sigma y)^2}$$

n being the number of observations (sets of x and y values) to be summed. In order to compute the constants by this method it is first necessary to calculate Σx, Σy, Σy^2, and Σxy. These operations are carried out to more places than the number of significant figures in the experimental data because the experimental values are assumed to be exact for the purposes of the calculations.

Example: Given the following data to be graphed, find the best line to fit the points:

Absorbance	Solute Concentration mg/l
0.10	29.8
0.20	32.6
0.30	38.1
0.40	39.2
0.50	41.3
0.60	44.1
0.70	48.7

Let y equal the absorbance values and x the concentration of solute. The first step is to find the summations (Σ) of x, y, y^2, and xy:

x	y	y^2	xy
29.8	0.10	0.01	2.98
32.6	0.20	0.04	6.52
38.1	0.30	0.09	11.43
39.2	0.40	0.16	15.68
41.3	0.50	0.25	20.65
44.1	0.60	0.36	26.46
48.7	0.70	0.49	34.09
$\Sigma = 273.8$	2.80	1.40	117.81

The next step is to substitute the summations in the equations for m and b; $n = 7$ as there are seven sets of x and y values:

$$m = \frac{7(117.81) - 2.80(273.8)}{7(1.40) - (2.80)^2}$$
$$= 29.6$$

$$b = \frac{1.4(273.8) - 2.80(117.81)}{7(1.40) - (2.80)^2}$$
$$= 27.27$$

To plot the line, three convenient values of y are selected—say, 0, 0.20, 0.60—and corresponding values of x calculated:

$$x_0 = 29.6(0) + 27.27 = 27.27$$
$$x_1 = 29.6(0.20) + 27.27 = 33.19$$
$$x_2 = 29.6(0.60) + 27.27 = 45.04$$

When the points representing these values are plotted on the graph, they will lie in a straight line (unless an error in calculation has been made), which is the line of best fit for the given data. The points representing the latter are also plotted on the graph, as in Fig. 2.

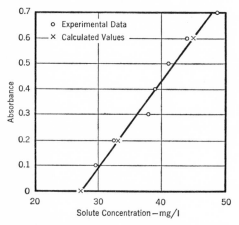

Fig. 2. Example of least-squares method

3. Self-Evaluation (Desirable Philosophy for the Analyst)

A good analyst continually tempers his confidence with doubt. Such doubt stimulates a search for new and different methods of confirmation for his reassurance. The frequent self-appraisals should embrace every step from collecting samples to reporting results.

His first critical scrutiny should be directed at the entire sample collection process in order to guarantee a representative sample for the purpose of the analysis and to avoid any possible losses or contamination during the act of collection. Attention should also be given to the type of container and to the manner of transport and storage, as discussed elsewhere in this volume.

A periodic re-assessment should be made of the available analytical methods, with an eye to applicability for the purpose and the situation. In addition, each selected method must be evaluated by the analyst himself for sensitivity, precision, and accuracy, because only in this way can he determine whether his technique is satisfactory and whether he has interpreted the directions properly. Self-evaluation on these points can give the analyst confidence regarding the value and significance of his reported results.

The benefits of less rigid intra-laboratory as well as inter-laboratory evaluations deserve serious consideration. The analyst can regularly check standard or unknown concentrations with and without interfering elements, and compare results on the same sample with other individuals in the laboratory. Such programs can uncover weaknesses in the analytical chain and enable improvements to be instituted without delay. The results can disclose whether the trouble stems from faulty sample treatment, improper elimination of interference, poor calibration practices, sloppy experimental technique, impure or incorrectly standardized reagents, defective instrumentation, or even inadvertent mistakes in arithmetic.

Other checks of a water analysis are described in Part I, Introduction, C, and involve anion-cation balance, specific conductance, ion exchange, and the recovery of added substance in the sample (General Introduction, A, Sec. 10).

All of these approaches are designed to appraise and upgrade the level of laboratory performance and thus inspire greater faith in the final reported results.

Bibliography

General

1. WELCH, P. S. *Limnological Methods.* Blakiston Co., Philadelphia (1948).
2. HAUCK, C. F. Gaging and Sampling Waterborne Industrial Wastes. *ASTM Bull.* (Dec. 1949).
3. BLACK, H. H. Procedures for Sampling and Measuring Industrial Wastes. *Sew. Ind. Wastes* 24:45 (1952).
4. WELCH, P. S. *Limnology.* McGraw-Hill Book Co., New York (2nd ed., 1952).
5. *Guide for Safety in the Chemical Laboratory.* Prepared by and published for General Safety Committee of Manufacturing Chemists' Assn. D. Van Nostrand Co., Princeton, N.J. (1954).
6. MINISTRY OF HOUSING AND LOCAL GOVERNMENT. *Methods of Chemical Analysis as Applied to Sewage and Sewage Effluents.* Her Majesty's Stationery Office, London (2nd ed., 1956).
7. *Safety Practice for Water Utilities.* Manual M6, Am. Water Works Assoc., New York (1958).
8. TAYLOR, E. W. *Examination of Waters and Water Supplies.* Little, Brown & Co., Boston, Mass. (7th ed., 1958).
9. *International Standards for Drinking Water.* World Health Organization, Geneva (1958).
10. HEM, J. D. Study and Interpretation of the Chemical Characteristics of Natural Water. *US Geol. Survey Water Supply Paper* 1473 (1959).
11. KLEIN, LOUIS. *River Pollution, I. Chemical Analysis.* Academic Press, New York (1959).
12. *Approved Methods for the Physical and Chemical Examination of Water.* Inst. Water Engineers, London (3rd ed., 1960).
13. RAINWATER, F. H. & THATCHER, L. L. Methods for Collection and Analysis of Water Samples. *US Geol. Survey Water Supply Paper* 1454 (1960).
14. SAWYER, C. N. *Chemistry for Sanitary Engineers.* McGraw-Hill Book Co., New York (1960).
15. *Manual on Industrial Water and Industrial Waste Water.* Special Tech. Pub. 148–F, Am. Soc. Testing Materials, Philadelphia (2nd ed., 1962).
16. Public Health Service Drinking Water Standards, 1962. *Public Health Service Pub.* 956 (1963).
17. CAMP, T. R. *Water and Its Impurities.* Reinhold Publishing Corp., New York (1963).
18. *Water Quality Criteria.* California State Water Pollution Control Board, Sacramento (2nd ed., 1963).
19. *Water Quality and Treatment.* Am. Water Works Assoc., New York (3rd ed., 1965).

Water Supply Data

20. LOHR, E. W. & LOVE, S. K. The Industrial Utility of Public Water Supplies in the United States, 1952. Parts 1 and 2. *US Geol. Survey Water Supply Papers* 1299 and 1300 (1954).

Laboratory Reagents

21. *The Pharmacopoeia of the United States of America.* Mack Printing Co., Easton, Pa. (16th rev., 1960) pp. 943–1065.
22. *Reagent Chemicals—American Chemical Society Specifications, 1960.* Am. Chem. Soc., Washington, D.C. (1961).
23. ROSIN, J. *Reagent Chemicals and Standards,* D. Van Nostrand Co., Princeton, N.J. (4th ed., 1961).
24. Standard Materials Issued by the National Bureau of Standards. *Natl. Bur. Standards Misc. Pub.* 241 (1962).

General Analytical Techniques

25. FOULK, C. W.; MOYER, H. V.; & MACNEVIN, W. M. *Quantitative Chemical Analysis.* McGraw-Hill Book Co., New York (1952).
26. KOLTHOFF, I. M. & SANDELL, E. B. *Textbook of Quantitative Inorganic Analysis.* Macmillan Co., New York (3rd ed., 1952).
27. WILLARD, H. H.; FURMAN, N. H.; & BRICKER, C. E. *Elements of Quantitative Analysis.* D. Van Nostrand Co., Princeton, N.J. (4th ed., 1956).
28. HUGHES, J. C. Testing of Glass Volumetric Apparatus. *Natl. Bur. Standards Circ.* No. 602 (1959).
29. WILSON, C. L. & WILSON, D. W., ed. *Comprehensive Analytical Chemistry.* Elsevier Publishing Co., New York. Vol. 1A (1959), Vol. 1B (1960), Vol. 1C (1962).
30. VOGEL, A. I. *Textbook of Quantitative Inorganic Analysis Including Elementary Instrumental Analysis.* John

Wiley & Sons, New York (3rd ed., 1961).

31. WELCHER, F. J., ed. *Standard Methods of Chemical Analysis*. D. Van Nostrand Co., Princeton, N.J. (6th ed., 1963), Vol. IIA.

Colorimetric Techniques

32. MELLON, M. G. Colorimetry and Photometry in Water Analysis. *J. AWWA* 39:341 (1947).
33. Terminology and Symbols for Use in Ultraviolet, Visible, and Infrared Absorptiometry. *Natl. Bur. Standards Letter Circ.* LC-857 (May 19, 1947).
34. GIBSON, K. S. & BALCOM, M. M. Transmission Measurements With the Beckman Quartz Spectrophotometer. *J. Research Natl. Bur. Standards* 38:601 (1947).
35. SNELL, F. D. & SNELL, C. T. *Colorimetric Methods of Analysis*. D. Van Nostrand Co., Princeton, N.J. (3rd ed., 1948). Vol. 1.
36. MELLON, M. G., ed. *Analytical Absorption Spectroscopy*. John Wiley & Sons, New York (1950).
37. DISKANT, E. M. Photometric Methods in Water Analysis. *J. AWWA* 44:625 (1952).
38. BOLTZ, D. F., ed. *Colorimetric Determination of Nonmetals*. Interscience Publishers, New York (1958).
39. SANDELL, E. B. *Colorimetric Determination of Traces of Metals*. Interscience Publishers, New York (3rd ed., 1959).

Potentiometric Titration

40. FURMAN, N. H. Potentiometric Titrations. *Anal. Chem.* 22:33 (1950); 23:21 (1951); 26:84 (1954).
41. KOLTHOFF, I. M. & LAITINEN, H. A. *pH and Electrotitrations*. John Wiley & Sons, New York (1958).
42. REILLEY, C. N. Potentiometric Titrations. *Anal. Chem.* 28:671 (1956); 30:765 (1958); 32:185R (1960); 34:313R (1962).
43. WILLARD, H. H.; MERRITT, L. L.; & DEAN, J. A. *Instrumental Methods of Analysis*. D. Van Nostrand Co., Princeton, N.J. (3rd ed., 1958).

Polarography

44. LINGANE, J. J. Polarographic Theory, Instrumentation, and Methodology.

Anal. Chem. 21:45 (1949); 23:86 (1951).

45. BUTTS, P. G. & MELLON, M. G. Polarographic Determination of Metals in Industrial Wastes. *Sew. Ind. Wastes* 23:59 (1951).
46. MULLER, O. H. *Polarographic Method of Analysis*. Chemical Education Publishing Co., Easton, Pa. (2nd ed., 1951).
47. KOLTHOFF, I. M. & LINGANE, J. J. *Polarography*. Interscience Publishers, New York (2nd ed., 1952).
48. *Bibliography of Polarographic Literature, 1922–1955*. E. H. Sargent Co., Chicago (1956).
49. HUME, D. N. Polarographic Theory, Instrumentation, and Methodology. *Anal. Chem.* 28:625 (1956); 30:675 (1958); 32:137R (1960); 34:172R (1962).

Emission Spectroscopy

50. HARRISON, G. R. *Wavelength Tables*. John Wiley & Sons, New York (1939).
51. BRODE, W. *Chemical Spectroscopy*. John Wiley & Sons, New York (2nd ed., 1943).
52. HARRISON, G. R.; LORD, R. C.; & LOOFBOUROW, J. R. *Practical Spectroscopy*. Prentice-Hall, New York (1948).
53. NACHTRIEB, N. H. *Principles and Practice of Spectrochemical Analysis*. McGraw-Hill Book Co., New York (1950).
54. HARVEY, C. E. *Spectrochemical Procedures*. Applied Research Labs., Glendale, Calif. (1950).
55. SAWYER, R. A. *Experimental Spectroscopy*. Prentice-Hall, New York (2nd ed., 1951).
56. TWYMAN, F. *Metal Spectroscopy*. Charles Griffin & Co., London (2nd ed., 1951).
57. AHRENS, L. A. *Quantitative Spectrochemical Analysis of Silicates*. Pergamon Press, London (1954).
58. MEGGERS, W. F. Emission Spectroscopy. *Anal. Chem.* 21:29 (1949); 22:18 (1950); 24:23 (1952); 26:54 (1954); 28:616 (1956).
59. AHRENS, L. H. & TAYLOR, S. R. *Spectrochemical Analysis*. Addison-Wesley Publishing Co., Reading, Mass. (2nd ed., 1961).
60. *Methods for Emission Spectrochemical*

Analysis. Am. Soc. Testing Materials, Philadelphia (3rd ed., 1961).

61. SCRIBNER, B. F. Emission Spectroscopy. *Anal. Chem.* 30:596 (1958); 32:229R (1960); 34:200R (1962).

Other New Methods of Analysis

62. LOVE, S. K. Analytical Instruments Used in the Modern Water Plant Laboratory. *J. AWWA* 43:725 (1951).

63. BOLTZ, D. F., ed. *Selected Topics in Modern Instrumental Analysis.* Prentice-Hall, New York (1952).

64. SAMUELSON, O. *Ion Exchangers in Analytical Chemistry.* John Wiley & Sons, New York (1953).

65. OSBORN, G. H. Bibliography on the Analytical Applications of Ion-Exchange Resins. *Analyst* 78:221 (1953).

66. EWING, G. W. *Instrumental Methods of Chemical Analysis.* McGraw-Hill Book Co., New York (1954).

67. HARLEY, J. H. & WIBERLEY, S. E. *Instrumental Analysis.* John Wiley & Sons, New York (1954).

68. YOE, J. H. & KOCH, H. J., ed. *Trace Analysis.* John Wiley & Sons, New York (1957).

69. LEDERER, E. & LEDERER, M. *Chromatography.* Elsevier Press, Houston, Tex. (2nd ed., 1957).

70. BLOCK, R. J.; CURRUM, E. L.; & ZWEIG, G. *A Manual of Paper Chromatography and Paper Electrophoresis.* Academic Press, New York (2nd ed., 1958).

71. WILLARD, H. H.; MERRITT, L. L.; & DEAN, J. A. *Instrumental Methods of Analysis.* D. Van Nostrand Co., Princeton, N.J. (3rd ed., 1958).

72. LINGANE, J. J. *Electroanalytical Chemistry.* Interscience Publishers, New York (2nd ed., 1958).

73. HEFTMANN, E., ed., *Chromatography.* Reinhold Publishing Corp., New York (1961).

General Analytical Reviews and Bibliographies

74. WEIL, B. H., ET AL. *Bibliography on Water and Sewage Analysis.* State Eng. Expt. Sta., Georgia Inst. Technol., Atlanta (1948).

75. Annual Reviews of Analytical Chemistry. *Anal. Chem.* 21:2, 196 (1949); 22:2, 206 (1950); 23:2, 212 (1951); 24:2,

232 (1952); 25:2 (1953); 26:2 (1954); 27:574 (1955); 28:559 (1956); 29:589 (1957); 30:553 (1958); 31:776 (1959); 32:3R (1960); 33:3R (1961); 34:3R (1962); 35:3R (1963); 36:3R (1964).

76. Annual Literature Review, Analytical Methods. *J. WPCF* 32:443 (1960); 33:445 (1961); 34:419 (1962); 35:553 (1963); 36:535 (1964).

Statistics

77. BENEDETTI-PICHLER, A. A. The Application of Statistics to Quantitative Analysis. *Ind. Eng. Chem., Anal. Ed.* 8:373 (1936).

78. CRUMPLER, T. B. & YOE, J. H. *Chemical Computations and Errors.* John Wiley & Sons, New York (1940). Chap. 2.

79. MILLS, C. F. *Statistical Methods.* H. Holt & Co., New York (1940).

80. WORTHING, A. G. & GEFFNER, J. *Treatment of Experimental Data.* John Wiley & Sons, New York (1943).

81. WAUGH, A. E. *Elements of Statistical Method.* McGraw-Hill Book Co., New York (2nd ed., 1943). Chap. 2.

82. YOUDEN, W. J. Technique for Testing the Accuracy of Analytical Data. *Anal. Chem.* 19:946 (1947).

83. *Symposium on Usefulness and Limitations of Samples.* Am. Soc. Testing Materials, Philadelphia (1948).

84. HINTERMAIER, J. C. Foundations for Experimental Design. *Anal. Chem.* 20:1144 (1948).

85. YOUDEN, W. J. Multiple Factor Experiments in Analytical Chemistry. *Anal. Chem.* 20:1136 (1948).

86. DANIELS, F., ET AL. *Experimental Physical Chemistry.* McGraw-Hill Book Co., New York (1949).

87. BROWNLEE, K. A. *Industrial Experimentation.* Chemical Publishing Co., New York (1949).

88. *Symposium on Application of Statistics.* Special Tech. Pub. 103, Am. Soc. Testing Materials, Philadelphia (1950).

89. *Manual on Quality Control of Materials.* Special Tech. Pub. 15C, Am. Soc. Testing Materials, Philadelphia (1951).

90. DEAN, R. B. & DIXON, W. J. Simplified Statistics for Small Numbers of Observations. *Anal. Chem.* 23:636 (1951).

91. LIEBHAFSKY, H. A.; PFEIFFER, H. G.; & BALIS, E. W. Statistical Operating

Rule for Analytical Chemists. *Anal. Chem.* 23:1531 (1951). [See also comments on this paper by G. Wernimont and the authors. *Anal. Chem.* 25:677 (1953).]

92. WERNIMONT, G. Design and Interpretation of Interlaboratory Studies of Test Methods. *Anal. Chem.* 23:1572 (1951).

93. YOUDEN, W. J. *Statistical Methods for Chemists.* John Wiley & Sons, New York (1951).

94. KOLTHOFF, I. M. & SANDELL, E. B. *Textbook of Quantitative Inorganic Analysis.* Macmillan Co., New York (3rd ed., 1952). Chap. 15.

95. GORE, W. L. *Statistical Methods for Chemical Experimentation.* Interscience Publishers, New York (1952).

PART I

Physical and Chemical Examination
of Natural and Treated Waters
in the Absence of Gross Pollution

Introduction

The procedures described in Part I of this manual are intended for the physical and chemical examination of natural and treated waters in the absence of gross pollution. Such waters include surface water, ground water, softened water, cooling or circulating water, process water, boiler water, and boiler feedwater. Other parts of this manual are applicable to examination of sewages and industrial wastes. The examination of water as an industrial raw material is described in the ASTM *Manual on Industrial Water,*[38] which is intended to cover only methods of examination and analysis, not standards of quality. For the effects of various constituents, see the 1962 U.S. Public Health Service Drinking Water Standards,[1] *Water Quality and Treatment,*[4] and *Water Quality Criteria.*[3]

The physical and chemical recommendations of the 1962 U.S. Public Health Service Drinking Water Standards [1] are presented in Table 2. The concentrations in the first column should not be present in a water supply in excess of the listed concentrations where, in the judgment of the reporting agency and the certifying authority, other more suitable supplies are or can be made available. The values listed in the second column constitute grounds for the rejection of the drinking water. In the matter of radioactivity the supply shall be approved if the amounts of radium-226 and strontium-90 do not exceed 3 and 10 $\mu\mu c/l$, respectively, and, in the known absence of strontium-90 and alpha emitters, gross beta concentrations do not exceed 1,000 $\mu\mu c/l$.

A. Collection of Samples

1. Quantity

A 2-liter sample should suffice for most physical and chemical analyses. For certain special determinations, larger samples may be necessary. No attempt should be made to use the same sample for chemical, bacteriologic, and microscopic examinations because the methods of collection and handling are quite different.

2. Time Interval Between Collection and Analysis

In general, the shorter the time that elapses between collection of a sample and its analysis, the more reliable will be the analytical results. For certain constituents and physical values, immediate analysis in the field is required in order to obtain dependable results, because the composition of the sample may change before it arrives at the laboratory.

It is impossible to state unequivocally how much time may be allowed to elapse between collection of a sample and its analysis; this depends upon the character of the sample, the particular analyses to be made, and the conditions of storage. Changes caused by the growth of organisms may be greatly retarded by keeping the sample in the dark and at a low temperature until it

TABLE 2—U.S. PUBLIC HEALTH SERVICE DRINKING WATER STANDARDS, 1962

Characteristic	Limit Not to Be Exceeded	Cause for Rejection
Physical		
Color	15 units	
Taste	Unobjectionable	
Threshold odor number	3	
Turbidity	5 units	
Chemical	*mg/l*	*mg/l*
Alkyl benzene sulfonate	0.5	
Arsenic	0.01	0.05
Barium		1.0
Cadmium		0.01
Chloride	250	
Chromium (hexavalent)		0.05
Copper	1	
Carbon chloroform extract *	0.2	
Cyanide	0.01	0.2
Fluoride †	0.7–1.2	1.4–2.4
Iron	0.3	
Lead		0.05
Manganese	0.05	
Nitrate	45	
Phenols	0.001	
Selenium		0.01
Silver		0.05
Sulfate	250	
Total dissolved solids	500	
Zinc	5	

* Organic contaminants.
† The concentration of fluoride should be between 0.6 and 1.7 mg/l, depending on the listed annual average maximum daily air temperatures.

can be analyzed. The following maximum limits are suggested as reasonable for samples for physical and chemical analysis:

Unpolluted waters .... 72 hr
Slightly polluted waters .... 48 hr
Polluted waters .... 12 hr

The time elapsed between collection and analysis should be recorded on the laboratory report. If the samples are preserved by the addition of acid or other germicide, they may be allowed to stand for longer periods than those just mentioned, but no specific recommendations can be offered. The laboratory report should state which, if any, preservative was added.

Some determinations are more likely to be affected than others by storage of samples prior to analysis. Certain cations are subject to loss by adsorption on or ion exchange with the walls of glass containers. Such cations include aluminum, cadmium, chromium, copper, iron, lead, manganese, silver, and zinc which are best collected in a separate clean bottle and acidified with concentrated hydrochloric or nitric acid to a pH of approximately 3.5 in order to minimize precipitation and adsorption on the walls of the container.

Temperature can change very quickly; pH may change significantly in a matter of minutes; dissolved gases may be lost (oxygen, carbon dioxide, hydrogen sulfide, chlorine) or gained (oxygen, carbon dioxide). For this reason, determinations of temperature, pH, and dissolved gases should always be carried out in the field. With changes in the pH-alkalinity-carbon dioxide balance, calcium carbonate may precipitate and cause a decrease in the values for calcium and for total hardness.

Iron and manganese form readily soluble compounds in their lower (reduced) valence states, and relatively insoluble compounds in their higher (oxidized) valence states; therefore, these cations may precipitate out, or may dissolve out of a sediment, depending upon the redox potential of the sample. Microbiologic activity may be responsible for changes in the nitrate-nitrite-ammonia balance, for decreases in phenols and in BOD, or for the reduction of sulfate to sulfide. Any residual chlorine is converted to chloride. Sulfide, sulfite, ferrous iron, iodide, and cyanide may be lost through oxidation. Color, odor, and turbidity may increase, decrease, or change in quality. Sodium, silica, and boron may be leached out of the glass container. Hexavalent chromium may be reduced to the trivalent state.

This list is by no means all inclusive. It is clearly impossible to prescribe absolute rules for the prevention of all possible changes. Some advice will be found in the discussions under individual determinations, but to a large degree the dependability of water analyses must rest upon the experience and good judgment of the analyst.

3. Representative Samples

Often much time and trouble can be saved if the analyst and the person for whom the tests are to be made will confer in advance concerning the best technique for collecting and analyzing the sample.

Care should be taken to obtain a sample that is truly representative of existing conditions, and to handle it in such a way that it does not deteriorate or become contaminated before it reaches the laboratory. Prior to filling, the sample bottle should be rinsed out two or three times with the water to be collected. Representative samples of some supplies can be obtained only by making composites of samples which have been collected over a period of time or at many different sampling points. The details of collection vary so much with local conditions that no specific recommendations would be universally applicable. Sometimes it will be more informative to analyze numerous separate samples instead of one composite.

Care must be exercised to insure that the analyses are representative of the actual composition of the water sample. Important factors affecting the results are the presence of turbidity, the method chosen for its removal, and the physical and chemical changes brought about by storage or aeration. Each sample containing turbidity must be treated individually with regard to the substances to be determined, the amount and nature of the turbidity present, and other conditions which may influence the results.

It is impossible to give directions covering all conditions which will be encountered, and the choice of technique must be left to the analyst's judgment. In general, any significant amount of suspended matter should be separated by decantation, centrifugation, or an appropriate filtration procedure. Often a slight amount of turbidity can be tolerated if experience shows that it will cause no interference in gravimetric or volumetric tests, and that it can be corrected for in colorimetric tests, where it has potentially the greatest interfering effect. When pertinent, the analyst should state whether or not the sample has been filtered.

A record should be made of every sample collected, and every bottle should be identified, preferably by attaching an appropriately inscribed tag or label. The record should include sufficient information to provide positive identification of the sample at a later date, as well as the name of the sample collector, the date, hour, and exact location, the water temperature, and any data which may be needed in the future for correlation, such as weather conditions, water level, stream flow, or the like. Sampling points should be fixed by detailed description, by maps, or with the aid of stakes, buoys, or landmarks in such a manner as to permit their identification by other persons without reliance upon memory or personal guidance.

Hot samples collected under pressure should be cooled while under pressure (see *E,* Sec. 1 and Fig. 6).

Before collecting samples from distribution systems, the lines should be flushed for a sufficient period to insure that the sample is representative of the supply, taking into account the diameter and length of the pipe to be flushed and the velocity of flow.

Samples from wells should be collected only after the well has been pumped for a sufficient time to insure that the sample will represent the ground water which feeds the well. Sometimes it will be necessary to pump at a specified rate to achieve a characteristic drawdown, if this determines the zones from which the well is supplied. It may be desirable to record the pumping rate and the drawdown as part of the sample record.

When samples are collected from a river or stream, the analytical values may vary with depth, stream flow, and distance from shore, and from one shore to the other. If equipment is available, it is best to take an "integrated" sample from top to bottom in the middle of the stream in such a way that the sample is made composite according to the flow. If only a grab sample can be collected, it is best taken in the middle of the stream and at mid-depth.

Lakes and reservoirs are subject to considerable variations due to normal causes such as seasonal stratification, rainfall, runoff, and wind. The choice of location, depth, and frequency of sampling will depend upon local conditions and upon the purpose of the investigation.

These general directions do not provide enough information for collecting samples in which dissolved gases are to be determined, and specific instructions will be found in the sections which describe these determinations.

B. Ion-Exchange Resins

Ion-exchange resins have in recent years provided the chemist with an important analytical tool. In water analysis, ion exchangers can be applied to: (a) remove interfering ions, (b) determine total ion content, (c) indicate the approximate volume of sample for certain gravimetric determinations,

(d) concentrate trace quantities of cations, and (e) separate anions from cations. This manual recommends the use of ion-exchange resins for the removal of interference in the sulfate determination, and for the determination of total ion content. Inasmuch as the ion-exchange process can be applied in other determinations, a brief description of typical operations will be given here for convenient use where supplementary applications are warranted.

1. Selection of Method

The batch method of ion exchange is satisfactory for sample volumes below 100 ml, while the column method is recommended for larger sample volumes. In the batch method, the resin is agitated with the sample for a given period, after which the resin is removed by filtration. The column method is more efficient in that it provides continuous contact between the sample and the resin, thereby enabling the exchange reaction to go to completion. In this modification, the solution passes slowly through the resin bed and the given ions are quantitatively removed from the sample. Elution of the resin permits recovery of the adsorbed substances.

2. Procedure

Use resins specifically manufactured for analytical applications. Prepare the ion exchanger by rinsing the resin with several volumes of ion-free water (good-quality distilled water) to remove any coloring matter and other leachable material which might interfere with subsequent colorimetric procedures.

2.1. *Batch method for cation removal:* Pipet an aliquot containing 0.1 to 0.2 me

of cations into a 250-ml erlenmeyer flask or beaker and add enough distilled water to bring the final volume to 75 ml. Add 2.0 g strongly acidic cation-exchange resin and stir the mixture at moderate speed for 15 min. Filter through a plug of glass wool placed in the neck of a 4-in. pyrex funnel. When the filtration is complete, wash the resin with two 10-ml portions of distilled water and make up to 100 ml total volume with distilled water.

Regeneration and storage of resin: Transfer the spent resin from the batch procedure to a flask containing 500 ml $3N$ nitric acid. When sufficient resin has accumulated, wash into a column (Fig. 3) and regenerate by passing $3N$

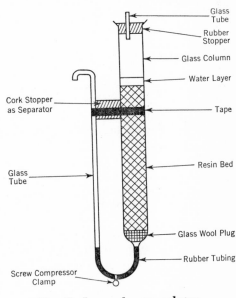

Fig. 3. Ion-exchange column

nitric acid through the column at a rate of 0.1 to 0.2 ml of acid per milliliter of resin per minute. Use 50 me of $3N$ nitric acid per milliliter of resin in the column. Finally, wash the resin with sufficient distilled water until the pH of the effluent is 5–7, using the same rate of flow as in the regeneration step. If desired, remove the resin from the column and store under distilled water in a wide-mouth container. Should the water become colored during storage, decant and replace with fresh distilled water. Prior to use, filter the resin through a plug of glass wool placed in the neck of a funnel, wash with distilled water, and allow to drain. The resin is then ready for use.

2.2. *Column method for cation removal:* Prepare the column as depicted in Fig. 3 (length of resin bed, 21.5 cm; diameter of column, 1.3 cm; representing approximately 21 ml or 20 g of resin). Other ion-exchange columns can be used equally well. One of the simplest consists of a buret containing a plug of glass wool immediately above the stopcock. (Whatever type of column is adopted, the liquid level in the column should never be allowed to fall below the upper surface of the resin because the trapped air causes uneven flow rates and poor efficiency of ion exchange.)

Charge the column by stirring the resin in a beaker with distilled water and then carefully washing the suspension into the column through a funnel. Backwash the column immediately by introducing distilled water at the bottom and passing it upward through the column until all air bubbles and channels are removed from the column. Connect a separatory funnel to the top of the column. Allow the sample to flow through the column at the rate of 0.2 ml of solution per milliliter of resin in the column per minute. After all of the sample has passed through the column, wash the resin with distilled water until the effluent pH is 5–7. Use strips of blue litmus paper or other indicating methods to determine when the column is washed free of acid. (When adsorbing cations from such large volumes of sample as one or more liters, it is advantageous to start this operation before the close of a work day and allow the exchange process to proceed overnight. The column will not run dry because of the curved outlet.)

Column elution: After the distilled-water wash, elute the adsorbed cations by passing 100 ml of 3N nitric acid through the column at a rate of 0.2 ml of acid per milliliter of resin per minute. (A volume of 100 ml 3N nitric acid quantitatively removes 3 me of cations. For quantities of adsorbed cations in excess of 3 me, additional increments of 100 ml 3N nitric acid are needed.) After the elution step, rinse the column free of acid with enough distilled water to produce an effluent pH of 5–7. Conduct the wash at the same flow rate as the acid elution. The acid elution and wash regenerate the column for future use. The combined acid eluate and wash water effluent contain the cations originally present in the sample.

C. Checking of Correctness of Analyses

1. Anion-Cation Balance

Theoretically, the sum of the anions, expressed in me/l, must exactly equal the sum of the cations, in me/l, in any sample. In practice, the sums are seldom equal because of unavoidable variations in the analyses. This inequality increases as the ionic concentration increases. A control chart can be constructed so that it will be immediately evident if the difference between the sum of the anions and cations, in me/l, falls between acceptable limits, which have been taken as ±1 standard deviation. If the difference is plotted against the sum of the anions, the lines showing ±1 standard deviation, that is, the acceptable limits, are given by the equation:

Σ anions $-\ \Sigma$ cations
$$= \pm (0.1065 + 0.0155 \ \Sigma \text{ anions})$$

This is shown in Fig. 4 and 5, which represent modified control charts. Values of differences of the sums fall-

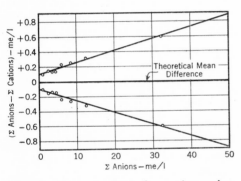

Fig. 4. Control chart for anion-cation balances

ing outside of the limits set by the equations indicate that at least one of the determinations deserves to be rechecked.

By a fortuitous combination of erroneous analyses which result in the balancing of errors, it is possible for the sum of the anions to agree with the sum of the cations even though two or more individual analytical results are seriously incorrect. The additional methods of checking which follow are useful for detecting such discrepancies.

2. Specific Conductance

In using specific conductance to check analyses, two methods of calculation may be employed.

2.1. *Rough calculation:* In most natural waters it has been found that when specific conductance (in micromhos/cm at 25°C) is multiplied by a factor which ordinarily lies in the range 0.55–0.7, the product is equal to mg/l total filtrable residue. For waters which contain ap-

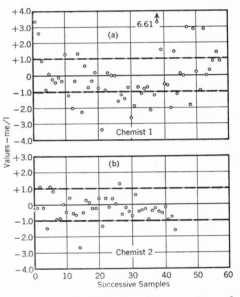

Fig. 5. Control chart with transformed limits

The vertical scale is plotted:
$$\frac{\Sigma \text{ anions } - \Sigma \text{ cations}}{0.1065 + 0.0155 \ \Sigma \text{ anions}}$$

preciable concentrations of free acid or caustic alkalinity, the factor may be much lower than 0.55, and for highly saline waters it may be much higher than 0.7. An approximate check based on this principle will reveal gross mistakes in analysis.

2.2. *More refined calculation:* In order to obtain better results based upon electrical conductance, it is necessary to dilute the sample so that its conductance falls within a narrow range and to take into account the contribution of each separate ion to the total measured conductance. Distilled water, boiled and cooled, is used to dilute the sample in a known ratio until the conductance lies between 90 and 120 micromhos/cm. Some trial may be necessary to achieve the proper dilution, because the conductance does not vary in exact ratio to the dilution; if it did, dilution would be unnecessary. The exact dilution ratio, D, must be known:

$$D = \frac{V_s + V_w}{V_s}$$

in which V_s is volume of sample and V_w is volume of distilled water. The conductance of the distilled water must be determined; it should not be greater than 2 micromhos/cm. Conductance is determined in the usual way. The "diluted conductance," K_d, is calculated from the equation:

$$K_d = \frac{AD \times 10^6}{R_d} - (D - 1) K_w$$

where A is the cell constant, R_d is the measured resistance, in ohms, of the diluted sample, and K_w is the distilled-water conductance.

Next the diluted conductance is computed from the chemical analysis by multiplying the concentration found (as either me/l or mg/l) by the appropriate factor in Table 3 and summing the products. If this computed diluted conductance is more than 1.5 per cent greater or more than 2 per cent lower than the measured value of the diluted conductance, it is advisable to recheck the chemical analysis.

The diluted-conductance method of checking is not applicable to samples which have conductances initially lower

TABLE 3—CONDUCTANCE FACTORS OF IONS COMMONLY FOUND IN WATER

Ion	Conductance (25°C) micromhos/cm	
	Per me/l	Per mg/l
Bicarbonate	43.6	0.715
Calcium	52.0	2.60
Carbonate	84.6	2.82
Chloride	75.9	2.14
Magnesium	46.6	3.82
Nitrate	71.0	1.15
Potassium	72.0	1.84
Sodium	48.9	2.13
Sulfate	73.9	1.54

than 90 micromhos/cm or pH values less than 6 or greater than 9, or to samples which contain significant quantities of ions not listed in Table 3. The conductances due to hydrogen ion and hydroxyl ion are much greater than those due to other ions, and will cause the method to be invalid for samples outside of the pH 6–9 range.

3. Ion Exchange

When all the major ionic constituents of a simple natural water are quantitatively determined, the accuracy of the chemical analysis can also be checked by means of an ion-exchange method. A serious discrepancy between the cations, me/l, obtained by titration of the sample after ion exchange and the total cation concentration found by the summation of the determined constituents can uncover a gross error in the water analysis.

The ion-exchange method is based upon the replacement of the cations in the original sample with hydrogen ions supplied by a strongly acidic cation-exchange resin. The acid produced by mixing the sample with the resin is titrated with standard sodium hydroxide. The total alkalinity of the original sample must also be ascertained in order to complete the calculation.

The apparatus required for the ion-exchange method consists of a pH meter (line or battery operated) or methyl orange indicator; a magnetic or mechanical stirrer provided with a speed control; a 10-ml buret graduated in 0.05-ml steps; and glass wool. The reagents comprise $0.02N$ standard acid, $0.02N$ standard sodium hydroxide, a strongly acidic cation-exchange resin like Amberlite IR-120 (H) * of analytical grade, and distilled water.

The procedure is carried out by pipeting a sample of water containing 0.1 to 0.2 me of cations into a 250-ml erlenmeyer flask or beaker and adding enough distilled water to bring the final volume to 100 ml. Then 2.0 g of cation-exchange resin is added and the mixture is stirred at moderate speed for 15 min. The resin is removed by filtration through a plug of glass wool placed in the neck of a 4-in. pyrex funnel and is washed with two 15-ml portions of distilled water. The combined filtrate and washings are titrated to pH 4.5 with $0.02N$ standard sodium hydroxide, using a pH meter or methyl orange as endpoint indicator, and stirring the solution during the titration.

The cation exchange can also be performed by the column method described in B, Sec. 2.2, above.

The alkalinity present in the water sample, in me/l, is determined by titrating an aliquot of the original water sample to a pH of 4.5 with $0.02N$ standard acid, using a pH meter or methyl orange as endpoint indicator.

The total cations in the sample (E, me/l) is finally computed by the equation:

* Rohm and Haas Company.

$$E = \frac{AB \times 1{,}000}{C} + D \qquad (1)$$

in which A is the volume (ml) of the standard sodium hydroxide used in titrating the filtrate from the ion exchange, B is the normality of the standard sodium hydroxide, C is the volume (ml) of water sample taken, and D is the alkalinity (me/l) present in the water sample.

The column method of ion exchange is preferred for checking the results of the gravimetric determinations for filtrable residues because less attention to the total milliequivalents of cations in the sample is required.

The filtrable and fixed filtrable residues are determined by multiplying the quantity $(E - D)$ from the preceding Eq 1 by a factor—usually found to be between 70 and 90, depending on the water tested and the resin used in the column—and adding $50D$. For more accurate determinations, the factors can be derived for the type of water tested routinely by subtracting $50D$ from the filtrable residues and dividing the results by the quantity $(E - D)$, thus:

$$\frac{R_{fg} - 50D}{E - D} = F_1 \qquad (2)$$

$$\frac{R_{ffg} - 50D}{E - D} = F_2 \qquad (3)$$

where R_{fg} and R_{ffg} are the filtrable and fixed filtrable residues determined gravimetrically and F_1 and F_2 are the resulting factors. The equations for calculating the filtrable residues are then:

$$(E - D) F_1 + 50D = R_{fx} \qquad (4)$$
$$(E - D) F_2 + 50D = R_{ffx} \qquad (5)$$

where R_{fx} and R_{ffx} are the filtrable and fixed filtrable residues determined by ion exchange.

Once these factors are derived for the particular water, the filtrable-residue values can be determined by ion exchange and the gravimetric values obtained less frequently, or only when there is a major change in the water being checked.

For approximation purposes, a factor of 80 may be used in either Eq 4 or Eq 5. If the water tested has an unusually high sulfate or bicarbonate content compared to chloride (mg/l), or has unusually high organic content, the factor in Eq 4 approaches 90. If the water tested has an unusually high chloride content compared to sulfate (mg/l), the factor more nearly approximates 70.

D. Evaluation of Methods in Water Section

The precision and accuracy data cited in Part I for a number of laboratory determinations are based on results of studies by the Analytical Reference Service * which is conducted by the Public Health Service, Robert A. Taft Sanitary Engineering Center in Cincinnati.

This activity is devoted to the cooperative study of analytical methods that are or may be applied to environmental samples—water, air, foods. These studies provide a basis for evaluation of selected analytical methods, both existing standard methods and new methods that offer promise. They supply a factual basis for judgment of what may be expected by practitioners applying such methods. Currently almost 200 agencies—public, private, and universities—comprise the membership of the Analytical Reference Service.

E. Examination of Industrial Water Supplies

The following brief paragraphs summarize the reasons for conducting an examination of an industrial water supply. Inasmuch as this section is limited in scope, the reader is urged to refer to comprehensive reference books on industrial water treatment [28, 36, 37, 38] for an appreciation of the complexities of the subject.

The matter of examination assumes great importance during the selection of a proper water supply for a specific industrial application or a variety of uses. [41, 45, 46] After the most suitable raw water supply and the method of

treatment have been chosen, control of the necessary water conditioning procedures is required to insure the adequate treatment of the water. [38]

Boiler feed and cooling are probably the leading uses of industrial water. Additionally, a multitude of other process applications may dictate that many specialized treatments and specific analytical procedures be instituted, particularly when water is used under high or varied temperature conditions. For example, analysis for only chloride and phosphate concentrations may be necessary for treatment control in one type of system, whereas in the case of a very high-pressure boiler, alkalinity, phos-

---

* Information brochure available.

phate, pH, copper, iron, hydrazine or sulfite, morpholine, sulfate, chloride, and others may be required.

Table 4 lists the determinations most frequently performed to control the quality of water destined for steam generation, heating, cooling, and other manufacturing processes. The method of analysis for each particular constituent is set forth under the appropriate heading in the Water Section, and in a few cases in Part IV, the Industrial Waste Section. Procedures for chromate,[40] hydrazine,[32] morpholine,[39] nickel,[35] nitrite,[42] and octadecylamine [43] are described in the references cited in the bibliography at the end of this section.

1. Collection of Samples

Samples not collected under pressure are obtained in the usual manner, observing the precautions outlined in Section A. Boiler waters collected under pressure should be cooled to approximately 20°C while still under pressure. Figure 6 illustrates typical sampling-cooling installations. Certain determinations demand specialized sampling equipment and procedures, and/or analyses conducted immediately after collection of samples. Specific examples include dissolved oxygen, dissolved and total iron, carbon dioxide, hydrogen sulfide, octadecylamine in condensate, etc. For such determinations, the sampling procedures are generally specified as part of the analytical method.

2. Expression of Results

As a general rule, results are expressed in milligrams per liter or parts per million in terms of the substances actually determined, and then converted into milliequivalents per liter for the purpose of comparing the positive and negative ions.

TABLE 4—ROUTINE AND SPECIAL DETERMINATIONS ON INDUSTRIAL WATER SAMPLES

Determination	Applications *
Acidity	B, C, P
Alkalinity :	
Hydroxyl (OH)	B, P
Phenolphthalein (P)	B, C, P
Total, methyl orange or	
mixed indicator (M)	B, C, P
Ammonia	B, P
Boron	C, P
Calcium	B, C, P
Carbon dioxide	B, P
Chloride	B, C, P
Chlorine, residual	C, P
Chromium, hexavalent	B, C, P
Color	P
Copper	B, C, P
Fluoride	C, P
Hardness	B, C, P
Hydrazine	B
Iron	B, C, P
Lead	P
Magnesium	B, C, P
Manganese	C, P
Morpholine	B
Nickel	B, P
Nitrate	B, C, P
Nitrite	B, C, P
Octadecylamine	B
Oil and grease	B, C, P
Oxygen, dissolved	B, P
pH	B, C, P
Phosphate :	
Ortho	B, C, P
Poly	B, C, P
Residue, total (103°C) :	
Filtrable	B, C, P
Non-filtrable	B, C, P
Silica	B, C, P
Sodium	B, C, P
Specific conductance	B, C, P
Sulfate	B, C, P
Sulfide	C, P
Sulfite	B, C, P
Tannin and lignin	B, C, P
Turbidity	P
Zinc	B, C, P

* Key: B—boiler water, feedwater, or condensate; C—cooling water, recirculating (open and closed systems) or once-through; P—Industrial process applications.

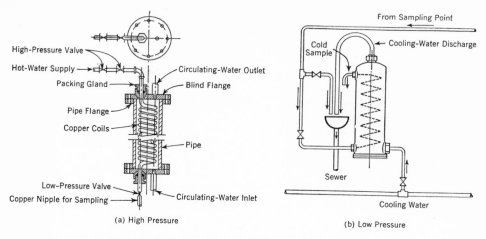

High-Pressure Valve
Hot-Water Supply
Packing Gland
Pipe Flange
Copper Coils
Circulating-Water Outlet
Blind Flange
Pipe
Low-Pressure Valve
Copper Nipple for Sampling
Circulating-Water Inlet

(a) High Pressure

From Sampling Point
Cold Sample
Cooling-Water Discharge
Sewer
Cooling Water

(b) Low Pressure

Fig. 6. Cooling coils for boiler water sampling

These illustrations do not represent standardized equipment, but exemplify the characteristics of the devices that should be used.

3. Scale

The occurrence of scale or sludge formation in industrial water systems may cause equipment failures, such as boiler tube ruptures or plugged heat exchanger tubing. Such occurrences frequently result from increased temperature, evaporation or aeration, which cause insolubility of some of the ions or ion combinations present. Common scale deposits may consist of calcium carbonate, sulfate, silicate, or phosphate and magnesium hydroxide, silicate, and phosphate. Others may be iron oxides, silica, and related substances.

In distribution systems of 0–93°C (32–200°F) temperature, the tendency of a water supply to form calcium carbonate scale may be estimated by calculating the Langelier pH of saturation (pH_s) from the calcium, alkalinity, dissolved solids of the water (see Saturation and Stability) and subtracting this pH from the actual measured pH of the water. A positive value indicates scale-forming tendency; a negative value

indicates scale dissolving (or corrosive) tendency. A balanced or stable water generally has a zero or slightly positive index. The literature also includes methods for calculating indices or solubilities of calcium phosphate,[25] calcium sulfate,[34] and magnesium hydroxide.[33]

Scale prevention in boilers [28, 30] is usually attained by ion exchange or other hardness reduction methods. The residual hardness is then precipitated inside the boiler by the addition of phosphate and organic sludge conditioning chemicals, producing a non-adhering sludge rather than a scale.

For sludge removal and maintenance of scale-free conditions, and for the control of steam quality, maximum limits are designated for the total dissolved solids, and control is accomplished by blowdown as necessary.

Pre-softening of makeup water for cooling towers is also practiced, and the application of acid for alkalinity reduction is generally employed. Polyphosphates and other chemicals are also applied to control calcium carbonate, calcium phosphate, and silica deposit formation.[44] Proper and adequate bleedoff is an important part of treatment of cooling water.

4. Corrosion

Corrosion causes metal in the system to dissolve and possibly to redeposit later as oxides. Certain constituents or contaminants in the water, including dissolved oxygen, carbon dioxide, anions (such as chloride and sulfate) and acidity (low pH) increase the corrosive tendency of the water. Microorganisms such as sulfate-reducing or iron bacteria also cause corrosion.

Development of a thin protective layer of calcium carbonate on the metal surfaces is often effective for preventing corrosion of the metal in the water distribution system. The Saturation Index or Ryznar [24] Stability Index may be used to suggest corrosive tendency, or the degree of stability or balance.

Another procedure [31] for estimating corrosive tendency is calculation of the

$$\text{ratio}: \frac{\text{me per liter } (Cl^- + SO_4^=)}{\text{me per liter alkalinity as } CaCO_3}.$$

In the neutral pH range (7 to 8) and the presence of dissolved oxygen, ratios below about 0.2 indicate general freedom from corrosion, whereas increasingly higher ratios are indicative of more aggressive waters.

Corrosion in boilers is controlled by removal of the oxygen from the feedwater by deaeration, and by the reaction of residual oxygen with sodium sulfite or hydrazine. The corrosion of iron is also effectively reduced by the application of alkaline chemicals such as caustic soda and sodium phosphates to provide boiler water pH in the range of 10–12.

Carbonate and bicarbonate decompose in the boiler to release carbon dioxide in the steam. This causes formation of carbonic acid in the steam condensate,[23, 26] and acidic corrosion results. The presence of dissolved oxygen accelerates carbonic acid attack.

Steam condensate corrosion can be minimized by maintaining minimum carbonate content in the boiler water, and by the use of low bicarbonate or carbonate makeup waters. The neutralizing amines such as morpholine and cyclohexylamine are helpful in reducing condensate system corrosion. Octadecylamine,[29] which forms a monomolecular film on the walls of the condensate piping, is also effective in reducing corrosion.

Inhibition of corrosion in cooling towers is provided by the application of corrosion inhibitors such as chromates, phosphates, and silicates, applied singly or in various combinations. Open recirculating cooling systems,[27, 44] in which water is continuously saturated with dissolved oxygen, offer more difficult corrosion control problems than do closed recirculating systems.

F. Standard Specifications for Water Treatment Chemicals

Many laboratories perform analyses on the bulk chemicals received at the plant for the treatment of water. The standards usually followed for such analyses are those prepared and issued by a committee of the American Water Works Association. Each separate standard describes the acceptable physical and chemical characteristics of the material, and presents methods for collecting the sample and determining the major components in order to ascertain compliance with the specifications. The detailed standards for the common water treatment chemicals are available at nominal cost from the American Water Works Association.[47]

Bibliography

General

1. Public Health Service Drinking Water Standards, 1962. *US Public Health Service Pub.* No. 956 (1963).
2. TAYLOR, F. B. Significance of Trace Elements in Public Finished Water Supplies. *J. AWWA* 55:619 (1963).
3. *Water Quality Criteria.* California State Water Pollution Control Board, Sacramento (2nd ed., 1963).
4. *Water Quality and Treatment.* Am. Water Works Assoc., New York (3rd ed., 1965).

Collection of Samples

5. ELLISON, G.; HACKLER, H. W.; & BUICE, W. A. Effects of Age and Storage Temperatures on Growth of Bacteria in Water Samples. *J. AWWA* 24: 895 (1932).
6. WELCH, P. S. *Limnological Methods.* Blakiston Co., Philadelphia (1948). Chap. 14.
7. HAUCK, C. F. Gaging and Sampling Waterborne Industrial Wastes. *ASTM Bull.* (Dec. 1949). pp. 38–43.
8. BLACK, H. H. Procedures for Sampling and Measuring Industrial Wastes. *Sew. Ind. Wastes* 24:45 (1952).
9. WELCH, P. S. *Limnology.* McGraw-Hill Book Co., New York (2nd ed., 1952). Chap. 5.
10. *Standard Methods of Sampling Industrial Water—D510-57.* Am. Soc. Testing Materials, Philadelphia (1957).
11. TAYLOR, E. W. *Examination of Waters and Water Supplies.* Little, Brown & Co., Boston, Mass. (7th ed., 1958). Chap. 11.
12. RAINWATER, F. H. & THATCHER, L. L. Methods for Collection and Analysis of Water Samples. *US Geol. Survey Water Supply Paper* No. 1454 (1960).

Ion Exchange

13. KUNIN, R., ET AL. Ion Exchange. *Anal.*
    Chem. 21:87 (1949); 22:64 (1950); 23:45 (1951); 24:64 (1952); 26:104 (1954); 28:729 (1956); 30:681 (1958); 32:67R (1960); 34:101R (1962).
14. SAMUELSON, O. *Ion Exchange in Analytical Chemistry.* John Wiley & Sons, New York (1953).

Checking of Analyses

15. ROSSUM, J. R. Conductance Method for Checking Accuracy of Water Analyses. *Anal. Chem.* 21:631 (1949).
16. ROBERTSON, R. S. & NIELSEN, M. F. Quick Test Determines Dissolved Solids. *Power* 95:87 (Feb. 1951).
17. NAVONE, R. Sodium Determination With Ion-Exchange Resin. *J. AWWA* 46: 479 (1954).
18. GREENBERG, A. E. & NAVONE, R. Use of the Control Chart in Checking Anion-Cation Balances in Water. *J. AWWA* 50:1365 (1958).

Evaluation of Methods

19. KRAMER, H. P. & KRONER, R. C. Cooperative Studies on Laboratory Methodology. *J. AWWA* 51:607 (1959).
20. KRONER, R. C.; BALLINGER, D. G.; & KRAMER, H. P. Evaluation of Laboratory Methods for Analysis of Heavy Metals in Water. *J. AWWA* 52:117 (1960).
21. MULLINS, J. W., ET AL. Evaluation of Methods for Counting Gross Radioactivity in Water. *J. AWWA* 53: 1466 (1961).
22. LISHKA, R. J.; KELSO, F. S.; & KRAMER, H. P. Evaluation of Methods for Determination of Minerals in Water. *J. AWWA* 55:647 (1963).

Industrial Water Supplies

23. COLLINS, L. F. More Information Concerning Corrosion in Steam Heating Systems. *Fourth Water Conf., Engineers Soc. W. Pennsylvania.* 33 (1943).
24. RYZNAR, J. W. A New Index for Determining Amount of Calcium Carbonate Scale Formed by a Water. *J. AWWA* 36:472 (1944).
25. GREEN, J. & HOLMES, J. A. Calculation of the pH of Saturation of Tricalcium Phosphate. *J. AWWA* 39:1090 (1947).
26. BERK, A. A. & NIGON, J. Amine Volatility and Alkalinity in Relation to

Corrosion Control in Steam Heating Systems. *U.S. Bureau of Mines Tech. Paper* 714 (1948).

27. APPLEBAUM, S. B. Treatment of Cooling Water. *Combustion.* 22:No. 5, 41–48 (Nov. 1950).

28. Boiler Water Chemistry Symposium. *Ind. Eng. Chem.* 46:953 (1954).

29. WILKES, J. F., ET AL. Filming Amines —Use and Misuse in Power Plant Water-Steam Cycles. *American Power Conf.* XVII, 527 (1955).

30. APPLEBAUM, S. B. & ZUMBRUNNEN, R. J. Selecting Water-Treating Processes for Medium-Pressure Boilers. *A.S.M.E. Paper No. 56–A–191* (1956).

31. LARSON, T. E. & SKOLD, R. V. Laboratory Studies Relating Mineral Quality of Water to Corrosion of Steel and Cast Iron. *Corrosion* 14:No. 6, 285t (1958).

32. *Tentative Method of Test for Hydrazine in Industrial Water.* D1385–58T. Am. Soc. Testing Materials, Philadelphia. (1958).

33. LARSON, T. E., ET AL. Stabilization of Magnesium Hydroxides in the Solids-Contact Process. *J. AWWA* 51:1551 (1959).

34. DENMAN, W. L. Maximum Re-Use of Cooling Water. *Ind. Eng. Chem.* 53:817 (1961).

35. *Tentative Method for Nickel in Industrial Water, D1886–61T.* Am. Soc. Testing Materials, Philadelphia (1961).

36. NORDELL, E. *Water Treatment for Industrial and Other Uses.* Reinhold Publishing Corp., New York (2nd ed., 1961).

37. HAMER, P.; JACKSON, J.; & THURSTON, E. F. *Industrial Water Treatment Practice.* Butterworths, London (1961).

38. *Manual on Industrial Water and Industrial Waste Water.* Special Tech. Pub. 148-F. Am. Soc. Testing Materials, Philadelphia (2nd ed., 1962), Chap. IV, p. 37 and Chap. V, p. 53.

39. *Tentative Method of Test for Morpholine in Industrial Water.* (ASTM Designation D 1942–62T), ASTM Spec. Tech. Pub. 148F. Am. Soc. Testing Materials, Philadelphia (1962).

40. FURMAN, N. H., ed. *Standard Methods of Chemical Analysis.* D. Van Nostrand Co., Princeton, N.J. (6th ed., 1962). Vol. I, pp. 354 & 360.

41. *Public Health Service Drinking Water Standards, 1962.* U.S. Public Health Service Pub. No. 956. (1963).

42. *Nitrite Ion in Industrial Water, Non-Referee Method, Tentative* (ASTM Designation D 1254–63T). Report of Committee D-19, 1963 preprint. Am. Soc. Testing Materials, Philadelphia.

43. *Tentative Method for Primary and Secondary Amines in Industrial Water.* Report of Committee D-19, 1963 preprint. Am. Soc. Testing Materials, Philadelphia.

44. LANE, R. W. & LARSON, T. E. Role of Water Treatment in the Economic Operation of Cooling Towers. *American Power Conf.* XXV, 687–701 (1963).

45. *Water Quality Criteria.* California State Water Pollution Control Board, Sacramento (2nd ed., 1963).

46. *Water Quality and Treatment.* Am. Water Works Assoc., New York (3rd ed., 1965).

Standard Specifications for Water Treatment Chemicals

47. *AWWA Standards for Water Treatment Chemicals.* Am. Water Works Assoc., New York: (separates)

B200–64 Sodium Chloride
B201–59 Soda Ash
B202–54 Quicklime and Hydrated Lime
B250–51 Cation Exchanger Test Procedures
B300–64 Hypochlorites
B301–59 Liquid Chlorine
B302–64 Ammonium Sulfate
B401–53 Bauxite
B402–53 Ferrous Sulfate
B403–64 Aluminum Sulfate
B404–58 Liquid Sodium Silicate
B405–60 Sodium Aluminate
B406–61T (Tentative) Ferric Sulfate
B500–53 Trisodium Phosphate
B501–64 Caustic Soda
B600–53 Powdered Activated Carbon
B601–64 Sodium Pyrosulfite
B602–59 Copper Sulfate
B701–60 Sodium Fluoride
B702–60 Sodium Silicofluoride
B703–60 Fluosilicic Acid

Acidity

The acidity of a water is the capacity of that water to donate protons. This includes the un-ionized portions of weakly ionizing acids such as carbonic acid and tannic acid, as well as hydrolyzing salts like ferrous and/or aluminum sulfate. Mineral acids contribute to acidity when the sample has a low pH value. The acidity is significant because acids contribute to the corrosiveness of water.

1. General Discussion

1.1. *Principle:* An equilibrium between carbonate, bicarbonate, and carbon dioxide exists in many natural waters used for potable purposes. The carbonate and bicarbonate can be estimated by titrating the alkalinity with standard acid to the bicarbonate equivalence point of pH 8.3 and then to the carbonic acid equivalence point in the pH range of 4 to 5. Acid pollutants entering a water supply in sufficient quantity will disturb the carbonate-bicarbonate-carbon dioxide equilibrium. The extent of this disturbance may be estimated by titrating with standard alkali to the endpoints of pH 4.5 and 8.3.

The titration of the sample at boiling temperature in the presence of phenolphthalein indicator has been found useful for water plant control where the source of supply is polluted with mineral acids and acid salts originating from acid mine drainage and some industrial wastes. Heat speeds the hydrolysis of iron and aluminum sulfate, enabling the rapid completion of the titration. This determination provides an estimate of the lime application which may be required to make such water supplies satisfactory for general use.

1.2. *Interference:* A fading and impermanent endpoint characterizes the phenolphthalein acidity titration performed at room temperature on a sample containing iron and aluminum sulfate. Better results are obtained by titrating the sample at boiling temperature. Free available residual chlorine may bleach methyl orange indicator in an acid medium, an effect which can be overcome by dechlorinating the sample with 1 drop of $0.1N$ sodium thiosulfate.

1.3. *Sampling and storage:* Samples should be collected in polyethylene or pyrex bottles and stored at a low temperature. Determinations should be performed as soon after sampling as practicable, preferably within 1 day.

2. Apparatus

Refer to Alkalinity, Sec. 2.1 and 2.2, below. The apparatus there described is also suitable for the acidity titrations.

3. Reagents

Except for standard $0.02N$ sulfuric acid or hydrochloric acid, all the reagents listed for the determination of Alkalinity, Sec. 3, are required, and in addition:

3.1. *Sodium hydroxide, saturated, 15N.* To prepare a carbonate-free solution, dissolve 625 g NaOH in 800 ml distilled water (or 454 g NaOH in 650 ml distilled water) and let stand at least 48 hr in an alkali-resistant container (wax lined or polyethylene), protected from atmospheric CO_2 with a soda lime tube. Consult the General Introduction, A, Sec. 4.7, for additional details on the preparation and handling of this general reagent.

3.2. *Sodium hydroxide, 1N.* Dilute 67 ml 15N NaOH with CO_2-free distilled water to 1 liter. Protect this solution from atmospheric CO_2 with a soda lime tube.

3.3. *Standard sodium hydroxide titrant, 0.02N.* Dilute 20.0 ml 1N NaOH with CO_2-free distilled water to 1 liter. Store in a tightly rubber-stoppered pyrex glass bottle protected from atmospheric CO_2 by a soda lime tube. For best results, prepare weekly. Standardize the solution against 0.0200N potassium biphthalate solution which has been prepared by dissolving 4.085 g anhydrous $KHC_8H_4O_4$, and diluting to the mark of a 1-liter volumetric flask with CO_2-free distilled water. Perform the standardization exactly as the typical acidity titration, using the identical volumes of final solution, phenolphthalein or methyl orange indicator, and the same time interval for the determination. For best results, take for standardization a volume of 0.0200N potassium biphthalate solution which approximates the average acidity of the water samples normally encountered in the given laboratory. Since the response to endpoint color changes varies among individuals, each analyst should perform the standardization independently and use the normality factor appropriate for his own technique. A standard NaOH solution, exactly 0.0200N, is equivalent to 1.00 mg $CaCO_3$ per 1.00 ml.

4. Procedure

4.1. Sample volumes requiring less than 25 ml of titrant yield the sharpest color changes at the endpoint and, therefore, are recommended. If indicator methods are used, remove the free available residual chlorine by adding 0.05 ml (1 drop) 0.1N sodium thiosulfate solution.

4.2. *Methyl orange acidity:* Add 0.1 ml (2 drops) methyl orange indicator to a sample of suitable size, 50.0 or 100 ml if possible, in a white porcelain casserole or an erlenmeyer flask over a white surface. Titrate with standard 0.02N NaOH until the color changes to the faint orange characteristic of pH 4.5.

4.3. *Phenolphthalein acidity:* Add 0.15 ml (3 drops) phenolphthalein indicator to a sample of suitable size, 50.0 or 100 ml if possible, in a white porcelain casserole or an erlenmeyer flask over a white surface. Titrate with standard 0.02N NaOH to the appearance of the faint pink color characteristic of pH 8.3.

4.4. *Phenolphthalein acidity at boiling temperature:* Add 0.15–0.5 ml (3–10 drops) phenolphthalein indicator to a sample of suitable size, 50.0 to 100 ml if possible (or an aliquot diluted to these volumes), in a white porcelain casserole or an erlenmeyer flask over a white surface. Heat the sample to boiling and boil for 2 min. Titrate the hot sample with standard 0.02N NaOH to a permanent pink endpoint.

5. Calculation

$$\text{Acidity as mg/1 } CaCO_3 = \frac{A \times N \times 50,000}{\text{ml sample}}$$

where A = ml titration for sample, and N = normality of NaOH.

In reporting the results, state the indicator used and the temperature at which the titration was performed.

Bibliography

1. ELLMS, J. & BENEKER, J. C. The Estimation of Carbonic Acid in Water. *J. Am. Chem. Soc.* 23:405 (1901).
2. JOHNSTON, J. The Determination of Carbonic Acid, Combined and Free, in Solution, Particularly in Natural Waters.

J. Am. Chem. Soc. 38:947 (1916).
3. KOLTHOFF, I. M. Titration of Carbonic Acid and Its Salts. *Chem. Weekblad.* 14:781 (1917).
4. SELVIG, W. A. & RATLIFF, W. C. The Nature of Acid Water From Coal Mines and the Determination of Acidity. *Ind. Eng. Chem.* 14:125 (1922).

Alkalinity*

The alkalinity of a water is the capacity of that water to accept protons. Alkalinity is usually imparted by the bicarbonate, carbonate, and hydroxide components of a natural or treated water supply. It is determined by titration with a standard solution of a strong mineral acid to the successive bicarbonate and carbonic acid equivalence points, indicated electrometrically or by means of color. Phenolphthalein indicator enables the measurement of that alkalinity fraction contributed by the hydroxide and half of the carbonate. Indicators responding in the pH range 4–5 are used to measure the alkalinity contributed by hydroxide, carbonate, and bicarbonate. The phenolphthalein alkalinity and total-alkalinity titrations are useful for the calculation of chemical dosages required in the treatment of natural water supplies. The stoichiometric relationships between hydroxide, carbonate, and bicarbonate are valid only in the absence of significant concentrations of weak acid radicals other than hydroxyl, carbonate, or bicarbonate.

1. General Discussion

1.1. *Selection of potentiometric or indicator method:* A number of advantages make the potentiometric titration the method of choice for accurate determinations. The equivalence point can be identified by the inflection in the titration curve or by the differential method of calculation.† The plot of a potentiometric titration curve also reveals any shift in the equivalence point caused by temperature, ionic strength, and, in the case of the total alkalinity, the effect of the carbon dioxide concentration at the equivalence point. Moreover, the potentiometric method is free from residual-chlorine interference, the influence of color and turbidity, and individual visual idiosyncrasies. Properly performed, however, the more rapid and simple indicator method is satisfactory for control and routine applications.

1.2. *Equivalence points:* The equivalence point to which the total-alkalinity titration must be carried is determined by the concentration of CO_2 present at the end of the titration. If the sample originally contained relatively little CO_2 or hydroxide, and if the mixing during the titration is not vigorous, then the alkalinity will determine the equivalence point. The following pH values are suggested as the equivalence points for the corresponding alkalinity concentrations as calcium car-

---

* See also Carbon Dioxide and the Three Forms of Alkalinity, and Saturation and Stability with Respect to Calcium Carbonate.

† For an illustration of this method, see Part III, Chloride, *C*, Sec. 4.4 and 4.5.

bonate: pH 5.1 for total alkalinities of about 30 mg/l, pH 4.8 for 150 mg/l, and pH 4.5 for 500 mg/l. Indicators effective in these ranges will give the most reliable results. A mixed indicator prepared from bromcresol green and methyl red is suitable for the higher pH values, while methyl orange can be used for those below 4.6. Since a written description of color shadings can frequently mislead rather than inform, dominant wavelength being a more exact method of defining color, the analyst is urged to prepare buffer solutions of the applicable pH, add the proper volume of indicator, and use these solutions as standards for color comparison until acquaintance with the various indicator color transitions is achieved. The same considerations apply to the phenolphthalein endpoint. For purposes of ascertaining the faint phenolphthalein endpoint, it is advisable to employ a buffer solution with a pH value of 8.3, to which the proper volume of indicator is added, as a standard of comparison. (See Carbon Dioxide, Method B, Sec. 3.3.)

1.3. *Interference:* Free available residual chlorine markedly affects the indicator color response in some water supplies through bleaching action. The addition of minimal volumes of sodium thiosulfate eliminates this interference without significant loss of accuracy. Where an error is demonstrated, the appropriate correction should be applied. Ultraviolet irradiation also removes residual chlorine. Another interfering factor is the finely divided calcium carbonate and magnesium hydroxide produced during the lime-soda softening process, which may cause a fading endpoint. This suspended material should be removed by filtering the sample through fine filter paper prior to titration. Salts of weak inorganic (phosphoric, silicic) and organic acids may contribute to alkalinity.

1.4. *Sampling and storage:* For best results, samples should be collected in polyethylene or pyrex bottles. Because of the instability of samples containing considerable causticity or carbon dioxide, the alkalinity determinations should be performed as soon as practicable, and preferably within 1 day.

2. Apparatus

2.1. *Daylight fluorescent lamps* have proved satisfactory for use in identifying the alkalinity endpoints by virtue of the fact that they enable the maintenance of uniform lighting conditions at all times, and, in particular cases, accentuate certain indicator color changes.

2.2. *Electrically operated titrators,* suitably calibrated. Where such devices are available, the alkalinity titrations may be performed using the standard solutions. The alkalinity determinations can also be performed by means of a properly calibrated pH meter, titrating with the standard solutions to the proper equivalence pH.

3. Reagents

3.1. *Carbon dioxide–free distilled water:* Prepare all stock and standard solutions, and dilution water for the standardization procedure, with distilled water which has a pH of not less than 6.0. If the water has a lower pH, it should be freshly boiled for 15 min and cooled to room temperature. Deionized water may be substituted for distilled water provided that it has a conductance of less than 2 micromhos/cm and a pH greater than 6.0.

3.2. *Phenolphthalein indicator solu-*

tion: Either the aqueous (*a*) or alcoholic (*b*) solution may be used.

a. Dissolve 5 g phenolphthalein disodium salt in distilled water and dilute to 1 liter. If necessary, add 0.02N NaOH dropwise until a faint pink color appears.

b. Dissolve 5 g phenolphthalein in 500 ml 95 per cent ethyl alcohol or isopropyl alcohol and add 500 ml distilled water. Then add 0.02N NaOH dropwise until a faint pink color appears.

3.3. *Standard sulfuric acid or hydrochloric acid titrant,* 0.02N. Prepare stock solutions approximately 0.1N by diluting either 9.5 ml conc HCl or 3 ml conc H_2SO_4 to 1 liter. Dilute 200 ml of the 0.1N stock solution to 1 liter with CO_2-free distilled water. Standardize the 0.02N acid against a 0.0200N sodium carbonate solution which has been prepared by dissolving 1.060 g anhydrous Na_2CO_3 (primary standard grade), oven dried at 140°C, and diluting to the mark of a 1-liter volumetric flask with CO_2-free distilled water. Perform the standardization exactly as the typical alkalinity titration, using the identical volumes of final solution, sodium thiosulfate, phenolphthalein, and total-alkalinity indicator, and the same time interval as for the sample determination. For best results take for standardization a volume of 0.0200N sodium carbonate solution which approximates the average alkalinity of the water samples normally encountered in the given laboratory. Since the response to endpoint color changes varies among individuals, each analyst should perform the standardization independently and use the normality factor appropriate for his own technique. A standard acid

solution, exactly 0.0200N, is equivalent to 1.00 mg $CaCO_3$ per 1.00 ml.

3.4. *Mixed bromcresol green-methyl red indicator solution:* Either the aqueous (*a*) or alcoholic (*b*) solution may be used.

a. Dissolve 0.02 g methyl red sodium salt and 0.10 g bromcresol green sodium salt in 100 ml distilled water.

b. Dissolve 0.02 g methyl red and 0.10 g bromcresol green in 100 ml 95 per cent ethyl alcohol or isopropyl alcohol.

3.5. *Methyl orange indicator solution:* Dissolve 0.5 g methyl orange in 1 liter distilled water.

3.6. *Sodium thiosulfate,* 0.1N. Dissolve 25 g $Na_2S_2O_3 \cdot 5H_2O$ and dilute to 1 liter with distilled water.

4. Procedure

Sample volumes requiring less than 25 ml of titrant yield the sharpest color changes at the endpoint and, therefore, are recommended. If indicator methods are used, remove the free residual chlorine by adding 0.05 ml (1 drop) 0.1N sodium thiosulfate solution or by ultraviolet irradiation.

4.1. *Phenolphthalein alkalinity:* Add 0.1 ml (2 drops) phenolphthalein indicator to a sample of suitable size, 50.0 or 100 ml if possible, in an erlenmeyer flask. Titrate over a white surface with 0.02N standard acid to the coloration corresponding to the proper equivalence point of pH 8.3.

4.2. *Total alkalinity by mixed bromcresol green–methyl red indicator method:* Add 0.15 ml (3 drops) indicator to the solution in which the phenolphthalein alkalinity has been determined, or to a sample of suitable size, 50.0 or 100 ml if possible, in an erlenmeyer flask. Titrate over a white surface with $0.02N$ standard acid to the proper equivalence point. The indicator yields the following color responses: above pH 5.2, greenish blue; pH 5.0, light blue with lavender gray; pH 4.8, light pink gray with bluish cast; pH 4.6, light pink.

4.3. *Total alkalinity by methyl orange indicator method:* Add 0.1 ml (2 drops) indicator to the solution in which the phenolphthalein alkalinity has been determined, or to a sample of suitable size, 50.0 or 100 ml if possible, in an erlenmeyer flask. Titrate over a white surface with $0.02N$ standard acid to the proper equivalence point. The indicator changes to orange at pH 4.6 and pink at 4.0.

5. Calculation

Phenolphthalein alkalinity as mg/l $CaCO_3$
$$= \frac{A \times N \times 50,000}{\text{ml sample}}$$

Total alkalinity as mg/l $CaCO_3$
$$= \frac{B \times N \times 50,000}{\text{ml sample}}$$

where $A = $ ml titration for sample to reach the phenolphthalein endpoint, $B = $ total ml titration for sample to reach second endpoint, and $N = $ normality of acid.

NOTE: If total alkalinity is determined on the same solution used for phenolphthalein alkalinity, be sure to include the volume of acid required for the phenolphthalein titration, A, in the total milliliters, B, of standard acid.

6. Low Alkalinity by Potentiometric Titration

Low alkalinities of less than 10 mg/l may be determined more accurately by potentiometric titration than by indicator methods. Potentiometric titra-

tion eliminates the error due to the sliding endpoint caused by free CO_2 in the sample at the end of the titration.

A sample of suitable size, 100 to 200 ml, is titrated carefully to pH 4.5 using a microburet. The required volume, X_1, of standard acid is recorded. The titration is then continued to pH 4.2 and the total volume, X_2, of acid is again recorded. The total alkalinity is calculated as shown below. Precise standardization of the pH meter is not required.

Total alkalinity as mg/l $CaCO_3$
$$= \frac{(2X_1 \text{ ml} - X_2 \text{ ml}) \times N \times 50,000}{\text{ml sample}}$$

where $N = $ normality of acid.

7. Calculation of Alkalinity Relationships

The results obtained from the phenolphthalein and total alkalinity determinations offer a means for the stoichiometric classification of the three principal forms of alkalinity present in many water supplies. The classification ascribes the entire alkalinity to bicarbonate, carbonate, and hydroxide, and assumes the absence of other (weak) acids of inorganic or organic composition, such as silicic, phosphoric, and boric. This classification system further presupposes the incompatibility of hydroxide and bicarbonate alkalinities in the same sample. Since the calculations are on a stoichiometric basis, ion concentrations in the strictest sense are not represented in the results. According to this scheme:

a. Carbonate alkalinity is present when the phenolphthalein alkalinity is not zero but is less than the total alkalinity.

b. Hydroxide alkalinity is present if the phenolphthalein alkalinity is more than half the total alkalinity.

c. Bicarbonate alkalinity is present if the phenolphthalein alkalinity is less than half the total alkalinity.

The mathematical conversion of the results is shown in Table 5.

TABLE 5—ALKALINITY RELATIONSHIPS *

Result of Titration	Hydroxide Alkalinity as CaCO₃	Carbonate Alkalinity as CaCO₃	Bicarbonate Alkalinity as CaCO₃
$P = 0$	0	0	T
$P < \frac{1}{2}T$	0	2P	$T - 2P$
$P = \frac{1}{2}T$	0	2P	0
$P > \frac{1}{2}T$	$2P - T$	$2(T - P)$	0
$P = T$	T	0	0

* Key: P—phenolphthalein alkalinity; T—total alkalinity.

The various alkalinity relationships may also be computed nomographically (see Carbon Dioxide, Method A). If the pH value of the water has been determined accurately by electrometric means, and from this the mg/l OH⁻ as CaCO₃ is calculated, then the mg/l CO_3^{--} and HCO_3^- may also be calculated as CaCO₃ from the mg/l OH⁻ and the phenolphthalein and total alkalinities by the following equations:

$$CO_3^{--} = 2P - 2[OH^-]$$

$$HCO_3^- = T - 2P + OH^-$$

Similarly, if difficulty is experienced with the phenolphthalein endpoint, or if it is desired to check the phenolphthalein titration, the phenolphthalein alkalinity may be calculated as CaCO₃ from the results of the nomographic determinations of the carbonate (CO_3^{--}) and hydroxide (OH⁻) ion concentrations, by the use of the relationship:

$$P = \frac{1}{2}[CO_3^{--}] + OH^-$$

8. Precision and Accuracy

A precision of ± 1 mg/l and an accuracy of ± 3 mg/l, expressed as CaCO₃, can be achieved with reasonably good technique in the range between 10 and 500 mg/l.

Bibliography

1. BAYLIS, J. R. The Use of Acids With Alum in Water Purification and the Importance of Hydrogen Ion Concentration. *J. AWWA* 10:365 (1923).
2. STRAUB, F. G. Determination of Alkalinity in Boiler Waters. *Ind. Eng. Chem., Anal. Ed.* 4:290 (1932).
3. SCHROEDER, W. C. Errors in Determination of Carbonate in Boiler Waters. *Ind. Eng. Chem., Anal. Ed.* 5:389 (1933).
4. COOPER, S. S. The Mixed Indicator Bromcresol Green-Methyl Red for Carbonates in Water. *Ind. Eng. Chem., Anal. Ed.* 13:466 (1941).
5. FLEISHER, H. Sensitive Indicator for Volumetric Determination of Boiler Feedwater Alkalinity. *Ind. Eng. Chem., Anal. Ed.* 15:742 (1943).
6. TARAS, M. Two New Total Alkalinity Indicators. *J. AWWA* 40:468 (1948).
7. TARAS, M. New Indicator for Carbonate Alkalinity. *J. AWWA* 41:527 (1949).
8. LARSON, T. E. & HENLEY, L. M. Determination of Low Alkalinity or Acidity in Water. *Anal. Chem.* 27:85 (1955).
9. DONG, G.; GIUSTI, R. L.; & GREENBERG, A. E. How to Make Alkalinity Measurements in Water. *Water & Sewage Works* 104:509 (1957).
10. DYE, J. F. Correlation of the Two Principal Methods of Calculating the Three Kinds of Alkalinity. *J. AWWA* 50:800 (1958).
11. THOMAS, J. F. J. & LYNCH, J. J. Determination of Carbonate Alkalinity in Natural Waters. *J. AWWA* 52:259 (1960).

Aluminum

Aluminum is the third most abundant element of the earth's crust, occurring in minerals, rocks, and clays. This wide distribution accounts for the presence of aluminum in practically all natural water supplies, as a soluble salt, colloid, or insoluble compound. Soluble, colloidal, and insoluble aluminum may appear additionally in treated water as a residual from alum coagulation.

1. General Discussion

1.1. *Principle:* Dilute aluminum solutions buffered to a pH of about 4.0 produce with an ammonium salt of aurin tricarboxylic acid ("aluminon") a red to pink lake which exhibits maximum absorption near 525 mμ. The intensity of the developed color is influenced by the aluminum concentration, reaction time, temperature, pH, the quality of the aluminon used, and the concentration of the various accompanying ions in the sample. Thioglycolic acid inhibits the interference of iron, normal phosphate, and certain other ions. The presence of gum arabic stabilizes the colloidal color system. The addition of citric acid to a sample blank containing color or turbidity prevents the aluminum in the sample from reacting with the aluminon.

The optimum aluminum range lies between 0.02 and 1.0 mg/l, but can be extended upward by sample dilution.

1.2. *Interference:* Negative errors approaching 25 and 40 per cent are caused by fluoride concentrations of 0.5 and 1.0 mg/l, respectively. (A procedure for fluoride removal is given in Sec. 4.7.) Polyphosphates lead to low results. Although they will be eliminated in the fluoride removal, they can also be removed by boiling a 50- to 100-ml sample in the presence of 4 ml of $6N$ sulfuric acid. Sulfite in excess of 10 mg/l introduces a negative error, but can be eliminated by oxidation with 3 per cent hydrogen peroxide. Residual chlorine in concentrations greater than 0.5 mg/l should be removed with sodium thiosulfate. In the presence of 1.0 mg/l Al, calcium concentrations yield a positive error progressing from 0.02 mg/l Al at 2.4 mg Ca to 0.1 mg/l Al at 15 mg Ca in the portion taken for analysis.

1.3. *Minimum detectable concentration:* The minimum aluminum concentration detectable by this method is 0.001 mg in a 50-ml sample, which corresponds to 0.02 mg/l.

1.4. *Sampling and storage:* Samples should be collected in clean, acid-rinsed bottles and should be examined as soon as possible after collection.

2. Apparatus

2.1. *Colorimetric equipment:* One of the following is required:

a. Spectrophotometer, for use at 525 mμ and utilizing a light path of 1 cm or longer.

b. Filter photometer, providing a light path of 1 cm or longer and equipped with a green filter showing maximum transmittance between 520 and 540 mμ.

c. Nessler tubes, 100 ml, tall form, matched.

2.2. *Glassware:* All glassware should be rinsed with $1 + 1$ HCl and then with aluminum-free distilled water to avoid errors due to contamination.

3. Reagents

All reagents should be low in aluminum. Aluminum-free distilled water is required.

3.1. *Stock aluminum solution:* The metal (a) or the salt (b) may be used for the preparation of the stock solution, which contains 0.500 mg Al per 1.00 ml:

a. Dissolve 0.5000 g ACS grade aluminum metal in 10 ml of conc HCl by heating gently. Dilute to 1 liter in a volumetric flask with distilled water.

b. Dissolve 8.792 g potassium aluminum sulfate (also called potassium alum), $K_2Al_2(SO_4)_4 \cdot 24H_2O$, in distilled water and dilute to 1 liter in a volumetric flask.

3.2. *Standard aluminum solution:* Dilute 10.00 ml of the stock aluminum solution to 1 liter in a volumetric flask with distilled water; 1.00 ml = 5 μg Al. Prepare daily.

3.3. *Paranitrophenol indicator solution:* Dissolve 1 g of the indicator in distilled water and make up to 100 ml.

3.4. *Hydrochloric acid,* 1 + 11.

3.5. *Ammonium hydroxide,* 1 + 4.

3.6. *Citric acid solution:* Dissolve 10 g citric acid monohydrate, $H_3C_6H_5O_7 \cdot H_2O$, in distilled water and make up to 100 ml.

3.7. *Thioglycolic acid inhibitor:* Dilute 1 ml of thioglycolic acid (also called mercaptoacetic acid, and available commercially in strengths from 80 to 95 per cent) to 100 ml with distilled water. If desired, ammonium thioglycolate may be substituted. Since neither solution is stable, it should be made up fresh every few days.

3.8. *Aluminon buffer solution:* Dissolve separately the following reagents in approximately 100-ml portions of distilled water, and mix the resulting solutions in the order named: 133 g ammonium acetate ($NH_4C_2H_3O_2$), 126 ml conc HCl, 0.9 g ammonium salt of aurin tricarboxylic acid, and 10 g gum arabic (also called gum acacia). Dilute to 1 liter with distilled water and mix. Let stand overnight and filter through fine glass wool if any turbidity develops. The pH of this solution should be between 3.8 and 4.0. The mixed reagent should be stable up to 6 months.

3.9. *Reagents for removal of fluoride interference:*

a. *Sulfuric acid,* conc.

b. *Sodium carbonate,* anhydrous, ACS grade powder.

c. *Hydrochloric acid,* conc.

4. Procedure

4.1. Prepare a series of aluminum standards from 0.000 to 0.05 mg by accurately measuring the calculated volumes of standard aluminum solution into 250-ml erlenmeyer flasks. Add distilled water to a total volume of approximately 50 ml.

4.2. Place two 50.0-ml portions of the sample, or aliquots diluted to 50 ml, in 250-ml erlenmeyer flasks. To each add 1 drop (0.05 ml) paranitrophenol indicator. If the solution turns yellow, add 1 + 11 HCl dropwise until the color is just discharged. If no color is evident, add ammonium hydroxide dropwise until a faint yellow appears. Then proceed with the dropwise addition of the acid as before.

4.3. If the sample is adjusted to pH 3.8–4.0 upon addition of the aluminon buffer reagent, the preliminary pH adjustment in Sec. 4.2 can be omitted. If a sample contains color or turbidity, add with mixing 1 ml citric acid solution to the second 50-ml sample, which serves as the sample blank.

4.4. To each 50.0-ml sample, standard, and blank, add 2 ml thioglycolic acid inhibitor, and mix. Add 10.00 ml of aluminon buffer reagent using a volumetric pipet, and mix. Place treated samples, standards, and blanks at once in a boiling-water bath for exactly 15 min. Be sure that the water continues to boil actively during the entire period of immersion and that its level is above the liquid level in the flasks. The flasks should be supported on a perforated plate to insure intimate contact with the boiling water. Lead collars may be used to keep the flasks from tipping over. At the end of the heating period, remove the flasks and cool them in an ice bath to a temperature between 20° and 25°C. Make up to 100 ml with distilled water in a volumetric flask or nessler tube. It is important that the temperature be controlled within the specified range.

4.5. Read the transmittance or absorbance using a wavelength of 525 mμ or a green filter providing maximum transmittance between 520 and 540 mμ. Use the sample blank to adjust the instrument to 100 per cent transmittance or zero absorbance, to compensate for natural color and turbidity. Plot a calibration curve of mg Al versus photometric reading, and read the mg Al in the sample from the curve. Construct a calibration curve each time a new aluminon buffer solution is prepared.

4.6. If photometric equipment is not available, transfer the samples and standards, after withdrawal from the boiling-water bath and cooling, to 100-ml nessler tubes; make up to the mark; and compare the color of the sample with the standards.

4.7. *Removal of fluoride interference:* Place the sample in a 100-ml platinum evaporating dish and evaporate to dryness on a steam bath. Add 5 ml conc H_2SO_4, taking care to wet all the residue, and carefully evaporate to dryness on a hot plate. Control the temperature to avoid spattering. Fuse the residue with 0.5 g sodium carbonate, and extract the cooled cake with 10 ml hot distilled water. Add 5 ml conc HCl, heat gently for a few minutes, add 10 ml distilled water, and wash the contents of the dish into a beaker. Boil the solution for a few minutes, then wash the contents of the beaker into an erlenmeyer flask and proceed as described in the beginning of Sec. 4.2. A blank should be run using distilled water and all of the reagents, including 0.5 g sodium carbonate. Keep in mind that the acid-fusion treatment, while eliminating fluoride and complex metaphosphate interference, may also bring certain insoluble aluminum compounds into solution.

5. Calculation

$$\text{mg/l Al} = \frac{\text{mg Al} \times 1,000}{\text{ml sample}}$$

6. Precision and Accuracy

In the absence of fluoride, polyphosphate, or other interfering substances not inhibited by thioglycolic acid, the precision and accuracy of this method approach 0.05 mg/l.

A synthetic unknown sample containing 1.80 mg/l Al, 0.42 mg/l Cu, 0.18 mg/l Cr, 0.25 mg/l Mn, 0.62 mg/l Fe, and 0.90 mg/l Zn was determined by 37 laboratories with a standard deviation of ±0.14 mg/l. One-half of the reported results were within ±0.40 mg/l of the known aluminum concentration. The individual laboratories reproduced their own results within ±0.08 mg/l.

Bibliography

1. ROLLER, P. S. Colorimetric Determination of Aluminum With Aurintricarboxylic Acid. *J. Am. Chem. Soc.* 55: 2437 (1933).
2. OLSEN, A. L.; GEE, E. A.; & McLENDON, V. Precision and Accuracy of Colorimetric Procedures as Analytical Control Methods—Determination of Aluminum. *Ind. Eng. Chem., Anal. Ed.* 16:169 (1944).
3. CRAFT, C. H. & MAKEPEACE, G. R. Colorimetric Estimation of Aluminum in Aluminum Steel. *Ind. Eng. Chem., Anal. Ed.* 17:206 (1945).
4. NELSON, J. J. & BACON, G. H. Determination of Alum in Water. *Public Health News* 30:187 (1949).
5. SMITH, W. H.; SAGER, E. E.; & SIEWERS, I. J. Preparation and Colorimetric Properties of Aluminon. *Anal Chem.* 21:1334 (1949).
6. LUKE, C. L. & BRAUN, K. C. Photomet-ric Determination of Aluminum. *Anal. Chem.* 24:1120 (1952).
7. POOLE, P. & SEGROVE, H. D. The Absorptiometric Determination of Aluminum Oxide in Glass Sands. *J. Soc. Glass Technol.* 39:205 (1955).
8. HORTON, A. D. Ion Exchange—Spectrophotometric Determination of Aluminum. *Anal. Chem.* 28:1326 (1956).
9. BANERJEE, D. K. Spectrophotometric Determination of Aluminum in Titanium and Titanium Alloys—An Aluminon Method. *Anal. Chem.* 29:55 (1957).
10. PACKHAM, R. F. The Absorptiometric Determination of Aluminum in Water. *Proc. Soc. Water Treatment & Examination* 7:102 (1958).
11. SANDELL, E. B. *Colorimetric Determination of Traces of Metals.* Interscience Publishers, New York (3rd ed., 1959). pp. 228–231.
12. SHULL, K. E. Suggested Modified Aluminon Method for Aluminum. *J. AWWA* 52:779 (1960).

Arsenic

Severe poisoning can arise from the ingestion of as little as 100 mg arsenic; chronic effects can appear from its accumulation in the body at low intake levels. Carcinogenic properties have also been imputed to arsenic. The arsenic concentration of most potable waters seldom exceeds 0.01 mg/l although values as high as 0.1 mg/l have been reported. Arsenic may occur in water as a result of mineral dissolution, industrial discharges, or the application of insecticides.

Selection of method: The silver diethyldithiocarbamate method should be used when greater precision and accuracy are desired than that possible with the mercuric bromide stain method. Although its minimum detectable concentration is 1 μg As, the mercuric bromide stain method should be confined to qualitative or semiquantitative (± 5 μg) determinations. Successful application of both methods often requires considerable practice.

A. Silver Diethyldithiocarbamate Method

1. General Discussion

1.1. *Principle:* Inorganic arsenic is reduced to arsine, AsH_3, by zinc in acid solution in a Gutzeit generator. The arsine is then passed through a scrubber containing glass wool impregnated with lead acetate solution and into an absorber tube containing silver diethyldithiocarbamate dissolved in pyridine. In the absorber, arsenic reacts with the silver salt forming a soluble red complex which is suitable for photometric measurement.

1.2. *Interference:* Although certain metals—cobalt, nickel, mercury, silver, platinum, copper, chromium, and molybdenum—interfere in the generation of arsine, the concentrations of these metals normally present in water samples do not constitute significant interference in the method. Antimony salts in the sample form stibine which may interfere with color development by yielding a red color with maximum absorbance at 510 mμ.

1.3. *Minimum detectable concentration:* 1 μg As.

2. Apparatus

2.1. *Arsine generator and absorption tube:* See Fig. 7.

2.2. *Photometric equipment:*

a. *Spectrophotometer,* for use at 535 mμ with 1-cm cells.

b. *Filter photometer,* with blue filter having a maximum transmittance in the range 530–540 mμ, with 1-cm cells.

3. Reagents

3.1. *Hydrochloric acid,* conc.

3.2. *Potassium iodide solution:* Dissolve 15 g KI in 100 ml distilled water. Store in a brown bottle.

3.3. *Stannous chloride reagent:* Dissolve 40 g arsenic-free $SnCl_2 \cdot 2H_2O$ in 100 ml conc hydrochloric acid.

3.4. *Lead acetate solution:* Dissolve 10 g $Pb(C_2H_3O_2)_2 \cdot 3H_2O$ in 100 ml distilled water.

3.5. *Silver diethyldithiocarbamate reagent:* Dissolve 1 g $AgSCSN(C_2H_5)$

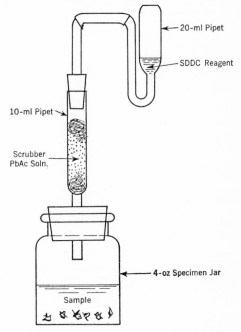

20-ml Pipet

SDDC Reagent

10-ml Pipet

Scrubber PbAc Soln.

4-oz Specimen Jar

Sample

Fig. 7. Arsine generator and absorber assembly

in 200 ml pyridine. Store in a brown bottle.

3.6. *Zinc:* 20–30 mesh, arsenic free.

3.7. *Stock arsenic solution:* Dissolve 1.320 g arsenic trioxide, As_2O_3, in 10 ml distilled water containing 4 g NaOH, and dilute to 1,000 ml with distilled water; 1.00 ml = 1.00 mg As.

3.8. *Intermediate arsenic solution:* Dilute 5.00 ml stock solution to 500 ml with distilled water; 1.00 ml = 10.0 μg As.

3.9. *Standard arsenic solution:* Dilute 10.00 ml intermediate solution to 100 ml with distilled water; 1.00 ml = 1.00 μg As.

4. Procedure

4.1. Pipet 35.0 ml sample into a clean generator bottle.

4.2. Add successively, with thorough

mixing after each addition, 5 ml conc HCl, 2 ml KI solution, and 8 drops (0.40 ml) SnCl₂ reagent. Allow 15 min for reduction of arsenic to the trivalent state.

4.3. Impregnate the glass wool in the scrubber with lead acetate solution. Pipet 4.00 ml silver diethyldithiocarbamate reagent into the absorber tube.

4.4. Add 3 g zinc to the generator and connect the scrubber-absorber assembly immediately. Make certain that all connections are tightly fitted.

4.5 Allow 30 min for complete evolution of arsine. Warm the generator slightly to make sure that all arsine is released. Pour the solution from the absorber directly into a 1-cm cell, and measure the absorbance of the solution at 535 mμ, using the reagent blank as the reference.

4.6. *Preparation of standard curve:* Treat aliquots of the standard solution containing 0, 1.0, 2.0, 5.0, and 10.0 μg As as described under Sec. 4.1 through 4.5. Plot absorbance versus concentration of arsenic in the standard.

5. Calculation

$$\text{mg/l As} = \frac{\mu\text{g As}}{\text{ml sample}}$$

6. Precision and Accuracy

A synthetic unknown sample containing 0.05 mg/l arsenic, 0.18 mg/l boron, 0.40 mg/l beryllium, and 0.05 mg/l selenium was determined in 13 laboratories with a standard deviation of $\pm$0.01 mg/l by means of the silver diethyldithiocarbamate method. Three-fourths of the reported results were within $\pm$0.01 mg/l of the known arsenic concentration. The individual laboratories reproduced their own results within $\pm$0.001 mg/l.

B. Mercuric Bromide Stain Method

1. General Discussion

1.1. *Principle:* After concentration of the sample, arsenic is liberated as arsine, AsH₃, by zinc in acid solution in a Gutzeit generator. The generated arsine is then passed through a column containing a roll of cotton, moistened with lead acetate solution. The generated arsine is allowed to produce a yellow-brown stain on test paper strips impregnated with mercuric bromide. The length of the stain is roughly proportional to the amount of arsenic present.

1.2. *Interference:* Antimony interferes by giving a similar stain if present in quantities greater than 0.10 mg.

1.3. *Minimum detectable concentration:* 1 μg As.

2. Apparatus

Arsine generator: See Fig. 8.

3. Reagents

3.1. *Sulfuric acid,* 1 + 1.

3.2. *Nitric acid,* conc.

3.3. *Roll cotton:* Cut a roll of dentist's cotton into 25-mm lengths.

3.4. *Lead acetate solution:* Prepare as directed in Method A, Sec. 3.4.

3.5. *Mercuric bromide paper:* Use commercial arsenic papers cut uniformly into strips about 12 cm long and 2.5 mm wide (papers can be obtained

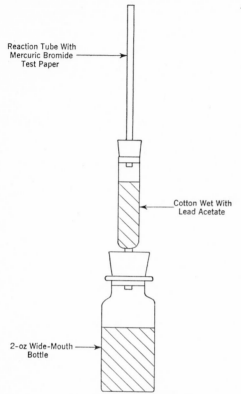

Reaction Tube With Mercuric Bromide Test Paper

Cotton Wet With Lead Acetate

2-oz Wide-Mouth Bottle

Fig. 8. Generator used with mercuric bromide stain method

already cut and sensitized). Soak strips for at least 1 hr in filtered solution prepared by dissolving 3–6 g HgBr₂ in 95 per cent ethyl or isopropyl alcohol; dry by waving in air. Store in dry, dark place. For best results, papers should be made up just prior to use.

3.6. *Potassium iodide solution:* Prepare as directed in Method A, Sec. 3.2.

3.7. *Stannous chloride reagent:* Prepare as directed in Method A, Sec. 3.3.

3.8. *Zinc,* 20–30 mesh, arsenic free.

3.9. *Standard arsenic solution:* Prepare as directed in Method A, Sec. 3.9.

4. Procedure

4.1. *Concentration of sample and oxidation of any organic matter:* To a suitable aliquot of sample containing from 2 to 30 μg As, add 7 ml 1 + 1 H_2SO_4 and 5 ml conc HNO_3 and evaporate to SO_3 fumes. Cool; add about 25 ml distilled water; and again evaporate to SO_3 fumes, to expel oxides of nitrogen. Maintain an excess of HNO_3 until the organic matter is destroyed. Do not allow the solution to darken while organic matter is destroyed because arsenic is likely to be reduced and lost.

4.2. *Preparation of guard column and reaction tube:* Dip one end of the 2.5-cm length of cotton into the lead acetate solution and introduce into the glass column. Then put the dried narrow glass tube in place and insert the $HgBr_2$ test paper. Make sure that the paper strip is straight.

4.3. *Treatment of sample concentrate:* To the 25 ml sample concentrate in the generator, add 7 ml 1 + 1 H_2SO_4 and cool. Add 5 ml KI solution, 4 drops $SnCl_2$ reagent and, finally, 2 to 5 g zinc. Immediately connect the reaction tube to the generator. Immerse the apparatus to within 2.5 cm of the top of the narrow tube in a water bath kept at 20° to 25°C and allow evolution to proceed for 1.5 hr. Remove the strip and compute the average length of stains on both sides. Using a calibration curve, the preparation of which is described below, estimate the amount of arsenic present.

4.4. *Preparation of calibration curve:* Prepare a blank and standards at 3-μg intervals in the 0- to 30-μg As range with 14 ml 1 + 1 H_2SO_4 and bring the total solution volume to 25 ml. Place in the generator and treat in the same manner as described for the sample concentrate. Remove the strip and compute the average length of stains on both sides, in millimeters. Plot the length in millimeters against micrograms of arsenic and use as a standard curve.

5. Precision and Accuracy

A synthetic unknown sample containing 0.05 mg/l arsenic, 0.18 mg/l boron, 0.40 mg/l beryllium, and 0.05 mg/l selenium was determined in five laboratories with a standard deviation of ±0.06 mg/l by means of the mercuric bromide stain method. One-half of the reported results were within ±0.01 mg/l of the known arsenic concentration. The individual laboratories reproduced their own results within ±0.003 mg/l.

Bibliography

Silver Diethyldithiocarbamate Method

1. VASAK, V. & SEDIVEC, V. Colorimetric Determination of Arsenic. *Chem. Listy.* 46:341 (1952).
2. STRATTON, G. & WHITEHEAD, H. C. Colorimetric Determination of Arsenic in Water with Silver Diethyldithiocarbamate. *J. AWWA* 54:861 (1962).
3. BALLINGER, D. G.; LISHKA, R. J.; & GALES, M. E. Application of Silver Diethyldithiocarbamate Method to Determination of Arsenic. *J. AWWA* 54: 1424 (1962).

Mercuric Bromide Stain Method

4. *Official Methods of Analysis.* Assoc. Official Agricultural Chemists, Washington, D.C. (9th ed., 1960) pp. 305–307.
5. FURMAN, N. H., ed. *Standard Methods of Chemical Analysis.* D. Van Nostrand Co., Princeton, N. J. (6th ed., 1962). Vol. I, pp. 118–124.

Boron

Boron in excess of 2.0 mg/l in irrigation water is deleterious to certain plants, and there is evidence that some are adversely affected by concentrations as low as 1.0 mg/l (or even less in commercial greenhouses). Drinking waters rarely contain more than 1 mg/l boron, and generally less than 0.1 mg/l, concentrations which are considered innocuous for human consumption. Boron may occur naturally in some waters or find its way into a watercourse by virtue of its presence in some cleaning compounds and industrial waste effluents.

Selection of method: The curcumin method (A) is applicable in the 0.10–1.0 mg/l range, while the carmine method (B) is suitable for the determination of boron concentrations in the 1–10 mg/l range. The potentiometric titration method (C) is useful for the boron range of 0.10–5 mg/l. The range of all three methods can be extended by dilution or concentration of the original sample. The colorimetric methods offer some advantages over the potentiometric titration method. Smaller aliquots (1–25 ml) are needed, in contrast to the 250-ml volume required for the titrimetric method. In addition, phosphate does not interfere with the colorimetric methods. The curcumin method, however, fails in the presence of nitrate nitrogen exceeding 20 mg/l. The potentiometric method, on the other hand, is especially applicable to waters of high boron concentration where accuracy is important.

Sampling and storage: Samples should be stored in polyethylene bottles or alkali-resistant, boron-free glassware.

A. Curcumin Colorimetric Method

1. General Discussion

1.1. *Principle:* When a sample of water containing boron is acidified and evaporated in the presence of curcumin, a red-colored product, called rosocyanine, is formed. The rosocyanine is taken up in a suitable solvent, and the red color is compared with standards visually or photometrically.

1.2. *Interference:* Ions commonly found in water do not interfere with this method, except nitrate at concentrations above 20 mg/l as nitrate nitrogen.

1.3. *Minimum detectable concentration:* 0.2 μg B.

2. Apparatus

2.1. *Colorimetric equipment:* One of the following is required:

a. Spectrophotometer, for use at 540 mμ, with a minimum light path of 1 cm.

b. Filter photometer, equipped with a filter having a maximum transmittance near 540 mμ, with a minimum light path of 1 cm.

2.2. *Evaporating dishes,* 45–150-ml capacity, of Vycor glass,* platinum, or other materials found suitable through use.

2.3. *Water bath,* set at 55° ± 2°C.

2.4. *Glass-stoppered volumetric flasks,* 25-ml capacity.

3. Reagents

3.1. *Stock boron solution:* Dissolve 0.5716 g anhydrous boric acid, H_3BO_3, in distilled water and dilute to 1,000 ml; 1.00 ml = 0.100 mg B. Because H_3BO_3 loses weight on drying at 105°C, use a reagent meeting ACS specifications and keep the bottle tightly stoppered to prevent the entrance of air moisture.

3.2. *Standard boron solution:* Dilute 10.00 ml stock boron solution to 1,000 ml with distilled water; 1.00 ml = 1.00 μg B.

3.3. *Curcumin reagent:* Dissolve 0.040 g of finely ground curcumin † and 5.0 g oxalic acid in 80 ml of 95 per cent ethyl alcohol. Add 4.2 ml conc HCl and make the solution up to 100 ml with ethyl alcohol in a 100-ml volumetric flask. (Isopropyl alcohol, 95 per cent, may be used in place of ethyl alcohol.) This reagent will be stable for several days, if stored in a refrigerator.

3.4. *Ethyl alcohol,* 95 per cent.

4. Procedure

4.1. *Precautions:* Close control of such variables as volumes and concentrations of reagents, as well as time and temperature of drying, must be practiced for a successful determination. Evaporating dishes must be identical in shape, size, and composition to insure equal evaporation time. Increasing the time of evaporation results in the intensification of the resulting color.

4.2. *Preparation of calibration curve:* Pipet 0.00 (blank), 0.25, 0.50, 0.75, and 1.00 μg boron into evaporating dishes of the same type, shape, and size. Add 4.0 ml curcumin reagent to each and swirl the dish gently to mix contents thoroughly. Float the dishes on a water bath set at 55° ± 2°C and evaporate the contents to complete dryness. Remove each dish from the water

---

* A product of Corning Glass Works.

† Eastman No. 1179 or equivalent.

bath as soon as the contents appear dry and the odor of HCl is gone. After the dishes cool to room temperature, add 10.0 ml 95 per cent ethyl alcohol to each dish, stirring gently with a polyethylene rod to insure complete dissolution of the red-colored product.

Wash the contents of each dish into a 25-ml volumetric flask using 95 per cent ethyl alcohol. Make up to the mark with 95 per cent ethyl alcohol, and mix thoroughly by inverting the flask. Read the transmittance or absorbance of the standards and samples at a wavelength of 540 mμ after setting the reagent blank at 100 per cent transmittance or zero absorbance. The calibration curve is linear from 0.00 to 1.00 μg boron. Make the photometric readings within 1 hr of drying the samples.

4.3. *Sample treatment:* For waters containing 0.10–1.00 mg/1 boron, use 1.00 ml of sample. For waters containing more than 1.00 mg/1 boron, make an appropriate dilution with boron-free distilled water, so that a 1.00-ml aliquot contains approximately 0.50 μg boron.

Pipet the 1.00 ml of sample or dilution into an evaporating dish. Unless the calibration curve is being determined at the same time, prepare a blank and a standard containing 0.50 μg boron and run it in conjunction with the unknown. Proceed as in Sec. 4.2, beginning with "Add 4.0 ml curcumin reagent. . . ." Obtain the boron content from the calibration curve.

4.4. *Visual comparison:* The photometric method may be adapted to visual estimation of low boron concentrations, from 0.05 to 0.20 mg/1, as follows: Dilute standard boron solution so that 1.00 ml equals 0.20 μg boron. Pipet 0.00, 0.05, 0.10, 0.15, and 0.20 μg boron into the evaporating dishes as indicated in Sec. 4.2. At the same time add an appropriate volume of sample (1.00 ml or less) to an identical evaporating dish. The boron content of the sample taken should be between 0.05 and 0.20 μg. Proceed as in Sec. 4.2, beginning with "Add 4.0 ml curcumin reagent. . . ." Compare the color of the unknowns with the standards within 1 hr after solution of the red color in the alcohol.

5. Calculation

The following equation may be used in calculating the boron concentration from the absorbance readings:

$$\text{mg/1 B} = \frac{A_2 \times C}{A_1 \times S}$$

in which $A_1 =$ absorbance of the standard taken, $A_2 =$ absorbance of unknown water sample, $C =$ micrograms boron in standard taken, and $S =$ ml unknown water sample used.

6. Precision and Accuracy

A synthetic unknown sample containing 0.18 mg/1 boron, 0.05 mg/1 arsenic, 0.40 mg/1 beryllium, and 0.05 mg/1 selenium was determined in 12 laboratories with a standard deviation of ±0.04 mg/1 by means of the curcumin method. One-half of the reported results were within ±0.02 mg/1 of the known boron concentration. The individual laboratories reproduced their own results within ±0.01 mg/1.

B. Carmine Colorimetric Method

1. General Discussion

1.1. *Principle:* In the presence of boron, a solution of carmine or carminic acid in concentrated sulfuric acid changes from a bright red to a bluish red or blue, depending on the concentration of boron present.

1.2. *Interference:* The ions more commonly found in water and sewage do not interfere in this method.

1.3. *Minimum detectable concentration:* 2 μg B.

2. Apparatus

Colorimetric equipment: One of the following is required:

2.1. *Spectrophotometer,* for use at 585 mμ, with a minimum light path of 1 cm.

2.2. *Filter photometer,* equipped with an orange filter having a maximum transmittance near 585 mμ, with a minimum light path of 1 cm.

3. Reagents

Store all reagents in polyethylene or boron-free containers.

3.1 *Standard boron solution:* Prepare as directed in Method A, Sec. 3.2.

3.2. *Hydrochloric acid,* conc and 1 + 11.

3.3. *Sulfuric acid,* conc.

3.4 *Carmine reagent:* Dissolve 0.92 g carmine N.F. 40, or carminic acid, in 1 liter conc H_2SO_4.

3.5. *Sodium hydroxide,* 1N. Dissolve 40 g NaOH and dilute to 1 liter with distilled water.

4. Procedure

4.1. *Preliminary sample treatment:* If the sample contains less than 1 mg/l

B, pipet an aliquot containing 2–20 μg B into a platinum dish, make alkaline with 1N NaOH plus a slight excess, and evaporate to dryness on a steam or hot water bath. If necessary, destroy any organic material at this point by ignition at 500–550°C. Acidify the cooled residue (ignited or not) with 2.5 ml 1 + 11 HCl, and triturate with a rubber policeman to dissolve. Centrifuge if need be to obtain a clear solution. Pipet 2.00 ml clear concentrate into a small flask or 30-ml test tube. Subject a reagent blank to the same steps as the sample.

4.2. *Color development:* Prepare a series of boron standard solutions (0.100, 0.250, 0.500, 0.750, and 1.00 mg) in 100 ml volume with distilled water. Pipet 2.00 ml of each standard solution into a small flask or 30-ml test tube.

Treat the blank and calibration standards exactly as the sample throughout the procedure. Add 2 drops (0.1 ml) conc HCl, then carefully introduce 10.0 ml conc H_2SO_4, mix, and allow to cool to room temperature. Add 10.0 ml carmine reagent, mix well, and after 45–60 min measure the absorbance at 585 mμ in a cell of 1-cm or longer light path, using the blank as the reference.

To avoid error, make sure that no bubbles are present in the optical cell when the photometric readings are being made. The bubbles may appear as a result of the incomplete mixing of the reagents. Because the carmine reagent deteriorates, check the calibration curve daily.

5. Calculation

$$mg/l\ B = \frac{mg\ B \times 1,000}{ml\ sample}$$

6. Precision and Accuracy

A synthetic unknown sample containing 0.18 mg/l boron, 0.05 mg/l arsenic, 0.40 mg/l beryllium, and 0.05 mg/l selenium was determined in nine laboratories with a standard deviation of ±0.06 mg/l by means of the carmine method. One-half of the reported results were within ±0.05 mg/l of the known boron concentration. The individual laboratories reproduced their own results within ±0.01 mg/l.

C. Potentiometric Titration Method

1. General Discussion

1.1. *Principle:* When a dilute solution containing boric acid or borate is neutralized and then treated with mannitol, there is produced a complex acid which can be titrated with dilute NaOH. The amount of boron is proportional to the amount of NaOH needed to return the pH of the solution to the initial pH.

1.2. *Interference:* Phosphate reacts with mannitol but not quantitatively, and if the phosphate concentration exceeds 10 mg/l, it should be removed. This can be done by precipitation with lead nitrate, followed by removal of the excess lead with sodium bicarbonate. Germanium and tetravalent vanadium react like boron, but are not normally present in water supplies. Buffer substances, such as carbonate, ammonia, or phosphate, may interfere by decreasing the sharpness of the endpoint. The absorption of acidic or alkaline gases from the laboratory air during the course of the titration may cause a drift of the meter and resultant error. Hydrochloric acid or ammonia should not be permitted in the room while boron titrations are being carried out. The error from atmospheric carbon dioxide can be minimized by titrating rapidly. The titration of the blanks and standards, if carried out under conditions as closely similar as possible to those of the sample titrations, will nearly compensate for any carbon dioxide error.

2. Apparatus

2.1. *Buret,* so calibrated that the volume can be read to 0.01 ml.

2.2. *Glassware:* Pyrex beakers can be used, but new beakers should be cleaned by filling with dilute acid and heating on a steam bath.

2.3. *Motor stirrer or magnetic stirrer.*

2.4. *Electrical equipment:* Either a potentiometer [10] or a pH meter sensitive to 0.01–0.05 pH may be used as an indicating system, set so that at balance the solution under test will have a pH of 7.00. The glass-saturated calomel electrode pair commonly used in pH measurements is satisfactory. The indicator needle of the pH meter should remain steady and unaffected by drift from a reading of pH 7.00 when the initial point of the titration is established in Sec. 4.4.

3. Reagents

3.1. *Bromthymol blue indicator solution:* Dissolve 1.0 g water-soluble bromthymol blue sodium salt in distilled water and dilute to 100 ml.

3.2. *Sulfuric acid, 1N.* Dilute cautiously 28 ml conc H_2SO_4 to 1 liter with distilled water.

3.3. *Standard buffer,* pH 7.00, commercially prepared for standardizing a pH meter.

3.4. *Sodium hydroxide solution,* carbonate free, saturated. Dissolve 50 g NaOH in 50 ml freshly boiled distilled water and let stand at least 48 hr in an alkali-resistant container (wax-lined or polyethylene), protected by a CO_2 trap.

3.5. *Sodium hydroxide,* 0.5N. Dilute 2.9 ml of the supernatant from the saturated NaOH solution to 100 ml with freshly boiled distilled water. Prepare each day.

3.6. *Standard sodium hydroxide titrant,* 0.0231N. Measure a volume of the supernatant from the carbonate-free saturated NaOH solution to give about 1 g NaOH and dilute to 1 liter with CO_2-free distilled water. Standardize against 5.00 ml standard boron solution plus 250 ml distilled water as described in the procedure. Dilute with CO_2-free distilled water so that 1.00 ml = 0.250 mg B. Store in a boron-free container (low-boron glass, paraffin-lined, or polyethylene bottle) protected by a CO_2 trap, filled with soda-lime or a sodium hydroxide asbestos absorbent.*

3.7. *Mannitol,* boron free. The blank titration for 5 g mannitol should not exceed 0.1 ml standard NaOH.

3.8. *Standard boron solution:* Prepare as directed in Method A, Sec. 3.2.

4. Procedure

4.1. Transfer 250 ml of the sample to a 400-ml tall-form beaker. This should contain not more than 1 mg boron. If the sample is high in boron, an aliquot portion diluted to 250 ml should be taken.

4.2. Add a few drops of bromthymol blue indicator and acidify with 1N H_2SO_4, adding 0.5–1 ml in excess. Bring to a boil and stir—cautiously at first, then vigorously—to expel carbon dioxide. Cover and cool to room temperature, preferably in a water bath.

4.3. Standardize the pH meter to 7.00 with standard buffer solution. Wash the electrodes thoroughly with distilled water, and introduce the electrodes into the solution to be titrated. Add carbonate-free 0.5N NaOH to approximately pH 5.0. Gently stir the solution during the titration procedure.

4.4. Adjust the solution to exactly pH 7.00 with the standard NaOH titrant (Sec. 3.6). This is the initial point of the titration.

4.5. Add 5 g ± 0.1 g mannitol. If boron is present, the indicator will change to the acid color, and the pH meter will show an acid pH. Add standard NaOH titrant until the pH meter indicates 7.00. Note the number of milliliters of standard NaOH titrant required after adding mannitol at the initial point of the titration.

4.6. Determine a reagent blank by using 250 ml boiled distilled water instead of the sample. Proceed as indicated above, beginning with Sec. 4.1.

4.7. It is advisable to run a standard boron solution (0.500 mg boron) in conjunction with the unknown in order to check reagents and technique.

5. Calculation

$$mg/l\ B = \frac{(A - C) \times N \times 10,820}{ml\ sample}$$

where A = ml titration for sample, C = ml titration for blank, N = normality of standard NaOH titrant, and B = boron.

---

* Ascarite (A. H. Thomas Company) or equal.

6. Precision and Accuracy

A precision and accuracy of ± 0.01 mg/l can be achieved at a boron concentration of 0.18 mg/l.

Bibliography

Curcumin Colorimetric Method

1. SILVERMAN, L. & TREGO, K. Colorimetric Microdetermination of Boron by the Curcumin-Acetone Solution Method. *Anal. Chem.* 25:1264 (1953).
2. DIBLE, W. T.; TRUOG, E.; & BERGER, K. C. Boron Determination in Soils and Plants—Simplified Curcumin Procedure. *Anal. Chem.* 26:418 (1954).
3. LUKE, C. L. Determination of Traces of Boron in Silicon, Germanium, and Germanium Dioxide. *Anal. Chem.* 27:1150 (1955).
4. LISHKA, R. J. Comparison of Analyti-cal Procedures for Boron. *J. AWWA* 53:1517 (1961).

Carmine Colorimetric Method

5. HATCHER, J. T. & WILCOX, L. V. Colorimetric Determination of Boron Using Carmine. *Anal. Chem.* 22:567 (1950).

Potentiometric Titration Method

6. FOOTE, F. J. Determination of Boron in Waters. *Ind. Eng. Chem., Anal. Ed.* 4:39 (1932).
7. WILCOX, L. V. Electrometric Titration of Boric Acid. *Ind. Eng. Chem., Anal. Ed.* 4:38 (1932).
8. WILCOX, L. V. Determination of Boron in Plant Material. *Ind. Eng. Chem., Anal. Ed.* 12:341 (1940).
9. Ref. 5.
10. *Standard Methods for the Examination of Water, Sewage, and Industrial Wastes.* APHA, AWWA & FSIWA, New York (10th ed., 1955). p. 48.

Bromide

Bromide may occur in varying amounts in well supplies in coastal areas as a result of sea water intrusion. The bromide content of some ground water supplies has been ascribed to connate water. Industrial discharges may contribute the bromide found in some fresh-water streams. Under normal circumstances, the bromide content of most drinking waters is negligible, seldom surmounting the 1-mg/l level.

1. General Discussion

1.1. *Principle:* Phenol red undergoes a color change from yellow to red over the pH range 6.4–8.0. With dilute hypobromite, phenol red forms an indicator of the bromphenol blue type, which changes from yellow to blue-purple over the pH range of 3.2–4.6. The oxidation of the bromide and the bromination of the phenol red take place readily in the presence of chloramine-T (sodium paratoluenesulfonchloramine). If the color comparison is made at a pH of 5.0–5.4, the brominated compound will be reddish to violet, depending upon its concentration. Thus, a sharp differentiation can be made between varying quantities of bromide. The concentration of chloramine-T and the timing of the reaction before dechlorination are critical.

1.2. *Interference:* Materials present in ordinary tap water do not interfere.

1.3. *Minimum detectable concentration:* 0.1 mg/l Br.

2. Apparatus

2.1. *Colorimetric equipment:* One of the following is required:

a. *Spectrophotometer,* for use at 590 mμ providing a light path of 1 cm.

b. *Filter photometer,* providing a

1-cm light path and equipped with an orange filter having a maximum transmittance near 590 mμ.

c. Nessler tubes, matched, 100 ml, tall form.

2.2. *Acid-washed glassware:* Wash all glassware with $1 + 6$ HNO$_3$ and rinse with distilled water to remove all trace of adsorbed bromide.

3. Reagents

3.1. *Acetate buffer solution:* Dissolve 68 g sodium acetate trihydrate, NaC$_2$H$_3$O$_2 \cdot 3$H$_2$O, in distilled water. Add 30 ml glacial acetic acid and make up to 1 liter. The pH should be 4.6–4.7.

3.2. *Phenol red indicator solution:* Dissolve 0.021 g phenolsulfonephthalein sodium salt and dilute to 100 ml with distilled water.

3.3. *Chloramine-T solution:* Dissolve 0.50 g chloramine-T and dilute to 100 ml with distilled water. Store in a dark bottle and refrigerate.

3.4. *Sodium thiosulfate, 2M.* Dissolve 49.6 g Na$_2$S$_2$O$_3 \cdot 5$H$_2$O or 31.6 g Na$_2$S$_2$O$_3$ and dilute to 100 ml with distilled water.

3.5. *Stock bromide solution:* Dissolve 0.7446 g anhydrous potassium bromide, KBr, in distilled water and make up to 1,000 ml; 1.00 ml = 0.500 mg Br.

3.6. *Standard bromide solution:* Dilute 10.00 ml stock bromide solution to 1,000 ml with distilled water; 1.00 ml = 5 μg Br.

4. Procedure

4.1. To 50.0 ml of sample containing 0.1–1.0 mg/1 Br, add 2 ml buffer solution, 2 ml phenol red solution, and 0.5 ml chloramine-T solution. Mix thoroughly. After exactly 20 min following the chloramine-T addition, dechlorinate by adding, with mixing, 0.5 ml sodium thiosulfate solution. Compare visually in nessler tubes against bromide standards prepared simultaneously, or preferably read in a photometer at 590 mμ and determine the bromide values from a calibration curve.

4.2. Prepare standards by diluting aliquots of the standard bromide solution to 50.0 ml; 1.00 ml of the standard solution diluted to 50.0 ml is equivalent to 0.1 mg/1 Br.

4.3. Construct a calibration curve consisting of 10 to 15 points in the concentration range of 0.1–1.0 mg/1 Br. Read standards at 590 mμ on a spectrophotometer or a filter photometer against a distilled-water blank.

5. Calculation

$$\text{mg/1 Br} = \frac{\mu\text{g Br}}{\text{ml sample}}$$

Bibliography

1. STENGER, V. A. & KOLTHOFF, I. M. Detection and Colorimetric Estimation of Microquantities of Bromide. *J. Am. Chem. Soc.* 57:831 (1935).
2. HOUGHTON, G. U. The Bromide Content of Underground Waters. *J. Soc. Chem. Ind. (London)* 65:277 (1946).
3. GOLDMAN, E. & BYLES, D. Suggested Revision of Phenol Red Method for Bromide. *J. AWWA* 51:1051 (1959).

Cadmium

Cadmium has high toxic potential, having been implicated in some cases of poisoning through food. Minute quantities of cadmium are suspected of being responsible for adverse renal arterial changes in human kidneys. A cadmium concentration of 0.20 mg/l has been found toxic to certain fish. On the other hand, there is an indication that cadmium might possibly be a dietary essential. The cadmium concentration of U.S. drinking waters has been reported to vary between 0.0004 and 0.06 mg/l with a mean of 0.0082 mg/l. Cadmium may enter a water as a result of industrial discharges or the deterioration of galvanized pipe.

1. General Discussion

1.1. *Principle:* Cadmium ions under suitable conditions react with dithizone to form a pink to red color which can be extracted with chloroform. The chloroform extracts are measured photometrically and the cadmium concentration is obtained from a calibration curve prepared from a standard cadmium solution treated in the same manner as the sample.

1.2. *Interference:* Under the conditions of this method, concentrations of metal ions normally found in water do not interfere. Lead concentrations up to 6 mg, zinc up to 3 mg, and copper up to 1 mg in the aliquot taken for analysis do not interfere. Ordinary room lighting does not affect the cadmium dithizonate color.

1.3. *Minimum detectable concentration:* 0.5 μg Cd with a 2-cm light path.

2. Apparatus

2.1. *Colorimetric equipment:* One of the following is required:

a. *Spectrophotometer,* for use at 518 mμ with a minimum light path of 1 cm.

b. *Filter photometer,* equipped with a green filter having a maximum light transmittance near 518 mμ, with a minimum light path of 1 cm.

2.2. *Separatory funnels,* 125–150 ml, preferably with teflon stopcocks.

2.3. *Glassware:* All glassware, including sample bottles, should be cleaned with $1 + 1$ HCl, and then rinsed thoroughly with tap water and distilled water.

3. Reagents

3.1. *Stock cadmium solution:* Weigh 0.1000 g pure cadmium metal and dissolve in a solution composed of 20 ml distilled water plus 5 ml conc HCl. Use heat to assist the dissolution of the metal. Transfer the solution quantitatively to a 1-liter volumetric flask and dilute to the mark with distilled water: 1.00 ml = 100 μg Cd. Store in a polyethylene container.

3.2. *Standard cadmium solution:* Pipet 10.00 ml stock cadmium solution into a 1-liter volumetric flask, add 10 ml conc HCl, and dilute to the mark with distilled water. Prepare as needed and use the same day; 1.00 ml = 1.00 μg Cd.

3.3. *Sodium potassium tartrate solution:* Dissolve 250 g NaKC$_4$H$_4$O$_6$·4H$_2$O in distilled water and make up to 1 liter.

3.4. *Sodium hydroxide—potassium cyanide solutions:*

a. *Solution (I):* Dissolve 400 g NaOH and 10 g KCN in distilled water and make up to 1 liter. Store in a polyethylene bottle. This solution is stable for 1–2 months.

b. *Solution (II):* Dissolve 400 g NaOH and 0.5 g KCN in distilled water and make up to 1 liter. Store in a polyethylene bottle. This solution is stable for 1–2 months.

CAUTION: Potassium cyanide is extremely poisonous and more than customary precautions should be observed in its handling. Never use mouth pipets to deliver volumes of cyanide solutions.

3.5. *Hydroxylamine hydrochloride solution:* Dissolve 20 g $NH_2OH \cdot HCl$ in distilled water and make up to 100 ml.

3.6. *Stock dithizone solution:* Dissolve 0.100 g diphenylthiocarbazone (Eastman No. 3092 or equivalent) in 1 liter chloroform, $CHCl_3$. Keep in a brown bottle in the refrigerator until required and use while still cold.

3.7. *Chloroform:* ACS grade passed for "suitability for use in dithizone test." Test for a satisfactory chloroform by adding a minute amount of dithizone to a portion of the $CHCl_3$ in a stoppered test tube so that a faint green is produced; the green color should be stable for a day.

3.8. *Tartaric acid solution:* Dissolve 20 g $H_2C_4H_4O_6$ in distilled water and make up to 1 liter. Keep the solution in the refrigerator, as it must be cold when used.

3.9. *Standard dithizone solution:* Dilute 100 ml stock dithizone solution to 1 liter with $CHCl_3$. Keep in a brown bottle in the refrigerator and allow to warm to room temperature before using.

3.10. *Hydrochloric acid,* conc.

3.11. *Thymol blue indicator solution:* Dissolve 0.4 g thymolsulfonephthalein sodium salt in 100 ml distilled water.

3.12. *Sodium hydroxide, 6N.* Dissolve 240 g NaOH in distilled water and make up to 1,000 ml. Store in a polyethylene bottle.

4. Procedure

4.1. *Preparation of standard curve:* Pipet 0 (blank), 2.00, 4.00, 6.00, 8.00, and 10.00 μg Cd into a series of separatory funnels. Add sufficient distilled water to make up to a final volume of 25 ml.

4.2. *Addition of reagents:* Add reagents in the following order, mixing after each addition: 1 ml sodium potassium tartrate solution, 5 ml NaOH— KCN solution (I), 1 ml hydroxylamine hydrochloride solution, and 15 ml stock dithizone solution. Stopper the funnels and shake for 1 min, relieving the vapor pressure in the funnels through the stopper rather than the stopcock. Drain the $CHCl_3$ layer into a second funnel containing 25 ml cold tartaric acid solution. Add 10 ml $CHCl_3$ to the first funnel; shake for 1 min and drain into the second funnel again. Do not permit the aqueous layer to enter the second funnel in these operations. As the time of contact of the $CHCl_3$ with the strong alkali must be kept to a minimum, perform the two extractions without delay after the addition of the dithizone. Cadmium dithizonate decomposes on prolonged contact with strong alkali saturated with $CHCl_3$.

Shake the second funnel for 2 min and discard the $CHCl_3$ layer. Add 5 ml $CHCl_3$, shake 1 min, and discard the $CHCl_3$ layer, making as close a separation as possible. In the following order, add 0.25 ml hydroxylamine hydrochloride solution, and 15.0 ml standard dithizone solution. Add 5 ml NaOH—KCN solution (II), and *immediately* shake for 1 min. Insert a pledget of cotton in the stem of the funnel and filter the $CHCl_3$ layer into a dry photometer tube. Read the absorbance at 518 mμ against the blank. Plot a calibration curve.

4.3. *Treatment of samples:* Pipet the appropriate volume of the sample containing 1–10 μg Cd into a separatory funnel and make up to 25 ml with distilled water. In the case of a potable water containing 0.01 mg/l Cd or less, add 0.5 ml conc HCl to 100 ml sample and evaporate to 20 ml. Add a few drops of thymol blue indicator solution and then 6N NaOH solution until the indicator just turns yellow at a pH of approximately 2.8. Make up to 25 ml with distilled water. Adjust in a similar fashion the pH of a sample which has been processed by acid digestion. Unless the calibration curve is being prepared at the same time, prepare a blank and a standard containing 6.00 μg Cd in a final volume of 25 ml and run it in conjunction with the unknown. Proceed as in Sec. 4.2. Obtain the Cd concentration from the calibration curve.

5. Calculation

The following equation may be used for calculating the Cd concentration from the absorbance readings:

$$\text{mg/l Cd} = \frac{A_2 \times C}{A_1 \times S}$$

in which A_1 = absorbance of the standard taken, A_2 = absorbance of unknown water sample, C = micrograms Cd in standard taken, and S = ml unknown water sample used.

6. Precision and Accuracy

A synthetic unknown sample containing 0.01 mg/l Cd, 0.05 mg/l Pb, 3.0 mg/l Cu, and 15.0 mg/l Zn was determined with a standard deviation of ±0.002 mg/l in five laboratories by means of this method. The individual laboratories reproduced their own results within ±0.001 mg/l.

A second synthetic unknown sample containing 0.10 mg/l Cd, 0.5 mg/l Pb, 6.0 mg/l Cu, and 30 mg/l Zn was determined with a standard deviation of ±0.02 mg/l by the same five laboratories. The individual laboratories reproduced their own results within ±0.01 mg/l on this sample.

A third synthetic unknown sample containing 0.50 mg/l Cd, 10.0 mg/l Pb, 30 mg/l Cu and 30 mg/l Zn was determined with a standard deviation of ±0.07 mg/l by the same five laboratories. The individual laboratories reproduced their own results within ±0.03 mg/l on this sample.

Bibliography

1. SALTZMAN, B. E. Colorimetric Microdetermination of Cadmium with Dithizone. *Anal. Chem.* 25:493 (1953).
2. GANOTES, J.; LARSON, E.; & NAVONE, R. Suggested Dithizone Method for Cadmium Determination. *J. AWWA* 54:852 (1962).

Calcium

The presence of calcium (fifth amongst the elements in order of abundance) in water supplies results from passage through or over deposits of limestone, dolomite, gypsum, and gypsiferous shale. The calcium content may range from zero to several hundred mg/l, depending on the source and treatment of the water. Small concentrations of calcium carbonate combat corrosion of metallic pipes by laying down a protective coating. Appreciable calcium salts, on the other hand, break down on heating to form harmful scale in boilers, pipes, and cooking utensils. The matter of "Saturation and Stability with Respect to Calcium Carbonate" is discussed under that heading elsewhere in this volume. Chemical softening treatment or ion exchange are employed to reduce the calcium and the associated hardness to tolerable levels.

Selection of method: Personal preference often dictates whether the classical gravimetric or the permanganate titrimetric method will be used for the accurate determination of calcium. The longer time required for gravimetric manipulations may restrict this method to occasional samples. The permanganate method, on the other hand, is often preferred for the determination of a large number of simultaneous samples. The rapidity and simplicity of the EDTA titrimetric method make it suitable for control and routine applications.

Storage of samples: The customary precautions are sufficient if care is taken to redissolve any calcium carbonate that may precipitate on standing.

A. Gravimetric Method

1. General Discussion

1.1. *Principle:* Ammonium oxalate precipitates calcium quantitatively as calcium oxalate. An excess of oxalate overcomes the adverse effects of magnesium. Optimum crystal formation and minimum occlusion are obtained only when the pH is brought slowly to the desired value. This is accomplished in two stages, with intervening digestion to promote seed crystal formation. The precipitate is ignited to, and weighed as, calcium oxide.

1.2. *Interference:* The sample should be free of interfering amounts of strontium, silica, aluminum, iron, manganese, phosphate, and suspended matter. Strontium may precipitate as the oxalate and cause high results. In such an event, a flame photometric determination should be performed for strontium and the proper correction applied to the gravimetric estimate in order to obtain a reliable calcium result. Silica interference should be disposed of by the classical dehydration procedure. Aluminum, iron, and manganese should be precipitated by ammonium hydroxide after treatment with persulfate. Precipitation as the ferric salt is an accepted procedure for eliminating phosphate. Suspended matter can be removed by centrifuging or by filtration through paper, sintered glass, or a cellulose acetate membrane (see Residue, Methods B and C, Sec. 2 and 3).

2. Reagents

2.1. *Methyl red indicator solution:* Dissolve 0.1 g methyl red sodium salt and dilute to 100 ml with distilled water.

2.2. *Hydrochloric acid,* 1 + 1.

2.3. *Ammonium oxalate solution:* Dissolve 10 g $(NH_4)_2C_2O_4 \cdot H_2O$ in 250 ml distilled water. Filter if necessary.

2.4. *Ammonium hydroxide,* 3N. Add 240 ml conc NH_4OH to about 700 ml distilled water and dilute to 1 liter. Filter before use to remove suspended silica flakes.

2.5. *Ammonium hydroxide,* 1 + 99.

2.6. *Special reagents for removal of*

*aluminum, iron, and manganese inter-
ference:*

   a. Ammonium persulfate, solid.

   b. Ammonium chloride solution:
Dissolve 20 g NH$_4$Cl in 1 liter of distilled water. Filter if necessary.

3. Procedure

3.1. Remove interfering amounts of
silica from the sample by the gravimetric procedure described in Silica,
Method A, Sec. 4.1–4.3 or 4.6. Discard the silica precipitate and save the
filtrate for removal of interfering
amounts of combined oxides described
in Sec. 3.2. If combined oxides are
absent, proceed to Sec. 3.3.

3.2. Remove interfering amounts of
aluminum, iron, and manganese by concentrating the filtrate from the gravimetric silica determination to 120–150
ml. Add enough HCl so that the filtrate from the silica removal contains
at least 10 ml conc HCl at this point.
Add 2–3 drops of methyl red indicator and 3N NH$_4$OH until the indicator color turns yellow. Add 1 g ammonium persulfate; when the solution
begins to boil, add 3N NH$_4$OH carefully until the solution becomes slightly
alkaline and the steam bears a distinct
but not a strong odor of ammonia. Test
the solution with litmus paper. Boil
the solution a minute or two and let the
hot solution stand 10 min, until the
hydroxides coagulate, but no longer.
Filter the precipitate and wash three or
four times with ammonium chloride
solution. Treat the filtrate as described
in Sec. 3.3.

3.3. To 200 ml of the sample, which
must not contain more than 250 mg Ca,
or to a smaller aliquot diluted to 200
ml, add 2 or 3 drops methyl red indicator solution. Neutralize with 1 + 1
HCl and boil for 1 min. Add 50 ml

ammonium oxalate solution, and if any
precipitate forms add just enough 1 + 1
HCl to redissolve it.

3.4. Keeping the solution just below
the boiling point, add 3N NH$_4$OH
dropwise from a buret, stirring constantly. Continue the addition until
the solution is quite turbid (about 5 ml
is required). Digest for 90 min at
90°C. Complete the precipitation by
slowly adding 3N NH$_4$OH over a period of several minutes until the solution turns yellow. Digest for 15 min at
90°C; then filter through S&S No. 589
Red Ribbon or equivalent filter paper.
Wash with cold 1 + 99 NH$_4$OH at
once. (If magnesium is to be determined gravimetrically, set aside the
combined filtrate and washings for this
purpose.)

3.5. Where time is not a factor and
interferences are suspected or known
to be present in the sample, repeat the
precipitation in the following manner.
Dissolve the precipitate with 50 ml
warm 1 + 9 HCl and wash the filter
paper thoroughly with hot distilled
water. Capture the solution and washings in the beaker in which the first precipitation was performed. Add 2–3
drops methyl red indicator solution.
Dilute or concentrate the volume to
150 ml. Add 50 ml ammonium oxalate
solution and repeat the precipitation as
described in Sec. 3.4.

3.6. Ignite the precipitate in a
covered crucible, preferably platinum,
at 1,100°–1,200°C for 15-min intervals
until constant weight is attained. Because calcium oxide is extremely hygroscopic, take suitable precautions in
cooling and weighing the crucible.
Weigh immediately after the crucible
reaches balance temperature. For best
results, use a fresh charge of an efficient desiccant such as anhydrous mag-

nesium perchlorate or activated aluminum oxide in the desiccator.

4. Calculation

$$\text{mg/l Ca} = \frac{\text{mg CaO} \times 714.7}{\text{ml sample}}$$

5. Precision and Accuracy

The standard deviation was ± 4.1 mg/l for four laboratories which determined calcium by the gravimetric method in a synthetic unknown containing 108 mg/l Ca and 82 mg/l Mg. One-half of the reported results were within ± 2 mg/l of the known calcium concentration. The individual laboratories reproduced their own results within ± 1.6 mg/l.

B. Permanganate Titrimetric Method

1. General Discussion

1.1. *Principle:* The titrimetric method differs from the gravimetric in that the precipitated calcium oxalate is redissolved in acid and titrated with permanganate. The amount of permanganate required to oxidize the oxalate is proportional to the amount of calcium.

1.2. *Interference:* See Method A, Sec 1.2.

2. Apparatus

2.1. *Vacuum pump,* or other source of vacuum.

2.2. *Filter flasks.*

2.3 *Filter crucibles,* 30 ml. Medium-porosity crucibles are recommended. Either glass or porcelain crucibles may be used. Gooch crucibles with specially prepared asbestos mats may be used, but are less convenient. Paper filters may be used but are not recommended. Crucibles of all-porous construction are difficult to wash quantitatively.

3. Reagents

All of the reagents listed in Method A, Sec. 2, are required, plus the following:

3.1. *Sodium oxalate:* Obtain primary standard grade $Na_2C_2O_4$ from the National Bureau of Standards or the Mallinckrodt Chemical Works. Dry it at 105°C overnight and store the dried material in a desiccator.

3.2. *Sulfuric acid,* 1 + 1.

3.3 *Standard potassium permanganate titrant,* 0.05N. Dissolve 1.6 g $KMnO_4$ in 1 liter distilled water. Keep in a brown glass-stoppered bottle and permit it to age for at least a week. Carefully decant or pipet the supernatant without stirring up any sediment. This solution requires frequent standardization by the following procedure (standard potassium permanganate solution, exactly 0.0500N, is equivalent to 1.002 mg Ca per 1.00 ml):

Weigh several samples of anhydrous sodium oxalate, $Na_2C_2O_4$, into 400-ml beakers. The charges should be between 0.1 and 0.2 g and be weighed to the nearest 0.1 mg. To each beaker in turn, add 100 ml distilled water and stir to dissolve. Add 10 ml 1 + 1 H_2SO_4 and heat rapidly to 90°–95°C. Titrate rapidly with the permanganate solution to be standardized, while stirring. The endpoint is a slight pink color which persists for at least 1 min. The temperature should not fall below 85°C and may, if desired, be maintained by a heater during the course of the titration; 0.1 g sodium oxalate will consume about 30 ml permanganate solution. Run a blank on the distilled water and H_2SO_4.

$$\text{Normality of } KMnO_4 = \frac{g\ Na_2C_2O_4}{(A - B) \times 0.06701}$$

where $A =$ ml titration for sample and $B =$ ml titration for blank. Average the results of several titrations.

4. Procedure

4.1. Using 200 ml of the sample, containing not more than 50 mg Ca (or a smaller aliquot diluted to 200 ml), follow the procedure described in Method A, Sec. 3.1–3.4, up to and including the directions, "Digest for 15 min at 90°C." Then filter, preferably through a filter crucible using suction. Wash at once with $1 + 99\ NH_4OH$. It is not necessary to transfer all of the precipitate to the filter crucible, but all excess ammonium oxalate must be removed from the beaker and crucible. (If magnesium is to be determined gravimetrically, set aside the combined filtrate and washings for this purpose.)

4.2. Place the filter crucible on its side in the beaker and cover with distilled water. Add 10 ml H_2SO_4 and, while stirring, heat rapidly to 90°–95°C. Titrate rapidly with permanganate solution to a slight pink endpoint which persists for at least 1 min. The temperature must not fall below 85°C, and may, if desired, be maintained by a heater during the course of the titration. The crucible must be agitated sufficiently to insure reaction of the oxalate it contains. Run a blank using a clean beaker and crucible, 10 ml H_2SO_4, and about the same volume of distilled water as was used in the actual titration.

5. Calculation

$$\text{mg/l Ca} = \frac{(A - B) \times N \times 20{,}040}{\text{ml sample}}$$

where $A =$ ml titration for sample, $B =$ ml titration for blank, and $N =$ normality of $KMnO_4$.

6. Precision and Accuracy

The standard deviation was ± 3.1 mg/l for five laboratories which determined calcium by the permanganate titrimetric method in a synthetic unknown sample containing 108 mg/l Ca and 82 mg/l Mg. One-half of the reported results were within ± 3 mg/l of the known calcium concentration. The individual laboratories reproduced their own results within ± 1.4 mg/l.

C. EDTA Titrimetric Method*

1. General Discussion

1.1. *Principle:* When EDTA (ethylenediaminetetraacetic acid or its salts) is added to water containing both calcium and magnesium, it combines first with the calcium that is present. Calcium can be determined directly using EDTA when the pH is made suffi-

---

* Two United States patents (No. 2,583,890 and 2,583,891) have been issued to G. Schwarzenbach disclosing titration and complexometric methods for quantitative determination of water hardness. Nothing contained in this manual is to be construed as granting any right, by implication or otherwise, for manufacture, sale, or use in connection with any method, apparatus, or product covered by patent, nor as insuring anyone against liability for infringement of patent.

ciently high so that the magnesium is largely precipitated as the hydroxide and an indicator is used which combines with calcium only. Several indicators are available that will give a color change at the point where all of the calcium has been complexed by the EDTA at a pH of 12–13.

1.2. *Interference:* Under conditions of this test, the following concentrations of ions cause no interference with the calcium hardness determination: copper, 2 mg/l; ferrous iron, 20 mg/l; ferric iron, 20 mg/l; manganese, 10 mg/l; zinc, 5 mg/l; lead, 5 mg/l; aluminum, 5 mg/l; tin, 5 mg/l. Orthophosphate will precipitate calcium at the pH of the test. Strontium and barium interfere with the calcium determination, and alkalinity in excess of 30 mg/l may cause an indistinct endpoint with hard waters.

2. Reagents

2.1. *Sodium hydroxide,* $1N$. Dissolve 40 g NaOH and dilute to 1 liter with distilled water.

2.2. *Indicators:* Many indicators are available for the calcium titration. Some are described in the literature (see bibliography), others are commercial preparations and may also be used. Murexide (ammonium purpurate) was the first indicator available for the detection of the calcium endpoint, and directions are presented for its use in this procedure. Individuals who have difficulty recognizing the murexide endpoint may find the indicator Eriochrome Blue Black R (color index number 202) or Solochrome Dark Blue an improvement because of its color change from red to pure blue. The chemical formula for Eriochrome Blue Black R is sodium-1-(2-hydroxy-1-naphthylazo)-2-naphthol-4-sulfonic

acid. Other indicators specifically designed for use as endpoint detectors in the EDTA titration of calcium may be employed.

Murexide (ammonium purpurate) indicator: This indicator changes from pink to purple at the endpoint. An indicator solution can be prepared by dissolving 0.15 g of the dye in 100 g of absolute ethylene glycol. Water solutions of the dye are not stable for longer than a day. A ground mixture of the dye powder and sodium chloride provides a stable form of the indicator. It is prepared by mixing 0.20 g of murexide with 100 g of solid NaCl and grinding the mixture to 40–50 mesh. The titration should be performed immediately after the addition of the indicator because it is unstable under alkaline conditions. Endpoint recognition is facilitated by the preparation of a color comparison blank containing 2.0 ml NaOH solution, 0.2 g solid indicator mixture (or 1–2 drops if a solution is used), and sufficient standard EDTA titrant (0.05–0.10 ml) to produce an unchanging color.

Eriochrome Blue Black R indicator: Prepare a stable form of the indicator by grinding together in a mortar 0.20 g powdered dye and 100 g solid NaCl to a 40–50 mesh. Store in a tightly stoppered bottle. Use 0.2 g of the ground mixture for the titration in the same manner as murexide indicator. During the course of the titration the color changes from red through purple to bluish purple to a pure blue without any trace of reddish or purple tint. The pH of some (not all) waters must be raised to 14 (rather than 12–13) by the use of $8N$ NaOH in order to get a good color change.

2.3. *Standard EDTA titrant,* $0.01M$. The standard EDTA titrant prepared as described for the EDTA total-hard-ness method (Hardness, Method B, Sec. 2.4, below) may be used. Standard EDTA titrant, exactly 0.0100M, is equivalent to 0.4008 mg Ca per 1.00 ml.

3. Procedure

3.1 Because of the high pH used in this procedure, the titration should be performed immediately after the addition of the alkali.

3.2. Use 50.0 ml of sample, or a smaller aliquot diluted to 50 ml, so that the calcium content is about 5–10 mg. For hard waters with alkalinity higher than 300 mg/l $CaCO_3$ the endpoint may be improved by taking a smaller aliquot and diluting to 50 ml, or by neutralization of the alkalinity with acid, boiling 1 min, and cooling before continuing the test.

3.3. Add 2.0 ml NaOH solution, or a volume sufficient to produce a pH of 12–13. Stir. Add 0.1–0.2 g of the indicator mixture selected (or 1–2 drops if a solution is used). Add EDTA titrant slowly, with continuous stirring to the proper endpoint. When using murexide, the endpoint may be checked by adding 1 or 2 drops of titrant in excess to make certain that no further color change occurs.

4. Calculation

$$mg/l\ Ca = \frac{A \times B \times 400.8}{ml\ sample}$$

Calcium hardness as mg/l $CaCO_3$
$$= \frac{A \times B \times 1,000}{ml\ sample}$$

where $A =$ ml titration for sample, and $B =$ mg $CaCO_3$ equivalent to 1.00 ml EDTA titrant at the calcium indicator endpoint.

5. Precision and Accuracy

The standard deviation among 40 laboratories which determined the calcium complexometrically in a synthetic unknown sample containing 108 mg/l Ca and 82 mg/l Mg was ±6.2 mg/l. One-half of the reported results were within ±2 mg/l of the known calcium concentration. The individual laboratories reproduced their own results within ±1.4 mg/l.

Bibliography

Gravimetric and Permanganate Titrimetric Methods

1. POPOFF, S.; WALDBAUER, L.; & McCANN, D. C. Quantitative Spectrographic Studies of Coprecipitation. I. Magnesium in Calcium Oxalate. *Ind. Eng. Chem., Anal. Ed.* 4:43 (1932).
2. INGOLS, R. S. & MURRAY, P. E. Urea Hydrolysis for Precipitating Calcium Oxalate. *Anal. Chem.* 21:525 (1949).
3. KOLTHOFF, I. M. & SANDELL, E. B. *Textbook of Quantitative Inorganic Analysis.* Macmillan Co., New York (3rd ed., 1952). Chap. 21 and pp. 575–577.
4. HILLEBRAND, W. F., ET AL. *Applied Inorganic Analysis.* John Wiley & Sons, New York (2nd ed., 1953). Chap. 31 and 40.
5. WILLARD, H. H.; FURMAN, N. H.; & BRICKER, C. E. *Elements of Quantitative Analysis.* D. Van Nostrand Co., Princeton, N.J. (4th ed., 1956).

EDTA Titrimetric Method

6. BETZ, J. D. & NOLL, C. A. Further Studies With the Direct Colorimetric Hardness Titration. *J. AWWA* 42:749 (1950).
7. KNIGHT, A. G. Estimation of Calcium in Water. *Chem. & Ind.* (London) No. 49, p. 1141 (Dec. 22, 1951).
8. DIEHL, H. & ELLINGBOE, J. L. Indicator for Titration of Calcium in the Presence of Magnesium Using Disodium Dihydrogen Ethylenediaminetetraacetate. *Anal. Chem.* 28:882 (1956).

9. PATTON, J. & REEDER, W. New Indicator for Titration of Calcium with (Ethylenedinitrilo) Tetraacetate. *Anal Chem.* 28:1026 (1956).

10. HILDEBRAND, G. P. & REILLEY, C. N. New Indicator for Complexometric Titration of Calcium in the Presence of Magnesium. *Anal. Chem.* 29:258 (1957).

11. SCHWARZENBACH, G. *Complexometric Titrations.* Interscience Publishers, New York (1957).

12. GOETZ, C. A. & SMITH, R. C. Evaluation of Various Methods and Reagents for Total Hardness and Calcium Hardness in Water. *Iowa State J. Sci.* 34:104 (Aug. 15, 1959).

13. KATZ, H. & NAVONE, R. Method for Simultaneous Determination of Calcium and Magnesium. *J. AWWA* 56: 121 (1964).

Carbon Dioxide

Surface waters normally contain less than 10 mg/l free carbon dioxide while some ground waters may easily exceed that concentration. The carbon dioxide content of a water may contribute significantly to some corrosive situations. The recarbonation of a supply during the terminal stages of water softening is a recognized treatment process. (The subject of saturation with respect to calcium carbonate is discussed elsewhere in this volume.)

Selection of method: A nomographic and a titrimetric method are described for the estimation of free carbon dioxide in water. The titration may be performed potentiometrically or conventionally in the presence of phenolphthalein indicator. Properly conducted, the more rapid, simple indicator method for the determination of free carbon dioxide is satisfactory for field tests and control and routine applications if it is understood that the method gives, at best, only an approximation.

The nomographic method (*A*) usually gives a closer estimation of the total free carbon dioxide when the pH and alkalinity determinations are made immediately and correctly at the time of sampling. The pH measurement should preferably be made with an electrometric pH meter, properly calibrated with standard buffer solutions in the pH range of 7 to 8. The error resulting from inaccurate pH measurements grows with an increase in the total alkalinity. For example, an inaccuracy of 0.1 in the pH determination causes a carbon dioxide error of 2 to 4 mg/l in the pH range of 7.0 to 7.3 and a total alkalinity of 100 mg/l as $CaCO_3$. In the same pH range, the error approaches 10 to 15 mg/l when the total alkalinity is 400 mg/l as $CaCO_3$.

Under favorable conditions the agreement between the titrimetric and nomographic methods is usually reasonably good. When the agreement is not precise, and the carbon dioxide determination is of particular importance, the analyst should state which method was used.

The calculation of the total carbon dioxide, free and combined, is given in Method C.

A. Nomographic Determination of Free Carbon Dioxide and the Three Forms of Alkalinity*

1. General Discussion

Within recent years, diagrams and nomographs have been proposed for the rapid calculation of the carbon dioxide, bicarbonate, normal carbonate, and hydroxide content of natural and treated waters. These graphical presentations

* See also Alkalinity.

are based on equations relating the ionization equilibria of the carbonates and water. Knowing the pH, total alkalinity, temperature, and total mineral content, any or all of the alkalinity forms and carbon dioxide can be determined nomographically.

A set of charts, Fig. 9 through 12, is presented for use where their ac-

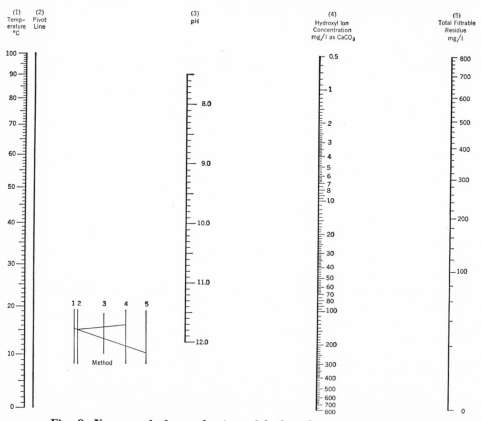

Fig. 9. Nomograph for evaluation of hydroxyl ion concentration *

To use: align temperature (Scale 1) and total filtrable residue (Scale 5); pivot on Line 2 to proper pH (Scale 3); read hydroxyl ion concentration, as mg/l CaCO₃, on Scale 4.

* Copies of the nomographs in Figs. 9–12, enlarged to 2.5 times the size shown here, may be obtained from American Water Works Association, 2 Park Ave., New York, N.Y. 10016, for 50 cents a set.

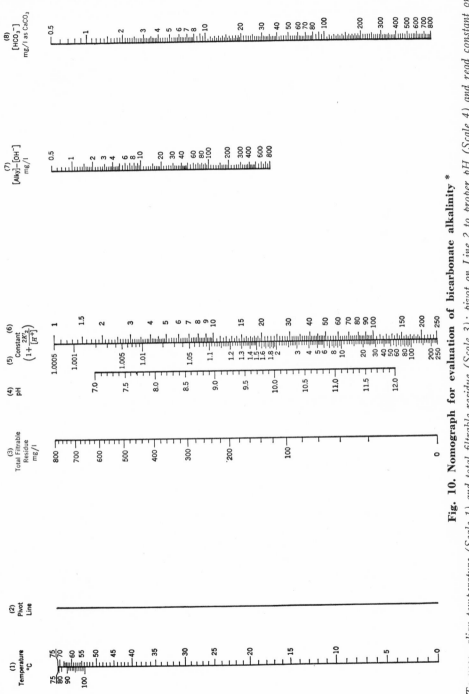

Fig. 10. Nomograph for evaluation of bicarbonate alkalinity *

To use: align temperature (Scale 1) and total filtrable residue (Scale 3); pivot on Line 2 to proper pH (Scale 4) and read constant on Scale 5; locate constant on Scale 6 and align with nonhydroxide alkalinity (found with aid of Fig. 9) on Scale 7; read bicarbonate alkalinity on Scale 8.

---

* See note to Fig. 9.

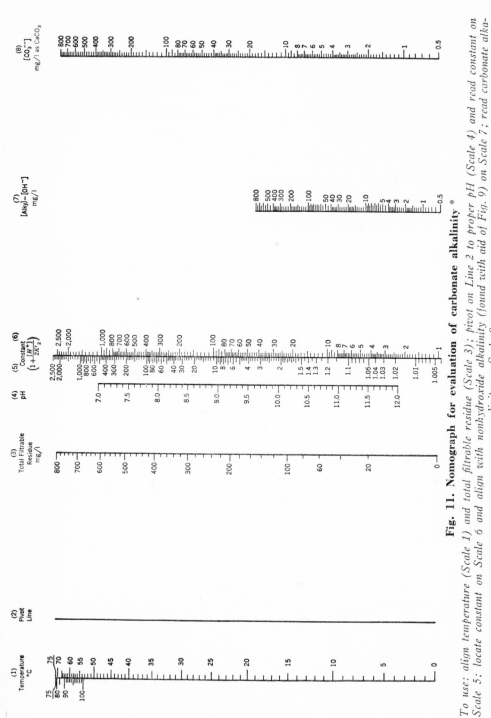

Fig. 11. Nomograph for evaluation of carbonate alkalinity *

To use: align temperature (Scale 1) and total filtrable residue (Scale 3); pivot on Line 2 to proper pH (Scale 4) and read constant on Scale 5; locate constant on Scale 6 and align with nonhydroxide alkalinity (found with aid of Fig. 9) on Scale 7; read carbonate alkalinity on Scale 8.

* See note to Fig. 9.

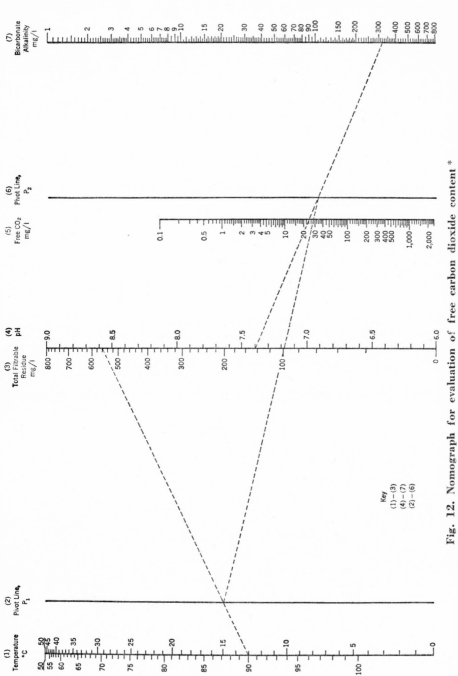

Fig. 12. Nomograph for evaluation of free carbon dioxide content *

To use: align temperature (Scale 1) and total filtrable residue (Scale 3), which determines Point P_1 on Line 2; align pH (Scale 4) and bicarbonate alkalinity (Scale 7), which determines Point P_2 on Line 6; align P_1 with P_2 and read free carbon dioxide on Scale 5. (Example: for 13°C temperature, 560 mg/l total filtrable residue, pH 7.4, and 320 mg/l alkalinity, the free carbon dioxide content is found to be 28 mg/l.)

* See note to Fig. 9.

curacy for the individual water supply is confirmed. The nomographs and the equations on which they are based are valid only where the salts of weak acids other than carbonic acid are present only in extremely small amounts or not at all.

Some treatment processes, such as superchlorination and coagulation, can significantly affect the pH and total-alkalinity values of a poorly buffered water of low alkalinity and low total-dissolved-mineral content. In such instances, the concentration of chloride and sulfate may overshadow the concentration of carbonic acid salts in the sample, thereby invalidating the applicability and accuracy of the nomographs.

Where the variables of temperature, total mineral content, and pH, alone or severally, exert an insignificant effect on the final result, the Moore charts [3] may be employed optionally. The limitations of these charts, however, must be completely comprehended and their applicability to the given water supply thoroughly demonstrated.

2. Precision and Accuracy

The precision possible with the nomographs is contingent upon the size and range of the scales. With practice, the recommended nomographs can be read with a precision of 1 per cent. The overall accuracy of the results is limited, however, by the accuracy of the analytical data which are applied to the nomographs and, additionally, by the validity of the theoretical equations and the numerical constants on which the nomographs are based. An approximate check of the accuracy of the calculations can be made by the summation of the three forms of alkalinity. Their sum should equal the total alkalinity.

B. Titrimetric Method for Free Carbon Dioxide

1. General Discussion

1.1. *Principle:* Free carbon dioxide reacts with sodium carbonate or sodium hydroxide to form sodium bicarbonate. Completion of the reaction is indicated potentiometrically or by the development of the pink color characteristic of phenolphthalein indicator at the equivalence pH of 8.3. An $0.01N$ sodium bicarbonate solution containing the recommended volume of phenolphthalein indicator is a suitable color standard until familiarity is obtained with the color prevalent at the endpoint.

1.2. *Interference:* Cations and anions which quantitatively disturb the normal carbon dioxide-carbonate equilibrium have a detrimental effect on the determination. Aluminum, iron, chromium, and copper are examples of metals whose salts contribute high results. The ferrous-ion level should not exceed 1.0 mg/l. Positive errors are also caused by ammonia, amines, phosphate, borate, silicate, sulfide, and nitrite. Mineral acids, and salts of strong acids and weak bases, affect the determination, and therefore should be absent. Experience has demonstrated that the titrimetric method for carbon dioxide is inapplicable to samples containing acid mine wastes and effluent from acid-regenerated cation exchangers. Negative errors may be introduced by high total dissolved solids, such as encountered in sea water, or by adding excess indicator. Fortunately, the concentration of these interferences is low in many water supplies used for potable purposes.

1.3. *Sampling and storage:* Even with a careful collection technique, some loss in free carbon dioxide can be expected in the storage and transit of the sample. This situation occurs more frequently when the gas is present in large amounts. Occasionally a sample may show an increase in free carbon dioxide content on standing. Consequently, the field determination of free carbon dioxide immediately at the point of sampling is advisable. Where a field determination is impractical, a bottle of sample filled to the top should be collected separately for laboratory examination. The bottled sample should be kept, until tested, at a temperature lower than that at which the water was collected. Moreover, the laboratory examination should be performed as soon as possible in order to minimize the effect of carbon dioxide changes in the sample.

2. Apparatus

2.1. *Daylight fluorescent lamps* have proved satisfactory and may be used in identifying the endpoint, by virtue of the fact that they enable the maintenance of uniform lighting conditions at all times, and, in particular cases, accentuate certain indicator color changes.

2.2. *Electrically operated titrators or pH meters,* suitably calibrated. Where such devices are available, the titrations may be performed using the same standard solutions that are given in the indicator method. Gentle agitation with a magnetic stirrer is recommended, as well as insulation of the sample from

the heat of the mixer motor by means of a sheet of $1/8$-in. asbestos paper. The titration can be made to selected pH values, appropriate for the temperature and total-dissolved-solids content of the samples.[7] The equivalence point may also be identified by the inflection of the titration curve or by the differential method of calculation. The potentiometric method is free from residual chlorine interference, the influence of color and turbidity, and individual visual idiosyncrasies.

3. Reagents

3.1. *Phenolphthalein indicator solution:* Either the aqueous (*a*) or alcoholic (*b*) solution may be used.

a. Dissolve 5 g phenolphthalein disodium salt in distilled water and dilute to 1 liter. Use distilled water which has been freshly boiled for at least 15 min to expel the carbon dioxide and has then been cooled to room temperature. If necessary, add 0.02N NaOH dropwise until a faint pink color appears.

b. Dissolve 5 g phenolphthalein in 500 ml 95 per cent ethyl alcohol or isopropyl alcohol and add 500 ml distilled water which has been freshly boiled for at least 15 min to expel the carbon dioxide and has then been cooled to room temperature. Then add 0.02N NaOH dropwise until a faint pink color appears.

3.2. *Standard alkali titrant:* Either 0.0454N sodium carbonate or 0.0227N sodium hydroxide solution may be used. One equivalent of sodium hydroxide or two equivalents of sodium carbonate (1 mol) are required to convert 1 mol of carbon dioxide to the bicarbonate endpoint. Both titrants are made up so that 1.00 ml $= 1.00$ mg CO_2:

a. *Standard sodium carbonate titrant,* 0.0454N. Dissolve 2.407 g anhydrous Na_2CO_3 (primary standard grade), oven dried at 140° C, and dilute to the mark of a 1-liter volumetric flask with distilled water which has been freshly boiled for at least 15 min to expel the carbon dioxide and has then been cooled to room temperature. Prepare the solution daily or protect from atmospheric carbon dioxide in a pyrex bottle.

b. *Standard sodium hydroxide titrant,* 0.0227N. Dilute 22.7 ml 1N NaOH (prepare as directed in Acidity, Sec. 3.1 and 3.2) to 1 liter with distilled water which has been freshly boiled for at least 15 min to expel the carbon dioxide and has then been cooled to room temperature. Prepare the reagent daily and protect from atmospheric carbon dioxide in a pyrex bottle. Standardize as described in Acidity, Sec. 3.3.

3.3. *Sodium bicarbonate,* 0.01N. Dissolve approximately 0.1 g anhydrous sodium hydrogen carbonate, $NaHCO_3$, and dilute to 100 ml with distilled water which has been freshly boiled for at least 15 min to expel the carbon dioxide and has then been cooled to room temperature. Prepare immediately before use.

4. Procedure

4.1. *Field determination:*

a. Collect the sample by means of rubber tubing discharging at the bottom of a 100-ml graduated cylinder or nessler tube. Allow the sample to overflow for a few minutes and withdraw the tubing while the sample is flowing. Flick the cylinder to throw off the excess sample above the 100-ml mark.

b. Add 5–10 drops of phenolphthalein indicator. (Always use the same volume of indicator for the sample as for the standardization procedure.) If the sample turns red, free carbon dioxide is absent. If the sample remains colorless, titrate rapidly into the cylinder with standard alkali solution, stirring gently with a stirring rod until a definite pink color persists for 30 sec when viewed through the depth of the sample. This color change is the endpoint. For best results, use a color comparison standard prepared by adding the identical volume of phenolphthalein indicator to 100 ml sodium bicarbonate solution in a similar graduated cylinder or nessler tube.

c. Where the free carbon dioxide content of the water sample is high, some loss of carbon dioxide to the atmosphere may occur even with this titration technique. Check this possibility by securing a second sample in the recommended manner and immediately run in the full amount of standard alkali solution used in the first titration. Apply 5–10 drops of phenolphthalein indicator, and, if the sample remains colorless, add sufficient extra alkali solution to titrate to the proper endpoint. Accept the second result as the more reliable titration.

4.2. *Laboratory determination:* Collect the sample in a 500-ml pyrex bottle as described in Sec. 4.1a, completely filling the bottle and leaving no air space. At the laboratory, siphon the sample into a 100-ml graduated cylinder or nessler tube, allowing overflow to occur. Proceed as in Sec. 4.1b.

5. Calculation

If the titrant is Na_2CO_3:

$$\text{mg/l } CO_2 = \frac{A \times N \times 22,000}{\text{ml sample}}$$

If the titrant is NaOH:

$$\text{mg/1 } CO_2 = \frac{A \times N \times 44,000}{\text{ml sample}}$$

where A = ml titration for sample, and N = normality of Na_2CO_3 or NaOH.

6. Precision and Accuracy

Precision and accuracy of the titrimetric method are on the order of ± 10 per cent of the known carbon dioxide concentration.

C. Total Carbon Dioxide by Calculation

The total carbon dioxide in a water is the sum of the free carbon dioxide and the carbon dioxide existing in the form of bicarbonate and carbonate ions as determined nomographically; or the free carbon dioxide and the carbonate and bicarbonate alkalinities as determined stoichiometrically by titration.

The total carbon dioxide can be calculated from the concentrations of free carbon dioxide, bicarbonate alkalinity, and carbonate alkalinity by the following equation, using alkalinities expressed as $CaCO_3$:

mg/1 total CO_2
$$= \text{mg/1 free } CO_2 + 0.88 \ (A + B)$$

where A = mg/1 bicarbonate alkalinity, and $B = \frac{1}{2}$ (mg/1 carbonate alkalinity).

Bibliography

Nomographic Method

1. LANGELIER, W. F. The Analytical Control of Anticorrosion Water Treatment. *J. AWWA* 28:1500 (1936).
2. DeMARTINI, F. E. Corrosion and the Langelier Calcium Carbonate Saturation Index. *J. AWWA* 30:85 (1938).
3. MOORE, E. W. Graphic Determination of Carbon Dioxide and the Three Forms of Alkalinity. *J. AWWA* 31:51 (1939).
4. LARSON, T. E. & BUSWELL, A. M. Calcium Carbonate Saturation Index and Alkalinity Interpretations. *J. AWWA* 34:1667 (1942).
5. DYE, J. F. The Calculation of Alkalinities and Free Carbon Dioxide in Water by the Use of Nomographs. *J. AWWA* 36:895 (1944).
6. DYE, J. F. Calculation of Effect of Temperature on pH, Free Carbon Dioxide, and the Three Forms of Alkalinity. *J. AWWA* 44:356 (1952).
7. DYE, J. F. Correlation of the Two Principal Methods of Calculating the Three Kinds of Alkalinity. *J. AWWA* 50: 812 (1958).

Titrimetric Method

8. *Standard Methods for the Examination of Water and Sewage.* APHA & AWWA, New York (8th ed., 1936). pp. 69, 122.
9. NORDELL, E. *Water Treatment for Industrial and Other Uses.* Reinhold Publishing Corp., New York (2nd ed., 1961). pp. 87–98.
10. *Approved Methods for the Physical and Chemical Examination of Water.* Inst. Water Engineers, Royal Inst. Chemistry, and Soc. Public Analysts & Other Analytical Chemists, London (3rd ed., 1960), p. 40.

Chloride

Chloride is one of the major anions in water and sewage. The salty taste produced by chloride concentrations is variable and dependent on the chemical composition of the water. Some waters containing 250 mg/1 chloride may evidence a detectable salty taste with sodium ions. On the other hand, the typical salty taste may be absent in waters containing as much chloride as 1,000 mg/l when there is a predominance of calcium and magnesium ions.

A high chloride content also exerts a deleterious effect on metallic pipes and structures, as well as on agricultural plants.

Selection of method: Two methods are presented for the determination of chloride in potable water. Since the two methods are similar in most respects, selection is largely a matter of preference. Where color offers a problem in the water sample, the determination can be performed potentiometrically, as described in Part III, Chloride, Method C.

A. Argentometric Method

1. General Discussion

1.1. *Principle:* In a neutral or slightly alkaline solution, potassium chromate can be used to indicate the endpoint of the silver nitrate titration of chloride. Silver chloride is quantitatively precipitated before red silver chromate is formed.

1.2. *Interference:* Substances in amounts normally found in potable waters will not interfere. Bromide, iodide, and cyanide register as equivalent chloride concentrations. Sulfide, thiosulfate, and sulfite ions interfere. However, sulfite can be removed by treatment with hydrogen peroxide in a neutral solution, while sulfide and thiosulfate can be removed by treatment with hydrogen peroxide in alkaline solution. Orthophosphate in excess of 25 mg/l interferes by precipitation as silver phosphate. Iron in excess of 10 mg/l will interfere by masking the endpoint.

2. Reagents

2.1. *Chloride-free water:* If necessary, remove any chloride impurity from distilled water by redistillation from an all-pyrex apparatus or passage through a mixed bed of ion-exchange resins. See General Introduction, A, Sec. 2, and Nitrogen (Ammonia), Method A, Sec. 3.1 b.

2.2. *Potassium chromate indicator solution:* Dissolve 50 g K_2CrO_4 in a little distilled water. Add silver nitrate solution until a definite red precipitate is formed. Allow to stand 12 hr, filter, and dilute filtrate to 1 liter with distilled water.

2.3. *Standard silver nitrate titrant,* 0.0141N. Dissolve 2.396 g $AgNO_3$ in distilled water and dilute to 1,000 ml. Standardize against 0.0141N NaCl by means of the procedure described in Sec. 3.4. Store in a brown bottle. Standard silver nitrate solution, exactly 0.0141N, is equivalent to 0.500 mg Cl per 1.00 ml.

2.4. *Standard sodium chloride,* 0.0141N. Dissolve 0.8241 g NaCl (dried at 140°C) in chloride-free water and dilute to 1,000 ml; 1.00 ml = 0.500 mg Cl.

2.5. *Special reagents for removal of interference:*

a. *Aluminum hydroxide suspension:* Dissolve 125 g potassium or ammonium alum, $K_2Al_2(SO_4)_4 \cdot 24H_2O$ or $(NH_4)_2Al_2(SO_4)_4 \cdot 24H_2O$, in 1 liter of distilled water. Warm to 60°C and add 55 ml conc NH_4OH slowly with stirring. After allowing it to stand about 1 hr transfer the mixture to a large bottle and wash the precipitate by successive additions, with thorough mixing, and decantations of distilled water, until free from chloride. When freshly prepared, the suspension occupies a volume of approximately 1 liter.

b. Phenolphthalein indicator solution. Either the aqueous (I) or alcoholic (II) solution may be used.

I. Dissolve 5 g phenolphthalein disodium salt in distilled water and dilute to 1,000 ml with distilled water. If necessary, add $0.02N$ NaOH dropwise until a faint pink color appears.

II. Dissolve 5 g phenolphthalein in 500 ml 95 per cent ethyl alcohol or isopropyl alcohol and add 500 ml distilled water. Add $0.02N$ NaOH dropwise until a faint pink color appears.

c. Sodium hydroxide, 1N. Dissolve 40 g NaOH in distilled water and dilute to 1 liter.

d. Sulfuric acid, 1N. While stirring, add 28 ml conc H_2SO_4 cautiously to distilled water and dilute to 1 liter.

e. Hydrogen peroxide, 30 per cent.

3. Procedure

3.1. Use a 100-ml sample or a suitable aliquot diluted to 100 ml.

3.2. If the sample is highly colored, add 3 ml $Al(OH)_3$ suspension, mix, allow to settle, filter, wash, and combine filtrate and washing.

3.3. If sulfide, sulfite, or thiosulfate is present, make the water alkaline to phenolphthalein with sodium hydroxide solution. Add 1 ml H_2O_2 and stir. Neutralize with sulfuric acid.

3.4. Titration: Samples in the pH range 7–10 may be titrated directly. Adjust samples not in this range with sulfuric acid or sodium hydroxide solution. Add 1.0 ml K_2CrO_4 indicator solution. Titrate with standard silver nitrate titrant to a pinkish-yellow endpoint. The means of consistent endpoint detection are left to the individual analyst.

Standardize the silver nitrate titrant and establish the reagent blank value by the titration method outlined above. A blank of 0.2 to 0.3 ml is usual for the method.

4. Calculation

$$\text{mg/1 Cl} = \frac{(A - B) \times N \times 35{,}450}{\text{ml sample}}$$

where $A =$ ml titration for sample, $B =$ ml titration for blank, and $N =$ normality of $AgNO_3$.

$$\text{mg/1 NaCl} = \text{mg/1 Cl} \times 1.65$$

5. Precision and Accuracy

A synthetic unknown sample containing 241 mg/1 chloride was determined in 41 laboratories with a standard deviation of ± 9.4 mg/1 by means of the argentometric method. One-half of the reported results were within ± 6 mg/1 of the known chloride concentration. The individual laboratories reproduced their own results within ± 1.7 mg/1.

B. Mercuric Nitrate Method*

1. General Discussion

1.1. *Principle:* Chloride can be titrated with mercuric nitrate because of the formation of soluble, slightly dissociated mercuric chloride. In the pH range 2.3–2.8, diphenylcarbazone in-

---

* United States Patent 2,784,064 has been issued to F. E. Clarke, relative to the mer-curimetric titration of chloride. Nothing contained in this manual is to be construed

dicates the endpoint of this titration by formation of a purple complex with the excess mercuric ions. The error in titration is about 1 per cent of the volume of titrant used per change of 0.1 pH unit in the pH range 2.1–2.8. Since exact pH adjustment is not feasible except by use of a pH meter, it is felt that keeping within a range of ±0.1 pH unit is sufficient for most water analyses. Therefore, in this method a specific mixture of nitric acid and diphenylcarbazone is added to a water sample, automatically adjusting the pH of most potable waters to pH 2.5 ± 0.1. A third substance in this alcoholic mixture, xylene cyanol FF, is used as a pH indicator and a background color to facilitate endpoint detection. The introduction of 10 mg sodium bicarbonate to both the blank and standard titration provides a pH of 2.5 ± 0.1 when 1.0 ml indicator-acidifier reagent (2.1 a) is added.

1.2. *Interference:* Iodide and bromide are titrated with mercuric nitrate in the same manner as chloride. Sulfite, chromate, and ferric ions interfere when present in excess of 10 mg/l.

2. Reagents

2.1. *Indicator-acidifier reagent:* The nitric acid concentration of this reagent is an important factor in the success of the determination and can be varied as indicated in (*a*) or (*b*) to suit the alkalinity range of the sample being titrated. Reagent (*a*) contains sufficient nitric acid to neutralize a total

alkalinity of 150 mg/l as $CaCO_3$ to the proper pH in a 100-ml sample.

a. Dissolve in the order named 0.25 g s-diphenylcarbazone, 4.0 ml conc HNO_3, and 0.03 g xylene cyanol FF in 100 ml of 95 per cent ethyl alcohol or isopropyl alcohol. Store in a dark bottle in a refrigerator. This reagent is not stable indefinitely. Deterioration causes a slow endpoint and high results.

b. Inasmuch as pH control plays a critical role in this method, the pH of highly alkaline or acid samples should be adjusted to 2.5 ± 0.1 with 0.1N nitric acid or sodium hydroxide, not with sodium bicarbonate. A pH meter with a non-chloride type of reference electrode should be used for the pH adjustment. If the usual chloride-type reference electrode alone is available for the pH adjustment, the amount of acid or alkali required to achieve a pH of 2.5 ± 0.1 should be determined and this particular sample portion should be discarded. A separate sample portion should then be treated with the determined amount of acid or alkali and the analysis continued to its prescribed end. Under these circumstances, the nitric acid should be omitted from the indicator reagent to maintain the proper sample pH. Alternatively, the nitric acid concentration of the indicator-acidifier reagent can be varied to accommodate the conditions wherein the work is centered exclusively on water samples of very high or low alkalinity.

2.2. *Standard mercuric nitrate titrant,* 0.0141N. Dissolve 2.3 g $Hg(NO_3)_2$, or 2.5 g $Hg(NO_3)_2 \cdot H_2O$, in 100 ml distilled water containing 0.25 ml conc HNO_3. Dilute to just under 1 liter. Perform a preliminary standardization by following the procedure described in Sec. 3.2–3.4. Use replicates containing 5.00 ml standard NaCl solution and 10 mg NaHCO₃ diluted to 100 ml with distilled water. Adjust the mercuric nitrate titrant to exactly 0.0141N and perform a final standardization. Store away from the light in a dark bottle. Standard mercuric nitrate titrant, exactly 0.0141N, is equivalent to 0.500 mg Cl per 1.00 ml.

2.3. *S t a n d a r d sodium chloride,* 0.0141N. See Method A, Sec. 2.4.

2.4. *Sodium bicarbonate,* powder.

2.5. *Special reagents for pH adjustment:*

a. *Nitric acid,* 0.1N. Dilute 6.4 ml conc HNO₃ to 1 liter with distilled water.

b. *Sodium hydroxide,* 0.1N. Dissolve 4.0 g NaOH in distilled water and dilute to 1 liter.

3. Procedure

3.1. Use a 100-ml sample or smaller aliquot so that the chloride content is less than 10 mg.

3.2. Add 1.0 ml of indicator-acidifier reagent to the sample. The color of the solution should be green-blue at this point. A light green indicates a pH of less than 2.0; a pure blue indicates a pH of more than 3.8. For most potable waters, the pH after this addition will be 2.5 ± 0.1. When highly alkaline or acid waters are encountered, a preliminary pH adjustment to about pH 8 will be necessary before the indicator-acidifier reagent is added.

3.3 Titrate the treated sample with mercuric nitrate titrant to a definite purple endpoint. The solution will turn from green-blue to a blue a few drops from the endpoint.

3.4. Perform a blank determination as in Sec. 3.3 by titration of 100 ml of

distilled water containing 10 mg NaHCO₃.

4. Calculation

If 100 ml of sample is taken, if the mercuric nitrate solution is exactly 0.0141N, and if the blank (B) takes 0.1 ml, then the calculation is as follows:

$$mg/l\,Cl = 5.0\,(A - 0.1)$$

If the above conditions are not all met, then the calculation is:

$$mg/l\,Cl = \frac{(A - B) \times N \times 35{,}450}{ml\ sample}$$

where $A =$ ml titration for sample, $B =$ ml titration for blank, and $N =$ normality of $Hg(NO_3)_2$.

$$mg/l\,NaCl = mg/l\,Cl \times 1.65$$

5. Precision and Accuracy

A synthetic unknown sample containing 241 mg/l chloride was determined mercurimetrically by nine laboratories with a standard deviation of ±3.5 mg/l. One-half of the reported results were within ±6 mg/l of the known chloride concentration. The individual laboratories reproduced their own results within ±1.1 mg/l.

Bibliography

Argentometric Method

1. HAZEN, A. On the Determination of Chlorine in Water. *Am. Chem. J.* 11: 409 (1889).
2. KOLTHOFF, I. M. & STENGER, V. A. *Volumetric Analysis.* Interscience Publishers, New York (2nd ed., 1947). Vol. 2, pp. 242–245, 256–258.

Mercuric Nitrate Method

3. Ref. 2, pp. 334–335.

4. DOMASK, W. C. & KOBE, K. A. Mercuri-
   metric Determination of Chlorides and
   Water-Soluble Chlorohydrins. *Anal.
   Chem.* 24:989 (1952).

5. GOLDMAN, E. New Indicator for the Mer-
   curimetric Chloride Determination in
   Potable Water. *Anal Chem.* 31:1127
   (1959).

Chlorine (Residual)

The chlorination of water supplies accomplishes a number of treatment objectives. The destruction of micro-organisms is a primary function. However, overall improvement in the finished water can result from chlorine's reaction with ammonia, iron, manganese, sulfide, and protein substances. With some taste- and odor-producing compounds such as phenols, chlorine may intensify the problem or under careful control may improve the water quality.

Most methods for the determination of free or combined available chlorine are based on reactions with reducing agents that are not specific for these materials. Definite test conditions under which specificity is attained despite the presence of particular interfering oxidizing agents have been described by a number of investigators, and the results have been considered in formulating this section. Chlorine in water may be present as free available chlorine (in the form of hypochlorous acid or hypochlorite ion, or both); or as combined available chlorine (chloramines and other chloro derivatives). Both free and combined chlorine may be present simultaneously.

Some oxidizing agents, including free halogens other than chlorine, will appear quantitatively as free chlorine; this is also true of chlorine dioxide. A small proportion of nitrogen trichloride (trichloramine) will titrate as free chlorine. These substances rarely appear in sufficient quantity to introduce a significant error; nevertheless, their action should be familiar to the analyst as they will affect all the chlorine methods described.

The following methods are intended for moderately polluted water, water in the process of purification, water treatment plant effluent, potable water in the distribution system, swimming pool water, and industrial cooling and process water. Highly polluted waters may require other methods for satisfactory analysis as described in Part IV.

Selection of method: The iodometric method (A) is employed as a standard and is the basis for the standardization of chlorine water used in preparing temporary standards. It is also suitable for determining high chlorine residuals, which are more frequently encountered now than heretofore. The iodometric method is more precise than the orthotolidine method when the residual chlorine concentration is greater than 1 mg/l.

The orthotolidine methods (B and D) are widely used for routine measurement of residual chlorine in plant control and in the field. Both procedures can be rapidly completed by simple visual apparatus or by photometric techniques. When proper precautions are observed, reasonable accuracy may be expected from the orthotolidine procedures described below.

The orthotolidine flash method (C)

is a qualitative technique for free available chlorine and is affected but slightly by the slow-acting interfering agents, usually nitrites or oxidized iron. It is affected by colloidal manganese dioxide.

The orthotolidine-arsenite method (D) is a technique for the differentiation of free available chlorine, combined available chlorine, and color due to interfering substances.

A drop dilution method (E) for orthotolidine tests is included for field use. It is not accurate and should not be substituted for titrimetric methods.

The amperometric titration method (F) appears to be one of the most accurate available for the determination of free or combined available chlorine. The method is usually unaffected by the presence of various oxidizing agents, temperature variations, and turbidity and color which interfere with the accuracy of the other methods.

Not enough experience has been gained with methods for differentiation of monochloramine and dichloramine to warrant their inclusion as standard methods. Since such information may be valuable in chlorination treatment control and research, however, the differential amperometric titration method (G) and the ferrous titrimetric method (H) are included as tentative methods.

Sampling and storage: Chlorine in aqueous solution is not stable, and the chlorine content of samples or solutions, particularly weak solutions, will rapidly decrease. Exposure to sunlight or other strong light or agitation will accelerate the reduction of chlorine present in such solutions. Therefore, it is recommended that chlorine determinations be started immediately after sampling, avoiding excessive light and agitation. Samples to be analyzed for chlorine cannot be stored.

A. Iodometric Method

1. General Discussion

1.1. *Principle:* Chlorine will liberate free iodine from potassium iodide solutions when its pH is 8 or less. The liberated iodine is titrated with a standard solution of sodium thiosulfate, using starch as the indicator. The reaction is preferably carried out at pH 3 to 4.

1.2. *Interference:* Although the neutral titration minimizes the interfering effect of nitrites and manganic and ferric ions, the acid titration is preferred; it is most accurate for determination of total available residual chlorine. Acetic acid should be used for the acid titration; sulfuric acid may be used only when the analyst has satisfied himself that interfering substances are absent; but hydrochloric acid should never be used.

1.3. *Minimum detectable concentration:* The minimum detectable concentration approximates 0.04 mg/l Cl if $0.01N$ sodium thiosulfate is used with a 500-ml sample.

2. Reagents

2.1. *Acetic acid,* conc (glacial).

2.2. *Potassium iodide,* crystals.

2.3. *Standard sodium thiosulfate,* $0.1N$. Dissolve 25 g $Na_2S_2O_3 \cdot 5H_2O$ in 1 liter freshly boiled distilled water, and standardize the solution against potassium biniodate or potassium dichromate after at least 2 weeks' storage. Use boiled distilled water and add a few milliliters of chloroform to minimize bacterial decomposition of the thiosulfate solution.

Standardization: Standardize the 0.1N sodium thiosulfate by one of the following procedures:

a. Biniodate method: Dissolve 3.249 g anhydrous potassium biniodate, KH(IO$_3$)$_2$, of primary standard quality,* in distilled water and dilute to 1,000 ml to yield a 0.1000N solution. Store in a glass-stoppered bottle.

To 80 ml distilled water, add, with constant stirring, 1 ml conc H$_2$SO$_4$, 10.00 ml 0.1000N KH(IO$_3$)$_2$, and 1 g potassium iodide. Titrate immediately with 0.1N Na$_2$S$_2$O$_3$ titrant until the yellow color of the liberated iodine is almost discharged. Add 1 ml starch indicator solution and continue titrating until the blue color disappears.

b. Dichromate method: Dissolve 4.904 g anhydrous potassium dichromate, K$_2$Cr$_2$O$_7$, of primary standard quality, in distilled water and dilute to 1,000 ml to yield a 0.1000N solution. Store in a glass-stoppered bottle.

Proceed as in the biniodate method, with the following exceptions: Substitute 10.00 ml 0.1000N K$_2$Cr$_2$O$_7$ for the KH(IO$_3$)$_2$, and allow the reaction mixture to stand 6 min in the dark before titration with the 0.1N Na$_2$S$_2$O$_3$ titrant.

Calculation of normality:

$$\text{Normality Na}_2\text{S}_2\text{O}_3 = \frac{1,000}{\text{ml Na}_2\text{S}_2\text{O}_3 \text{ consumed}}$$

2.4. Standard sodium thiosulfate titrant, 0.01N or 0.025N. Stability of 0.01N or 0.025N Na$_2$S$_2$O$_3$ is improved if it is prepared by diluting an aged 0.1N solution, made as directed above,

---

* Such as is obtainable from G. F. Smith Chemical Company, Columbus, Ohio.

with freshly boiled distilled water. Trouble may be avoided by the addition of a few milliliters of chloroform. Another suggested method of preservation of a few milliliters of chloroform. and 10 mg mercuric iodide per liter of solution. For accurate work, this solution should be standardized daily, in accordance with the directions given above, using 0.01N or 0.025N KH(IO$_3$)$_2$ or K$_2$Cr$_2$O$_7$. The use of an automatic buret, of a type in which rubber does not come in contact with the solution, speeds up operations where many samples must be titrated. Standard sodium thiosulfate titrants, exactly 0.0100N and 0.0250N, are equivalent, respectively, to 0.3545 mg and 0.8863 mg available Cl per 1.00 ml.

2.5. Starch indicator solution: To 5 g starch (potato, arrowroot, or soluble), add a little cold water and grind in a mortar to a thin paste. Pour into 1 liter of boiling distilled water, stir, and allow to settle overnight. Use the clear supernatant. Preserve with 1.25 g salicylic acid, 4 g zinc chloride, or a combination of 4 g sodium propionate and 2 g sodium azide added to 1 liter of starch solution.

2.6. Standard iodine, 0.1N. Refer to Method F, Sec. 3.1b.

2.7. Dilute standard iodine, 0.0282N. Refer to Method F, Sec. 3.1c.

3. Procedure

3.1. Volume of sample: The volume of sample to be taken for titration is governed by the chlorine concentration. It is suggested that, for concentrations of residual chlorine of 1 mg/l or less, 1 liter be titrated; for residual chlorine concentrations between 1 and 10 mg/l, 500 ml; and for residual chlorine concentrations above 10 mg/l, proportionately less. It is preferable to regulate the sample volume so that not more than 20 ml $0.01N$ thiosulfate is required.

3.2. Preparation for titration: Place 5 ml acetic acid, or sufficient to reduce the pH to between 3.0 and 4.0, in a flask or white porcelain casserole; add about 1 g potassium iodide estimated on a spatula; pour in the sample and mix with a stirring rod. Distilled water may be added at the discretion of the analyst if a larger volume is preferred for titration. The titration must not be performed in direct sunlight.

3.3. Titration: Add $0.025N$ or $0.01N$ thiosulfate from a buret until the yellow color of the liberated iodine is almost discharged. Add 1 ml starch solution and titrate until the blue color is discharged.

If the titration is made with $0.025N$ thiosulfate instead of 0.01, then, with a 1-liter sample, 1 drop is equivalent to about 0.05 mg/l. It is not possible to discern the endpoint with greater accuracy than this. If a 500-ml sample is titrated, 1 drop will correspond to about 0.1 mg/l, which is within the limit of sensitivity. Hence, use of $0.025N$ solution should be considered acceptable. Many laboratories have this on hand.

3.4. Blank titration: Correct the result of the sample titration by determining the blank contributed by such reagent impurities as: (a) the free iodine or iodate in the potassium iodide which liberates extra iodine; or (b) the traces of reducing agents that might reduce some of the iodine which is liberated.

Take a volume of distilled water corresponding to the sample used for titration in Sec. 3.1–3.3, add 5 ml acetic acid, 1 g KI, and 1 ml starch solution. Perform either Blank Titration A or B, whichever applies.

Blank Titration A: If a blue color occurs, titrate with $0.01N$ or $0.025N$ sodium thiosulfate to the disappearance of the blue, and record the result.

Blank Titration B: If no blue color occurs, titrate with $0.0282N$ iodine solution until a blue color appears. Back-titrate with $0.01N$ or 0.025 N sodium thiosulfate and record the difference as Titration B.

Before calculating the chlorine, subtract Blank Titration A from the sample titration; or, if necessary, add the net equivalent value of Blank Titration B.

4. Calculation

For standardizing chlorine solution for temporary standards:

$$mg/ml\ Cl = \frac{(A \pm B) \times N \times 35.45}{ml\ sample}$$

For the determination of total available residual chlorine in a water sample:

$$mg/l\ Cl = \frac{(A \pm B) \times N \times 35,450}{ml\ sample}$$

where $A =$ ml titration for sample, $B =$ ml titration for blank which may be positive or negative, and $N =$ normality of $Na_2S_2O_3$.

B. Orthotolidine Method

1. General Discussion

The orthotolidine method measures both free and combined available chlorine. If it is desired to determine whether the chlorine is present in the free or the combined form, the flash test (Method C) or the OTA test (Method D) may be used.

1.1. *Principle:* To obtain the correct color development with chlorine and orthotolidine: (a) the solution must be at pH 1.3 or lower during the contact period; (b) the ratio by weight of orthotolidine to chlorine must be at least 3:1; and (c) the chlorine concentration must not exceed 10 mg/l.

Commercially available orthotolidine dihydrochloride is considerably purer than the free orthotolidine base. Moreover, the dihydrochloride readily dissolves in water, which makes it easier to prepare the test reagent.

The concentration of the acid in the orthotolidine reagent must be such that it will produce a suitable pH even if the sample has up to 1,000 mg/l of alkalinity.

To insure color development at a pH of 1.3 or lower and a ratio of orthotolidine to chlorine of at least 3:1, the reagent must be placed in the cell, tube, or comparison bottle first, and the sample added to it.

A 6-month stability limit is specified for the orthotolidine reagent as an arbitrary precaution against any discoloration or precipitation due to occasional exposure to high temperatures or direct sunlight. The caution against permitting the reagent to come in contact with rubber is based on observations that significant amounts of reducing substances are extracted from some types of rubber closures by orthotolidine.

The reaction time and the temperature specified were selected to permit measurement of a maximum proportion of the combined available chlorine present, while minimizing loss of color by fading, or increase of color due to interfering oxidizing agents such as nitrite, ferric iron, and certain compounds formed by chlorine with organic matter.

The method given in Sec. 3.1 below for preparation of chlorine-demand-free water was selected for convenience; although ammonia-free water is not required, the preference expressed for it is based on difficulties encountered in removing large amounts of ammonia with chlorine alone. Due to the rapidity with which this water may absorb some laboratory fumes, it should be examined for nitrite, chlorine, and reducing agents immediately before use when determining very low concentrations of chlorine.

The permanent chromate-dichromate color standards give good visual matches and almost exact spectrophotometric matches when the determination is made at pH 1.3 or less and the orthotolidine-chlorine ratio is at least 3:1. The choice of buffer solutions and their application are the result of spectrophotometric studies.

Excellent accuracy in determination of residual chlorine with orthotolidine may be obtained by photometric methods. A method for calibration of photometric instruments for residual chlorine testing is referred to in the bibliography.[26]

1.2. *Interference:* When orthotolidine is used to measure residual chlorine, the analyst must satisfy himself as to the presence and amount of interfering substances in the sample to be tested. Such interferences include nitrite, ferric compounds, manganic compounds, and, possibly, organic iron compounds, lignocellulose, and algae. The effect of these substances is to increase the apparent residual chlorine content of the sample under examination.

Suspended matter interferes and should be removed by centrifuging prior to test; or, if the turbidity is not high, a compensating colorimeter, which also corrects for existing color and turbidity in the sample, may be used. Compensation of color and turbidity can also be accomplished by adding 1 or 2 drops of a reducing reagent containing an oxidizable sulfur group (see Sec. 6), and stirring until the color disappears. This simple procedure is particularly suited to photometric measurements and for use with samples containing acid-soluble turbidity such as alum floc.

In chlorinated water containing no more than 0.3 mg/l iron, 0.01 mg/l manganic manganese, and 0.10 mg/l nitrite nitrogen, the development of the characteristic yellow color with orthotolidine may be accepted as being due to chlorine. If iron and manganese are present in more than the above concentrations, the development of the characteristic yellow color with orthotolidine cannot be accepted as being due to chlorine alone. If nitrite is present in an interfering concentration, color development in total darkness minimizes interference. It should be noted that significant amounts of nitrite will not exist in water containing free available chlorine but may exist in the presence of chloramines.

It is recommended that the orthotolidine-arsenite method (D) be employed to determine the amount of any additional color produced by the above interferences. When such additional color is found, the quantity is deducted to correct the chlorine values and the OTA test should be used as a routine procedure.

1.3. *Minimum detectable concentration:* The orthotolidine-chlorine reaction is sensitive to residual chlorine concentrations as low as approximately 0.01 mg/l.

2. Apparatus

2.1. *Illumination:* All readings should be taken by looking through the samples against an illuminated white surface. The surface may be opaque and illuminated by reflection or may be an opal diffusing glass illuminated from behind. Since chlorine determinations are made both day and night in plant control, it is preferable that all comparisons be made with a standard artificial light. The permanent standards give greater accuracy when used with either of the two artificial light sources specified below, both of which are close approximations of average "north" daylight:

a. *Filament lamp assembly,* consisting of a light source, color filter, and diffuser glass, suitably mounted in a cabinet. It is essential that the diffuser glass be placed in contact with the color filter and on the sample side. The light source should be a 150-w Mazda "C" lamp,* with clear envelope. The color filter should be Corning "daylight" No. 5900 having a thickness equivalent to 163 microreciprocal degrees. The diffuser glass should be thin flashed opal glass without color tint.

b. *Fluorescent "daylight" lamp assembly:* The white reflecting or diffusing surface may be illuminated by a fluorescent "daylight" lamp without the use of a color filter. Those manufactured by General Electric Company or Westinghouse Electric and Manufacturing Company, or equal, should be specified.

---

* A product of General Electric Company.

If artificial light is not provided, comparisons should be made with good "north" daylight. Under no circumstances should the comparisons be made in sunlight.

2.2. Colorimetric equipment: One of the following is required:

a. Nessler tubes, matched, 100 ml, tall form.

b. Filter photometer, providing a light path of 1 cm or longer and equipped with a violet filter having maximum transmittance in the range of 400 mμ to 450 mμ, and a blue-green filter having maximum transmittance near 490 mμ.

c. Spectrophotometer, for use at 435 mμ, and 490 mμ, providing a light path of 1 cm or longer.

3. Temporary Chlorine Standards

Temporary chlorine standards are not recommended for routine use because extreme care is required in their preparation. These standards are recommended for calibration purposes and for research. The yellow holoquinone color developed obeys Beer's law over a considerable chlorine range when measurements are made with a 1-cm light path. Although the maximum absorption occurs near 435 mμ, filters transmitting in the range between 400 mμ and 450 mμ may be employed for the photometric measurement of low chlorine values. The following information will serve as a guide in the selection of color filters and light paths:

Chlorine Range mg/l	Light Path cm	Wavelength mμ
0.02–0.3	5	400–450
0.1 –1.5	1	400–450
0.5 –7.0	1	490

3.1. Chlorine-demand-free water: Add sufficient chlorine to distilled water to destroy the ammonia. The amount of

chlorine required will be about ten times the amount of ammonia nitrogen present; in no case should the initial residual be less than 1.0 mg/l free chlorine. Allow the chlorinated distilled water to stand overnight or longer; then expose to direct sunlight until all residual chlorine is discharged. The use of distilled water free from nitrite and ammonia makes it simpler to obtain a chlorine-demand-free water.

3.2. Chlorine solution for temporary standards: Chlorine solutions or hypochlorite solutions for research and calibration purposes should be prepared from purified reagents and standardized as described below. Certain commercial solutions of hypochlorite have been found to be of relatively constant composition and of a high degree of stability.* Because of their convenience, their use is preferred for routine purposes.

3.3. Preparation of temporary standards: All glassware must be exposed to water containing at least 10 mg/l chlorine for 3 hr or more before use and then rinsed with chlorine-demand-free water. Add calculated volumes of chlorine or hypochlorite solution to a series of flasks containing chlorine-demand-free water to cover the range desired. Make up each one to 500 ml and mix gently. Pipet 100 ml from each flask into a series of smaller flasks, each containing 5 ml orthotolidine. Add the chlorine solution slowly, mixing well as it is added. Pour the required amount into the comparator cell or tube. If 100-ml nessler tubes are used, the sec-

---

* Of those available at the present time, Zonite (Zonite Products Corporation) and household bleach have been found satisfactory. Zonite contains approximately 1 per cent available chlorine.

ond series of flasks may be omitted.

3.4. *Titration of chlorine solution:* Pour the remaining 400 ml of each temporary standard into a white porcelain casserole and titrate with thiosulfate according to Method A, Sec. 3.2 and 3.3.

3.5. *Calibration of photometer:* Construct a calibration curve for the photometer by making dilutions of standardized hypochlorite solution prepared as directed under Chlorine Demand, Method A, Sec. 3.1. Special precautions must be taken when diluting to low concentrations, because of possible consumption of small amounts of chlorine by trace impurities. Use chlorine-demand-free water (Sec. 3.1 above) in making the dilutions. Expose all glassware to be used in the dilutions to water containing at least 10 mg/l of chlorine, leaving it in contact for a few hours. Then rinse with the chlorine-demand-free water.

Make a suitable series of dilutions; subject these to the analytical procedures described in the orthotolidine method (*B* and *D*); then use the results to construct a calibration curve.

4. Permanent Chlorine Standards

It cannot be emphasized too strongly that precision in the preparation of the buffer solutions is necessary; therefore, the directions must be followed explicitly.

4.1. *Phosphate buffer stock solution, 0.5M.* Dry anhydrous disodium hydrogen phosphate, Na_2HPO_4, and anhydrous potassium dihydrogen phosphate, KH_2PO_4, overnight at 105°–110°C, and store in a desiccator. Dissolve 22.86 g Na_2HPO_4 together with 46.16 g KH_2PO_4 in distilled water and dilute to 1 liter. Let the solution stand for several days to allow time

for any precipitate to form. Filter before using.

4.2. *Phosphate buffer solution, 0.1M.* This is a standard buffer, pH 6.45. Filter the stock solution as prepared above and dilute 200 ml to 1 liter with distilled water.

4.3. *Strong chromate-dichromate solution:* Dissolve 1.55 g potassium dichromate, $K_2Cr_2O_7$, and 4.65 g potassium chromate, K_2CrO_4, in 0.1M phosphate buffer and dilute to 1 liter with 0.1M phosphate buffer. This solution corresponds to the color produced by 10 mg/l chlorine in the standard orthotolidine procedure when viewed through a depth of 24–30 cm.

4.4. *Dilute chromate-dichromate solution:* Dissolve 0.155 g potassium dichromate and 0.465 g potassium chromate in 0.1M phosphate buffer and dilute to 1 liter with 0.1M phosphate buffer. The solution may also be prepared by diluting 100 ml of strong chromate-dichromate solution to 1 liter with 0.1M phosphate buffer. This solution corresponds to the color produced by 1 mg/l chlorine in the standard orthotolidine procedure when viewed through all cell depths.

TABLE 6—LOW-RANGE CHLORINE STANDARDS
—0.01–1.0 MG/L *

Chlorine *mg/l*	Chromate-Dichromate Solution *ml*	Chlorine *mg/l*	Chromate-Dichromate Solution *ml*
0.01	1	0.35	35
0.02	2	0.40	40
0.05	5	0.45	45
0.07	7	0.50	50
0.10	10	0.60	60
0.15	15	0.70	70
0.20	20	0.80	80
0.25	25	0.90	90
0.30	30	1.00	100

* These standards are very close visual matches of the chlorine-orthotolidine color and are preferable to temporary standards, which are difficult to prepare accurately.

4.5. *Low-range permanent chlorine standards,* 0.01–1.0 mg/l. The volumes of dilute chromate-dichromate solution indicated in Table 6 for the range of cell depths given are pipeted into 100-ml tubes of any uniform length and diameter or into 100-ml volumetric flasks. The volume is then made up to the 100-ml mark with $0.1M$ phosphate buffer solution. These standards can be read at any cell depth up to 30 cm.

4.6. *High-range permanent chlorine standards,* 1.0–10.0 mg/l. The volumes of strong chromate-dichromate solution indicated in Table 7 for the range of cell depths given are pipeted into 100-ml tubes of any uniform length and diameter or into 100-ml volumetric flasks. The volume is then made up to the 100-ml mark with $0.1M$ phosphate buffer solution. Standards for other cell depths or for other concentrations can be prepared by interpolating between the values in Tables 6 and 7.

4.7. *Comparison tube specifications:* Variations in the viewing depth in any

TABLE 7—HIGH-RANGE CHLORINE STANDARDS—1.0–10.0 MG/L *

Chlorine mg/l	Cell Depth—cm			
	2.5–5	10	20	24–30
	Chromate-Dichromate Solution—ml			
1	10.0	10.0	10.0	10.0
1.5	15.0	15.0	15.0	15.0
2	19.5	19.5	19.7	20.0
3	27.0	27.5	29.0	30.0
4	34.5	35.0	39.0	40.0
5	42.0	43.0	48.0	50.0
6	49.0	51.0	58.0	60.0
7	56.5	59.0	68.0	70.0
8	64.0	67.0	77.5	80.0
9	72.0	75.5	87.0	90.0
10	80.0	84.0	97.0	100.0

* These standards are very close visual matches of the chlorine-orthotolidine color and are preferable to temporary standards, which are difficult to prepare accurately.

set of color comparison tubes, cells, or bottles used in this determination must not be more than ±3 per cent.

4.8. *Protection of standards:* The tubes should be protected from dust and evaporation by sealing on microcover glasses with collodion, Canada balsam, or similar material. The material may be applied to the top of the nessler tube by means of a camel's-hair brush and the cover glass put into position promptly with forceps. After it is spot sealed, the circumference may be reinforced with additional, brush-applied, sealing material until the joining of the tube and cover glass is complete. The use of rubber stoppers is not recommended. Convenient nessler tubes with special ground-glass caps that permit optical comparison are now on the market. The standards should be neither stored nor used in direct sunlight. They should be renewed whenever turbidity appears.

4.9. *Commercial standards:* Commercially prepared permanent standards may be used for routine tests, provided the analyst checks them frequently to satisfy himself of their accuracy.

5. Orthotolidine Reagent

5.1. *Preparation:* Dissolve 1.35 g orthotolidine dihydrochloride in 500 ml distilled water. Add this solution, with constant stirring, to a mixture of 350 ml distilled water and 150 ml conc HCl. The use of orthotolidine base in the preparation of this reagent is not recommended.

5.2. *Storage:* The orthotolidine solution should be: (a) stored in amber bottles or in the dark; (b) protected at all times from direct sunlight; (c) used no longer than 6 months; (d) kept from contact with rubber; and (e) maintained at normal temperatures. At temperatures below 0°C, the orthotolidine will precipitate from solution and cannot be redissolved easily. The use of a reagent from which part of the orthotolidine has precipitated may lead to errors due to a deficiency of orthotolidine.

6. Decolorizing Solution

One of the following reducing reagents with a sulfur group will discharge the yellow holoquinone color formed by the reaction of chlorine and orthotolidine. Mercaptosuccinic acid (thiomalic acid) is preferred because greater quantities of the compound can be tolerated in an acid medium before sulfur begins to precipitate. The use of excess sodium thiosulfate and sodium sulfite leads to the formation of a sulfur colloid. However, 1 or 2 drops of any of these agents can be used with safety:

6.1. *Mercaptosuccinic acid solution:* Dissolve 10 g mercaptosuccinic acid (also called thiomalic acid), practical grade, and dilute to 100 ml with distilled water. This solution is stable for at least 6 months when stored away from strong light in a glass-stoppered bottle.

6.2. *Sodium thiosulfate,* 0.1N. Dissolve 25 g $Na_2S_2O_3 \cdot 5H_2O$ and dilute to 1 liter with distilled water.

6.3. *Sodium sulfite solution:* Dissolve 10 g Na_2SO_3 and dilute to 100 ml with distilled water.

7. Procedure

7.1. *Addition of sample to reagent:* Use 0.5 ml orthotolidine reagent in 10-ml cells, 0.75 ml in 15-ml cells, 5 ml in 100-ml, and the same ratio for other volumes. Place the orthotolidine reagent in the nessler tube, colorimeter cell, or other container; add sample to the proper mark or volume; and mix.

7.2. *Temperature:* When the temperature of the sample is less than 20°C, bring it to that temperature quickly after mixing it with orthotolidine. If a comparator cell is used, place it in hot water until the specified temperature is reached. If a nessler tube is used, it may be handled in the same manner as the cell, or the contents may be transferred to a flask for heating.

7.3. *Color development and comparison:* Color comparison should be made at the time of maximum color development. If the potable sample contains predominantly free chlorine, the maximum color appears almost instantly and begins to fade. Samples containing combined chlorine develop their maximum color at a rate that is largely dependent on temperature, although the nitrogenous compounds present may influence this rate. Usually at 20°C maximum color develops in about 3 min; at 25°C, in about 2.5 min; and at 0°C, in about 6 min. About 5 min after maximum color develops, a slight fading begins. Therefore, samples containing combined chlorine should be read within 5 min and should, preferably, be allowed to develop color in the dark. When color comparison is made against chromate-dichromate standards, use the same cell depth for both samples and standards.

7.4. *Compensation for interference:* Interference due to the presence of natural color or turbidity can be compensated for in one of two ways: (a) view the sample and standard horizontally after placing an untreated sample of the same thickness behind the standard and the same thickness of clean water behind the sample under comparison; (b) add 1 or 2 drops (0.05–0.1 ml) of decolorizing solution (Sec. 6) to the developed chlorine-orthotolidine color and mix until the yellow color disappears (within a minute). The approach in (b) is adaptable for photometric work by enabling measurements to be made before and after the addition of the decolorizing solution. The values are read from the calibration curve as "apparent chlorine" and "interferences as chlorine" and then subtracted. Alternatively, a portion of the developed sample can be decolorized and used to null the photometer, whereupon the chlorine value is obtained directly from the curve. In the presence of excessive turbidity a brief period of centrifuging may be needed to bring the sample within nulling range of the photometer.

C. Orthotolidine Flash Test Method

1. General Discussion

A qualitative determination of the presence of free chlorine is afforded by the flash test.

Interference: Oxidized manganese will produce flash colors with orthotolidine reagent in this test, similar in shade and rate of development to that of free available chlorine residuals. The presence of combined chlorine in the sample will produce a slightly higher reading than the total amount of free chlorine actually present. This effect may be minimized by lowering the temperature of the sample to as near $1°C$ as practical, as the orthotolidine reacts more slowly with chloramines at low temperatures. Speed in making the color comparison is essential when chloramines are present. Free chlorine reacts almost instantaneously, even at $0°C$.

2. Procedure

Place a sample of water cooled to less than $20°C$ in a comparator cell or other small container, of such dimensions as to insure immediate and complete mixture of the reagent with the sample. Hold the container against a white background and, using a medicine dropper, add, with force, 0.5–1 ml orthotolidine reagent to the sample of water, paying close attention to color development. Read as rapidly as possible. Take a second reading after 3 min. If the second reading is higher than the first, combined chlorine is present; therefore, the sample should be chilled (as rapidly as circumstances permit) to as near $1°C$ as possible, and the determination repeated.

3. Interpretation of Results

If oxidized manganese and combined available chlorine are absent, instantaneous color development indicates the presence of free chlorine. Combined available chlorine develops color gradually, and the free-chlorine reading taken in its presence will generally be somewhat high, the error increasing with increased temperature and concentration of combined available chlorine. Free-chlorine concentrations greater than 0.3 mg/l are above the most accurate range of this method.

D. Orthotolidine-Arsenite (OTA) Method

1. General Discussion

Within the limitations specified, the orthotolidine-arsenite (OTA) method permits the measurement of the relative amounts of free available chlorine, combined available chlorine, and color due to interfering substances. In samples containing a high proportion of combined available chlorine, more free available chlorine may be indicated than is actually present, because temperature plays an important role in the determination of the free-available-chlorine fraction. At room temperature some of the combined available chlorine can react with orthotolidine in the OTA method, yielding a spurious or high free-available-chlorine value. To minimize this interference, the sample should be chilled (as rapidly as circumstances permit) to as near 1°C as possible before the addition of the orthotolidine and arsenite reagents (steps described in Sec. 4.1b).

Too much emphasis cannot be placed on the fact that the precision of the results depends on strict adherence to (a) the recommended time intervals for the addition of reagents and (b) the temperature of the sample. Since precision is affected by the relative concentrations of free and combined available chlorine in the sample, the temperature of the sample under examination should never exceed 20°C in Sec. 4.1b of the procedure. The precision of the determination for the free-available-chlorine fraction improves with decreasing temperature.

2. Apparatus

Colorimetric equipment: One of the following is required:

2.1. *Spectrophotometer or filter photometer,* for use in the wavelength range of 400 to 490 mμ and providing a light path of 1 cm or longer.

2.2. *Comparator,* color and turbidity compensating.

2.3. *French square bottles,* capacity 1 or 2 oz.

3. Reagents

3.1. *Orthotolidine reagent,* prepared and stored as directed in Method B, Sec. 5.

3.2. *Sodium arsenite solution:* Dissolve 5.0 g $NaAsO_2$ in distilled water and dilute to 1 liter. (CAUTION: *Toxic; take care to avoid ingestion.*)

3.3. *Permanent chlorine standards,* prepared commercially or as directed in Method B, Sec. 4 (to be used in comparator tubes or French square bottles).

4. Procedure

4.1. *Visual comparison:*

a. Label three comparator cells or French square bottles "A," "B," and "C." Use 0.5 ml orthotolidine reagent in 10-ml cells, 0.75 ml in 15-ml cells, and the same ratio for other volumes of sample. Use the same volume of arsenite solution as orthotolidine.

b. To Cell A, containing orthotolidine reagent, add a measured volume of water sample. Mix quickly, and immediately (within 5 sec) add arsenite solution. Mix quickly again and compare with color standards as rapidly as possible. Record the result. The value obtained (A) represents free available chlorine and interfering colors.

c. To Cell B, containing arsenite solution, add a measured volume of water sample. Mix quickly, and immediately add orthotolidine reagent. Mix quickly again and compare with color standards as rapidly as possible. Record the result (B_1). Compare with color standards again in exactly 5 min and record the result (B_2). The values obtained represent the interfering colors present in the immediate reading (B_1) and in the 5-min reading (B_2).

d. To Cell C, containing orthotolidine reagent, add a measured volume of water sample. Mix quickly and compare with color standards in exactly 5 min. Record the result. The value obtained (C) represents the total amount of residual chlorine present

and the total amount of interfering colors.

4.2. Photometric measurement: The colors developed by following the directions in Sec. 4.1 can be measured photometrically and the readings converted to the proper chlorine values by referring to a calibration curve prepared by treating known chlorine concentrations in the same manner as the unknown samples.

5. Calculation

Total available residual chlorine $= C - B_2$

Free available residual chlorine $= A - B_1$

Combined available residual chlorine
    $=$ total available residual Cl
      $-$ free available residual Cl

E. Drop Dilution Method for Field Use

1. General Discussion

The drop dilution method is designed for field measurements of free residual chlorine where concentrations are greater than 10 mg/l and where speed of estimation is of importance. It is particularly useful in connection with the disinfection of mains or tanks where laboratory apparatus is not available. The test is not intended to displace titration methods and should not be used where accuracy is desired. This test must not be made in direct sunlight.

2. Apparatus

2.1. Color comparison equipment: One of the following may be used with due consideration being given the amount of chlorine solution taken for the test:

a. Comparator.

b. Nessler tubes, 100 ml.

2.2. Medicine dropper, calibrated to deliver 20 drops per milliliter.

3. Reagents

3.1. Orthotolidine reagent, prepared and stored as directed in Method B, Sec. 5.

3.2. Permanent chlorine standards, prepared as directed in Method B, Sec. 4.

4. Procedure

4.1. If the comparator cell holds 10 or 15 ml, place 0.5 ml orthotolidine reagent in the cell. If a 100-ml nessler tube is used, place 5.0 ml orthotolidine reagent in the tube. Fill the cell or tube to the mark with distilled water and mix thoroughly. Add to the cell or tube 1 drop of the water under test. Mix thoroughly.

4.2. A sample of water with such concentrations of chlorine as may be estimated by this method usually contains only free available chlorine, although traces of combined available chlorine are occasionally found. For this reason, the color development is very rapid and the reading may be made almost at once. Color comparisons against chromate-dichromate standards must be made with the same cell depth for samples and standards.

4.3. If the addition of 1 drop of the water under test produces no color, discard the contents of the cell. Refill with orthotolidine and distilled water as before and add 2 drops of the water under test. Continue this procedure with increasing amounts of sample until an easily readable color, equivalent to not less than 0.1 mg/l, is produced.

5. Calculation

Free available residual chlorine:

$$\text{mg/l Cl} = \frac{\text{ml cell volume} \times \text{reading} \times 20}{\text{drops of sample}}$$

F. Amperometric Titration Method

1. General Discussion

Amperometric titration is generally considered to be an excellent laboratory method for the determination of chlorine residuals, particularly when extreme accuracy is desired. It is more practical for the laboratory than for field use, as it requires a source of 110-v current. Amperometric titration requires a higher degree of skill and care than the orthotolidine method. Chlorine residuals over 2 mg/l may best be measured by using smaller samples, or by dilution. The method can be used to determine total residual chlorine and can also differentiate between free and combined available chlorine.

1.1. *Principle:* The amperometric method is a special adaptation of the polarographic principle. Free available chlorine is determined by titration at a pH between 6.0 and 7.5, a range in which the combined chlorine does not react. The combined chlorine, in turn, is titrated in the presence of the proper amount of potassium iodide in the pH range 3.5–4.5. When determining free chlorine, the pH must not be greater than 7.5—because the reaction becomes sluggish at higher pH values—or less than 6.0, because at lower pH values some combined chlorine may react even in the absence of iodide. When determining combined chlorine, the pH must not be less than 3.5—because substances such as oxidized manganese interfere at lower pH values—or greater than 4.5, because the reaction is not quantitative at higher pH values.

For the titrating reagent, phenylarsine oxide solution is used. Its reaction with chlorine is independent of pH. It is stable even in dilute solution. Each mole of phenylarsine oxide reacts with two equivalents of halogen. In the procedure, the chlorine residual is titrated with a standard solution of phenylarsine oxide, and a special galvanic cell is used to detect the endpoint. The cell consists of a nonpolarizable reference electrode which is immersed in a salt solution, and a readily polarizable noble-metal electrode which is in contact both with the salt solution and with the sample that is to be titrated. The electrode circuit is connected to a microammeter. If there is no chlorine residual in the sample, the microammeter reading will be comparatively low because of cell polarization. The greater the residual in the sample, the more effectively the cell is depolarized and the greater the microammeter reading. The meter acts merely as a null-point indicator—that is, the actual meter reading is not important, but rather the relative readings as the titration proceeds. As phenylarsine oxide is added gradually, the cell becomes more and more polarized due to the decrease in available chlorine. The endpoint is recognized when no further decrease in meter reading can be obtained by adding more phenylarsine oxide.

1.2. *Interference:* Accurate determinations of free chlorine cannot be made in the presence of nitrogen trichloride or chlorine dioxide, which titrate partly as free chlorine. Free halogens other than chlorine will also titrate as free chlorine. If the sample contains bromide or iodide and combined chlorine, an apparent increase in the free-chlorine reading may occur. Interference from copper has been noted in samples after heavy copper sulfate treatment of reservoirs, with metallic copper plating out on the electrode. Silver ions also poison the electrode. Interference has also been noted in some highly colored waters, but the interfering substance has not been established. Very low temperatures slow the response of the electrode, and longer time is required for the titration, but the precision is not affected. A reduction in reaction rate is also caused by pH values above 7.5, but this is overcome by buffering all samples to pH 7.0 or less. On the other hand, some substances—such as manganese, nitrite, and iron—that interfere with the orthotolidine method do not interfere with amperometric titration.

2. Apparatus

2.1. *Endpoint detection apparatus,* consisting of a cell unit connected to a microammeter, with the necessary electrical accessories. The cell unit comprises a noble-metal electrode of sufficient surface area, a salt bridge to provide an electrical connection without diffusion of electrolyte, and a reference electrode of silver-silver chloride in a saturated sodium choride solution which is connected into the circuit by means of the salt bridge. It is important that the noble-metal electrode be kept free of deposits and similar foreign matter. Vigorous chemical cleaning is fortunately not necessary in ordinary usage. Occasional mechanical cleaning with a suitable abrasive is usually sufficient. The salt bridge should be kept in good operating condition, which means that it should neither become plugged nor permit appreciable flow of electrolyte through it. It is important that the solution surrounding the reference electrode be kept free of contamination and be maintained at constant composition by insuring an adequate supply of undissolved salt at all times. For descriptions of various forms of this device see the bibliography.

2.2. *Agitator,* designed to give the greatest possible degree of agitation at the noble-metal electrode surface in order to insure proper sensitivity. The agitator and the exposed electrode system should be thoroughly cleaned to remove all chlorine-consuming contaminants by immersing them in water containing 1 to 2 mg/1 free available residual chlorine for a few minutes. Then potassium iodide is added to the same water and the agitator and electrodes allowed to remain immersed another 5 min. After thorough rinsing with chlorine-demand-free water or the sample to be tested, the sensitized electrodes and agitator are ready for use.

2.3. *Buret:* A convenient form is made from a 1-ml pipet with 0.01-ml graduations. This is connected to a delivery tube with a finely drawn tip by means of suitable plastic tubing. Glass beads may be inserted in the plastic tubing to act as valves.

2.4. *All glassware* must be exposed to water containing at least 10 mg/l residual chlorine for 3 hr or more before use and then rinsed with chlorine-demand-free water.

3. Reagents

3.1. *Standard phenylarsine oxide titrant:* Dissolve approximately 0.8 g phenylarsine oxide powder, C_6H_5AsO, in 150 ml 0.3N sodium hydroxide. After settling, decant 110 ml of this solution into 800 ml distilled water and mix thoroughly. Bring the solution to pH 6–7 with dilute hydrochloric acid solution and finally dilute to 1 liter. Standardize to 0.00564N against standard 0.0282N iodine solution, using the amperometric titrator for the normality determinations; 1.00 ml = 0.200 mg available chlorine. Preserve with 1 ml chloroform. (CAUTION: *Toxic; take care to avoid ingestion.*)

a. *Standard sodium arsenite, 0.1N.* Accurately weigh a stoppered weighing bottle containing approximately 4.95 g arsenic trioxide, As_2O_3, primary standard grade. Transfer without loss to a 1-liter volumetric flask and again weigh the bottle. Do not attempt to brush out the adhering oxide. Moisten the As_2O_3 with distilled water, and add 15 g NaOH and 100 ml distilled water. Swirl the contents of the flask gently

until the As_2O_3 is in solution. Dilute to 250 ml with distilled water and saturate the solution with CO_2, thus converting all the NaOH to sodium bicarbonate. Dilute to the mark, stopper the flask, and mix thoroughly. A solution thus prepared will preserve its titer almost indefinitely. (CAUTION: *Toxic; take care to avoid ingestion.*)

$$\text{Normality} = \frac{\text{g } As_2O_3}{49.455}$$

b. *Standard iodine,* 0.1N. Dissolve 40 g potassium iodide in 25 ml distilled water and then add 13 g resublimed iodine and stir until dissolved. Transfer to a 1-liter volumetric flask and dilute to the mark.

Standardization: Accurately measure 40–50 ml of 0.1N sodium arsenite solution into a flask and titrate with 0.1N iodine solution using starch solution as indicator. In order to obtain accurate results, it is absolutely necessary that the solution be saturated with carbon dioxide at the end of the titration. A current of carbon dioxide may be passed through the solution for a few minutes just before the endpoint is reached, or a few drops of hydrochloric acid may be added to liberate sufficient carbon dioxide to saturate the solution.

c. *Dilute standard iodine,* 0.0282N. Dissolve 25 g potassium iodide in a little distilled water in a 1-liter volumetric flask; add the proper amount of 0.1N iodine solution exactly standardized to yield a 0.0282N solution; and dilute to 1 liter. For accurate work this solution should be standardized daily in accordance with directions given in the preceding paragraph, using 5–10 ml of 0.1N sodium arsenite solution.

Storage: Place in amber bottle or store in the dark, making certain that the solution is protected from direct sunlight at all times and kept from all contact with rubber.

3.2. *Phosphate buffer solution,* pH 7. Dissolve 25.4 g anhydrous potassium dihydrogen phosphate, KH_2PO_4, and 34.1 g anhydrous disodium hydrogen phosphate, Na_2HPO_4, in 800 ml distilled water. Add 2 ml sodium hypochlorite solution containing 1 per cent available chlorine and mix thoroughly. Protect from sunlight for several days and then expose to sunlight until no residual chlorine remains. If necessary the final dechlorination can be carried out with a sodium sulfite solution, leaving just a trace of chlorine as shown by a qualitative orthotolidine test. Finally dilute to 1 liter with distilled water and filter if any precipitate is present.

3.3. *Potassium iodide solution:* Dissolve 50 g KI and dilute to 1 liter, using freshly boiled and cooled distilled water. Store in a brown, glass-stoppered bottle, preferably in the refrigerator. Discard the solution when a yellow color has developed.

3.4. *Acetate buffer solution,* pH 4. Dissolve 480 g glacial acetic acid and 243 g sodium acetate trihydrate, $NaC_2H_3O_2 \cdot 3H_2O$, in 400 ml distilled water and make up to 1 liter.

4. Procedure

4.1. *Volume of sample:* It is suggested that, for residual chlorine concentrations of 2 mg/l or less, 200 ml be titrated. For residual chlorine concentrations above this range, a 100-ml sample is more suitable. It is preferable to use a sample such that not more than 2 ml phenylarsine oxide solution is required.

4.2. *Titration of free available chlorine:* Unless the pH of the sample is definitely known to lie between 6.0 and 7.5, add 1 ml pH 7 phosphate buffer solution. Then titrate by adding phenylarsine oxide solution from the buret and observing current changes on the microammeter. As long as addition of phenylarsine oxide produces a definite decrease in current, free available chlorine is present. As the endpoint is approached, the response of the microammeter to each increment becomes more sluggish, and smaller increments of phenylarsine oxide are added. The endpoint is just passed when a very small increment of phenylarsine oxide no longer causes a decrease in current. The buret is then read and the last increment of titrating solution subtracted from the reading to give a value representing the free available chlorine concentration.

4.3. *Titration of combined available chlorine:* To the sample remaining from the free-chlorine titration add exactly 1 ml potassium iodide solution and then 1 ml acetate buffer solution in that order. Titrate with phenylarsine oxide solution to an endpoint just as above. It is most convenient not to refill the buret but simply to continue the titration after recording the figure for free available chlorine. After concluding the titration, subtraction of the last increment again gives the amount of titrating solution actually used in reaction with the chlorine. If the titration was continued without refilling the buret, this figure represents the total residual chlorine. Subtracting the free available chlorine from the total gives the combined residual chlorine. It is essential to wash the apparatus and sample cell thoroughly to remove iodide ion after this determination, in order to avoid inaccuracies if the titrator is subsequently used for a free available chlorine determination.

4.4. If desired, the determination of the total residual chlorine and the free available chlorine may be made on separate samples. If only the value for total available chlorine is required, it is permissible to treat the sample immediately with 1 ml potassium iodide solution followed by 1 ml acetate buffer solution. The titration is carried out with phenylarsine oxide solution as described above.

5. Calculation

$$\text{mg/1 Cl} = \frac{A \times 200}{\text{ml sample}}$$

where $A =$ ml titration for sample.

6. Interpretation of Results

It is unnecessary to use chlorine-demand-free water in making up the reagent solutions. Such small volumes of these solutions are used that the slight chlorine demand of ordinary distilled water has no significance. On the other hand, the destruction of all ammonia contamination contributed by the phosphate salts should be insured through chlorination of the pH 7 buffer solution. Otherwise the ammonia traces often present in phosphate salts may convert significant amounts of free available chlorine in the sample to combined chlorine when the pH 7 buffer is added prior to titration for free available chlorine. Since the pH 4 buffer is added after that titration, traces of ammonia which might be present in this buffer will cause no similar error. Of course, the pH 7 buffer must be carefully dechlorinated after the ammonia has been destroyed.

G. Method for Differentiation of Monochloramine and Dichloramine by Amperometric Titration (Tentative)

1. General Discussion

1.1. *Principle:* This method is merely an extension of the method (F) for determining free available chlorine and combined residual chlorine by amperometric titration. By a slight alteration in procedure, it is possible to separate the combined chlorine into two fractions, one of which is monochloramine and the other dichloramine. The differentiation depends on the fact that monochloramine reacts more readily with iodide than does dichloramine. Different potassium iodide concentrations and pH values are used to determine these two chloramines separately. It is important to use the specified amounts of potassium iodide solution in each case.

1.2. *Interference:* The method is subject to the same interferences as the general amperometric titration method. The limitations of this method are: (a) if nitrogen trichloride is present, it titrates partly as free available chlorine and partly as dichloramine, which makes both of these values slightly high; (b) it is known that different organic chloramines are titrated in each step.

2. Apparatus

The apparatus is the same as in Method F, Sec. 2.

3. Reagents

The reagents are the same as in Method F, Sec. 3.

4. Procedure

4.1. It is suggested that for residual chlorine concentrations of 2 mg/l or less, 200 ml be titrated. For residual chlorine concentrations above this range, 100 ml is more suitable. It is preferable to use a sample such that not more than 2 ml phenylarsine oxide titrant is required.

4.2. Titrate for free available chlorine as in Method F, Sec. 4.2.

4.3. Then, to the same sample, add 0.2 ml potassium iodide solution. Again titrate with phenylarsine oxide titrant to the usual endpoint. It is most convenient not to refill the buret but simply to continue the titration after recording the figure for free available chlorine. After concluding the titration, subtraction of the last increment again gives the amount of titrating solution actually used in reaction with the chlorine. The second titration represents monochloramine.

4.4. Still using the same sample, add 1 ml acetate buffer solution and 1 ml potassium iodide solution. Titrate as usual, subtracting the last increment of phenylarsine oxide. This titration represents dichloramine.

5. Calculation

For each titration, the concentration of available residual chlorine in the particular form represented is given as follows:

$$\text{mg/l Cl} = \frac{A \times 200}{\text{ml sample}}$$

where $A =$ ml titration for sample.

H. Ferrous Titrimetric Method for Free Available Chlorine, Monochloramine, and Dichloramine, and Estimation of Nitrogen Trichloride (Tentative)

1. General Discussion

1.1. *Principle:* A system has been developed by Palin using a serial titration for the differentiation of free available chlorine, nitrogen trichloride, and ochloramine, and dichloramine. Three steps are used: In the first, free available chlorine, nitrogen trichloride, and chlorine dioxide are titrated with standard ferrous solution at pH 6.3 to 6.5 with orthotolidine as the indicator. The second step titrates monochloramine by the addition of a small amount of iodide ion, the liberated iodine reacting with the orthotolidine. The third step requires, first, the addition of acid to permit the dichloramine to react with the iodide; then, the adjustment of the pH back to 6.5 for the titration. The absence of color in the first step also indicates the absence of nitrogen trichloride (trichloramine) and chlorine dioxide; and while the presence of free available chlorine does not prove the presence of the other two components, it does indicate that they may be present. Nitrogen trichloride, readily identified by its distinctive odor, may be estimated by one of two procedures. The first involves the extraction of the nitrogen trichloride by means of carbon tetrachloride and titration of the water layer for free available chlorine. (Carbon tetrachloride also partially extracts chlorine dioxide.) The second procedure depends on the destruction of the free available chlorine residual with oxalic acid, leaving nitrogen trichloride for subsequent titration. If organic chloramines are present, it is not known in which fraction they will be titrated.

1.2. *pH control:* For accurate results, careful pH control is essential. At the proper pH of 6.3 to 6.5, the orthotolidine will be a true, clear blue and the endpoint sharp and colorless, except in the presence of nitrogen trichloride when a yellow color may persist in spite of a correct pH. The titration should be carried to the disappearance of the blue color. Too low a pH in the first step will tend to make the monochloramine show in the free-chlorine step and the dichloramine in the monochloramine step. Too high a pH in the first step will give a poor recovery and a difficult endpoint. Thus, the orthotolidine will give a green color which leaves a yellow color at the endpoint when the pH is above 7.0. Further, at pH 7.0 the recovery may be only 50 per cent and at pH 7.5 only 20 per cent, or less. Only part of the nitrogen trichloride is recovered in the free-chlorine step. At times the rest of the nitrogen trichloride is recovered as dichloramine, and at times there is no evidence of dichloramine in the presence of nitrogen trichloride; this is apparently a function of the pH of the solution before starting the titration. If stale bicarbonate solution is used for adjusting the pH for the third step, it will give low recovery and an off color.

1.3. *Care required:* Unless the carbon tetrachloride is iodine-free for the nitrogen trichloride extraction, some monochloramine will appear as free chlorine in the titration of the second aliquot. *The titration must be carried out as soon as the blue color is formed in each step.* The standard ferrous sulfate solution should be added dropwise, yet without wasting time. For complete recovery, the temperature of the solution titrated should not be above 20° C. At temperatures of 10° to 12° C the titration should be carried out somewhat more slowly than at 20° C. As the endpoints are approached, additions of standard solution should be spaced about 5 sec apart.

1.4. *Interference:* The only interfering substance likely to be encountered in water is oxidized manganese. To correct for this interference, place 5 ml buffer solution, 1 ml potassium iodide solution, and 0.5 ml sodium arsenite solution (0.5 g $NaAsO_2$ plus 100 ml distilled water) in the titration flask. Add 100 ml of sample and mix. Add 5 ml orthotolidine and mix. Titrate with standard ferrous ammonium sulfate titrant until any blue color is discharged. This reading is subtracted from Reading A obtained by the normal procedure as described in Sec. 3.1a of this method.

2. Reagents

2.1. *Phosphate buffer solution:* This buffer must bring a 100-ml sample to a pH between 6.3 and 6.5. Dissolve 12 g anhydrous disodium hydrogen phosphate, Na_2HPO_4, 60 g anhydrous potassium dihydrogen phosphate, KH_2PO_4, and 100 g sodium hexametaphosphate, $(NaPO_3)_6$, in distilled water and make up to 1 liter. Add 20 mg mercuric chloride to prevent mold growth.

2.2. *Neutral orthotolidine indicator solution:* Dissolve 1.33 g orthotolidine dihydrochloride in about 500 ml distilled water, add 5 ml 1 + 19 HCl, dilute to 1 liter, and store in an amber glass-stoppered bottle.

2.3. *Standard ferrous ammonium sulfate titrant:* Dissolve 1.106 g Mohr's salt, $Fe(NH_4)_2(SO_4)_2 \cdot 6H_2O$, in distilled water containing 1 ml 1 + 3 H_2SO_4, and make up to 1,000 ml with freshly boiled and cooled distilled water. This is a primary standard and may be used for 1 month. Potassium dichromate may be used to check the titer. This solution is equivalent to 0.100 mg Cl per 1.00 ml.

2.4. *Potassium iodide solution:* Dissolve 2 g potassium iodide in 1 liter distilled water.

2.5. *Sulfuric acid, 1N.* Dilute cautiously 28 ml conc H_2SO_4 to 1 liter with distilled water.

2.6. *Sodium bicarbonate solution:* Dissolve 4.7 g sodium hydrogen carbonate, $NaHCO_3$, in 100 ml distilled water. This solution must be made daily.

2.7. *Carbon tetrachloride,* iodine free.

2.8. *Oxalic acid solution:* Dissolve 20 g oxalic acid dihydrate, $H_2C_2O_4 \cdot 2H_2O$, in distilled water and dilute to 1 liter. Store in an amber bottle.

3. Procedure

The quantities given below are suitable for concentrations of total available chlorine up to 8 mg/l. Where the total available chlorine exceeds 8 mg/l or the dichloramine exceeds 4 mg/l, use a smaller sample and dilute to a total volume of 100 ml. Mix the usual volumes of buffer reagent and orthotolidine solution with distilled water before adding sufficient sample to bring the total volume to 100 ml.

3.1. *Free available chlorine or chloramine:* Place 5 ml each of buffer reagent and orthotolidine solution in the titration flask and mix. Add 100 ml of sample and mix.

a. Free available chlorine: Titrate with standard ferrous ammonium sulfate titrant until the blue color is discharged. The titration should be dropwise, yet without wasting time (Reading A). This step will yield a fading and yellow endpoint in the presence of a large proportion of nitrogen trichloride.

b. Monochloramine: Add 1 ml potassium iodide solution and mix. Continue titration until the blue color is again discharged (Reading B).

c. Dichloramine: Add 2 ml sulfuric acid solution and mix. Allow to stand 1 min. Add 5 ml sodium bicarbonate solution and mix. Continue titration until the blue color is again discharged (Reading C). In executing this titration, add as much as possible of the standard ferrous titrant while the color mixture is still acid and before the final neutralization with sodium bicarbonate. The color of the solution at the acid stage provides a guide to the amount of ferrous titrant that may safely be added without overshooting the endpoint when the color mixture is restored to a neutral pH:

Color	Ferrous Titrant Addition *ml*
yellow	none
brown	0.5
purple	1.0
blue	1.5
green	2.0
dark green	3.0

3.2. *Nitrogen trichloride or chlorine dioxide:*

a. Place 100 ml of sample in a separatory funnel and extract with 10 ml carbon tetrachloride. Run off the carbon tetrachloride. Add the aqueous layer to the titration flask containing

5 ml each of buffer and orthotolidine reagents. Titrate with standard ferrous ammonium sulfate titrant until the blue color is discharged (Reading D).

b. Alternate procedure: Place 5 ml each of buffer and oxalic acid reagents in the titration flask. Add 100 ml of sample and mix. Allow to stand 15 min. Add 5 ml sodium bicarbonate and 5 ml orthotolidine solution. Mix and titrate with standard ferrous titrant until the blue color is discharged (Reading E).

4. Calculation

For a 100-ml sample, 1.00 ml standard ferrous titrant equals 1.00 mg/l available residual chlorine.

Reading	NCl_3 Absent	NCl_3 Present
A	free Cl	free Cl — NCl_3
B — A	NH_2Cl	NH_2Cl
C — B	$NHCl_2$	$NHCl_2$
D	—	free Cl
2(A — D)	—	approx. NCl_3
2E	—	approx. NCl_3
A — E	—	free Cl

Bibliography

General

1. ELLMS, J. W. & HAUSER, S. J. Orthotolidine as a Reagent for the Colorimetric Estimation of Small Quantities of Free Chlorine. *Ind. Eng. Chem.* 5:915 (1913).
2. THERIAULT, E. J. The Orthotolidine Reagent for Free Chlorine in Water. *Pub. Health Repts.* 42:668 (1927).
3. ADAMS, H. W. & BUSWELL, A. M. Orthotolidine Test for Chlorine. *J. AWWA* 25:1118 (1933).
4. SCOTT, R. D. Eliminating False Chlorine Tests. *J. AWWA* 26:634 (1934).
5. DAVIS, W. S. & KELLY, C. B. Photodiscoloration of Orthotolidine and Artificial Standards for Free Chlorine Test in Water. *J. AWWA* 26:757 (1934).
6. SCOTT, R. D. Effect of Iron in the Determination of Residual Chlorine. *J. AWWA* 26:1234 (1934).
7. HULBERT, R. Chlorine and the Orthotolidine Test in the Presence of Nitrite. *J. AWWA* 26:1638 (1934).
8. SCOTT, R. D. Improved Standards for the Residual Chlorine Test. *Water Works & Sewerage* 82:399 (1935).
9. GRIFFIN, A. E. Evaluation of Residual Chlorine. *J. AWWA* 27:888 (1935).
10. HALLINAN, F. J. & THOMPSON, W. R. A Critical Study of the Thiosulfate Titration of Chlorine. *J. Am. Chem. Soc.* 61:265 (1939).
11. LAUX, P. C. Breakpoint Chlorination at Anderson. *J. AWWA* 32:1027 (1940).
12. GRIFFIN, A. E. & CHAMBERLIN, N. S. Estimation of High Chlorine Residuals. *J. AWWA* 35:571 (1943).
13. CHAMBERLIN, N. S. & GLASS, J. R. Colorimetric Determination of Chlorine Residuals up to 10 ppm With Orthotolidine. *J. AWWA* 35:1065 (1943).
14. COMMITTEE REPORT. Control of Chlorination. *J. AWWA* 35:1315 (1943).
15. GILCREAS, F. W. & HALLINAN, F. J. The Practical Use of the Orthotolidine-Arsenite Test for Residual Chlorine. *J. AWWA* 36:1343 (1944).

Amperometric Titration

16. FOULK, C. W. & BAWDEN, A. T. A New Type of Endpoint in Electrometric Titration and Its Application to Iodimetry. *J. Am. Chem. Soc.* 48:2045 (1926).
17. MARKS, H. C. & GLASS, J. R. A New Method of Determining Residual Chlorine. *J. AWWA* 34:1227 (1942).
18. HALLER, J. F. & LISTEK, S. S. Determination of Chlorine Dioxide and Other Active Chlorine Compounds in Water. *Anal. Chem.* 20:639 (1948).
19. MAHAN, W. A. Simplified Amperometric Titration Apparatus for Determining Residual Chlorine in Water. *Water Works & Sewerage* 96:171 (1949).
20. MARKS, H. C.; WILLIAMS, D. B.; & GLASGOW, G. U. Determination of Residual Chlorine Compounds. *J. AWWA* 43:201 (1951).
21. KOLTHOFF, I. M. & LINGANE, J. J. *Polarography.* Interscience Publishers, New York (2nd ed., 1952).

Differentiation of Chloramines

22. PALIN, A. T. Estimation of Free Chlo-

rine and Chloramine in Water. *J. Inst. Water Engrs.* 3:100 (1949).

23. Ref. 20.

24. PALIN, A. T. Determining Residual Chlorine in Water by Neutral Orthotolidine Methods. *Water & Sewage Works* 101:74 (1954).

25. PALIN, A. T. The Determination of Free and Combined Chlorine in Water by the Use of Diethyl-p-phenylene Diamine. *J. AWWA* 49:873 (1957).

Photometric Method

26. TARAS, M. J. Simplified Calibration of Photometric Instruments for Residual Chlorine. *Water & Sewage Works* 97:404 (1950).

Chlorine Demand

The chlorine demand of a water is caused by such inorganic reductants as ferrous, manganous, nitrite, sulfide, and sulfite ions. Ammonia and cyanide consume considerable chlorine during the free residual chlorination process. Chlorine substitutes on phenols and other similar aromatic compounds to form chloro derivative compounds, but may also oxidize the aromatic compounds when larger amounts of chlorine are added. It may also react with ammonia and naturally occurring amino compounds to form chloramines with an active or oxidizing chlorine atom. The destruction of the chloramine compounds can be achieved by the addition of more chlorine and subsequently with the addition of enough chlorine a free available residual (hypochlorous acid) may be attained.

The chlorine demand of water is the difference between the amount of chlorine applied to a treated supply and the amount of free, combined, or total available chlorine remaining at the end of the contact period. The chlorine demand of any given water varies with the amount of chlorine applied, time of contact, pH, and temperature. For comparative purposes it is imperative that *all test conditions be stated*. The smallest amount of residual chlorine considered significant is 0.1 mg/l Cl. Presented here are a method for laboratory use and a field procedure which gives less exact results.

A. Method for Laboratory Use

1. Principle

The laboratory method is designed to determine the so-called immediate demand as well as other demands at longer contact periods. Chlorine demand determinations are made to determine the amount of chlorine that must be applied to a water to produce a specific free, combined, or total available chlorine residual after a selected period of contact. If the amount of chlorine applied to waters containing ammonium or organic nitrogen compounds is not sufficient to reach what is termed the "breakpoint," chloramines and certain other chloro derivatives which react as combined available residual chlorine are produced. When sufficient chlorine has been added to reach the breakpoint, which depends on pH, ratio of chlorine to nitrogenous compounds present, and other factors, subsequent additions of chlorine remain in the free available state.

2. Apparatus

Colorimetric equipment: One of the following is required:

2.1. *Spectrophotometer or filter photometer,* for use in the wavelength range of 400–490 mμ and providing a light path of 1 cm or longer.

2.2. *Comparator,* color and turbidity compensating.

2.3. *French square bottles,* capacity 1 or 2 oz.

3. Reagents

3.1. *Standard chlorine solution:* A suitable solution may be obtained from the chlorinator solution hose or by bubbling chlorine gas through distilled or tap water. The stability of the chlorine solution may be improved by storing in the dark or in amber glass-stoppered bottles. Even so, it will lose strength and must be standardized each day that it is used. Alternatively, household hypochlorite solution, which contains about 30,000–50,000 mg/l chlorine equivalent, may be diluted to suitable strength. This is more stable than a chlorine solution, but should not be used more than a week without re-standardizing. The solution used for determining chlorine demand should preferably be the same kind of chlorine solution as is actually applied in plant treatment. For making temporary standards for calibrating a photometer, it is preferable that hypochlorite be used. Depending on the intended use, a suitable strength of chlorine so-

lution will usually be between 100 mg/l and 1,000 mg/l. If used for chlorine demand determination, it should be sufficiently strong so that the volume of treated portions will not be increased more than 5 per cent by addition of the chlorine solution.

Standardization: Place 2 ml acetic acid and 10 to 25 ml distilled water in a flask. Add about 1 g potassium iodide. It is sufficient for the analyst to estimate this on a spatula or small spoon, after first having familiarized himself with the quantity by one or more weighings. Measure into the flask a suitable volume of the chlorine solution. In choosing a convenient volume, note that 1 ml of 0.025N thiosulfate titrant to be used for titrating is equivalent to about 0.9 mg chlorine.

Titrate with standardized 0.025N sodium thiosulfate titrant until the yellow iodine color is almost gone. Add 1 to 2 ml starch indicator solution and continue the titration to disappearance of the blue color.

Determine the blank by adding identical quantities of acid, KI, and starch indicator to a volume of distilled water corresponding to the sample used for titration.

$$\text{mg/ml Cl} = \frac{(A \pm B) \times N \times 35.45}{\text{ml sample}}$$

where $A = $ ml titration for sample, $B = $ ml titration for blank which may be positive or negative, and $N = $ normality of $Na_2S_2O_3$.

3.2. *Acetic acid,* conc (glacial).

3.3. *Potassium iodide crystals.*

3.4. *Standard sodium thiosulfate titrant,* 0.025N. Prepare as directed in Chlorine, Method A, Sec. 2.4.

3.5. *Starch indicator solution:* Prepare as directed in Chlorine, Method A, Sec. 2.5.

3.6. *Orthotolidine reagent:* Prepare

as directed in Chlorine, Method B, Sec. 5.

3.7. *Sodium arsenite solution:* Prepare as directed in Chlorine, Method D, Sec. 3.2.

4. Procedure

4.1. *Volume of sample:* Measure at least ten equal portions of the sample, preferably into amber glass-stoppered bottles or erlenmeyer flasks of ample capacity to permit mixing. If the object of the test is to determine chlorine demand, 200-ml portions are suitable. If the purpose of the test is to relate chlorine demand to bacterial removal, the effect on taste and odor, or the chemical constituents of the water, portions of 500 ml or more will be required. All glassware for bacteriologic investigation should be properly sterilized.

4.2. *Addition of chlorine water:* The amount of chlorine added to the first portion should leave no chlorine residual at the end of the contact period, especially if low demands are being studied. Add increasing amounts of chlorine to the successive portions in the series. The increase in dosage between portions may be as low as 0.1 mg/l for determining low demands, and up to 1.0 mg/l or more for higher demands. Mixing while the chlorine solution is being added to the sample is imperative. It may be advantageous to dose the portions of the sample according to a staggered schedule that will permit the determination of chlorine residuals at the predetermined contact time.

4.3. *Contact time:* The usual purpose of a chlorine demand test is to determine the amount of chlorine required to produce a specific free, combined,

or total available chlorine residual after a definite, record time interval. It is recommended, therefore, that the testing be carried out at the end of the contact period corresponding to the contact time at the point of control. This may vary from a few minutes to several hours. To determine in advance the effect of chlorination, the plant contact time and temperature should be duplicated in the laboratory. Under some circumstances it is desirable to make several chlorine determinations after different periods of contact, such as 15, 30, and 60 min. Such a procedure will give an indication of the stability of the residual chlorine as related to time, which will be very useful information in plant control. The time of contact must be recorded. During the contact period the chlorinated samples must be protected from strong daylight.

4.4. *Examination of samples:* At the end of the contact period, determine the free and the combined available residual chlorine by the OTA test—Chlorine, Method D—or other adequate test on a small aliquot from each portion. Plotting the residual chlorine or the amount consumed versus the dosage will aid in studying the results. Samples for bacteriologic examination may be removed at desired intervals.

4.5. *Taste and odor:* Taste and odor of the treated samples may be observed at ordinary temperatures with or without dechlorination. For odor observation at elevated temperatures, samples should be dechlorinated before heating. Choice of the dechlorinating agent must be made with due regard to its effect on odor in the water under examination. Generally, sodium sulfite is satisfactory if only a slight excess is used.

B. Method for Field Use

1. General Discussion

The test below is designed for the measurement of chlorine demand in the plant or field when facilities or personnel are not adequate to employ the more exact method. Results obtained in this test are approximations only.

2. Apparatus

2.1. *Chlorine comparator,* color and turbidity compensating.

2.2. *Medicine dropper,* which will deliver 20 drops per milliliter. When measuring by drops, it is essential that the end of the dropper be well cleaned, so that water adheres all around the periphery, and that the dropper be held in a strictly vertical position, with the drops being formed slowly.

2.3. *Ten 1-qt fruit jars or other suitable containers,* marked at the 500-ml level.

2.4. *Ten 2-oz bottles,* marked at the 20-ml level.

2.5. *Glass stirring rod.*

2.6. *Glass-stemmed thermometer.*

3. Reagents

3.1. *Standard chlorine solution:* Dilute a 5 per cent household bleaching solution 1 + 4. Standardize as directed in Method A, Sec. 3.1, but taking 20 drops of the diluted hypochlorite solution as the sample to be titrated; use the same dropper that will be used in the procedure. For each drop:

$$\text{mg available Cl} = \frac{A \times N \times 35}{20}$$

where A = ml titration for sample, and N = normality of $Na_2S_2O_3$.

Adjust this solution to a strength of 10 mg/ml (0.5 mg chlorine per drop) so that one drop added to a 500-ml water sample will represent a dosage of 1 mg/1.

3.2. *Orthotolidine reagent:* Prepare as directed in Chlorine, Method B, Sec. 5.

3.3. *Sodium arsenite solution:* Prepare as directed in Chlorine, Method D, Sec. 3.2.

4. Procedure

4.1. *Measurement of samples:* Fill each jar or container to the 500-ml mark with the water under test. Record the temperature at which the samples are held.

4.2. *Addition of chlorine:* While stirring constantly, add 1 drop of chlorine solution to the water in the first fruit jar, 2 drops to that in the second jar, 3 drops to that in the third jar, etc.

4.3. *Contact time:* Follow directions given in Method A, Sec. 4.3.

4.4. *Examination of samples:* At the end of the contact period, remove a 20-ml portion from each sample, place it in a 2-oz bottle, and proceed with the OTA method as outlined in Chlorine, Method D, Sec. 4.1.

5. Calculation

mg/1 Cl demand
= mg/1 Cl added − mg/1 residual Cl

6. Interpretation of Results

This chlorine demand refers only to the particular dosage, contact time, and temperature used in this test. Plotting the residual chlorine or the amount consumed versus the chlorine added will aid in studying the results.

Bibliography

1. GRIFFIN, A. E. & CHAMBERLIN, N. S. Relation of Ammonia-Nitrogen to Breakpoint Chlorination. *A.J.P.H.* 31:803 (1941).

2. COMMITTEE REPORT. Control of Chlorination. *J. AWWA* 35:1315 (1943).

3. PALIN, A. T. Chemical Aspects of Chlorination. *J. Inst. Water Engrs.* 4:565 (1950).

4. TARAS, M. J. Effect of Free Residual Chlorination on Nitrogen Compounds in Water. *J. AWWA* 45:47 (1953).

Chlorine Dioxide

Because the physical and chemical properties of chlorine dioxide resemble those of chlorine in many respects, the entire writeup on Chlorine (Residual) should be read before a chlorine dioxide determination is attempted.

Chlorine dioxide is applied to water supplies for the purpose of combatting tastes and odors due to phenolic-type wastes, Actinomycetes, and algae, as well as for the purpose of oxidizing soluble iron and manganese to a more easily removable form.

Chlorine dioxide is a deep yellow, volatile, and unpleasant-smelling gas which is produced at the site of application by reacting a solution of sodium chlorite with a strong chlorine solution. An excess of chlorine over the theoretical amount is needed so that the final mixture consists of chlorine and chlorine dioxide. When the source of chlorine is a hypochlorite compound, an acid must be added to insure the production of chlorine dioxide.

The reaction between sodium chlorite and chlorine is inhibited at pH values above 4 in dilute solutions. Therefore, chlorine dioxide solutions are prepared for laboratory studies by acidifying a sodium chlorite solution to a pH of 2.5. The evolved chlorine dioxide is scrubbed with sodium chlorite solution to remove free-chlorine impurity

and then passed into distilled water by means of a smooth current of air when a pure chlorine dioxide solution is desired.

Selection of method: The iodometric method (*A*) is designed for standardizing the chlorine dioxide solutions which are needed for the preparation of temporary standards. Temporary standards are valuable for checking the permanent color standards, for the construction of photometric calibration curves required in the OTO method (*B*), and for securing evidence on the accuracy of the amperometric method (*C*). It cannot be used to check chlorine dioxide residuals after running a chlorine dioxide demand test because of the presence of the chlorite ion.

The orthotolidine-oxalic acid colorimetric method (*B*), generally abbreviated OTO, is a flash test which finds greatest application in the routine determination of chlorine dioxide both in the control laboratory and in the field. The method requires common reagents and the simplest of operations once the visual standards or the photometric calibration curve have been prepared. Reasonable accuracy can be expected when the proper precautions governing orthotolidine reactions are observed.

The amperometric method (*C*) is

useful when a knowledge of the various chlorine fractions in a water sample is desired.

Sampling and storage: Like residual chlorine, chlorine dioxide determinations should be performed promptly after the sample has been collected. Exposure of the sample to sunlight or strong artificial light, and agitation which excessively aerates the sample, should be avoided. Minimum chlorine dioxide losses will occur when the determination is immediately completed at the site of the sample collection.

A. Iodometric Method

1. General Discussion

1.1. *Principle:* A pure solution of chlorine dioxide is prepared by slowly adding dilute sulfuric acid to a sodium chlorite solution, removing any contaminants such as chlorine by means of a sodium chlorite scrubber, and passing the gas into distilled water by means of a steady stream of air.

Chlorine dioxide releases free iodine from a potassium iodide solution which has been acidified with acetic or sulfuric acid. The liberated iodine is titrated with a standard solution of sodium thiosulfate using starch as the indicator.

1.2. *Interference:* Little interference is encountered when a pure solution of chlorine dioxide is determined by the iodometric method. However, temperature and strong light affect the stability of the solution. Chlorine dioxide losses can be minimized by storing the stock chlorine dioxide solution in a dark refrigerator, and preparing and titrating the dilute chlorine dioxide solutions for standardization purposes at the lowest practicable temperature and in subdued light.

1.3. *Minimum detectable concentration:* One drop (0.05 ml) of 0.01N sodium thiosulfate is equivalent to 0.02 mg/l chlorine dioxide (or 0.04 mg/l in terms of available chlorine) when a 500-ml sample is titrated.

2. Reagents

All the reagents listed for the determination of residual chlorine by Method A, Sec. 2, are required. Also needed are:

2.1. *Stock chlorine dioxide solution:* Prepare a gas generating and absorbing system similar to the one illustrated in Fig. 13. Connect aspirator

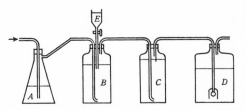

Fig. 13. Chlorine dioxide generation and absorption system

flask A of 500-ml capacity by means of rubber tubing to a source of compressed air. Allow the air to bubble through a layer of 300 ml of distilled water in flask A and then pass over and down through a glass tube to within 5 mm of the bottom of the 1-liter gas generating bottle B. Conduct the evolved gas via glass tubing through a scrubber bottle C containing saturated sodium chlorite solution or a

tower packed with flaked sodium chlorite, and finally via glass tubing into a
2-liter pyrex collecting bottle D where
the gas is absorbed in 1,500 ml of distilled water.   Provide an air outlet tube
on bottle D for the escape of the moving
air.   Select for a gas generating bottle
one which is constructed of strong pyrex glass and has a mouth wide enough
to permit the insertion of three separate glass tubes : the first leading almost
to the bottom for the admission of the
air, the second reaching below the liquid surface for the gradual introduction of the sulfuric acid, and the third
near the top for the exit of the evolved
gas and air.   Fit to the second tube a
graduated cylinder E for the contain-
ment of the sulfuric acid.   If available,
locate this entire system in a good fuming hood equipped with an adequate
shield.

Dissolve   10   g   sodium   chlorite
($NaClO_2$), analytical   reagent   grade,
in 750 ml distilled water and place in
bottle B.

Carefully add 2 ml conc sulfuric acid
to 18 ml distilled water and mix.   Transfer to cylinder E.

Connect flask A to bottle B and the
latter to bottles C and D.   Pass a
smooth current of air through the system, as evidenced by the bubbling rate
in all bottles.

Introduce 5-ml increments of sulfuric
acid from cylinder E into bottle B at 5-
min intervals.

Continue the air flow for 30 min
after the last portion of acid has been
added.

Store the yellow-colored stock solution in a dark refrigerator to minimize
loss in strength.   The concentration of
the chlorine dioxide thus prepared may
vary between 250 and 600 mg/l which
corresponds to approximately 600 to

1,600 mg/l when expressed as available
chlorine.

*2.2.   Standard chlorine dioxide solu-
tion:* Use   this   solution   for   preparing
the desired temporary chlorine dioxide
standards.   Dilute the required volume
of stock chlorine dioxide solution to
the desired strength with chlorine-demand-free water which has been prepared as described in Chlorine (Residual), Method B, Sec. 3.1.   Standardize
the solution by titrating with standard
$0.01N$ or $0.025N$ sodium thiosulfate titrant in the presence of potassium iodide, acid, and starch indicator by following the procedure given in Sec. 3.
A full or nearly full bottle of chlorine
or chlorine dioxide solution retains its
titer longer than a bottle which is half
full.   If repeated withdrawals reduce
the volume to a critical level, standardize the solution at the beginning, mid-
way in the series of withdrawals, and
at the end of the series.   Shake the contents thoroughly before drawing off the
needed solution from the middle of the
glass-stoppered,   dark-colored   bottle.
Frequent preparation of this solution is
desirable.

3. Procedure

Select the volume of sample, prepare
the sample for titration, titrate the sample, and conduct the blank titration as
described   in   Chlorine   (Residual),
Method A, Sec. 3.   The only exception
is the following: *allow the chlorine dioxide to react in the dark with the acid
and the potassium iodide for 5 min
before starting the titration.*

4. Calculations

Chlorine dioxide concentrations may
be expressed in terms of chlorine dioxide alone or in terms of available

chlorine content. The available chlorine is defined as the total oxidizing power of the chlorine dioxide measured by titrating the iodine released by the chlorine dioxide from an acidic solution of potassium iodide and then calculating the result in terms of chlorine itself.

For standardizing chlorine dioxide solution:

$$\text{mg/ml } ClO_2 = \frac{(A \pm B) \times N \times 13.49}{\text{ml sample titrated}}$$

$$\text{mg/ml } Cl = \frac{(A \pm B) \times N \times 35.45}{\text{ml sample titrated}}$$

For determination of chlorine dioxide in temporary standards:

$$\text{mg/l } ClO_2 = \frac{(A \pm B) \times N \times 13,490}{\text{ml sample}}$$

$$\text{mg/l } Cl = \frac{(A \pm B) \times N \times 35,450}{\text{ml sample}}$$

where $A =$ ml titration for sample, $B =$ ml titration for blank which may be positive or negative, and $N =$ normality of $Na_2S_2O_3$.

B. Orthotolidine-Oxalic Acid (OTO) Method

1. General Discussion

1.1. *Principle:* After the sample has been treated with oxalic acid to eliminate the residual chlorine, acidic orthotolidine reagent is added for the purpose of producing a yellow color. Sodium arsenite serves to minimize interference and arrest color development. Chlorine dioxide produces less yellow color than residual chlorine, the intensity corresponding to approximately one-half that of a similar concentration of residual chlorine when the result is reported in terms of chlorine dioxide itself. However, the color developed by chlorine dioxide is one-fifth that of the available chlorine content.

The yellow orthotolidine color can be measured by visual or photometric methods. The best results are obtained with photometric instruments which have been carefully calibrated with known chlorine dioxide solutions. Visual comparison is satisfactory for routine determinations in the control laboratory.

1.2. *Precautions:* The same attention should be paid to details as in the residual chlorine determinations. Because the amounts of chlorine dioxide normally applied to water supplies are quite small, the following considerations assume conspicuous importance. All glassware used in the determinations should be kept scrupulously clean. An average of two or three determinations may have to be performed on a sample to avoid questionable values. The fact that the readings must be multiplied by two or five to obtain the final result makes such practices both desirable and prudent.

1.3. *Interferences:* The same interferences apply in the case of chlorine dioxide as those described in Chlorine (Residual), Method D, Sec. 1. In addition, the calcium content of hard waters may precipitate following the introduction of the saturated oxalic acid solution. Although chlorite ion reacts slowly with orthotolidine, the chlorite ion may react with the oxalic acid solution during the standing period and subsequently with the hydrochloric acid of the orthotolidine reagent to form chlorous acid, which in turn can disproportionate to chlorine dioxide.

1.4. *Minimum detectable concentra-*

tion: The minimum detectable concentration depends on the terms in which the chlorine dioxide result is reported. If the result is reported as chlorine dioxide, a minimum of 0.02 mg/l can be detected. When the result is reported in terms of available chlorine content, the minimum becomes 0.05 mg/l.

2. Apparatus

The same apparatus is required as in Chlorine (Residual), Method D, Sec. 2.

3. Reagents

All reagents listed for the determination of residual chlorine by Method D, Sec. 3, are required. Also needed is:

3.1. *Oxalic acid saturated solution:* Dissolve 110 g $H_2C_2O_4$ in 1 liter distilled water by heating the solution. When the solution has cooled to room temperature, decant the supernatant liquid into the storage bottle. Use only the clear liquid in the test procedure. Dispense with an automatic or safety pipet. (CAUTION: Toxic; take care to avoid ingestion.)

4. Procedure

4.1. *Visual comparison:*

a. Label two comparator cells or French square bottles "D" and "E". Use 0.5 ml orthotolidine reagent in 10-ml cells, 0.75 ml in 15-ml cells, and the same ratio for other volumes of sample. Use the same volume of sodium arsenite solution as orthotolidine reagent.

b. To Cell D, containing a measured volume of water sample, add 1 ml oxalic acid saturated solution. Mix well and allow to stand 10 min in the dark. Depending on the volume of sample used, next add the proper volume of orthotolidine reagent. Mix quickly, and immediately (within 5 sec) add sodium arsenite solution. Mix quickly again and compare with color standards as rapidly as possible. Record the result, D, which represents approximately one-half the chlorine dioxide and all of the interfering colors. (If it is desired to report the results in terms of available chlorine, the value D represents one-fifth the available chlorine and all of the interfering colors.)

c. To Cell E, containing sodium arsenite solution and 1 ml oxalic acid saturated solution, add a measured volume of water sample. Mix quickly, and immediately add orthotolidine reagent. Mix quickly again, and compare with color standards as rapidly as possible. Record the result, B_3, which represents the interfering colors present in the sample.

4.2. *Photometric measurement:* Measure photometrically the colors developed by following the directions in Sec. 4.1. Convert the absorbance readings to the proper chlorine dioxide readings by referring to a calibration curve prepared by treating known chlorine dioxide concentrations in the same manner as the unknown samples.

5. Calculations

mg/l ClO_2 as $ClO_2 = (D - B_3) \times 1.9$

mg/l ClO_2 as available chlorine
$$= (D - B_3) \times 5$$

Inasmuch as chlorine dioxide and residual chlorine coexist in many samples, the residual chlorine determinations can be performed as described in Chlorine (Residual), Method D, Sec. 4, and the following calculations then made in terms of available chlorine:

Free available residual chlorine
$$= (A - B_1) - (D - B_3)$$

Combined available residual chlorine
$$= (C - B_2) - (A - B_1)$$

C. Amperometric Method

1. General Discussion

1.1. *Principle:* The amperometric titration of chlorine dioxide is an extension of the amperometric method for residual chlorine. By performing four titrations with phenylarsine oxide, free chlorine (including hypochlorite and hypochlorous acid), chloramines, chlorite, and chlorine dioxide may be separately determined. In stage one the chlorine dioxide is converted to chlorite and chlorate through the addition of sufficient sodium hydroxide to produce a pH of 12, followed by neutralization to a pH of 7, and the titration of the free chlorine. When potassium iodide is added to a sample which has been similarly treated with alkali and the pH readjusted to 7, the titration yields free chlorine and monochloramine. The third stage involves the addition of potassium iodide and pH adjustment to 7, followed by titration of the free chlorine, monochloramine, and one-fifth of the available chlorine dioxide. The addition of sufficient sulfuric acid to lower the pH to 2 enables all of the available chlorine dioxide and chlorite, as well as the total available chlorine, to liberate an equivalent amount of iodine from the added potassium iodide, and thus be titrated.

1.2. *Precautions:* In order to minimize the effects of pH and the time and temperature of reaction, all conditions should be standardized as much as practicable. All samples should be titrated at pH 7. A reaction period of 10 min or longer should be used on the samples which are treated with sodium hydroxide at a pH of 12, as well as those that are treated with sulfuric acid at a pH of 2. A 10-min reaction period is suggested even though the reaction rate is faster in warm samples.

1.3. *Interference:* The same interferences apply in the case of chlorine dioxide as those described in Chlorine (Residual), Methods F and G, Sec. 1.2.

2. Apparatus

The same apparatus is required as in Chlorine (Residual), Method F, Sec. 2.

3. Reagents

All reagents listed for the determination of residual chlorine by Method F, Sec. 3, are required. Also needed are:

3.1. *Sodium hydroxide, 6N.* Dissolve 240 g NaOH and dilute to 1 liter with chlorine-demand-free water.

3.2. *Sulfuric acid, 6N.* $1 + 5$.

4. Procedure

4.1. *Titration of free available chlorine (hypochlorite and hypochlorous acid):* Add sufficient 6N sodium hydroxide solution to raise the sample pH to 12. After 10 min, add sufficient 6N sulfuric acid solution to lower the pH to 7. Titrate with standard phenylarsine oxide titrant to the amperometric endpoint as described in Chlorine (Residual), Method F, Sec. 4. Record the result as A.

4.2. *Titration of free available chlorine and chloramine:* Add sufficient 6N sodium hydroxide solution to raise the sample pH to 12. After 10 min, add sufficient 6N sulfuric acid solution to reduce the pH to 7. Add 1 ml potassium iodide solution. Titrate with standard phenylarsine oxide titrant to the amperometric endpoint. Record the result as B.

4.3. *Titration of free available chlorine, chloramine, and one-fifth of the available chlorine dioxide:* Add sufficient pH 7 phosphate buffer solution to adjust the sample pH to 7. Add 1 ml potassium iodide solution. Titrate with standard phenylarsine oxide titrant to the amperometric endpoint. Record the result as C.

4.4. *Titration of free available chlorine, chloramines, chlorine dioxide, and chlorite:* Add 1 ml potassium iodide solution to the sample. Add sufficient $6N$ sulfuric acid solution to lower the sample pH to 2. After 10 min, add sufficient $6N$ sodium hydroxide solution to raise the pH to 7. Titrate with standard phenylarsine oxide titrant to the amperometric endpoint. Record the result as D.

5. Calculation

Convert the individual titrations (A, B, C, and D) into mg/l Cl by the following equation:

$$\text{mg/l chlorine} = \frac{E \times 200}{\text{ml sample}}$$

where $E =$ ml phenylarsine oxide titration for each individual sample A, B, C, or D.

Calculate the chlorine dioxide and the individual chlorine fractions as follows:

mg/l ClO_2 as chlorine dioxide $= 1.9\ (C - B)$

mg/l ClO_2 as chlorine $\quad = 5\ (C - B)$

mg/l free available residual
$\qquad\qquad$ chlorine $= A$

mg/l chloramine as chlorine $\ = B - A$

mg/l chlorite as chlorine $\quad = 4B - 5C + D$

Bibliography

General

1. INGOLS, R. S. & RIDENOUR, G. M. Chemical Properties of Chlorine Dioxide in Water Treatment. *J. AWWA* 40:1207 (1948).
2. HODGDEN, H. W. & INGOLS, R. S. Direct Colorimetric Method for Determination of Chlorine Dioxide in Water. *Anal. Chem.* 26:1224 (1954).
3. PALIN, A. T. Colorimetric Determination of Chlorine Dioxide in Water. *Water & Sewage Works* 107:457 (1960).

Iodometric Method

4. POST, M. A. & MOORE, W. A. Determination of Chlorine Dioxide in Treated Surface Waters. *Anal. Chem.* 31:1872 (1959).

Orthotolidine—Oxalic Acid (OTO) Method

5. ASTON, R. N. Developments in the Chlorine Dioxide Process. *J. AWWA* 42:151 (1950).

Amperometric Method

6. HALLER, J. F. & LISTEK, S. S. Determination of Chlorine Dioxide and Other Active Chlorine Compounds in Water. *Anal. Chem.* 20:639 (1948).

Chromium

The carcinogenic potential of hexavalent chromium is a good reason to protect a potable water supply against its intrusion. The hexavalent chromium concentration of U.S. drinking waters has been reported to vary between 0.0003 and 0.04 mg/l with a mean of 0.0032 mg/l. Chromium salts are used extensively in industrial processes and may enter a water supply through the discharge of wastes. Chromate compounds are frequently added to cooling water for corrosion control. Chromium may exist in water supplies in both the hexavalent and the trivalent state, although the trivalent form rarely occurs in potable water supplies.

Selection of method: Method A is applicable for the determination of hexavalent chromium present in a natural or treated water intended for potable purposes. The permanganate-azide method (*B*) is recommended for the determination of total chromium in samples containing organic material. It is the method of choice for the determination of total chromium in unknown samples. The alkaline hypobromite method (*C*) is useful as a control method for total chromium in treated waters. It is not designed for samples containing an appreciable amount of organic matter.

Sampling and storage: Because chromate ions have a tendency to be adsorbed on the surface of the container, and also may be reduced by various agents, precautions should be observed in sample collection and storage. New bottles rather than old, etched containers should be used for sample collection. The sample should be tested during the day of collection if hexavalent chromium is to be determined. Storage for more than 2 to 3 days is not recommended.

A. Hexavalent Chromium

1. General Discussion

1.1. *Principle:* Hexavalent chromium reacts with diphenylcarbazide to produce a reddish-purple color in slightly acid solutions.

1.2. *Interference:* In the color development step the following substances may cause interference. Mercury, both mercurous and mercuric, gives a blue or blue-purple color, but the reaction is not very sensitive at the acidity employed. Iron in concentrations greater than 1 mg/l interferes by producing a yellow color with the reagent. Vanadium interferes in the same manner but more strongly. The color produced with vanadium fades fairly rapidly and is negligible 10 min after the addition of the diphenylcarbazide.

1.3. *Minimum detectable concentration:* A chromium concentration of 3 µg/l can be detected by visual comparison in 50-ml nessler tubes. The limit is 5 µg/l when a 5-cm light path is used for photometric measurement.

2. Apparatus

Colorimetric equipment: One of the following is required:

2.1. *Spectrophotometer,* for use at 540 mµ, providing a light path of 1 cm or longer.

2.2. *Filter photometer,* providing a light path of 1 cm or longer and equipped with a green filter having maximum transmittance near 540 mµ.

2.3. *Nessler tubes,* 50 ml, matched, tall form.

3. Reagents

3.1. *Chromium-free water:* Redistill from an all-pyrex apparatus if necessary. A satisfactory water can also be prepared by passing distilled water through a mixed bed of ion-exchange resins. See General Introduction, A, Sec. 2, and Nitrogen (Ammonia), Method A, Sec. 3.1b.

3.2. *s-Diphenylcarbazide reagent:* Dissolve 0.2 g s-diphenylcarbazide (also called 1,5-diphenylcarbohydrazide) in 100 ml 95 per cent ethyl alcohol or isopropyl alcohol; add, with mixing, an acid solution prepared from 40 ml conc H_2SO_4 and 360 ml distilled water. Kept under refrigeration, the solution is stable for about a month. Its color will change from colorless to tan without affecting its usefulness.

3.3. *Stock chromium solution:* Dissolve 0.1414 g anhydrous potassium dichromate, $K_2Cr_2O_7$, in distilled water and dilute to 1,000 ml; 1.00 ml = 50 μg Cr.

3.4. *Standard chromium solution:* Dilute 20.00 ml stock chromium solution to 1,000 ml; 1.00 ml = 1 μg hexavalent Cr. Prepare daily.

4. Procedure

Use a 50.0-ml sample or an aliquot diluted to 50 ml with chromium-free distilled water. If necessary, clarify by centrifuging. Add 2.5 ml diphenylcarbazide reagent and mix well. Compare visually against standards containing 3 to 200 μg/l Cr. Prepare a calibration curve in the chromium range of 5 to 400 μg/l if photometric measurements are made at 540 mμ with a 5-cm light path. Make comparisons or readings at least 5 min, but not later than 15 min, after the reagent is added.

5. Calculation

$$\text{mg/l hexavalent Cr} = \frac{\mu\text{g hexavalent Cr}}{\text{ml sample}}$$

6. Precision and Accuracy

Photometric measurements in the range below 0.4 mg/l can be made with a precision of ± 0.01 mg/l Cr. Accuracy depends on the promptness with which the determination for hexavalent chromium is undertaken. Storage in glass or polyethylene containers may result in low chromate values.

B. Permanganate-Azide Method for Total Chromium

1. General Discussion

1.1. *Principle:* The original hexavalent chromium in the sample is first reduced with sodium sulfite to the trivalent form. The sample is evaporated and fumed with sulfuric acid to destroy the organic matter. The trivalent chromium is oxidized to the hexavalent condition by a slight excess of potassium permanganate. The chromium is reacted with diphenylcarbazide after the excess permanganate has been removed by means of sodium azide.

1.2. *Interference:* Same as Method A, Sec. 1.2.

2. Apparatus

2.1. *Colorimetric equipment:* Same as Method A, Sec. 2.

2.2. *Acid-washed glassware:* New and unscratched glassware will minimize chromium adsorption on the glass surface during the oxidation procedure. Glassware previously treated with chromic acid, as well as new glassware, should be thoroughly cleaned with hydrochloric or nitric acid for removal of chromium traces.

3. Reagents

All of the reagents listed in Method A, Sec. 3, are required, plus the following:

3.1. *Sulfuric acid,* $1 + 1$.

3.2. *Sodium sulfite solution:* Dissolve 1.26 g Na_2SO_3 in distilled water and dilute to 100 ml. Prepare daily. One milliliter of this solution will reduce approximately 3.4 mg of hexavalent to trivalent chromium.

3.3. *Potassium permanganate,* $0.1N$. Dissolve 3.16 g $KMnO_4$ in distilled water and dilute to 1,000 ml.

3.4. *Sodium azide solution:* Dissolve 0.5 g NaN_3 in distilled water and dilute to 100 ml.

4. Procedure

4.1. Pipet a sample volume containing 0.3–10 μg Cr into an erlenmeyer flask, and add 5 ml H_2SO_4 and 1 ml Na_2SO_3 solution. Allow to stand 10 min for complete reduction of hexavalent chromium. Add three glass beads or Berl saddles to control bumping. Evaporate to fumes and fume for 15 min or until clear. Cool and carefully dilute to about 50–80 ml. Bring to a boil and add sufficient $KMnO_4$ dropwise so that a faint pink color persists as the solution continues to boil for 10 min. Then add the NaN_3 solution dropwise and continue boiling until the solution becomes colorless. Boil

for about 2 min between azide additions to guard against the use of excess azide. Cool the sample.

4.2. If suspended matter and color are absent, transfer to a 50-ml nessler tube or volumetric flask. Remove any suspended matter by filtration through a sintered-glass filter of coarse or medium porosity. Use a filter of coarse porosity for colorless samples. If manganese dioxide precipitate is present, pass the sample through a filter of medium porosity under suction. Wash the filter well. Collect the filtrate in a 100-ml nessler tube or volumetric flask to permit sufficient washing.

4.3. Proceed as in Method A, Sec. 4, for hexavalent chromium and make the reading at least 5 min, but no later than 15 min, after the reagent is added. Prepare the photometric curve from known amounts of chromium handled in the same manner as the unknown sample. Correct the results with a blank carried through all the steps of the procedure.

5. Calculation

$$\text{mg/l total Cr} = \frac{\mu\text{g total Cr}}{\text{ml sample}}$$

6. Precision and Accuracy

A synthetic unknown sample containing 0.18 mg/l Cr, 1.80 mg/l Al, 0.42 mg/l Cu, 0.62 mg/l Fe, 0.25 mg/l Mn, and 0.90 mg/l Zn was determined in 30 laboratories with a standard deviation of ±0.04 mg/l by means of the permanganate-azide method. One-half of the reported results were within ±0.05 mg/l of the known chromium concentration. The individual laboratories reproduced their own results within ±0.01 mg/l.

C. Alkaline Hypobromite Method for Total Chromium

1. General Discussion

1.1. *Principle:* Total chromium is determined by oxidizing the trivalent form to the hexavalent state with an alkaline hypobromite solution. After the removal of the excess bromine with phenol, the color is developed in the normal manner with diphenylcarbazide.

1.2. *I n t e r f e r e n c e :* Significant amounts of organic matter or other reducing substances may prevent the complete oxidation of chromic ion, thereby resulting in low chromium values. Other interferences are described in Method A, Sec. 1.2.

2. Apparatus

2.1. *Colorimetric equipment:* Same as Method A, Sec. 2.

2.2. *Acid-washed glassware:* Same as Method B, Sec. 2.2.

3. Reagents

All of the reagents listed in Method A, Sec. 3, are required, plus the following:

3.1. *Oxidizing reagent:* Add 50 ml $1N$ NaOH to 3 ml saturated bromine water.

3.2. *Sulfuric acid, 6N.* Add cautiously 167 ml conc H_2SO_4 to distilled water and dilute to 1 liter.

3.3. *Phenol solution:* Dissolve 1.2 g redistilled phenol in distilled water and dilute to 100 ml. Store in an amber bottle.

3.4. *Sodium hydroxide, 1N.* Dissolve 40 g NaOH and dilute to 1 liter with distilled water.

4. Procedure

Determine the sample size by a rough preliminary analysis. To 25.0 ml of sample, or an aliquot diluted to 25 ml, in a 125-ml erlenmeyer flask, add 2 ml oxidizing reagent and place the flask on a steam bath for 45 min. Remove any precipitate at this point by filtration through a sintered-glass filter of coarse or medium porosity. Cool the sample, add 0.4 ml $6N$ H_2SO_4, and mix. Add 0.5 ml phenol solution and 2.5 ml $1N$ NaOH, mixing after each addition. Dilute to 50 ml in a nessler tube or volumetric flask and complete the color development and measurement as described in Method A, Sec. 4, for hexavalent chromium. Correct the results with a blank carried through all the steps of the procedure.

5. Calculation

$$\text{mg/l total Cr} = \frac{\mu\text{g total Cr}}{\text{ml sample}}$$

6. Precision and Accuracy

A synthetic unknown sample containing 0.18 mg/l Cr, 1.80 mg/l Al, 0.42 mg/l Cu, 0.62 mg/l Fe, 0.25 mg/l Mn, and 0.90 mg/l Zn was determined in 12 laboratories with a standard deviation of ±0.06 mg/l by means of the alkaline hypobromite method. One-half of the reported results were within ±0.05 mg/l of the known chromium concentration. The individual laboratories reproduced their own results within ±0.01 mg/l.

Bibliography

General

1. GRAHAM, D. W. Chromium, A Water and Sewage Problem. *J. AWWA* 35:159 (1943).
2. EGE, J. F., JR. & SILVERMAN, L. Stable Colorimetric Reagent for Chromium. *Anal. Chem.* 19:693 (1947).

3. Ruchhoft, C. C., et al. *Tentative Analytical Methods for Cadmium, Chromium, and Cyanide in Water.* US Public Health Service Environmental Health Center, Cincinnati, Ohio (1949).

4. Urone, P. F. Stability of Colorimetric Reagent for Chromium, *s*-Diphenylcarbazide, in Various Solvents. *Anal. Chem.* 27:1354 (1955).

Permanganate-Azide Method

5. Saltzman, B. E. Microdetermination

of Chromium with Diphenycarbazide by Permanganate Oxidation. *Anal. Chem.* 24:1016 (1952).

6. Lieber, M. Permanganate-Azide Test for Total Chromium in Water. *J. AWWA* 48:295 (1956).

Alkaline Hypobromite Method

7. Urone, P. F. & Anders, H. K. Microdetermination of Small Amounts of Chromium in Human Bloods, Tissues, and Urine. *Anal. Chem.* 22:1317 (1950).

Color

Color in water may result from the presence of natural metallic ions (iron and manganese), humus and peat materials, plankton, weeds, and industrial wastes. Color removal is practiced in order to make a water suitable for general and industrial applications.

The term "color" is used herein to mean "true color"—that is, the color of the water from which the turbidity has been removed. The term "apparent color" includes not only the color due to substances in solution, but also that due to suspended matter. Apparent color is determined on the original sample without filtration or centrifugation.

The following method for the determination of color is applicable to nearly all samples of potable water. Pollution by certain industrial wastes may produce unusual colors which cannot be matched; such samples may be examined by the procedures for color in Part IV.

1. General Discussion

1.1. *Principle:* Color is determined by visual comparison of the sample with known concentrations of colored solutions. Comparison may also be made with special glass color discs if they have been properly calibrated. The

platinum-cobalt method of measuring color is given as the standard method, the unit of color being that produced by 1 mg/l platinum, in the form of the chloroplatinate ion. The ratio of cobalt to platinum may be varied to match the hue in special cases; the proportion given below is usually satisfactory to match the color of natural waters.

1.2. *Interference:* Even a slight turbidity causes the apparent color to be noticeably higher than the true color; therefore, it is necessary to remove turbidity before true color can be approximated by differential reading with different color filters [6] or by differential scattering measurements.[5] Neither of these techniques, however, has reached the status of a standard method. The recommended method for the removal of turbidity is centrifugation. Filtration cannot be used because it may remove some of the true color as well as turbidity. If centrifuging will not suffice to remove all of the turbidity, the analyst is referred to the method described by Lamar.[4]

The color value of a water is extremely pH dependent, and invariably increases as the pH of the water is raised. For this reason it is necessary, when reporting a color value, to specify the pH at which the color is determined. For research purposes or when color values are to be compared between laboratories, it is advisable to determine the color response of a given water over a wide range of pH values. This procedure has been described by Black and Christman.[9]

1.3. *Field method:* Since the platinum-cobalt standard method is not convenient for field use, the color of water may be compared with that of glass discs held at the end of metallic tubes which contain glass comparator tubes of the sample and colorless distilled water. The color of the sample is matched with the color of the tube of clear water plus the calibrated colored glass when viewed by looking toward a white surface. Every individual disc must be calibrated to correspond with the colors on the platinum-cobalt scale. Experience has shown that the glass discs used by the U. S. Geological Survey give results in substantial agreement with those obtained by the platinum-cobalt method, and their use is recognized as a standard field procedure.

1.4. *Nonstandard laboratory methods:* The use of glass discs or of liquids other than water as standards for laboratory work is permissible only if these have been individually calibrated against platinum-cobalt standards. Waters of highly unusual color, such as may occur as a result of mixture with certain industrial wastes may have hues so far removed from those of the platinum-cobalt standards that comparison by the standard method is difficult or impossible. For such waters, the color methods in Part IV may be employed. The results so obtained are not, however, directly comparable to those obtained with platinum-cobalt standards.

1.5. *Sampling:* Samples for the color determination should be representative and must be taken in clean glassware. The color determination should be made within a reasonable period, as biologic changes occurring in storage may affect the color.

2. Apparatus

2.1. *Nessler tubes,* matched, 50 ml, tall form.

2.2. *pH meter,* for determining the sample pH as described in pH Value. The pH may also be determined colorimetrically.

3. Preparation of Standards

3.1. If a reliable supply of potassium chloroplatinate cannot be purchased, it may be replaced by chloroplatinic acid, which the analyst can prepare from metallic platinum. Commercial chloroplatinic acid should not be used because it is very hygroscopic and therefore may vary in platinum content. Potassium chloroplatinate is not hygroscopic.

3.2. Dissolve 1.246 g potassium chloroplatinate, K_2PtCl_6 (equivalent to 0.500 g metallic platinum) and 1 g crystallized cobaltous chloride, $CoCl_2 \cdot 6H_2O$ (equivalent to about 0.25 g metallic cobalt) in distilled water with 100 ml conc HCl and dilute to 1 liter with distilled water. This stock standard has a color of 500 units.

3.3. If potassium chloroplatinate is not available, dissolve 0.500 g pure metallic platinum in aqua regia with the aid of heat; remove nitric acid by repeated evaporation with fresh portions of conc HCl. Dissolve this product together with 1 g crystallized cobaltous chloride as directed above.

3.4. Prepare standards having colors of 5, 10, 15, 20, 25, 30, 35, 40, 45, 50, 60, and 70 by diluting 0.5, 1.0, 1.5, 2.0, 2.5, 3.0, 3.5, 4.0, 4.5, 5.0, 6.0, and 7.0 ml stock color standard with distilled water to 50 ml in nessler tubes. Protect these standards against evaporation and contamination when not in use.

4. Procedure

4.1. Observe the color of a sample by filling a matched nessler tube to the 50-ml mark with the water to be examined and comparing it with the standards. Look vertically downward through the tubes toward a white or specular surface placed at such an angle that light is reflected upward through the columns of liquid. If turbidity is present and has not been removed by the procedure given below, report the color as "apparent color." If the color exceeds 70 units, dilute the sample with distilled water in known proportions until the color is within the range of the standards.

4.2. To determine true color if turbidity is present, first place the sample in a suitable centrifuge tube or tubes and centrifuge until the supernatant is clear. The time required will depend upon the nature of the sample, the speed of the motor, and the radius of the centrifuge, but rarely will more than 1 hr be necessary. Compare the centrifuged sample in a nessler tube with distilled water to insure that all turbidity has been eliminated. If clear, the sample is then compared with the standards.

4.3. Since the color is related to pH, measure the pH of each sample.

5. Calculation

5.1. Calculate the color units by means of the following equation:

$$\text{Color units} = \frac{\overline{B}}{A \times 50}$$

where A = estimated color of a diluted sample, and B = ml sample taken for dilution.

5.2. Report the color results in whole numbers and record as follows:

Color Units	Record to Nearest
1–50	1
51–100	5
101–250	10
251–500	20

5.3. Report the pH of the water sample whose color was determined.

Bibliography

1. HAZEN, A. A New Color Standard for Natural Waters. *Am. Chem. J.* 14:300 (1892).
2. HAZEN, A. The Measurement of the Colors of Natural Waters. *J. Am. Chem. Soc.* 18:264 (1896).
3. *Measurement of Color and Turbidity in Water.* Circ. 8, Div. of Hydrography, US Geological Survey, Washington, D.C. (1902).
4. LAMAR, W. L. Determination of Color of Turbid Waters. *Anal. Chem.* 21:726 (1949).
5. JULLANDER, I. & BRUNE, K. Light Absorption Measurements on Turbid Solutions. *Acta Chem. Scand.* 4:870 (1950).
6. KNIGHT, A. G. The Photometric Estimation of Color in Turbid Waters. *J. Inst. Water Engrs.* 5:623 (1951).
7. RUDOLFS, W. & HANLON, W. D. Color in Industrial Wastes. *Sew. Ind. Wastes* 23:1125 (1951).
8. PALIN, A. T. Photometric Determination of the Colour and Turbidity of Water. *Water & Water Eng.* 59:341 (1955).
9. BLACK, A. P. & CHRISTMAN, R. F. Characteristics of Colored Surface Waters. *J. AWWA* 55:753 (1963).
10. BLACK, A. P. & CHRISTMAN, R. F. Chemical Characteristics of Fulvic Acids. *J. AWWA* 55:897 (1963).

Copper

Copper is an essential element to the human body and the adult daily requirement has been estimated at 2.0 mg. Large oral doses may, however, produce emesis, and, if prolonged, may result in liver damage. In amounts above 1.0 mg/l copper can impart a bitter taste to the water. The copper content of drinking waters seldom exceeds 0.6 mg/l but generally falls below 0.03 mg/l. Copper salts are used in controlling growths in reservoirs, for catalyzing the oxidation of manganese, and for controlling slime in the distribution system. The corrosion of copper, brass, and bronze pipe and fittings may result in the introduction of measurable concentrations of copper into a water, as evidenced by blue-green stains on plumbing fixtures.

Selection of method: The "cuprethol" method (*A*) is intended for the determination of traces of copper in relatively unpolluted water. It is also intended for those who prefer a non-extraction method. If iron is present in concentrations lower than 0.3 mg/l, the modification suggested in Sec. 4.4 offers a simple and highly sensitive procedure ideally adapted to field work. The "bathocuproine" method (*B*) is recommended for unknown and polluted waters because of its high degree of freedom from interferences. The "neocuproine" extraction method, for the determination of copper in industrial wastes, can also be applied to many water samples; see Part IV, Metals (Heavy), Method D (Copper).

Sampling and storage: Copper ion has a tendency to be adsorbed on the surface of the sample container. Samples should, therefore, be analyzed as soon as possible after collection. If storage is necessary, 0.5 ml 1 + 1 HCl per 100 ml of sample will prevent "plating out." When such acidified samples are analyzed, a volume correction must be made for the added acid, and the addition of acid called for in the procedure below is not made.

A. 'Cuprethol' Method

1. General Discussion

1.1. *Principle:* Cupric ions form a yellow-colored chelate with the reagent bis (2-hydroxyethyl) dithiocarbamate, whose popular name is "cuprethol." The colored compound is soluble and is formed quantitatively. Hydrochloric acid and sodium acetate buffer the solution at a favorable pH, between 5 and 6. Pyrophosphate overcomes the interference of iron up to 20 mg/l as ferric ion and 50 mg/l as ferrous ion.

1.2. *Interference:* Bismuth, cobalt, mercurous, nickel, and silver ions interfere seriously and must be absent. Other ions which interfere must be limited to the concentration shown:

Ion	Upper Limit mg/l
Aluminum	20
Cadmium	20
Calcium	400
Chromate	2
Chromic	5
Cyanide	20
Dichromate	2
Ferric	20
Ferrous	50
Lead	10
Manganous	10
Mercuric	20
Nitrite	20
Stannic	10
Stannous	20
Sulfite	100
Uranyl	10
Zinc	20

No interference is caused by up to 1,000 mg/l of sodium, potassium, ammonium, magnesium, carbonate, chloride, fluoride, iodide, nitrate, phosphate, silicate, or borate. It is believed that excessive concentrations of interfering ions will seldom be encountered in unpolluted waters; however, certain sewage, industrial, and boiler waters may require Method B. Turbidity or color may be corrected by the usual photometric compensation techniques or by extraction of the copper chelate with isoamyl alcohol.

1.3. *Minimum detectable concentration:* A copper concentration of 0.02 mg/l can be detected by visual comparison in 100-ml nessler tubes.

2. Apparatus

2.1. *Colorimetric equipment:* One of the following is required:

a. Spectrophotometer, for use at 435 mμ, providing a light path of 1 cm or longer.

b. Filter photometer, providing a light path of 1 cm or longer and equipped with a violet filter having maximum transmittance near 435 to 440 mμ.

c. Nessler tubes, matched, 100 ml, tall form.

2.2. *Acid-washed glassware:* All glassware must be rinsed with conc HCl and then with copper-free water (Sec. 3.1).

3. Reagents

3.1. *Copper-free water:* The water used throughout this procedure must be prepared by redistilling single-distilled water from an all-pyrex still. Ordinary distilled water usually contains traces of copper because of its use in still construction. A satisfactory water can also be prepared by passing distilled water through a mixed bed of ion-exchange resins; see General Introduction, A, Sec. 2, and Nitrogen (Ammonia), Method A, Sec. 3.1b.

3.2. *Stock copper solution:* Weigh 0.1000 g copper metal foil; place it in a 250-ml beaker under a hood; add 3 ml copper-free water and 3 ml conc HNO_3 and cover the beaker with a watch glass. After the metal has all dissolved, add 1 ml conc H_2SO_4 and heat on a hot plate to volatilize the acids. Stop heating just short of complete dryness. Do not bake the residue. Cool and dissolve in copper-free water, washing down the sides of the beaker and the bottom of the watch glass. Transfer quantitatively to a 1-liter volumetric flask and make up to the mark with copper-free water. This stock solution contains 0.100 mg Cu per 1.00 ml.

3.3. *Standard copper solution:* Dilute 50.00 ml stock copper solution to 1,000 ml with copper-free water; 1.00 ml = 5 μg Cu.

3.4. *Hydrochloric acid,* 1 + 1. Use copper-free water.

3.5. *Sodium pyrophosphate solution:* Dissolve 30 g $Na_4P_2O_7 \cdot 10H_2O$ in copper-free water and make up to 1 liter.

3.6. *Sodium acetate solution:* Dissolve 400 g $NaC_2H_3O_2 \cdot 3H_2O$ in 600 ml copper-free water. The solution of the salt is endothermic and requires heat.

3.7. *Cuprethol reagent mixture:*

a. Solution (I): Dissolve 4.0 g diethanolamine (also called 2,2'-iminodiethanol) in 200 ml methyl alcohol.

b. Solution (II): Dissolve 3.0 ml carbon disulfide in 200 ml methyl alcohol.

Solutions I and II are quite stable. Prepare the reagent by mixing equal volumes of the two solutions. If tightly stoppered, the reagent mixture is stable for about one week; it slowly decomposes, liberating sulfur, which causes turbidity when added to the sample. (CAUTION: *Keep the reagent away from flame. Dispense it with a safety pipet because of toxicity.*)

3.8. *Isoamyl alcohol.*

4. Procedure

4.1. Standards for visual comparison or for the preparation or checking of a calibration curve may be prepared from the standard copper solution according to the following schedule:

Copper *mg/l*	Vol. of Std. Copper Soln. to Be Diluted to 100 ml *ml*
0.000	0.00
0.025	0.50
0.050	1.00
0.100	2.00
0.150	3.00
0.200	4.00
0.300	6.00
0.400	8.00
0.500	10.00

The standards are treated exactly as described for samples.

4.2. To a 100-ml sample, or an aliquot diluted to 100 ml, add, mixing after each addition, 0.5 ml HCl, 2 ml sodium pyrophosphate solution, and sufficient sodium acetate solution to give a pH between 5 and 6. Let stand for 5 min. Add 1 ml cuprethol reagent mixture. Allow to stand at least 10 min, but not more than 30 min. Compare visually in nessler tubes against simultaneously prepared standards in the recommended copper range of 0–0.5 mg/l, or use a photometer and evaluate on a calibration curve obtained from simultaneously prepared standards.

4.3. A photometer can be used if the sample is initially turbid or colored. All reagents except cuprethol are added to a 100-ml sample as directed in Sec. 4.2; 2 ml methyl alcohol is added in lieu of the cuprethol solution. This mixture is used to correct for the turbidity or color and is set at 100 per cent transmittance. If turbidity develops upon the addition of cuprethol to a clear solution, it indicates either a stale cuprethol reagent or the presence of an interfering ion in excessive concentration.

Extraction by isoamyl alcohol may also be used to overcome the problem of turbidity. In visual determinations using nessler tubes, a convenient technique consists of adding 5 ml isoamyl alcohol to the samples after the color has been developed as described in Sec. 4.2, and mixing by constantly inverting the tubes for 3 min. The bulk of the color collects in the droplets of isoamyl alcohol which are buoyed up to the surface and there form a layer. The color of the layer can then be compared, without removal, with standards prepared in a like manner. The emulsion may be broken up by the addition of a few drops of ethyl alcohol to the isoamyl alcohol layer and gently stirring this layer with a stirring rod.

4.4. *Modified procedure for field work:* The procedure may be simplified with waters containing tolerable concentrations of interfering ions. Iron must be less than 0.3 mg/l as ferric ion and 0.6 mg/l as ferrous ion; the pH should be between 1.5 and 9. Under these circumstances, the simplification is especially adaptable to field work and consists only of adding 1 ml cuprethol to a 100-ml sample, mixing, and immediately comparing the color to simultaneously prepared standards.

5. Calculation

$$\text{mg/l Cu} = \frac{\text{mg Cu} \times 1,000}{\text{ml sample}}$$

6. Precision and Accuracy

A synthetic unknown sample containing 0.42 mg/l Cu, 1.80 mg/l Al, 0.18 mg/l Cr, 0.62 mg/l Fe, 0.25 mg/l Mn, and 0.90 mg/l Zn was determined in 30 laboratories with a standard deviation of ±0.13 mg/l by means of the cuprethol method. One-half of the reported results were within ±0.04 mg/l of the known copper concentration. The individual laboratories reproduced their own results within ±0.01 mg/l.

B. 'Bathocuproine' Method

1. General Discussion

1.1. *Principle:* Cuprous ions form an orange-colored bisphenanthroline chelate with 2,9-dimethyl-4,7-diphenyl-1,10-phenanthroline ("bathocuproine"). Hydrochloric acid assures dissolution of the copper, prevents its adsorption on vessel walls, and forms a buffer system with the sodium acetate. The pH should be maintained between 4 and 10 for maximum color development. Hydroxylamine hydrochloride serves as the reducing agent. Sunlight oxidizes the cuprous complex and thereby causes a gradual fading of the color. Undue exposure to light should, therefore, be avoided.

1.2. *Interference:* No known metallic ion interferes if present in concentrations below 1 mg/l. The maximum permissible concentration for zinc is 10 mg/l. Nitrate does not interfere to at least 250 mg/l. Ferrous, ferric, manganous, chromate, plumbous, aluminum, sodium, ammonium, potassium, phosphate, sulfate, and chloride ions do not seriously interfere to 1,000 mg/l.

1.3. *Minimum detectable concentration:* A copper concentration of 0.02 mg/l can be detected by the bathocuproine method.

2. Apparatus

2.1. *Colorimetric equipment:* One of the following is required:

a. Spectrophotometer, for use at 480 mμ, providing a light path of 1 cm or longer.

b. Filter photometer, providing a light path of 1 cm or longer and equipped with a blue filter having a maximum transmittance near 480 mμ.

c. Nessler tubes, matched, 100 ml, tall form (for use only in the modification described in Sec. 4.3.)

2.2. *Separatory funnels,* 250 ml, preferably with inert teflon stopcocks.

2.3. *Acid-washed glassware:* All glassware must be rinsed with conc HCl and then with copper-free water (Method A, Sec. 3.1).

3. Reagents

3.1. *Copper-free water:* Prepare as directed in Method A, Sec. 3.1.

3.2. *Bathocuproine reagent:* Add 5 ml 95 per cent ethyl alcohol to 0.2 g bathocuproine and stir into a paste. Add 95 ml 1 + 1 HCl and apply gentle heat until dissolution is effected. Insufficient acidity will cause precipitation of the bathocuproine.

3.3. *Hydroxylamine hydrochloride*

solution: Dissolve 100 g $NH_2OH \cdot HCl$ in 900 ml of copper-free water.

3.4. *Sodium acetate solution:* Prepare as directed in Method A, Sec. 3.6.

3.5. *Standard copper solution:* Prepare as directed in Method A, Sec. 3.3.

3.6. *Chloroform.*

4. Procedure

4.1. See Method A, Sec. 4.1.

4.2. To a separatory funnel containing 100 ml of sample, or an aliquot diluted to 100 ml, add, mixing after each addition, 2 ml of bathocuproine reagent, 5 ml of hydroxylamine hydrochloride solution, and sufficient sodium acetate solution to produce a pH of about 4.5; this should require approximately 5 ml and the same determined quantity should be used throughout. Add 10.0 ml chloroform and shake in the separatory funnel for 2 min. Let stand for 5 min and draw off the chloroform layer into a 25-ml glass-stoppered flask. Filter the solution through glass wool into the absorption cell. Read in the photometer. Evaluate the result on the calibration curve made with simultaneously prepared standards.

4.3. *Modified method:* Extraction can be omitted and the determination made on the aqueous solution after color development. In this circumstance, close pH control is essential. A pH lower than approximately 4.0 does not produce full color, and a pH higher than 4.2 tends to cloud up and deposit the copper complex. The copper-bathocuproine complex also deposits with excessive amounts of bathocuproine reagent.

The method consists of adding to a 100-ml sample, mixing after each addition, 1 ml bathocuproine reagent, 5 ml hydroxylamine solution, and enough sodium acetate to maintain a pH of 4.0 to 4.2. The determination may then be completed visually or instrumentally. The recommended copper range is 0–0.5 mg/l.

5. Calculation

$$mg/l \ Cu = \frac{mg \ Cu \times 1,000}{ml \ sample}$$

6. Precision and Accuracy

The extraction method, using a spectrophotometer, is estimated to have an accuracy within ±5 per cent under routine conditions. The precision approximates ±0.02 mg/l in the neighborhood of 0.3 mg/l copper.

Bibliography

Cuprethol Method

1. WOELFEL, W. C. Colorimetric Determination of Copper With Carbon Disulfide and Diethanolamine—An Improved Dithiocarbamate Reagent. *Anal. Chem.* 20:722 (1948).

Bathocuproine Method

2. SMITH, G. F. & WILKINS, D. H. New Colorimetric Reagent Specific for Copper. *Anal. Chem.* 25:510 (1953).

3. BORCHARDT, L. G. & BUTLER, J. P. Determination of Trace Amounts of Copper. *Anal. Chem.* 29:414 (1957).

Cyanide

The determination of cyanide in a potable water supply can be performed by the methods described in Part IV.

Detergents

See Surfactants.

Fluoride

A fluoride concentration of approximately 1.0 mg/l is an effective preventive of dental caries without harmful effects on health. Fluoride may occur naturally in water or may be added in controlled amounts. Some fluorosis may occur when the fluoride level exceeds the recommended limits. In rare instances the fluoride concentration naturally occurring may approach 10 mg/l. Such waters should be defluoridated to reduce the fluoride content to the acceptable levels.

The accurate determination of fluoride in water supplies has increased in importance with the growth of the practice of fluoridation of supplies as a public health measure. The maintenance of a constant fluoride concentration is essential in maintaining the effectiveness and safety of the fluoridation procedure.

Among the many methods suggested for the determination of fluoride ion in water, the colorimetric methods are believed to be the most satisfactory at the present time. They are based on the reaction between fluoride and a zirconium-dye lake. The fluoride reacts with the dye lake, dissociating a portion of it into a colorless complex anion (ZrF_6^{--}) and the dye. As the amount of fluoride is increased, the color produced becomes progressively lighter or different in hue, depending on the reagent used.

Because all of the methods are subject to errors where interfering ions are present, it may be necessary to distill the sample as directed in Preliminary Step I or II prior to making the fluoride determination. When interfering ions are not present in excess of the tolerances of the method, the fluoride determination may be made directly without distillation. The analysis is completed by using one of the three colorimetric methods (A, B, C).

Selection of method: Each method is sensitive to 0.05 mg/l fluoride. Photometric methods (B) (alizarin) and (C) (SPADNS) are directly applicable to samples containing up to 2.5 mg/l and 1.4 mg/l F, respectively. The visual modification (A) is directly applicable to samples containing up to 1.4 mg/l F.

The alizarin photometric method (B) is adaptable to a greater concentration range, 0–2.5 mg/l F, but it requires that the sample be read at exactly 60 ± 2 min. The SPADNS method (C) does not require any waiting period after reagent addition. The alizarin visual and photometric methods, on the other hand, require that an hour elapse between reagent addition to the samples and subsequent reading.

The visual method requires no special equipment. It does not, except under special circumstances, require accurate time control, because sample and standards are treated at the same time under the same conditions. However, a waiting period after reagent addition is mandatory.

TABLE 8—CONCENTRATION OF INTERFERING SUBSTANCES CAUSING 0.1-MG/L ERROR AT
1.0 MG/L F *

Substance	Method A (Alizarin Visual)		Method B (Alizarin Photometric)		Method C (SPADNS)	
	Conc. *mg/l*	Type of Error	Conc. *mg/l*	Type of Error	Conc. *mg/l*	Type of Error
Alkalinity ($CaCO_3$)	400	—	325	—	5,000	—
Aluminum (Al^{+++})	0.25	—	0.2	—	0.1†	—
Chloride (Cl^-)	2,000	—	1,800	—	7,000	+
Iron (Fe^{+++})	2	+	5	—	10	—
Hexametaphosphate ($[NaPO_3]_6$)	1.0	+	1.1	+	1.0	+
Phosphate (PO_4^{---})	5	+	5	+	16	+
Sulfate (SO_4^{--})	300	+	400	+	200	+

* Residual chlorine must be completely removed with arsenite reagent. Color and turbidity must be removed or compensated for.
† On immediate reading. Tolerance increases with time: after 2 hr, 3.0; after 4 hr, 30.

Permanent colored standards, commercially or otherwise prepared, may be used if appropriate precautions are taken. These include strict adherence to the manufacturer's directions and careful calibration of the permanent standards against standards prepared by the analyst. (See General Introduction, A, Sec. 7, for further discussion of their use.)

Interference: In general, the methods are susceptible to the same interfering substances, but to varying degrees. Table 8 lists the substances which commonly cause interference with the various methods. As these interferences are neither linear in effect nor algebraically additive, mathematical compensation is extremely hazardous. Whenever any one substance is present in sufficient quantity to produce an error of 0.1 mg/1, or whenever the total interfering effect is in doubt, the sample should be distilled. (Distillation is also recommended for colored or turbid samples.) In some instances, sample dilution or addition of the appropriate amounts of interfering substances to the standards may be used to eliminate the interference effect. If alkalinity is the only significant interference, it may be neutralized with either hydrochloric or nitric acid.

Chlorine interferes in all of the methods and provision for its removal is made.

The volume of water sample and, particularly, the volume of reagent added are of utmost importance to the accuracy of the determinations. The temperature and, in Method B, the time of reaction are also important factors in reproducibility of results.

Sampling and storage: Polyethylene bottles are preferred for collecting and storing water samples for fluoride analysis. Glass bottles are satisfactory provided precautions are taken to prevent the use of containers which previously contained high-fluoride solutions. The usual precaution of rinsing the bottle with a portion of the sample should be observed.

Laboratories which use water samples collected for bacteriologic analysis should be cautioned against an excess of dechlorinating agent in the sample. Sodium thiosulfate in excess of 100 mg/1 will interfere by producing a precipitate.

I. Preliminary Direct Distillation Step

1. Principle

The basic difference between the steam and direct distillation procedures is that the latter produces no dilution of the water sample, making preconcentration unnecessary. This is accomplished by using a larger sample and carrying out the distillation over a broader temperature range. Although the sulfate carryover during the latter portion of the distillation is pronounced due to the higher temperature, the large volume of distillate and the lower starting temperature serve to hold the final sulfate concentration within tolerable limits by dilution.

2. Apparatus

Distillation apparatus consisting of a 1-liter round-bottom, long-neck pyrex boiling flask, a connecting tube, an efficient condenser, a thermometer adapter, and a thermometer reading to 200°C is illustrated in Fig. 14, but any comparable apparatus may be used, provided the essential design features are observed. Fig. 17 shows the general type of distillation apparatus * which is satisfactory for the fluoride, ammonia, albuminoid nitrogen, phenol, and selenium distillations. The critical points to observe are those which could affect complete fluoride recovery— such as obstruction in the vapor path and trapping of liquid in the adapter and condenser—and conditions which might enhance sulfate carryover. In this regard, the use of an asbestos shield or similar device is recommended to protect the upper part of the distilling flask from the burner flame. If desired,

---

* Such as Corning No. 3360 or equivalent.

this apparatus can be modified so that the heat is automatically shut off when distillation is completed.[2]

3. Reagents

3.1. *Sulfuric acid,* conc.
3.2. *Silver sulfate,* crystals.

4. Procedure

4.1. Place 400 ml distilled water in the distilling flask and carefully add 200 ml conc H_2SO_4. Swirl until the flask contents are homogeneous. Add

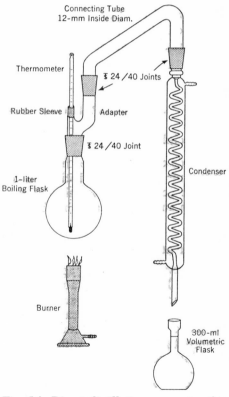

Fig. 14. Direct distillation apparatus for fluoride

25–35 glass beads and connect the apparatus as shown in Fig. 14, making sure all joints are tight. Begin heating slowly at first, then as rapidly as the efficiency of the condenser will permit (the distillate must be cool) until the temperature of the flask contents reaches exactly 180°C. Discard the distillate. This process serves to remove fluoride contamination and to adjust the acid-water ratio for subsequent distillations.

4.2. After cooling the acid mixture remaining from Sec. 4.1, or previous distillations, to 120°C or below, add 300 ml of sample, mix thoroughly, and distill as before until the temperature reaches 180°C. To prevent sulfate carryover, do not permit the temperature to exceed 180°C.

4.3. Add silver sulfate to the distilling flask at the rate of 5 mg per milligram of chloride when high-chloride samples are distilled.

4.4. The sulfuric acid solution in the flask may be used repeatedly until the contaminants from the water samples accumulate to an extent that recovery is affected or interferences appear in the distillate. The suitability of the acid should be periodically checked by distilling standard fluoride samples. After high-fluoride samples are distilled, the still should be flushed with 300 ml of distilled water before samples containing lower fluoride concentrations (less than about 10 per cent of the fluoride concentration of the previous sample) are run.

5. Interpretation of Results

The recovery of fluoride is quantitative within the accuracy of the methods used for its measurement.

II. Preliminary Steam Distillation Step

1. Principle

Fluoride can be separated from other constituents in water by distillation of fluosilicic acid from a solution of the sample in an acid with a higher boiling point.

2. Apparatus

The commercial distilling apparatus * shown in Fig. 15 (Apparatus A) or any comparable apparatus (such as Apparatus B in Fig. 15) is satisfactory. The funnel on such apparatus may be modified by replacing it with a glass steam inlet connected to a steam generator as shown in the diagram (Fig. 15).[3]

The thermometer bulb or well and steam inlet should extend to within 2 mm of the bottom of the flask. When a separatory funnel is used, the inlet to the flask should terminate with a capillary tip. Bumping is minimized by placing glass beads in the steam generator and distilling flask.

Any of the apparatus illustrated which will distill fluoride quantitatively can be used provided the analyst has assured himself of its reliability. The critical points in the design are the diameter and slope of the delivery tube, the distance between the surface of the boiling liquid and the lower end of the delivery tube, and the fit of ground-

---

* Listed as Catalog No. 6431 by Ace Glass Co. and as Catalog No. JD 2130 by Scientific Glass Apparatus Co.

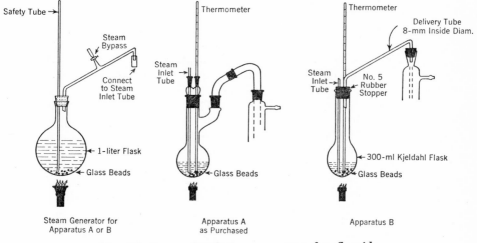

Fig. 15. Steam distillation apparatus for fluoride

glass joints or rubber stoppers. The principal source of difficulty in distilling fluoride samples is the carryover of sulfate from the boiling acid, and frequently this occurrence is caused by faulty apparatus. The delivery tube must be at least 8 mm in internal diameter, and must slope upward from the distilling flask. The lower end of the delivery tube, which should be cut at an angle to prevent the formation of a sealing bubble, must be at least 6 in. from the boiling liquid to preclude carryover of droplets. The tight fit of joints and stoppers is a necessity for quantitative recovery of fluoride. It is advisable to make a quantitative test for both sulfate and fluoride on the distillate in order to check both the apparatus and the technique.

3. Reagents

3.1. *Sulfuric acid,* conc.

3.2. *Silver sulfate,* solid.

3.3. *Reagents for sample concentration:*

a. Sodium hydroxide, 1N. Dissolve 40 g NaOH and dilute to 1 liter with distilled water.

b. Phenolphthalein indicator solution: Either the aqueous (I) or alcoholic (II) solution may be used.

I. Dissolve 5 g phenolphthalein disodium salt in distilled water and dilute to 1 liter. If necessary, add $0.02N$ NaOH dropwise until a faint pink color appears.

II. Dissolve 5 g phenolphthalein in 500 ml 95 per cent ethyl alcohol or isopropyl alcohol and add 500 ml distilled water. Then add $0.02N$ NaOH dropwise until a faint pink color appears.

4. Procedure

4.1. *Concentration of sample:* Concentrate the sample in the following way if it contains less than 0.4 mg/l F. Make a 200-ml sample alkaline with NaOH, using phenolphthalein indicator, and add a few drops of NaOH in excess. Concentrate to 25–50 ml on a steam bath or hot plate, avoiding splashing which might result in loss of liquid.

When cool, transfer quantitatively to a distillation flask which has been prepared as in Sec. 4.2. Distilled water may be used for washing the concentrated sample into the distilling flask, but in no case should the total volume of water exceed 100 ml.

4.2. *Preparation of apparatus:* Place 125 ml distilled water in the distillation flask and carefully add 25 ml conc H_2SO_4. Mix thoroughly by swirling and add a few glass beads. Connect the condenser, thermometer, and steam inlet assembly with the steam bypass open. Heat the mixture to boiling. As the distillate is collected, the water in the steam generator is brought to a boil and the steam permitted to escape. As soon as the temperature reaches 135°C, the steam is introduced into the distillation flask by closing the bypass. Heat from the two burners is regulated to maintain a temperature of 135°–145°C and a distillation rate of not less than 3 ml/min. The distillation is continued until 200 ml of distillate is collected.

This process of steaming out the apparatus with distilled water serves to remove any fluoride with which both glassware and sulfuric acid are often contaminated.

4.3. *Distillation of sample:* Either the concentrated sample from Sec. 4.1 or, if the sample contains 0.4 mg/l F or more, a 100-ml portion of the water sample is transferred directly to a cool distillation flask prepared as above. Approximately 50 ml of sulfuric acid solution should remain in the flask at the completion of the steaming-out process. This acid may be used repeatedly, provided the contaminants from the water samples do not accumulate to such a degree that recovery is affected or interferences appear in the distillate. The analyst can ascertain the condition of the acid in the flask by periodically distilling standard fluoride samples.

The distillation is carried out exactly as in Sec. 4.2 until 200 ml of distillate is collected, the excess over original volume coming from the steam.

The volatilization of hydrochloric acid can be kept to a minimum by the addition of solid silver sulfate, at the rate of 5 mg for each milligram chloride, to the distilling flask. (However, the chloride tolerances of the methods are usually high enough to make this step unnecessary.)

5. Interpretation of Results

The recovery of fluoride by distillation is quantitative within the accuracy of the methods for its measurement, provided the requisite precautions are taken. The dilution of the sample by the addition of steam results in multiplication of any errors stemming from faulty distillation. The hazard of sulfate carryover cannot be stressed too much. When not due to poor apparatus design, this difficulty can often be traced to temperatures higher than 145°C or to superheating of the vapor by a burner flame which is not kept below the surface of the liquid in the distilling flask. The use of an asbestos shield or similar device is recommended to protect the sides of the flask from a higher burner flame. The carryover of volatile materials other than sulfate or chloride is seldom a problem.

A. Alizarin Visual Method

1. Apparatus

Color comparison equipment: One of the following is required:
1.1. *Nessler tubes,* matched, 100 ml, tall form.
1.2. *Comparator,* visual.

2. Reagents

2.1. *Stock fluoride solution:* Dissolve 0.2210 g anhydrous sodium fluoride, NaF, in distilled water and dilute to 1,000 ml; 1.00 ml = 0.100 mg F.

2.2. *Standard fluoride solution:* Dilute 100.0 ml stock fluoride solution to 1,000 ml with distilled water; 1.00 ml = 10.0 μg F.

2.3. *Zirconyl-alizarin reagent:* Dissolve 0.30 g zirconyl chloride octahydrate, $ZrOCl_2 \cdot 8H_2O$, in 50 ml distilled water contained in a 1-liter glass-stoppered volumetric flask. Dissolve 0.07 g 3-alizarinsulfonic acid sodium salt (also called alizarin red S) in 50 ml distilled water and pour slowly into the zirconyl solution, while stirring. The resulting solution clears on standing for a few minutes.

2.4. *Mixed acid solution:* Dilute 101 ml conc HCl to approximately 400 ml with distilled water. Add carefully 33.3 ml conc H_2SO_4 to approximately 400 ml distilled water. After cooling, mix the two acids.

2.5. *Acid zirconyl-alizarin reagent:* To the clear zirconyl-alizarin reagent in the 1-liter volumetric flask, add the mixed acid solution, add distilled water up to the mark, and mix. The reagent changes in color from red to yellow within an hour and is then ready for use. Store away from direct sunlight to extend the reagent stability to 6 months.

2.6. *Sodium arsenite solution:* Dissolve 5.0 g $NaAsO_2$ and dilute to 1 liter with distilled water. (CAUTION: *Toxic; take care to avoid ingestion.*)

3. Procedure

3.1. *Sample pretreatment:* If the sample contains residual chlorine, remove it by adding 1 drop (0.05 ml) of arsenite for each 0.1 mg Cl and mix.

3.2. *Preparation of standards:* Prepare a series of standards by diluting various volumes of standard fluoride solution (1.00 ml = 10.0 μg F) to 100 ml in nessler tubes. The standards should be chosen so that there is at least one with lower and one with higher fluoride concentration than the unknown sample. The interval between standards determines the accuracy of the determination. An interval of 0.05 mg/l is usually sufficient.

3.3. *Color development:* Adjust the temperature of samples and standards so that the deviation between them is no more than 2°C. A temperature near that of the room is satisfactory. To 100 ml of the clear sample, or an aliquot diluted to 100 ml, and to the standards in nessler tubes, add 5.00 ml of the acid zirconyl-alizarin reagent from a volumetric pipet. Mix thoroughly, exercising care to avoid contamination during the process, and compare the samples and standards after 1 hr.

4. Calculation

$$\text{mg/l F} = \frac{A \times 1,000}{\text{ml sample}} \times \frac{B}{C}$$

where A = mg F determined visually. The ratio B/C applies only when a sample is distilled to a volume B, and an aliquot *C* taken from it for color development.

5. Precision and Accuracy

A synthetic unknown sample containing 0.92 mg/l fluoride and no interference was determined with a standard deviation of ±0.02 mg/l in twelve laboratories using the alizarin visual method. Following the steam distillation of the sample, the standard deviation was ±0.07 mg/l. The individual laboratories reproduced their own results within ±0.01 mg/l in the alizarin visual determination and ±0.04 mg/l in the steam-distilled samples.

A synthetic unknown sample containing 0.76 mg/l fluoride, 2.0 mg/l trivalent aluminum ion, and 200 mg/l sulfate was determined with a standard deviation of ±0.11 mg/l in twelve laboratories using steam distillation and the alizarin visual method. The individual laboratories reproduced their own results within ±0.04 mg/l.

A synthetic unknown sample containing 0.87 mg/l fluoride and 2.5 mg/l sodium hexametaphosphate was determined with a standard deviation of ±0.09 mg/l in twelve laboratories using steam distillation and the alizarin visual method. The individual laboratories reproduced their own results within ±0.05 mg/l.

A synthetic unknown sample containing 0.83 mg/l fluoride and no interference was determined by the alizarin visual method with a standard deviation of ±0.05 mg/l in 19 laboratories without recourse to distillation. Following the direct distillation of the sample, the standard deviation was ±0.06 mg/l. The individual laboratories reproduced their own results within ±0.01 mg/l in the alizarin visual determination and ±0.03 mg/l in the distilled samples.

A synthetic unknown sample containing 0.57 mg/l fluoride, 10 mg/l aluminum, 200 mg/l sulfate, and 300 mg/l total alkalinity was determined with a standard deviation of ±0.07 mg/l in 19 laboratories which followed the direct distillation and alizarin visual methods. The individual laboratories reproduced their own results within ±0.01 mg/l by using the combined methods.

A synthetic unknown sample containing 0.68 mg/l fluoride, 2 mg/l aluminum, 2.5 mg/l sodium hexametaphosphate, 200 mg/l sulfate, and 300 mg/l total alkalinity was determined with a standard deviation of ±0.07 mg/l in 19 laboratories which followed the direct distillation and alizarin visual methods. The individual laboratories reproduced their own results within ±0.01 mg/l by using the combined methods.

B. Alizarin Photometric Method

1. Apparatus

Colorimetric equipment: One of the following is required:

1.1. *Spectrophotometer,* for use at 520 to 550 mμ, providing a light path of at least 1 cm.

1.2. *Filter photometer,* providing a light path of at least 1 cm and equipped with a green filter having maximum transmittance at 520 to 550 mμ.

2. Reagents

2.1. *Standard fluoride solution:* Prepare as in Method A, Sec. 2.2.

2.2. *Alizarin red solution:* Dissolve 0.75 g 3-alizarinsulfonic acid sodium salt (alizarin red S) in distilled water and dilute to 1 liter. If insoluble material is present, filter through filter paper. Protect from direct sunlight.

2.3. *Zirconyl-acid reagent:* Dissolve 0.354 g zirconyl chloride octahydrate, $ZrOCl_2 \cdot 8H_2O$, in 600–800 ml distilled water. Add 33.3 ml conc H_2SO_4 slowly, with stirring. Add 101 ml conc HCl with stirring. Cool to room temperature. Dilute to 1 liter with distilled water and mix well. After 1 hr the reagent is ready for use.

2.4. *Sodium arsenite solution:* Prepare as directed in Method A, Sec. 2.6.

3. Procedure

3.1. *Preparation of standard curve:* Prepare fluoride standards in the range 0.00 to 2.50 mg/l by diluting appropriate quantities of the standard fluoride solution to 100 ml with distilled water. Pipet 5.00 ml of alizarin red solution and 5.00 ml of zirconyl-acid reagent to each standard, mix well, exercising care to avoid contamination during the process, and allow the reaction to proceed for 60 ± 2 min. Set the photometer to zero absorbance (100 per cent transmittance) with distilled water. (The instrument must not drift, since the standard, being subject to progressive color development, cannot be rechecked at a later time. In direct-reading instruments, initial light intensity must not fluctuate during a series of determinations.) At the end of 60 ± 2 min, take a reading on each standard using a wavelength in the 520 to 550 mμ range. Plot a curve of fluoride-absorbance relationships. A new standard curve must be prepared whenever a fresh batch of either of the two reagents is prepared, or when a

different standard temperature is desired.

3.2. *Sample pretreatment:* If the sample contains residual chlorine, remove it by adding 1 drop (0.05 ml) of arsenite solution for each 0.1 mg Cl and mix.

3.3 *Color development:* Use a 100-ml sample or an aliquot diluted to 100 ml. Adjust the temperature of the sample to that used for the standard curve. Add 5.00 ml alizarin red solution and 5.00 ml zirconyl-acid reagent and mix well, exercising care to avoid contamination during the process. Read the absorbance after 60 ± 2 min, first setting the reference point of the photometer as was done for the standard curve.

4. Calculation

$$\text{mg/l F} = \frac{A \times 1.000}{\text{ml sample}} \times \frac{B}{C}$$

where $A = \text{mg F}$ determined photometrically. The ratio B/C applies only when a sample is distilled to a volume B, and an aliquot C taken from it for color development.

5. Precision and Accuracy

A synthetic unknown sample containing 0.83 mg/l fluoride and no interference was determined by the alizarin photometric method with a standard deviation of ± 0.06 mg/l in 17 laboratories without recourse to distillation. Following the direct distillation of the sample, the standard deviation was ± 0.08 mg/l. The individual laboratories reproduced their own results within ± 0.01 mg/l in the alizarin photometric determination and ± 0.03 mg/l in the distilled samples.

A synthetic unknown sample containing 0.57 mg/l fluoride, 10 mg/l aluminum, 200 mg/l sulfate, and 300 mg/l total alkalinity was determined with a standard deviation of ±0.10 mg/l in 16 laboratories which followed the direct distillation and alizarin photometric methods. The individual laboratories reproduced their own results within ±0.02 mg/l by using the combined methods.

A synthetic unknown sample containing 0.68 mg/l fluoride, 2 mg/l aluminum, 2.5 mg/l sodium hexametaphosphate, 200 mg/l sulfate, and 300 mg/l total alkalinity was determined with a standard deviation of ±0.07 mg/l in 16 laboratories which followed the direct distillation and alizarin photometric methods. The individual laboratories reproduced their own results within ±0.02 mg/l by using the combined methods.

C. SPADNS Method

1. Principle

The reaction rate between fluoride and zirconium ions is influenced greatly by the acidity of the reaction mixture. By increasing the proportion of acid in the reagent, the reaction can be made practically instantaneous. Under such conditions, however, the effect of various ions differs from that in the conventional alizarin methods. The selection of dye for this rapid fluoride method is governed largely by the resulting tolerance to these ions.

2. Apparatus

Colorimetric equipment: One of the following is required:

2.1. *Spectrophotometer,* for use at 570 mμ, providing a light path of at least 1 cm.

2.2. *Filter photometer,* providing a light path of at least 1 cm and equipped with a greenish-yellow filter having maximum transmittance at 550 to 580 mμ.

3. Reagents

3.1. *Standard fluoride solution:* Prepare as directed in Method A, Sec. 2.2.

3.2. *SPADNS solution:* Dissolve 0.958 g SPADNS, sodium 2-(parasulfophenylazo)-1,8-dihydroxy-3,6-naphthalene disulfonate, also called 4,5-dihydroxy-3-(parasulfophenylazo)-2,7-naphthalenedisulfonic acid trisodium salt,* in distilled water and dilute to 500 ml. This solution is stable indefinitely if protected from direct sunlight.

3.3. *Zirconyl-acid reagent:* Dissolve 0.133 g zirconyl chloride octahydrate, $ZrOCl_2 \cdot 8H_2O$, in about 25 ml distilled water. Add 350 ml conc HCl and dilute to 500 ml with distilled water.

3.4. *Acid zirconyl-SPADNS reagent:* Mix equal volumes of SPADNS solution and zirconyl-acid reagent to produce a single reagent which is stable for at least 2 years.

3.5. *Reference solution:* Add 10 ml SPADNS solution to 100 ml distilled water. Dilute 7 ml conc HCl to 10 ml and add to the diluted SPADNS solution. The resulting solution, used for setting the reference point (zero) of the spectrophotometer or photometer, is stable and may be reused indefinitely. This reference solution can be eliminated by using, if desired, one of the prepared standards as a reference.

_____
* Eastman No. 7309 or equivalent.

3.6. *Sodium arsenite solution:* Prepare as directed in Method A, Sec. 2.6.

4. Procedure

4.1. *Preparation of standard curve:* Prepare fluoride standards in the range of 0 to 1.40 mg/l by diluting appropriate quantities of the standard fluoride solution to 50 ml with distilled water. Pipet 5.00 ml each of SPADNS solution and zirconyl-acid reagent, or 10.00 ml of the mixed acid zirconyl-SPADNS reagent, to each standard and mix well, exercising care to avoid contamination during the process. Set the photometer to zero absorbance with the reference solution and obtain the absorbance readings of the standards immediately. Plot a curve of the fluoride-absorbance relationships. Prepare a new standard curve whenever a fresh batch of reagent is made up or a different standard temperature is desired. If no reference solution is used, set the photometer at some convenient point established with a prepared fluoride standard.

4.2. *Sample pretreatment:* If the sample contains residual chlorine, remove it by adding 1 drop (0.05 ml) of sodium arsenite solution for each 0.1 mg Cl and mix. (Sodium arsenite concentrations of 1,300 mg/l produce an error of 0.1 mg/l at 1.0 mg/l F.)

4.3. *Color development:* Use a 50.0-ml sample or an aliquot diluted to 50 ml. Adjust the temperature of the sample to that used for the standard curve. Add 5.00 ml each of the SPADNS solution and zirconyl-acid reagent, or 10.00 ml of the acid zirconyl-SPADNS reagent; mix well, exercising care to prevent contamination during the process; and read the absorbance immediately or at any subsequent time, first setting the reference

point of the photometer as above. If the absorbance falls beyond the range of the standard curve, repeat the procedure using a smaller sample aliquot.

5. Calculation

$$\text{mg/l F} = \frac{A \times 1,000}{\text{ml sample}} \times \frac{B}{C}$$

where $A = $ mg F determined photometrically. The ratio B/C applies only when a sample is distilled to a volume B, and an aliquot C taken from it for color development.

6. Precision and Accuracy

A synthetic unknown sample containing 0.83 mg/l fluoride and no interference was determined by the SPADNS method with a standard deviation of ±0.07 mg/l in 51 laboratories without recourse to distillation. Following the direct distillation of the sample, the standard deviation was ±0.10 mg/l. The individual laboratories reproduced their own results within ±0.02 mg/l in the SPADNS determination and ±0.02 mg/l in the distilled samples.

A synthetic unknown sample containing 0.57 mg/l fluoride, 10 mg/l aluminum, 200 mg/l sulfate, and 300 mg/l total alkalinity was determined with a standard deviation of ±0.10 mg/l in 50 laboratories without resort to distillation. Following the direct distillation of the sample, the standard deviation was ±0.10 mg/l in 49 laboratories. The individual laboratories reproduced their own results within ±0.03 mg/l in the SPADNS determination and ±0.02 mg/l in the distilled samples.

A synthetic unknown sample containing 0.68 mg/l fluoride, 2 mg/l aluminum, 2.5 mg/l sodium hexametaphosphate, 200 mg/l sulfate, and 300 mg/l total alkalinity was determined with a standard deviation of ±0.10 mg/l in 48 laboratories which followed the direct distillation and SPADNS methods. The individual laboratories reproduced their own results within ±0.02 mg/l by using the combined methods.

Bibliography

Direct Distillation Step

1. BELLACK, E. Simplified Fluoride Distillation Method. *J. AWWA* 50:530 (1958).
2. BELLACK, E. Automatic Fluoride Distillation. *J. AWWA* 53:98 (1961).

Steam Distillation Step

3. WILLARD, H. H. & WINTER, O. B. Volumetric Method for Determination of Fluorine. *Ind. Eng. Chem., Anal. Ed.* 5:7 (1933).

4. MEGREGIAN, S. & SOLET, I. Critical Factors in Fluoride Distillation Technique. *J. AWWA* 45:1110 (1953).

Alizarin Visual Method

5. SANCHIS, J. M. Determination of Fluorides in Natural Waters. *Ind. Eng. Chem., Anal. Ed.* 6:134 (1934).
6. SCOTT, R. D. Modification of Fluoride Determination. *J. AWWA* 33:2018 (1941).
7. TARAS, M. J.; CISCO, H. D.; & GARNELL, M. Interferences in Alizarin Method of Fluoride Determination. *J. AWWA* 42:583 (1950).

Alizarin Photometric Method

8. MEGREGIAN, S. & MAIER, F. J. Modified Zirconium-Alizarin Reagent for Determination of Fluoride in Water. *J. AWWA* 44:239 (1952).

SPADNS Method

9. BELLACK, E. & SCHOUBOE, P. J. Rapid Photometric Determination of Fluoride with SPADNS-Zirconium Lake. *Anal. Chem.* 30:2032 (1958).

Grease

See Oil and Grease.

Hardness

Originally, the hardness of a water was understood to be a measure of the capacity of the water for precipitating soap. Soap is precipitated chiefly by the calcium and magnesium ions commonly present in water, but may also be precipitated by ions of other polyvalent metals, such as iron, aluminum, manganese, strontium, and zinc, and by hydrogen ions. Because all but the first two are usually present in insignificant concentrations in natural waters, hardness is defined as a characteristic of water which represents the total concentration of just the calcium and magnesium ions expressed as calcium carbonate. However, if present in significant amounts, other hardness-producing metallic ions should be included.

When the hardness is numerically greater than the sum of the carbonate alkalinity and the bicarbonate alkalinity, that amount of hardness which is equivalent to the total alkalinity is called "carbonate hardness"; the amount of hardness in excess of this is called "noncarbonate hardness." When the hardness is numerically equal to, or less than, the sum of carbonate and bicarbonate alkalinity, all of the hardness is "carbonate hardness," and there is no "noncarbonate hardness." The hardness may range from zero to hundreds of milligrams per liter in terms of calcium carbonate, depending on the source and treatment to which the water has been subjected.

Selection of method: Two approaches are presented for the determination of hardness. Method A, hardness by calculation, is applicable to all waters and is considered to yield the higher accuracy. If a complete mineral analysis is performed, the hardness can be reported by calculation. Method B, the EDTA titration method, which measures the calcium and magnesium ions, may be applied with appropriate modification to any kind of water. The procedure described affords a means of rapid analysis.

Reporting of results: When reporting hardness, the analyst should state either the ions determined or the method used—e.g., "hardness (Ca, Mg)," "hardness (Ca, Mg, Sr, Fe, Al, etc.)," "hardness (EDTA)."

A. Hardness by Calculation

1. Principle

The accurate method for determining hardness is to compute it from the results of the calcium and the magnesium determinations. If present in significant amounts, other hardness-producing cations must be determined and included in the computation.

2. Procedure

Hardness is computed by multiplying the concentration of each hardness-producing cation by the proper factor to obtain equivalent calcium carbonate concentrations, and summing these $CaCO_3$ concentrations. To obtain the $CaCO_3$ equivalent (mg/l) of the following cations, multiply the concentration found (mg/l) by the factor shown.

Cation	Factor	Cation	Factor
Ca	2.497	Al	3.710
Mg	4.116	Zn	1.531
Sr	1.142	Mn	1.822
Fe	1.792		

B. EDTA Titrimetric Method*

1. General Discussion

1.1. *Principle:* Ethylenediamine tetraacetic acid and its sodium salts (abbreviated EDTA) form a chelated soluble complex when added to a solution of certain metal cations. If a

---

* Two United States patents (No. 2,583,890 and 2,583,891) have been issued to G. Schwarzenbach disclosing titration and complexometric methods for quantitative determination of water hardness. Nothing contained in this manual is to be construed as granting any right, by implication or otherwise, for manufacture, sale, or use in connection with any method, apparatus, or product covered by patent, nor as insuring anyone against liability for infringement of patent.

small amount of a dye such as Erio-chrome Black T is added to an aqueous solution containing calcium and mag-nesium ions at a pH of 10.0 ± 0.1, the solution will become wine red. If EDTA is then added as a titrant, the calcium and magnesium will be com-plexed. After sufficient EDTA has been added to complex all the magne-sium and calcium, the solution will turn from wine red to blue. This is the endpoint of the titration. Magnesium ion must be present to yield a satisfac-tory endpoint in the titration. A small amount of complexometrically neutral magnesium salt of EDTA is therefore added to the buffer, a step which auto-matically introduces sufficient magne-sium and at the same time obviates a blank correction.

The sharpness of the endpoint in-creases with increasing pH. The pH, however, cannot be increased indefi-nitely because of the danger of precipi-tating $CaCO_3$ or $Mg(OH)_2$, and be-cause the dye changes color at high pH values. The pH value of 10.0 ± 0.1 recommended in this procedure is a satisfactory compromise. A limit of 5 min is set for the duration of the titra-tion in order to minimize the tendency toward $CaCO_3$ precipitation.

1.2. *Interference:* Some metal ions interfere with this procedure by caus-ing fading or indistinct endpoints. This interference is reduced by the addition of certain inhibitors to the water sample prior to titration with EDTA. The maximum concentrations of interfering substances which may be present in the original sample and still permit titra-tion with EDTA are shown in Table 9. The figures are intended as a rough guide only and are based on the use of a 25-ml aliquot diluted to 50 ml.

Suspended or colloidal organic mat-

TABLE 9—MAXIMUM CONCENTRATIONS OF
INTERFERENCES PERMISSIBLE WITH
VARIOUS INHIBITORS *

Interfering Substance	Max. Interference Concentration *mg/l*		
	Inhibitor I	Inhibitor II	Inhibitor III
Aluminum	20	20	20
Barium	†	†	†
Cadmium	†	20	†
Cobalt	over 20	0.3	0‡
Copper	over 30	20	0.3
Iron	over 30	5	20
Lead	†	20	†
Manganese (Mn^{++})	†	1	1
Nickel	over 20	0.3	0‡
Strontium	†	†	†
Zinc	†	200	†
Polyphosphate		10	

* Based on 25-ml aliquot diluted to 50 ml.
† Titrates as hardness.
‡ Inhibitor fails if substance present.

ter in the sample may also interfere with the endpoint but may be overcome by evaporating the aliquot to dryness on a steam bath, followed by heating in a muffle furnace at 600°C until the or-ganic matter is completely oxidized. Dissolve the residue in 20 ml $1N$ HCl, neutralize to pH 7 with $1N$ NaOH, and make up to 50 ml with distilled water; cool to room temperature and continue according to the general pro-cedure.

1.3. *Titration precautions:* Titra-tions are best conducted at or near normal room temperatures. The color change becomes impractically slow as the sample approaches freezing tem-perature. Indicator decomposition pre-sents a problem in hot water.

The pH specified in the recommended procedure may result in an environ-ment conducive to $CaCO_3$ precipitation. Although the titrant can slowly redis-solve such precipitates, a drifting end-point will often yield low results. A time limit of 5 min for the overall procedure minimizes the tendency for $CaCO_3$ to precipitate. The following three methods also combat precipitation loss:

a. The sample can be diluted with distilled water to reduce the $CaCO_3$ concentration. The simple expedient of diluting a 25-ml aliquot to 50 ml has been incorporated in the recommended procedure. If precipitation occurs at this dilution, Modification b or c can be followed. Reliance upon too small an aliquot contributes a systematic error originating from the buret-reading error.

b. If the approximate hardness of a sample is known or is ascertained by a preliminary titration, 90 per cent or more of the titrant can be added to the sample *before* the pH is adjusted with the buffer.

c. The sample can be acidified and stirred for 2 min to expel CO_2 *before* pH adjustment with the buffer. A prior alkalinity determination can indicate the amount of acid to be added to the sample for this purpose.

2. Reagents

2.1. *Buffer solution:*

a. Dissolve 16.9 g ammonium chloride, NH_4Cl, in 143 ml conc ammonium hydroxide, NH_4OH; add 1.25 g of magnesium salt of EDTA (this salt is available commercially) and dilute to 250 ml with distilled water.

b. In the absence of the magnesium salt of EDTA, dissolve 1.179 g disodium salt of ethylenediamine tetraacetic acid dihydrate (analytical reagent grade) and 0.780 g $MgSO_4 \cdot 7H_2O$ or 0.644 g $MgCl_2 \cdot 6H_2O$ in 50 ml distilled water. Add this solution to 16.9 g NH_4Cl and 143 ml conc NH_4OH with mixing and dilute to 250 ml with dis-

tilled water. To attain the highest accuracy, adjust to exact equivalence through appropriate addition of a small amount of EDTA or magnesium sulfate or chloride.

Keep the solution (a or b) in a plastic or resistant-glass container, tightly stoppered to prevent loss of NH_3 or pickup of CO_2. A frequently opened container should not hold more than a month's supply. The buffer solution is best dispensed by means of a bulb-operated pipet. Discard the buffer when 1 or 2 ml added to the sample fails to produce a pH of 10.0 ± 0.1 at the endpoint of the titration.

c. Satisfactory alternate "odorless buffers" are described in the literature [6] and are also available commercially. They contain the magnesium salt of EDTA and have the advantage of being relatively odorless and much more stable than the NH_4Cl-NH_4OH buffer. One of these buffers may be prepared by mixing 55 ml conc HCl with 400 ml distilled water, and then, slowly and with stirring, adding 310 ml 2-aminoethanol. The magnesium salt of EDTA in the amount of 5.0 g is next added to the solution, and the volume diluted to 1 liter with distilled water.

2.2. *Inhibitors:* For most waters there is no need to utilize an inhibitor. However, instances arise where waters contain interfering ions, requiring the addition of an appropriate inhibitor to give a clear, sharp change in color at the endpoint. The following inhibitor reagents have been found satisfactory:

a. *Inhibitor I:* Add 0.25 g sodium cyanide in powder form to the solution to be titrated. When this inhibitor is used, it is necessary to add sufficient buffer to adjust the pH to 10.0 ± 0.1 in order to offset the additional alkalinity resulting from the hydrolysis of the sodium cyanide. (CAUTION: *So-*

*dium cyanide is extremely poisonous
and more than customary precautions
should be observed in its use.* Solutions containing this inhibitor may be
flushed down the drain with large
quantities of water provided no acid is
present, because acids liberate volatile,
poisonous HCN.)

b. Inhibitor II: Dissolve 5.0 g
$Na_2S \cdot 9H_2O$ or 3.7 g $Na_2S \cdot 5H_2O$ in
100 ml distilled water. Exclude air
with a tightly fitting rubber stopper.
This inhibitor deteriorates through air
oxidation. The inhibitor will give a
sulfide precipitate which tends to ob-
scure the endpoint when appreciable
concentrations of heavy metals are
present. Use 1 ml of Inhibitor II in
Sec. 3.2.

c. Inhibitor III: Dissolve 4.5 g hydroxylamine hydrochloride in 100 ml
of 95 per cent ethyl or isopropyl alcohol.
Since this inhibitor is added to the dye
solution (see Sec. 2.3a), the solution
may be used both as endpoint indicator
and inhibitor for interfering ions indicated in Table 9.

Commercial preparations incorporating the buffer and an inhibitor are
available. These products may be used
if found satisfactory for the specific
needs of the analyst. Mixtures of inhibitors and buffers should maintain a
pH of 10.0 ± 0.1 during titration and
give a clear, sharp endpoint when added
to the sample.

2.3. *Indicator:* The dye Eriochrome
Black T is the sodium salt of 1-(1-hy-
droxy-2-naphthylazo)-5-nitro-2-naph-
thol-4-sulfonic acid, No. 203 in the
Color Index. Commercial grades are
available.* Many types of indicator so-

---

* Satisfactory commercial grades include
"Eriochrome Black T" (Geigy), "Ponta-
chrome Black TA" (du Pont), "Solochrome
Black WDFA" (C.I.E.), "Omega Chrome
Black S," and "Potting Black C."

lutions are advocated in the literature
and for the most part are satisfactory.
The prime difficulty with indicator solutions is their instability through aging, giving rise to indistinct endpoints
in the EDTA titration. For example,
alkaline solutions of the dye are sensitive to oxidants, and aqueous or alcoholic solutions are stable for only about
a week. Dry mixtures of the dye and
sodium chloride are stable. Prepared
dry mixtures of the indicator and an
inert salt are available commercially.

The following formulations have
been widely used and are generally
satisfactory:

a. Mix 0.5 g of dye with 4.5 g hydroxylamine hydrochloride. Dissolve
this mixture in 100 ml of 95 per cent
ethyl or isopropyl alcohol.

b. Mix 0.5 to 1.0 g dye in 100 g of
an appropriate solvent such as 2,2′,2″-
nitrilotriethanol (also called triethanol-
amine) or 2-methoxyethanol (also
called ethylene glycol monomethyl
ether).

c. Mix together 0.5 g dye and 100 g
NaCl to prepare a dry powder mixture.

All indicator formulations tend to
deteriorate, especially when exposed to
moist air. If the endpoint color change
is not clear and sharp, it usually means
that an appropriate inhibitor is needed.
If sodium cyanide inhibitor does not
sharpen the endpoint, the indicator is
probably at fault.

2.4. *Standard EDTA titrant,* $0.01M$.

a. Analytical reagent grade disodium
ethylenediamine tetraacetate dihydrate,
also called (ethylenedinitrilo) tetraacetic
acid disodium salt [EDTA], Na_2H_2-
$C_{10}H_{12}O_8N_2 \cdot 2H_2O$, is commercially
available. Weigh 3.723 g of the dry
reagent, dissolve in distilled water, and
dilute to 1,000 ml. Check the titer by
standardizing against standard calcium

solution (see Sec. 2.5) as described in Sec. 3.2.

b. The technical grade of the disodium salt of EDTA dihydrate may also be used if the titrant is allowed to stand for several days and is then filtered. Dissolve 4.0 g of such material in 800 ml distilled water. Standardize against standard calcium solution (see Sec. 2.5) as described in Sec. 3.2. Adjust the titrant so that 1.00 ml = 1.00 mg $CaCO_3$.

Because the titrant extracts hardness-producing cations from soft-glass containers, store preferably in polyethylene and secondarily in pyrex bottles. Compensate for gradual deterioration by periodic restandardization and a suitable correction factor.

2.5. Standard calcium solution: Weigh 1.000 g anhydrous calcium carbonate, $CaCO_3$, powder (primary standard or special reagent low in heavy metals, alkalis, and magnesium) into a 500-ml erlenmeyer flask. Place a funnel in the neck of the flask and add, a little at a time, 1 + 1 HCl until all the $CaCO_3$ has dissolved. Add 200 ml distilled water and boil for a few minutes to expel CO_2. Cool, add a few drops of methyl red indicator, and adjust to the intermediate orange color by adding $3N$ NH_4OH or 1 + 1 HCl, as required. Transfer quantitatively to a 1-liter volumetric flask and fill to the mark with distilled water. This standard solution is equivalent to 1.00 mg $CaCO_3$ per 1.00 ml.

3. Procedure

3.1. The aliquot of sample taken for the titration should require less than 15 ml of EDTA titrant. The duration of titration should not exceed 5 min measured from the time of the buffer addition.

3.2. Dilute 25.0 ml of sample to about 50 ml with distilled water in a porcelain casserole or other suitable vessel. Add 1–2 ml of buffer solution. Usually 1 ml will be sufficient to give a pH of 10.0 to 10.1. If in the titration a sharp endpoint color change is not obtained, it usually means that an inhibitor needs to be added at this point in the procedure (see Sec. 2.2) or that the indicator has deteriorated.

Add 1–2 drops of indicator solution or an appropriate amount of dry-powder indicator formulation (Sec. 2.3c). Add the standard EDTA titrant slowly, with continuous stirring, until the last reddish tinge disappears from the solution, adding the last few drops at 3–5-sec intervals. The color of the solution at the endpoint is blue under normal conditions. (Daylight or a daylight fluorescent lamp is highly recommended. Ordinary incandescent lights tend to produce a reddish tinge in the blue at the endpoint.)

3.3. Low-hardness sample: This modification is used for ion exchanger effluent or other softened water and for natural waters of low hardness (less than 5 mg/l). A larger sample, 100 to 1,000 ml, is taken for titration, and proportionately larger amounts of buffer, inhibitor, and indicator are added. The standard EDTA titrant should be added slowly from a microburet, and a blank should be run using redistilled, distilled, or deionized water of the same volume as the sample, to which identical amounts of buffer, inhibitor, and indicator have been added.

4. Calculation

Hardness (EDTA) as mg/l $CaCO_3$

$$= \frac{A \times B \times 1,000}{\text{ml sample}}$$

where A = ml titration for sample,

and $B = $ mg $CaCO_3$ equivalent to 1.00 ml EDTA titrant.

5. Precision and Accuracy

The standard deviation was ±17.4 mg/l among 52 laboratories which determined the hardness complexometrically on a synthetic unknown sample containing a total hardness of 610 mg/l as $CaCO_3$ (270 mg/l calcium hardness and 340 mg/l magnesium hardness), with no interference present. One-half of the reported results were within ±9 mg/l of the known hardness concentration. The individual laboratories reproduced their own results within ±1.9 mg/l.

Bibliography

1. Connors, J. J. Advances in Chemical and Colorimetric Methods. *J. AWWA* 42:33 (1950).
2. Diehl, H.; Goetz, C. A.; & Hach, C. C. The Versenate Titration for Total Hardness. *J. AWWA* 42:40 (1950).
3. Betz, J. D. & Noll, C. A. Total Hardness Determination by Direct Colorimetric Titration. *J. AWWA* 42:49 (1950).
4. Goetz, C. A.; Loomis, T. C.; & Diehl, H. Total Hardness in Water: the Stability of Standard Disodium Dihydrogen Ethylenediaminetetraacetate Solutions. *Anal. Chem.* 22:798 (1950).
5. Diskant, E. M. Stable Indicator Solutions for Complexometric Determination of Total Hardness in Water. *Anal. Chem.* 24:1856 (1952).
6. Patton, J. & Reeder, W. New Indicator for Titration of Calcium with (Ethylenedinitrilo) Tetraacetate. *Anal. Chem.* 28:1026 (1956).
7. Barnard, A. J., Jr.; Broad, W. C.; & Flaschka, H. The EDTA Titration. *Chemist Analyst* 45:86 (1956); 46:46 (1957).
8. Schwarzenbach, G. *Complexometric Titrations.* Interscience Publishers, New York (1957).
9. Goetz, C. A. & Smith, R. C. Evaluation of Various Methods and Reagents for Total Hardness and Calcium Hardness in Water. *Iowa State J. Sci.* 34:81 (Aug. 15, 1959).

Iodide

Only trace quantities of iodide are normally present in natural waters. Increased concentrations are found in natural brines or may be associated with certain industrial wastes. Iodide has been used as one possible indicator of sea water intrusion. Although physiologically important, iodide is now added in common table salt rather than in water supplies.

Photometric Method (Tentative)

1. General Discussion

1.1. *Principle:* Iodide can be determined in water supplies by utilizing its ability to catalyze the reduction of ceric ions by arsenious acid, the effect being proportional, but not linearly, to the amount of iodide present. Photometric determination of the loss of ceric ion color directly is difficult without a recording device, since the color fades rapidly while it is being read in the photometer. If the reaction is stopped after a specific time interval by the addition of ferrous ammonium sulfate, the resulting ferric ions, which are directly proportional to the remaining ceric ions, develop a color complex with potassium thiocyanate that is relatively stable. This method has the advantages of requiring only small untreated water samples, eliminating distillation procedures, minimizing certain interferences, and giving stable colors for spectrophotometric determinations.

Digestion with chromic acid and distillation must be undertaken where an estimate is desired of the organically bound and other nonsusceptible forms of iodine in addition to the usual iodide ion. The pertinent procedures for these special applications may be found elsewhere.[2]

1.2. *Interference:* An excess of sodium chloride is added to the sample aliquot to eliminate the interference of chloride already present in the water by attaining a stable maximum chloride concentration which sensitizes the reaction. The formation of noncatalytic forms of iodine and the inhibitory effects of silver and mercury are reduced by this addition.

2. Apparatus

2.1. *Water bath,* capable of temperature control to $30° \pm 0.5°C$.

2.2. *Colorimetric equipment:* One of the following is required:

a. Spectrophotometer, for use at wavelengths of 510 or 525 mμ, and providing a light path of 1 cm.

b. Filter photometer, providing a light path of 1 cm and equipped with a green filter having maximum transmittance near 525 mμ.

2.3. *Test tubes,* 2×15 cm.

2.4. *Stop watch.*

3. Reagents

Store all of the following stock solutions in tightly stoppered containers in a dark place.

3.1. *Distilled water,* containing less than 0.3 $\mu g/1$ iodine.

3.2. *Sodium chloride solution:* Dissolve 200.0 g NaCl in distilled water and dilute to 1 liter. Recrystallize the NaCl if an interfering amount of iodine is present, using a water-ethanol mixture.

3.3. *Arsenious acid,* 0.1N. Dissolve 4.946 g arsenious oxide, As_2O_3, in distilled water, add 0.20 ml conc H_2SO_4, and dilute to 1,000 ml.

3.4. *Sulfuric acid,* conc.

3.5. *Ceric ammonium sulfate,* 0.02N. Dissolve 13.38 g $Ce(NH_4)_4(SO_4)_4 \cdot 4H_2O$ in distilled water, add 44 ml conc H_2SO_4, and make up to 1 liter.

3.6. *Ferrous ammonium sulfate reagent:* Dissolve 1.50 g $Fe(NH_4)_2(SO_4)_2 \cdot 6H_2O$ in 100 ml distilled water containing 0.6 ml conc H_2SO_4. Prepare daily.

3.7. *Potassium thiocyanate solution:* Dissolve 4.00 g KSCN in 100 ml distilled water.

3.8. *Stock iodide solution:* Dissolve 0.2616 g anhydrous potassium iodide, KI, in distilled water and dilute to 1,000 ml; 1.00 ml = 200 μg I.

3.9. *Intermediate iodide solution:* Dilute 20.00 ml stock iodide solution to 1,000 ml with distilled water; 1.00 ml = 4.00 μg I.

3.10. *Standard iodide solution:* Dilute 25.00 ml intermediate iodide solution to 1,000 ml with distilled water; 1.00 ml = 0.100 μg I.

4. Procedure

4.1. Add 10.00 ml water sample, or an aliquot made up to 10.00 ml with iodine-free distilled water, to a 2 × 15-cm test tube. If possible, keep the iodide content of the diluted sample in the range 0.2–0.6 μg. Use scrupulously clean glassware and apparatus.

4.2. Add reagents to the sample in the following order: 1.00 ml NaCl solution, 0.50 ml arsenious acid solution, and 0.50 ml conc H_2SO_4.

4.3. Place the reaction mixture and the ceric ammonium sulfate solution in the 30°C water bath and allow to come to temperature equilibrium. Add 1.00 ml ceric ammonium sulfate solution, mix the contents of the test tube by inversion, and start the stop watch to time the reaction. Use an inert, clean test tube stopper when mixing. After 15 ± 0.1 min remove the sample from the water bath and add immediately 1.00 ml ferrous ammonium sulfate reagent with mixing, whereupon the yellow ceric ion color should disappear. Then add, with mixing, 1.00 ml potassium thiocyanate solution. Replace the sample in the water bath. Within 1 hr after the thiocyanate addition, read the red color as per cent transmittance in a photometric instrument. Maintain the temperature of the solution and the cell compartment at 30° ± 0.5°C until the transmittance is determined. If several samples are run, start the reactions at 1-min intervals, to allow time for additions of ferrous ammonium sulfate and thiocyanate. (If temperature control of the cell compartment is not possible, allow the final solution to come to room temperature and measure the transmittance with the cell compartment at room temperature.)

4.4. Treat standards containing 0.0, 0.2, 0.4, 0.6, and 0.8 μg I per 10.00 ml of solution as in Sec. 4.1–4.3. Run with each set of samples for the purpose of establishing a calibration curve.

5. Calculation

$$mg/l\ I = \frac{\mu g\ I}{ml\ sample}$$

6. Precision and Accuracy

Results obtained by this tentative method are reproducible on samples of Los Angeles source waters, and have been reported to be accurate to ±0.3 μg/l I on samples of Yugoslavian water containing from 0.0 to 14.0 μg/l I.

Bibliography

1. ROGINA, B. & DUBRAVCIC, M. Microdetermination of Iodides by Arresting the Catalytic Reduction of Ceric Ions. *Analyst* 78:594 (1953).
2. *Standard Methods for the Examination of Water, Sewage, and Industrial Wastes.* APHA, AWWA & FSIWA (10th ed., 1955). pp. 120–124.
3. DUBRAVCIC, M. Determination of Iodine in Natural Waters (Sodium Chloride as a Reagent in the Catalytic Reduction of Ceric Ions). *Analyst* 80:295 (1955).

Iron

Iron ranks next to aluminum in abundance of metals in the earth's crust. Despite the wide distribution, natural waters contain variable but minor amounts of iron. The total iron of surface waters may vary widely, depending on the quantity of turbidity. In filtered samples of alkaline surface waters iron concentrations seldom approach a maximum of 1 mg/l. Some ground waters and acid surface waters, on the other hand, may contain considerably more iron. Iron's importance in water derives from the stains imparted to laundry and porcelain, and also the bitter, sweet, astringent taste which may be detectable by some persons at levels above 0.3 mg/l.

Under reducing conditions, iron which exists in the ferrous state is relatively soluble in natural waters. In the absence of complex formers, ferric iron is significantly soluble only at pH values less than 5. Upon exposure to air, or on addition of chlorine, the iron is oxidized to the ferric state and may hydrolyze to form insoluble hydrated ferric oxide. This is the form of iron in most laboratory samples unless the samples are collected under specific conditions to avoid oxidation.

The form of iron may also undergo alteration as a result of the growth of iron bacteria in the sample during storage or shipment (see Part VIII). In acid wastes at pH less than 3.5, iron in the ferric state may also be soluble.

Accordingly, iron in water may be either in true solution, in a colloidal state which may be peptized by organic matter, in the form of inorganic or organic iron complexes, or in the form of relatively coarse suspended particles. Furthermore, it may be either ferrous or ferric, or both.

Silt and clay in suspension may contain acid-soluble iron. Iron oxide particles are sometimes collected with a water sample as a result of flaking of rust from pipes. Iron may come from a metal cap used to close the sample bottle.

Selection of method: For natural and treated waters, the phenanthroline method has attained the greatest acceptance for reliability. In the presence of interfering substances, two alternative methods are available: a method employing tripyridine, with ethylenediamine as a complexing agent for interfering substances; or an extraction method using diisopropyl ether to extract the iron from interfering substances.

It is difficult to distinguish analytically between dissolved and suspended iron because on exposure to air, soluble ferrous iron can be oxidized by dissolved oxygen and hydrolyzed at pH greater than 5 to insoluble ferric iron. Soluble iron might be determined (Sec. 4.2) by subsequent analysis of a portion of the sample which has been filtered through a fine filter paper immediately after collection at the site. This procedure suffers from oxidation of ferrous iron and hydrolysis during filtration and tends to yield low results.

A rigorous quantitative distinction between ferrous and ferric iron is not included, but may be obtained with a special procedure using bathophenanthroline.[15] Both the phenanthroline and the tripyridine reagent tend to shift the soluble ferric-ferrous equilibrium to ferrous iron. The suggested procedure (Sec 4.3) has limited application and requires a large excess of phenanthroline (mol ratio to ferrous plus ferric greater than 30). The sample is stabilized with hydrochloric acid rather than acetic acid because the latter catalyzes the oxidation of ferrous to ferric iron.

Sampling and storage: Methods of collecting, storing, and pretreating samples should be planned in advance. The sample container should be cleaned with acid and rinsed with distilled water. The value of the determination is greatly dependent upon the care taken to obtain a representative sample. Iron in well water or tap samples may vary in concentration and form with period and degree of flushing before and during sampling. When taking the portion of the sample for the determination, the sample bottle must often be shaken vigorously to obtain a uniform suspension of the precipitated iron. Particular care must be taken when colloidal iron adheres to the sample bottle. This problem can be acute with plastic bottles.

For a precise determination of total iron, a separate container should be used for collection of the sample. This sample may be treated with acid at the time of collection to prevent a deposit on the container wall, or prior to the removal of the portion for analysis of total iron, to dissolve the colloidal deposit on the container wall.

A. Phenanthroline Method

1. General Discussion

1.1. *Principle:* Iron is brought into solution and reduced to the ferrous state by boiling with acid and hydroxylamine, and treated with 1,10-phenanthroline at pH 3.2–3.3. Three molecules of phenanthroline chelate each atom of ferrous iron to form an orange-red complex. The colored solution obeys Beer's law; its intensity is independent of pH from 3 to 9 and is stable for at least 6 months. A pH between 2.9 and 3.5 insures rapid color development in the presence of an excess of phenanthroline.

1.2. *Interference:* Among the interfering substances are strong oxidizing reagents, cyanide, nitrite, and phosphates—polyphosphates more so than orthophosphate; chromium; zinc in concentrations exceeding ten times that of iron; cobalt and copper in excess of 5 mg/l, and nickel in excess of 2 mg/l. Bismuth, cadmium, mercury, molybdate, and silver precipitate phenanthroline. The initial boiling with acid reverts polyphosphates to orthophosphate and removes cyanide and nitrite, which would otherwise interfere. The addition of more hydroxylamine will eliminate errors caused by excessive concentrations of strong oxidizing re-

agents. In the presence of interfering metal ions, a larger excess of phenanthroline is required to replace that which is complexed by these interferences. With excessive concentrations of interfering metal ions, the procedure for iron in the Industrial Wastes Section may be used, or preferably the tripyridine or the extraction method.

If much color or organic matter is present, it may be necessary to evaporate the sample, gently ash the residue, and then redissolve in acid. The ashing may be carried out in silica, porcelain, or platinum crucibles which have previously been boiled for several hours in $1 + 1$ HCl.

1.3. *Minimum detectable concentration:* Total, dissolved, or ferrous iron concentrations between 0.02 and 4.0 mg/l can be determined directly, and higher concentrations can be determined by use of aliquots. The minimum is 3 μg with a spectrophotometer (510 mμ) using a 10-cm cell, or with nessler tubes.

2. Apparatus

2.1. *Colorimetric equipment:* One of the following is required:

a. Spectrophotometer, for use at 510

$m\mu$, providing a light path of 1 cm or longer.

b. Filter photometer, providing a light path of 1 cm or longer and equipped with a green filter having maximum transmittance near 510 $m\mu$.

c. Nessler tubes, matched, 100 ml, tall form.

2.2. *Acid-washed glassware:* All glassware must be washed with conc HC1 and rinsed with distilled water prior to use, in order to remove the thin film of adsorbed iron oxide which is frequently present as a result of employing the glassware for other purposes.

3. Reagents

All reagents must be low in iron. Iron-free distilled water is required. Glass-stoppered bottles are recommended for storage. The hydrochloric acid, ammonium acetate solution, and stock iron solutions are stable indefinitely if tightly stoppered. The hydroxylamine and phenanthroline solutions are stable for several months. The standard iron solutions are not stable and must be prepared freshly as needed by diluting the stock solution. Visual standards in nessler tubes are stable for 3 months if protected from light.

3.1. *Hydrochloric acid,* conc.

3.2. *Hydroxylamine solution:* Dissolve 10 g $NH_2OH \cdot HC1$ in 100 ml distilled water.

3.3. *Ammonium acetate buffer solution:* Dissolve 250 g $NH_4C_2H_3O_2$ in 150 ml distilled water. Add 700 ml glacial acetic acid and dilute to 1 liter. (Since even good grade $NH_4C_2H_3O_2$ contains a significant amount of iron, new reference standards should be prepared with each buffer preparation).

3.4. *Phenanthroline solution:* Dissolve 0.1 g 1,10-phenanthroline mono-

hydrate, $C_{12}H_8N_2 \cdot H_2O$, in 100 ml distilled water by stirring and heating to 80°C; do not boil. Discard the solution if it darkens. Heating is not necessary if 2 drops of conc HCl are added to the distilled water. (Note that 1 ml of this reagent is sufficient for no more than 0.1 mg Fe.)

3.5. *Stock iron solution:* The metal (*a*) or the salt (*b*) may be used for the preparation of the stock solution, which contains 0.200 mg Fe per 1.00 ml.

a. Use electrolytic iron wire, or "iron wire for standardizing" to prepare the solution. If necessary, clean the wire with fine sandpaper to remove any oxide coating and to produce a bright surface. Weigh 0.2000 g wire and place in a 1-liter volumetric flask. Dissolve in 20 ml $6N$ H_2SO_4 and dilute to the mark with iron-free distilled water.

b. If ferrous ammonium sulfate is preferred, add slowly 20 ml conc H_2SO_4 to 50 ml distilled water and dissolve 1.404 g $Fe(NH_4)_2(SO_4)_2 \cdot 6H_2O$. Add dropwise 0.1$N$ $KMnO_4$ until a faint pink color persists. Dilute with iron-free distilled water to 1,000 ml and mix.

3.6. *Standard iron solutions:* These should be prepared the day they are used.

a. Pipet 50.00 ml stock solution into a 1-liter volumetric flask and dilute to the mark with iron-free distilled water; 1.00 ml = 10.0 μg Fe.

b. Pipet 5.00 ml stock solution into a 1-liter volumetric flask and dilute to the mark with iron-free distilled water; 1.00 ml = 1.00 μg Fe.

4. Procedure

4.1. *Total iron:* Mix the sample thoroughly and measure 50.0 ml into a 125-ml erlenmeyer flask. (If the sample contains more than 2 mg/1 Fe, an accurately measured aliquot containing not more than 0.1 mg should be diluted to 50 ml; or more phenanthroline and a 1- or 2-cm light path may be used.) Add 2 ml conc HCl and 1 ml hydroxylamine solution. Add a few glass beads and heat to boiling. To insure dissolution of all the iron, continue boiling until the volume is reduced to 15–20 ml. (If the sample is ashed as described in Sec. 1.2, take up the residue in 2 ml conc HCl and 5 ml distilled water.) Cool to room temperature and transfer to a 50- or 100-ml volumetric flask or nessler tube. Add 10 ml ammonium acetate buffer solution and 2 ml phenanthroline solution, and dilute to the mark with distilled water. Mix thoroughly and allow at least 10–15 min for maximum color development.

4.2. *Dissolved iron:* Allow the sample to settle, and decant the supernate through fine (Whatman No. 42 or equivalent) filter paper,* discarding the first 25 ml. Treat a measured volume as in Sec. 4.1.

4.3. *Ferrous iron:* To determine the ferrous iron concentration stabilize a separate sample with mineral acid at the time of collection to prevent oxidation of ferrous iron. Place 4 ml conc HCl in a 100-ml stoppered sampling bottle. Fill the bottle directly from the sampling source and stopper until facilities for color development and measurement become available. Immediately before analysis, withdraw a 50-ml portion of the acidified sample, and add 20 ml phenanthroline solution and 10 ml ammonium acetate solution with vigorous stirring. Dilute to 100 ml and measure the color intensity within 5 to 10 min after the addition of the reagents. Do not expose to sunlight.

The color development is rapid in the presence of excess phenanthroline. (The phenanthroline volume given is for less than 50 μg total iron; if larger amounts are present, a correspondingly larger volume of phenanthroline or a more concentrated reagent must be used.)

4.4. *Color measurement:* Prepare a series of standards by accurately pipeting the calculated volumes of standard iron solutions (the weaker solution should be used to measure the 1–10-μg portions) into 125-ml erlenmeyer flasks, diluting to 50 ml, and carrying out the steps in Sec. 4.1.

For photometric measurement, Table 10 may be used as a rough guide for selection of the proper light path.

For visual comparison, a set of at least ten standards is desirable, ranging from 1 to 100 μg Fe in the final 100-ml volume. Comparison should be carried out using 100-ml, tall-form nessler tubes.

For photometric measurement (see General Introduction, A, Sec. 7), the standards should be read against distilled water set at 100 per cent transmittance (zero absorbance) and a calibration curve plotted, including a blank (see Sec. 3.3).

If the samples are colored or turbid, a second set of identical aliquots of the samples may be carried through all of the steps of the procedure except that no phenanthroline is to be added. Then, instead of distilled water, the prepared blanks are used to set the photometer to 100 per cent transmittance, and each developed sample, with phenanthroline, is read against the corresponding blank, without phenanthroline. Observed pho-

---

* A membrane filter will permit less "dissolved" iron to appear in the filtrate from some samples.

TABLE 10—SELECTION OF LIGHT PATH
LENGTH FOR VARIOUS IRON
CONCENTRATIONS

50-ml Final Volume	100-ml Final Volume	Light Path cm
Fe—μg		
50–200	100–400	1
25–100	50–200	2
10– 40	20– 80	5
5– 20	10– 40	10

tometer readings are translated into iron values by means of the calibration curve. This procedure does *not* compensate for the presence of interfering ions. If color and turbidity are absent, it is quicker and just as satisfactory to read the developed samples, as well as the standards, against distilled water.

5. Calculation

$$\text{mg/l Fe} = \frac{\mu\text{g Fe}}{\text{ml sample}}$$

Details of sample collection, storage, and pretreatment should be reported together with the iron value obtained, if they are pertinent to the interpretation.

6. Precision and Accuracy

6.1. The precision and accuracy will depend upon the method of sample col-lection and storage, the method of color measurement, the iron concentration, and the presence of interfering color, turbidity, and foreign ions. In general, optimum reliability of visual compari-son in nessler tubes is not better than 5 per cent, and often only 10 per cent, whereas, under optimum conditions, photometric measurement may be reli-able to 3 per cent or 3 μg, which-ever is the greater. The sensitivity limit for visual observation in nessler tubes is approximately 1 μg Fe. The variability and instability of the sample may limit the precision and accuracy of this determination more than will the errors of the analysis it-self. In the past, serious divergences have been found in reports of different laboratories because of variations in methods of collecting and treating the samples.

6.2. A synthetic unknown sample containing 0.62 mg/l Fe, 1.80 mg/l Al, 0.42 mg/l Cu, 0.18 mg/l Cr, 0.25 mg/l Mn, and 0.90 mg/l Zn was determined in 37 laboratories with a standard devi-ation of ±0.14 mg/l by means of the phenanthroline method. One-half of the reported results were within ±0.15 mg/l of the known iron concentration. The individual laboratories reproduced their own results within ±0.02 mg/l.

B. Tripyridine Method

1. General Discussion

1.1. *Principle:* Iron is brought into solution by boiling with acid, is reduced to the ferrous state by hydroxylamine, and is then treated with 2,2',2''-tri-pyridine. Two molecules of tripyridine chelate each atom of ferrous iron to form a reddish-purple complex. The color system obeys Beer's law, is in-dependent of pH over the range 1.5 to 12, and is stable for at least 3 months. Ethylenediamine is used to buffer the mixture at pH 9.6 and to complex heavy metals which might otherwise interfere.

1.2. *Interference:* This method is subject to the same type of interference from strong oxidizing agents, color, turbidity, cyanide, and nitrite as the phenanthroline method, and the treatment applied for correction is similar. However, phosphates and heavy metals, in concentrations which might be expected as a result of the pollution of a water supply, do not interfere. If much color or organic matter is present, it may be necessary to evaporate the sample, gently ash the residue, and then redissolve it in acid. The ashing should be carried out in silica, porcelain, or platinum crucibles which have been cleaned by boiling for several hours in $1 + 1$ HCl.

1.3. *Minimum detectable concentration:* See Method A, Sec. 1.3.

2. Apparatus

The same apparatus is required as for Method A, except that the spectrophotometer must be used at 555 mμ and the filter photometer provided with a green or greenish-yellow filter having maximum transmittance near 555 mμ.

3. Reagents

All reagents must be low in iron. Iron-free distilled water is required. Glass-stoppered reagent bottles are recommended. The hydrochloric acid, ethylenediamine, and stock iron solutions are stable indefinitely if tightly stoppered. The hydroxylamine and tripyridine solutions are stable for several months, but not indefinitely. The standard iron solutions are not stable and must be prepared freshly as needed by diluting the stock solution.

3.1. *Hydrochloric acid,* conc.

3.2. *Ethylenediamine,* full strength.*

---

* Eastman practical grade, No. P1915, or equivalent.

(CAUTION: *Do not pipet this liquid by mouth.*)

3.3. *Hydroxylamine solution:* See Method A, Sec. 3.2.

3.4. *Tripyridine reagent:* With gentle warming, dissolve 0.1 g 2,2′,2″-tripyridine † in 100 ml 0.1N HCl.

3.5. *Standard iron solutions:* See Method A, Sec. 3.5 and 3.6.

4. Procedure

4.1. *Treatment of sample:* Into a 125-ml erlenmeyer flask, pipet a 50.0-ml portion of the sample. If the iron concentration is high, accurately pipet a smaller aliquot—to contain less than 0.4 mg Fe for photometric measurement, or less than 0.2 mg Fe for visual comparison—and add enough distilled water to bring the volume up to approximately 50 ml. Add 2 ml conc HCl and boil to insure dissolution of all the iron. Cool to room temperature and add 1 ml hydroxylamine solution, 5 ml ethylenediamine, and 5 ml tripyridine solution, in that order. Dilute to 100 ml in a volumetric flask or nessler tube, mix thoroughly, and compare visually or instrumentally with standards after 1 min.

4.2. *Color measurement:* Prepare a series of standards by accurately pipeting the calculated volumes of working iron solution into 125-ml erlenmeyer flasks and carrying out the above steps. For visual comparison, a set of at least twelve standards is desirable, ranging from 1 to 200 μg Fe in the final 100-ml volume. For photometric measurement, the light paths specified in Table 10 may be used as a rough guide.

Visual comparison should be carried out in matched nessler tubes. For

---

† Obtainable from G. F. Smith Chemical Company, Columbus, Ohio, under the name "2,2′,2″-terpyridine."

photometric measurements, the standards should be read against distilled water set at 100 per cent transmittance (zero absorbance) and a calibration curve plotted. If the samples are colored or turbid, a second set of identical aliquots of the samples may be carried through all of the steps of the procedure except that no tripyridine is to be added. Then, instead of distilled water, the prepared blanks are used to set the photometer to 100 per cent transmittance, and each developed sample, containing tripyridine, is read against the corresponding prepared blank, without tripyridine. Observed photometer readings are translated into iron values by means of the calibration curve. If color and turbidity are absent, it is quicker and just as satisfactory to read the developed samples, as well as the standards, against distilled water.

5. Calculation

See Method A, Sec. 5.

6. Precision and Accuracy

6.1. See Method A, Sec. 6.

6.2. A synthetic unknown sample containing 0.62 mg/l Fe, 1.80 mg/l Al, 0.42 mg/l Cu, 0.18 mg/l Cr, 0.25 mg/l Mn, and 0.90 mg/l Zn was determined in five laboratories with a standard deviation of ± 0.08 mg/l by means of the tripyridine method. One-half of the reported results were within ± 0.14 mg/l of the known iron concentration. The individual laboratories reproduced their own results within ± 0.01 mg/l.

C. Extraction Method

1. General Discussion

1.1. *Principle:* This is a modification of the phenanthroline method (*A*). If interference caused by the presence of metal ions or of anions that may complex iron is suspected, iron can be separated by extraction from $7N$–$8N$ HCl solution with diisopropyl ether. The colorimetric determination is made on a subsequent aqueous extract of the iron from the ether by the phenanthroline method.

1.2. *Interference:* This method may be subject to the same type of nonionic interference as the phenanthroline method (*A*) and treatment is similar.

1.3. *Minimum detectable concentration:* A 10.0-ml aliquot of the sample provides a concentration range between 0.1 and 20 mg/l with a possible sensitivity of 0.001 mg with a spectrophotometer (510 mμ) using a 10-cm cell, or nessler tubes.

2. Apparatus

The same apparatus as indicated in Method A, Sec. 2, is required. In addition, separatory funnels, 125 ml, Squibb form, with ground-glass or inert teflon stoppers, should be used in performing the extraction.

3. Reagents

The same reagents as indicated in Method A, Sec. 3, are required, as well as diisopropyl ether.

4. Procedure

4.1. *Extraction to ether phase:* Select an aliquot of the sample and, if smaller or larger than 10 ml, dilute or concentrate it to that volume. Transfer to a 125-ml separatory funnel and add 15 ml conc HCl. Cool the solution and then extract the iron with 25 ml diisopropyl ether, shaking for 30 sec.

Draw off the lower acidic layer into a second separatory funnel, and extract twice with two 10-ml portions of ether. Combine the ether extracts in the original funnel and discard the acidic layer. Failure to decolorize the HCl solution should not be taken as evidence of incomplete extraction of iron. Copper, which is not extracted, has a similar yellow color. A blank with all reagents must be carried through the procedure for a zero instrument setting for photometric measurement.

4.2. *Extraction to water phase:* Extract the iron to the aqueous phase with 25 ml iron-free distilled water, shaking for 30 sec. Draw off the lower aqueous layer into a 50-ml volumetric flask. Repeat the extraction with 10-ml iron-free distilled water; add the aqueous extract to the first one in the volumetric flask and dilute to the mark with distilled water. Discard the ether layer.

4.3. *Color development:* See Method A, Sec. 4.1.

4.4. *Color measurement:* See Method A, Sec. 4.4.

5. Calculation

See Method A, Sec. 5.

6. Precision and Accuracy

See Method A, Sec. 6.

Bibliography

Phenanthroline Method

1. FORTUNE, W. B., & MELLON, M. G. Determination of Iron with *o*-Phenanthroline: a Spectrophotometric Study. *Ind. Eng. Chem., Anal. Ed.* 10:60 (1938).
2. MEHLIG, R. P. & HULETT, R. H. Spectrophotometric Determination of Iron with *o*-Phenanthroline and with Nitro-*o*-Phenanthroline. *Ind. Eng. Chem., Anal. Ed.* 14:869 (1942).
3. MOSS, M. L. & MELLON, M. G. Color Reactions of 1,10-Phenanthroline Derivatives. *Ind. Eng. Chem., Anal. Ed.* 14:931 (1942).
4. CRONHEIM, G. & WINK, W. Determination of Divalent Iron (by *o*-Nitrosophenol). *Ind. Eng. Chem., Anal. Ed.* 14:447 (1942).
5. HALLINAN, F. J. Determination of Iron in Water. *Ind. Eng. Chem., Anal. Ed.* 15:510 (1943).
6. CALDWELL, D. H. & ADAMS, R. B. Colorimetric Determination of Iron in Water With *o*-Phenanthroline. *J. AWWA* 38:727 (1946).
7. *Standard Methods for the Examination of Water and Sewage.* APHA & AWWA, New York (9th ed., 1946). pp. 51–52.
8. WELCHER, F. J. *Organic Analytical Reagents.* D. Van Nostrand Co., Princeton, N.J. (1947). Vol. 3, pp. 85–98.
9. KOLTHOFF, I. M.; LEE, T. S.; & LEUSSING, D. L. Equilibrium and Kinetic Studies on the Formation and Dissociation of Ferroin and Ferriin. *Anal. Chem.* 20:985 (1948).
10. RYAN, J. A. & BOTHAM, G. H. Iron in Aluminum Alloys: Colorimetric Determination Using 1,10-Phenanthroline. *Anal. Chem.* 21:1521 (1949).
11. REITZ, L. K.; O'BRIEN, A. S.; & DAVIS, T. L. Evaluation of Three Iron Methods Using a Factorial Experiment. *Anal. Chem.* 22:1470 (1950).
12. *Tentative Method of Test for Iron in Industrial Water—D1068–62T.* Am. Soc. Testing Materials, Philadelphia (1964).
13. SANDELL, E. B. *Colorimetric Determination of Traces of Metals.* Interscience Publishers, New York (3rd ed., 1959). Chap. 22.
14. RAINWATER, F. H. & THATCHER, L. L. Methods of Collection and Analysis of Water Samples. *US Geol. Survey Water Supply Paper* No. 1454 (1960).
15. LEE, G. F. & STUMM, W. Determination

of Ferrous Iron in the Presence of Ferric Iron Using Bathophenanthroline. *J. AWWA.* 52:1567 (1960).

Tripyridine Method

16. Moss, M. L. & Mellon, M. G. Colorimetric Determination of Iron with

2,2'-Bipyridine and with 2,2',2''-Tripyridine. *Ind. Eng. Chem., Anal. Ed.* 14:862 (1942).

17. Ref. 8. Vol. 3, pp. 100–104.

18. Morris, R. L. Determination of Iron in Water in the Presence of Heavy Metals. *Anal. Chem.* 25:1376 (1952).

Lead

Lead is a serious, cumulative body poison and is to be avoided. Natural waters seldom contain more than 0.02 mg/l, although values as high as 0.4 mg/l have been reported. The presence of lead in a water supply may arise from industrial, mine, and smelter discharges, or from the dissolution of old lead plumbing. Tap waters which are soft, acid, and not suitably treated may contain lead resulting from an attack on the lead service pipes.

For normal drinking waters, low in organic matter and tin, the brief method given here should prove adequate. The method for lead described in Part IV is recommended for waters high in organic matter, such as sewage and industrial wastes.

1. General Discussion

1.1. *Principle:* Dithizone dissolved in carbon tetrachloride will extract lead from a slightly basic solution. Lead and dithizone form a metal complex, lead dithizonate, which is soluble in carbon tetrachloride, with the formation of a red color. Measurement of the amount of red color formed yields an estimation of the lead present.

1.2. *Interference:* Before attempting this method, the analyst is urged to acquaint himself thoroughly with the theory and practice of dithizone pro-

cedures. The use of careful technique in this method is of the utmost importance. The necessity of checking and preventing contamination by lead and other metals cannot be overemphasized. The procedure is extremely sensitive and measurable amounts of lead may be picked up from glassware and reagents. Samples should be collected in bottles made of lead-free glass or plastic containers. If possible, separatory funnels used in the lead determination should be reserved for this purpose only. Reagents should be extracted with a dithizone solution to remove all traces of lead. A reagent blank should be carried through the procedure to compensate for the lead which may be introduced from glassware and reagents.

Interference by most metals which form dithizonates is eliminated by double extraction at controlled pH. In the first extraction ammonium citrate and cyanide will complex many heavy metals. Hydroxylamine inhibits dithizone oxidation by ferricyanide produced by iron. Tin in large amounts can be removed by volatilization as $SnBr_4$.

Organic material, if present, must be removed by acid digestion, or, less satisfactorily, by ignition. The analysis should be carried out in diffused light since bright sunlight tends to oxidize dithizone and dithizonate.

1.3. Minimum detectable concentration: Approximately 2 μg Pb.

2. Apparatus

2.1. Colorimetric equipment: One of the following is required:

a. Spectrophotometer, for use at 510 mμ with a light path of 1 cm or longer.

b. Filter photometer, equipped with a green filter having a maximum transmittance near 510 mμ and a light path of 1 cm or longer.

2.2. Separatory funnels, 125–150 ml, preferably with inert teflon stopcocks.

2.3. Glassware: All glassware, including sample bottles, should be cleaned with $1 + 1$ HNO$_3$, and then rinsed thoroughly with lead-free water. A finishing rinse with a dithizone solution may also be advisable.

3. Reagents

3.1. Lead-free water: Prepare by redistilling distilled water in an all-pyrex apparatus, or by passing distilled water through a mixed bed of ion-exchange resins—see General Introduction, A, Sec. 2, and Nitrogen (Ammonia), Method A, Sec. 3.1b. Use lead-free water for the preparation of all reagents and dilutions.

3.2. Stock lead solution: Dissolve 1.599 g anhydrous lead nitrate, Pb(NO$_3$)$_2$, in lead-free water to which has been added 1 ml conc HNO$_3$. Dilute to 1,000 ml. This solution contains 1.00 mg Pb per 1.00 ml.

3.3. Intermediate lead solution: Dilute 10.00 ml stock solution to 200 ml with lead-free water; 1.00 ml = 50.0 μg Pb. Prepare the intermediate solution immediately before use.

3.4. Standard lead solution: Dilute 10.00 ml intermediate lead solution to 250 ml with lead-free water; 1.00 ml = 2.00 μg Pb. Prepare the standard solution immediately before use.

3.5. Ammonium citrate reagent: Dissolve 50 g (NH$_4$)$_3$C$_6$H$_5$O$_7$ in 100 ml lead-free water. Add lead-free NH$_4$OH to adjust the pH to between 8.5 and 9.0. Extract with 10-ml portions dithizone solution until the last portion remains green. Wash with carbon tetrachloride to remove excess dithizone.

3.6. Hydroxylamine hydrochloride reagent: Dissolve 20 g NH$_2$OH·HCl in 65 ml lead-free water. Add conc NH$_4$OH to make the solution alkaline to thymol blue. Extract with 10-ml portions dithizone solution until the last portion remains green. Wash with carbon tetrachloride to remove excess dithizone. Make the solution just acid with HCl and dilute to 100 ml.

3.7. Thymol blue indicator solution: Dissolve 0.1 g thymolsulfonephthalein sodium salt in 100 ml lead-free water.

3.8. Ammonium hydroxide, conc.

3.9. Potassium cyanide solution: Dissolve 5.0 g KCN in lead-free water and dilute to about 50 ml. Extract with 10-ml portions dithizone solution until the last portion remains green. Wash with carbon tetrachloride to remove excess dithizone.

CAUTION: *Potassium cyanide is extremely poisonous and more than customary precautions should be observed in its handling. Never use mouth pipets to deliver volumes of cyanide solutions.*

3.10. Nitric acid, conc, and $1 + 99$.

3.11. Dithizone solution: Dissolve 0.050 g diphenylthiocarbazone in 1 liter carbon tetrachloride, CCl$_4$. Refrigerate this solution to preserve its stability for several weeks.

3.12. Ammoniacal cyanide-citrate reagent: Dissolve 10 g KCN in 500 ml conc NH$_4$OH. Add 10 g citric acid,

$H_3C_6H_5O_7 \cdot H_2O$, and dilute to 1 liter with lead-free water. *Handle with the same caution as in Sec. 3.9.*

3.13. *Carbon tetrachloride, CCl_4.*

3.14. *Methyl orange indicator solution:* Dissolve 0.5 g methyl orange in 1 liter lead-free water.

4. Procedure

4.1. *Preparation of calibration curve:* Prepare a series of standards containing 0, 2.00, 5.00, 10.0, 15.0, and 20.0 μg Pb per 25.0 ml. Use lead-free water for diluting the standard lead solution. Transfer 25 ml into a separatory funnel. Add 10 ml ammonium citrate reagent, 2 ml hydroxylamine hydrochloride reagent, and 5 drops thymol blue indicator solution. Make alkaline with conc NH_4OH. Carefully add 4 ml KCN solution and adjust the pH to 8.5–9 (green color) with $1 + 99$ HNO_3. Immediately extract by shaking vigorously for 30 sec with 5-ml portions dithizone solution until the color in the last portion remains unchanged. To the combined extracts in a second separatory funnel, add 20 ml $1 + 99$ HNO_3. Shake for 1 min and discard the CCl_4 layer. Dilute the acid extract with $1 + 99$ HNO_3 to 50.0 ml. Add 4.0 ml ammoniacal cyanide-citrate reagent, 5.0 ml dithizone solution and immediately shake for 1 minute. After allowing the layers to separate, transfer the CCl_4 extract into a dry absorption cell. Set the blank at 100 per cent transmittance or zero absorbance and determine the transmittance or absorbance of the standards at 510 mμ. Plot a calibration curve, which should be linear.

4.2. *Sample treatment:* Pipet a suitable volume of sample containing not more than 15 μg Pb in 25 ml of the sample into a separatory funnel. (If the sample contains less than 0.05 mg/l Pb, concentrate the sample by measuring 100 ml sample into a beaker, acidifying to methyl orange indicator with conc HNO_3, and adding 1 ml excess conc HNO_3. Cover with a watch glass and evaporate to about 10 ml on a steam bath. Adjust the volume to 25.0 ml with lead-free water.) Prepare a comparison blank using lead-free water and treat in the same manner as the sample. Unless the calibration is being determined simultaneously, prepare at least one standard containing 15.0 μg Pb and run it in conjunction with the sample. Proceed as in Sec. 4.1. Read the lead content from the calibration curve.

5. Calculation

$$\text{mg/l Pb} = \frac{\mu\text{g Pb}}{\text{ml sample}}$$

6. Precision and Accuracy

Results obtained by this procedure are usually accurate and reproducible to about 2 μg.

Bibliography

1. SANDELL, E. B. *Colorimetric Determination of Traces of Metals.* Interscience Publishers, New York (3rd ed., 1959). Chap. 23, and pp. 144–176.
2. RAINWATER, F. H. & THATCHER, L. L. Methods for Collection and Analysis of Water Samples. *US Geological Survey Water Supply Paper* No. 1454 (1960). Chap. D:20.

Lignin

See Tannin and Lignin.

Lithium

A minor constituent of minerals, lithium is present in fresh waters in concentrations below 10 mg/l. Brines and thermal waters may contain higher lithium levels. The use of lithium or its salts in dehumidifying units, medicinal waters, metallurgical processes, and the manufacture of some types of glass and storage batteries may contribute to its presence in wastes. Lithium hypochlorite is available commercially as a source of chlorine and may be used in swimming pools.

Flame Photometric Method (Tentative)

1. General Discussion

1.1. *Principle:* Like its sister elements, sodium and potassium, lithium can be determined in trace amounts by flame photometric methods. The measurement can be performed at a wavelength of 671 mμ.

1.2. *Interference:* Barium, strontium, and calcium interfere in the flame photometric determination of lithium and can be removed by the addition of a sodium sulfate-sodium carbonate solution which precipitates $BaSO_4$, $SrCO_3$, and $CaCO_3$. The content of either sodium or magnesium individually must not exceed 10 mg in the aliquot taken for analysis .

1.3. *Minimum detectable concentration:* The minimum lithium concentration detectable by the flame photometric method is of the order of 0.1 mg/l.

1.4. *Sampling and storage:* Collect the sample in a pyrex bottle. Polyethylene bottles are not recommended because of the contamination which may result from the occasional use of lithium chloride as a catalyst in the manufacture of polyethylene.

2. Apparatus

Flame photometer: a Perkin-Elmer Model 52-C flame photometer; or a Beckman Model DU spectrophotometer equipped with photomultiplier tube and flame accessory; or the equivalent.

3. Reagents

3.1. *Sodium sulfate and sodium carbonate reagent:* Dissolve 5 g Na_2SO_4 and 10 g Na_2CO_3 in distilled water and dilute to 1 liter.

3.2. *Stock lithium solution:* Dissolve 0.6109 g anhydrous lithium chloride, LiCl, in distilled water and dilute to 1,000 ml; 1.00 ml $= 0.100$ mg Li. Weigh the LiCl very rapidly because the salt is highly deliquescent. Dry the salt overnight in an oven at 105°C.

3.3. Standard lithium solution: Dilute 20.00 ml stock lithium chloride solution to 1,000 ml with distilled water. This solution contains 2.0 μg Li per ml.

4. Procedure

4.1. Removal of interference from sample: Take a sample of 50.0 ml or less, so that the concentrations in the aliquot do not exceed the following: Na, 10 mg; Mg, 10 mg. Add 5.0 ml Na_2SO_4-Na_2CO_3 reagent. Bring the solution to a boil to coagulate the precipitate of $BaSO_4$, $SrCO_3$, $CaCO_3$, and possibly $MgCO_3$. Allow enough time for complete precipitation; otherwise, a feathery precipitate of $BaSO_4$ will appear after filtration. Pass the sample through Whatman No. 42 filter paper, wash with distilled water, and dilute the filtrate to 50.0 ml for the flame photometric measurement.

4.2. Treatment of standard solution: Add 5.0 ml Na_2SO_4-Na_2CO_3 reagent to 50.0 ml of the standard lithium solution. Boiling is unnecessary because no precipitation occurs in the standard. When boiling is avoided, the treated standard contains 1.8 μg Li per ml.

4.3. Flame photometric measurement: Determine the unknown lithium concentration by direct intensity measurements at a wavelength of 671 mμ. The bracketing method can be used with some instruments, while the construction of a calibration curve is necessary with other photometric instruments. Run the sample, distilled water (0 mg/l Li), and the lithium standard as nearly simultaneously as possible. For best results, take the average of several readings on each solution. In many cases, the calibration readings on distilled water and the lithium standard will suffice. The manufacturer's instructions for operation of the instrument used in the determination should be followed.

5. Calculation

$$\text{mg/l Li} = \frac{\mu\text{g Li}}{\text{ml sample}}$$

6. Accuracy

The lithium concentration can be determined with an accuracy of ±0.1–0.2 mg/l in the lithium range of 0.7 to 1.2 mg/l.

Bibliography

1. KUEMMEL, D. F. & KARL, H. L. Flame Photometric Determination of Alkali and Alkaline Earth Elements in Cast Iron. *Anal. Chem.* 26:386 (1954).
2. BRUMBAUGH, R. J. & FANUS, W. E. Determination of Lithium in Spodumene by Flame Photometry. *Anal. Chem.* 26:463 (1954).
3. ELLESTAD, R. B. & HORSTMAN, E. L. Flame Photometric Determination of Lithium in Silicate Rocks. *Anal. Chem.* 27:1229 (1955).
4. WHISMAN, M. & ECCLESTON, B. H. Flame Spectra of Twenty Metals Using a Recording Flame Spectrophotometer. *Anal. Chem.* 27:1861 (1955).
5. HORSTMAN, E. L. Flame Photometric Determination of Lithium, Rubidium, and Cesium in Silicate Rocks. *Anal. Chem.* 28:1417 (1956).

Magnesium

Magnesium ranks eighth amongst the elements in order of abundance and is a common constituent of natural water supplies. Important contributors to the hardness of a water, magnesium salts break down on heating to form deleterious scale in boilers. Concentrations in excess of 125 mg/l can also exert a cathartic and diuretic action. Chemical softening treatment or ion exchange is employed to reduce the magnesium and associated hardness to tolerable levels. The magnesium concentration may vary from zero to several hundred mg/l, depending on the source and the treatment of the water.

Selection of method: The two methods presented for the determination of magnesium are applicable to all natural waters. Magnesium can be determined by the gravimetric method (A) only after prior removal of calcium salts and is generally determined by this method on the filtrate and washings from the gravimetric and permanganate calcium determination (Calcium, Methods A and B). By the photometric method (B), magnesium can be determined in the presence of calcium salts directly on the water sample. Both methods can be applied to all concentrations by the selection of suitable aliquots. Choice of method is largely a matter of personal preference.

A. Gravimetric Method

1. General Discussion

1.1. *Principle:* Diammonium hydrogen phosphate precipitates magnesium quantitatively in ammoniacal solution as magnesium ammonium phosphate. The precipitate is ignited to, and weighed as, magnesium pyrophosphate. A choice is presented between: (a) destruction of ammonium salts and oxalate, followed by single precipitation of magnesium ammonium phosphate; and (b) double precipitation without pretreatment. Where time is not a factor, double precipitation is preferable. Pretreatment is faster but requires close attention to avoid mechanical loss.

1.2. *Interference:* The solution should be reasonably free from calcium, silica, iron, manganese, aluminum, strontium, and suspended matter. The solution should not contain more than about 3.5 g NH_4Cl.

2. Reagents

2.1. *Nitric acid,* conc.

2.2. *Hydrochloric acid,* conc; also $1 + 1$; $1 + 9$; and $1 + 99$.

2.3. *Methyl red indicator solution:* Dissolve 0.1 g methyl red sodium salt in distilled water and dilute to 100 ml.

2.4. *Diammonium hydrogen phosphate solution:* Dissolve 30 g $(NH_4)_2HPO_4$ in distilled water and make up to 100 ml.

2.5. *Ammonium hydroxide,* conc; also $1 + 19$.

3. Procedure

3.1. *By removal of oxalate and ammonium salts:* To the combined filtrate and washings from the calcium determination, which should not contain more than 60 mg Mg, or to an aliquot containing less than this amount in a 600- or 800-ml beaker, add 50 ml conc HNO_3 and evaporate carefully to dryness on a hot plate. Care must be taken that the reaction does not become too violent during the latter part of the evaporation; the analyst should be in constant attendance to avoid losses through spattering. Moisten the residue with 2–3 ml conc HCl; add 20 ml distilled water; warm; filter; and wash.

To the filtrate add 3 ml conc HCl, 2–3 drops of methyl red solution, and 10 ml $(NH_4)_2HPO_4$ solution. Cool and add conc NH_4OH, drop by drop, stirring constantly, until the color changes to yellow. Stir for 5 min; add 5 ml conc NH_4OH; and stir vigorously for 10 min more. Allow to stand overnight and then filter through S&S No. 589 White Ribbon or equivalent filter paper. Wash with $1 + 19$ NH_4OH. Transfer to a crucible which has been ignited, cooled, and weighed. Dry the precipitate thoroughly in the crucible and then burn the paper off *slowly,* allowing circulation of air. Heat at about 500°C until the residue is white. Then ignite for 30-min periods at 1,100°C to constant weight.

3.2. By *double precipitation:* To the combined filtrate and washings from the calcium determination, which should not contain more than 60 mg Mg, or to an aliquot containing less than this amount, add 2–3 drops of methyl red solution; adjust the volume to 150 ml; and acidify with $1 + 1$ HCl. Add 10 ml $(NH_4)_2HPO_4$ solution. Cool the solution. Then add conc NH_4OH, drop by drop, stirring constantly, until the color changes to yellow. Stir for 5 min; add 5 ml conc NH_4OH; and stir vigorously for 10 min more. Allow to stand overnight and then filter through S&S No. 589 White Ribbon or equivalent filter paper. Wash with $1 + 19$ NH_4OH. Discard the filtrate and washings. Dissolve the precipitate with 50 ml warm $1 + 9$ HCl and wash the paper well with hot $1 + 99$ HCl. Add 2–3 drops methyl red solution, 1–2 ml $(NH_4)_2HPO_4$ solution, and precipitate as before, after adjusting the volume to 100–150 ml. Allow the solution to stand in a cool place for at least 4 hr or preferably overnight. Filter through S&S No. 589 White Ribbon or equivalent filter paper and wash with $1 + 19$ NH_4OH. Transfer to a crucible which has been ignited, cooled, and weighed. Dry the precipitate thoroughly in the crucible and then burn the paper off *slowly,* allowing circulation of air. Heat at about 500°C until the residue is white. Then ignite for 30-min periods at 1,100°C to constant weight.

4. Calculation

$$\text{mg/l Mg} = \frac{\text{mg } Mg_2P_2O_7 \times 218.5}{\text{ml sample}}$$

5. Precision and Accuracy

A synthetic unknown sample containing 82 mg/l Mg and 108 mg/l Ca was determined gravimetrically by eight laboratories with a standard deviation of ±5.4 mg/l magnesium. One-half of the reported results were within ±3 mg/l of the known magnesium concentration. The individual laboratories reproduced their own results within ±1.7 mg/l.

B. Photometric Method

1. General Discussion

1.1. *Principle:* When magnesium hydroxide is precipitated in the presence of brilliant yellow, the dye is adsorbed on the precipitate and its color changes from orange to red. A stabilizer is added to maintain the $Mg(OH)_2$ in colloidal suspension.

1.2. *Interference:* Interference from calcium and aluminum is avoided by raising the concentrations of these ions to a level where their influence is constant and predictable. Iron is without effect in amounts below 2.5 mg/l, but in excess of that concentration it contributes to the magnesium color. Tolerable limits for other ions are: chloride, 250 mg/l; orthophosphate, 5 mg/l; fluoride, 5 mg/l. Manganic and zinc ions must be absent. Samples containing more than 0.5 mg/l chlorine must be dechlorinated.

1.3. Minimum detectable concentration: 0.10 mg Mg.

2. Apparatus

Colorimetric equipment: One of the following is required (visual comparison is difficult due to the intensity of color):

2.1. Spectrophotometer, for use at 525 mμ, providing a light path of 1 cm or longer.

2.2. Filter photometer, providing a light path of 1 cm or longer and equipped with a green filter having maximum transmittance near 525 mμ.

2.3. Glassware: All glassware should be cleaned with concentrated hydrochloric acid or nitric acid, followed by thorough rinsing with distilled water.

3. Reagents

All solutions are stable except the dechlorinating, brilliant yellow, and stabilizing solutions.

3.1. Sulfuric acid, 0.02N. Add 0.6 ml conc H_2SO_4 to 1 liter distilled water.

3.2. Saturated calcium sulfate solution, approximately 20 g/l $CaSO_4$. Add a large excess of $CaSO_4$ to distilled water; let stand as long as possible (preferably overnight); then filter through a filter paper sufficiently retentive for fine particles.

3.3. Aluminum sulfate reagent: Dissolve 0.31 g $Al_2(SO_4)_3 \cdot 18H_2O$ in distilled water, add 0.3 ml conc H_2SO_4, and dilute to 1 liter.

3.4. Stabilizing solution: The following stabilizing solutions are listed in the order of preference:

a. Colloresin: Place 1.0 g Colloresin 25 * or Colloresine LV * in a glass-stoppered pyrex bottle containing 100 ml distilled water and shake a few times. Store in a refrigerator; allow to reach the temperature of other reagents before use. Deterioration of the solution is indicated by the appearance of mold growth or sediment. Prepare a new solution if such conditions are observed.

b. Methocel: Place 1.0 g Methocel 25 * in a glass-stoppered bottle containing 100 ml distilled water and shake a few times. Store in a refrigerator. Allow to reach the temperature of other reagents before use. Observe precautions regarding deterioration (see Sec. *a* above).

3.5. Brilliant yellow solution: Dissolve 0.50 g solid dye † in 1 liter distilled water. Prepare every 2 or 3 days.

3.6. Sodium hydroxide, 6N. Dissolve 240 g NaOH in distilled water, cool, and dilute to 1 liter.

3.7. Stock magnesium solution: The metal (a) or the salt (b) may be used for the preparation of the stock solu-

---

* Colloresin 25 (Irwin Dyestuff Company, Montreal, Que.) and Colloresine LV (General Dyestuff Corporation) are said to be the same product. Both, as well as Methocel 25 (Dow Chemical Company), are commercial products for which no specifications can be given. It will be necessary for the analyst to confirm product quality for this application.

† National Aniline Company, Color Index No. 364, or equivalent.

tion, which contains 1.00 mg Mg per 1.00 ml:

a. Weigh out 1.000 g rough turnings of pure magnesium metal, not less than 99.9 per cent Mg. Transfer quantitatively to a 500-ml erlenmeyer flask. Place a funnel in the neck of the flask and add about 150 ml distilled water. Add, 1 ml at a time, 5.0 ml $1 + 1$ H_2SO_4. Mix well after each addition and allow the reaction to subside before making the next addition of acid. When all the acid has been added and the reaction becomes quiet, bring to a gentle boil and continue boiling for about 10 min to insure complete dissolution. Cool, transfer quantitatively to a 1-liter volumetric flask, and make up to the mark. The solution should be water white and crystal clear.

b. Dissolve 10.136 g magnesium sulfate heptahydrate, $MgSO_4 \cdot 7H_2O$, in distilled water and dilute to 1,000 ml. Determine the exact magnesium concentration in this solution by Method A.

3.8. Standard magnesium solution: Dilute 100.0 ml magnesium stock solution to 1,000 ml with distilled water; 1.00 ml = 0.100 mg Mg.

3.9. Reagent for removal of chlorine interference—sodium sulfite solution: Dissolve 1.0 g anhydrous Na_2SO_3 in 100 ml distilled water. Prepare daily.

4. Procedure

Measure into a 100-ml volumetric flask a sample aliquot containing between 0.1 and 0.8 mg Mg if using Colloresin stabilizer, or between 0.1 and 0.6 mg Mg if using Methocel stabilizer. If necessary, add 1 ml sodium sulfite solution to dechlorinate. Add, in order, 1 ml H_2SO_4 solution (or sufficient acid to prevent precipitation of succeeding calcium and aluminum additions), 20

ml calcium sulfate solution, and 5.0 ml aluminum sulfate reagent. Bring volume to about 80 ml with distilled water and mix. Add 5.0 ml stabilizer reagent, 2.0 ml brilliant yellow solution, and 3.5 ml NaOH solution. Dilute to the mark, shake vigorously, and wait 5 min for full color development. Measure photometrically within 1 hr against a blank prepared from distilled water and all of the reagents. Use a light path of 1 cm for Colloresin-treated samples and 2 cm or longer for Methocel-treated samples. Prepare a standard curve from 0.0, 0.100, 0.200, 0.400, and 0.600 or 0.800 mg Mg. Check at least two points with each set of determinations.

5. Calculation

$$mg/l \ Mg = \frac{mg \ Mg \times 1,000}{ml \ sample}$$

6. Precision and Accuracy

A precision of ± 1 mg/1 and an accuracy of ± 2 mg/1 can be achieved in the magnesium range 2–75 mg/l.

Bibliography

Gravimetric Method

1. EPPERSON, A. W. The Pyrophosphate Method for the Determination of Magnesium and Phosphoric Anhydride. *J. Am. Chem. Soc.* 50:321 (1928).
2. KOLTHOFF, I. M. & SANDELL, E. B. *Textbook of Quantitative Inorganic Analysis.* Macmillan Co., New York (3rd ed., 1952). Chap. 22.
3. HILLEBRAND, W. F., ET AL. *Applied Inorganic Analysis.* John Wiley & Sons, New York (2nd ed., 1953). Chap. 41 and pp. 133–134.

Photometric Method

4. TARAS, M. Photometric Determination of Magnesium in Water with Brilliant Yellow. *Anal. Chem.* 20:1156 (1948).

Manganese

Although manganese in ground water is generally present in the soluble divalent ionic form because of the complete absence of oxygen, there are times when part or all of the manganese in a water treatment plant may occur in a higher valence state. The total manganese determination does not differentiate the various manganese valence states. At present, the permanganate ion in the heptavalent state is used as a treatment procedure for removal of manganese and/or organic matter causing taste. The presence of excess permanganate, complexed trivalent manganese, or a suspension of quadrivalent manganese must be detected with great sensitivity to control the treatment to prevent their discharge into the distribution system. There is evidence to indicate that manganese occurs in surface waters both in suspension in the quadrivalent state as well as in the trivalent state in a relatively stable, soluble complex. Although rarely present in excess of 1 mg/l, manganese imparts objectionable and tenacious stains to laundry and plumbing fixtures. The low manganese limits imposed on an acceptable water stem from these practical considerations rather than for toxicological reasons. Special means of removal are often necessary, such as chemical precipitation, pH adjustment, aeration, superchlorination, and the use of special ion-exchange materials.

Selection of method: The persulfate method (*A*) is preferred for the determination of manganese in unknown samples both because the use of mercuric ion can control the interference from a limited chloride ion concentra-tion, and, also, the method is more rapid in the presence of low manganese concentrations. The periodate method (*B*) is suitable for samples which contain more than 0.01 mg manganese and in which chloride and organic matter are absent. The orthotolidine method (*C*) may be used for determining the total oxidative capacity of manganese in the higher valence states. A comparison of the total moles of manganese in solution to the oxidative equivalents can indicate the apparent valence state of the manganese. Although the tetra-base method for manganese is not fully quantitative, it provides a very rapid and highly sensitive (0.01 mg/l Mn) procedure which can be used in the field or laboratory to indicate the presence of manganese.[10]

Sampling and storage: Manganese may exist in a soluble form in a neutral water when first collected but oxidizes readily to a higher oxidation state and precipitates from solution or becomes adsorbed on the walls of the container. Manganese should be determined very soon after sample collection. When delay is unavoidable, a total manganese can be determined if the sample is acidified at the time of collection. Method C for the valence state must be applied as soon as possible after sample collection. Chlorine and oxygen at high pH will increase the oxidation and valence state of manganese. Organic compounds will reduce the oxidation state with time of contact. The total manganese may remain constant but changes in the valence state of this element are favored by the presence of the most stable form; that is, the presence of manganese dioxide will favor the breakdown of the permanganate and the formation of more manganese dioxide. In a solution of manganous ion, the presence of manganese dioxide will increase the rate of formation of manganese dioxide.

A. Persulfate Method

1. General Discussion

1.1. *Principle:* Persulfate oxidation of soluble manganous compounds to form permanganate is carried out in the presence of silver nitrate under the conditions shown by Nydahl[2] to be most effective. The resulting color is stable for at least 24 hr if excess persulfate is present and organic matter is absent.

1.2. *Interference:* As much as 0.1 g sodium chloride is prevented from interfering by the addition of mercuric sulfate to form slightly dissociated complexes. Only minute amounts of bromide and iodide may be present. Reasonable amounts of organic matter may be present if the period of heating is increased and more persulfate is added.

1.3. *Minimum detectable concentration:* 5 μg Mn.

2. Apparatus

Colorimetric equipment: One of the following is required:

2.1. *Spectrophotometer,* for use at 525 mμ, providing a light path of 1 cm or longer.

2.2. *Filter photometer,* providing a light path of 1 cm or longer and equipped with a green filter having maximum transmittance near 525 mμ.

2.3. *Nessler tubes,* matched, 100 ml, tall form.

Visual comparison is recommended only in the range of 5–100 μg Mn

(in the 100-ml final solution). For photometric measurement, the following tabulation shows the length of light path appropriate for various concentrations of manganese in the 100-ml final solution:

Mn Range	Light Path
mg	*cm*
0.005–0.2	15
0.02 –0.4	5
0.05 –1.0	2
0.1 –1.5	1

3. Reagents

3.1. *Special reagent:* Dissolve 75 g mercuric sulfate, $HgSO_4$, in 400 ml conc HNO_3 and 200 ml distilled water. Add 200 ml 85 per cent phosphoric acid, H_3PO_4, and 0.035 g silver nitrate, $AgNO_3$, and dilute the cooled solution to 1 liter.

3.2. *Ammonium persulfate,* $(NH_4)_2S_2O_8$, solid.

3.3. *Standard manganese solution:* Prepare a 0.1N KMnO$_4$ solution in the usual manner by dissolving 3.2 g KMnO$_4$ in distilled water and making up to 1 liter. This solution must be aged for several weeks in sunlight or heated for several hours near the boiling point, then filtered through a fritted-glass filter crucible and carefully standardized against sodium oxalate. (The standard KMnO$_4$ solution prepared for the titrimetric calcium determination—Calcium, Method B, Sec. 3.3—may be conveniently used.) Calculate the volume of this solution necessary to prepare 1 liter of solution of such strength that 1.00 ml $= 0.050$ mg Mn, as follows:

$$\text{ml KMnO}_4 = \frac{4.55}{\text{normality KMnO}_4}$$

To this volume add 2 to 3 ml conc H_2SO_4 and then sodium bisulfite solution (10 g $NaHSO_3$ plus 100 ml distilled water) dropwise, with stirring, until the permanganate color disappears. Boil to remove excess SO_2; cool; and dilute to 1,000 ml with distilled water. This solution may be diluted further in order to measure small amounts of manganese.

3.4. *Hydrogen peroxide,* 30 per cent.

4. Procedure

4.1. *Treatment of sample:* To a suitable aliquot of the sample, add 5 ml special reagent. Concentrate to 90 ml by boiling, or dilute to 90 ml. Add 1 g ammonium persulfate, bring to boiling, and boil for 1 min. Do not heat on a water bath. Remove from the heat source, allow to stand for 1 min, then cool under the tap. (Too long a boiling time results in decomposition of excess persulfate and subsequent loss of permanganate color; too slow cooling has the same effect.) Dilute to 100 ml with distilled water free from reducing substances, and mix. Compare visually or measure photometrically, using standards containing 0, 0.005, etc., to 1.5 mg Mn, prepared by treating various amounts of the standard Mn solution in the same way. Make the photometric measurements against a distilled-water blank. (Refer to Sec. 2 for information concerning the appropriate wavelength and the proper optical cells to use with different amounts of Mn.)

4.2. *Correction for turbidity or interfering color:* Filtration is not recommended because of the possibility that some of the permanganate may be retained on the filter paper. If visual comparison is used, the effect of turbidity can only be estimated, and no correction can be made for the effect of interfering colored ions. When photometric measurements are made, the following "bleaching" method is used, which also corrects for interfering color. As soon as the photometer reading has been made, add 0.05 ml hydrogen peroxide solution directly to the sample in the optical cell. Mix the solution and, as soon as the permanganate color has completely faded and no bubbles are left, take the reading again. The readings can be converted to absorbance and subtracted, or they can be read from the calibration curve as "apparent manganese" and "interferences as manganese," and then subtracted.

5. Calculation

$$\text{mg/l Mn} = \frac{\text{mg Mn} \times 1,000}{\text{ml sample}}$$

6. Precision and Accuracy

A synthetic unknown sample containing 0.25 mg/l Mn, 1.80 mg/l Al, 0.42 mg/l Cu, 0.18 mg/l Cr, 0.62 mg/l Fe, and 0.90 mg/l Zn was determined in 32 laboratories with a standard deviation of ± 0.10 mg/l by means of the persulfate method. One-half of the reported results were within ± 0.03 mg/l of the known manganese concentration. The individual laboratories reproduced their own results within ± 0.01 mg/l.

B. Periodate Method

1. General Discussion

1.1. *Principle:* With periodate as the oxidizing agent acting upon soluble manganous compounds to form permanganate, Beer's law holds closely up to 15 mg. The intensity of the color is not affected by variation in acid or periodate concentration, and the color is stable for many months. To obtain complete oxidation of small amounts of manganese (10 μg or less), silver nitrate is added and the heating time increased.

1.2. *Interference:* Reducing substances capable of reacting with periodate or permanganate must be removed or destroyed before the periodate oxidation is attempted. Although chloride in small amounts can be oxidized by periodate, removal by evaporation with sulfuric acid is preferred, especially when the sample contains only a small amount of manganese. This treatment, however, usually results in the dehydration of silica and the production of turbidity. Interference from other oxidizable substances, including organic materials, is eliminated by boiling the sample with nitric acid. Phosphoric acid is added to decolorize ferric iron by complex formation and prevent possible precipitation of periodates or iodates of manganese. Foreign metals, with a few exceptions, do not interfere, except those whose ions are colored; for these a method of correction is described.

1.3. *Minimum detectable concentration:* 5 μg Mn.

2. Apparatus

See Method A, Sec. 2.

3. Reagents

3.1. *Sulfuric acid,* conc.

3.2. *Nitric acid,* conc.

3.3. *Phosphoric acid,* syrupy, 85 per cent.

3.4. *Periodate:*

a. *Potassium metaperiodate,* KIO_4, solid; or

b. *Sodium paraperiodate,* $Na_3H_2IO_6$ (also called trisodium periodate [para]), solid.

3.5. *Silver nitrate.*

3.6. *Standard manganese solution:* Prepare as described in Method A, Sec. 3.3.

3.7. *Hydrogen peroxide,* 30 per cent.

4. Procedure

4.1. *Pretreatment of samples:* To remove chloride or other oxidizable substances such as organic matter, take a suitable aliquot of sample and add 5 ml conc H_2SO_4 and 5 ml conc HNO_3, mixing between additions. Evaporate to SO_3 fumes. Cool, add 85 ml distilled water, and cool again. Add 5 ml HNO_3 and 5 ml H_3PO_4 and mix. Treat as described in Sec. 4.2, beginning with ". . . add 0.3 g KIO_4."

4.2. *Oxidation:* To a suitable aliquot of the sample, add 5 ml conc H_2SO_4, mix, and cool. Add 5 ml HNO_3 and 5 ml H_3PO_4, and mix. Concentrate to about 90 ml by boiling. Cool; add 0.3 g KIO_4 or 0.5 g $Na_3H_2IO_6$. If the amount of Mn is 0.01 mg or less, also add 20 mg $AgNO_3$. Heat to boiling, with stirring, and keep at or slightly below the boiling point for 10 min (or at least 1 hr for very small amounts of Mn). Cool; dilute to 100 ml with distilled water free from reducing substances; and mix. Compare visually or measure photometrically, using standards containing 0, 0.005, etc., to 1.5 mg Mn, prepared by treating the various amounts of standard Mn solution in the same way. Make the photometric measurements against a distilled-water blank. (Refer to Method A, Sec. 2, for information concerning the appropriate wavelength and the proper optical cells to be used with different amounts of Mn.)

4.3. *Correction for turbidity or interfering color:* Follow the procedure described in Method A, Sec. 4.2.

5. Calculation

$$\text{mg/l Mn} = \frac{\text{mg Mn} \times 1,000}{\text{ml sample}}$$

6. Precision and Accuracy

A synthetic unknown sample containing 0.25 mg/l Mn, 1.80 mg/l Al, 0.42 mg/l Cu, 0.18 mg/l Cr, 0.62 mg/l Fe, and 0.90 mg/l Zn was determined in 19 laboratories with a standard deviation of ±0.18 mg/l by means of the periodate method. One-half of the reported results were within ±0.04 mg/l of the known manganese concentration. The individual laboratories reproduced their own results within ±0.01 mg/l.

C. Orthotolidine Method for Manganese in Higher Oxidation States (Tentative)

1. General Discussion

1.1. *Principle:* For many years, the higher oxidation states of manganese have been known to interfere with the orthotolidine method for determining residual chlorine. Therefore, it is obvious that residual chlorine will interfere in the orthotolidine method for the determination of manganese in the higher oxidation states. On the other hand, the use of the acid orthotolidine reagent makes it possible to determine the total oxidative capacity of the solution or suspension. Nitrite and ferric compounds may also interfere. To remove the interference of residual chlorine, an arsenite solution may be added before the orthotolidine addition, as suggested in the OTA method for Chlorine (Residual).

2. Apparatus

For a complete discussion of the use of the orthotolidine color system, consult the pertinent directions for determining Chlorine (Residual), Method B.

Colorimetric equipment: One of the following is required:

2.1. *Nessler tubes,* matched, 100 ml, tall form.

2.2. *Filter photometer,* providing a light path of 1 cm or longer and equipped with a violet filter having maximum transmittance in the range 400 to 450 mμ and a blue-green filter having maximum transmittance near 490 mμ.

2.3. *Spectrophotometer,* providing a light path of 1 cm or longer for use at 435 and 490 mμ.

2.4. *Commercial permanent chlorine standards:* A standard commercial residual chlorine kit may be used for routine observations. A reading of 0.35 mg/l residual chlorine will indicate 10 microequivalents of oxidizing capacity.

3. Reagents

3.1. *Orthotolidine reagent:* Dissolve 1.35 g orthotolidine dihydrochloride in 500 ml distilled water. Add this solution with constant stirring to a mixture of 350 ml distilled water and 150 ml conc hydrochloric acid. Store the reagent in an amber bottle.

3.2. *Sodium arsenite solution:* Dissolve 5 g $NaAsO_2$ in distilled water and dilute to 1 liter. (CAUTION: *Toxic; take care to avoid ingestion.*)

3.3. *Stock permanganate solution:* Dissolve 9.09 g $KMnO_4$ in freshly boiled and cooled distilled water and dilute to 1,000 ml. To maintain reasonable stability for one month, store in a clean pyrex bottle.

3.4. *Intermediate permanganate solution:* Daily dilute 10.0 ml stock permanganate solution to 1,000 ml with distilled water.

3.5. *Standard permanganate solution:* Daily dilute 1.0 ml intermediate permanganate solution to 100 ml with distilled water. This solution containing 0.091 mg $KMnO_4$ per 100 ml will develop a yellow color with orthotolidine reagent which will be the same as that developed by a solution of 1.0 mg/l residual chlorine.

4. Procedure

4.1. With raw water, add 1 ml orthotolidine reagent to 10 ml sample, and wait one minute for maximum color development. Compare with standards or read the absorbance in a photometric instrument.

4.2. With chlorine-treated water, add 0.5 ml sodium arsenite solution to 10 ml sample, mix, and add 1.0 ml orthotolidine reagent as quickly as possible. Wait for color development and compare with standards or read the absorbance in a photometric instru-

ment. If both permanganate and a manganese dioxide floc are present, remove the manganese dioxide by filtering the sample through a medium filter paper, and determine the permanganate immediately in the filtrate.

5. Interpretation of Results

In order to interpret the results of the orthotolidine method for manganese, the total manganese must also be ascertained by the persulfate or periodate method.

Trivalent manganese will be indicated when 1.5 mg/l Mn produces a yellow orthotolidine color equivalent to 1 mg/l residual chlorine.

Quadrivalent manganese will be indicated when 0.75 mg/l Mn suspension produces a yellow orthotolidine color equivalent to 1 mg/l residual chlorine.

Permanganate will be indicated when 0.32 mg/l Mn produces a yellow orthotolidine color equivalent to 1 mg/l residual chlorine.

Bibliography

Persulfate Method

1. RICHARDS, M. B. Colorimetric Determination of Manganese in Biological Material. *Analyst* 55:554 (1930).
2. NYDAHL, F. Determination of Manganese by the Persulfate Method. *Anal. Chem. Acta.* 3:144 (1949).
3. MILLS, S. M. Elusive Manganese. *Water & Sewage Works* 97:92 (1950).
4. SANDELL, E. B. *Colorimetric Determination of Traces of Metals.* Interscience Publishers, New York (3rd ed., 1959). Chap. 26.

Periodate Method

5. MEHLIG, J. P. Colorimetric Determination of Manganese with Periodate. *Ind. Eng. Chem., Anal. Ed.* 11:274 (1939).
6. ROWLAND, G. P., JR. Photoelectric Colorimetry: An Optical Study of Permanganate Ion and of the Chromium-Di-

phenyl Carbazide System. *Ind. Eng. Chem., Anal. Ed.* 11:442 (1939).

7. COOPER, M. D. Periodate Method for Manganese and Effect of Band Width. *Anal. Chem.* 25:411 (1953).

8. Ref. 4.

Orthotolidine Method

9. INGOLS, R. S. & WILROY, R. D. Mecha-

nism of Manganese Solution in Lake Waters. *J. AWWA* 55:282 (1963).

Tetrabase Method

10. RAINWATER, F. H. & THATCHER, L. L. Methods for Collection and Analysis of Water Samples. *US Geol. Survey Water Supply Paper* No. 1454 (1960) pp. 207–209.

Methane

Methane is a colorless, odorless, tasteless, combustible gas occasionally found in ground waters. The escape of this gas from water may develop an explosive atmosphere not only in the utility's facilities, such as tanks and pumphouses, but also on the consumer's property, particularly where water is sprayed through poorly ventilated spaces like public showers.

The explosive limits of methane in air are 5–15 per cent by volume. At sea level, a 5 per cent methane concentration in air could theoretically be reached in a poorly ventilated space sprayed with hot (68°C) water having a methane concentration of only 0.7 mg/l. At higher water temperatures, the vapor pressure of water is so great that no explosive mixture can form. At lower barometric pressures, the theoretical hazardous concentration of methane in water will be reduced proportionately. In an atmosphere of nitrogen or other inert gas, oxygen must be present at least to the extent of 12.8 per cent.

A qualitative test for high methane concentration can be made as follows: Invert a 1-qt bottle of water and immerse the neck in a pan or trough of water. Insert a tube or hose from a tap upward through the mouth of the bottle and allow the tap water to flow into the bottle, displacing the original water and permitting "gas" to accumulate at the top of the inverted bottle. After approximately $\frac{1}{8}$–$\frac{1}{4}$ of the bottle is filled with "gas," remove the hose, place a hand over the mouth of the bottle, and again invert to an upright position, holding the hand in place. If a lighted match is brought to the mouth of the bottle immediately on removing the hand, a brief wisp of blue flame will be apparent in the neck of the bottle if the "gas" is methane in high concentration. The blue flame is best observed in a darkened room. This is not a quantitative test but may indicate as low as 2 mg/l methane (1 cu ft per 1,000 gal). A positive result warrants precautionary measures. A negative one would require a quantitative analysis for certainty. The qualitative test should be performed with the utmost care. Every safeguard should be taken against bodily injury which might result from the shattering of the glass container during the flaming operation. Adequate shielding of the container and the wearing of goggles or a face shield are among the elementary precautions to be observed.

Selection of method: The combustible-gas indicator method (*A*) offers the advantages of simplicity, speed, and great sensitivity. The combustion-absorption method (B) can be made more accurate for concentrations of 4–5 mg/l and higher, but will not be satisfactory for very low concentrations. The combustion-absorption method is also applicable in a situation demanding a differentiation between methane and other gases. Such a situation might arise when a water supply is contaminated by a liquid-petroleum gas or other volatile combustible materials.

Methane may also be determined with the gas chromatograph as described in Part V, Digester Gases. The gas chromatograph enables a differentiation to be made between hydrogen, methane, and/or the higher homologues.

A. Combustible-Gas Indicator Method

1. General Discussion

1.1. *Principle:* An equilibrium according to Henry's law is established between methane (CH_4) in solution and the partial pressure of methane in the gas phase above the solution. The partial pressure of methane may be determined with a combustible-gas indicator. The operation of the instrument is based upon the catalytic oxidation of a combustible gas on a heated platinum filament which is made a part of a Wheatstone bridge. The heat generated by the oxidation of the gas increases the electrical resistance of the filament. The resulting imbalance of the electrical circuit causes deflection of a milliammeter. The milliammeter may be calibrated in terms of the percentage of methane or the percentage of the lower explosive limit of the gas sampled.

1.2. *Interference:* Small amounts of ethane are usually associated with methane in natural gas, and presumably would be present in water that contains methane. Hydrogen gas has been observed in well waters and would behave similarly to methane in this procedure. Hydrogen sulfide may interfere if the pH of the water is low enough for an appreciable fraction of the total sulfides to exist in the un-ionized form. The vapors of combustible oils may also interfere. In general, these interferences are of no practical importance, as the analyst is primarily interested in calculating the explosion hazard to which all combustible gases and vapors contribute.

Interference due to hydrogen sulfide can be reduced by the addition of solid sodium hydroxide to the container prior to sampling.

1.3. *Minimum detectable concentration:* The limit of sensitivity of the test is approximately 0.2 mg/l.

1.4. *Sampling:* If the water is supersaturated with methane, a representative sample cannot be obtained unless the water is under sufficient pressure to keep all of the gas dissolved. Wells should be operated for a sufficient period to insure that water coming directly from the aquifer is being sampled. Representative samples can be expected only if the well is equipped with a pump operating at sufficient submergence to assure that no gas escapes from the water.

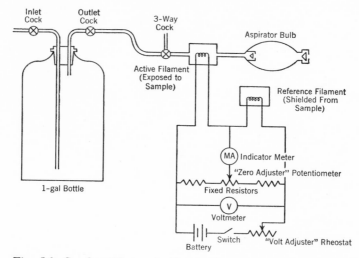

Fig. 16. Combustible-gas indicator circuit and flow diagram

2. Apparatus

2.1. *Combustible-gas indicator* *: A three-way stopcock should be connected to the inlet so that the instrument may be zeroed on atmospheric air immediately prior to obtaining the sample reading. For laboratory use, the suction bulb may be replaced with a filter pump throttled so as to draw gas through the instrument at a rate of approximately 600 ml/min. A diagrammatic view of the apparatus is shown in Fig. 16.

2.2. *Laboratory filter pump.*

2.3. *Glass bottle,* 1 gal, fitted with a two-hole rubber stopper. The inlet tube should extend to within 1 cm of the bottom, and the outlet tube should terminate approximately 1 cm from

the stopper. The tubes may be metal or glass. Each should be fitted with stopcocks or with short (approximately 5 cm) lengths of rubber tubing and pinchcocks. The entire assembly should be capable of holding a low vacuum for several hours. The volume of the assembly should be determined by filling with water and measuring the volume, or weight, of the water contained.

3. Reagents

Sodium hydroxide, pellets.

4. Procedure

4.1. If the approximate methane concentration of the water is unknown, it should be roughly determined as follows. Fill the bottle about half full of water, using a rubber tube connecting the sampling tap and the inlet tube, with the outlet tube open. With both the inlet and outlet tubes closed, shake the bottle vigorously for approximately 15 sec and allow the water to stand for approximately 1 min. Sample the gas

---

* Marketed under the following trade names: "Explosimeter," "Methane Gas Detector," and "Methane Tester," all manufactured by Mine Safety Appliance Company, Pittsburgh, Pa.; "J-W Combustible Gas Indicator," manufactured by Johnson-Williams, Inc., Palo Alto, Calif.; and "Vapotester," manufactured by Davis Emergency Equipment Company, Newark, N.J.

phase by withdrawing gas from the outlet, leaving the inlet open to admit air. If the needle swings rapidly to a high level on the meter and then drops to zero, the methane-air mixture is too rich to burn, and a smaller volume of water should be taken for the final test; if the needle deflection is too small to read accurately, a larger volume of water should be taken.

4.2. If the water contains hydrogen sulfide, approximately 0.5 g NaOH pellets may be added to the empty bottle to suppress interference from this gas. Evacuate the bottle using the filter pump. Fill the bottle not more than three-quarters full by connecting the inlet tube to the sampling cock, with the outlet tube closed. After the desired volume of water has been collected, allow the bottle to fill with air through the inlet tube. Close the inlet cock, shake the bottle vigorously for 60 sec, and let stand for at least 2 hr. Sample the gas phase through the outlet tube with the inlet cock open, taking the reading as rapidly as possible before the entering air has appreciably diluted the sample. Measure the volume of water sampled.

5. Calculation

The weight of methane (w), in milligrams, in the sample is given by the equation:

$$w = P \left(\frac{0.257 V_g}{T} + \frac{890 V_1}{H} \right)$$

where P is the partial pressure of methane, in millimeters of mercury; T is the temperature, in degrees Kelvin; V_g is the volume of the gas phase, in milliliters; V_1 is the volume of the liquid phase, in milliliters; and H is the Henry's law constant, in millimeters of mercury per mole of CH_4

per mole of water. The values for Henry's constant are as follows:

Temperature °C	Henry's Constant $10^6 H$	Temperature °C	Henry's Constant $10^6 H$
0	16.99	40	39.46
5	19.69	45	41.83
10	22.58	50	43.85
15	25.60	60	47.57
20	28.53	70	50.62
25	31.36	80	51.84
30	34.08	90	52.60
35	36.95	100	53.30

For most determinations, it may be assumed that atmospheric pressure is 760 mm and that the temperature is 20° C. The concentration of methane in the sample is then given by:

$$\text{mg/l } CH_4 = Rf \left(6.7 \frac{V_0 - V_1}{V_1} + 0.24 \right)$$

where R is the scale reading, V_0 the total volume of the sample bottle, V_1 the volume of water sampled, and f a factor depending upon the instrument used. If the instrument reads directly in percentage of methane, $f = 1.00$. If the instrument reads in percentage of the lower explosive limit of methane, the factor is 0.05. For instruments which require additional factors, the manufacturer should be consulted. For example, one commercial instrument with a scale that reads in percentage of the lower explosive limit of combustible gases requires an additional factor of 0.77 for methane. Hence, the value of f in the above equation would be 0.77 × 0.05, or 0.0385.

For more accurate work, or in locations where the normal barometric pressure is significantly lower than 760 mm, the following equation should be used:

$$\text{mg/l } CH_4 = RBf \left(2.57 \frac{V_0 - V_1}{TV_1} + \frac{8,900}{H} \right)$$

where B is the barometric pressure in millimeters of mercury, and the other symbols are the same as above.

6. Precision and Accuracy

The accuracy of the determination is limited by the accuracy of the instrument used, which is generally ±10 per cent at midscale reading. The precision is ±2 per cent at midscale reading, so that, by frequent calibration of the instrument on known methane-air mixtures, the accuracy can be greatly improved.

B. Combustion-Absorption Method

1. General Discussion

1.1. *Principle:* If methane is slowly mixed with oxygen in the presence of a platinum coil heated to yellow incandescence, most of the methane will be converted to carbon dioxide and water in a smooth reaction. Several subsequent passes of the mixed gases over the hot coil will serve to burn substantially all of the methane present in the sample. Oxygen must be removed from the original sample before the slow combustion is started; and the concentration of methane in the sample should not exceed 20 per cent, the remainder being an inert gas such as nitrogen.

Methane may also be converted to carbon dioxide and water in a catalytic oxidation assembly. If this procedure is used, an excess of oxygen is mixed with the sample prior to passage through the assembly.

1.2. *Interference:* Low-boiling hydrocarbons, other than ethane, and vapors from combustible oils could interfere in this analysis. These substances, however, are not likely to be present in water in sufficiently high concentration to affect the results significantly.

1.3. *Minimum detectable concentration:* This method is not satisfactory for determining methane in water where the concentration is less than 2 mg/l.

1.4. *Sampling:* The sample may be collected in the same way as for analysis by the combustible-gas indicator method, and the same precautions are necessary to obtain representative samples (see Method A, Sec. 1.4). The sodium hydroxide pellets may be omitted, however, and the sample bottle may be filled with water up to 90 per cent of its capacity.

2. Apparatus

Orsat-type gas analysis apparatus, consisting of at least: (a) a water-jacketed gas buret with leveling bulb; (b) a carbon dioxide absorption pipet; (c) an oxygen absorption pipet; (d) a slow-combustion pipet fitted with a safety-glass plate, or a catalytic oxidation assembly; and (e) a leveling bulb. If the slow-combustion pipet is used, a controlled source of current should be available to heat the platinum filament electrically. The units should be placed in a rigid assembly and connected by a manifold of capillary glass tubing fitted with stopcocks to permit controlled communication between any of the units. Mercury is recommended as the confining liquid. Dilute solutions (1–5 per cent) of sulfuric acid containing 15–20 per cent sodium sulfate have also been used successfully. Any of the commercially available gas analyzers having these units may be used.

3. Reagents

3.1. *Potassium hydroxide solution:* Dissolve 500 g KOH in distilled water and dilute to 1 liter.

3.2. *Alkaline pyrogallol reagent:* Dissolve 30 g pyrogallol (also called pyrogallic acid) in water and make up to 100 ml. Add 500 ml potassium hydroxide solution.

3.3. *Oxygen gas.*

4. Procedure

4.1. Transfer 5–10 ml of the gas phase of the sample into the gas buret through a capillary-tube connection to the sample bottle. Expel this portion of the sample to the atmosphere to purge the system. Select a sample which will result in a volume of approximately 60 ml at the step recorded as V_2 in the procedure. Transfer the sample to the buret, replacing it with water admitted through the inlet tube of the sample bottle. Bring the sample in the buret to atmospheric or reference pressure by adjusting the leveling bulb. Measure the volume accurately and record as V_1. Remove the carbon dioxide from the sample by three or four passes through the carbon dioxide absorption pipet charged with the potassium hydroxide solution. Before opening the stopcocks between the buret and any absorption pipet, make sure that the gas in the buret is under a slight positive pressure. This procedure will prevent the reagent in the pipet from contaminating the stopcock or manifold. Remove the oxygen by passing the sample through the oxygen absorption pipet charged with alkaline pyrogallol reagent, until the volume of the sample remains constant. Measure the volume accurately and record as V_2. Store the sample in the carbon dioxide pipet.

4.2. Purge the inlet connections to the buret with oxygen by drawing 5–10 ml into the buret and expelling to the atmosphere. Transfer 35–40 ml of oxygen to the buret and measure accurately. Record this volume as V_3. Transfer the oxygen to the slow-combustion pipet and then transfer the sample from the carbon dioxide pipet to the buret. Heat the platinum coil in the combustion pipet to yellow heat, controlling the temperature by adjusting the current passing through the coil. Reduce the pressure of the oxygen in the pipet to somewhat less than atmospheric by means of the leveling bulb attached to the pipet. If a catalytic oxidation assembly is used, proceed directly to 4.4.

4.3. Pass the sample into the slow-combustion pipet at the rate of approximately 10 ml/min. After the first pass, transfer the sample and oxygen mixture back and forth between the pipet and buret several times at a faster rate, allowing the mercury in the pipet to rise to a point just below the heated coil. Collect the sample in the combustion pipet, turn off the coil, and cool the pipet and sample with a jet of compressed air. Transfer the sample to the buret and measure its volume. Record as V_4.

4.4. If a catalytic oxidation assembly is used, mix 40 ml oxygen with not more than 60 ml of the stored gas sample, V_2. Pass the entire mixture through the assembly at a rate not greater than 30 ml/min. After the first pass, transfer the mixture back and forth through the assembly between the buret and the reservoir at a rate not greater than 60 ml/min until a constant residual volume is obtained. Record as V_4. During the usual three or four passes, the pressure should be maintained near atmospheric.

4.5. Determine the amount of carbon dioxide formed in the reaction by passing the sample through the carbon dioxide absorption pipet until the volume remains constant. Record the volume after this procedure as V_5.

4.6. A further check on the accuracy of the determination may be made by absorbing the residual oxygen from the sample. After this absorption, record the final volume as V_6.

5. Calculation

5.1. If methane is the only combustible gas present, the methane content of the sample will be given by any one of the following equations:

$$\text{volume } CH_4 = \frac{V_2 + V_3 - V_4}{2}$$

$$\% \, CH_4 = \frac{(V_2 + V_3 - V_4) \, 100}{2V_1}$$

$$\text{volume } CH_4 = V_4 - V_5$$

$$\% \, CH_4 = \frac{(V_4 - V_5) \, 100}{V_1}$$

$$\text{volume } CH_4 = \frac{V_3 - V_5 + V_6}{2}$$

$$\% \, CH_4 = \frac{(V_3 - V_5 + V_6) \, 100}{2V_1}$$

Results from these calculations should be in reasonable agreement. If they are not, ethane may be present. For methane and ethane (C_2H_6) together, the following equations apply:

$$\text{volume } CH_4 = \frac{4(V_2 + V_3) - 9V_4 + 5V_5}{3}$$

$$\% \, CH_4 = \frac{4(V_2 + V_3) - 9V_4 + 5V_5}{3V_1} 100$$

$$\text{volume } C_2H_6 = \frac{2(3V_4 - 2V_5 - V_2 - V_3)}{3}$$

$$\% \, C_2H_6 = \frac{2(3V_4 - 2V_5 - V_2 - V_3) \, 100}{3V_1}$$

Each volume of methane will react with 2 volumes of oxygen and each volume of ethane will use 3.5 volumes of oxygen. This relationship may be used as a check on the accuracy of the analysis:

$$2w_m + 3.5w_e = V_3 - V_5 + V_6$$

where w_m is the volume of methane and w_e, of ethane. Or, if volumes are not calculated:

$$V_2 + 3V_4 - V_5 = 2V_3 + 3V_6$$

If agreement is not obtained, the analysis should be repeated after the apparatus has been thoroughly checked for sources of error, such as leaky stopcocks or connections. The possibility that the sample contains other combustible gases, such as propane or butane, should be considered.

5.2. The percentage of methane given by this analysis may be used in applying Henry's law to obtain the concentration of methane in the original water sample (see Method A, Sec. 5). The percentage of methane as determined by this analysis should be substituted for R (scale reading) in the calculation, and $f = 1$.

6. Precision and Accuracy

A gas buret can measure gas volume with a precision of 0.05 ml and a probable accuracy of 0.1 ml. With methane (gas phase) concentrations larger than 2 per cent, the overall error of the gas determination can be made less than ±5 per cent.

Bibliography

Combustible-Gas Indicator Method

1. ROSSUM, J. R.; VILLARRUZ, P. A.; & WADE, J. A. A New Method for Determining Methane in Water. *J. AWWA* 42:413 (1950).

Combustion-Absorption Method

2. DENNIS, L. M. & NICHOLS, M. L. *Gas Analysis.* Macmillan Co., New York (1929).
3. HALDANE, J. S. & GRAHAM, J. I. *Methods of Air Analysis.* Charles Griffin & Co., London (1935).
4. YANT, W. P. & BERGER, L. B. Sampling of Mine Gases and the Use of the Bureau of Mines Portable Orsat Apparatus in Their Analysis. *Miners' Circ. (US Bur. Mines)* No. 34 (1936).

5. BUSWELL, A. M. & LARSON, T. E. Methane in Ground Waters. *J. AWWA* 29:1978 (1937).
6. BERGER, L. B. & SCHRENK, H. H. Bureau of Mines Haldane Gas Analysis Apparatus. *US Bur. Mines Inform. Circ.* No. 7017 (1938).
7. LARSON, T. E. Properties and Determination of Methane in Ground Waters. *J. AWWA* 30:1828 (1938).
8. MULLEN, P. W. *Modern Gas Analysis.* Interscience Publishers, New York (1955).

Nitrogen (Albuminoid)

The albuminoid-nitrogen determination gives an approximate indication of the quantity of proteinaceous nitrogen present in water. This largely derives from the animal and plant life normal to the aquatic environment.

Following the distillation of free ammonia nitrogen, the addition of a strongly alkaline potassium permanganate solution to a water sample often causes an additional evolution of ammonia. This supplementary release of ammonia represents the albuminoid nitrogen and results largely from the action of potassium permanganate on the unsubstituted amino groups of many amino acids, polypeptides, and proteins in an alkaline medium. These nitrogenous materials are important constituents of organic pollution in a water supply. Like free ammonia nitrogen, albuminoid nitrogen frequently exerts a significant influence on the chlorine demand in treatment plants practicing free residual chlorination.

1. General Discussion

1.1. *Principle:* After conversion of unsubstituted amino groups by alkaline potassium permanganate to ammonia, the ammonia is distilled and determined by nesslerization. The determination can also be completed by titration with a standard solution of a strong mineral acid as described in Part III, Nitrogen (Organic).

1.2. *Storage of sample:* Samples should be stored as directed under Nitrogen (Ammonia).

2. Apparatus

The same type of apparatus (Fig. 17) is required as in Nitrogen (Ammonia), Method A, Sec. 2.

3. Reagents

All the reagents listed for the determination of ammonia nitrogen by Method A, Sec. 3, are required. Also needed is:

Alkaline potassium permanganate reagent: In a 3-liter pyrex beaker, dissolve 16 g $KMnO_4$ in sufficient ammonia-free distilled water to effect dissolution. Add 288 g NaOH or 404 g KOH and enough ammonia-free water to make up to 2.5 liters. Concentrate to 2 liters on an electric hot plate. Determine the ammonia blank in 50 ml of the reagent and use the results as a basis for correction in subsequent determinations.

4. Procedure

Perform the albuminoid nitrogen determination immediately following the ammonia nitrogen determination on the same sample—see Nitrogen (Ammonia), Method A, Sec. 4.1 and 4.2, for the preparation of the distillation apparatus and the sample. Measure 700 to 1,000 ml of the neutralized and dechlorinated sample into a 2-liter distilling flask. Add 10 ml phosphate buffer solution together with several glass beads or boiling chips, and collect 50 to 300 ml of the ammonia nitrogen distillate (Method A, Sec. 4.3 and 4.4). Add 50 ml alkaline potassium permanganate reagent and continue distillation. Collect 200 or 250 ml of distillate (Method A, Sec. 4.3 and 4.4). Complete the determination by nesslerization (Method A, Sec. 4.5).

5. Calculation

Calculate the albuminoid nitrogen as for ammonia nitrogen (Method A, Sec. 5), correcting for the blank on the alkaline permanganate reagent, instead of for the phosphate buffer solution. Report as mg/l albuminoid N.

$$\text{mg/l albuminoid N} = \frac{A \times 1,000}{\text{ml sample}} \times \frac{B}{C}$$

where A = mg N found colorimetrically, B = ml total distillate collected including the H_3BO_3, and C = ml distillate taken for nesslerization.

6. Precision and Accuracy

The recovery of unsubstituted amino nitrogen in the albuminoid nitrogen determination is estimated at approximately 80 per cent. The results can be reproduced within ± 5 per cent of the concentration determined.

Bibliography

1. PHELPS, E. B. A Critical Study of the Methods in Current Use for the Determination of Free and Albuminoid Ammonia in Sewage. *APHA Public Health Papers & Repts.* 29:354 (1903) ; *J. Infectious Diseases* 1:327 (1904).
2. TARAS, M. J. Preliminary Studies on the Chlorine Demand of Specific Chemical Compounds. *J. AWWA* 42:462 (1950).
3. TARAS, M. J. Effect of Free Residual Chlorination on Nitrogen Compounds in Water. *J. AWWA* 45:47 (1953).
4. BOLTZ, D. F., ed. *Colorimetric Determination of Nonmetals.* Interscience Publishers, New York (1958). pp. 75–97.

Nitrogen (Ammonia)

Ammonia nitrogen is present in variable concentrations in many surface and ground waters. A product of microbiologic activity, ammonia nitrogen is sometimes accepted as chemical evidence of sanitary pollution when encountered in raw surface supplies. Its occurrence in ground supplies is quite general, as a result of natural reduction processes. At some water treatment plants ammonia is added in the combined residual chlorination of water. Where the free residual chlorination process is employed, the presence of ammonia in the water supply may require the addition of large amounts of chlorine in order to produce a free chlorine residual. If a sample contains residual chlorine, then monochloramine, dichloramine, or trichloramine (nitrogen trichloride) may be present. Dechlorination prior to analysis will convert these substances to ammonia.

Selection of method: The distillation method (*A*) is preferred for the determination of ammonia nitrogen, in trace or appreciable amounts, especially when interferences of any nature are suspected or when it is necessary to make a subsequent determination of the albuminoid or organic nitrogen, in which case the sample must be freed of ammonia. The nesslerization procedure for estimating ammonia gives acceptable results for samples in which all the free ammonia appears in the first 50 to 100 ml of distillate, and therefore can be collected as the free distillate. The ammonia nitrogen content of such distillates approximates 0.05 mg or less where 500 ml of sample is used for distillation. Nesslerization and titration alike can be practiced on distillates bearing as much as 1 mg ammonia nitrogen. It is important in the latter instances to use sufficient boric acid to absorb the ammonia, thereby preventing volatilization losses.

The titration procedure described in Part III, Nitrogen (Organic) should be tried on distilled samples which are subject to serious nessler interference from neutral organic compounds.

The direct nesslerization method (*B*) is usually reserved for samples containing in excess of 0.2 mg/l ammonia nitrogen. The relative simplicity and speed of the method recommend it for control operations in the demonstrated absence of significant interference from colored ions or other materials.

Storage of sample: The most reliable results are obtained on fresh samples. In the event that a prompt analysis is impossible, precautions should be taken to retard biologic activity by storing the sample at a low temperature, preferably just above freezing. Where such a measure is impractical, the addition of 0.8 ml conc H_2SO_4 to 1 liter of sample may serve to maintain the nitrogen balance. If acid preservation is practiced, the sample acidity should be neutralized with sodium or potassium hydroxide immediately before the procedure is undertaken. Residual chlorine should also be reduced immediately after the sample is collected in order to arrest the consumption of ammonia.

A. Distillation Method

1. General Discussion

1.1. *Principle:* Free ammonia nitrogen can be recovered when the distillation mixture is kept near pH 7.4. Since natural waters exhibit varying pH values and buffering properties, a phosphate buffer is applied for the purpose of maintaining the required pH

during the distillation process. Trace amounts of ammonia characteristic of relatively unpolluted supplies can be collected as the free distillate and determined by nesslerization. Ammonia nitrogen concentrations in excess of 50 μg are best absorbed in boric acid to minimize ammonia losses. Each milligram of ammonia nitrogen requires the use of an added increment of 50 ml of boric acid solution for effective ammonia absorption. The isolated ammonia can be determined by nesslerization or by titration with a standard solution of a strong mineral acid as in Part III, Nitrogen (Organic). An indicator which responds at the pH (approximately 5.0) of the dilute boric acid absorbent solution is suitable for the titration of the ammonia.

The graduated series of yellow to brown colors produced by the nessler-ammonia reaction absorb strongly over a wide wavelength range. The yellow color characteristic of low ammonia nitrogen strengths (20–250 μg per 50 ml of solution) can be measured with acceptable sensitivity in the wavelength region from 400 to 425 mμ when a 1-cm light path is available. A light path of 5 cm extends measurements into the nitrogen range of 5 to 60 μg. The reddish-brown hues typical of ammonia nitrogen levels approaching 0.5 mg may be measured in the wavelength region of 450 to 500 mμ. A judicious selection of light path and wavelength available with a given instrument thus enables the photometric determination of ammonia nitrogen concentrations over a considerable range.

Departures from Beer's law may be experienced with photometers equipped with broad-band color filters. For this reason, the calibration curve should be prepared under conditions identical with those adopted for the samples.

1.2. *Interference:* Ammonia recovery will be low on water samples containing more than 250 mg/l calcium unless the treatment prescribed in Sec. 4.2 is followed. The calcium and the phosphate buffer react to precipitate calcium phosphate, releasing hydrogen ions and lowering the pH. A number of aliphatic and aromatic amines, organic chloramines, acetone, aldehydes, and alcohols, among other undefined organic compounds, cause trouble in direct nesslerization. Compounds of this type have been found to yield a yellowish or greenish off color or a turbidity following the addition of nessler reagent to distillates collected from dechlorinated polluted samples. The titration procedure is also subject to amine interference because the standard acid can react with such alkaline bodies. However, the titration procedure is free of interference from neutral organic compounds. Sulfide has also been reported to cause turbidity following nesslerization, a condition which may be avoided by adding lead carbonate to the flask prior to distillation. Volatile substances such as formaldehyde can be removed by boiling at low pH, after which the sample can be distilled and nesslerized in the normal manner.

1.3. *Minimum detectable concentration:* A carefully prepared nessler reagent may respond under optimum conditions to as little as 1 μg ammonia nitrogen in 50 ml of solution. However, reproducibility below 5 μg may often be erratic.

2. Apparatus

2.1. *Distillation apparatus:* A glass flask of 800–2,000-ml capacity attached to a vertical condenser is so arranged that the distillate falls directly into the collecting glassware. An all-pyrex apparatus (Fig. 17) or one with condensing units constructed of block tin or aluminum tubes may be employed.

2.2. *Colorimetric equipment:* One of the following is required:

a. *Spectrophotometer,* for use at 400

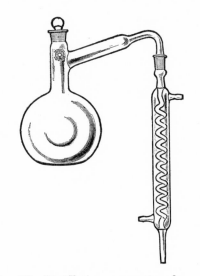

Fig. 17. Distillation apparatus for ammonia, albuminoid nitrogen, phenol, selenium, and fluoride determinations

to 425 mμ, providing a light path of 1 cm or longer.

b. Filter photometer, providing a light path of 1 cm or longer and equipped with a violet filter having maximum transmittance at 400 to 425 mμ.

c. Nessler tubes, matched, 50 ml, tall form.

3. Reagents

All solutions should preferably be stored in pyrex glassware.

3.1. *Ammonia-free water:* Ammonia-free water may be made by distillation or ion-exchange methods:

a. Distillation: Traces of ammonia in distilled water may be eliminated by the addition of sufficient bromine or chlorine water to produce a free halogen residual of 2–5 mg/l. After standing at least 1 hr, and preferably overnight, the first 100 ml of the distillate

is discarded before collection is commenced.

b. Ion exchange: Removal of ammonia alone can be accomplished by a cation exchanger. For most work a satisfactory water can be obtained by shaking 1 gal of distilled water with 10 g of a strong cation exchanger * or by passing the distilled water through a column of such an ion exchanger.

Where it is important to produce an all-purpose, high-purity water, free of the common trace ions and therefore suitable for other determinations, a convenient preparatory method consists of slowly passing distilled water through a 10-in. column of glass tubing (0.5 to 1 in. in diameter) which has been charged with 2 parts by volume of a strongly basic anion-exchange resin in the hydroxyl form and 1 part by volume of a strongly acidic cation-exchange resin in the hydrogen form. Ion-exchange resins of a quality suitable for analytical work should be used. The reagent blank obtained by distilling "ammonia-free" water prepared by the exchange process and adding 10 ml of phosphate buffer solution may have an ammonia nitrogen content approaching 0.01 mg/l. Although the resins may be used repeatedly, regular blanks should be run to guard against unsuspected exhaustion and the attendant release of ammonia to the "ammonia-free" water.

c. Traces of magnesium in some distilled waters cause cloudiness following nesslerization, a condition which may be prevented by the use of 1 or 2 drops of EDTA or Rochelle salt solution (see Method B, Sec. 2.3).

3.2. *Phosphate buffer solution,* pH 7.4. Dissolve 14.3 g anhydrous potas-

---

* Folin's ammonia permutit (a product of The Permutit Company) or equal.

sium dihydrogen phosphate, KH_2PO_4, and 68.8 g anhydrous dipotassium hydrogen phosphate, K_2HPO_4, and dilute to 1 liter with ammonia-free water. A blank ammonia determination should be run on the buffer solution.

3.3. *Boric acid solution:* Dissolve 20 g anhydrous boric acid, H_3BO_3, in ammonia-free water and dilute to 1 liter.

3.4. *Stock ammonium solution:* Dissolve 3.819 g anhydrous ammonium chloride, NH_4Cl, dried at 100°C, in ammonia-free water and dilute to 1,000 ml; 1.00 ml = 1.00 mg N = 1.22 mg NH_3.

3.5. *Standard ammonium solution:* Dilute 10.00 ml stock ammonium chloride solution to 1,000 ml with ammonia-free water; 1.00 ml = 10.0 μg N = 12.2 μg NH_3.

3.6. *Neutralization agent:*

a. *Sodium hydroxide,* 1N. Dissolve 40 g NaOH in ammonia-free water and dilute to 1 liter.

b. *Sulfuric acid,* 1N. Add 28 ml conc H_2SO_4 cautiously to 500 ml ammonia-free water and dilute to 1 liter.

3.7. *Dechlorinating agent:* Any of the following reagents is satisfactory; 1 ml will remove 1 mg/l of residual chlorine in 500 ml of sample. The thiosulfate and sulfite solutions are unstable and should be prepared fresh.

a. *Sodium thiosulfate,* $\frac{1}{70}N$. Dissolve 3.5 g $Na_2S_2O_3\cdot5H_2O$ in ammonia-free water and dilute to 1 liter.

b. *Sodium arsenite,* $\frac{1}{70}N$. Dissolve 1.0 g $NaAsO_2$ in ammonia-free water and dilute to 1 liter. (CAUTION: *Toxic; take care to avoid ingestion.*)

c. *Sodium sulfite,* $\frac{1}{70}N$. Dissolve 0.9 g Na_2SO_3 in ammonia-free water and dilute to 1 liter.

d. *Phenylarsine oxide,* $\frac{1}{70}N$. Dissolve 1.2 g phenylarsine oxide, C_6H_5AsO, in 200 ml 0.3N sodium hy-

droxide solution, filter if necessary, and dilute to 1 liter with ammonia-free water. (CAUTION: *Toxic; take care to avoid ingestion.*)

3.8. *Nessler reagent:* Dissolve 100 g mercuric iodide, HgI_2, and 70 g potassium iodide, KI, in a small quantity of ammonia-free water and add this mixture slowly, with stirring, to a cool solution of 160 g NaOH in 500 ml ammonia-free water. Dilute to 1 liter with ammonia-free water. Stored in pyrex glassware and out of the sunlight, this reagent is stable for periods up to a year under normal laboratory conditions. The reagent should give the characteristic color with 0.1 mg/l ammonia nitrogen within 10 min after addition and should not produce a precipitate with small amounts of ammonia within 2 hr. (CAUTION: *Toxic; take care to avoid ingestion.*)

3.9. *Permanent color solutions:*

a. *Potassium chloroplatinate solution:* Dissolve 2.0 g K_2PtCl_6 in 300–400 ml distilled water; add 100 ml conc HCl and dilute to 1 liter.

b. *Cobaltous chloride solution:* Dissolve 12.0 g $CoCl_2\cdot6H_2O$ in 200 ml distilled water; add 100 ml conc HCl and dilute to 1 liter.

4. Procedure

Carry out the following steps without any intervening delay.

4.1. *Preparation of equipment:* Add 500 ml distilled water, 10 ml phosphate buffer solution, and a few glass beads or boiling chips to a flask of appropriate capacity; steam out the entire distillation apparatus until the distillate shows no trace of ammonia.

4.2. *Sample preparation:* Use a 500-ml sample or an aliquot diluted to 500 ml with ammonia-free water. When the ammonia nitrogen content falls below

0.05 mg/l, or when an albuminoid nitrogen determination is to be made following the ammonia determination, use sample volumes up to 1,000 ml. Remove the residual chlorine in the sample by adding an equivalent amount of dechlorinating-agent solution. If necessary, neutralize the sample to about pH 7 with the dilute acid or base, using a pH meter. Add 10 ml phosphate buffer solution. For most water samples this volume is sufficient to maintain a pH of 7.4 ± 0.2 during distillation; if not, add another 10-ml portion of buffer solution. For samples containing more than 250 mg/l calcium add up to 40 ml of buffer solution first and then adjust the pH to 7.4 with acid or base.

4.3. *Distillation:* In order to avoid any possibility of contamination, leave the entire distillation apparatus assembled after the steaming-out process until just before the actual sample distillation is to be started. Empty the distilling flask, taking care to leave the glass beads or boiling chips in it. Pour in the dechlorinated, neutralized, and buffered sample. Distill at the rate of 6–10 ml/min, collecting the distillate in successive separate 50-ml, or larger, portions until free of ammonia. Nessler tubes or volumetric flasks are suitable receivers for nitrogen concentrations below 0.05 mg.

4.4. *Ammonia absorption:* When the ammonia nitrogen content exceeds 50 μg, absorb the distillate below the surface of 50 ml boric acid solution. Use an additional 50-ml increment of boric acid solution for every milligram of ammonia nitrogen in the distillate. Collect at least 300 ml of the distillate. Lower the collected distillate free of contact with the delivery tube, and continue distillation during the last minute or two to cleanse the condenser.

4.5. *Color development:* Add 1.0 ml nessler reagent to a 50.0-ml portion of the distillate, or to a suitable aliquot diluted to 50.0 ml with ammonia-free water. Mix thoroughly by capping the nessler tubes or flasks with clean rubber stoppers (which have been thoroughly washed with ammonia-free water) and then inverting the tubes at least six times to insure complete mixing. Keep such experimental conditions as temperature and reaction time the same in the blank, samples, and standards. Allow the reaction to proceed for at least 10 min after the addition of the reagent; then read the color in the distillate and the standards. Use a 30-min contact time if the ammonia nitrogen is very low, but in this event run the blank and standards for the same length of time. Measure the color either photometrically (Sec. 4.6) or visually (Sec. 4.7).

4.6. *Photometric measurement:* Measure the absorbance or transmittance in a spectrophotometer or a filter photometer. The calibration curve should be prepared under the same conditions of temperature and reaction time prevailing for the samples. Transmittance readings should be made against a reagent blank, and parallel checks should be run frequently against known ammonia standards, preferably in the nitrogen range of the samples. Complete calibration curves should be redetermined following the preparation of each batch of nessler reagent.

4.7. *Visual comparison:* Compare the colors produced in the samples against those of the ammonia standards. Prepare temporary or permanent standards as directed below:

a. Temporary standards: Prepare a series of visual standards in nessler tubes by adding the following volumes of standard ammonium chloride solution and diluting to 50 ml with ammonia-free water: 0.0, 0.2, 0.4, 0.7, 1.0, 1.4, 1.7, 2.0, 2.5, 3.0, 3.5, 4.0, 4.5, 5.0, and 6.0 ml. Nesslerize the standards and the portions of distillate by adding 1.0 ml nessler reagent to each tube and mixing well.

b. Permanent standards: Measure into 50-ml nessler tubes the volumes of potassium chloroplatinate and cobaltous chloride solutions indicated in Table 11; dilute to the mark and mix thor-

TABLE 11—PREPARATION OF PERMANENT COLOR STANDARDS FOR VISUAL DE-TERMINATION OF AMMONIA NITROGEN

Value in Ammonia Nitrogen μg	Approx. Vol. of Platinum Solution ml	Approx. Vol. of Cobalt Solution ml
0	1.2	0.0
2	2.8	0.0
4	4.7	0.1
7	5.9	0.2
10	7.7	0.5
14	9.9	1.1
17	11.4	1.7
20	12.7	2.2
25	15.0	3.3
30	17.3	4.5
35	19.0	5.7
40	19.7	7.1
45	19.9	8.7
50	20.0	10.4
60	20.0	15.0

oughly. The values given in the table are *approximate;* actual equivalents of the standards thus prepared will differ with the quality of the nessler reagent, the kind of illumination used, and the color sensitiveness of the analyst's eye. The color standards should be compared with the nesslerized temporary ammonia standards and the tints modified as necessary. Such comparisons should be made for each newly prepared nessler solution and checked by each analyst. These standards may be kept for several months if protected from dust. Comparison with them is

made at either 10 or 30 min after nesslerization, depending upon the reaction time used in the preparation of the nesslerized ammonia standards against which they were matched.

5. Calculation

5.1. The amount of nitrogen in the volume of ammonia-free water which has been used for diluting the original sample should be deducted before the final nitrogen value is computed.

5.2. A reagent blank should also be deducted for the volume of phosphate buffer solution used with the sample.

5.3. The total ammonia nitrogen in the original volume of sample taken for distillation is equal to the sum of the ammonia nitrogen found in each separate portion of distillate. If a representative aliquot of a cumulative distillate is taken for nesslerization, the nitrogen is computed by the following equation:

$$\text{mg/l ammonia N} = \frac{A}{\text{ml sample}} \times \frac{B}{C}$$

where $A = \mu g$ N found colorimetrically, $B =$ ml total distillate collected including the H_3BO_3, and $C =$ ml distillate taken for nesslerization.

5.4. The free NH_3 and NH_4 values can be calculated by multiplying the ammonia nitrogen results by the factors 1.216 and 1.288, respectively.

6. Precision and Accuracy

6.1. Since the ammonia content of the ammonia-free water plus the phosphate buffer may approach or slightly exceed 0.01 mg/l N, depending on the purity of the reagents and the excellence of experimental technique, the proper course is to report the N values to the second decimal where trace quantities of ammonia are involved. A precision of ±5 per cent of the nitrogen value can be attained with a little practice by resort to photometric methods if 500-ml samples are used.

6.2. Where better than average accuracy—i.e., less variation than ±10 per cent of the true value—is required in the ammonia determination, it is recommended that the photometric calibration curve be prepared by taking the ammonia nitrogen s t a n d a r d s through all of the procedural steps, including distillation. Such an approach will compensate for deficiencies in the nitrogen recovery which may be peculiar to the distillation procedure and the technique being used.

6.3. Ammonia nitrogen can be determined photometrically within less than ±5 per cent of the nitrogen value.

B. Direct Nesslerization Method

1. General Discussion

1.1. *Principle:* With samples that have a high ammonia content, the distillation step is sometimes omitted and the sample is nesslerized directly. Pretreatment with zinc sulfate and alkali is used to precipitate calcium, magnesium, iron, and sulfide, which might cause turbidity with nessler reagent. The floc also removes suspended matter and sometimes colored matter. The addition of EDTA or Rochelle salt solution prevents the precipitation of residual calcium and magnesium ions in the presence of the alkaline nessler reagent.

1.2. *Interference:* A number of aliphatic and aromatic amines, organic chloramines, acetone, aldehydes, and alcohols, among other undefined organic compounds, have been found to yield a yellowish or greenish off color or a turbidity following the addition of nessler reagent. Such interferences may arise during the course of a direct nesslerization. No specific procedure can be recommended for eliminating all of them, but recourse should be had to distillation when they occur. Some volatile substances such as formaldehyde can be removed by boiling at low pH, after which the sample can be nesslerized.

1.3. *Minimum detectable concentration:* Same as Method A, Sec. 1.3.

2. Apparatus and Reagents

The colorimetric equipment described in Method A, Sec. 2.2, and all the reagents listed in Method A, Sec. 3, except the phosphate buffer and boric acid solutions, are required, plus the following:

2.1. *Zinc sulfate solution:* Dissolve 100 g $ZnSO_4 \cdot 7H_2O$ in ammonia-free water and dilute to 1 liter.

2.2. *Sodium hydroxide, 6N.* Dissolve 240 g NaOH in 500 ml ammonia-free water and dilute to 1 liter.

2.3. *Stabilizer reagent:* Either EDTA or Rochelle salt may be used to prevent calcium or magnesium precipitation following the addition of the alkaline nessler reagent.

a. *EDTA reagent:* Dissolve 50 g disodium ethylenediamine tetraacetate dihydrate, also called (ethylenedinitrilo) tetraacetic acid disodium salt, in 60 ml ammonia-free water containing 10 g sodium hydroxide. If necessary, apply gentle heat to complete the dissolution. Cool to room temperature and dilute to 100 ml.

b. *Rochelle salt solution:* Dissolve 50 g potassium sodium tartrate tetrahydrate, $KNaC_4H_4O_6 \cdot 4H_2O$, in 100 ml ammonia-free water. Remove the ammonia usually present in the salt by boiling off 30 ml of the solution. After cooling, dilute to 100 ml.

3. Procedure

3.1. If necessary, remove the residual chlorine of the sample with an equivalent amount of dechlorinating-agent solution.

3.2. Add 1 ml zinc sulfate solution to 100 ml of sample; mix thoroughly; add 0.4 to 0.5 ml sodium hydroxide solution to obtain a pH of 10.5 as determined with a pH meter and a high-pH glass electrode; again mix thoroughly. Allow the treated sample to stand for a few minutes, whereupon a heavy precipitate should fall, leaving the supernatant liquid clear and colorless. Clarify by centrifuging or filtering.

3.3. Test any filter paper used to be sure no ammonia is present. This may be done by running ammonia-free water through and testing the filtrate by nesslerization. Filter the sample and discard the first 25 ml of the filtrate.

3.4. Take 50.0 ml, or an aliquot portion diluted to 50.0 ml with ammonia-free water, add 1 drop of EDTA reagent or 1 or 2 drops of Rochelle salt solution, and mix well. Add 2.0 ml nessler reagent if EDTA reagent is used, or 1.0 ml nessler reagent if Rochelle salt is used; and mix thoroughly. Measure the color developed, either photometrically or visually, as described in Method A, Sec. 4.5–4.7.

4. Calculation

$$\text{mg/1 ammonia } N = \frac{\text{mg ammonia } N \times 1,000}{\text{ml sample}}$$

The free NH_3 and NH_4 values can be calculated by multiplying the ammonia nitrogen results by the factors 1.216 and 1.288, respectively.

5. Precision and Accuracy

A precision of ± 5 per cent of the nitrogen value can be attained with a little practice by resort to photometric methods. A river water "unknown" sample to which was added 0.40 mg/1 ammonia nitrogen was determined with a standard deviation of ± 0.09 mg/1 in seventeen laboratories, using the direct nesslerization method.

Bibliography

1. JACKSON, D. D. Permanent Standards for Use in the Analysis of Water. *Mass. Inst. Technol. Quart.* 13:314 (1900).
2. NICHOLS, M. S. & FOOTE, M. E. Distillation of Free Ammonia from Buffered Solutions. *Ind. Eng. Chem., Anal. Ed.* 3:311 (1931).
3. GRIFFIN, A. E. & CHAMBERLIN, N. S. Relation of Ammonia Nitrogen to Break-Point Chlorination. *A.J.P.H.* 31:803 (1941).
4. PALIN, A. T. Symposium on the Sterilization of Water: Chemical Aspects of Chlorination. *J. Inst. Water Engrs.* 4:565 (1950).
5. SAWYER, C. N. pH Adjustment for Determination of Ammonia Nitrogen. *Anal. Chem.* 25:816 (1953).
6. TARAS, M. J. Effect of Free Residual Chlorination of Nitrogen Compounds in Water. *J. AWWA* 45:47 (1953).
7. BOLTZ, D. F., ed. *Colorimetric Determination of Nonmetals.* Interscience Publishers, New York (1958) pp. 75–97.

Nitrogen (Nitrate)

Nitrate represents the most highly oxidized phase in the nitrogen cycle and normally reaches important concentrations in the final stages of biologic oxidation. It generally occurs in trace quantities in surface water supplies but may attain high levels in some ground waters. In excessive amounts, it contributes to the illness known as infant methemoglobinemia. A limit of 45 mg/l nitrate has accordingly been imposed on drinking waters as a means of averting this condition. The nitrate concentration of most drinking waters usually falls below 10 mg/l.

Selection of Method: Nitrate is a difficult determination in the presence of interfering ions. The phenoldisulfonic acid method (*A*) is subject to severe chloride interference, necessitating complete chloride removal for a correct result. Nitrite responds like nitrate, but this interference is relatively minor because of the low nitrite concentrations prevalent in potable water supplies. Nitrate nitrogen levels down to 0.01 mg/l may be estimated by the method.

The brucine method (*B*) is satisfactory for the determination of nitrate nitrogen in the range of 1–10 mg/l. Although chloride offers no special difficulties, strong oxidizing and reducing agents must be absent. Samples and standards must be treated in an identical manner for a successful determination.

Methods *A* and *B* have been used over the longest period of time and are considered standard.

The ultraviolet spectrophotometric (*C*) and polarographic (*D*) methods are useful in screening a large number of drinking water samples for public health acceptability. Both methods enable the identification of those samples which yield high uncorrected nitrate values. The nitrate results of such samples should then be checked by the standard methods (*A* or *B*) to ascertain the correct nitrate values.

A reduction method for the determination of nitrate nitrogen in sewage is described in Part III. With the proper precautions, this method can be applied to water samples.

Storage of sample: To prevent any change in the nitrogen balance through biologic activity, the nitrate determinations should be started promptly after sampling. If such a step is impractical, storage near freezing temperature is advisable. If acid preservation is employed, it is important that the sample acidity be neutralized to at least pH 7 immediately before the procedure is undertaken.

A. Phenoldisulfonic Acid Method

1. General Discussion

1.1. *Principle:* The yellow color produced by the reaction between nitrate and phenoldisulfonic acid obeys Beer's law up to at least 12 mg/l N at a wavelength of 480 mμ when a light path of 1 cm is used. At a wavelength of 410 mμ, the point of maximum absorption, determinations may be made up to 2 mg/l with the same cell path.

1.2. *Interference:* As even small concentrations of chloride result in nitrate losses in this method, it is important that the chloride content be reduced to a minimum, preferably below 10 mg/l. However, the silver sulfate used for this purpose presents problems with some water samples owing to the incomplete precipitation of silver ion, which produces an off color or turbidity when the final color is developed. The preferred alkali for color development in the final stage of the determination is ammonium hydroxide, particularly where chloride removal must be practiced on the sample. Potassium hydroxide should be used only if ammonia fumes must be reduced to a minimum in the laboratory atmosphere (for example, when trace amounts of ammonia nitrogen are being determined concurrently). A faint tinge of brown is imparted by potassium hydroxide to the final color when a silver compound has been previously applied for chloride precipitation. Nitrite levels in excess of 0.2 mg/l N erratically increase the apparent nitrate concentration. Colored ions and materials physically modifying the color system should be absent.

1.3. *Minimum detectable concentration:* In the absence of interference, the phenoldisulfonic acid method is sensitive to 1 μg of nitrate nitrogen, which represents 0.01 mg/l in a 100-ml sample.

2. Apparatus

Colorimetric equipment: One of the following is required:

2.1. *Spectrophotometer,* for use at 410 mμ, providing a light path of 1 cm or longer.

2.2. *Filter photometer,* providing a light path of 1 cm or longer and equipped with a violet filter having maximum transmittance near 410 mμ.

2.3. *Nessler tubes,* matched, 50 or 100 ml.

3. Reagents

All reagents must be prepared from chemicals which are white in color, and all solutions must be stored in pyrex containers.

3.1. *Standard silver sulfate solution:* Dissolve 4.40 g Ag_2SO_4, free from nitrate, in distilled water and dilute to 1.0 liter; 1.00 ml is equivalent to 1.00 mg Cl.

3.2. *Phenoldisulfonic acid reagent:* Dissolve 25 g pure white phenol in 150 ml conc H_2SO_4. Add 75 ml fuming H_2SO_4 (15 per cent free SO_3); stir well; and heat for 2 hr on a hot water bath.

3.3. *Ammonium hydroxide,* conc. If this cannot be used, prepare 12N potassium hydroxide solution by dissolving 673 g KOH in distilled water and diluting to 1 liter.

3.4. *EDTA reagent:* Rub 50 g disodium ethylenediamine tetraacetate dihydrate, also called (ethylenedinitrilo)-tetraacetic acid sodium salt, with 20 ml distilled water to form a thoroughly wetted paste. Add 60 ml conc NH_4OH and mix well to dissolve the paste. (The EDTA solution described under Nitrogen (Ammonia), Method B, Sec. 2.3a, can also be used.)

3.5. *Stock nitrate solution:* Dissolve 0.7218 g anhydrous potassium nitrate, KNO_3, and dilute to 1,000 ml with distilled water. This solution contains 100 mg/l N.

3.6. *Standard nitrate solution:* Evaporate 50.0 ml stock nitrate solution to dryness on a steam or hot water bath; dissolve the residue by rubbing with 2.0 ml phenoldisulfonic acid reagent, and dilute to 500 ml with distilled water; 1.00 ml $= 10.0 \ \mu g \ N = 44.3 \ \mu g \ NO_3$.

3.7. *Reagents for treatment of unusual interference:*

a. *Aluminum hydroxide suspension:* Dissolve 125 g potassium or ammonium alum, $K_2Al_2(SO_4)_4 \cdot 24H_2O$ or $(NH_4)_2Al_2(SO_4)_4 \cdot 24H_2O$, in 1 liter distilled water. Warm to 60°C; and add 55 ml conc NH_4OH slowly, with stirring. After permitting the mixture to stand about 1 hr, transfer to a large bottle and wash the precipitate by successive additions (with thorough mixing) and decantations of distilled water, until free from ammonia, chloride, nitrite, and nitrate.

b. *Sulfuric acid, 1N.* Dilute cautiously 28 ml conc H_2SO_4 to 1 liter with distilled water.

c. *Potassium permanganate, 0.1N.* Dissolve 0.316 g $KMnO_4$ in distilled water and dilute to 100 ml.

d. *Dilute hydrogen peroxide solution:* Dilute 10 ml of 30 per cent hydrogen peroxide (low in nitrate) to 100 ml with distilled water.

e. *Sodium hydroxide, 1N.* Dissolve 40 g NaOH and dilute to 1 liter with distilled water.

4. Procedure

4.1. *Color removal:* If the sample has a color of more than 10, decolorize by adding 3 ml aluminum hydroxide suspension to 150 ml of sample; stir very thoroughly; allow to stand for a few minutes; then filter, discarding the first portion of the filtrate.

4.2. *Nitrite conversion:* To 100 ml of sample add 1 ml of H_2SO_4 and stir. Add dropwise, with stirring, either $KMnO_4$ or H_2O_2 solution. Let the treated sample stand for 15 min to complete the conversion of nitrite to

nitrate. (A faint pink color persists for at least 15 min when sufficient $KMnO_4$ is used.) Make the proper deduction at the end of the nitrate determination for the nitrite concentration as determined by the method described in Nitrogen (Nitrite).

4.3. *Chloride removal:* Determine the chloride content of the water (see under Chloride) and treat 100 ml of sample with an equivalent amount of standard silver sulfate solution. Remove the precipitated chloride either by centrifugation or by filtration, coagulating the silver chloride by heat if necessary. (Excellent removal of silver chloride can be achieved by allowing the treated sample to stand overnight at laboratory temperature away from strong light. This approach is applicable to samples free of contamination by nitrifying organisms.)

4.4. Neutralize the clarified sample to approximately pH 7, transfer to a casserole, and evaporate to dryness over a hot water bath. Using a glass rod, rub the residue thoroughly with 2.0 ml phenoldisulfonic acid reagent to insure dissolution of all solids. If need be, heat mildly on the hot water bath a short time to dissolve the entire residue. Dilute with 20 ml distilled water and add with stirring about 6 to 7 ml NH_4OH or about 5 to 6 ml KOH until maximum color is developed. Remove any resulting flocculent hydroxides by passing through a filter paper or filtering crucible, or add the EDTA reagent dropwise with stirring until the turbidity redissolves. Transfer the filtrate or clear solution to a 50- or 100-ml volumetric flask or nessler tube, dilute to the mark, and mix.

4.5. Photometric readings can be made in cells with a 1-cm or longer light path at a wavelength of 410 mμ or with violet filters exhibiting maximum transmission in the range from 400 to 425 mμ. A 5-cm light path is suitable for measurements in the nitrogen interval from 5 to 50 μg, while a 1-cm light path can be used in a proportionate range. Readings should be made against a blank prepared from the same volumes of phenoldisulfonic acid reagent and NH_4OH or KOH as used for the samples.

4.6. For visual comparison in 50-ml nessler tubes, the following volumes of standard nitrate solution are suggested: 0.0, 0.1, 0.3, 0.5, 0.7, 1.0, 1.5, 2.0, 3.5, 6.0, 10, 15, 20, and 30 ml. Where it is more convenient to use a total volume of 100 ml, the volumes of standard solution may be doubled. To each of these standards must be added 2.0 ml phenoldisulfonic acid reagent and the same volume of the same alkali as is used in the preparation of the sample. These standards may be kept several weeks without deterioration.

5. Calculation

$$mg/l \text{ nitrate N} = \frac{mg \text{ nitrate N} \times 1{,}000}{ml \text{ sample}}$$

$$mg/l \; NO_3 = mg/l \text{ nitrate N} \times 4.43$$

6. Precision and Accuracy

Accuracy of the order of ± 0.1 mg/l nitrate nitrogen can be obtained only by the proper treatment of the chloride and nitrite interference. Many laboratories appear to have difficulty in coping with these interferences.

A synthetic unknown sample containing 1.1 mg/l nitrate nitrogen, 0.25 mg/l nitrite nitrogen, and 241 mg/l chloride was determined in 40 laboratories with a standard deviation of ± 1.1 mg/l nitrogen. One-half of the reported results were within ± 0.4 mg/l of the known nitrate nitrogen concentration. The individual laboratories reproduced their own results within ± 0.1 mg/l.

B. Brucine Method*

1. General Discussion

1.1. *Principle:* The reaction between nitrate and brucine yields a sulfur yellow color employed for colorimetric estimation. The color system does not obey Beer's law, although in plotting transmittance against nitrate concentration a smooth curve is produced. It is necessary to develop color simultaneously in a series of standards and samples. The intensity of the color is measured at 410 mμ.

The intensity of the maximum color produced varies more or less inversely with the temperature, while the rate of color development varies more or less directly with the temperature. The temperature generated upon mixing sulfuric acid with water can be controlled by adjusting the acid concentration. Both the acid concentration and the reaction time have been selected to yield optimum results and to compensate for any normal variations in room temperature.

1.2. *Interference:* All strong oxidizing or reducing agents interfere. The presence of oxidizing agents may be

* This method, with modifications, is identical in source and substance to ASTM D992–52.

determined by the addition of orthotolidine reagent as in the measurement of residual chlorine. The interference by residual chlorine may be eliminated by the addition of sodium arsenite, provided that the residual chlorine does not exceed 5 mg/1. A slight excess of sodium arsenite will not affect the determination. Ferrous and ferric iron and quadrivalent manganese give slight positive interferences, but in concentrations less than 1 mg/1 these are negligible. The interference due to nitrite is eliminated by the use of sulfanilic acid. Chloride does not interfere.

2. Apparatus

2.1. *Colorimetric equipment:* One of the following is required:

a. Spectrophotometer, for use at 410 mμ, providing a light path of 1 cm or longer.

b. Filter photometer, providing a light path of 1 cm or longer and equipped with a violet filter having maximum transmittance between 400 and 425 mμ.

2.2. *Safety pipet.*

3. Reagents

3.1. *Stock nitrate solution:* Prepare as described in Method A, Sec. 3.5.

3.2. *Standard nitrate solution:* Dilute 100.0 ml stock nitrate solution to 1,000 ml with distilled water; 1.00 ml = 10.0 μg N.

3.3. *Sodium arsenite solution:* Dissolve 5.0 g $NaAsO_2$ and dilute to 1 liter with distilled water. (CAUTION: *Toxic; take care to avoid ingestion.*)

3.4. *Brucine-sulfanilic acid reagent:* Dissolve 1 g brucine sulfate and 0.1 g sulfanilic acid in approximately 70 ml hot distilled water. Add 3 ml conc HCl, cool, and make up to 100 ml. This solution is stable for several months. The pink color that develops slowly does not affect its usefulness. (CAUTION: *Brucine is toxic; take care to avoid ingestion.*)

3.5. *Sulfuric acid solution:* Carefully add 500 ml of conc H_2SO_4 to 75 ml distilled water. Cool to room temperature before use. Keep tightly stoppered to prevent absorption of atmospheric moisture.

4. Procedure

4.1. *Preparation of standard curve:* Prepare nitrate standards in the range 0.0–10.0 mg/1 N by diluting appropriate quantities of the standard nitrate solution to 100 ml with distilled water. Suggested volumes of standard nitrate solution are: 0, 5, 15, 25, 35, 50, 75, and 100 ml. Treat 2.00 ml of each solution as described under Sec. 4.3, and determine the photometer readings.

4.2. *Pretreatment of sample:* If the sample contains chlorine, remove it by adding 1 drop (0.05 ml) sodium arsenite solution for each 0.10 mg Cl, and mix. Add 1 drop in excess to a 50-ml portion.

4.3. *Color development:* Carefully pipet 2.00 ml of sample containing not more than 10 mg/1 nitrogen into a 50-ml beaker. Add 1.0 ml brucine-sulfanilic acid reagent, using a safety pipet. Into a second 50-ml beaker measure 10 ml H_2SO_4. (An automatic buret is convenient for this purpose. The intensity of color is affected slightly by the heat capacity of the containers. The concentration of H_2SO_4 has been chosen so that normal variations in heat capacities of beakers will not affect the result. It is important, however, that only 50-ml beakers be used.) Mix the contents of the two beakers by carefully adding the sample with brucine-sulfanilic acid reagent to the beaker containing acid. Pour from one beaker to the other four to six times to insure mixing. Allow the treated sample to remain in the dark for 10 ± 1 min. (The beaker may conveniently be covered with a cardboard carton during this period.) While the sample is standing for color development, measure 10 ml distilled water into the empty beaker. After 10 min add the water to the sample and mix as before. Allow to cool in the dark for 20–30 min. Set the blank at 100 per cent transmittance at a wavelength of 410 mμ. It is advisable to run a series of standards with each set of samples. With a proper arrangement of work, as many as twelve samples may be determined in a batch along with eight standards.

5. Calculation

Refer to Method A, Sec. 5.

6. Precision and Accuracy

A synthetic unknown sample containing 1.1 mg/l nitrate nitrogen, 0.25 mg/l nitrite nitrogen, and 241 mg/l chloride was determined by the brucine method in seven laboratories with a standard deviation of ± 0.49 mg/l nitrogen. One-half of the reported results were within ± 0.1 mg/l of the known nitrate nitrogen concentration. The individual laboratories reproduced their own results within ± 0.1 mg/l.

C. Ultraviolet Spectrophotometric Method (Tentative)

1. General Discussion

1.1. *Principle:* Measurement of the ultraviolet absorption at 220 mμ enables a rapid means of determining nitrate. The nitrate calibration curve follows Beer's law up to 11 mg/l N. Because dissolved organic matter may also absorb at 220 mμ and nitrate does not absorb at 275 mμ, a second measurement is made at 275 mμ for the purpose of correcting the nitrate value. The extent of this empirical correction is related to the nature and concentration of the organic matter, and, consequently, may vary from one water sample to another. Filtration of the sample is intended to remove possible interference from suspended particles. Acidification with $1N$ hydrochloric acid is designed to prevent interference from hydroxide or carbonate concentrations up to 1,000 mg/l as $CaCO_3$. Chloride is without effect on the determination.

1.2. *Interference:* Dissolved organic matter, nitrite, hexavalent chromium, and surfactants interfere. The latter three substances may be compensated for by the preparation of individual correction curves.

Organic matter can cause a positive but variable interference, the degree depending on the nature and concentration of the organic material. For this reason, sufficient data must be accumulated in order to obtain a factor which can be used for a given water. This factor may not apply to another water containing organic matter of a different chemical structure.

In this connection, organic contaminants determined by the carbon chloroform extract method or chemical oxygen demand values in excess of 50 $\mu g/l$ or 5 mg/l, respectively, are significant indicators of organic pollution. Dilution of the sample represents one way of minimizing organic interference.

Occasionally high quality well waters and river waters give ultraviolet nitrate values which are at first higher than those obtained by the usual determinations of nitrite and nitrate. When such samples are kept for several weeks, the nitrate values obtained by the customary colorimetric methods eventually rise to those found by the ultraviolet method.

Thorough cleaning and rinsing of all glassware must be practiced in order to reduce the error which might result from streaks or particles on the outside of the cuvets, as well as traces of surfactants or dichromate cleaning solution which might adhere on the interior glass surfaces.

Highly colored samples should be decolorized or diluted to minimize color interference.

Sulfate, ammonium bicarbonate, phosphate, and fluoride in the concentrations normally present in drinking water offer negligible interference.

1.3. *Minimum detectable concentration:* 0.02 mg/l nitrate N.

2. Apparatus

2.1. *Spectrophotometer,* for use at 220 mμ and 275 mμ with matched silica cells of 1-cm or longer light path. A Beckman Model DU spectrophotometer with a photomultiplier attachment and hydrogen lamp source, or equivalent, is satisfactory.

2.2. *Filter:* One of the following is required:

a. Membrane filter. A Millipore filter type HA and appropriate filter assembly, or equivalent, is satisfactory.

b. Paper: Acid-washed, ashless, hard-finish filter paper sufficiently retentive for fine precipitates.

2.3. *Nessler tubes,* 50 ml, short form.

3. Reagents

3.1. *Redistilled water:* Redistill single-distilled water from an all-pyrex still. Use the redistilled water for the preparation of all solutions and dilutions.

3.2. *Stock nitrate solution:* Prepare as described in Method A, Sec. 3.5; 1.00 ml = 0.100 mg N = 0.443 mg NO_3.

3.3. *Standard nitrate solution:* Prepare as described in Method B, Sec. 3.2; 1.00 ml = 10.0 μg N = 44.3 μg NO_3.

3.4. *Hydrochloric acid solution, 1N:* 1 + 11.

4. Procedure

4.1. *Preparation of standard curve:* Prepare nitrate calibration standards in the range 0–0.35 mg N by diluting to 50 ml the following volumes of the standard nitrate solution: 0, 1.00, 2.00, 4.00, 7.00. . . . 35.0 ml. Add to each standard 1 ml 1N HCl, mix, and measure the absorbance or transmittance at 220 mμ against redistilled water. Check the standard curve periodically in the area of interest.

4.2. *Treatment of sample:* Pass sufficient sample through an appropriate filter and collect 50 ml filtrate in the nessler tube. If filter paper is used, wash the paper well with redistilled water and discard the first 25 ml of the filtrate before collecting the filtrate. Add 1 ml $1N$ HCl to the filtrate, and invert the tube a dozen times to insure complete reaction of the carbonate.

4.3. *Spectrophotometric measurement:* Read the absorbance or transmittance of the sample against redistilled water set at zero absorbance or 100 per cent transmittance. Use a wavelength of 220 mμ to obtain the nitrate reading and a wavelength of 275 mμ to obtain the interference due to dissolved organic matter.

4.4. *Preparation of correction curves for nitrite, hexavalent chromium, and surfactants:* When nitrite, chromium and anionic surfactants are known to be present in the sample, prepare correction curves for each of these substances at 2-mg/l intervals up to 10 mg/l. Use potassium nitrite, KNO_2, potassium dichromate, $K_2Cr_2O_7$, and alkyl benzene sulfonate (or linear alkylate sulfonate), and redistilled water for this purpose. Measure the absorbances given by varying concentrations of each substance at wavelength 220 mμ against redistilled water, and plot a separate curve for each of these interfering materials.

5. Calculation

5.1. *Correction for dissolved organic matter:* Convert the absorbance or transmittance measurement at 275 mμ into equivalent nitrate by reading the nitrate value from the standard calibration curve obtained at 220 mμ. Multiply the value by a suitable correction factor which has been determined on a sufficient number of samples of the particular water. (In some cases a factor of 2 may apply, while in other instances the empirical factor of 2 may be too high. A good general rule is to rely on the ultraviolet method only when the correction for organic matter amounts to less than 20 per cent of the total apparent nitrate reading.) Deduct the organic correction from the gross nitrate result.

5.2. *Correction for nitrite, hexavalent chromium, or surfactants:* Deduct the equivalent nitrate values for each of these interfering substances from the gross nitrate result.

5.3.

$$\text{mg/l nitrate N} = \frac{\text{net mg nitrate N} \times 1{,}000}{\text{ml sample}}$$

$$\text{mg/l NO}_3 = \text{mg/l nitrate N} \times 4.43$$

D. Polarographic Method (Tentative)

1. General Discussion

1.1. *Principle:* The method is based on the reduction of nitrate nitrogen at the dropping mercury electrode in slightly acid solution in the presence of uranyl ion.

1.2. *Interference:* Nitrite interferes by producing a wave similar to that of nitrate, the response for nitrite nitrogen being somewhat over half as high as that obtained from an equiva-

lent concentration of nitrate nitrogen. Correction for nitrite nitrogen can be made by determining the nitrite with another method. The precise correction factor for nitrite should be determined under identical conditions used for the nitrate determination, because nitrite is not completely stable in the acid solution used. Phosphates interfere if present in concentrations greater than 4 mg/l as phosphorus in samples containing more than 20 mg/l nitrate nitrogen. Because phosphates interfere only in samples containing high concentrations of nitrate nitrogen, the interference can be eliminated by dilution. Ferric iron interferes slightly and should be allowed to settle out of the sample before withdrawal of the portion for nitrate analysis. Fluoride up to 5 mg/l, sulfate up to 2,500 mg/l, and alkalinities of 1,000 mg/l as calcium carbonate do not interfere.

1.3. *Minimum detectable concentration:* The procedure will determine 0.2 mg/l nitrate nitrogen; however, best results are obtained in the range above 0.5 mg/l. Concentration of the sample by evaporation will lower the nitrate nitrogen minimum which can be determined, provided the level of interfering substances is not increased beyond the permissible limits.

2. Apparatus

Polarograph, with a low-resistance reference electrode and salt bridge system. A commercially available polarograph may be used or one may be constructed according to directions found in any standard text on polarography. A reference electrode with a flexible salt bridge that can be immersed in the sample is convenient (Fig. 18). Relatively large diffusion currents are involved in this procedure; therefore, it is important that the voltage drops through the system be kept at a minimum. The reference electrode and its associated salt bridge and liquid junction should be of low electrical resistance.

3. Reagents

3.1. *Uranyl catalyst:* Dissolve 25 ml glacial (conc) acetic acid, 0.34 g uranyl acetate dihydrate,

$$UO_2(C_2H_3O_2)_2 \cdot 2H_2O,$$

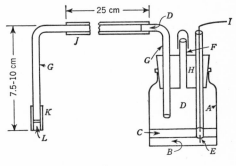

LEGEND

A. 60-ml (2-oz) wide-mouth bottle.
B. Mercury layer.
C. Mercury-mercurous chloride paste.
D. Saturated potassium chloride solution.
E. Platinum sealed in glass.
F. Vent and fill tube.
G. 6.5-mm (1/4-in.) O. D. glass tube.
H. Rubber stopper.
I. Wire lead.
J. 6.5-mm (1/4-in.) I. D. Tygon tubing; 1.5-mm (1/16-in.) wall.
K. Thin-wall teflon sleeve.
L. Porous glass plug from Corning No. 7930 glass or equivalent.

Fig. 18. Reference electrode and salt bridge for polarographic method for nitrate

14.8 g KCl, and 1.7 ml conc hydrochloric acid in distilled water, and make up to 1 liter.

3.2. *Stock nitrate solution:* Prepare as described in Method A, Sec. 3.5.

3.3. *Standard nitrate solution:* Dilute 10.00 ml stock nitrate solution to 100 ml for a standard having a concentration of 10 mg/l N.

4. Procedure

4.1. *Preparation of sample and standard:* Adjust both standard and sample to room temperature. If necessary, dilute the sample to a nitrate nitrogen concentration below 30 mg/l. Measure 5.0 ml sample, 5.0 ml distilled water, and 5.0 ml of 10-mg/l standard nitrate nitrogen solution into

separate ¾-oz paper souffle cups or
15-ml beakers. Add 5.0 ml uranyl
catalyst to each cup and allow to stand
a few minutes.

4.2. *Polarographic measurement:* At
−1.2 volt vs SCE (saturated calomel
electrode), zero the polarograph with
the electrodes in the air. Place the
electrodes in the blank and adjust the
sensitivity to give a reading of about
25 per cent of full scale. Suppress this
reading to zero with the zero set adjustment. Read the sample and standard at these settings.

5. Calculation

$$\text{mg/l nitrate nitrogen} = \frac{A \times 10}{B}$$

where A = reading for sample, and B
= reading for standard. This relation
holds up to about 35 mg/l nitrate nitrogen. Samples with higher nitrogen
concentrations should be appropriately
diluted and the determination repeated.

$$\text{mg/l } NO_3 = \text{mg/l nitrate N} \times 4.43$$

6. Precision and Accuracy

Nitrate nitrogen concentrations in
excess of 2 mg/l can be determined
with an estimated precision and accuracy of ±5 per cent.

Bibliography

Phenoldisulfonic Acid Method

1. CHAMOT, E. M.; PRATT, D. S.; & RED-
   FIELD, H. W. A Study on the Phenoldisulfonic Acid Method for the Determination of Nitrates in Water. *J. Am.
   Chem. Soc.* 31:922 (1909); 32:630
   (1910); 33:366 (1911).
2. TARAS, M. J. Phenoldisulfonic Acid
   Method of Determining Nitrate in
   Water: Photometric Study. *Anal.
   Chem.* 22:1020 (1950).
3. BOLTZ, D. F., ed. *Colorimetric Determi-*
nation of Nonmetals. Interscience
Publishers, New York (1958). pp.
135–147.

Brucine Method

4. HAASE, L. W. Colorimetric Determination of Nitrate. [In German.]
   Chemiker-Ztg. 50:372 (1926).
5. NOLL, C. A. Determination of Nitrate
   in Boiler Water by Brucine Reagent.
   Ind. Eng. Chem., Anal. Ed. 17:426
   (1945).
6. *Method of Test for Nitrate Ion in Industrial Water—D992-52.* Am. Soc.
   Testing Materials, Philadelphia
   (1952).
7. GREENBERG, A. E., ET AL. Study of Methods for the Determination of Nitrates.
   J. AWWA 50:821 (1958).

Ultraviolet Spectrophotometric Method

8. HOATHER, R. C. Applications of Spectrophotometry in the Examination of
   Waters. *Proc. Soc. Water Treatment and Exam.* 2:9 (1953).
9. BASTIAN, R., ET AL. Ultraviolet Spectrophotometric Determination of Nitrate. *Anal. Chem.* 29:1795 (1957).
10. HOATHER, R. C. & RACKHAM, R. F. Ox-
    idized Nitrogen and Sewage Effluents
    Observed by Ultraviolet Spectro-
    photometry. *Analyst* 84:549 (1959).
11. GOLDMAN, E. & JACOBS, R. Determina-
    tion of Nitrates by Ultraviolet Ab-
    sorption. *J. AWWA* 53:187 (1961).
12. ARMSTRONG, F. A. J. Determination of
    Nitrate in Water by Ultraviolet Spec-
    trophotometry. *Anal. Chem.* 35:1292
    (1963).
13. NAVONE, R. Proposed Method for Ni-
    trate in Potable Waters, *J. AWWA*
    56:781 (1964).

Polarographic Method

14. HUME, D. N. & HARRIS, W. E. An
    Improved Salt Bridge for Polaro-
    graphic and Potentiometric Measure-
    ments. *Ind. Eng. Chem., Anal. Ed.*
    15:465 (1943).
15. KOLTHOFF, I. M., ET AL. A New Method
    for the Polarographic Determination
    of Nitrate. *J. Am. Chem. Soc.* 66:1782
    (1944).
16. CHOW, D. T-W. & ROBINSON, R. J.

Polarographic Determination of Nitrate in Sea Water. *J. Marine Res.* 12:1 (1953).

17. RAND, M. C. & HEUKELEKIAN, H. Polarographic Determination of Nitrates

in Sanitary Analysis. *Anal. Chem.* 25:878 (1953).

18. FRAZIER, R. E. Polarographic Determination of Nitrate Nitrogen in Water. *J. AWWA* 55:624 (1963).

Nitrogen (Nitrite)

Nitrite, an intermediate stage in the nitrogen cycle, may occur in water as a result of the biological decomposition of proteinaceous materials. When correlated with the concentration of other nitrogen forms, trace amounts of nitrite may indicate organic pollution. Nitrite may also be produced in water treatment plants or in the distribution system through the action of bacteria or other organisms on ammonia nitrogen fed at elevated temperatures in the combined residual chlorination of water. Nitrite can likewise enter a water supply through its use as a corrosion inhibitor in industrial process water. The nitrite concentration of a drinking water rarely exceeds 0.1 mg/l.

1. General Discussion

1.1. *Principle:* The nitrite concentration is determined through the formation of a reddish-purple azo dye produced at pH 2.0 to 2.5 by the coupling of diazotized sulfanilic acid with naphthylamine hydrochloride. The diazotization method is suitable for the visual determination of nitrite nitrogen in the range 1–25 μg/l N. Photometric measurements can be performed in the range 5–50 μg/l if a 5-cm light path and a green color filter are available. The color system obeys Beer's law up to 0.18 mg/l N or 0.6 mg/l NO_2, with a 1-cm light path at 520 mμ.

1.2. *Interference:* Chemical incompatibility makes it unlikely that nitrite, free available chlorine, and nitrogen trichloride will coexist in a sample. Nitrogen trichloride imparts a false red color when the normal order of reagent addition is followed. Although this effect may be minimized somewhat by adding the naphthylamine hydrochloride reagent first and then the sulfanilic acid reagent, an orange color may still result when a substantial nitrogen trichloride concentration is present. A check for a free available chlorine and nitrogen trichloride residual is advisable under such circumstances. The following ions interfere due to precipitation under the conditions of the test and, therefore, should be absent: ferric, mercurous, silver, bismuth, antimonous, lead, auric, chloroplatinate, and metavanadate. Cupric ion may cause low results by catalyzing the decomposition of the diazonium salt. Colored ions which alter the color system should likewise be absent.

1.3. *Minimum detectable concentration:* In the absence of interference, the minimum nitrite nitrogen concentration detectable in a 50-ml nessler tube is 1 μg/l.

1.4. *Storage of sample:* The determination should be made promptly on fresh samples to prevent bacterial conversion of the nitrite to nitrate or ammonia.

2. Apparatus

Colorimetric equipment: One of the following is required:

2.1. *Spectrophotometer,* for use at 520 mμ, providing a light path of 1 cm or longer.

2.2. *Filter photometer,* providing a light path of 1 cm or longer and equipped with a green color filter having maximum transmittance near 520 mμ.

2.3. *Nessler tubes,* matched, 50 ml, tall form.

3. Reagents

All reagents must be prepared from chemicals which are white in color.

3.1. *Nitrite-free water:* Prepare nitrite-free water by either of the following methods:

a. Add to 1 liter distilled water one small crystal each of potassium permanganate and an alkali such as barium or calcium hydroxide (1 or 2 drops of the alkaline permanganate reagent used for the albuminoid nitrogen determination, Sec. 3, is also a satisfactory reagent; add to 1 liter of distilled water). Redistill in an all-pyrex apparatus, discarding the initial 50 ml of distillate. Collect that fraction of the distillate which is free of permanganate. (A yellow color with the orthotolidine reagent, used for the residual chlorine determination, Method B, Sec. 5.1, indicates the presence of permanganate.)

b. See Part III, Nitrogen (Nitrite), Sec. 3.9.

3.2. *EDTA solution:* Dissolve 0.5 g disodium ethylenediamine tetraacetate dihydrate, also called (ethylenedinitrilo)tetraacetic acid sodium salt, in nitrite-free water and dilute to 100 ml.

3.3. *Sulfanilic acid reagent:* Completely dissolve 0.60 g sulfanilic acid in 70 ml hot distilled water, cool, add 20 ml conc HCl, dilute to 100 ml with distilled water, and mix thoroughly.

3.4. *Naphthylamine hydrochloride reagent:* Dissolve 0.60 g 1-naphthylamine hydrochloride in distilled water to which 1.0 ml conc HCl has been added. Dilute to 100 ml with distilled water, and mix thoroughly. The reagent becomes discolored and a precipitate may form after 1 week, but it is still usable. Discard when the sensitivity or reproducibility is affected. Store in a refrigerator to prolong the useful life of the reagent. Filter before using.

3.5. *Sodium acetate buffer solution, 2M.* Dissolve 16.4 g $NaC_2H_3O_2$ or 27.2 g $NaC_2H_3O_2 \cdot 3H_2O$ in nitrite-free water and dilute to 100 ml. Filter if necessary.

3.6. *Stock nitrite solution:* The reagent grade sodium nitrite available commercially assays at less than 99 per cent. Since nitrite is readily oxidized in the presence of moisture, fresh bottles of reagent are desirable for the preparation of the stock solution. The preferred approach is to determine the sodium nitrite content immediately before the preparation of the stock solution and to keep the bottles tightly stoppered against the free access of air when not in use. The sodium nitrite content may be determined by adding an excess of standard potassium permanganate solution, discharging the permanganate color with a standard reductant such as sodium oxalate or ferrous ammonium sulfate solution, and finally back-titrating with standard permanganate solution.

Preparation of stock solution: Dissolve 1.232 g sodium nitrite, $NaNO_2$, in nitrite-free water and dilute to 1,000 ml; 1.0 ml = 0.25 mg N. Preserve with 1 ml chloroform.

Standardization of stock solution: [4,5] Pipet in order 50.00 ml standard 0.05N KMnO₄ (prepared and standardized as described under Calcium, Method B, Sec. 3.3), 5 ml conc sulfuric acid, and 50.00 ml stock nitrite solution into a glass-stoppered flask or bottle. Submerge the tip of the nitrite pipet well below the surface of the permanganate acid solution. Shake the stoppered flask gently. Warm the flask contents to 70°–80°C on a hot plate. Discharge the permanganate color by adding sufficient standard 0.05N sodium oxalate (3.350 g Na₂C₂O₄, primary standard grade, per 1,000 ml solution) in 10.00-ml portions. Titrate the excess sodium oxalate with standard 0.05N KMnO₄ to the faint pink endpoint. Carry a nitrite-free water blank through the entire procedure and make the necessary corrections in the final calculation.

When standard 0.05N ferrous ammonium sulfate solution is substituted for sodium oxalate, omit the heating to 70°–80°C and instead extend the reaction period between the permanganate and ferrous ions to 5 min before the final KMnO₄ titration is undertaken. This standard 0.05N ferrous solution contains 19.607 g Fe(NH₄)₂(SO₄)₂·6H₂O and 20 ml conc H₂SO₄ per 1,000 ml solution and may be standardized as described under Oxygen Demand (Chemical), Sec. 3.3, Part IV.

Calculate the nitrite nitrogen content of the stock solution by the following equation:

$$A = \frac{[(B \times C) - (D \times E)] \times 7}{F}$$

where A = mg/ml nitrite nitrogen in stock nitrite solution, B = total ml standard KMnO₄ used, C = normality of standard KMnO₄, D = total ml standard reductant added, E = normality of standard reductant, and F = ml stock NaNO₂ solution taken for titration. Each 1.00 ml 0.05N KMnO₄ consumed by the nitrite corresponds to 1.725 mg NaNO₂ or 0.350 mg N.

Titration of high nitrite samples: The standardization procedure can also be used for the titration of water samples containing nitrite nitrogen concentrations in excess of 2 mg/l. In such a case, the water sample volume is substituted for F in the previous equation and the factor 7 is increased to 7,000 for the purpose of calculating the nitrite nitrogen value in terms of mg/l.

3.7. *Intermediate nitrite solution:* Calculate the volume, G, of stock nitrite solution required for the intermediate nitrite solution by means of the following equation: $G = 12.5/A$. Dilute to 250 ml the calculated volume, G (approximately 50 ml), of the stock nitrite solution with nitrite-free water; 1.00 ml = 50.0 μg N. Prepare daily.

3.8. *Standard nitrite solution:* Dilute 10.00 ml intermediate nitrite solution to 1,000 ml with nitrite-free water; 1.00 ml = 0.500 μg N. Prepare daily.

3.9. *Aluminum hydroxide suspension:* Prepare as directed in Nitrogen (Nitrate), Method A, Sec. 3.7a.

4. Procedure

4.1. If the sample contains suspended solids and color, add 2 ml aluminum hydroxide suspension to 100 ml sample, stir thoroughly, allow to stand for a few minutes, and filter, discarding the first portion of the filtrate. Coagulation with zinc sulfate and hydroxide may also be practiced as described under Nitrogen (Ammonia), Method B, Sec. 3.2.

4.2. To 50.0 ml clear sample which has been neutralized to pH 7, or to an aliquot diluted to 50.0 ml, add 1.0 ml EDTA solution and 1.0 ml sulfanilic acid reagent. Mix thoroughly. At this point, the pH of the solution should be about 1.4. After it has been standing 3 to 10 min, add 1.0 ml naphthylamine hydrochloride reagent and 1.0 ml sodium acetate buffer solution; mix well. At this point, the pH of the solution should be 2.0 to 2.5. Measure the reddish-purple color after 10 to 30 min.

4.3. Measure the absorbance at or near 520 mμ against a reagent blank, and run parallel checks frequently against known nitrite standards, preferably in the nitrogen range of the samples. Redetermine complete calibration curves following the preparation of new reagents.

4.4. Prepare a suitably spaced series of visual color standards in nessler tubes by adding the following volumes of standard sodium nitrite solution and diluting to 50 ml with nitrite-free water: 0, 0.1, 0.2, 0.4, 0.7, 1.0, 1.4, 1.7, 2.0, and 2.5 ml.

5. Calculation

$$\text{mg/l nitrite N} = \frac{\mu\text{g nitrite N}}{\text{ml sample}}$$

$$\text{mg/l NO}_2 = \text{mg/l nitrite N} \times 3.29$$

6. Precision and Accuracy

The standard deviation was ± 0.03 mg/l among 43 laboratories which determined the nitrite nitrogen by the diazotization method in a synthetic unknown sample containing 0.25 mg/l nitrite nitrogen. One-half of the reported results were within ± 0.04 mg/l of the known nitrite nitrogen concentration. The individual laboratories reproduced their own results within ± 0.02 mg/l.

Bibliography

1. RIDER, B. F. & MELLON, M. G. Colorimetric Determination of Nitrates. *Ind. Eng. Chem., Anal. Ed.* 18:96 (1946).
2. BARNES, H. & FOLKARD, A. R. The Determination of Nitrites. *Analyst* 76:599 (1951).
3. BOLTZ, D. F., ed. *Colorimetric Determination of Nonmetals.* Interscience Publishers, New York (1958). pp. 124–132.
4. *Reagent Chemicals—American Chemical Society Specifications, 1960.* Am. Chem. Soc., Washington, D.C. (1961). p. 474.
5. FURMAN, N. H., ed. *Standard Methods of Chemical Analysis.* D. Van Nostrand Co., Princeton, N. J. (6th ed., 1962). Vol. I, pp. 746–747.

Nitrogen (Organic)

The classical kjeldahl method determines organically bound nitrogen in the trinegative state. The organic nitrogen content of a water is contributed in various degrees by amino acids, polypeptides, and proteins—all products of biologic processes—and, thus, includes albuminoid nitrogen. A rise in the organic nitrogen content may often be related to the sewage or industrial-waste pollution of a given water supply.

The method offered in this manual fails to account for nitrate and nitrite nitrogen. If the ammonia nitrogen is not removed as described in the initial phase (Sec. 4.1) of the organic nitrogen procedure, the term "total kjeldahl nitrogen" is applied to the result. Should the total kjeldahl nitrogen and ammonia nitrogen be determined individually, the "organic nitrogen" can then be obtained by difference.

1. General Discussion

1.1. *Principle:* In the presence of sulfuric acid, potassium sulfate, and mercuric sulfate catalyst, the amino nitrogen of many organic materials is converted to ammonium bisulfate. After the mercury ammonium complex in the digestate has been decomposed by sodium thiosulfate, the ammonia is distilled from an alkaline medium and absorbed in boric acid. The ammonia is determined by nesslerization, or, if preferred, by titration with a standard mineral acid as described in Part III, Nitrogen (Organic), Sec. 4.

1.2. *Selection of modification:* The sensitivity of the nessler reaction makes the nesslerization method useful for the determination of organic nitrogen levels below 1 mg/1. The titrimetric method of measuring the ammonia in the distillate is suitable for the determination of a wide range of organic nitrogen concentrations, depending on the volume of boric acid absorbent used and the concentration of the standard acid titrant.

1.3. *Storage of sample:* The most reliable results are obtained on fresh samples. If a prompt analysis is impossible, every precaution should be taken to retard biologic activity by storing the sample at a low temperature, preferably just above freezing. Where such a measure is impractical, the addition of 0.8 ml conc H_2SO_4 per liter of sample may serve to maintain the nitrogen balance.

2. Apparatus

2.1. *Digestion apparatus:* Kjeldahl flasks with a total capacity of 800 ml yield the best results. Digestions should be conducted over a heating device adjusted in such a manner that 250 ml of distilled water at an initial temperature of 25°C can be heated to a rolling boil in approximately 5 min. A heating device meeting this specification will usually provide the temperature range of 344°–371°C which is desirable for an effective digestion.

2.2. *Distillation apparatus:* The entire assembly consists of a kjeldahl flask, an efficient bulb or trap, and a vertical condenser. Connections between these units can be made with short lengths of rubber tubing. Although gas-heated distillation apparatus may be used, electrically-heated units often offer smoother operation and less bumping. The entire apparatus should be steamed out prior to use, by distilling 500 ml of distilled water (low in ammonia) until the distillate becomes free of ammonia.

2.3. *Colorimetric equipment:* One of the following is required:

a. Spectrophotometer, for use at 400 to 425 mμ, providing a light path of 1 cm or longer.

b. Filter photometer, providing a light path of 1 cm or longer and equipped with a violet filter having maximum transmittance at 400 to 425 mμ.

c. Nessler tubes, matched, 50 ml, tall form.

3. Reagents

All the reagents listed for the determination of Nitrogen (Ammonia), Method A, Sec. 3, are required, plus the following:

3.1. *Digestion reagent:* Dissolve 134

g potassium sulfate, K_2SO_4, in 650 ml ammonia-free distilled water and 200 ml conc H_2SO_4. Add, with stirring, a solution prepared by dissolving 2 g red mercuric oxide, HgO, in 25 ml $6N$ H_2SO_4. Dilute the combined solution to 1 liter. Keep this solution at a temperature above 14°C to prevent crystallization.

3.2. *Phenolphthalein indicator solution:* Either the aqueous (*a*) or alcoholic solution (*b*) may be used.

a. Dissolve 5 g phenolphthalein disodium salt in ammonia-free distilled water and dilute to 1 liter. If necessary, add $0.02N$ NaOH dropwise until a faint pink color appears.

b. Dissolve 5 g phenolphthalein in 500 ml 95 per cent ethyl alcohol or isopropyl alcohol and add 500 ml ammonia-free distilled water. Then add $0.02N$ NaOH dropwise until a faint pink color appears.

3.3. *Sodium hydroxide-sodium thiosulfate reagent:* Dissolve 500 g NaOH and 25 g $Na_2S_2O_3 \cdot 5H_2O$ in ammonia-free distilled water and dilute to 1 liter.

4. Procedure

4.1. Add 10 ml phosphate buffer solution and a few glass beads or boiling chips to a 500-ml sample or less, in an 800-ml kjeldahl flask, and boil off 300 ml. If desired, distill this fraction and determine the ammonia nitrogen.

4.2. Cool and add carefully 50 ml digestion reagent. After mixing, heat under a hood or with suitable ejection equipment to fumes of SO_3, and continue to boil briskly until the solution clears (becomes colorless or a pale straw color). Then digest for an additional 30 min. Allow the flask and contents to cool; dilute to 300 ml with ammonia-free water, and add 0.5 ml phenolphthalein indicator solution and

mix. Tilt the flask and add carefully sufficient (approximately 50 ml) hydroxide-thiosulfate reagent so that an alkaline layer forms at the bottom of the flask.

Connect the flask to the steamed-out distillation apparatus and shake the flask to insure complete mixing. Add more hydroxide-thiosulfate reagent in the prescribed manner if a red phenolphthalein color fails to appear at this stage.

4.3. Distill and collect 200 ml distillate below the surface of 50 ml boric acid solution. Lower the collected distillate free of contact with the delivery tube, and continue distillation during the last minute or two to cleanse the condenser.

4.4. Mix the distillate thoroughly and measure a 50.0-ml portion or less. Complete the determination as described in Nitrogen (Ammonia), Method A, Sec. 4.5–4.7.

4.5. Carry a blank through all the steps of the procedure and apply the necessary correction to the results.

5. Calculation

$$\text{mg/l organic N} = \frac{A \times 1,000}{\text{ml sample}} \times \frac{B}{C}$$

where A = mg N found colorimetrically, B = ml total distillate collected including the H_3BO_3, and C = ml distillate taken for nesslerization.

6. Precision

A precision of ± 5 per cent can be attained with a little practice in the organic nitrogen range up to 1 mg/l by the photometric method, if 500-ml samples are used.

Bibliography

1. MACKENZIE, H. A. & WALLACE, H. S. The Kjeldahl Determination of Nitro-

gen: A Critical Study of Digestion Conditions. *Austral. J. Chem.* 7:55 (1954).

2. MORGAN, G. B.; LACKEY, J. B.; & GILCREAS, F. W. Quantitative Determination of Organic Nitrogen in Water, Sewage, and Industrial Wastes. *Anal. Chem.* 29:833 (1957).

3. BOLTZ, D. F., ed. *Colorimetric Determination of Nonmetals.* Interscience Publishers, New York (1958). pp. 75-97.

4. *Official Methods of Analysis.* Assoc. Official Agricultural Chemists, Washington, D.C. (9th ed., 1960). pp. 12, 643.

Odor

See Taste and Odor.

Oil and Grease

Oil or grease may be present in water as an emulsion from industrial wastes or similar sources, or a light petroleum fraction may be in solution. Some oils in natural waters may derive from the decomposition of plankton or higher forms of aquatic life. Most heavy oils and greases are insoluble in water but may be emulsified or saponified by detergents, alkalis, or other chemicals. Low-boiling fractions are lost in ordinary oil and grease analysis, and special techniques for their determination have been developed.[3-7] Even lubricating oil fractions evaporate at a significant rate at the temperature which is necessary for removal of the last traces of the extraction solvent. Kerosene is still more volatile, and gasoline cannot be determined with any reliability by the petroleum ether extraction method, which is designed for waters that may contain small amounts of oil or grease in solution or suspension. For heavily polluted water or wastes use the methods described under Grease in Part III.

1. General Discussion

1.1. *Principle:* Dissolved or emulsified oil or grease is extracted from water by intimate contact with various organic solvents. Some extractables, especially unsaturated fats and fatty acids, oxidize readily; hence, special precautions regarding temperature and solvent vapor displacement are included to minimize this effect.

1.2. *Interference:* Solvents vary considerably in their ability to dissolve not only oil and grease, but other organic substances as well. No solvent is known that will selectively dissolve only oil and grease. On standing, most solvents tend to form oxidation products which leave a gummy residue on evaporation. Saponified oil or grease tends to remain as an emulsion, but acidification of the sample to about pH 1 or addition of sodium chloride aids in breaking this emulsion. Directions for breaking stubborn emulsions have been described by Pomeroy and Wakeman.[1]

1.3. *Sampling:* Care should be taken that the sample is representative. Samples of oil films taken from the surface of a stream or other body of water will be almost impossible to evaluate in comparison to the total volume of water, the total film area, and the thickness involved. Samples should be taken in clean, glass-stoppered bottles, previously washed with solvent and air dried before use. The bottle should not be completely filled, as a loss of floating oil may occur in stoppering. It is advisable to collect the desired quantity of sample in an oversized bottle that has previously been marked on the outside at the desired volume.

1.4. *Storage of sample:* Stored samples should be acidified with 5 ml of $1 + 1$ H_2SO_4 per liter to inhibit bacterial activity. Since many oils and hydrocarbons are utilized by bacteria, storage is obviously detrimental.

2. Apparatus

Separatory funnel: In the absence of the preferred inert teflon stopcock, all greasy lubricants should be removed from the ground-glass surfaces. A stopcock lubricant that is insoluble in organic solvents may be prepared by making a paste of bentonite and glycerol. This lubricant dissolves very slowly in water and is not affected by petroleum ether. After using apparatus greased with this lubricant, clean the stopcock thoroughly, as the lubricant tends to harden over a period of time. Other suitable lubricants are listed in handbooks or are available commercially.

3. Reagents

3.1. *Sulfuric acid,* $1 + 1$.

3.2. *Petroleum ether,* boiling point 35° to 60°C. Distill at least twice in all-glass apparatus, discarding the last 10 per cent remaining in the flask at each distillation. The residue on evaporation should be less than 0.1 mg per 100 ml. Observe all safety precautions when using petroleum ether because of its potential fire and explosion hazard.

4. Procedure

4.1. Place the sample, usually 1 liter, in a separatory funnel of sufficient size to allow the addition of acid and solvent, and still have space for proper agitation.

4.2. Acidify the sample with 5 ml H_2SO_4 per liter.

4.3. Rinse the sample bottle carefully with 15 ml petroleum ether, and add the ether washings to the separatory funnel. Add an additional 25 ml ether to the separatory funnel, shaking vigorously for 2 min.

4.4. Allow the ether layer to separate. Withdraw the aqueous portion of the sample into a clean container, and transfer the solvent layer into a clean, tared distilling flask capable of holding at least three volumes of solvent. If a clear ether layer cannot be obtained, filter the solvent layer into the tared distilling flask through a funnel containing an ether-moistened Whatman No. 40 (or equivalent) filter paper. Use as small a funnel and filter paper as practical. After all the ether from the two extractions and the final rinsing is included, wash down the funnel and filter paper twice with fresh 5-ml increments of petroleum ether.

4.5. Return the sample to the separatory funnel, rinsing the container with 15 ml ether. Add the ether washings and an additional 25 ml ether to the separatory funnel, and agitate for another 2 min.

4.6. Allow the solvent layer to separate, and discard the aqueous phase. Add the ether extraction to the tared distilling flask, and rinse the separatory funnel with 20 ml ether. Add the ether washings to the tared distilling flask.

4.7. Distill off all but approximately 10 ml of the ether extract by means of a water bath or an electric heating mantle, observing all necessary safety precautions and keeping the heat source at about 70°C. Disconnect the condenser and boil off the remaining solvent from the tared flask at the same temperature. Dry on a water or steam bath.

4.8. When dry, lay the flask on its side to facilitate the removal of solvent vapor. Introduce approximately three volumes of dry illuminating gas into the flask to displace the solvent vapor.

4.9. Cool in a desiccator for 30 min and weigh.

5. Calculation

If the petroleum ether used is known to be free of residue, the gain in weight of the tared distilling flask is mainly due to oil and grease. The total gain in weight, A, of the tared flask less the calculated residue, B, from the solvent, as determined by the distillation or evaporation of a measured quantity, indicates the amount of oil or grease in the water sample:

$$mg/l \text{ oil or grease} = \frac{(A - B) \times 1,000}{ml \text{ sample}}$$

6. Interpretation of Results

This method attempts to avoid most errors that can affect the determination of oil and grease, and should produce satisfactory results when small amounts of oil or grease are present. If the quantity of oil or grease is extremely small, the technical skill of the analyst may be the most important factor in the accuracy of the analysis.

Bibliography

1. POMEROY, R. & WAKEMAN, C. M. Determination of Grease in Sewage, Sludge, and Industrial Wastes. *Ind. Eng. Chem., Anal. Ed.* 13:795 (1941).
2. KIRSCHMAN, H. D. & POMEROY, R. Determination of Oil in Oil Field Waste Waters. *Anal. Chem.* 21:793 (1949).
3. WEBBER, L. A. & BURKS, C. E. The Determination of Light Hydrocarbons in Water. *Anal. Chem.* 24:1086 (1952).
4. MIDDLETON, F. M., ET AL. Fundamental Studies of Taste and Odor in Water Supplies. *J. AWWA* 44:538 (1952).
5. ROSEN, A. A. & MIDDLETON, F. M. Identification of Petroleum Refinery Wastes in Surface Water. *Anal. Chem.* 27:790 (1955).
6. LUDZACK, F. J. & WHITFIELD, C. E. Determination of High-Boiling Paraffin Hydrocarbons in Polluted Water. *Anal. Chem.* 28:157 (1956).
7. LINDGREN, C. Measurement of Small Quantities of Hydrocarbons in Water. *J. AWWA* 49:55 (1957).

Organic Contaminants

Organic contaminants—in natural substances, insecticides, herbicides, and other agricultural chemicals — enter water supplies from runoff. Domestic sewage and industrial wastes, depending on the degree of treatment, contribute contaminants in v a r i o u s amounts. As a result of accidental spills and leaks, industrial organic wastes also enter streams. Some of the contaminants, extremely persistent and only partially removed by treatment, reach the consumer in drinking water.

Contaminants, both natural and manmade, can conceivably have undesirable effects on health. Some of the materials interfere with water quality, and kill fish. A few micrograms per liter may be significant. Where concentrations of 200 μg/l have been found, the taste and odor of the water have nearly always been poor.

The isolation and recovery of DDT, nitriles, orthonitrochlorobenzene, aromatic ethers, and many other synthetic chemicals suggest that a method for assessing these materials in water is desirable.

Carbon Chloroform Extract (CCE) Method (Tentative)

1. General Discussion

1.1. *Principle:* Activated carbon is a remarkable adsorption medium for many types of organic materials. As used in a carbon adsorption unit (Fig. 19), it aids in the detection of low, but significant, quantities of organic contaminants in large volumes of water.

When a sufficient quantity of water has been run through the unit, the carbon containing the adsorbed sample is removed, dried, and extracted with chloroform. The removal of the chloroform by distillation leaves a weighable residue of contaminants. Other solvents, such as ethyl alcohol, will remove additional organics, but for monitoring and control purposes the chloroform extraction is considered adequate.

This method does not determine the total organic content of water. Although it is very effective, the carbon does not adsorb all the organics, and the solvent does not recover all of the materials adsorbed. Synthetic detergents are not measured by this procedure.

Using known amounts of easily adsorbed materials, recoveries may range from 50 to 90 per cent. Replicate samples agree within ± 10 per cent. The technique provides a relative measure of pollution load not obtainable by

other techniques. It reveals undue stress on a water from most industrial contaminants, particularly synthetic chemicals, and furnishes materials that can be subjected to physical, chemical, and physiological tests. The residues can be analyzed in a variety of ways, and constant collection of such data constitutes a valuable index of water quality.

1.2. *Application:* This method is applicable to drinking waters, but not limited to them.

2. Apparatus

2.1. *Carbon adsorption assembly* (Fig. 20) :

a. *Pyrex pipe,* 3-in. diameter, 18-in. length.

b. *Asbestos inserts* (two), for 3-in. pipe.

c. *Flange sets* (two), for 3-in. pipe.

d. *Neoprene gaskets* * (two), ¼-in. thickness, with 3-in. hole slotted to ⅜-in. depth to take screen. Drill 3 holes, ⁵⁄₁₆-in. diameter to match flange.

e. *Stainless-steel screens* * (two), 40 mesh, 3¾-in. diameter.

f. *Brass plates* (two), ³⁄₁₆-in. thickness × 6¼-in. diameter. Tap hole in center for ¾-in. nipple. Score a cir-

---

* Such as can be obtained from Netherland Rubber Co., Cincinnati, Ohio.

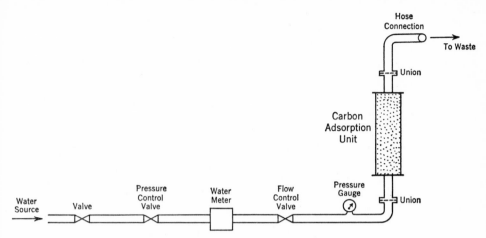

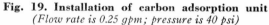

Fig. 19. Installation of carbon adsorption unit
(Flow rate is 0.25 gpm; pressure is 40 psi)

cular groove (⅟₁₆-in. depth × ⅟₁₆-in. width and 3⅜-in. diameter) into the plate to prevent leakage. Drill three holes, ⅝₁₆-in. diameter, to coincide with the flange.

g. Galvanized nipples (two), ¾-in. × 3 in. Thread nipple into brass plate and weld in place.

h. Aluminum bolts and nuts (six), ⅝₁₆-in. × 2 in., for holding assembly together.

2.2. *Extraction apparatus:*

a. Large-capacity Soxhlet extractor.†

b. Heating mantle, 3-liter.‡

2.3. *Variable transformer,** 0–135 v, 7.5 amp.

2.4. *Glass wool:* Extracted before use to remove organic coating. It is convenient to pack about ¼ lb into the large-capacity extractor and extract with chloroform for several cycles.

2.5. *Erlenmeyer flask,* 300 ml.

2.6. *Glass vials,* 5 drams or 18.5 ml.

---

† Corning No. 3885 (Corning Glass Works, Corning, N.Y.), or equivalent.

‡ Glas-Col Series M (Apparatus Co., Terre Haute, Ind.), or equivalent.

* Powerstat, Type 116 (Superior Electric Co., Bristol, Conn.), or equivalent.

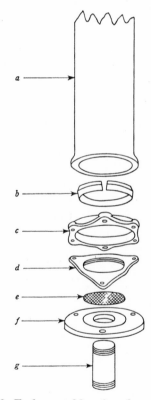

Fig. 20. End assembly of carbon adsorption unit *(for complete dimensions and explanations see Sec. 2.1)*

2.7. Pressure control valve, 40 psi.

2.8. Flow control valve, 0.25 gpm.

2.9. Water meter, ⅝-in. household type.

3. Reagents

3.1. Activated carbon: Upon receipt of each shipment of 4 × 10-mesh carbon † and 30-mesh carbon, ‡ test for impurities. Fill extractors (Sec. 2.2) with each type of carbon, and extract with chloroform. Recover the residues, which should be less than 40 mg for the 4 × 10 mesh and 20 mg for 30 mesh (volume that fits extractor). If larger recoveries are obtained, look for possible sources of contamination. Store the carbon in areas free from paint fumes and other organic vapors. Deduct one-half of the value found on blanks from the sample results.

3.2. Chloroform: If possible, distill all chloroform used. If this cannot be done, check the impurities by distilling 1 liter of solvent and evaporating to dryness. Use the chloroform if the residue is less than 5 mg, and deduct the blank found from the results of the sample extraction.

4. Procedure

4.1. Assembly of carbon adsorption unit: Attach the end fittings of the adsorption unit to the glass pipe. Draw up the bolts evenly, holding the brass plate to the glass pipe in order to get a good seal on the gasket. Add 4 × 10-mesh carbon to a depth of 4.5 in.; add 30-mesh carbon to a depth of

9 in. Complete filling the glass pipe with 4 × 10-mesh carbon (4.5 in.) Be sure the unit is full. Tap the cylinder gently but do not tamp the carbon. Attach the end fittings on the adsorption unit, and install on the water source as shown in Fig. 19.

NOTE: Organic contaminants must be avoided in making pipe joints or other plumbing. Red-lead powder and water mixed to a paste is suitable for pipe joints. Clean all new fittings with kerosene and follow with a detergent wash. Rinse thoroughly with clean water.

4.2. Sample collection: Start the unit by passing water through slowly, because fine carbon washes out at first. Turn on the full flow after a few minutes. Check the operation of the meter and the rate of flow (0.25 gpm). Slight variations from the rate of flow can be tolerated. Measure the total volume accurately. Continue operation until 5,000 gal of water has passed through the unit. Record the meter readings daily.

4.3. Handling the carbon after use: Immediately after the necessary amount of water has passed through the unit, take the unit apart and remove the carbon for drying. Spread the carbon out in a thin layer on a tray of impervious material such as copper or glass.

NOTE: Do not use aluminum and galvanized metals for trays because wet carbon reacts with these metals.

Dry the carbon in clean surroundings. Otherwise, paint fumes, spraying operations, or other organic vapors will be taken up by the carbon and false results will be obtained. To speed drying, pass heated air (35°–40°C) over the trays. Avoid high heat. Regard the carbon as dry when it is free flowing and appears like

---

† Cliff Char 4 × 10 mesh (Cliffs Dow Chemical Co., Marquette, Mich.), or equivalent.

‡ Nuchar C-190 (West Virginia Pulp & Paper Co., New York, N.Y.), or equivalent.

fresh, unused carbon. Some moisture that is left will disappear in later processing. The dried carbon is now ready for extraction with chloroform. If the dried carbon must be held, place in a tight vessel for storage. A crimped-lid paint can is a satisfactory storage container.

4.4. *Carbon extraction:* Remove the glass plate from the bottom of the Soxhlet extractor. Pack the previously extracted glass wool (Sec. 2.4) lightly into the bottom of the extractor in order to keep the fine carbon from passing into the boiling flask. Charge the extractor with the carbon to be extracted. The amount of carbon in a sampling unit fits the extractor. Pour chloroform over the carbon fairly rapidly to help absorb the heat evolved. Continue adding chloroform until siphon action is started. When the chloroform has siphoned into the boiling flask, refill the extraction chamber with chloroform. Add glass beads, or porous chips, to the boiling flask to prevent bumping, and then begin passing water through the condensers. Turn on the heating mantles. A voltage setting of 80 on the variable transformer is usually sufficient. When first starting the extractors, or after the siphon cycle during the run, the solvent in the boiling flask may superheat and bump. Tap the flask or vibrate the apparatus just at the boiling point of the solvent to prevent superheating. Extraction units do not always siphon automatically. Although regular siphoning is not necessary, application of air pressure to the vent of the extractor with a rubber bulb will start the siphon action. Extract the carbon with chloroform for 35 hr. Discard the carbon if no additional work with the carbon is planned.

NOTE: The carbon retains a substantial amount of solvent even after draining. Burning generates hydrochloric acid and storage releases fumes. If a good hood is available, pass warm air over the carbon for 4 or 5 hr to dry it while still in the extractor. Dispose of the carbon by broadcasting on the ground.

When the extraction is completed, siphon all chloroform into the boiling flask. Remove the flask from the extraction system and distill to about 250 ml (avoid overheating). Filter into a 300-ml erlenmeyer flask and evaporate to about 15–20 ml on a steam bath. Blow a stream of clean air into the flask to hasten evaporation. Transfer to a tared vial and evaporate to dryness by allowing to stand in an open hood (without heat) overnight or longer. Judge completeness of solvent removal by odor. It is better to leave traces of solvent rather than to risk loss of sample by prolonged heating and evaporation.

Weigh the sample and record the weight. Deduct the amount due to the carbon blank (Sec. 3.1) and the solvent blank (Sec. 3.2).

5. Calculation

It is convenient to record the CCE in micrograms per liter:

$$\mu g/l = \frac{g\ CCE \times 10^6}{gal\ sample \times 3.785}$$

6. Interpretation of Results

According to the 1962 USPHS Drinking Water Standards,[6] a concentration of 200 $\mu g/l$ of CCE should not be exceeded. Waters containing more than this amount are likely to be of poor quality (judged by taste and odor) and may exhibit some of the damaging effects noted in the introduction. The source and kind of contaminants should be investigated if waters consistently exceed 200 $\mu g/l$ of CCE. Clean surface and ground waters will usually contain only 25 to 50 $\mu g/l$ of CCE; highly colored waters may exceed this level.

Bibliography

1. Middleton, F. M.; Grant, W.; & Rosen, A. A. Drinking Water Taste and Odor, Correlation with Organic Content. *Ind. Eng. Chem.* 48:268 (1956).
2. Middleton, F. M.; Rosen, A. A.; & Burttschell, R. H. Taste and Odor Research Tools for Water Utilities. *J. AWWA* 50:21 (1958).
3. Middleton, F. M.; Rosen, A. A.; & Burttschell, R. H. *Manual for Recovery and Identification of Organic Chemicals in Water.* Robert A. Taft San. Eng. Center, Cincinnati, Ohio (1959).
4. Middleton, F. M. & Lichtenberg, J. J. Measurement of Organic Contaminants in the Nation's Rivers. *Ind. Eng. Chem.* 52:99A (1960).
5. Ettinger, M. B. Proposed Toxicity Screening Procedure for Use in Protecting Drinking-Water Quality. *J. AWWA* 52:689 (1960).
6. Public Health Service Drinking Water Standards, 1962. *Public Health Service Pub.* 956 (1963).

Oxygen (Dissolved)

Adequate dissolved oxygen (DO) is necessary for the life of fish and other aquatic organisms. The DO concentration may also be associated with corrosivity of water, photosynthetic activity, and septicity. The DO test is used in the biochemical oxygen demand (BOD) determination in Part III.

The azide modification of the iodometric method is recommended for most conditions. (See Part III, Oxygen [Dissolved], Method A.) The unmodified iodometric method can be used only with waters containing less than 0.1 mg/l nitrite nitrogen and less than 0.5 mg/l ferrous iron, and free of other possible interferences. (The procedure for the unmodified iodometric method is the same in all respects as that described in Part III for the azide modification, except that no sodium azide is used in the preparation of the alkali-iodide reagent, Sec. 2.2 of Method A, and potassium fluoride solution, Sec. 2.7, is not required, because iron interference must be absent to begin with.) Depending on the type of interference, other modifications may be necessary. For a detailed discussion, see Part III.

Oxygen Demand (Biochemical)

Biochemical oxygen demand (BOD) in water is determined as described in Part III. Seeding with sewage organisms, if necessary, and elimination of interferences from residual chlorine and other bactericidal substances should be carried out as indicated there. The amount of pollution in the sample will govern the need for and the degree of dilution.

Samples with low DO values can be aerated to increase the initial DO content above that required by the BOD. Air is bubbled through a diffusion tube into the sample for 5 min, or until the DO is at least 7 mg/l. On one portion of the aerated sample the DO is determined; another portion is seeded and incubated for the BOD determination.

Oxygen Demand (Chemical)

The chemical oxygen demand (COD) test indicates the quantity of oxidizable compounds present in a water and will vary with water composition, concentration of reagent, temperature, period of contact, and other factors. In some instances, a rough correlation between BOD and COD has been established. Since chemical oxidation and biologic oxidation are different processes, the results may differ to a large degree. Methods for determining COD values will be found in Part IV.

Ozone (Residual)

Ozone, a potent germicide, is also employed as an oxidizing agent for the destruction of organic compounds producing taste and odor in water, as well as for the destruction of organic coloring matter and the oxidation of reduced iron or manganese salts to insoluble oxides, which can then be precipitated or filtered from the water. Waters containing such oxidizable minerals must necessarily be filtered after ozonation. The presence of ozone residuals of even less than 0.1 mg/l at the outlet of the ozonation chamber is generally effective for disinfection; therefore, the demonstration of an ozone residual in the water is generally sufficient. For other purposes, perhaps as much as 0.2 mg/l may be necessary.

Selection of method: Three methods are described for the determination of ozone in water. The iodometric method (A) is quantitative, subject to the fewest interferences, and capable of good precision. The method can also be used for the determination of ozone in air by absorption of the ozone in iodide solution.

The orthotolidine-manganese sulfate method (B), generally abbreviated OTM, is semiquantitative. It is subject to relatively slight interference from other common oxidants.

The orthotolidine-arsenite method (C), usually designated OTA, is largely qualitative because of its liability to interference. However, it is useful for such control purposes as determinations at the outlet of the ozonation chamber.

The ozone concentration in water or air can also be determined continuously by photometric instruments which can measure the strong absorption ozone exerts at the wavelength of 253.7 mμ.

Sampling and storage: A determination for ozone must be performed immediately because samples cannot be preserved or stored, owing to the instability of the residual. The stability of residual ozone is markedly improved at low temperatures and low pH values. Samples should be collected in a manner to minimize aeration. Frequency of sampling should be dictated by the variations in the quality of the supply and the demands of plant operation.

A. Iodometric Method

1. General Discussion

1.1. *Principle:* Ozone liberates free iodine from a potassium iodide solution. For accurate results the solution should be alkaline during the absorption of ozone. In practice, solutions of potassium iodide quickly become alkaline during the process. After acidification, the liberated iodine is titrated with standard 0.005N sodium thiosulfate using starch indicator.

1.2. *Interference:* Because ozonated water may contain manganese dioxide, ferric ion, nitrite, possibly peroxide, and other oxidation products, these interferences are avoided by passing the ozone through the gaseous phase into a potassium iodide solution for titration. The stability of ozone solutions decreases progressively at each increment in temperature above freezing and with each increment in pH above 3.0.

1.3. *Minimum detectable concentration:* Approximately 0.03 mg/l ozone.

2. Apparatus

The following are required for sample collection:

2.1. *Standard gas washing bottles and absorbers,* 1-liter and 500-ml capacities, with medium-permeability porous-plate diffusers at bottom.

2.2. *Pure air or pure nitrogen gas supply,* 0.2–1.0-liter/min capacity.

2.3. *Glass, stainless steel, or aluminum piping,* for carrying ozonized air. Good quality Tygon * tubing may also be used for short runs, but not rubber.

3. Reagents

3.1. *Potassium iodide solution:* Dissolve 20 g KI, free from iodine, iodate, and reducing agents, in 1 liter of freshly boiled and cooled distilled water. Store in an amber bottle.

3.2. *Sulfuric acid,* 1N. Add 28 ml conc H_2SO_4 slowly and cautiously to approximately 750 ml distilled water and dilute to 1 liter.

3.3. *Standard sodium thiosulfate,* 0.1N. Dissolve 25 g $Na_2S_2O_3 \cdot 5H_2O$ in 1 liter of freshly boiled distilled water. Standardize against potassium biniodate (also called potassium hydrogen iodate) or potassium dichromate according to the procedure described in Chlorine (Residual), Method A, Sec. 2.3.

3.4. *Standard sodium thiosulfate titrant,* 0.005N. Dilute the proper volume (approximately 50 ml) of 0.1N sodium thiosulfate to 1,000 ml. For accurate work, standardize this solution

---

* US Stoneware Company.

daily, using either 0.005N potassium biniodate or potassium dichromate solution for the purpose. Perform the standardization in exactly the same manner as the procedure described in Sec. 4.3. Standard sodium thiosulfate titrant, exactly 0.0050N, is equivalent to 0.120 mg ozone per 1.00 ml.

3.5. *Starch indicator solution:* To 5 g potato, arrowroot, or soluble starch, in a mortar, add a little cold distilled water and grind to a thin paste. Pour into 1 liter boiling distilled water, stir, and allow to settle overnight. Use the clear supernate. Preserve with 1.25 g salicylic acid, 4 g zinc chloride, or a combination of 4 g sodium propionate and 2 g sodium azide added to 1 liter of starch solution.

3.6. *Standard iodine,* 0.1N. Dissolve 40 g KI in 25 ml distilled water; then add 13 g resublimed iodine and stir until dissolved. Dilute to 1 liter and standardize against sodium arsenite, primary standard grade, as described in Chlorine (Residual), Method F, Sec. 3.1b.

3.7. *Standard iodine,* 0.005N. Dissolve 16 g KI in a little distilled water in a 1-liter volumetric flask, add the proper volume (approximately 50 ml) of 0.1N iodine solution, and dilute to the mark. For accurate work standardize this solution daily. Store the solution in an amber bottle or in the dark. Protect from direct sunlight at all times and keep from all contact with rubber.

4. Procedure

4.1. *Sample collection:* Collect an 800-ml sample in a 1-liter washing bottle with a porous diffuser at the bottom. (Some prefer to add 8 ml 1N H_2SO_4 before proceeding to Sec. 4.2; others state this may result in in-

creased interference from the acid itself or from breakdown of substances in the sample.)

4.2. *Ozone absorption:* Pass a stream of pure air or nitrogen through the sample, and then through an absorber containing 400 ml potassium iodide solution. Continue for not less than 5 min at a rate of 0.2–1.0 liter/min to insure that all ozone is swept from the sample and absorbed in the potassium iodide solution.

4.3. *Titration:* Transfer the potassium iodide solution to a 1-liter beaker, rinse the absorber, and add 20 ml H_2SO_4 to produce a pH below 2.0. Titrate with 0.005N sodium thiosulfate titrant until the yellow color of the liberated iodine is almost discharged. Add 4 ml starch indicator solution to impart a blue color, and continue the titration carefully but rapidly to the endpoint at which the blue color just disappears. Long contact of iodine and starch develops a blue compound which is difficult to decolorize. (The endpoint may be determined amperometrically as described in Chlorine [Residual], Method F, Sec. 4.3, except that sodium thiosulfate can be used as the titrant.)

4.4. *Blank test:* Correct the result of the sample titration by determining the blank contributed by such reagent impurities as (a) the free iodine or iodate in the potassium iodide, which liberates extra iodine, or (b) the traces of reducing agents that might reduce some of the iodine which is liberated.

Take 400 ml potassium iodide solution, 20 ml H_2SO_4, and 4 ml starch indicator solution. Perform whichever one of the blank titrations below applies:

a. If a blue color occurs, titrate with 0.005N sodium thiosulfate to the disappearance of the blue, and record the result.

b. If no blue color occurs, titrate with $0.005N$ iodine solution until a blue color appears. Back-titrate with $0.005N$ sodium thiosulfate and record the difference.

Before calculating the ozone, subtract the result of the blank titration in Sec. 4.4a from the sample titration, or add the result of Sec. 4.4b.

5. Calculation

$$\text{mg/l } O_3 = \frac{(A \pm B) \times N \times 24{,}000}{\text{ml sample}}$$

where $A = $ ml titration for sample, $B = $ ml titration for blank which may be positive or negative, and $N = $ normality of $Na_2S_2O_3$.

6. Interpretation of Results

The precision of the actual test is within ± 1 per cent. However, rapid deterioration of the residual occurs in the time elapsing between sampling and performance of the test. Temperature is also an important factor in the deterioration.

B. Orthotolidine—Manganese Sulfate (OTM) Method

1. General Discussion

1.1. *Principle:* Residual ozone oxidizes manganous ion to the manganic state, which in turn reacts with the acidic orthotolidine reagent. The final yellow color can be measured visually with a comparator suitable for residual chlorine estimations or photometrically in the wavelength range of 400–450 mμ.

1.2. *Interference:* This method may be affected by the presence of a high oxide of manganese in the original sample but not by such slow-acting interfering agents as nitrite or oxidized iron. The correction for interferences can be determined by thoroughly aerating a second portion of the sample and then following the procedure described in Sec. 4.

1.3. *Minimum detectable concentration:* Approximately 0.02 mg/l ozone.

2. Apparatus

Color comparison equipment: One of the following is required:

2.1. *Comparator,* color and turbidity compensating, equipped with permanent glass standards suitable for the estimation of residual chlorine by the orthotolidine method.

2.2. *Filter photometer,* providing a light path of 1 cm or longer and equipped with a violet filter exhibiting maximum transmittance in the wavelength range of 400–450 mμ.

2.3. *Spectrophotometer,* for use at 435 mμ and providing a light path of 1 cm or longer.

3. Reagents

3.1. *Manganese sulfate reagent:* Dissolve 3.1 g $MnSO_4 \cdot H_2O$ in distilled water containing 3 ml conc H_2SO_4, and dilute to 1 liter. This solution contains approximately 1 g/l Mn and may be used for many months.

3.2. *Orthotolidine reagent:* Dissolve 1.35 g orthotolidine dihydrochloride in 500 ml distilled water. Add this solution, with constant stirring, to a mixture of 350 ml distilled water and 150 ml conc HCl. Store the reagent in amber bottles or in the dark, and observe the precautions prescribed for its storage in Chlorine (Residual), Method B, Sec. 5.2.

4. Procedure

Place 5 ml manganese sulfate reagent in a 250-ml flask. Add 95 ml of sample and mix quickly. Add 5 ml orthotolidine reagent and mix quickly. Measure the developed yellow color in a comparator fitted with a chlorine color disc, or photometrically in the wavelength range of 400–450 mμ.

5. Calculation

$$\text{mg/l } O_3 = \frac{\text{mg/l apparent ``chlorine''}}{1.45}$$

6. Interpretation of Results

The yellow color developed by ozone in this method is theoretically equal to 1.45 times the amount produced by an equal quantity of chlorine. Interfering compounds and uncertainties in reading a color disc comparator may cause appreciable variations in this theoretical factor. Photometric measurement of the color density improves the test accuracy.

C. Orthotolidine-Arsenite (OTA) Method

1. General Discussion

1.1. *Principle:* Ozone produces an instantaneous yellow color with the acid orthotolidine reagent. This addition of arsenite reagent minimizes interference from such slower-acting ions as nitrite or oxidized iron.

1.2. *Interference:* This method is affected by colloidal manganese dioxide, which rapidly reacts with the acid orthotolidine reagent.

1.3. *Minimum detectable concentration:* Approximately 0.02 mg/l ozone.

2. Apparatus

Color comparison equipment: One of the following is required:

2.1. *Comparator,* color and turbidity compensating, equipped with permanent glass standards for the estimation of residual chlorine by the orthotolidine method.

2.2. *French square bottles,* capacity 1 or 2 oz.

3. Reagents

3.1. *Orthotolidine reagent:* Prepare and store as directed in Method B, Sec. 3.2.

3.2. *Sodium arsenite solution:* Dissolve 5 g $NaAsO_2$ in distilled water and dilute to 1 liter. The solution may be used for several months. (CAUTION: *Toxic; take care to avoid ingestion.*)

4. Procedure

4.1. Label two comparator cells, or French square bottles, "A" and "B." Add 0.5 ml orthotolidine reagent to 10-ml cells, 0.75 ml to 15-ml cells, and the same ratio for other volumes of sample. Use the same volume of arsenite solution after color development in Sec. 4.2, and also for the determination of the interference correction in Sec. 4.3.

4.2. To Cell A, containing orthotolidine reagent, add a measured volume of water sample. Mix quickly and thoroughly, and within 5 sec add the sodium arsenite solution. Mix quickly and compare with color standards in the comparator as rapidly as possible. Record the result as *A*.

4.3. To Cell B, containing arsenite solution, add a measured volume of water sample. Mix quickly and thoroughly, and add orthotolidine reagent. Again mix quickly and compare with color standards in the comparator as rapidly as possible. Record the result as *B,* which represents the interfering substances in the water.

5. Calculation

$$\text{mg/l } O_3 = A - B$$

6. Interpretation of Results

The color developed in this test by a given amount of ozone varies greatly in different waters. On the average it approximates the color produced by an equal quantity of chlorine. The method is qualitative only.

Bibliography

1. FOULK, C. W. & BAWDEN, A. T. A New Type of Endpoint in Electrometric Titration and Its Application of Iodimetry. *J. Am. Chem. Soc.* 48:2045 (1926).
2. HANN, V. A. & MANLEY, T. C. OZONE. In *Encyclopedia of Chemical Technology.* Interscience Publishers, New York (1952). Vol. 9, pp. 735–753.
3. BIRDSALL, C. M.; JENKINS, A. C.; & SPADINGER, E. The Iodometric Determination of Ozone. *Anal. Chem.* 24:662 (1952).
4. ZEHENDER, F. & STUMM, W. Determination of Ozone in Drinking Water. [In German.] *Mitt. Gebiete Lebensm. u. Hyg.* 44:206 (1953).
5. INGOLS, R. S. & FETNER, R. H. *Sterilization of Water by Ozone Under Arctic Conditions.* Report PB 124786, Office of Technical Services, US Dept. of Commerce, Washington, D.C.
6. INGOLS, R. S.; FETNER, R. H.; & EBERHARDT, W. H. Determination of Ozone in Solution. *Proc. Intern. Ozone Conf.* (1956).
7. HANN, V. A. Disinfection of Drinking Water with Ozone. *J. AWWA* 48:1316 (1956).
8. INGOLS, R. S. & FETNER, R. H. Some Studies of Ozone for Use in Water Treatment. *Proc. Soc. Water Treatment & Examination* 6:8 (1957).

Pesticides

Organic pesticides may be present in ground and surface waters as the result of (a) direct application for aquatic insect or aquatic plant control, (b) residues resulting from runoff from rural or urban lands, (c) residues occurring in ground water from percolation of rainfall, (d) accidental or deliberate discharge from manufacturing wastewater effluents, (e) accidental contamination from drift when being applied to agricultural lands, and (f) discharge of wastes from cleanup of equipment used in insecticide application. Widespread use of pesticides has resulted in fish kills and in detectable residues in many major streams.

Adverse effects on water quality may result from (a) the pesticide itself or solvent carriers used in commercial formulations, (b) chlorination products of the pesticide, and (c) impurities in the manufactured technical products.

Quantitative analytical techniques

have been developed for organic pesticides residues in crops, soils, and biological samples. In general, these procedures are limited in sensitivity to relatively macro quantities in microgram and milligram amounts. These methods also require cleanup procedures to remove interfering substances. Application of these methods can not be made directly for the analysis of pesticides in water because of the inadequate sensitivity and specificity. With suitable modification, such as increasing sample size by solvent extraction or carbon adsorption, published methods can be used in water analysis.

The published literature on methods developed specifically for water analysis is sparse. Until more methods become available, the reader is directed to the following general references.

Bibliography

1. GUNTHER, F. A. & BLINN, R. C. *Analysis of Insecticides and Acaricides.* Interscience Publishers, New York (1955).
2. METCALF, R. L., ed. *Advances in Pest Control Research.* Interscience Publishers, New York (1957–1963), Vol. I–V.
3. GUNTHER, F. A. *Residue Reviews.* Academic Press, New York. Vol. I (1962), Vol. II (1963), Vol. III (1963).
4. ZWEIG, G. *Analytical Methods for Pesticides, Plant Growth Regulators, and Food Additives. Principles, Methods, and General Applications.* Academic Press, New York (1963), Vol. I.
5. American Chemical Society. *Anal. Chem., Anal. Review,* published annually.

pH Value

The pH of most natural waters falls within the range 4 to 9. The majority of waters are slightly basic due to the presence of carbonate and bicarbonate. A departure from the norm for a given water could be caused by the entry of strongly acidic or basic industrial wastes. A relatively common practice is the pH adjustment of the treatment plant effluent for the purpose of controlling corrosion in the distribution system.

pH is the logarithm of the reciprocal of the hydrogen ion concentration —more precisely, of the hydrogen ion activity—in moles per liter. pH enters into the calculation of carbonate, bicarbonate, and carbon dioxide, as well as of the corrosion or stability index; and into the control of water treatment processes. The practical pH scale extends from 0, very acidic, to 14, very alkaline, with the middle value (pH 7) corresponding to exact neutrality at 25°C. Whereas "alkalinity" and "acidity" express the total reserve or buffering capacity of a sample, the pH value represents the instantaneous hydrogen ion activity.

Selection of method: pH can be measured either colorimetrically or electrometrically. The colorimetric method requires a less expensive investment in equipment but suffers from severe interference contributed by color, turbidity, high saline content, colloidal matter, free chlorine, and various oxidants and reductants. The indicators are subject to deterioration, as are the color standards with which they are compared. Moreover, no single indicator encompasses the pH range of interest in water. In poorly buffered liquids, a description applicable to some waters, the indicators themselves may alter the pH of the sample which they are expected to measure, unless they are preadjusted to nearly the same pH as the sample. For these reasons, the colorimetric method is suitable only for rough estimation and will not be described in this section. (For details on the colorimetric method, see Clark,[1] Kolthoff,[2] and Ref. 12.) The electrometric method below is considered standard.

Glass Electrode Method

1. General Discussion

1.1. *Principle:* Several types of electrodes have been suggested for the electrometric determination of pH. Although the hydrogen gas electrode is recognized as the primary standard, the glass electrode in combination with the reference potential provided by a saturated calomel electrode is most generally used. The glass electrode system is based on the fact that a change of 1 pH unit produces an electrical change of 59.1 mv at 25°C.

1.2. *Interference:* The glass electrode is relatively immune to interference from color, turbidity, colloidal matter, free chlorine, oxidants, or reductants, as well as from high saline content, except for a sodium error at high pH. The error caused by high sodium ion concentrations at a pH above 10 may be reduced by using special "low sodium error" electrodes. When employing ordinary glass electrodes, approximate corrections for the sodium error may be made by consulting a chart which the manufacturer can furnish for the particular make and catalog number of electrode. Temperature exerts two significant effects on pH measurements: the electrodes themselves vary in potential, and ionization in the sample varies.* The first effect can be compensated by an adjustment which is provided on the better commercial instruments. The second effect is inherent in the sample and is taken into consideration by recording both the temperature and the pH of each sample.

2. Apparatus

Where flow-type electrodes are unavailable, or where stirring may be inadequate, as in the ordinary immersion (dipping)-type electrodes, the best procedure is to wash the glass electrode 6–8 times with portions of the sample, particularly when an unbuf-

---

* This ionization, dependent upon the values of K_1 and K_2 for H_2CO_3 as well as on K_w for H_2O at the various temperatures, is to a significant extent related to the alkalinity of the sample. Increasing alkalinity reduces the effect of temperature change on the pH. This effect of alkalinity is not a direct relationship and can be quite pronounced even at very low concentrations of alkalinity.

The temperature dial on pH meters is designed only to correct for the temperature characteristics of the electrodes. Instruments without a temperature dial are often provided with data from which this correction for the characteristics of the electrodes may be calculated.

Data for calculating, by interpolation, the pH of natural waters at other temperatures than that of the measurement are provided by Langelier.[6]

fered measurement follows one on a buffered solution. Flow-type electrodes are recommended for the accurate measurement of relatively unbuffered waters such as condensates. Measurements on buffered waters can be obtained on open samples. Equilibrium, as shown by the absence of drift, should be established between the sample and the electrode system before readings are accepted as final. If the water is hot or if the pH is over 10, special glass electrodes should be used and the assembly should be standardized under conditions of temperature and concentration as close as possible to those of the sample, taking into account the manufacturer's recommendations. The analyst should constantly be on the alert for possible erratic results arising from mechanical or electrical failures—weak batteries, cracked glass electrodes, plugged liquid junction, and fouling of the electrodes with oily or precipitated materials.

3. Buffer Solutions

Electrode systems are calibrated against buffer solutions of known pH value. Inasmuch as buffer solutions may deteriorate because of mold growth or contamination, it may be advisable to prepare them freshly as needed by dissolving dry buffer salts in distilled water. Commercially available buffer tablets or powders of tested quality may also be used. It is good practice to calibrate the electrodes with a buffer whose pH is close to that of the samples, so as to minimize any error resulting from nonlinear response of the electrode. In making up buffers from solid salts, it is imperative that all of the material be dissolved; otherwise the pH may be incorrect. Polyethylene bottles are preferable for the storage of buffers and samples, although pyrex glassware may be employed. Limitations of space permit information on the preparation of only three buffer solutions, at practically spaced intervals (pH 4, 7, and 9) for standardization purposes and for checking the linearity of electrode response.

In general, ACS grade chemicals are satisfactory for the preparation of the following buffer solutions. Where a high degree of accuracy is required, however, it is advisable to use salts of buffer quality supplied by the National Bureau of Standards. The pH values of the three buffer solutions at various temperatures listed in Table 12 were obtained with salts of the highest purity.

TABLE 12—EFFECT OF TEMPERATURE ON pH VALUES OF BUFFER SOLUTIONS

Temperature °C	pH Value		
	pH 4 Buffer	pH 7 Buffer	pH 9 Buffer
0	4.00	6.98	9.46
5	4.00	6.95	9.40
10	4.00	6.92	9.33
15	4.00	6.90	9.28
20	4.00	6.88	9.23
25	4.01	6.86	9.18
30	4.02	6.85	9.14
35	4.02	6.84	9.10
38	4.03	6.84	9.08
40	4.04	6.84	9.07
45	4.05	6.83	9.04
50	4.06	6.83	9.01
55	4.08	6.83	8.99
60	4.09	6.84	8.96

3.1. *Buffer solution*, pH 4.01 at 25°C: Dissolve 10.21 g anhydrous potassium biphthalate, $KHC_8H_4O_4$, in distilled water and dilute to 1,000 ml.

3.2. *Buffer solution*, pH 6.86 at 25°C: Dissolve 3.40 g anhydrous potassium dihydrogen phosphate,

KH_2PO_4, and 3.55 g anhydrous disodium hydrogen phosphate, Na_2HPO_4, both of which have been dried for 2 hr at 110° to 130°C. Use distilled water which has been boiled for 15 min and cooled to room temperature. Dilute to 1,000 ml.

3.3. *Buffer solution,* pH 9.18 at 25°C: Dissolve 3.81 g sodium borate decahydrate (borax), $Na_2B_4O_7 \cdot 10H_2O$, in distilled water that has been boiled for 15 min and cooled to room temperature. Dilute to 1,000 ml.

4. Procedure

Because of the differences between the many makes and models of pH meters which are available commercially, it is impossible to provide detailed instructions for the correct operation of every instrument. In each case, the manufacturer's instructions must be followed. The glass electrode and the calomel electrode should be thoroughly wetted and prepared for use in accordance with the instructions given. The instrument can be standardized against a buffer solution with a pH approaching that of the sample, and then the linearity of electrode response can be checked against at least one additional buffer of a different pH. The readings with the additional buffers will afford a rough idea of the limits of accuracy to be expected of the instrument and the technique of operation.

5. Precision and Accuracy

The precision and accuracy attainable with a given pH meter will depend upon the type and condition of the instrument employed and the technique of standardization and operation. With the proper care, a precision of ±0.02 pH unit and accuracy of ±0.05 pH unit can be achieved with the better battery models. Line-operated instruments, on the other hand, are less accurate, ±0.1 pH unit representing the limits of accuracy under normal conditions. A synthetic unknown sample consisting of a Clark and Lubs buffer solution of pH 7.3 was determined electrometrically with a standard deviation of ±0.13 pH unit in 30 laboratories.

Bibliography

1. CLARK, W. M. *The Determination of Hydrogen Ions.* Williams & Wilkins Co., Baltimore (3rd ed., 1928).
2. KOLTHOFF, I. M. *Acid-Base Indicators.* Macmillan Co., New York (4th ed., 1937).
3. DOLE, M. *The Glass Electrode.* John Wiley & Sons, New York (1941).
4. BATES, R. G. & ACREE, S. F. pH of Aqueous Mixtures of Potassium Dihydrogen Phosphate and Disodium Hydrogen Phosphate at 0° to 60°C. *J. Research Natl. Bur. Standards* 34:373 (1945).
5. LANGELIER, W. F. Effect of Temperature on the pH of Natural Waters. *J. AWWA* 38:179 (1946).
6. BATES, R. G. *Electrometric pH Determinations.* John Wiley & Sons, New York (1954).
7. FELDMAN, I. Use and Abuse of pH Measurements. *Anal. Chem.* 28:1859 (1956).
8. BRITTON, H. T. S. *Hydrogen Ions.* D. Van Nostrand Co., Princeton, N.J. (4th ed., 1956).
9. KOLTHOFF, I. M. & LAITINEN, H. A. *pH and Electrotitrations.* John Wiley & Sons, New York (1958).
10. BATES, R. G. Revised Standard Values for pH Measurements from 0° to 95°C. *J. Res. Natl. Bur. Std.* 66A:179 (1962).
11. BATES, R. G. *Determination of pH.* John Wiley & Sons, New York (1964).
12. *Simplified Procedures for Water Examination.* Manual M12. Am. Water Works Assoc., New York (1964). pp. 52–54.

Phenols

Phenols are waste products of oil refineries, coke plants, and some chemical producing facilities. Concentrations of the order of 0.01 to 0.1 mg/l are detectable by the taste and odor test. Trace amounts approaching 1 μg/l can impart an objectionable taste to a water following marginal chlorination. The removal of phenolic tastes from a water supply offers a serious challenge at the treatment plant. Among the processes used for coping with the phenol problem are superchlorination, chlorine dioxide or chlorine-ammonia treatment, ozonation, and activated-carbon adsorption.

The term "phenols" as used in this manual includes those hydroxy derivatives of benzene which can be determined under specified conditions by the methods presented in Part IV.

In a water supply containing phenol itself, there will usually be associated with it other phenolic compounds whose sensitivity to the reagents used in these methods may not necessarily be the same. As a general rule, the introduction of substituent groups in the benzene nucleus lowers the sensitivity of the particular compound to color formation with the two indicators.

The percentage composition of the various phenolic compounds present in a given sample is unpredictable. It is obvious, therefore, that a standard containing a mixture of phenols cannot be made applicable to all samples. For this reason, phenol itself has been selected as a standard, and any color produced by the reaction of other phenolic compounds is reported as phenol. This value will represent the minimum concentration of phenolic compounds present in the sample.

The same methods are used for the determination of phenols in water as in industrial wastes, although the preliminary distillation steps may be somewhat different. Directions for the distillation procedure for water samples are given below.

Storage of samples: For best results, the samples should be stored in accordance with directions in Part IV, Phenols, *Storage of samples.*

Preliminary Distillation Step

1. Apparatus

Distillation apparatus, all glass. A suitable assembly consists of a 1-liter pyrex distilling apparatus with Graham condenser (Fig. 17).*

2. Reagents

All reagents must be prepared with distilled water free of both phenols and chlorine.

-----
* Corning No. 3360 or equivalent.

2.1. *Copper sulfate solution:* Dissolve 100 g $CuSO_4 \cdot 5H_2O$ in distilled water and dilute to 1 liter.

2.2. *Phosphoric acid solution:* Dilute 10 ml 85 per cent H_3PO_4 to 100 ml with distilled water.

3. Procedure

To a 500-ml sample of water, add 5.0 ml copper sulfate solution, unless it has previously been added as a preservative. Lower the pH of the mixture to below 4.0 with phosphoric acid solution; 0.7 ml is sufficient for most samples. Place the mixture in the all-glass distillation apparatus and distill over 450 ml. Stop the distillation, and, when boiling ceases, add 50 ml distilled water to the distilling flask. Continue the distillation until a total of 500 ml has been collected.

If at this point a distinct odor of other organic compounds is noted in the distillate, or if an oily layer is noticeable, then further purification is necessary and reference should be made to the complete procedure given for polluted water and industrial wastes in Part IV.

Colorimetric Determination

The phenol in the above distillate can be determined by use of the amino-antipyrine methods outlined under Part IV, Phenols.

Phosphate

Phosphate occurs in traces in many natural waters, and often in appreciable amounts during periods of low biologic productivity. Traces of phosphate increase the tendency of troublesome algae to grow in reservoirs. Waters receiving raw or treated sewage, agricultural drainage, and certain industrial waters normally contain significant concentrations of phosphate. Also, phosphate is frequently added to domestic and industrial waters in various forms. Sometimes both orthophosphate and polyphosphates (molecularly dehydrated phosphates) will be found in the same sample. Trace amounts of phosphate may also be combined with organic matter. Such phosphate seldom exceeds a few tenths of a milligram per liter. Phosphate in its various forms may also appear in the suspended matter or sludge of the sample taken. As a general rule, unless reported otherwise, only the soluble phosphate is considered. Phosphate analyses are

made primarily to control chemical dosage, or as a means of tracing flow or contamination.

Selection of method: The amino-naphtholsulfonic acid method (A) is most useful for routine analysis in the range of 0.1 to 30 mg/l PO_4. The stannous chloride method (B) is more sensitive and better suited for the range 0.05 to 3 mg/l PO_4. With extraction, the range of Method B can be extended to 0.01 mg/l. Method B is more susceptible to interferences. When interferences are suspected or known to be present, the extraction step should be employed with Method B. A procedure, Method C, is given for converting polyphosphate into orthophosphate by heating with acid. After this treatment, total phosphate may be determined as the orthophosphate, and polyphosphate calculated by difference, if orthophosphate alone has also been determined.

Sampling and storage: The analysis

for orthophosphate is ordinarily limited to the soluble forms. However, consideration must be given to phosphate-containing sludge and suspended matter and to the possible precipitation, adsorption, or desorption of phosphate during sampling and storage. The water should be settled free of such matter before sampling. Where settling is not relatively rapid or the supernatant water is not perfectly clear, the water should be filtered before sampling. See Residue, Method B, for suitable filters. Certain filter papers and filter aids contain appreciable amounts of phosphate and should not be used. Other materials, such as as-bestos, can adsorb phosphate from solution and, therefore, should be thoroughly seasoned with sample water before use. Semicolloidal or colloidal matter passing through the filter will be included in the analysis. If precipitation occurs during storage prior to analysis, the sample bottle must be shaken vigorously to obtain a uniform suspension before withdrawing a portion for analysis. A field analysis is preferred to avoid this problem. Natural conversion of organic phosphorus and polyphosphate to orthophosphate through microbiologic activity can be retarded or arrested by the addition of 5 ml of chloroform to 1 liter of sample.

A. Aminonaphtholsulfonic Acid Method for Orthophosphate

1. General Discussion

1.1. *Principle:* In a dilute phosphate solution, ammonium molybdate reacts in an acid medium to form a heteropoly acid, molybdophosphoric acid, which is reduced to the intensely colored complex, molybdenum blue, by the combination of aminonaphtholsulfonic acid and sulfite reducing agents.

1.2. *Interference:* Arsenic and germanium must be absent. Sulfide must be removed by oxidation. Saturated bromine water may be used for this purpose. The soluble-iron content should not exceed 0.1 mg in the portion taken for analysis. Tannin, lignin, and hexavalent chromium (at concentrations normally encountered) will cause significant error only when the phosphate sought is below 1 mg/l. Soluble silicates do not interfere even at concentrations as high as 100 mg/l SiO_2.

The presence of high amounts of polyphosphate in the water can lead to slightly high orthophosphate values; however, in no case is it likely that this error will exceed 0.1 mg/l. When testing for phosphate in highly saline waters, such as brines, low results may be obtained. If so, readings should be taken on successive dilutions until two such dilutions give essentially the same value; or Method B should be employed with extraction.

1.3. *Minimum detectable concentration:* The minimum detectable concentration (that concentration which produces 1 per cent transmittance above the normal expected deviation in reading at zero concentration) with a spectrophotometer (690 mμ) using 10-cm cells is about 0.02 mg/l PO_4. The sensitivity of the method, measured at 50 per cent transmittance, under the same conditions as above, is about

22 $\mu g/l$ for 1 per cent change in transmittance.

2. Apparatus

2.1. *Colorimetric equipment:* Visual comparison in nessler tubes is not normally recommended, because of the difficulty in meeting the time requirements to obtain accurate results. One of the following is required:

a. *Spectrophotometer,* for use at approximately 690 mμ. The color system also obeys Beer's law at 650 mμ, with somewhat reduced sensitivity, in the event the instrument available cannot be operated at the optimum wavelength. A light path of 0.5 cm or longer yields satisfactory results.

b. *Filter photometer,* provided with a red filter exhibiting maximum transmittance in the wavelength range of 600–750 mμ. A light path of 0.5 cm or longer yields satisfactory results.

2.2. *Filtration equipment:* See Residue, Method B, Sec. 2.1.

2.3. *Acid-washed glassware:* This may be of great importance, particularly when determining low concentrations of phosphate. Phosphate contamination is common owing to the formation of thin films or adsorption on iron oxide films on glassware. *Commercial detergents containing phosphate should be avoided.* Glassware should be cleaned with hot dilute HCl and rinsed well with distilled water.

3. Reagents

3.1. *Phenolphthalein indicator solution:* Either the aqueous (a) or alcoholic (b) solution may be used.

a. Dissolve 5 g phenolphthalein disodium salt in distilled water and dilute to 1 liter. If necessary, add 0.02N NaOH dropwise until a faint pink color appears.

b. Dissolve 5 g phenolphthalein in 500 ml 95 per cent ethyl alcohol or isopropyl alcohol and add 500 ml distilled water. Then add 0.02N NaOH until a faint pink color appears.

3.2. *Strong-acid solution:* Slowly add 300 ml conc H_2SO_4 to about 600 ml distilled water. When cool add 4.0 ml conc HNO_3 and dilute to 1 liter.

3.3. *Ammonium molybdate reagent:* Dissolve 31.4 g $(NH_4)_6Mo_7O_{24} \cdot 4H_2O$ in about 200 ml distilled water. Cautiously add 252 ml conc H_2SO_4 to 400 ml distilled water. Cool, add 3.4 ml conc HNO_3, add the molybdate solution, and dilute to 1 liter.

3.4. *Aminonaphtholsulfonic acid reagent:* Weigh out separately 0.75 g 1-amino-2-naphthol-4-sulfonic acid * (use only a powder which is pale pink in color); 42 g anhydrous sodium sulfite, Na_2SO_3; and 70 g anhydrous sodium metabisulfite (also called sodium pyrosulfite), $Na_2S_2O_5$. Thoroughly grind the sulfonic acid with a small portion of the $Na_2S_2O_5$ powder in a clean, dry mortar. Dissolve the remaining salts in about 900 ml distilled water; dissolve the finely ground sulfonic acid in this mixture and dilute to 1 liter. Store in a brown glass-stoppered bottle at a temperature not exceeding 30°C. This solution will become slightly discolored with time; however, if not contaminated, it will give satisfactory results for most work for 4 months or more. For the most precise work, discard the solution when tests made with standards show a deviation from calibration of 2 per cent of concentration.

3.5. *Stock phosphate solution:* Dissolve in distilled water 0.7165 g anhydrous potassium dihydrogen phosphate,

---

* Eastman No. 360 or equivalent.

KH_2PO_4, and dilute to 1,000 ml; 1.00 ml = 0.500 mg PO_4.

3.6. *Standard phosphate solution:* Dilute 100.0 ml stock phosphate solution to 1,000 ml with distilled water; 1.00 ml = 50.0 μg PO_4.

4. Procedure

4.1. If precipitation has occurred during the transporting of the sample, mix thoroughly and filter a portion of the sample according to instructions under Residue, Method B, Sec. 3, avoiding possible contamination as explained above (see "sampling and storage" and Sec. 2.3). If polyphosphate concentration is to be determined, collect as much as 200 ml of filtrate. Save the filtered and unfiltered stored sample for use in Method C. If the pH of the sample is less than 4, dilute 50.0 ml to 100 ml in a volumetric flask with distilled water and mix thoroughly. Use this diluted sample in the following steps. If the pH is greater than 10, add 1 drop of phenolphthalein indicator to 50.0 ml of sample and discharge the red color with strong-acid solution before diluting to 100 ml. (Such dilution is also useful when concentrations greater than 30 mg/l are present. When dilutions are made, the correct interpretation of "ml sample" in Sec. 5 must be made. For example, when 50.0 ml of original sample has been diluted to 100 ml for pH adjustment, the "ml sample" in the calculation is 25, not 50, although 50.0 ml of diluted sample is still used in the following steps.)

4.2. Pipet 50.0 ml of filtered or clear sample containing not more than 1.5 mg (30 mg/1) PO_4 into a clean, dry 125-ml erlenmeyer flask. Add 2.0 ml molybdate reagent and mix by swirling. Add 2.0 ml sulfonic acid reagent and mix again. Because the rate and intensity of color development are dependent on temperature, the reagents, standards, and samples should be at the same temperature (20°–30°C).

4.3. After exactly 5 min, measure the color photometrically, adjusting the instrument to 100 per cent transmittance with a proper blank. Light path lengths suitable for various phosphate ranges are as follows:

Approx. PO_4 Range mg/l	Light Path cm
5–30	0.5
0.5–6	2
0.05–1	10

Interference from color, turbidity not removed by filtration, and chromate is greatly reduced or eliminated by preparing the blank from the sample in exactly the same manner, except that strong-acid solution is used in place of the molybdate solution. Distilled water treated in the same manner with the strong-acid and sulfonic acid solutions can be used where such interferences are absent. One distilled-water blank can be used for a number of interference-free samples.

4.4. Obtain the weight of orthophosphate in the sample taken by referring the reading to the standard curve. This curve is obtained by plotting on semilogarithmic paper the transmittance readings from a suitable number of orthophosphate standards. The plot should be a straight line. (The line may not quite pass through the 100 per cent transmittance point at zero PO_4 concentration, but the reading is usually between 98 and 100 per cent, depending on the instrument used.) At least one standard should be tested with each set of samples, or once each day that tests are made.

5. Calculation

$$\text{mg/l } PO_4 = \frac{\text{mg } PO_4 \times 1{,}000}{\text{ml sample}}.$$

6. Precision and Accuracy

The precision approximates ± 0.001 mg (0.02 mg/l) or about ± 2 per cent of the result, whichever is the larger numerical value. The accuracy depends on the amount of interferences and the apparatus used. Serious differences between laboratories reporting on the same sample can result from dirty glassware and inattention to phosphate-bearing suspended matter.

B. Stannous Chloride Method for Orthophosphate

1. General Discussion

1.1. *Principle:* The principle of this method is the same as that of Method A, except for the substitution of stannous chloride for aminonaphtholsulfonic acid as the reducing agent. This change increases the sensitivity of the molybdenum blue method. It also makes an extraction step feasible, increasing the reliability of the method at concentrations below 0.1 mg/l and lessening interference.

1.2. *Interference:* The interferences mentioned under Method A, Sec. 1.2, apply to the direct or nonextraction part of the stannous chloride method as well. Because the interference from iron is somewhat greater, the concentration should not exceed 0.04 mg Fe in the portion taken for analysis. At least 25 mg/l soluble silicates can be tolerated. Color and turbidity also interfere. Chromate and strong oxidizing agents, such as peroxide, bleach the blue color. Interference from nitrite (which also bleaches the blue color) can be overcome by adding 0.1 g sulfamic acid to the sample before adding the molybdate. Because of the very low PO_4 range, contamination is a problem. In general, the direct method should be used only if Method A does not provide adequate sensitivity. Extracting the heteropoly acid into an immiscible solvent before reduction greatly reduces the number of interferences; however, it does not remove interference from arsenic and germanium. Extraction also reduces the amount of polyphosphate determined with orthophosphate.

1.3. *Minimum detectable concentration:* The minimum detectable concentration is about 0.01 mg/l PO_4. The sensitivity at 50 per cent transmittance is about 0.01 mg/l for 1 per cent change in transmittance. (See Method A, Sec. 1.3, for definition of terms and conditions of measurement.)

2. Apparatus

The same apparatus is required as for Method A, Sec. 2, except when the extraction step is employed, in which case a safety aspirator is required. The spectrophotometer will be used at 625 mμ in the measurement of the benzene-isobutanol extracts, and at 690 mμ for the aqueous solutions. A wavelength of 650 mμ may be used for the aqueous solutions, with somewhat reduced sensitivity and precision, if the instrument available is not equipped to read at 690 mμ.

3. Reagents

3.1. *Phenolphthalein indicator solution:* Prepare as directed in Method A, Sec. 3.1.

3.2. *Strong-acid solution:* Prepare as directed in Method A, Sec. 3.2.

3.3. *Ammonium molybdate reagent (I):* Dissolve 25 g $(NH_4)_6Mo_7O_{24} \cdot 4H_2O$ in 175 ml distilled water. Cautiously add 280 ml conc H_2SO_4 to 400 ml distilled water. Cool, add the molybdate solution, and dilute to 1 liter.

3.4. *Stannous chloride reagent (I):* Dissolve 2.5 g of a fresh supply of $SnCl_2 \cdot 2H_2O$ in 100 ml glycerol. Heat in a water bath and stir with a glass rod to hasten dissolution. This reagent is stable and requires neither preservatives nor special storage.

3.5. *Standard phosphate solution:* Prepare as directed in Method A, Sec. 3.6.

3.6. *Reagents for extraction:*

a. *Benzene-isobutanol solvent:* Mix equal volumes of benzene and isobutyl alcohol. (CAUTION: *This solvent is highly flammable.*)

b. *Ammonium molybdate reagent (II):* Dissolve 40.1 g $(NH_4)_6Mo_7O_{24} \cdot 4H_2O$ in approximately 500 ml distilled water. Slowly add 396 ml molybdate reagent (I). Cool and dilute to 1 liter.

c. *Alcoholic sulfuric acid solution:* Cautiously add 20 ml conc H_2SO_4 to 980 ml methyl alcohol with continuous mixing.

d. *Dilute stannous chloride reagent (II):* Mix 8 ml stannous chloride reagent (I) with 50 ml glycerol. This reagent is stable for at least 6 months.

4. Procedure

4.1. If necessary, filter the sample as directed in Method A, Sec. 4.1. To a 100-ml sample containing not more than 0.6 mg PO_4 and free from color and turbidity, add 1 drop (0.05 ml) phenolphthalein indicator. If the sample turns pink, add strong-acid solution, dropwise, to discharge the color. If more than 5 drops are required, take a smaller sample and dilute to 100 ml with distilled water after first discharging the pink color with acid.

4.2. Add, with thorough mixing after each addition, 4.0 ml molybdate reagent (I) and 0.5 ml (10 drops) stannous chloride reagent (I). The rate of color development and the intensity of color depend on the temperature of the final solution, each 1°C increase producing about 1 per cent increase in color. Hence, samples, standards, and reagents should be within 2°C of one another and at a temperature between 20° and 30°C.

4.3. After 10 min, but before 12 min, employing the same specific interval for all determinations, measure the color photometrically at 690 mμ and compare with a calibration curve, using a distilled-water blank. Light path lengths suitable for various phosphate ranges are as follows:

Approx. PO_4 Range *mg/l*	Light Path *cm*
1–6	0.5
0.3–3	2
0.02–0.5	10

A blank must always be run on the reagents and distilled water. Inasmuch as the color at first develops progressively and later fades, it is essential that timing be the same for samples as for standards. At least one standard should be tested with each set of samples or once each day that tests are made. The calibration curve may deviate from a straight line at the upper concentrations of the 1–6 mg/l range.

4.4. *Extraction:* When increased

sensitivity is desired or interferences need to be overcome, extract the phosphate as follows: Pipet a suitable aliquot of sample into a 100-ml graduated extraction cylinder and dilute, if necessary, to 40 ml with distilled water. Add 50.0 ml benzene-isobutanol solvent and 15.0 ml molybdate reagent (II). Close at once and shake vigorously for exactly 15 sec. Any delay increases the amount of polyphosphate, if present, which will be included in the orthophosphate value. Remove the stopper and withdraw 25.0 ml of separated organic layer, using a pipet and a safety aspirator. Transfer to a 50-ml volumetric flask, add 15 to 16 ml alcoholic sulfuric acid solution, swirl, add 10 drops (0.50 ml) dilute stannous chloride reagent (II), swirl, and dilute to the mark with alcoholic sulfuric acid. Mix thoroughly; after 10 min, but before 30 min, read against the blank at

625 mμ. Prepare the blank by carrying 40 ml distilled water through the same procedure as the sample. Read the PO_4 concentration from a calibration curve prepared by taking known phosphate standards through the same procedural steps as the samples.

5. Calculation

The results from the direct and the extraction procedures can be calculated by the following equation:

$$\text{mg/l } PO_4 = \frac{\text{mg } PO_4 \times 1{,}000}{\text{ml sample}}$$

6. Precision and Accuracy

The precision, both with and without extraction, approximates ± 0.001 mg (0.02 mg/l) or about ± 2 per cent of the result, whichever is the larger numerical value. See Method A, Sec. 6, for comments on accuracy.

C. Total Phosphate and Polyphosphate

1. General Discussion

1.1. *Principle:* The total-phosphate content of the sample includes all the soluble orthophosphate and polyphosphates, and insoluble phosphates precipitated during storage. If any insoluble phosphates are present, for practical purposes they are assumed to be insoluble orthophosphate. It is understood that total phosphate is not to include insoluble phosphates that may have been present in the original water and removed in sampling, unless expressly requested; in that case, such insoluble phosphate will be reported separately. Condensed phosphates, such as pyro-, tripoly-, and higher-molecular-weight species (from commer-

cial phosphates like hexametaphosphate), are not normally present in natural waters, but are frequently added in the course of water treatment. The concentration employed depends on the application. Polyphosphates do not respond appreciably to the orthophosphate tests but can be hydrolyzed to orthophosphate by boiling with acid. Also, the insoluble phosphates can be dissolved by boiling with acid. Then, with the proper combinations of filtration and boiling with acid, and the orthophosphate value by Method A or B, both the polyphosphates and insoluble phosphates can be determined as their equivalent PO_4.

1.2. *Interference:* Interferences are the same as for Method A or B, Sec.

1.2, whichever is used to complete the analysis. The sample should be analyzed as soon as possible after collection, because polyphosphates will significantly decrease on long standing or on heating. The total-phosphate and polyphosphate values obtained may at times be 0.1–0.2 mg/l PO₄ high, owing to a small amount of phosphate contributed by natural organic matter.

1.3. *Minimum detectable concentration:* The minimum detectable concentration will depend on whether Method A or B is used after hydrolysis. The selection should be based on ease of use and sensitivity required. See Methods A and B, Sec. 1.3, for details.

2. Apparatus

In addition to the apparatus required in either Method A or B, Sec. 2, an autoclave or pressure cooker may be employed to speed hydrolysis.

3. Reagents

3.1. *Phenolphthalein indicator solution:* See Method A, Sec. 3.1.

3.2. *S t r o n g-a c i d solution:* See Method A, Sec. 3.2.

3.3. *Sodium hydroxide, 1N.* Dissolve 40 g NaOH in a small quantity of distilled water and dilute to 1 liter.

4. Procedure

4.1. If precipitate or turbidity is present in the bottled sample, two portions must be taken for analysis. One should consist of 100 ml of the filtered sample (see Method A, Sec. 4.1, for procedure on filtering the sample). The other portion should consist of 100 ml of thoroughly mixed unfiltered sample. To each of the two 100-ml portions, or aliquots diluted to 100 ml, add 1 drop of phenolphthalein in-

dicator solution. If a red color develops, add strong-acid solution dropwise to just discharge the color. Then add 1 ml in excess to each.

4.2. Boil gently for at least 90 min, adding distilled water to keep the volume between 25 and 50 ml. Alternatively, heat for 30 min in an autoclave or pressure cooker at 15–20 psi. Cool, neutralize to a faint pink color with sodium hydroxide solution, and restore the portions to the original 100-ml volume with distilled water.

4.3. Determine the orthophosphate content of each treated portion using either Method A or B. This gives the total phosphate present as PO₄ in each portion.

4.4. Determine the orthophosphate on the filtered original untreated sample by the same method as used in Sec. 4.3.

5. Calculation

5.1. If no precipitate or turbidity is present in the bottled sample, then:

Total phosphate $= C_1$
Orthophosphate $= C_3$
Polyphosphate $= C_1 - C_3$

where C_1 is the value obtained from Sec. 4.3, and C_3 is the value obtained from Sec. 4.4. All results are expressed as mg/l PO₄.

5.2. If a precipitate or turbidity is present in the bottled sample, then:

Total phosphate $= C_1$
Orthophosphate $= C_3 + C_1 - C_2$
Polyphosphate $= C_2 - C_3$

where C_1 is the value obtained on the unfiltered portion and C_2 is the value obtained on the filtered portion from Sec. 4.3. All results are expressed as mg/l PO₄.

6. Precision and Accuracy

The precision and accuracy are largely dependent on the method used for the determination of the phosphate contents after digesting with acid (see Sec. 6 of both Methods A and B). If samples do not filter clear and the matter causing turbidity contains phosphate, this phosphate is determined as part of the total and orthophosphate values in both Sec. 5.1 and 5.2. Such phosphates will be very low in concentration, and, by definition, are to be considered a part of the values sought.

Bibliography

1. TRUOG, E. & MEYER, A. H. Improvements in the Deniges Colorimetric Method for Phosphorus and Arsenic. *Ind. Eng. Chem., Anal. Ed.* 1:136 (1929).
2. SCHROEDER, W. C. & FELLOWS, C. H. Determination of Carbonate, Hydroxide, and Phosphate in Boiler Waters. *Trans. Am. Soc. Mech. Engrs.* 54:213 (1932).
3. WOODS, J. T. & MELLON, M. G. Molybdenum Blue Reaction. *Ind. Eng. Chem., Anal. Ed.* 13:760 (1941).
4. FONTAINE, T. D. Spectrophotometric Determination of Phosphorus. *Ind. Eng. Chem., Anal. Ed.* 14:77 (1942).
5. KITSON, R. E. & MELLON, M. G. Further Studies of the Molybdenum Blue Reaction. *Ind. Eng. Chem., Anal. Ed.* 16:466 (1944).
6. GOLDMAN, L. & LOVE, R. N. Colorimetric Phosphate Tests for Boiler Waters Containing Tannin. *Power Plant Eng.* 50:11:76 (1946).
7. BOLTZ, D. F. & MELLON, M. G. Determination of Phosphorus, Germanium, Silicon, and Arsenic by the Heteropoly Blue Method. *Ind. Eng. Chem., Anal. Ed.* 19:873 (1947).
8. GREENBERG, A. E.; WEINBERGER, L. W.; & SAWYER, C. N. Control of Nitrite Interference in Colorimetric Determination of Phosphorus. *Anal. Chem.* 22:499 (1950).
9. YOUNG, R. S. & GOLLEDGE, A. Determination of Hexametaphosphate in Water After Threshold Treatment. *Ind. Chemist* 26:13 (1950).
10. GRISWOLD, B. L.; HUMOLLER, F. L.; & McINTYRE, A. R. Inorganic Phosphates and Phosphate Esters in Tissue Extracts. *Anal. Chem.* 23:192 (1951).
11. BOLTZ, D. F., ed. *Colorimetric Determination of Nonmetals.* Interscience Publishers, New York (1958). pp. 29–40.
12. COMMITTEE REPORT. The Determination of Orthophosphate, Hydrolyzable Phosphate, and Total Phosphate in Surface Waters. *J. AWWA* 50:1563 (1958).
13. SLETTEN, O. & BACH, C. M. Modified Stannous Chloride Reagent for Orthophosphate Determination. *J. AWWA* 53:1031 (1961).

Potassium

Potassium ranks seventh amongst the elements in order of abundance, yet its concentration in most drinking waters is trivial, seldom reaching 20 mg/l. However, occasional brines may contain in excess of 100 mg/l potassium.

Selection of method: Two methods for the determination of potassium are given. The flame photometric method

(A) is more rapid, sensitive, and accurate but requires a special instrument and much preliminary work before samples can be run routinely. The colorimetric method (B) is usually inadvisable for potassium levels below 10 mg/l because the determination would then entail more than a tenfold concentration of the sample by evaporation.

Storage of sample: Samples should not be stored in soft-glass bottles because of the possibility of contamination from leaching of the glass. Polyethylene or pyrex bottles are preferable.

A. Flame Photometric Method

1. General Discussion

1.1. *Principle:* Trace amounts of potassium can be determined in either a direct-reading or internal-standard type of flame photometer at a wavelength of 768 mμ. The principles, applications, and interferences of the flame photometric method are described under Sodium. Because much of the information pertaining to sodium applies equally to the potassium determination, the entire discussion dealing with the flame photometric determination of sodium should be studied carefully in advance of the potassium determination.

1.2. *Interference:* Burner-clogging particulate matter should be removed from the sample by filtration through a quantitative filter paper of medium retentiveness. Inclusion of a nonionic detergent into the lithium standard may assure proper aspirator function. Interference in the internal-standard method has been reported at sodium-to-potassium ratios of 5:1 or greater. Calcium may interfere if the calcium-to-potassium ratio is 10:1 or more. Magnesium begins to interfere when the magnesium-to-potassium ratio exceeds 100.

1.3. *Minimum detectable concentration:* With expert technique, potassium levels approximating 0.1 mg/l can be determined in the better flame photometers.

2. Apparatus

See Sodium, Sec. 2.

3. Reagents

In order to minimize potassium pickup, all solutions should preferably be stored in plastic bottles. The use of small containers reduces the amount of dry element which may be picked up from the bottle walls when the solution is poured. Each container should be thoroughly shaken to wash the accumulated salts from the walls before the solution is poured.

3.1. *Deionized distilled water:* Prepare as described under Sodium, Sec. 3.1. Use this water for the preparation of all reagents, calibration standards, and as dilution water.

3.2. *Stock potassium solution:* Dissolve 1.907 g potassium chloride, KCl, dried at 110°C, and dilute to 1,000 ml with deionized distilled water to form a solution containing 1.00 mg K per 1.00 ml.

3.3. *Intermediate potassium solution:* Dilute 10.00 ml stock potassium solution with deionized distilled water to 100 ml to form a solution containing 0.100 mg K per 1.00 ml. Use this intermediate solution for preparing the calibration curve in the potassium range of 1–10 mg/l.

3.4. *Standard potassium solution:* Dilute 10.00 ml intermediate potassium solution with deionized distilled water to 100 ml to form a solution containing 10.0 μg K per 1.00 ml. Use this solution for preparing the calibration curve in the potassium range of 0.1–1.0 mg/l.

3.5. *Standard lithium solution.* See Sodium, Sec. 3.5.

4. Procedure

Perform the determination as described under Sodium, Sec. 4, but measure the emission intensity at 768 mμ.

5. Calculation

See Sodium, Sec. 5.

6. Precision and Accuracy

The potassium content of a synthetic unknown sample containing 3.6 mg/l potassium, 8 mg/l sodium, 120 mg/l calcium, and 75 mg/l magnesium was determined with a standard deviation of ±0.36 mg/l in 23 laboratories using the flame photometric method. The individual laboratories reproduced their own results within ±0.12 mg/l.

The potassium content of another synthetic unknown sample containing 3.1 mg/l potassium, 19.9 mg/l sodium, 108 mg/l calcium, and 82 mg/l magnesium was determined with a standard deviation of ±0.49 mg/l in 31 laboratories, using the flame photometric method. Half of the reported results were within ±0.3 mg/l of the known potassium concentration. The individual laboratories reproduced their own results within ±0.09 mg/l.

B. Colorimetric Method

1. General Discussion

1.1. *Principle:* Potassium is determined colorimetrically by precipitating it with sodium cobaltinitrite, oxidizing the dipotassium sodium cobaltinitrite with standard potassium dichromate solution in the presence of sulfuric acid, and measuring the excess dichromate colorimetrically. A series of solutions of known potassium concentration must be carried through the procedure together with each set of samples, because the temperature and the time of precipitation affect the results markedly.

1.2. *Interference:* Ammonium ion interferes and should be absent. Silica causes no difficulty unless a silica gel is formed either during evaporation or when the sample becomes acid upon addition of the reagent. If this occurs, as evidenced by turbidity in the final colored solution, filtration will be necessary. Other substances normally present in water do not interfere.

1.3. *Minimum detectable concentration:* 0.5 mg potassium can be detected by the photometric method when a 15-cm light path is used. This represents a potassium concentration of 5 mg/l when a 100-ml sample is taken for analysis.

2. Apparatus

2.1. *Colorimetric equipment:* One of the following is required:

a. *Spectrophotometer,* for use at 425 mμ, providing a light path of 1 cm or longer.

b. *Filter photometer,* providing a light path of 1 cm or longer and equipped with a violet filter having maximum transmittance near 425 mμ. Longer light paths are desirable for concentrations below 20 mg/1 K.

c. Nessler tubes, matched, 100 ml, tall form.

2.2. *Centrifuge.*

2.3. *Centrifuge tubes,* 25 ml.

2.4. *Small-diameter stirring rods,* 2–3 mm, to stir the precipitate in the centrifuge tube.

3. Reagents

3.1. *Nitric acid, 1N.* Dilute 64 ml conc HNO_3 to 1 liter with distilled water.

3.2. *Trisodium cobaltinitrite solution:* Dissolve 10 g $Na_3Co(NO_2)_6$ in 50 ml distilled water. Filter before use. Prepare the solution daily.

3.3. *Nitric acid, 0.01N.* Dilute 10 ml $1N$ HNO_3 to 1 liter with distilled water.

3.4. *Standard potassium dichromate,* 0.1000N. Dissolve 4.904 g anhydrous $K_2Cr_2O_7$ in distilled water, and make up to 1,000 ml. This solution is stable for long periods.

3.5. *Sulfuric acid,* conc.

3.6. *Standard potassium solution:* Prepare as directed in Method A, Sec. 3.2; 1.00 ml = 1.00 mg K.

4. Procedure

4.1. If the sample contains from 100 to 700 mg/1 K, a 10.00-ml portion is taken for analysis. If it contains less than this amount, concentrate a larger portion by evaporation to about 5 ml, transfer to a 25-ml centrifuge tube, and make up to 10.00 ml.

4.2. At room temperature, add, with mixing, 1 ml $1N$ HNO_3 and 5 ml cobaltinitrite solution. Allow to stand for 2 hr. Inasmuch as the composition of the precipitate is dependent on the time allowed for precipitation as well as on the temperature, the time should

be kept constant (±15 min) for all samples. A variation of 10°C in either direction will give an error of 2 per cent. Centrifuge for 10 min. Decant and wash the precipitate with 15 ml 0.01N HNO_3, using a small-diameter stirring rod; mix to insure complete contact between precipitate and wash solution. Centrifuge again; decant; and add, with mixing, 10.00 ml standard $K_2Cr_2O_7$ solution and 5 ml conc H_2SO_4. Cool to room temperature. Make up to 100 ml with distilled water. Filter if the solution is turbid.

4.3. Place 1.00, 2.00, 3.00, 4.00, 5.00, 6.00, and 7.00 ml standard potassium solution in 25-ml centrifuge tubes, dilute each to 10 ml, and treat in the same manner as the sample. This will give standards containing 1.00 to 7.00 mg K. Compare the sample against these standards. A wavelength of 425 mμ is suitable for photometric measurements. If visual comparison is used, the range of standards should be from 2 to 7 mg K, and the accuracy to be expected will be about ±0.5 mg K. When a filter photometer is used, with a 15-cm light path, the range of standards should be from 0.5 to 7 mg K, and the accuracy will be 2 to 3 per cent. If a spectrophotometer is used, with a 2-cm cell, the range should be from 2 to 7 mg K, and the accuracy will be ±0.5 mg. The solutions at this point are stable for at least a week, if protected from dust and strong light.

5. Calculation

$$mg/1\ K = \frac{mg\ K \times 1,000}{ml\ sample}$$

Bibliography

Flame Photometric Method

All of the references cited in the bibliography for the flame photometric method of sodium apply equally well to potassium. The following reference also deserves attention:

1. MEHLICH, A. & MONROE, R. J. Report on
Potassium Analyses by Means of Flame
Photometer Methods. *J. Assoc. Offic.
Agr. Chemists* 35:588 (1952).

Colorimetric Method

2. WANDER, I. W. Photometric Determination of Potassium. *Ind. Eng. Chem.,
Anal. Ed.* 14:471 (1942).

Residue

Waters yielding considerable residue are generally inferior with respect to palatability or may induce an unfavorable physiological reaction in the transient consumer. Highly mineralized waters are also unsuitable for many industrial applications. For these reasons, a limit of 500 mg/l residue is desirable for drinking waters.

"Total residue" is the term applied to the material left in the vessel after evaporation of a sample of water and its subsequent drying in an oven at a definite temperature. Total residue includes "nonfiltrable residue"—that is, the portion of the total residue retained by a filter—and "filtrable residue"—the portion of the total residue which passes through the filter.

In the past, the terms "suspended" and "dissolved" residue corresponded to nonfiltrable and filtrable residue, respectively. The latter are more precise designations, however, because these residues are still somewhat indistinct entities whose separation is dependent on a number of variables, some of which can be controlled only with difficulty. The chemical and physical nature of the material in suspension, the pore size of the filter, the area and thickness of the filter mat, and the amount and physical state of the materials deposited on it are the principal factors involved. A method designed to control all of the variables affecting filtration would be too cumbersome for practical use. It must be recognized, therefore, that residue determinations are not subject to the usual criteria of accuracy. The various types of residue are defined arbitrarily by the methods used for their determination, and these, in turn, represent practical approaches to what would otherwise be exceedingly complex operations.

The temperature at which the residue is dried has an important bearing on the results, since weight losses due to volatilization of organic matter, mechanically occluded water, water of crystallization, and gases from heat-induced chemical decomposition, as well as weight gains due to oxidation, are dependent on the temperature and the period of heating. Provision is made for a choice of drying temperatures and the analyst should be familiar with the probable effects of each.

"Fixed residue"—the residue remaining after ignition for 1 hr at 600° C—does not distinguish precisely between organic and inorganic residue because the loss on ignition is not confined to organic matter but includes losses due to decomposition or volatilization of certain mineral salts. A better approximation of the organic matter in water is available by biochemical oxygen demand or chemical oxygen demand methods described in Parts III and IV, respectively.

Specific conductance measurements

are roughly proportional to the filtrable residue and may be used to advantage in selecting the proper size of sample for residue determinations. Close correlation of results of the two tests should not, however, be expected in every instance.

An additional possibility for checking fixed filtrable residue is the utilization of ion-exchange procedures described in the Introduction, C, Sec. 3.

Selection of drying temperature: The methods described are gravimetric and permit freedom of choice with respect to the temperature of drying.

Residues dried at 103°–105°C may be expected to retain not only water of crystallization but also some mechanically occluded water. Loss of carbon dioxide will result in the conversion of bicarbonate to carbonate. Loss of organic matter by volatilization will be very slight at this temperature, if it occurs at all. Because the expulsion of occluded water is marginal at 105°C, attainment of constant weight is very slow.

Residues dried at 179°–181°C will lose almost all the mechanically occluded water, but some water of crystallization may remain, especially if sulfates are present. Organic matter is reduced by volatilization but is not completely destroyed. Bicarbonate is converted to carbonate, and carbonate may be partially decomposed to oxide or basic salts. Some chloride and nitrate salts may be lost. In general, evaporating and drying water samples at 179°–181°C yields values for total residue which conform more closely to those obtained through summation of individually determined mineral salts than do the values for total residue secured through drying at a lower temperature.

The analyst must select the drying temperature best suited to the type of water under examination. Waters that are low in organic matter and total mineral content and are intended for human consumption may be examined under either temperature, but waters containing considerable organic matter or those with pH over 9.0 should be dried at the higher temperature. In any case, the report should indicate the drying temperature.

Selection of method for nonfiltrable residue: The amount and type of suspended matter in the sample, the purpose of the water analysis, and the relative ease of making the determination will dictate whether the nonfiltrable residue is obtained by a direct determination or by calculation of the difference between the total residue and the filtrable residue.

Sampling and storage: Water has considerable solvent action on glass, and the mineral content of a sample will increase when the water is stored in a bottle made of nonresistant glass. This effect is especially pronounced with alkaline waters. Resistant-glass bottles are therefore desirable. Plastic bottles are satisfactory, provided that the material in suspension in the sample does not adhere to the walls of the container. Store samples likely to contain iron or manganese so that oxygen will not come into contact with the water. Analyze these samples promptly to minimize the possibility of the occurrence of chemical or physical change during storage.

A. Total Residue

1. General Discussion

1.1. *Principle:* The sample is evaporated in a weighed dish on a steam bath and then is dried to constant weight in an oven at either 103°–105°C or 179°–181°C. The increase in weight over that of the empty dish represents the total residue.

1.2. *Minimum detectable concentration:* Dependent on the sensitivity of the analytical balance used for weighing.

2. Apparatus

2.1. *Evaporating dishes:* Dishes of 150–200 ml capacity made of the following materials may be used as indicated:

a. Platinum: Generally satisfactory for all tests.

b. Nickel: Satisfactory if the residue is not to be ignited.

c. Porcelain, silica, Vycor, * or *pyrex:* Satisfactory for samples having a pH below 9.0.

Nickel oxidizes slightly at 600°C, and fixed residues may be difficult to remove. Porcelain, silica, Vycor, and pyrex glass are corroded by high-pH waters, and pyrex glass will soften at the ignition temperature. Platinum is the most satisfactory because it is relatively unattacked by mineral salts and suffers comparatively insignificant weight change during heating operations.

2.2. *Steam bath.*

2.3. *Drying oven,* equipped with a thermostatic control capable of maintaining the temperature within a 2°C range.

---

* A product of Corning Glass Works.

2.4. *Desiccator,* provided with a desiccant containing a color indicator of moisture concentration.

2.5. *Analytical balance,* 200-g capacity, capable of weighing to 0.1 mg.

3. Procedure

3.1. *Preparation of evaporating dish:* A dish to be used in the determination of total residue should receive a preliminary drying in an oven at the same temperature intended to be used for the residue. If ignition of the residue is to be carried out for determination of fixed total residue, preliminary ignition of the dish in a furnace for 30 min at 600°C is required.

3.2. Choose a volume of sample which will yield a residue between 25 and 250 mg, and preferably between 100 and 250 mg. A rough preliminary calculation from the value of specific conductance will usually suffice to estimate the volume to be evaporated.

3.3. Pour a measured portion of the well mixed sample into a weighed evaporating dish on a steam bath. After complete evaporation of the water from the residue, transfer the dish to an oven maintained at either 103°–105°C or 179°–181°C. Dry to constant weight. (Constant weight is considered attained when not more than a 0.5-mg weight change occurs between two successive series of operations consisting of heating, cooling in a desiccator, and weighing.) Drying for a long period may eliminate the necessity for checking for constant weight, but the analyst must either dry the dish overnight or determine by trial the minimum time required to attain constant weight with a given type of sample when a number of samples of the same kind are involved. Allow the dish to cool briefly in air before placing it, while still warm, in a desiccator to complete the cooling in a dry atmosphere. Do not overload the desiccator. Sufficient room must be available so that all dishes may remain flat on the desiccator shelf, and no part of a dish should touch another dish or the side of the desiccator.

3.4. Weigh the dish as soon as it has completely cooled. The residue should not remain overly long in a desiccator because some residues, especially those dried at 180°C, are very hygroscopic and may remove water from a desiccant that is not thoroughly dry. Report the increase in weight over the empty dish as "total residue on drying at —°C" in terms of mg/l and to the nearest whole number. For results ex-ceeding 1,000 mg/l report only three significant figures.

4. Calculation

$$\text{mg/l total residue} = \frac{\text{mg total residue} \times 1,000}{\text{ml sample}}$$

5. Precision and Accuracy

The precision of the method is about ±4 mg or ±5 per cent. Accuracy can-not be estimated, for residue as deter-mined by this method is an arbitrary quantity essentially defined by the pro-cedure followed. The determined val-ues, therefore, may not check with the theoretical value for solids calculated from the chemical analysis. Sokoloff [2] should be consulted for approximate methods by which to correlate the chemical analysis with the residue de-terminations.

B. Filtrable Residue

1. General Discussion

1.1. *Principle:* The sample is filtered and the filtrate is evaporated in a weighed dish on a steam bath. The residue left after evaporation is dried to constant weight in an oven at either 103°–105°C or 179°–181°C. The in-crease in weight over that of the empty dish represents filtrable residue and in-cludes all materials, liquid or solid, in solution or otherwise, which pass through the filter and are not volatil-ized during the drying process.

1.2. *Minimum detectable concentra-tion:* Dependent on the analytical bal-ance used for weighing.

2. Apparatus

All of the apparatus listed under Method A, Sec. 2, is required; and, in addition:

2.1. *Filter:* One of the following is required:

a. Membrane filter: The pore size should be chosen to include the critical item (like soil, algae, and bacteria) to be removed, but large enough to filter a reasonable volume in an hour's time or less.

b. Paper: Acid-washed, ashless, hard-finish filter paper sufficiently re-tentive for fine precipitates.

c. Crucible: Porous-bottom silica, fritted-glass, porcelain, stainless-steel, or alundum crucible with a maximum pore size of 5 microns.

d. Diatomaceous filter candles, with a maximum pore size of 5 microns.

e. *Gooch crucible,* 30-ml capacity, with asbestos mat.

2.2. *Filtering apparatus,* appropriate to the type of filter selected.

3. Procedure

Filter a portion of the sample through one of the filters listed in Sec. 2 and carry out the procedure outlined in Method A, Sec. 3, on an appropriate portion of the filtrate. Report the increase in weight over the empty dish as "filtrable residue on drying at —°C" in terms of mg/l and to the nearest whole number. For results exceeding 1,000 mg/l report only three significant figures. Report the type of filter used.

4. Calculation

$$\text{mg/l filtrable residue} = \frac{A \times 1,000}{\text{ml sample}}$$

where $A = $ mg filtrable residue.

5. Precision and Accuracy

Refer to Method A, Sec. 5. A synthetic unknown sample containing 134 mg/l filtrable residue was determined gravimetrically with a standard deviation of ± 13 mg/l in 18 laboratories, using a drying temperature of 103°–105°C.

C. Nonfiltrable Residue

1. General Discussion

1.1. *Principle:* The sample is filtered and the nonfiltrable residue is determined either directly or by difference between the total residue and the filtrable residue. If the determination is made directly, an appropriate portion of sample is passed through a weighed filter, and the filter with its contents is oven dried at either 103°–105°C or 179°–181°C. The increase in weight over that of the empty filter represents nonfiltrable residue.

1.2. *Interference:* Occasionally the physical nature of the suspended material may cause it to clog the filter and retard the passage of the water. If the time required for filtration in such instances is unduly long, determination by difference is recommended.

1.3. *Minimum detectable concentration:* Dependent upon efficiency of filtration and upon the sensitivity of the analytical balance used for weighing.

2. Apparatus

2.1. *Filters:* One of the following is required:

a. *Crucible:* Porous-bottom silica, fritted-glass, porcelain, stainless-steel or alundum crucible with a maximum pore size of 5 microns.

b. *Gooch crucible,* 30-ml capacity, with asbestos mat.

2.2. *Filtering apparatus,* appropriate to the type of filter selected.

2.3. *Drying oven,* equipped with a thermostatic control capable of maintaining the temperature within 2°C.

2.4. *Desiccator,* provided with a desiccant containing a color indicator of moisture content.

2.5. *Analytical balance,* capable of weighing to 0.1 mg.

3. Procedure

3.1. *Preparation of filter:* If the determination is to be made directly by weighing the residue, the filter must receive a preliminary drying in an oven at the same temperature intended to be used for the sample. If the fixed nonfiltrable residue is to be determined subsequently, the filter must be heated in a furnace for at least 30 min at 600°C and, because stainless-steel and glass filters should not be subjected to ignition temperatures, a porcelain, silica, or alundum filter is required.

3.2. As the amount of nonfiltrable residue in potable waters is usually very small, a relatively large volume of sample must be passed through the filter to secure a weighable residue. The minimum amount of residue to be considered significant in a direct weighing is 2.5 mg. A reasonable criterion of sample size may be found in the measurement of turbidity. If the sample has a turbidity of 50 units or less, filter 1 liter for nonfiltrable residue; if the turbidity is over 50 units, filter sufficient sample to yield from 50 to 100 mg of nonfiltrable residue. When the amount of residue left on the filter is greater than 100 mg, estimation of the nonfiltrable residue by difference between total residue and filtrable residue is recommended.

3.3. After filtration transfer the filter with its contents to an oven maintained at a temperature of either 103°–105°C or 179°–181°C and dry until constant weight is attained (see Method A, Sec. 3.3, for criterion on constant weight). Drying for a long period may eliminate the necessity for checking for constant weight, but the analyst must either dry the filter overnight or determine by trial the minimum time required to attain constant weight with a given type of sample when a number of the same kind of samples are involved. Cool briefly in air and transfer to a desiccator to complete the cooling in a dry atmosphere. Report the increase in weight over that of the empty filter as "nonfiltrable residue on drying at —°C" in terms of mg/1 and to the nearest whole number.

4. Calculation

$$\text{mg/1 nonfiltrable residue} = \frac{A \times 1,000}{\text{ml sample}}$$

where A = mg nonfiltrable residue.

5. Precision and Accuracy

Refer to Method A, Sec. 5.

D. Fixed Residue (Total, Filtrable, Nonfiltrable)

1. Principle

The dishes with the residue retained after completion of the tests for total residue and filtrable residue, or the filter with its residue retained after completion of the test for nonfiltrable residue, are subjected to heat for 1 hr in a furnace held at 600°C. The increase in weight over that of the ig-nited empty vessel represents fixed residue in each instance.

2. Procedure

Ignite the residue in the dish or filter in a muffle furnace at a temperature of 600°C. In order to insure reproducibility, it is preferable to have the furnace up to temperature and to ignite for 1 hr. After ignition, allow the vessels to partially cool in air until most of the heat has dissipated, and then transfer to a desiccator for final cooling in a dry atmosphere. Do not overload the desiccator. Weigh the vessel as soon as it has completely cooled. (See Method A, Sec. 3.4.) Report the increase in weight over the empty ignited vessel as "fixed total residue," "fixed filtrable residue," or "fixed nonfiltrable residue," whichever is appropriate to the sample, in terms of mg/l and to the nearest whole number. For results exceeding 1,000 mg/l report only three significant figures.

3. Calculation

$$\text{mg/l fixed residue} = \frac{\text{mg fixed residue} \times 1,000}{\text{ml sample}}$$

4. Precision and Accuracy

Refer to Method A, Sec. 5.

Bibliography

1. HOWARD, C. S. Determination of Total Dissolved Solids in Water Analysis. *Ind. Eng. Chem., Anal. Ed.* 5:4 (1933).
2. SOKOLOFF, V. P. Water of Crystallization in Total Solids of Water Analysis. *Ind. Eng. Chem., Anal. Ed.* 5:336 (1933).

Saturation and Stability with Respect to Calcium Carbonate

Theoretical and practical studies of the scale-forming and corrosive properties of water have been and are being made. An important value upon which theory and application have been built is the theoretical pH_s, the calculated pH at which, without change in total alkalinity and calcium content, a water would be in equilibrium with solid calcium carbonate. Another definition of pH_s is: the calculated pH at which, by the addition or removal of carbon dioxide, a water would be brought into equilibrium with solid calcium carbonate.

The calculation of pH_s, at a given temperature involves three variables— total alkalinity, calcium, and dissolved solids. (An average value applicable to most ordinary fresh waters is often used for the last, thereby reducing the number of variables to two.) The value for pH_s for a given water can be obtained directly by the use of one of the following aids: Langelier stability diagram,[13, 18] Riehl's nomogram,[4, 17] Hirsch's slide rule,[8, 9] and the Caldwell-Lawrence water-conditioning diagram.[20] The values of the various constants used in calculating pH_s are also available.[5, 10, 14, 19]

Saturation index and stability index are each calculated from the pH_s and the actual pH of the water. The most important determination is that of the actual pH in the field; a pH determination on a sample which has been exposed to temperature change, storage, agitation, or other conditions that can cause pH change is of negligible value. A change in temperature will cause a change in the value of either index, the direction of the change being determined both by the direction of the temperature change and by the alkalinity concentration.[12–15, 19]

The formula [1] for *saturation index* is $pH_{actual} - pH_s$. This value is an indication of the degree of instability with respect to calcium carbonate deposition and solution. A positive value indicates a tendency to deposit calcium carbonate and a negative value indicates a tendency to dissolve calcium carbonate.

The formula [11] for *stability index* is $2 \text{ pH}_s - \text{pH}_{actual}$. It has been proposed as a more quantitative measure of the $CaCO_3$ scale-forming tendency. The stability index for all waters will be positive. A water having a stability index of about 6.0 or less is considered definitely scale forming, provided the pH_s is not more than 7.5, whereas an index above 7.0 may not give a protective coating of carbonate scale. Scale deposition will become increasingly less and corrosion will become increasingly greater as the index increases above 7.5 or 8.0.

This discussion is necessarily brief and oversimplified. The reader is referred to the bibliography for detailed information regarding the derivation of the basic equations, their application, their limitations when applied to special types of waters, and comparisons between indicated and observed scale formation.

Another means of determining the stability of a water with respect to calcium carbonate is the "marble test," the procedure for which has been outlined by Hoover.[4] This test simply determines whether a water is supersaturated, just saturated, or unsaturated with calcium carbonate, by determining the change in total alkalinity or pH after contact with an excess of pure powdered calcium carbonate. The Enslow stability indicator [7] provides for a continuous flow of the water to be tested through powdered and granular calcium carbonate. Testing the influent to, and the effluent from, this apparatus should give the same results as the marble test. If the results of either test are expressed as a change in pH value, this change must not be confused with, or reported as, the Langelier saturation index, because the change in the pH value in the marble test is caused by a change in total alkalinity, which is assumed to be constant when calculating the pH_s for Langelier's saturation index. If these results are expressed as a change in mg/l total alkalinity, the tests give a quantitative measure of the tendency of the water to dissolve or deposit calcium carbonate scales. These tests are subject to the influence of contact time and temperature change during the test.

Bibliography

Classification according to subject matter: (a) theory and theoretical calculations—Ref. 1, 13, 14, 18, 19; (b) graphs and other aids for rapid calculations of pH_s—Ref. 4, 5, 8, 9, 10, 12, 13, 17, 18, 19, 20; (c) comparisons of observed and theoretical scale formation—Ref. 3, 15; (d) laboratory tests for measurement of calcium carbonate saturation—Ref. 2, 4, 6, 7, 16, 18; (e) general—Ref. 12, 17, 18, 19, 20.

1. Langelier, W. F. The Analytical Control of Anticorrosion Water Treatment. *J. AWWA* 28:1500 (1936).

2. McLaughlin, P. L. Determining the Necessary Treatment to Prevent Corrosion. *Water Works & Sewerage* 83:81 (1936).

3. DeMartini, F. E. Corrosion and the Langelier Calcium Carbonate Saturation Index. *J. AWWA* 30:85 (1938).

4. Hoover, C. P. Practical Application of the Langelier Method. *J. AWWA* 30:1802 (1938).

5. Moore, E. W. Calculation of Chemical Dosages Required for the Prevention of Corrosion. *J. New Engl. Water Works Assoc.* 52:311 (1938).

6. Amorosi, A. M. & McDermet, J. R. Calculation of the Distribution of Carbon Dioxide Between Water and Steam. *Proc. ASTM* 39:1204 (1939).

7. ENSLOW, L. H. The Continuous Stability Indicator. *Water Works & Sewerage* 86:107 (1939).

8. HIRSCH, A. A. A Special Slide Rule for Calcium Carbonate Equilibrium Problems. *Ind. Eng. Chem., Anal. Ed.* 14: 178 (1942).

9. HIRSCH, A. A. A Slide Rule for Carbonate Equilibria and Alkalinity in Water Supplies. *Ind. Eng. Chem., Anal. Ed.* 14:943 (1942).

10. LARSON, T. E. & BUSWELL, A. M. Calcium Carbonate Saturation Index and Alkalinity Interpretations. *J. AWWA* 34:1667 (1942).

11. RYZNAR, J. W. A New Index for Determining Amount of Calcium Carbonate Scale Formed by Water. *J. AWWA* 36:472 (1944).

12. POWELL, S. T.; BACON, H. E.; & LILL, J. R. Corrosion Prevention by Controlled Calcium Carbonate Scale. *Ind. Eng. Chem.* 37:842 (1945).

13. LANGELIER, W. F. Chemical Equilibria in Water Treatment. *J. AWWA* 38: 169 (1946).

14. LANGELIER, W. F. Effect of Temperature on the pH of Natural Waters. *J. AWWA* 38:179 (1946).

15. POWELL, S. T.; BACON, H. E.; & LILL, J. R. Recent Developments in Corrosion Control. *J. AWWA* 38:808 (1946).

16. HARTUNG, H. O. Stabilization of Lime-Softened Water. *Water & Sewage Works* 95:128 (1948).

17. BLACK, A. P. The Chemistry of Water Treatment. *Water & Sewage Works* 95:369 (1948).

18. *Water Quality and Treatment.* Am. Water Works Assoc., New York (2nd ed., 1950). p. 297.

19. LARSON, T. E. The Ideal Lime-Softened Water. *J. AWWA* 43:649 (1951).

20. CALDWELL, D. H. & LAWRENCE, W. B. Water Softening and Conditioning Problems. *Ind. Eng. Chem.* 45:535 (1953).

21. DYE, J. F. Correlation of the Two Principal Methods of Calculating the Three Kinds of Alkalinity. *J. AWWA* 50: 800 (1958).

Selenium

Selenium is toxic to man and livestock, with several instances of illness having been attributed to its presence in drinking water. Selenium has also been suspected of causing dental caries in man, and has been cited as a potential carcinogenic agent.

The selenium concentration of most drinking waters falls below 0.01 mg/l. Concentrations exceeding 0.5 mg/l are rare and limited to seepage from seleniferous soils. The sudden appearance of selenium in a water supply might indicate industrial pollution. Little is known regarding the valence state of selenium in natural waters, but because selenate and selenite are both found in soils, it is reasonable to expect that both may be present in seleniferous water.

Water contaminated with wastes may contain selenium in any of its four valence states. Many organic compounds of selenium are known.

Selection of method: The diaminobenzidine methods (*A* and *B*) react with smaller selenium concentrations and are shorter from the standpoint of manipulation than the colored sol method (*C*). Method C is the oldest of the three presented but requires that both the samples and the standards be distilled before the colored sol is produced. Method A involves the least time and is preferred in the absence of large amounts of iodide. Method B can be reserved for those instances where such interferences as iodide and bromide are present in the sample.

A. *Diaminobenzidine Method* (Tentative)

1. General Discussion

1.1. *Principle:* Oxidation by acid permanganate converts all selenium compounds to selenate. Many carbon compounds are not completely oxidized by acid permanganate, but it is improbable that the selenium-carbon bond will remain intact through this treatment. Experiments demonstrate that inorganic forms of selenium are oxidized by acid permanganate in the presence of much greater concentrations of organic matter than would be anticipated in water supplies.

There is substantial loss of selenium when solutions of sodium selenate are evaporated to complete dryness, but in the presence of calcium all the selenium is recovered. An excess of calcium over the sulfate is not necessary.

Selenate is reduced to selenite in warm $4N$ HCl. Temperature, time, and acid concentrations are specified to obtain quantitative reduction without loss of selenium. The optimum pH for the formation of piazselenol is approximately 1.5. Above pH 2, the rate of formation of the colored compound is critically dependent on the pH. When indicators are used to adjust the pH, the results are frequently erratic. Extraction of piazselenol is not quantitative, but equilibrium is attained rapidly. Above pH 6, the partition ratio of piazselenol between water and toluene is almost independent of the hydrogen ion concentration.

1.2. *Interference:* No inorganic compounds give a positive interference. It is possible that colored organic compounds exist that are extracted by toluene, but it seems improbable that interference of this nature will resist the initial acid permanganate oxidation. Negative interference results from compounds that lower the concentration of diaminobenzidine by oxidizing this reagent. The addition of EDTA eliminates negative interference from at least 2.5 mg ferric iron. Manganese has no effect in any reasonable concentration, probably because it is reduced along with the selenate. Iodide, and to a lesser extent bromide, causes low results. The recovery of selenium from a standard containing 25 μg Se in the presence of varying amounts of iodide and bromide is shown in Table 13. The percentage recovery improves

TABLE 13—PERCENTAGE OF SELENIUM RECOVERED

Iodide *mg*	Selenium Recovered—%		
	Br 0 mg	Br 1.25 mg	Br 2.50 mg
0	100	100	96
0.5	95	94	95
1.25	84	80	
2.50	75		70

slightly as the amount of selenium is decreased.

1.3. *Minimum detectable concentration:* 1 μg Se with a 4-cm light path.

2. Apparatus

2.1. *Colorimetric equipment:* One of the following is required:

a. *Spectrophotometer,* for use at 420 mμ, providing a light path of 1 cm or longer.

b. *Filter photometer,* providing a light path of 1 cm or longer and equipped with a violet filter having a maximum transmittance near 420 mμ.

2.2. *Separatory funnel,* 250 ml.

2.3. *Centrifuge,* for 12- or 15-ml tubes (optional).

3. Reagents

3.1. *Stock selenium solution:* Place an accurately weighed pellet of ACS-grade metallic selenium into a small beaker. Add 5 ml conc HNO_3. Warm until the reaction is complete and cautiously evaporate just to dryness. Dilute to 1,000 ml with distilled water.

3.3. *Standard selenium solution:* Dilute an appropriate volume of stock selenium solution with distilled water so that 1.00 ml $= 1.00$ μg Se.

3.3. *Methyl orange indicator solution:* Dissolve 0.5 g methyl orange in 1 liter distilled water.

3.4. *Hydrochloric acid, 0.1N.* Dilute 8.3 ml conc HCl to 1,000 ml with distilled water.

3.5. *Calcium chloride solution:* Dissolve 30 g $CaCl_2 \cdot 2H_2O$ in distilled water and dilute to 1 liter.

3.6. *Potassium permanganate, 0.1N.* Dissolve 3.2 g $KMnO_4$ in 1,000 ml distilled water.

3.7. *Sodium hydroxide, 0.1N.* Dissolve 4.0 g NaOH in distilled water and dilute to 1 liter.

3.8. *Hydrochloric acid,* conc.

3.9. *Ammonium chloride solution:* Dissolve 250 g NH_4Cl in 1 liter distilled water.

3.10. *EDTA-sulfate reagent:* Dissolve 100 g disodium ethylenediamine tetraacetate dihydrate, also called (ethylenedinitrilo)tetraacetic acid disodium salt, and 200 g sodium sulfate in 1 liter distilled water. Add conc ammonium hydroxide dropwise while stirring until the dissolution is complete.

3.11. *Ammonium hydroxide, 5N.* Dilute 330 ml conc NH_4OH to 1 liter with distilled water.

3.12. *Diaminobenzidine solution:* Dissolve 0.100 g 3,3'-diaminobenzidine hydrochloride in 10 ml distilled water. Prepare no more than 8 hr prior to use because this solution is unstable. (CAUTION: *Handle this suspected carcinogen with extreme care.*)

3.13. *Toluene.*

3.14. *Sodium sulfate,* anhydrous. Required if no centrifuge is available.

4. Procedure

4.1. *Oxidation to selenate:* Prepare standards containing 0, 10.0, 25.0, and 50.0 μg Se in 500-ml erlenmeyer flasks. Dilute to approximately 250 ml, add 10 drops methyl orange indicator solution, 2 ml 0.1N HCl, 5 ml $CaCl_2$ solution, 3 drops 0.1N $KMnO_4$, and a 5-ml measure of glass beads to prevent bumping. Boil vigorously for approximately 5 min.

To a 1,000-ml sample in a 2-liter beaker add 10 drops methyl orange indicator solution. Titrate to the methyl orange endpoint with 0.1N HCl and add 2-ml excess. Add 3 drops $KMnO_4$, 5 ml $CaCl_2$ solution, and a 5-ml measure of glass beads to prevent bumping. Heat to boiling, adding $KMnO_4$ as required to maintain a purple tint. Ignore a precipitate of MnO_2 because it will have no adverse effect. After the volume has been reduced to approximately 250 ml, quantitatively transfer the solution to a 500-ml erlenmeyer flask.

4.2. *Evaporation:* Add 5 ml NaOH to each flask and evaporate to dryness. Avoid prolonged heating of the residue.

4.3. *Reduction to selenite:* Cool the flask, add 5 ml conc HCl and 10 ml NH_4Cl solution. Heat in a boiling water bath or steam bath for 10 ± 0.5 min.

4.4. *Formation of piazselenol:* Transfer the warm solution and ammonium chloride precipitate, if present, from the flask to a beaker suitable for pH adjustment, washing the flask with 5 ml EDTA-sulfate reagent and 5 ml $5N$ NH$_4$OH. Adjust the pH to 1.5 ± 0.3 with NH$_4$OH using a pH meter. The precipitate of EDTA will not interfere. Add 1 ml diaminobenzidine solution and heat in a boiling water bath or steam bath for approximately 5 min.

4.5. *Extraction of piazselenol:* Cool and then add NH$_4$OH to adjust the pH to 8 ± 1; the precipitate of EDTA will dissolve. Pour the sample into a 50-ml graduate, and adjust the volume to 50 ± 1 ml with washings from the beaker.

Pour the contents of the graduate into a 250-ml separatory funnel. Add 10 ml toluene, shake for 30 ± 5 sec. Discard the aqueous layer, and transfer the organic phase to a 12- or 15-ml centrifuge tube. Centrifuge briefly to clear the toluene from water droplets. If a centrifuge is not available, filter the organic phase through a dry filter paper to which has been added approximately 0.1 g anhydrous Na$_2$SO$_4$.

4.6. *Determination of absorbance:* Read the absorbance at approximately 420 mμ using toluene to establish zero absorbance. The piazselenol color is stable, but evaporation of toluene concentrates the color to a marked degree in a few hours. Beer's Law is obeyed up to 50 μg.

5. Calculation

$$mg/l \; Se = \frac{\mu g \; Se}{ml \; sample}$$

6. Precision and Accuracy

A synthetic unknown sample containing 0.05 mg/l selenium (added as selenite), 100 mg/l CaCl$_2$, 100 mg/l MgSO$_4 \cdot 7H_2O$, and 50 mg/l NaHCO$_3$ was determined with a standard deviation of ± 0.006 mg/l in seven laboratories using the diaminobenzidine method. The individual laboratories reproduced their results within ± 0.004 mg/l.

A synthetic unknown sample containing 0.01 mg/l selenium (added equally as selenite and selenate) in distilled water was determined with a standard deviation of ± 0.005 mg/l in seven laboratories using the diaminobenzidine method. The individual laboratories reproduced their own results within ± 0.002 mg/l.

A synthetic unknown sample containing 0.05 mg/l selenium, 18 mg/l boron, 0.05 mg/l arsenic, and 0.40 mg/l beryllium in distilled water was determined with a standard deviation of ± 0.013 mg/l in six laboratories using the diaminobenzidine method. The individual laboratories reproduced their own results within ± 0.002 mg/l.

A synthetic unknown sample containing 0.10 mg/l selenium (added as selenate), 5 mg/l bromide, 5 mg/l iodide, 100 mg/l CaCl$_2$, 100 mg/l MgSO$_4 \cdot 7H_2O$, and 50 mg/l NaHCO$_3$ was determined with a standard deviation of ± 0.018 mg/l in seven laboratories using the diaminobenzidine method. The individual laboratories reproduced their own results within ± 0.004 mg/l.

B. *Distillation and Diaminobenzidine Method* (Tentative)

1. General Discussion

1.1. *Principle:* Selenium is quantitatively separated from most other elements by distillation of the volatile tetrabromide from an acid solution containing bromine. The bromine is generated by the reaction of bromide with hydrogen peroxide in order to avoid the inconvenience of handling the element. Selenium tetrabromide, along with a minimum of excess bromine, is absorbed in water. The excess bromine is removed by precipitation as tribromophenol, and the quadrivalent selenium determined with diaminobenzidine as in Method A.

1.2. *Interference:* No substances are known to interfere. The time-honored bromine distillation is satisfactory because recovery of selenium added to tap water is essentially complete.

1.3. *Minimum detectable concentration:* 1 μg Se with a 4-cm light path.

2. Apparatus

All of the apparatus in Method A, Sec. 2.1–2.3, plus:

Distillation assembly, all pyrex, for use with 500-ml erlenmeyer flasks with interchangeable ground-glass necks.

3. Reagents

All of the reagents described in Method A, Sec. 3, are needed except reagents 3.8 through 3.11. The following are also required:

3.1. *Potassium bromide-acid reagent:* Dissolve 10 g KBr in 25 ml distilled water. Cautiously add 25 ml conc H_2SO_4, mixing and cooling under tap water as each increment of acid is added. Prepare immediately before it

is to be used, because $KHSO_4$ will precipitate on cooling, and reheating to dissolve this salt will drive off some of the HBr.

3.2. *Hydrogen peroxide,* 30 per cent.

3.3. *Phenol solution:* Dissolve 5 g phenol in 100 ml distilled water.

3.4. *Ammonium hydroxide,* conc.

3.5. *Hydrochloric acid,* $1 + 1$.

4. Procedure

4.1. *Oxidation to selenate:* Same as Method A, Sec. 4.1, except that glass-stoppered erlenmeyer flasks are used.

4.2. *Evaporation:* Add 5 ml NaOH to each flask and evaporate to dryness. Avoid prolonged heating of the residue.

4.3. *Distillation:* Add 500 ml KBr-H_2SO_4 reagent to the cool flask. Add 1 ml 30 per cent H_2O_2 and fit the flask to the condenser without delay. Distill under the fume hood until the color of bromine is gone from the flask. Use as a receiver a beaker which is suitable for the subsequent pH adjustment and contains just enough water to immerse the tip of the condenser. Wash the small amount of distillate remaining in the condenser into the beaker with 5 ml distilled water.

4.4. *Formation of piazselenol:* Add phenol solution dropwise until the color of bromine is discharged. A white precipitate of tribromophenol will form, but a small proportion of the yellow tetrabromophenol causes no trouble. Adjust the pH to 1.5 ± 0.3 using conc NH_4OH and $1 + 1$ HCl. Add 1 ml diaminobenzidine solution and heat in a boiling water bath or steam bath for approximately 5 min.

4.5. *Extraction of piazselenol:* Cool and then add conc NH_4OH to adjust the pH to 8 ± 1. Pour the sample into a 50-ml graduate, and adjust the volume to 50 ± 1 ml with washings from the beaker. Pour the contents of the graduate into a 250-ml separatory funnel. Add 10 ml toluene, and shake for 30 ± 5 sec. Discard the aqueous layer, and transfer the organic phase to a 12- or 15-ml centrifuge tube. Centrifuge briefly to clear the toluene of water droplets. If a centrifuge is not available, filter the organic phase through a dry filter paper to which has been added approximately 0.100 g anhydrous Na_2SO_4.

4.6. *Determination of absorbance:* Read the absorbance at approximately 420 mμ using toluene to establish zero absorbance. The phenol used in Sec. 4.4 causes the yellow piazselenol color slowly to acquire a greenish tint, so that the absorbance readings should be made within 2 hr after extraction.

5. Calculation

Refer to Method A, Sec. 5.

6. Precision and Accuracy

Refer to Method A, Sec. 6.

C. Distillation and Colored-Sol Method (Tentative)

1. General Discussion

1.1. *Principle:* Selenium is evolved from a solution—by distillation with hydrobromic acid and bromine in the presence of sulfuric acid—as volatile selenium bromide, which in the aqueous distillate becomes selenious acid. The excess of bromine is reduced with sulfur dioxide and then the selenious acid is reduced to elemental selenium with hydroxylamine hydrochloride. The stable red selenium sol is suitable for visual color matching. Careful control of the sol formation is desirable for color reproducibility between standards and samples.

1.2. *Interference:* Excessive organic material may have to be oxidized by methods used for plant materials.[6] Arsenic, antimony, and germanium may distill over with the selenium.

1.3. *Minimum detectable concentration:* The sol method can detect 10 μg Se. Visual estimation is best performed in the selenium range of 10 to 100 μg.

2. Apparatus

2.1. *Distillation apparatus,* all pyrex. A suitable assembly consists of a 500- or 1,000-ml distilling flask, condenser, and adapter, with ground-glass connections throughout (see Fig. 17).

2.2. *Nessler tubes,* matched, 100 ml, tall form.

3. Reagents

3.1. *Sodium peroxide:* Use fresh Na_2O_2, which has a pale yellow color and is free flowing. White or caked material indicates deterioration and should be discarded.

3.2. *Sulfuric-nitric acid reagent:* Cautiously add 1 volume conc H_2SO_4 to 2 volumes conc HNO_3 and mix.

3.3. *Hydrobromic acid,* 48 per cent. Reserve for this determination a supply of HBr which will become completely decolorized when subjected to SO_2 treatment as described in Sec. 4.5. If the reagent in stock does not meet this specification, purify by distillation in an all-pyrex still, collecting the middle fraction of the distillate.

3.4. *Hydrobromic acid-bromine reagent:* Cautiously mix 15 ml liquid bromine with 985 ml 48 per cent HBr.

3.5. *Sulfuric acid,* conc.

3.6. *Stock selenium solution:* Place accurately weighed pellets of ACS-grade metallic selenium into a small beaker. Add 5 ml conc HNO_3. Warm until the reaction is complete and cautiously evaporate just to dryness. Dissolve in distilled water, add 80 ml 48 per cent HBr, and dilute with distilled water to 1,000 ml. Filter if necessary. The solution should contain 100 μg Se per 1.00 ml.

3.7. *Standard selenium solution:* Place 1 ml 48 per cent HBr in a volumetric flask, add 10.00 ml stock selenium solution, and dilute to 100 ml with distilled water; 1.00 ml = 10.0 μg Se. Prepare daily. Do not allow the acidity, as determined by titration, to fall below 0.05N, because neutral or very slightly acid solutions of dilute selenious acid tend to lose their titer.

3.8. *Sulfur dioxide,* safely assumed free of Se, contained in a small commercial cylinder equipped with a needle valve.

3.9. *Gum arabic reagent:* Dissolve 5 g gum arabic, also called gum acacia, and dilute to 100 ml with distilled water. Filter through a glass wool mat. Prepare daily.

3.10. *Hydroxylamine hydrochloride,* $NH_2OH \cdot HCl$. Use either the solid reagent, or a solution containing 10 g in 100 ml of distilled water.

4. Procedure

4.1. *Concentration of low-level selenium samples:* Evaporate 1–10 liters of sample in order to obtain a selenium concentration of no more than 0.5 mg. During the evaporation keep the sample definitely alkaline by adding a sufficient amount of fresh Na_2O_2. Carry out the initial phase of the evaporation on an electric hot plate. Transfer to a steam bath and evaporate the final 100 ml nearly to dryness.

4.2. *Treatment of organic material:* If a high concentration of sewage or other organic matter is present, digest the residue with a few drops of the H_2SO_4-HNO_3 reagent to oxidize the organic material prior to distillation.

4.3. *Distillation:* Steam out the entire distilling apparatus. Rub down the sides of the evaporating vessel with a rubber policeman and transfer the concentrate and residue to the distilling flask. Add to the evaporating vessel a volume of conc H_2SO_4 equal to the volume of the preceding concentrate. Again rub down the sides of the evaporating vessel to remove the remaining solids. Very carefully add the H_2SO_4 to the distilling flask. Repeat the transfer with another portion of 25 ml distilled water and a final volume of 25 ml conc H_2SO_4. Keep the total volume of water, including the concentrate, within 50–75 ml. *Conduct the entire distillation in an efficient fuming hood* because of the copious evolution of bromine fumes.

Mark off a line at the 85-ml liquid level on a 100-ml beaker or other suitable receiver. Place 10 ml of distilled water in the beaker, and tip the beaker so that the delivery end of the vertical condenser is below the water surface. (This precaution will provide for the entrapment of the bromine and volatile components evolved during distillation.) Add 60 ml hydrobromic acid-bromine reagent to the distilling flask, replace the glass stopper, and adjust the flame so that 30 min of distillation will yield 75 ml of distillate. Stop the distillation when the distillate level reaches the 85-ml mark on the beaker or receiver.

4.4. *Preparation of selenium standards:* Prepare a suitable series of selenium standards in the 0–100 μg range so that 50 ml of the total volume of 100 ml will be composed of conc H_2SO_4. (Example: Prepare the 50 μg Se standard from 5.0 ml Se standard solution, 45 ml distilled water, and 50 ml conc H_2SO_4). Transfer each standard to the distilling flask, add 60 ml hydrobromic acid-bromine reagent, and distill as described in Sec. 4.3.

4.5. *Sol formation in distilled sample and standards:* Screw the needle valve to the SO_2 cylinder. Connect a 1-ml measuring pipet by means of a 2-ft length of rubber tubing to the needle valve tip. Place the pipet end of the gas line in a beaker of distilled water and adjust the gas bubbling rate to about 5 bubbles per second. While stirring the beaker contents with the pipet, slowly bubble the gas through each distillate until the bromine color vanishes. Continue the bubbling and stirring for an additional 5 sec. (Within 5 min a pale pink sol usually appears in the 100-μg Se standard.) Add 1 ml gum arabic solution and stir. Then add either (a) 0.5 g of solid $NH_2OH \cdot HCl$ and stir to dissolve the crystals, or (b) 5 ml $NH_2OH \cdot HCl$ solution. Cover the beaker with a watch glass and allow the sample and standards to stand 1 hr. Quantitatively transfer the sample and standards to 100-ml tall-form nessler tubes for visual comparison.

5. Calculation

$$mg/1\ Se = \frac{\mu g\ Se}{ml\ sample}$$

6. Precision and Accuracy

A synthetic unknown sample containing 0.05 mg/1 selenium, 0.18 mg/1 boron, 0.05 mg/1 arsenic, and 0.40 mg/1 beryllium in distilled water was determined within ±0.02 mg/1 by three laboratories using the colored-sol method. Two of the laboratories were able to determine the selenium within ±0.01 mg/1. The individual laboratories reproduced their results within ±0.01 mg/1.

Bibliography

Diaminobenzidine Methods

1. HOSTE, J. & GILLIS, J. Spectrophotometric Determination of Traces of Selenium with 3,3'-Diaminobenzidine. *Anal. Chem. Acta* 12:158 (1955).
2. CHENG, K. Determination of Traces of Selenium. *Anal. Chem.* 28:1738 (1956).
3. MAGIN, G. B., ET AL. Suggested Modified Method for Colorimetric Determination of Selenium in Natural Water. *J. AWWA* 52:1199 (1960).
4. ROSSUM, J. R. & VILLARRUZ, P. A. Suggested Methods for Determining Selenium in Water. *J. AWWA* 54:746 (1962).

Colored-Sol Method

5. ROBINSON, W. O., ET AL. Determination of Selenium and Arsenic by Distillation. *Ind. Eng. Chem., Anal. Ed.* 6:274 (1934).
6. DUDLEY, H. C. & BYERS, H. G. Determination of Selenium. *Ind. Eng. Chem., Anal. Ed.* 7:3 (1935).
7. TRELEASE, S. F. & BEATH, O. A. *Selenium: Its Geological Occurrence and Its Biological Effects in Relation to Botany, Chemistry, Agriculture, Nutrition, and Medicine and the Chemistry of Selenium and Its Determination.* S. F. Trelease, Columbia Univ., New York (1949).
8. BOLTZ, D. F., ed. *Colorimetric Determination of Nonmetals.* Interscience Publishers, New York (1958). pp. 309–338.

Silica

Silicon ranks next to oxygen in abundance and is a common constituent of igneous rocks, quartz, and sand. Many natural waters contain less than 10 mg/l silica, although some may approach 60 mg/l. The formation of a hard coating on the steam-turbine blades of high-pressure boilers necessitates the removal of silica from such boiler feed waters. Among the methods employed for silica removal are ion exchange, distillation, the hot and cold lime-soda-magnesia processes, the ferric hydroxide process, and the fluosilicate process.

Silica is present in natural waters in soluble and colloidal forms. Volcanic waters often contain an abundance of silica. A silica cycle occurs in many bodies of water containing organisms, such as diatoms, that utilize silica in their skeletal structure. The silica removed from the water may be slowly returned by re-solution of the dead organisms.

Three methods applicable to natural waters, each subject to certain limitations discussed below, are provided: the gravimetric method (A); a colorimetric method with formation of yellow molybdosilicate (B); and a colorimetric method with formation of heteropoly blue (C). An optional alkali treatment step is provided in Methods B and C.

Selection of method: Method A must be used to standardize the sodium silicate solutions which are used as standards for Methods B and C. It is the preferred method for water samples which contain at least 20 mg/l silica, but is not recommended for determining lower concentrations. Method B is recommended for relatively pure waters containing from 0.4 to 25 mg/l silica. As with most colorimetric methods, the range can be extended, if necessary, by taking aliquots, concentrating, or varying the light path. The interferences due to tannin, color, and turbidity are more severe with this method than with Method C. Moreover, the yellow color produced by Method B has a limited stability and some attention to timing is necessary. When applicable, however, it offers greater speed and simplicity than Method C: one less reagent is used; one timing step is eliminated; and many natural waters can be analyzed without dilution, which is not often the case with Method C. Method C is recommended for the low range, from 0.04 to 2 mg/l silica. This range can also be extended, if necessary. Such extension may be desirable if interference is expected from tannin, color, or turbidity. A combination of factors renders Method C less susceptible than Method B to those interferences; also the blue color of Method C is more stable than the yellow color of Method B. Many samples, however, will require dilution because of the high sensitivity. Permanent artificial color standards are not available for the blue color developed in Method C.

Sampling and storage: Samples should be collected in bottles of polyethylene, other plastic, or hard rubber, especially if a delay between collection and analysis is unavoidable. Pyrex glass is a less desirable choice.

A. Gravimetric Method

1. General Discussion

1.1. *Principle:* Hydrochloric acid decomposes silicates and dissolved silica, forming silicic acids which are precipitated as partially dehydrated silica during evaporation and baking. Ignition completes the dehydration of the silica, which is weighed and then volatilized as silicon tetrafluoride, leaving any impurities behind as nonvolatile residue. The residue is weighed, and silica is determined as loss on volatilization. Perchloric acid may be used instead of hydrochloric acid to dehydrate the silica. A single fuming with perchloric acid will recover more silica than one with hydrochloric acid, although for complete silica recovery it is necessary to carry out two dehydrations with either acid. The use of perchloric acid lessens the tendency to spatter, yields a silica precipitate that is easier to filter, and shortens the time required for the determination. Because perchloric acid is explosive, a shield must be used.

1.2. *Interference:* As glassware may contribute silica, its use should be avoided as much as possible. The reagents and the distilled water should be low in silica. A blank determination should be carried out to correct for silica introduced by the reagents and apparatus.

2. Apparatus

2.1. *Platinum crucibles,* with covers.
2.2. *Platinum evaporating dishes,* 200 ml. In the dehydration steps, acid-leached, glazed porcelain evaporating dishes, free from etching, may be substituted for platinum.

3. Reagents

For maximum accuracy, batches of chemicals low in silica should be set aside for this method. It is advisable to store all reagents in plastic containers and to run blanks.

3.1. *Hydrochloric acid,* $1 + 1$ and $1 + 50$.
3.2. *Sulfuric acid,* $1 + 1$.
3.3. *Hydrofluoric acid,* 48 per cent.
3.4. *Perchloric acid,* 72 per cent.

4. Procedure

Before performing silica determinations, test the sulfuric acid and hydrofluoric acid for interfering nonvolatile matter by carrying out the procedure of Sec. 4.5. Use a clean, empty platinum crucible. If any increase in weight is observed, a correction should be made in the silica determinations.

4.1. *Hydrochloric acid dehydration:* To a clear sample containing at least 10 mg silica, add 5 ml $1 + 1$ HCl. Evaporate the mixture to dryness in a 200-ml platinum evaporating dish, in several portions, if necessary, on a water bath or suspended on an asbestos ring over a hot plate. Protect the contents against contamination by atmospheric dust. During the evaporation, add a total of 15 ml $1 + 1$ HCl in several portions. After the dish is dry, place it in a 110°C oven or over a hot plate to bake for half an hour.

4.2. To the residue in the dish, add 5 ml $1 + 1$ HCl; warm; and add 50 ml hot distilled water. While hot, filter the suspension through an ashless, medium-texture filter paper, decanting as much of the liquid as possible. Wash the dish and the residue with hot $1 + 50$ HCl and then with a minimum volume of distilled water until the washings are chloride free. Save all the washings. Set aside the filter paper with its residue.

4.3. Evaporate the filtrate and washings from the above operation to dryness in the original platinum dish and then bake the residue in a 110°C oven or over a hot plate for half an hour. Repeat the steps in Sec. 4.2. Use a separate filter paper, and a rubber policeman to aid in transferring all of the residue from the dish to the filter.

4.4. Transfer the two filter papers and residues to a covered platinum crucible; dry at 110°C; and ignite at 1,200°C to constant weight. Caution must be exercised to avoid mechanical loss of residue when first charring and burning off the paper. Cool the crucible in a desiccator; weigh it; and repeat the ignition and weighing until constant weight is attained. Record the weight of the crucible and contents.

4.5. Thoroughly moisten the weighed residue in the crucible with distilled water. Add 4 drops $1 + 1$ H_2SO_4, followed by 10 ml HF (measure the latter in a plastic graduated cylinder or pour an estimated 10 ml directly from the reagent bottle). Slowly evaporate the mixture to dryness over an air bath or hot plate in a hood and take precautions to avoid loss by spattering. Ignite the crucible to constant weight at 1,200°C. Record the weight of the crucible and contents.

4.6. *Perchloric acid dehydration:* Review Sec. 1.1. Follow the procedure in Sec. 4.1 until all but 50 ml of the sample has been evaporated. Add 5 ml perchloric acid and evaporate until dense white fumes appear. (CAU-

TION: *Explosive; place a shield between the personnel and the fuming dish.*)

Continue the dehydration for 10 min. Cool; add 5 ml $1 + 1$ HCl and then 50 ml hot distilled water. Bring to a boil and filter through an ashless quantitative filter paper. Wash thoroughly ten times with hot distilled water and proceed as directed in Sec. 4.4 and 4.5, with the single filter paper. For routine work, the silica precipitate is often sufficiently pure for the purpose intended and may be weighed directly, omitting the HF volatilization. An initial check against the longer procedure should be made, however, to be sure that the result is within the limits of accuracy required.

5. Calculation

Subtract the weight of crucible and contents after the HF treatment from the corresponding weight before HF treatment. The difference, A, in milligrams is "loss on volatilization" and represents silica:

$$mg/l\ SiO_2 = \frac{A \times 1,000}{ml\ sample}$$

6. Precision and Accuracy

The accuracy is limited both by the finite solubility of silica in water under the conditions of the analysis and by the sensitivity of the analytical balance. If all the precautions are observed, and if the analyst's quantitative technique is satisfactory, the precision will be approximately ± 0.2 mg SiO_2. If a 1-liter sample is taken for analysis, this will represent a precision of ± 0.2 mg/l.

B. Colorimetric Molybdosilicate Method

1. General Discussion

1.1. *Principle:* Ammonium molybdate at approximately pH 1.2 reacts with silica and also with any phosphate present to produce heteropoly acids. Oxalic acid is added to destroy the molybdophosphoric acid but not the molybdosilicic acid. Even if phosphate is known to be absent, the addition of oxalic acid has been found highly desirable, and is a mandatory step in both this method and Method C. The intensity of the yellow color is proportional to the concentration of "molybdate-reactive" silica. In at least one of its forms, silica does not react with molybdate even though it is capable of passing through filter paper and does not display noticeable turbidity. It is not known to what extent such "unreactive" silica occurs in waters, and the literature on the subject is contradictory. In the past, terms such as "colloidal," "crystalloidal," and "ionic" have been employed to distinguish between various forms of silica in waters, but such terminology cannot be substantiated. An optional step is included in the procedure to convert any "molybdate-unreactive" silica into the "molybdate-reactive" form. It must be clearly understood that these terms do not imply reactivity, or lack of it, toward *other* reagents or processes.

1.2. *Interference:* As apparatus and reagents may both contribute silica, care should be taken to avoid the use of glassware as much as possible and to use reagents low in silica. Also, a blank determination should be carried out to correct for silica so introduced. In both this method and Method C, tannin, large amounts of iron, color, turbidity, sulfide, and phosphate are potential sources of interference. The treatment with oxalic acid eliminates interference from phosphate and decreases interference from tannin. If necessary, photometric compensation may be used to cancel interference from color or turbidity in the sample.

1.3. *Minimum detectable concentration:* Approximately 1 mg/l SiO_2 can be detected in 50-ml nessler tubes.

2. Apparatus

2.1. *Platinum dishes,* 100 ml.

2.2. *Colorimetric equipment:* One of the following is required:

a. *Spectrophotometer,* for use at 410 $m\mu$, providing a light path of 1 cm or longer.

b. *Filter photometer,* providing a light path of 1 cm or longer and equipped with a violet filter having maximum transmittance near 410 $m\mu$.

c. *Nessler tubes,* matched, 50 ml, tall form.

3. Reagents

For maximum accuracy, batches of chemicals low in silica should be set aside for this method. It is advisable to store all reagents in plastic containers. Blanks are essential.

3.1. *Sodium bicarbonate,* powder. Label and set aside a batch which has been found silica free. A plastic storage container is desirable.

3.2. *Sulfuric acid,* 1N. Cautiously add 28 ml conc H_2SO_4 to approximately 800 ml distilled water while stirring; cool; and dilute to 1 liter.

3.3. *Hydrochloric acid,* 1 + 1.

3.4. *Ammonium molybdate reagent:* Dissolve 10 g $(NH_4)_6Mo_7O_{24}\cdot 4H_2O$ in distilled water with stirring and gentle warming, and dilute to 100 ml. Filter if necessary. If this solution is adjusted to pH 7–8 with silica-free ammonium or sodium hydroxide and is stored in polyethylene, it is stable indefinitely. If the pH is not adjusted, a precipitate gradually forms. If the solution is stored in glass, silica may be leached out and cause high blanks. If necessary, silica-free ammonium hydroxide may be prepared by passing gaseous ammonia into distilled water contained in a plastic bottle.

3.5. *Oxalic acid solution:* Dissolve 10 g $H_2C_2O_4 \cdot 2H_2O$ in distilled water and dilute to 100 ml.

3.6. *Stock silica solution:* Dissolve 4.73 g reagent grade sodium metasilicate nonahydrate, $Na_2SiO_3 \cdot 9H_2O$, in recently boiled and cooled distilled water and dilute to approximately 900 ml. Analyze 100.0-ml aliquots of this solution by Method A, and adjust the remainder of the solution to contain exactly 1,000 mg/l SiO_2. Store this stock solution in a tightly stoppered plastic bottle.

3.7. *Standard silica solution:* Dilute 10.00 ml of stock solution to 1,000 ml with recently boiled and cooled distilled water; this solution contains 10.0 mg/l SiO_2 or 1.00 ml = 10.0 μg SiO_2. Store in a tightly stoppered plastic bottle.

3.8. *Permanent color solutions:*

a. *Potassium chromate solution:* Dissolve 0.63 g K_2CrO_4 in distilled water and dilute to 1 liter.

b. *Borax solution:* Dissolve 10 g $Na_2B_4O_7 \cdot 10H_2O$ in distilled water and dilute to 1 liter.

4. Procedure

4.1. This step is designed to convert any molybdate-unreactive silica into the reactive form or state. If molybdate-unreactive silica is known to be absent, or if it is desired to determine only such silica as will react with molybdate, the analyst may omit this step and pass on to Sec. 4.2.

Prepare a clear sample by filtering if necessary. Place a 50.0-ml portion, or a smaller aliquot diluted to 50 ml, in a 100-ml platinum dish. Add 0.20 g silica-free sodium bicarbonate and digest on a steam bath for 1 hr. Cool and add slowly, with stirring, 2.4 ml H_2SO_4. Do not interrupt the analysis at this point but proceed *at once* with the remaining steps. Transfer the solution quantitatively to a 50-ml nessler tube and make up to the mark with distilled water. (Tall-form 50-ml nessler tubes are recommended for convenience in mixing even if the mixture is to be transferred subsequently to a photometer cell.)

4.2. To the prepared sample, or to 50.0 ml of an untreated sample if the conversion step is omitted, add in rapid succession 1.0 ml 1 + 1 HCl and 2.0 ml ammonium molybdate reagent; mix by inverting at least six times, and allow the solution to stand for 5 to 10 min. Add 1.5 ml oxalic acid solution and mix thoroughly. Read the color after 2 min but before 15 min, measuring time from the addition of oxalic acid. The yellow color obeys Beer's law; it may be read either visually as directed in Sec. 4.4 or, preferably, in a photometer as directed in Sec. 4.5.

4.3. If sodium bicarbonate pretreatment is used for the samples, the standards should also contain 0.20 g $NaHCO_3$ and 2.4 ml H_2SO_4, to compensate both for the slight amount of silica which may be introduced by the reagents and for the effect of the salinity upon the intensity of the color.

4.4. If visual comparison is to be

used, make up a set of permanent artificial color standards using potassium chromate and borax solutions. Mix the volumes of liquids specified in Table 14 and place them in well stoppered, appropriately labeled, 50-ml nessler tubes.

The correctness of these permanent artificial color standards should be verified by comparing them visually against standards prepared by carrying out determinations upon aliquots of the standard silica solution. The permanent artificial color standards are intended only for visual comparison and should never be used to calibrate a photometric instrument.

4.5. For photometric measurement, prepare a calibration curve from a series of approximately six standards to cover the optimum range, by carrying out the steps of Sec. 4.2 upon suitable aliquots of standard silica solution diluted to 50.0 ml. Nessler tubes, 50-ml size, are recommended for convenience in mixing. The following table suggests optimum ranges for the photometer:

Silica Range (54.5-ml Final Volume) *mg*	Light Path *cm*
0.2 –1.3	1
0.1 –0.7	2
0.04–0.25	5
0.02–0.13	10

Distilled water should be used to set the instrument to 100 per cent transmittance (zero absorbance); all the standards, including a reagent blank, should be read against the distilled water and a calibration curve prepared. It is convenient to plot milligrams of silica in the final (54.5-ml) developed solution against photometer readings. It is necessary to run a reagent blank and at least one standard with each group of samples, to verify that the calibration curve previously established has not shifted.

4.6. To correct for color or turbidity in a sample, prepare a special blank for every sample that needs such correction. Two identical aliquots of each such sample are to be carried through the procedure, including sodium bicarbonate treatment if this is elected. To one aliquot all of the reagents are added as directed in Sec. 4.2 To the other aliquot hydrochloric and oxalic

TABLE 14—PREPARATION OF PERMANENT COLOR STANDARDS FOR VISUAL DETERMINATION OF SILICA

Value in Silica *mg*	Potassium Chromate Solution *ml*	Borax Solution *ml*	Water *ml*
0.00	0.0	25	30
0.10	1.0	25	29
0.20	2.0	25	28
0.40	4.0	25	26
0.50	5.0	25	25
0.75	7.5	25	22
1.0	10.0	25	20

acid are added, but not molybdate. For each sample, the special blank aliquot without molybdate is used to set the photometer to 100 per cent transmittance, and the corresponding aliquot which has been molybdate treated is then placed in the light beam and read. The reading so obtained will be automatically corrected for the background color or turbidity present and may be interpreted on the calibration curve. If background color and turbidity are negligible, time is saved by reading developed samples against distilled water. The above photometer compensation process will not entirely eliminate interference from tannins, because these interact with molybdate somewhat like silica.

5. Calculation

$$\text{mg/l SiO}_2 = \frac{\text{mg SiO}_2 \times 1,000}{\text{ml sample}}$$

The result is reported either as "total dissolved silica, colorimetric" or as "molybdate-reactive dissolved silica, colorimetric," whichever the case may be.

6. Precision

Visual comparisons in nessler tubes are seldom reliable to better than ± 5 per cent, often only to ± 10 per cent; under favorable circumstances, photometric measurements may be reliable to ± 1 per cent or better.

C. Colorimetric Heteropoly Blue Method

1. General Discussion

1.1. *Principle:* The principles outlined under Method B, Sec. 1.1, also apply to this method. The yellow molybdosilicic acid is reduced by means of aminonaphtholsulfonic acid to heteropoly blue. The blue color is more intense than the yellow color of Method B and provides increased sensitivity.

1.2. *Interference:* The problems of interference discussed under Method B, Sec. 1.2, apply to this method.

1.3. *Minimum detectable concentration:* Approximately 0.02 mg/l SiO_2 can be detected in 50-ml nessler tubes.

2. Apparatus

2.1. *Platinum dishes,* 100 ml.

2.2. *Colorimetric equipment:* One of the following is required:

a. *Spectrophotometer,* for use at approximately 815 mμ. The color system also obeys Beer's law at 650 mμ, with appreciably reduced sensitivity, in the event the instrument available cannot be operated at the optimum wavelength. A light path of 1 cm or longer yields satisfactory results.

b. *Filter photometer,* provided with a red filter exhibiting maximum transmittance in the wavelength range of 600–815 mμ. Sensitivity improves

with increasing wavelength. A light path of 1 cm or longer yields satisfactory results.

c. *Nessler tubes,* matched, 50 ml, tall form.

3. Reagents

For maximum accuracy, batches of chemicals low in silica should be set aside for this method. Because of the sensitivity of the method, the use of plastic storage containers is strongly advised. Blanks are essential. Distilled water may contain detectable silica, especially if it has been stored in glass.

All of the reagents listed under Method B, Sec. 3, are required, and in addition:

3.1. *Reducing agent:* Dissolve 0.5 g 1-amino-2-naphthol-4-sulfonic acid and 1 g anhydrous sodium sulfite, Na_2SO_3, in 50 ml distilled water, with gentle warming if necessary; add this to a solution of 30 g sodium bisulfite, $NaHSO_3$, in 150 ml distilled water. Filter into a plastic bottle. Discard the solution when it becomes dark. The reducing agent will keep longer if it is stored in a refrigerator and away from light. Some batches of aminonaphtholsulfonic acid on the market are incompletely soluble or produce solutions which are dark even when freshly prepared; such material is *not* suitable for silica determinations.*

4. Procedure

4.1. Proceed as in Method B, Sec. 4.1 and 4.2, including the words "Add 1.5 ml oxalic acid solution and mix thoroughly." Measuring time from the moment of addition of oxalic acid, wait for at least 2 min, but not more than 15 min; then add 2.0 ml reducing agent and mix thoroughly. The blue color develops fully in approximately 5 min and is then stable for 12 hr; it conforms to Beer's law. The color may be read either visually in 50-ml nessler tubes or, preferably, photometrically. If sodium bicarbonate pretreatment is to be used, follow Method B, Sec. 4.3.

4.2. For visual comparison, prepare a series of not less than twelve standards, covering the range 0.00 to 0.12 mg SiO_2, by placing the calculated volumes of standard silica solution in 50-ml nessler tubes, diluting to the mark with distilled water, and developing the color as described in Sec. 4.1.

4.3. For photometric measurement, prepare a calibration curve from a series of approximately six standards to cover the optimum range, by carrying out the steps described above upon suitable aliquots of standard silica solution diluted to 50.0 ml. Nessler tubes, 50-ml size, are recommended for mixing. Table 15 may be used as a rough guide to the concentration range that can be covered without diluting or concentrating the sample.

Distilled water should be used to set the instrument to 100 per cent transmittance (zero absorbance), and all the standards, including a reagent

---

* Eastman No. 360 has been found satisfactory.

TABLE 15—SELECTION OF LIGHT PATH LENGTH FOR VARIOUS SILICA CONCENTRATIONS

Silica in 56.5-ml Final Volume—μg		Light Path cm
650-mμ Wavelength	815-mμ Wavelength	
40–300	20–100	1
20–150	10–50	2
7–50	4–20	5
4–30	2–10	10

blank, should be read against the distilled water. If it is desired to correct for color or turbidity in a sample, consult Method B, Sec. 4.6. To the special blank add hydrochloric acid and oxalic acid, but do *not* add molybdate or reducing agent. If background color and turbidity are absent, time is saved by reading developed samples against distilled water. It is convenient to plot milligrams of silica in the final (56.5-ml) developed solution against photometer readings. It is necessary to run a reagent blank and at least one standard with each group of samples to check the calibration curves.

5. Calculation

Refer to Method B, Sec. 5.

6. Precision

Refer to Method B, Sec. 6.

Bibliography

General

1. ROY, C. J. Silica in Natural Waters. *Am. J. Sci.* 243:393 (1945).
2. VAIL, J. G. *The Soluble Silicates, Their Properties and Uses.* Reinhold Publishing Corp., New York (1952). Vol. 1, pp. 95–97, 160–161.

Gravimetric Method

3. KOLTHOFF, I. M. & SANDELL, E. B. *Textbook of Quantitative Inorganic Anal-*

ysis. Macmillan Co., New York (3rd ed., 1952). Chap. 25.

4. HILLEBRAND, W. F., ET AL. *Applied Inorganic Analysis.* John Wiley & Sons, New York (2nd ed., 1953). Chap. 43.

Colorimetric Methods

5. DIENERT, F. & WANDENBULCKE, F. On the Determination of Silica in Waters. *Bull. Soc. Chim. France* 33:1131 (1923); *Compt. Rend.* 176:1478 (1923).

6. DIENERT, F. & WANDENBULCKE, F. A Study of Colloidal Silica. *Compt. Rend.* 178:564 (1924).

7. SWANK, H. W. & MELLON, M. G. Colorimetric Standards for Silica. *Ind. Eng. Chem., Anal. Ed.* 6:348 (1934).

8. TOURKY, A. R. & BANGHAM, D. H. Colloidal Silica in Natural Waters and the "Silicomolybdate" Colour Test. *Nature* 138:587 (1936).

9. BIRNBAUM, N. & WALDEN, G. H. Coprecipitation of Ammonium Silicomolybdate and Ammonium Phosphomolybdate. *J. Am. Chem. Soc.* 60:66 (1938).

10. KAHLER, H. L. Determination of Soluble Silica in Water: A Photometric Method. *Ind. Eng. Chem., Anal. Ed.* 13:536 (1941).

11. NOLL, C. A. & MAGUIRE, J. J. Effect of Container on Soluble Silica Content of Water Samples. *Ind. Eng. Chem., Anal. Ed.* 14:569 (1942).

12. SCHWARTZ, M. C. Photometric Determination of Silica in the Presence of Phosphates. *Ind. Eng. Chem., Anal. Ed.* 14:893 (1942).

13. BUNTING, W. E. Determination of Soluble Silica in Very Low Concentrations. *Ind. Eng. Chem., Anal. Ed.* 16:612 (1944).

14. STRAUB, F. G. & GRABOWSKI, H. A. Photometric Determination of Silica in Condensed Steam in the Presence of Phosphates. *Ind. Eng. Chem., Anal. Ed.* 16:574 (1944).

15. GUITER, H. Influence of pH on the Composition and Physical Aspects of the Ammonium Molybdates. *Compt. Rend.* 220:146 (1945).

16. BOLTZ, D. F. & MELLON, M. G. Determination of Phosphorus, Germanium, Silicon, and Arsenic by the Heteropoly Blue Method. *Ind. Eng. Chem., Anal. Ed.* 19:873 (1947).

17. MILTON, R. F. Formation of Silicomolybdate. *Analyst* 76:431 (1951).

18. MILTON, R. Estimation of Silica in Water. *J. Appl. Chem. (London)* 1: Supplement No. 2:126 (1951).

19. CARLSON, A. B. & BANKS, C. V. Spectrophotometric Determination of Silicon. *Anal. Chem.* 24:472 (1952).

20. KILLEFFER, D. H. & LINZ, A. *Molybdenum Compounds, Their Chemistry and Technology.* Interscience Publishers, New York (1952). pp. 1–2, 42–45, 67–82, 87–92.

21. STRICKLAND, J. D. H. The Preparation and Properties of Silicomolybdic Acid. *J. Am. Chem. Soc.* 74:862, 868, 872 (1952).

22. CHOW, D. T. W. & ROBINSON, R. J. The Forms of Silicate Available for Colorimetric Determination. *Anal. Chem.* 25:646 (1953).

Silver

Silver can cause argyria, a permanent, blue-gray discoloration of the skin and eyes which presents a ghostly appearance. Concentrations in the range of 0.4 to 1 mg/l have caused pathologic changes in the kidneys, liver, and spleen of rats. The silver concentration of U.S. drinking waters has been reported to vary between 0 and 2 $\mu g/l$ with a mean of 0.13 $\mu g/l$. Relatively small quantities of silver are bactericidal or bacteriostatic and find limited use for the disinfection of swimming pool waters.

Selection of method: The spectrographic method (A) is the preferred method for the determination of silver content. The dithizone colorimetric method (B) may be used in those instances where spectrographic equipment is unavailable.

Sampling and storage: Samples should be examined as soon as possible after collection because of the silver loss which may occur through adsorption on the container walls. The addition of a small volume of nitric acid of known purity is advisable when sample storage time is excessive. Sample containers should be washed with $1 + 1$ nitric acid and rinsed with silver-free water before use.

A. *Spectrographic Method* (Tentative)

1. General Discussion

1.1. *Principle:* A sample of potable water is diluted with lithium sulfate solution, and a palladium solution is added as an internal standard. Standards are made by adding appropriate amounts of silver to a potable-water blank with less than 0.5 μg/l silver and diluting this with the lithium sulfate spectrobuffer solution and the palladium internal-standard solution. The diluted sample is evaporated to dryness in a glass beaker, in a 150°C oven. The residue is scraped loose and crushed to homogeneity with a spatula, and an aliquot is transferred to a platform graphite electrode and arced to completion. Spectrogram densitometer readings are made on the Ag 3280.7 and the Pd 3242.7 line transmittances, and are converted to a ratio of line intensities from emulsion calibration data. The Ag/Pd intensity ratio is converted to mg/l Ag from the standard working curve. The method is suitable for the determination of silver in the concentration range 0.01–0.5 mg/l.

1.2. *Interference:* No elements in the concentrations encountered in potable water interfere.

1.3. *Minimum detectable concentration:* 0.2 μg Ag. With a 20-ml sample this represents 0.01 mg/l Ag. The 20-

ml Li_2SO_4 solution produces 114 mg residue at 150°C. A 20-ml sample for most potable waters produces about 7 mg residue or a 6 per cent contribution to the matrix. If a sample with half the total residue is determined, 40 ml can be taken and 5 μg/l Ag can be determined. The upper concentration limit can be extended by diluting the sample appropriately with a low-silver (less than 0.5 μg/l Ag) potable-water blank, such as is used to make up the standards.

2. Apparatus

Any commercially available spectrographic equipment meeting the following specifications is satisfactory:

2.1. *Excitation:* Excitation is provided by an ARL Multisource * Model No. 5700, or equivalent, adjusted to give a fully rectified d-c arc discharge, 13 amp at 300 v.

2.2. *Spectrograph:* The ARL 1.5-m grating spectrograph, or equivalent, with a reciprocal linear dispersion of 7 angstroms (Å) per millimeter over the 2,300–4,500 Å spectral range. For this method, only the 3,200–3,300 Å region is utilized.

2.3. *Electrode system:* The lower

* Manufactured by Applied Research Labs., Glendale, Calif.

sample electrode (anode) is a ¼-in. diameter, high-purity graphite preform, 30-deg angle platform with center post,† and the upper is a ¼-in. diameter (a slightly smaller diameter in the upper electrode may be preferable in instances of trouble caused by arc wandering), high-purity graphite preform with center post and $\frac{3}{16}$-in. diameter undercut. The analytical gap is maintained at 5 mm.

2.4. *Recording equipment:* The spectrum is recorded on Eastman SA No. 2 film or plates, or No. 1 film or plates, or equivalent.

2.5. *Densitometer:* Transmittance readings of spectral lines are measured with the ARL No. 5400 film densitometer, or equivalent.

2.6. *Developing equipment:* Films are developed in a thermostatically controlled, rocking, developing machine, washed in a film washer, and dried in a stream of warm air.

2.7. *Calculating equipment:* A sliding-scale calculating board is used to convert transmittance readings to intensity ratios based on film calibration data.

2.8. *Beakers,* 250-ml tall electrolytic type, Corning No. 1140, or equivalent.

2.9. *Balance,* capable of weighing to 0.1 mg.

3. Reagents

3.1. *Palladium internal-standard solution:* Dissolve 0.0667 g palladium chloride, $PdCl_2$, in 10 ml $0.1N$ HCl by heating up to 60°C and then dilute with distilled water to 1,000 ml. This solution contains 40 mg/l Pd.

3.2. *Lithium sulfate solution:* Dis-

solve 5.5 g $Li_2SO_4 \cdot H_2O$ in 1 liter distilled water. This solution contains 4.75 g/l Li_2SO_4 and yields a residue of 5.7 mg/ml at 150°C.

3.3. *Cementing solution:* Dissolve 39 g sucrose in 300 ml absolute methyl alcohol and 100 ml distilled water.

3.4. *Stock silver solution:* Dissolve 0.1260 g anhydrous silver nitrate, $AgNO_3$, in distilled water and dilute to 1,000 ml. This solution contains 80.0 mg/l Ag.

3.5. *Standard silver solution:* Dilute 5.00 ml stock silver solution to 1,000 ml with distilled water. Store overnight to allow the plating-out process to reach equilibrium. Discard this dilute solution and make again in the same flask just before using. This solution contains 0.40 mg/l Ag, or 0.40 μg Ag per 1.00 ml.

3.6. *Low-silver potable-water blank:* Use a potable water with about 250–450 mg/l total residue containing less than 0.5 μg/l Ag to make up the silver standards. Determine the silver concentration in the blank water by a semiquantitative spectrographic method.[1] This range of total residue enables samples of potable water with approximately 150–800 mg/l total residue to be analyzed within 5 per cent from the same standard working curve. When markedly different types of waters are to be analyzed, a similar type of blank water must be used to make the standard working curve.

4. Procedure

4.1. *Preparation of sample for arcing:* Take a sample containing 0.01–0.5 mg/l Ag and 150–800 mg/l total residue. See Sec. 1.3 and 3.6 for the analysis of other waters.

a. *Determination of total residue:* Determine the amount of total residue in 20.0 ml of the water sample to be analyzed after evaporation, either by weighing the residue on evaporation of 20 ml at 150°C or by multiplying its specific conductance in micromhos by 0.62 × 0.020. (Example: If the specific conductance is 646 μmho, then 646 × 0.62 × 0.020 = 8.0 mg total residue.)

b. *Sample treatment and evaporation:* Add 1.0 ml Pd internal-standard solution and 20 ml Li_2SO_4 solution to 20.0 ml sample to be analyzed in a 250-ml tall-type electrolytic beaker, and evaporate to dryness in a 150°C oven. When the volume is down to about 5–10 ml, swirl the beaker a bit to redissolve the salts which have dried on the sides of the beaker, thus concentrating the residue as much as possible on the bottom.

c. *Preparation of residue:* Scrape the residue in the beaker loose from the glass and grind to a homogeneous powder against the side of the beaker with a small stainless-steel spatula or a silver-free monel spatula.

d. *Transfer of residue to electrode:* Weigh a 5.0-mg sample of the ground residue, transfer to the sample electrode, add 3 drops of the cementing solution, and heat over a spirit lamp or small burner until caramelized (until further heating does not produce steam, and the residue smells like caramel). Sometimes it is easier to transfer the residue to the electrode if the electrode is first wetted with 1 drop of cementing solution.

4.2. *Preparation of standards for arcing:* Prepare exactly as the regular samples except that a standard sample is substituted for the 20.0 ml of sample to be analyzed (see Sec. 4.1b). Make the standard sample by admitting 0.50, 2.00, 8.00, and 25.0 ml, re-spectively, of the standard silver solution to each of four 20-ml aliquots of the low-silver potable-water blanks, corresponding, respectively, to 0.01, 0.04, 0.16, and 0.50 mg/1 Ag.

4.3. *Spectrograph operations:* Properly adjust the electrode system and operate the spectrograph and its accessories according to the manufacturer's instructions. Treat the sample and standards in the same manner.

a. *Excitation:* Set the following arc discharge circuit constants for Multisource (see Sec. 2.1): voltage, 300 v; capacitance, 62 microfarads; inductance, 460 microhenries; resistance, 20 ohms (10 + 10); average current, 13 amp on short, 11–12 amp during run.

b. *Exposure conditions:* In the spectral region of 2,300–4,500 Å, use 3,200–3,300 Å. The slit width and length depend on the spectrograph and densitometer used; however, a 55-μ width has been found satisfactory. Burn the sample and standards to completion (until the platform is gone). Use filters or sectors to expose to background (7.5 per cent of total light has proved satisfactory).

4.4. *Photographic processing:* Develop and fix the film as follows: Emulsion, Eastman SA No. 2; developer, Eastman D-19, rocked 3 min at 68°F; stop bath, 50 ml glacial acetic acid diluted to 1 liter, 10 sec; fixing, Eastman F-5, 3 min; washing, running water, 3 min; drying, blower and heater, 5 min.

4.5. *Estimation of silver concentration:* Read the transmittance of the spectral lines Ag 3280.7Å and Pd 3242.7Å with the film densitometer. Convert the transmittance readings to intensity ratios based on film calibration data. Convert the Ag/Pd intensity ratio to mg/1 Ag from the standard working curve.

4.6. *Standard working curve:* Plot mg Ag against the intensity ratio of Ag 3280.7 to Pd 3242.7 on log-log paper (2 × 2 cycles) with data from standard samples. Once the working curve is established, use it for all future samples unless they differ markedly (more than 100 per cent in total residue) from the low-silver potable-water blank used to make up the standard samples.

5. Accuracy

Based on the fit of standard samples with the working curve and the precision of independent determinations, the accuracy of the method is estimated to be within about 10 per cent of the true value.

B. Dithizone Method (Tentative)

1. General Discussion

1.1. *Principle:* Twenty metals are capable of reacting with dithizone to produce colored coordination compounds. Under the proper conditions or upon the removal of all interferences, the reaction can be made selective for a desired substance. In this mixed-color method a separation of the two colors is not attempted; either the green color of the dithizone or the yellow color of the silver dithizonate can be measured. In view of the sensitivity of the reaction and the numerous interferences among the common metals, the method is somewhat empirical, and demands careful adherence to the procedure. The final color evaluation can be made visually or photometrically. The visual finish has been found as accurate and more efficient than the photometric measurement because it circumvents the extra handling involved with a photometer. The use of cells having a volume greater than 1 ml requires final dilution with carbon tetrachloride or the selection of a larger sample.

1.2. *Interference:* Ferric ion, residual chlorine, and other oxidizing agents convert dithizone to a yellow-brown color. However, extraction of the silver along with other metals in a carbon tetrachloride solution of dithizone overcomes such oxidation interference from the contaminants which might be present in the water sample. The silver is then removed selectively from the other carryover metals by the use of an ammonium thiocyanate solution. The extreme sensitivity, as well as silver's affinity for being adsorbed, makes it desirable to prepare and segregate glassware especially for this determination, and to take unusual precautions at every step in the procedure. The necessity for checking and preventing contamination at all points cannot be overemphasized. Dithizone and the silver dithizonate both decompose rapidly in strong light; therefore, they should not be left in the light beam of the photometer for a longer period than is necessary. Direct sunlight should also be avoided at all times.

1.3. *Minimum detectable concentration:* 0.2 μg Ag.

2. Apparatus

2.1. *Colorimetric equipment:* One of the following is required:

a. *Spectrophotometer,* for measurements at either 620 mμ or 462 mμ, and providing a light path of 1 cm.

b. *Filter photometer,* providing a light path of 1 cm and equipped with a red filter having maximum transmittance at or near 620 mμ or a blue filter having maximum transmittance at or near 460 mμ.

c. *Micro test tubes,* 10-ml capacity, 1×7.5-cm size.

2.2. *Separatory funnels,* with a capacity of 500 ml or larger, and also funnels with a capacity of 60 ml, preferably with inert teflon stopcocks.

2.3. *Glassware:* All glassware, dishes, and crucibles should first be treated with a sulfuric-chromic acid mixture, and then washed in $1 + 1$ HNO$_3$ to dissolve any trace of chromium or silver adsorbed on the glassware. After thorough rinsing with silver-free water, "Desicote" * or a similar silicone coating fluid should be applied to establish a repellant surface. Omission of these extremely important steps will result in serious errors. If desired, glassware can be dried in an oven, but acetone rinses should be avoided because this solvent frequently contains enough interferences to affect the determination.

2.4. *Vycor dishes or silica crucibles.*

3. Reagents

3.1. *Silver-free water:* Redistill ordinary distilled water in all-pyrex apparatus, or pass distilled water through a mixed bed of ion-exchange resins— see General Introduction, A, Sec. 2

and Nitrogen (Ammonia), Method A, Sec. 3.1b. Use silver-free water for the preparation of all reagents and dilutions.

3.2. *Sulfuric acid,* conc.

3.3. *Carbon tetrachloride:* Store in a glass container and do not allow contact with any metals before use. If this reagent is found to contain traces of an interfering metal, redistill in an all-pyrex apparatus.

3.4. *Stock dithizone solution:* Dissolve without heating 0.100 g diphenylthiocarbazone † in 100 ml carbon tetrachloride, CCl$_4$, in a separatory funnel. Free the solution from copper as follows. To the solution contained in the separatory funnel, add 100 ml silver-free water and 5 ml conc ammonium hydroxide, and shake the mixture vigorously. Discard the CCl$_4$ layer and wash the alkaline liquid with two 5-ml portions CCl$_4$. Add 200 ml CCl$_4$ and then $1 + 1$ hydrochloric acid in small portions until the aqueous layer is colorless on shaking. Run off the CCl$_4$ layer and store in the dark in a brown glass bottle. This solution contains 0.5 mg dithizone per ml.

3.5. *Dithizone solution (I):* Dilute 50 ml stock dithizone solution to 500 ml with CCl$_4$ and store in the dark in a brown glass bottle. This solution contains 50 μg dithizone per ml.

3.6. *Dithizone solution (II):* Dilute 2.00 ml stock dithizone solution to 250.0 ml with CCl$_4$. Store in the dark in a brown glass bottle. This solution contains 0.4 μg dithizone per ml.

3.7. *Ammonium thiocyanate reagent:* Dissolve 10 g NH$_4$CNS in silver-free water to which 5 ml conc H$_2$SO$_4$ has been added, and dilute to 500 ml with silver-free water. Store this solu-

---

* Beckman Instruments, Inc.

† Eastman No. 3092 or equivalent.

tion in a bottle containing 25 ml dithizone solution (I).

3.8. *Nitric acid, 1N:* Dilute 6.4 ml conc HNO_3 to 100 ml with silver-free water.

3.9. *Urea solution:* Dissolve 10 g $(NH_2)_2CO$ in silver-free water and dilute to 100 ml. Store in a bottle containing 25 ml dithizone solution (I). Discard the solution upon the formation of a red film, which makes the pipeting of a clear solution impossible.

3.10. *Hydroxylamine sulfate solution:* Dissolve 20 g $(NH_2OH)_2 \cdot H_2SO_4$ in silver-free water and dilute to 100 ml. Store in a bottle containing 25 ml dithizone solution (I).

3.11. *Sulfuric acid, 1N:* Dilute 28 ml conc H_2SO_4 to 1 liter with silver-free water.

3.12. *Stock silver solution:* Dissolve 0.1574 g anhydrous silver nitrate, $AgNO_3$, in silver-free water to which 14 ml conc H_2SO_4 has been added, and dilute to 1,000 ml with silver-free water; 1.00 ml $= 100$ μg Ag.

3.13. *Standard silver solution:* Immediately before use, dilute 10.00 ml stock solution to 1,000 ml with silver-free water; 1.00 ml $= 1.00$ μg Ag.

4. Procedure

4.1. *Sample treatment:* To 100 ml sample in a 500-ml separatory funnel add 11 ml conc H_2SO_4. Extract the silver by adding 5 ml dithizone solution (I) and shaking for 1 min. Collect the organic phase and any scum in a 25-ml centrifuge tube. Transfer the scum formed to the centrifuge tube because it may contain an appreciable amount of silver. Repeat the extraction twice more with 5-ml portions of dithizone solution (I) and add the extracts and scum to the centrifuge tube. Reject the aqueous phase. If a larger

sample necessitates, use two centrifuge tubes to contain the dithizone extracts. For a 500-ml sample, use at least two 5-ml portions dithizone solution (I). Centrifuge, discard the aqueous phase, and add 2 ml silver-free water. Recentrifuge and discard the aqueous phase. Transfer the silver dithizonate layer to a 60-ml separatory funnel. Add 4 ml ammonium thiocyanate solution to the centrifuge tube to collect any remaining extract, gently agitate, and transfer quantitatively to the separatory funnel. Shake for 1 min, and, with a suction pipet, transfer as much of the aqueous phase as possible to a Vycor dish. Repeat the addition of 4 ml ammonium thiocyanate solution, gentle agitation, and the transfer of the aqueous phase two more times. Run off the organic layer and add the last few drops of the aqueous phase to the dish. Add 1.5 ml conc H_2SO_4 and evaporate to dryness by first evaporating to fumes by heating from above with an infrared lamp and then by heating the sample from below with a hot plate and above with an infrared lamp. Keep the heating temperature low enough to prevent bumping. Add 0.6 ml 1N HNO_3 and warm to dissolve all the solid residue. Add 1 ml each of urea and hydroxylamine sulfate solutions, and digest the solution for 5 min near the boiling point, adding silver-free water dropwise to prevent caking. Allow the solution to cool to room temperature. Transfer the solution to a 10-ml micro test tube, rinsing the Vycor dish twice with 2-ml portions 1N H_2SO_4.

4.2. *Extraction of silver:* Add 1 ml dithizone solution (II), and extract the silver by agitation of the organic and aqueous phases together for 2 min with the aid of a thin glass rod flattened at the bottom. If the organic phase has a greenish hue, the amount of silver can be estimated as less than 1.5 μg. If the organic phase is a clear yellow (showing there is no excess of dithizone), add further 1-ml portions dithizone solution (II), and repeat the extraction until a mixed color is obtained. Record the total volume, *A*, of dithizone solution (II) used.

4.3. *Visual colorimetric estimation:* Prepare the standards by placing in each of the nine micro test tubes 1 ml dithizone solution (II) and then 0, 0.20 . . . . 1.60 ml standard silver solution, and 3.0, 2.8 . . . . 1.4 ml 1N H$_2$SO$_4$. Extract the silver as described in Sec. 4.2, starting with the solution of lowest concentration.

4.4. *Photometric measurement:* Prepare a standard curve by adding known amounts of silver in the range 0.20 to 1.50 μg to 0.3 ml 1N HNO$_3$, 1 ml each of urea and hydroxylamine sulfate solutions. After the addition of 1 ml dithizone solution (II), extract the silver using the same method as with the samples. Measure the absorbance at or near 620 mμ using special cells of 1-cm light path, but of reduced width so as to contain, when full, no more than about 1 ml. Zero the spectrophotometer on a cell containing dithizone solution (II) at an absorb-

ance reading of 1.0 (or 10 per cent transmittance) and read the samples and standards against this setting. Since the samples and standards will give a lesser absorbance reading, plot the difference between the constant absorbance of 1.0 for the dithizone and the absorbance readings for each standard and sample in order to obtain a positive-sloping standard curve.

4.5. Subtract the blank value obtained by carrying 100 ml silver-free water through the entire process.

5. Calculation

$$\text{mg/l Ag} = \frac{\mu\text{g Ag}}{\text{ml sample}} \times A$$

where A = total volume of dithizone solution (II) used to extract the silver for the final colorimetric measurement.

Bibliography

Spectrographic Method

1. HARVEY, C. E. *A Method of Semiquantitative Spectrographic Analysis.* Applied Research Labs., Glendale, Calif. (1947).
2. UMAN, G. A. Spectrochemical Method for Silver. *J. AWWA* 55:205 (1963).

Dithizone Method

3. PIERCE, T. B. Determination of Trace Quantities of Silver in Trade Effluents. *Analyst* 85:166 (1960).

Sodium

Sodium ranks sixth among the elements in order of abundance; therefore, it is present in most natural waters. The levels may vary from negligible to appreciable. Relatively high concentrations may be found in brines and hard waters softened by the sodium exchange process. The ratio of sodium to total cations is important in agriculture and human pathology. Soil permeability has been found to be detrimentally affected by a high sodium ratio, while certain diseases require water with a low sodium concentration. A limiting concentration of 2 to 3 mg/l is recommended in feed waters destined for high-pressure boilers. When necessary, sodium is removed by the hydrogen exchange process or distillation.

Selection of method: The flame photometric method (A) is more rapid and sensitive, and generally more accurate, than the gravimetric method, especially for sodium concentrations below 10 mg/l; but a special instrument and much preliminary work is required before samples can be run routinely. The gravimetric method (B) is used if a flame photometer is not available or if a check on the flame photometric result by an independent method is desired.

Storage of sample: Alkaline samples or samples containing low sodium concentrations should be stored in polyethylene bottles in order to eliminate the possibility of contamination of the sample due to leaching of the glass container. Solutions attack glass and, consequently, become contaminated with sodium which is present in the glass.

A. Flame Photometric Method

1. General Discussion

1.1. *Principle:* Trace amounts of sodium can be determined in either a direct-reading or internal-standard type flame photometer at a wavelength of 589 mμ. The sample is sprayed into a gas flame and excitation is carried out under carefully controlled and reproducible conditions. The desired spectral line is isolated by the use of interference filters or by a suitable slit arrangement in light-dispersing devices such as prisms or gratings. The intensity of light is then measured by a phototube potentiometer or other appropriate circuit. The intensity of light at 589 mμ is approximately proportional to the concentration of the element. The calibration curve may be linear but has a tendency to level off in the upper reaches. The optimum lithium concentration may vary among individual flame photometers operating on the internal-standard principle and, therefore, must be ascertained for the instrument at hand. In those cases where the alignment of the wavelength dial with the prism is not precise in the available photometer, the exact wavelength setting, which may be slightly different than 589 mμ, can be determined from the maximum needle deflection and then used for the emission measurements.

1.2. *Interference:* Burner-clogging particulate matter should be removed from the sample by filtration through a quantitative filter paper of medium retentiveness. Incorporation of a nonionic detergent in the lithium standard may assure proper aspirator function.

The problem of interference can be minimized by the following approaches:

a. Operation in the lowest practical sodium range.

b. Resort to the internal-standard or standard-addition technique.

c. Addition of radiation buffers.

d. Introduction of identical amounts of the same interfering substances into the calibration standards that are present in the sample.

e. Preparation of a family of calibration curves embodying added concentrations of a common interference.

f. Application of an experimentally determined correction in those instances where the sample contains a single important interference.

g. Removal of the interfering ions.

The standard-addition approach is described in the flame photometric method for strontium. Its use involves the addition of an identical portion of the sample to each standard and determination of the sample concentration by mathematical or graphical evaluation of the calibration data.

Potassium and calcium have been reported to interfere with the sodium determination by the internal-standard method if the potassium-to-sodium ratio is 5:1 or greater, and the calcium-to-sodium ratio is 10:1 or higher. When these ratios are exceeded, the calcium and potassium should be determined first so that the approximate concentration of interfering ions may be added, if necessary, to the sodium calibration standards. Magnesium interference does not appear until the magnesium-to-sodium ratio exceeds 100, a rare occurrence. Among the common anions capable of causing radiation interference are chloride, sulfate, and bicarbonate in relatively large amounts.

1.3. *Minimum detectable concentration:* The better flame photometers can be used for the determination of sodium levels approximating 0.1 mg/l. With proper modifications in technique, the sodium level can be extended to 0.01 mg/l or lower.

2. Apparatus

2.1. *Flame photometer,* either direct-reading or internal-standard type.

2.2. *Glassware:* Rinse all glassware with $1 + 15$ nitric acid followed by several portions of deionized distilled water to avoid contamination errors.

3. Reagents

In order to minimize sodium pickup, all solutions should preferably be stored in plastic bottles. The use of small containers reduces the amount of dry element which may be picked up from the bottle walls when the solution is poured. Each container should be thoroughly shaken to wash the accumulated salts from the walls before the solution is poured.

3.1. *Deionized distilled water:* Prepare by passing distilled water through a mixed bed of ion-exchange resins as described in General Introduction, A, Sec. 2, and Nitrogen (Ammonia) Method A, Sec. 3.1b. Use deionized distilled water for the preparation of all reagents, calibration standards, and as dilution water.

3.2. *Stock sodium solution:* Dissolve 2.542 g NaCl dried at 140°C, and dilute to 1,000 ml with deionized distilled water to form a solution containing 1.00 mg Na per 1.00 ml.

3.3. *Intermediate sodium solution:* Dilute 10.00 ml stock sodium solution with deionized distilled water to 100.0 ml to form a solution containing 0.100 mg Na per 1.00 ml. Use this intermediate solution for preparing the calibration curve in the sodium range of 1–10 mg/l.

3.4. *Standard sodium solution:* Dilute 10.00 ml intermediate sodium solution with deionized distilled water to 100 ml to form a solution containing 10.0 μg Na per 1.00 ml. Use this solution for preparing the calibration curve in the sodium range of 0.1–1.0 mg/l.

3.5. *Standard lithium solution:* Use either lithium chloride (*a*) or lithium nitrate (*b*) for the preparation of the standard lithium solution which contains 1.00 mg Li per 1.00 ml.

a. Dry LiCl overnight in an oven at 105°C. Weigh rapidly 6.109 g, dissolve in deionized distilled water, and dilute to 1,000 ml.

b. Dry LiNO₃ overnight in an oven at 105°C. Weigh rapidly 9.935 g, dissolve in deionized distilled water, and dilute to 1,000 ml.

Prepare a new calibration curve whenever the standard lithium solution must be replenished. Where circumstances warrant, alternatively prepare a standard lithium solution containing 2.00 mg or even 5.00 mg Li per 1.00 ml.

4. Procedure

4.1. *Precautions:* Locate the flame photometer in an area away from direct sunlight or the constant light emitted by an overhead fixture, and free of drafts, dust, and tobacco smoke. Guard against contamination arising from corks, filter paper, perspiration, soap, cleansers, cleaning mixtures, and inadequately rinsed apparatus.

4.2. *Instrument operation:* Because the differences between the makes and models of satisfactory flame photometers render impossible the formulation of detailed instructions applicable to every instrument, follow the manufacturer's recommendation for the selection of the proper photocell and wavelength, the adjustment of the slit width and sensitivity, the appropriate fuel and air or oxygen pressures, and the steps for warmup, correcting for flame background, rinsing of the burner, ignition of sample, and measurement of the emission intensity.

4.3. *Direct-intensity measurement:* Prepare a blank and sodium calibration standards in stepped amounts in any of the following applicable ranges: 0–1.0, 0–10, or 0–100 mg/l. Starting with the highest calibration standard and working toward the most dilute, measure the emission at 589 mμ. Repeat the operation with both the calibration standards and the samples a sufficient number of times to secure a reliable average reading for each solution. Construct a calibration curve from the sodium standards. Determine the sodium concentration of the sample by consulting the calibration curve. Where a large number of samples must be run routinely, reference to the calibration curve provides sufficiently accurate results. If greater precision and accuracy are desired, and ample time is available, resort may be had to the bracketing approach described in Sec. 4.5.

4.4. *Internal-standard measurement:* To a carefully measured volume of the sample (or a diluted aliquot of the sample), each sodium calibration standard, and a blank, add, with a volumetric pipet, an appropriate volume of standard lithium solution. Then follow all the steps prescribed in Sec. 4.3 for the direct-intensity measurement.

4.5. *Bracketing approach:* From the calibration curve, select and prepare the sodium standards that immediately bracket the emission intensity of the sample. Determine the emission intensities of the bracketing standards (one sodium standard slightly less and the other slightly greater than the sample) and the sample as nearly simultaneously as possible. Repeat the determination on both the bracketing standards and the sample. Calculate the sodium concentration by the equation presented in Sec. 5, and average the several findings for a final result.

5. Calculation

5.1. For direct reference to the calibration curve:

$$mg/l\ Na = (mg/l\ Na\ in\ aliquot) \times D$$

5.2. For the bracketing approach:

$$mg/l\ Na = \left(\frac{(B-A)\ (s-a)}{(b-a)} + A \right) D$$

in which

B = mg/l Na concentration of the upper bracketing standard

A = mg/l Na concentration of the lower bracketing standard

b = emission intensity of the upper bracketing standard

a = emission intensity of the lower bracketing standard

s = emission intensity of the sample

D = dilution ratio

$$= \frac{ml\ sample + ml\ distilled\ water}{ml\ sample}$$

6. Precision and Accuracy

The sodium content of a synthetic unknown sample containing 8 mg/l sodium, 3.6 mg/l potassium, 120 mg/l calcium, and 75 mg/l magnesium was determined with a standard deviation of ±1.3 mg/l in 23 laboratories, using the flame photometric method. Seventeen laboratories reported results within ±1 mg/l of the sodium value. The individual laboratories reproduced their own results within ±0.5 mg/l.

The sodium content of another synthetic unknown sample containing 19.9 mg/l sodium, 3.1 mg/l potassium, 108 mg/l calcium, and 82 mg/l magnesium was determined with a standard deviation of ±1.8 mg/l in 32 laboratories, using the flame photometric method. Half of the reported results were within ±0.9 mg/l of the known sodium concentration. The individual laboratories reproduced their own results within ±0.4 mg/l.

B. Gravimetric Method

1. General Discussion

1.1. *Principle:* Sodium is precipitated as sodium zinc uranyl acetate hexahydrate, $NaC_2H_3O_2 \cdot Zn(C_2H_3O_2)_2 \cdot 3UO_2(C_2H_3O_2)_2 \cdot 6H_2O$, by adding a large volume of zinc uranyl acetate solution, previously saturated with the sodium salt, to a small volume of the concentrated sample. To precipitate sodium quantitatively, at least 10 ml reagent must be added for every 1 ml of sample, and the mixture must be allowed to stand for at least 60 min. Because the solubility of sodium zinc uranyl acetate hexahydrate in water is fairly great, the precipitate, after being collected in a filter crucible, is first washed with successive small portions of the reagent solution saturated with the triple salt, and then with 95 per cent alcohol, also saturated with the triple salt. Next, the precipitate is washed with ether to remove the alcohol, and finally a stream of air is drawn through the crucible to evaporate the ether. The precipitate is weighed in the air-dry state.

1.2. *Interference:* Lithium interferes by forming a slightly soluble salt with the reagent. Potassium interferes if there is more than 25 mg in the 1-ml solution being tested. Organic acids, such as oxalic, citric, and tartaric, interfere, as do anions like phosphate which give precipitates with the reagent. Sulfate must be absent when much potassium is present, because potassium sulfate is only slightly soluble in the reagent. If the potassium and sulfate concentrations are known, the maximum possible error due to the precipitation of K_2SO_4 can be calculated. Usually this error will be negligible because the potassium concentration in potable water is generally low, and also because the calculation factor, 0.01495, for converting weight of sodium is very low. Upon evaporation of the sample, silica may, if present, become partially dehydrated and precipitate out. Except in extreme cases, the error caused by silica will be negligible for various reasons: (a) the precipitation of silica is by no means complete; (b) some of the dehydrated silica adheres strongly to the glass surface of the beaker and is not transferred to the crucible to be weighed with the sodium salt; (c) because of the high ratio of the weight of the triple salt to that of sodium, the slight increase in the weight of precipitate due to precipitated silica has a relatively small effect on the calculated sodium concentration. A method for compensation of errors caused by precipitation of uranyl phosphate and silica is described in the procedure.

2. Apparatus

2.1. *Beakers,* 20 ml, pyrex.

2.2. *Fritted-glass crucibles,* 30 ml, pyrex, of medium porosity; or porous porcelain crucibles.

2.3. *Vacuum pump or aspirator,* with manifold and individual petcocks.

3. Reagents

3.1. *Zinc uranyl acetate reagent:* Mix 2.7 ml glacial acetic acid with 100 ml distilled water. Add 10 g uranyl acetate dihydrate, $UO_2(C_2H_3O_2)_2 \cdot 2H_2O$, and 30 g zinc acetate dihydrate, $Zn(C_2H_3O_2)_2 \cdot 2H_2O$, to the solution and warm to dissolve. On cooling, add 2–3 mg sodium chloride, NaCl, allow the mixture to stand for 24 hr or more, and filter off the precipitate of sodium zinc uranyl acetate, thus leaving the reagent saturated with the triple salt. Store the solution in a pyrex bottle.

3.2. *Ethyl alcohol wash solution:* Saturate 95 per cent ethyl alcohol with pure sodium zinc uranyl acetate, and decant or filter the solution just prior to use. Prepare the sodium zinc uranyl acetate by adding 25 ml zinc uranyl acetate reagent to 2 ml sodium chloride solution (10 mg NaCl), stirring, collecting the precipitate in a sintered-glass crucible, and washing 3 times with glacial acetic acid and finally 3 times with diethyl ether.

3.3 *Diethyl ether.*

4. Procedure

If necessary, remove any suspended matter from the sample by filtration. Select a sample volume containing less than 8 mg Na and less than 25 mg K. Pipet the clear sample into a 20- or 50-ml pyrex beaker, and evaporate to dryness on a steam or hot water bath. Cool the residue to room temperature, add 1.0 ml distilled water, and rub with a stirring rod. If the residue fails to dissolve, add more 1.0-ml increments of distilled water to put the residue into solution. Ignore a feathery turbidity of $CaSO_4$ at this point because of its subsequent solubility in the zinc uranyl acetate reagent. Treat with zinc uranyl acetate reagent in the ratio of 10 ml reagent for each 1.0-ml increment of distilled water required to dissolve the residue. Mix, cover the beaker, and allow to stand for 1 hr. Stir periodically to prevent the formation of a supersaturated solution. Collect the precipitate under suction in a weighed, medium-porosity, sintered-glass crucible. Substitute a porous-bottomed porcelain filtering crucible if desired. Drain the filter as dry as possible under suction. Wash the beaker, crucible, and precipitate 5 to 8 times with 2-ml portions of zinc uranyl acetate reagent. Drain the crucible completely after the last wash in order to remove traces of the zinc uranyl acetate reagent. Next wash 5 times with 2-ml portions of ethyl alcohol wash solution. Conclude the washing with 3 small portions of diethyl ether. Continue the suction for a few minutes until the ethyl ether is volatilized and the precipitate is dry. Wipe the outside and inner bottom ring of the crucible with a cloth if salts have crystallized there. Transfer the crucible to the balance case, and weigh after 10 to 15 min, and again 10 min later to check on the constancy of the weight. Return the crucible to the suction apparatus and dissolve the sodium zinc uranyl acetate by passing 100 ml warm distilled water in small portions through the filter. Dry the crucible with ethyl alcohol wash solution and diethyl ether as previously directed, and reweigh. The difference in the weight before and after the distilled water treatment represents the weight of the sodium zinc uranyl acetate.

5. Calculation

$$mg/l\ Na = \frac{A \times 14.95}{ml\ sample}$$

where $A =$ mg triple-salt precipitate.

Bibliography

Flame Photometric Method

1. BARNES, R. B., ET AL. Flame Photometry: A Rapid Analytical Method. *Ind. Eng. Chem., Anal. Ed.* 17:605 (1945).
2. BERRY, J. W.; CHAPPELL, D. G.; & BARNES, R. B. Improved Method of Flame Photometry. *Ind. Eng. Chem., Anal. Ed.* 18:19 (1946).
3. PARKS, T. D.; JOHNSON, H. O.; & LYKKEN, L. Errors in the Use of a Model 18 Perkin-Elmer Flame Photometer for the Determination of Alkali Metals. *Anal Chem.* 20:822 (1948).
4. BILLS, C. E., ET AL. Reduction of Error in Flame Photometry. *Anal. Chem.* 21:1076 (1949).
5. GILBERT, P. T.; HAWES, R. C.; & BECKMAN, A. O. Beckman Flame Spectrophotometer. *Anal. Chem.* 22:772 (1950).
6. WEST, P. W.; FOLSE, P.; & MONTGOMERY, D. Application of Flame Spectrophotometry to Water Analysis. *Anal. Chem.* 22:667 (1950).
7. FOX, C. L. Stable Internal-Standard Flame Photometer for Potassium and Sodium Analyses. *Anal. Chem.* 23:137 (1951).
8. *Symposium on Flame Photometry.* Special Tech. Pub. 116, Am. Soc. Testing Materials, Philadelphia (1952).
9. COLLINS, C. G. & POLKINHORNE, H. An Investigation of Anionic Interference in the Determination of Small Quantities of Potassium and Sodium with a New Flame Photometer. *Analyst* 77:430 (1952).
10. WHITE, J. U. Precision of a Simple Flame Photometer. *Anal. Chem.* 24:394 (1952).
11. MAVRODINEANU, R. Bibliography on Analytical Flame Spectroscopy. *Appl. Spectroscopy* 10:51 (1956).
12. MELOCHE, V. W. Flame Photometry. *Anal. Chem.* 28:1844 (1956).
13. BURRIEL-MARTI, F. & RAMIREZ-MUNOZ, J. *Flame Photometry: A Manual of*

Methods and Applications. D. Van
Nostrand, Princeton, N.J. (1957).
14. DEAN, J. A. *Flame Photometry.* Mc-
Graw-Hill, New York (1960).

Gravimetric Method

15. BARBER, H. H. & KOLTHOFF, I. M. A Specific Reagent for the Gravimetric Determination of Sodium. *J. Am. Chem.
Soc.* 50:1625 (1928); 51:3233 (1929).
16. KOLTHOFF, I. M. & SANDELL, E. B. *Textbook of Quantitative Inorganic Analysis.* Macmillan, New York (3rd ed.,
1952) pp. 400–402.

Specific Conductance

Specific conductance yields a measure of a water's capacity to convey an
electric current. This property is related to the total concentration of the
ionized substances in a water and the
temperature at which the measurement
is made. The nature of the various
dissolved substances, their actual and
relative concentrations, and the ionic
strength of the water sample vitally
affect the specific conductance.

An aqueous system containing dissociated molecules will conduct an electric current. In a direct-current field
the positive ions migrate toward the
negative electrode, while the negatively
charged ions migrate toward the positive electrode. Most inorganic acids,
bases, and salts (such as hydrochloric
acid, sodium carbonate, and sodium
chloride) are good conductors. Conversely, molecules of such organic compounds as sucrose and benzene do not
dissociate in aqueous solution and,
therefore, conduct a current very
poorly, if at all.

Freshly distilled water has a specific
conductance of 0.5 to 2 micromhos/cm,
rising after a few weeks of storage to
a value of 2 to 4 micromhos/cm. This
increase from zero results principally
from the absorption of atmospheric
carbon dioxide, and, to a lesser extent,
ammonia.

Most raw and finished waters in the
United States exhibit a specific conductance from about 50 to 500 micro-
mhos/cm, with highly mineralized
water being in the range of 500 to
1,000 micromhos/cm and even higher.
Domestic sewage reflects to a degree
the characteristics of the water supply
serving the district. Some industrial
wastes may have specific conductance
values well in excess of 10,000 micro-
mhos/cm.

A number of practical applications
are made of specific conductance measurements, as follows:

(a) The purity of distilled and deionized water can be checked by the
determination.

(b) The variations in the dissolved
mineral concentration of raw water or
wastewater samples can be quickly
noted. The minor seasonal variations
found in reservoir waters sharply contrast with the daily fluctuations prevailing in some polluted river waters.
Sewage containing significant trade
wastes may also evidence a considerable daily variation.

(c) Conductivity measurements afford an idea of the aliquots which may
prove useful for the common chemical
determinations. They also offer a
means for checking the results of a
chemical analysis, as described in the
Introduction, C, Sec. 2.

(d) Specific conductance measurements enable the determination of the amount of ionic reagent needed in certain precipitation and neutralization reactions, the endpoint being denoted by a change in the slope of the conductivity curve.

(e) The amount of dissolved ionic matter in a sample may often be estimated by multiplying the specific conductance by an empirical factor. This factor may vary from 0.55 to 0.9, depending on the soluble components of the particular water and the temperature of the measurement. Relatively high factors may be required for saline or boiler waters, whereas lower factors may apply where considerable hydroxide or free acid is present. Even though sample evaporation results in the change of bicarbonate to carbonate, an empirical factor is often derived for a comparatively constant water supply by dividing the dissolved residue by the specific conductance. The filtrable residue may be determined by evaporation. An approximation of the me/l of either cations or anions in some waters may be possible by multiplying the micromhos by 0.01.

1. General Discussion

The standard unit of electrical resistance is the ohm. The standard unit of electrical conductance is its inverse, the mho. Inasmuch as the measurement of conductance or resistance implies the use of two electrodes 1 cm square placed 1 cm apart, specific conductance is generally reported as micromhos/cm, although the unit micromhos alone is also widely accepted. A conductance cell and a Wheatstone bridge are essential for measuring the electrical resistances of the sample and of a potassium chloride solution of known specific conductance at the same

temperature. Inasmuch as specific conductance varies directly with the temperature of the sample, the result is conventionally reported at 25°C. For control work, factors based on 0.01M potassium chloride, as shown in Fig. 21, are frequently applied to correct to 25°C the specific conductance of simple water samples tested at any temperature from 0 to 30°C. A better curve

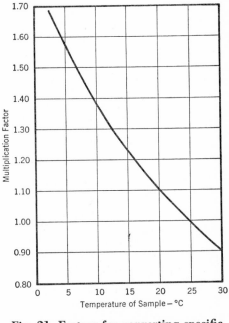

Fig. 21. Factors for converting specific conductance of water to equivalent values at 25° C (based on 0.01M KCl solution)

will be obtained for a water or wastewater by chilling the sample to 0°C, and then determining the specific conductance at intervals of a few degrees as the sample slowly warms to room temperature.

2. Apparatus

Self-contained conductance instruments meeting the specifications described in Sec. 2.1–2.3 are available commercially and are suitable for conductance measurements.

2.1. *Wheatstone bridge,* capable of being read with an accuracy of 1 per cent or better.

2.2. *Source of electrical current:* Either alternating or direct current may be used. A null indicator consisting of an a-c galvanometer or an electron-ray "magic eye" tube operates satisfactorily on 25 to 60 cycles, whereas an instrument incorporating a telephone receiver often requires 1,000 to 3,000 cycles. An isolating transformer will minimize electrical shock, equipment damage, and erroneous or erratic results when the current is derived from the electrical mains. Best results with direct current are obtained when the power input is limited to 1 watt.

2.3. *Specific conductance cell:*

a. *Platinum-electrode type:* Specific conductance cells containing platinized electrodes are available in either the pipet or immersion form. The cell choice will depend on the expected range of specific conductances. A cell constant of 0.1 is suitable for solutions of low conductivity, 100 micromhos/cm or less; a cell constant of 1 for solutions of moderate conductivity; and a cell constant of 10 for highly conducting solutions such as brines. In spite of the fact that the practical limits for measuring resistance are approximately 50 to 100,000 ohms, that cell should be used which will give an actual cell resistance in the range of 500 to 10,000 ohms. The range for the complete instrument assembly on hand should be checked experimentally by comparing the instrumental results with the true conductances of the potassium chloride solutions listed in Table 16. New cells

TABLE 16—CONDUCTANCES OF POTASSIUM
CHLORIDE SOLUTIONS AT 25°C*

Conc. M	Conductance (μmho/cm)	
	Equivalent	Specific
0	149.85	
0.0001	149.43	14.94†
0.0005	147.81	73.90
0.001	146.95	147.0
0.005	143.55	717.8
0.01	141.27	1,413
0.02	138.34	2,767
0.05	133.37	6,668
0.1	128.96	12,900
0.2	124.08	24,820
0.5	117.27	58,640
1	111.87	111,900

* Data drawn from Ref. 5.
† Computed from equation given in Ref. 4.

should be cleaned with chromic-sulfuric acid cleaning mixture and the electrodes platinized before use. Subsequently, they should be cleaned and replatinized whenever the readings become erratic or when inspection shows that any of the platinum black has flaked off. To platinize, prepare a solution of 1 g chloroplatinic acid (platinum chloride) and 0.012 g lead acetate in 100 ml water. Immerse the electrodes in this solution and connect both to the negative terminal of a 1.5-v dry cell battery. Connect the positive side of the battery to a piece of platinum wire and dip the wire into the solution. The amount of current should be such that only a small quantity of gas is evolved. The electrolysis should be continued until both cell electrodes are coated with platinum black. The platinizing solution may be saved for subsequent use. The electrodes should be rinsed thoroughly and, when not in use, must be kept immersed in distilled water.

b. *Non-platinum-electrode type:* Specific conductance cells containing electrodes constructed from durable common metals (stainless steel among others) are widely used for continuous monitoring and field studies.

2.4. *Water bath,* provided with racks of corrosion-resistant material, such as copper, brass, or stainless steel, in which tubes of samples may be held. Large test tubes are convenient for holding the samples.

3. Reagents

Standard potassium chloride, 0.0100*M*. Dissolve 0.7456 g anhydrous KCl in freshly boiled double-distilled water and make up to 1,000 ml at 25°C. This is the standard reference solution, which at 25°C has a specific conductance of 1,413 micromhos/cm. It is satisfactory for most waters when using a cell with a constant between 1 and 2. For other cell constants, stronger or weaker potassium chloride solutions listed in Table 16 will be needed. Store in glass-stoppered pyrex bottles.

4. Procedure

4.1. Specific conductance is reported in micromhos/cm at 25°C. It varies about 2 per cent per degree centigrade. It is desirable, but not imperative, that the water bath be maintained at exactly 25°C; however, any temperature between 20° and 30° will suffice, because the conductivity of the standard potassium chloride will vary to nearly the same extent with temperature as will that of the samples over the range stated. The water bath should be of sufficient size and in such a location that its temperature does not fluctuate rapidly.

4.2. Place four tubes of standard potassium chloride solution in the water bath. Place two tubes of each sample to be measured in the water bath, and allow the tubes 30 min to reach thermal equilibrium.

4.3. Rinse the conductivity cell in three of the tubes of potassium chloride solution and measure the resistance of the fourth solution. Record this value as R_{KCl}. Next rinse the cell with one tube of the first water sample, being sure that the rinsing is very thorough, and measure the resistance of the second tube; proceed in the same way until all of the water samples have been measured. It is not necessary to measure the resistance of the KCl solution again, unless there is a temperature drift of more than a few tenths of a degree during the set of measurements. The KCl measurement should, however, be made along with every subsequent set of water samples. If samples are encountered which differ in conductivity by a factor of 5 or more from the conductivity of the KCl, it would be safer, in order to minimize carryover from one sample to the next, to use three tubes of each sample. Where this is done, rinse the cell with two tubes and make the measurement in the third tube.

5. Calculation

5.1. The cell constant, C, is equal to the product of the measured resistance, in ohms, of the standard potassium chloride solution and the specific conductance, in mhos per centimeter, of this standard solution; $C = R_{KCl} \times 0.001413$ if the measurement is made at 25°C.

5.2. The specific conductance (mho/cm) of the water sample at 25°C is equal to the cell constant, C, divided by the resistance, in ohms, of the sample, R_s, measured at 25°C:

$$\text{Specific conductance} = \frac{C}{R_s}$$

The specific conductance of most waters is so low that it is standard practice to express it in micromhos/cm (the numerical value expressed in micromhos/cm is 1,000,000 times as large as the numerical value expressed in mhos/cm).

5.3. If the temperature of measurement is not exactly 25°C, it may be more convenient to calculate the specific conductance at 25°C according to the equation:

Specific conductance
$$= \frac{1,413 \times R_{KCl}}{R_s} \text{ micromhos/cm}$$

where R_{KCl} and R_s are measured at the same temperature, preferably near room temperature, and in the range from 20° to 30°C.

6. Precision and Accuracy

The precision and accuracy with which the conductance of water can be determined depends on the equipment used. A precision and accuracy of about ±5 per cent are possible with the better commercial instruments.

Bibliography

1. Jones, G. & Bradshaw, B. C. The Measurement of the Conductance of Electrolytes. V. A Redetermination of the Conductance of Standard Potassium Chloride Solutions in Absolute Units. *J. Am. Chem. Soc.* 55:1780 (1933).
2. Rossum, J. R. Conductance Method for Checking Accuracy of Water Analyses. *Anal. Chem.* 21:631 (1949).
3. Wilcox, L. V. Electrical Conductivity. *J. AWWA* 42:775 (1950).
4. Lind, J. E.; Zwolenik, J. J.; & Fuoss, R. M. Calibration of Conductance Cells at 25°C with Aqueous Solutions of Potassium Chloride. *J. Am. Chem. Soc.* 81:1557 (1959).
5. Robinson, R. A. & Stokes, R. H. *Electrolyte Solutions.* Academic Press, New York (2nd ed., 1959), p. 466.

Strontium

A typical alkaline-earth element, strontium chemically resembles calcium and thereby causes a positive error in gravimetric and titrimetric methods for the determination of calcium. As strontium has a tendency to accumulate in the bone structure, radioactive strontium-90, with a half-life of 28 years, presents a well-recognized peril to health. Naturally occurring strontium is not radioactive. For this reason, the determination of strontium in a water supply should be supplemented by a radiologic measurement to exclude the possibility that the strontium content may originate from radioactive contamination (see Part II).

Although most potable supplies contain little strontium, some well waters in the midwestern part of the United States have exhibited levels as high as 39 mg/l.

Flame Photometric Method (Tentative)

1. General Discussion

1.1. *Principle:* The flame photometric method enables the determination of strontium in the small concentrations prevalent in natural water supplies. The strontium emission is measured at a wavelength of 460.7 mμ. Because the background intensity at a wavelength of 454 mμ equals that at 460.7 mμ, and is unaffected by the variable strontium concentration, the difference in readings obtained at these two wavelengths allows an estimate of the light intensity emitted by strontium.

1.2. *Interference:* The emission intensity is a linear function of the strontium concentration and also the concentration of the other constituents in the sample. The standard addition technique distributes the same ions throughout the standards and the unknown, thereby equalizing the radiation effect of possible interfering substances in the standards and the unknown.

1.3. *Minimum detectable concentration:* Strontium levels of about 0.2 mg/l can be detected by the flame photometric method without prior concentration of the sample by evaporation.

1.4. *Sampling and storage:* Polyethylene bottles are preferable for sample storage, although pyrex containers may also be used. Analyses should be performed as soon as possible after sample collection.

2. Apparatus

*Spectrophotometer,** equipped with photomultiplier tube and flame accessories.

3. Reagents

3.1. *Stock strontium solution:* Weigh into a 500-ml erlenmeyer flask 1.685 g anhydrous strontium carbonate, $SrCO_3$, powder. Place a funnel in the neck of the flask and add, a little at a time, $1 + 1$ HCl until all the

---

* Beckman Model DU or equivalent.

$SrCO_3$ has dissolved. Add 200 ml distilled water and boil for a few minutes to expel the CO_2. Cool, add a few drops of methyl red indicator, and adjust to the intermediate orange color by adding $3N$ NH_4OH or $1 + 1$ HCl as required. Transfer quantitatively to a 1-liter volumetric flask and dilute to the mark with distilled water; 1.00 ml = 1.00 mg Sr.

3.2. *Standard strontium solution:* Dilute 25.00 ml stock strontium solution to 1,000 ml with distilled water; 1.00 ml = 0.025 mg Sr. Use this solution for preparing Sr standards in the 1–25 mg/l range.

3.3. *Nitric acid,* conc.

4. Procedure

4.1. *Preparation of strontium standards:* Add 25.0 ml of sample, containing less than 10 mg calcium or barium and less than 1 mg strontium, to 25.0 ml of each of a series of strontium standards. Use a minimum of four strontium standards from 0.0 mg/l to a concentration exceeding that of the sample. For most natural waters 0.0, 2.0, 5.0, and 10.0 mg/l Sr standards are sufficient. Brines may require a strontium series containing 0, 25, 50, and 75 mg/l. Dilute the brine sufficiently to eliminate burner splatter and clogging. Best results occur when the strontium concentration of the sample does not exceed 100 mg/l.

4.2. *Concentration of low-level strontium samples:* With waters containing less than 2 mg/l Sr, concentrate the samples for best results. Add 3–5 drops of conc HNO_3 to 250 ml of sample and evaporate to about 25 ml. Cool and make up to 50.0 ml with distilled water. Proceed as in Sec. 4.1. The HNO_3 concentration in the sample prepared for atomization can approach

0.2 ml per 25 ml without producing interference.

4.3. *Flame photometric measurement:* Measure the emission intensity of the prepared samples (standards plus sample) at wavelengths of 460.7 and 454 mμ. Follow the manufacturer's instructions for the correct operation of the instrument available for the determination.

5. Calculation

5.1. Plot the net intensity (reading at 460.7 mμ minus reading at 454 mμ) against the strontium concentration which was added to the unknown sample. Because the plot forms a straight calibration line that intersects the ordinate, the unknown strontium concentration can be computed from the equation:

$$mg/l\ Sr = \frac{A - B}{C} \times \frac{D}{E}$$

where A = sample emission intensity reading at 460.7 mμ, B = background radiation reading at 454 mμ, C = slope of calibration line. The ratio D/E applies only when E ml of sample is evaporated to form a concentrate of 25.0 ml, the value for D.

5.2. *Graphical method:* The strontium concentration of the sample can also be evaluated by the graphical method illustrated in Fig. 22. Plot the net intensity against the strontium concentration which was added to the unknown sample. The calibration line in the example intersects the ordinate at 12. Thus, $Y = 12$ and $2Y = 24$. The strontium concentration of the unknown sample is found by locating the abscissa value of the point on the calibration line which has an ordinate

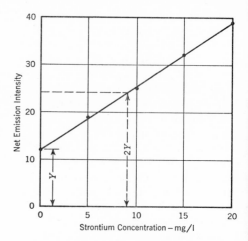

Fig. 22. Graphical method of computing strontium concentration

value of 24. In the example, the strontium concentration is 9.0 mg/l.

5.3. Report a strontium concentration below 10 mg/l to the nearest 0.1 mg/l, and one above 10 mg/l to the nearest whole number.

6. Accuracy

Strontium concentrations in the range 12.0–16.0 mg/l can be determined with an accuracy within ±1–2 mg/l.

Bibliography

1. CHOW, T. J. & THOMPSON, T. G. Flame Photometric Determination of Strontium in Sea Water. *Anal. Chem.* 27 :18 (1955).
2. NICHOLS, M. S. & McNALL, D. R. Strontium Content of Wisconsin Municipal Waters. *J. AWWA* 49 :1493 (1957).
3. HORR, C. A. A Survey of Analytical Methods for the Determination of Strontium in Natural Water. *US Geol. Survey Water Supply Paper* No. 1496-A (1959).

Sulfate

Sulfate is widely distributed in nature and may be present in natural waters in concentrations ranging from a few to several thousand mg/l. Mine drainage wastes may contribute high sulfate by virtue of pyrite oxidation. Because sodium and magnesium sulfate exert a cathartic action, the recommended sulfate concentration in potable supplies is limited to 250 mg/l.

The methods for sulfate described below are gravimetric (*A* and *B*) and turbidimetric (*C*). Several titrimetric methods are currently used for the direct or indirect determination of sulfate. Although quite satisfactory in some circumstances, they are not yet considered to be sufficiently developed to warrant recommendation for general use in water analysis. The analyst is urged, however, to become familiar with the literature on the subject of titrimetric determination of sulfate.

Selection of method: The choice of method will depend on the concentration range of sulfate and the degree of accuracy required. Dilution or concentration of the sample will bring most waters into the desired range for any of the methods. Although Method A is recognized as the preferred standard method and is the most accurate for sulfate concentrations above 10 mg/l, it is also the most time consuming. It should be used for obtaining the theoretical ion balances and whenever results of the greatest accuracy are required. Method B is similar but substitutes drying of the filter and residue for the more rigorous heat treatment by ignition at 800°C that is required to expel occluded water. This method is acceptable in routine work where the greatest attainable accuracy is not required. Method C is more rapid and may be either more or less accurate than Methods A or B for sulfate concentrations less than 10 mg/l, depending on a number of factors, including the skill of the analyst. Although usually less accurate than Methods A or B above 10 mg/l, Method C may be applied to concentrations up to 60 mg/l.

Sampling and storage: In the presence of organic matter certain bacteria may reduce sulfate to sulfide. To avoid this, heavily polluted or contaminated samples should be stored at low temperatures or treated with formaldehyde. Sulfite may be oxidized to sulfate by dissolved oxygen above pH 8.0. Samples containing sulfite should have the pH adjusted below this level.

A. Gravimetric Method With Ignition of Residue

1. General Discussion

1.1. *Principle:* Sulfate is precipitated in a hydrochloric acid medium as barium sulfate by the addition of barium chloride. The precipitation is carried out near the boiling temperature, and, after a period of digestion, the precipitate is filtered, washed with water until free of chlorides, ignited or dried, and weighed as $BaSO_4$.

1.2. *Interference:* The gravimetric determination of sulfate is subject to many errors, both positive and negative. In potable waters where the mineral concentration is low these may be of minor importance. The analyst should be familiar with the more common interferences, however, so that he may apply corrective measures when necessary.

a. *Interferences leading to high results:* Suspended matter, silica, barium chloride precipitant, nitrate, sulfite, and water are the principal factors in positive errors. Suspended matter may be present in both the sample and the precipitating solution; soluble silicate may be rendered insoluble and sulfite may be oxidized to sulfate during processing of the sample. Barium nitrate, barium chloride, and water are occluded to some extent with the barium sulfate, although water is driven off if the temperature of ignition is sufficiently high.

b. *Interferences leading to low results:* Alkali metal sulfates frequently yield low results. This is especially true of alkali hydrogen sulfates. Occlusion of alkali sulfate with barium sulfate causes the substitution of an element of lower atomic weight than barium in the precipitate. Hydrogen sulfates of alkali metals act similarly and, in addition, decompose on being heated. Heavy metals, such as chromium and iron, cause low results by interfering with the complete precipitation of sulfate and by formation of heavy metal sulfates. Barium sulfate has small but significant solubility, which is increased in the presence of acid. Although an acid medium is necessary to prevent precipitation of barium carbonate and phosphate, it is important to limit its concentration to minimize the solution effect.

2. Apparatus

2.1. *Steam bath.*

2.2. *Drying oven,* equipped with thermostatic control.

2.3. *Muffle furnace,* with heat indicator.

2.4. *Desiccator,* preferably containing a desiccant with color indicator of the water content.

2.5. *Analytical balance,* capable of weighing to 0.1 mg.

2.6. *Filters:* One of the following is required:

a. *Paper:* Acid-washed, ashless, hard-finish filter paper sufficiently retentive for fine precipitates.

b. *Crucible:* Porous-bottom silica or porcelain crucible with a maximum pore size of 5 microns.

c. *Gooch crucible,* 30-ml capacity, with asbestos mat.

2.7. *Filtering apparatus,* appropriate to the type of filter selected.

3. Reagents

3.1. *Methyl red indicator solution:* Dissolve 0.1 g methyl red sodium salt in distilled water and dilute to 100 ml.

3.2. *Hydrochloric acid,* $1 + 1$.

3.3. *Barium chloride solution:* Dissolve 100 g $BaCl_2 \cdot 2H_2O$ in 1 liter distilled water. Filter through a membrane filter or hard-finish filter paper before use; 1 ml of this reagent is capable of precipitating approximately 40 mg SO_4.

3.4. *Asbestos cream:* Add 15 g acid-washed medium-fiber asbestos, which is prepared especially for Gooch crucible determinations, to 1 liter distilled water. Remove the fine material from the asbestos before use by repeated decantations.

3.5. *Silver nitrate-nitric acid reagent:* Dissolve 8.5 g $AgNO_3$ and 0.5

ml conc HNO_3 in 500 ml distilled water.

4. Procedure

4.1. *Removal of cation interference:* If the total cation concentration in the sample is 250 mg/l or more, or if the total heavy metal ion concentration in the sample is 10 mg/l or more, pass the sample portion intended for sulfate precipitation through a cation-removing ion exchange column (Fig. 3) as described in the Introduction, B, Sec. 2.2.

4.2. *Removal of silica:* If the silica concentration exceeds 25 mg/l, evaporate the sample nearly to dryness in a platinum dish on a steam bath. Add 1 ml HCl, tilt the dish, and rotate it until the acid comes in contact with the residue on the sides; continue the evaporation to dryness. Complete the drying in an oven at 180°C and, if organic matter is present, char over the flame of a burner. Moisten the residue with 2 ml distilled water and 1 ml HCl, and evaporate to dryness on a steam bath. Add 2 ml HCl, take up the soluble residue in hot water, and filter. Wash the insoluble silica with several small portions of hot water. Combine the filtrate and washings.

4.3. *Precipitation of barium sulfate:* Adjust the clarified sample—treated if necessary to remove interfering agents —to contain approximately 50 mg of sulfate ion in a 250-ml volume. Adjust the acidity with HCl to pH 4.5–5.0 using a pH meter or the orange color of methyl red indicator. Then add an additional 1 to 2 ml HCl. Lower concentrations of sulfate ion may be tolerated if it is impracticable to concentrate the sample to the optimum level, but in such cases it is better to fix the total volume at 150 ml. Heat the solution to boiling and, while stirring gently, add warm barium chloride solution slowly until precipitation appears to be complete; then add about 2 ml in excess. If the amount of precipitate is small, add a total of 5 ml barium chloride solution. Digest the precipitate at 80°–90°C, preferably overnight but for not less than 2 hr.

4.4. *Preparation of filters:*

a. Paper: Prepare in the conventional manner.

b. Silica or porcelain crucible: Preignite at 800°C for 1 hr, cool in a desiccator, and weigh.

c. Gooch crucible: Prepare an asbestos filter mat in the crucible by using suitable suction apparatus. Wash with several portions of hot distilled water, dry, and ignite at 800°C for 1 hr. Cool the crucible in a desiccator and weigh.

4.5. Mix a small amount of ashless filter paper pulp with the barium sulfate, and filter at room temperature. The pulp aids filtration and reduces the tendency of the precipitate to creep. Wash the precipitate with small portions of warm distilled water until the washings are free of chloride, as indicated by testing with silver nitrate-nitric acid reagent. Dry the filter and precipitate and ignite at 800° C for 1 hr. *Do not allow the filter paper to flame.* Cool in a desiccator and weigh.

5. Calculation

$$\text{mg/l } SO_4 = \frac{\text{mg } BaSO_4 \times 411.5}{\text{ml sample}}$$

6. Precision and Accuracy

A synthetic unknown sample containing 259 mg/l sulfate was determined gravimetrically by 31 laboratories with a standard deviation of ±3.2 mg/l. One-half of the reported results were within ±6 mg/l of the known sulfate concentration. The individual laboratories reproduced their own results within ±3.8 mg/l.

B. Gravimetric Method with Drying of Residue

1. General Discussion

Refer to Method A.

2. Apparatus

2.1. *Steam bath.*

2.2. *Drying oven:* Conventional hot-air drying oven equipped with thermostatic control, or, preferably, a vacuum drying oven.

2.3. *Desiccator,* preferably containing a desiccant with a color indicator of the water content.

2.4. *Analytical balance,* capable of weighing to 0.1 mg.

2.5. *Filters:* One of the following is required:

a. *Crucible:* Porous-bottom silica or porcelain crucible with a maximum pore size of 5 microns.

b. *Fritted-glass filter,* fine ("F") porosity, with a maximum pore size of 5 microns.

c. *Membrane filter,* with a pore size of about 0.45 microns.

d. *Gooch crucible,* 30-ml capacity, with asbestos mat.

2.6. *Filtering apparatus,* appropriate to the type of filter selected. (Coat the holder used for the membrane filter with silicone fluid to prevent the precipitate from adhering to it.)

3. Reagents

All the reagents listed in Method A, Sec. 3, are required; and, in addition:

3.1. *Silicone fluid.**

---

* "Desicote" (Beckman) or similar.

3.2. *Anticreep fluid:* Commercial nonionic wetting agents are satisfactory.

4. Procedure

4.1. *Removal of interference:* Refer to Method A, Sec. 4.1 and 4.2.

4.2. *Precipitation of barium sulfate:* Refer to Method A, Sec. 4.3.

4.3. *Preparation of filters:*

a. *Silica or porcelain crucible:* Dry to constant weight † in an oven maintained at 105°C or more, cool in a desiccator, and weigh.

b. *Fritted-glass filter:* Dry as in (a).

c. *Membrane filter:* Place the filter on a piece of filter paper or a watch glass and dry to constant weight † in a vacuum oven at 80°C, while maintaining a vacuum of at least 25 in. of mercury, or in a conventional oven at a temperature of 103°–105°C. Cool in a desiccator and weigh the membrane only.

d. *Gooch crucible:* Prepare an asbestos filter mat in the crucible by using suitable suction apparatus. Wash with several portions of hot distilled water and dry to constant weight † in an oven maintained at 105°C or more; cool in a desiccator and weigh.

4.4. Filter the barium sulfate at room temperature. Wash the precipitate with several small portions of

---

† Constant weight is defined as a change of not more than 0.5 mg in two successive operations consisting of heating, cooling in a desiccator, and weighing.

warm distilled water until the washings are free of chloride, as indicated by testing with silver nitrate-nitric acid reagent. If the membrane filter is used, add a few drops of anticreep solution to the suspension before filtering and also to the wash water, to prevent adherence of the precipitate to the holder. Dry the filter with precipitate by the same procedure used in the preparation of the filter. Cool in a desiccator and weigh.

5. Calculation

$$\text{mg/l } SO_4 = \frac{\text{mg BaSO}_4 \times 411.5}{\text{ml sample}}$$

C. Turbidimetric Method

1. General Discussion

1.1. *Principle:* Sulfate ion is precipitated in a hydrochloric acid medium with barium chloride in such manner as to form barium sulfate crystals of uniform size. The absorbance of the barium sulfate suspension is measured by a nephelometer or transmission photometer and the sulfate ion concentration is determined by comparison of the reading with a standard curve.

1.2. *Interference:* Color or suspended matter in large amounts will interfere with this method. Some suspended matter may be removed by filtration. If both are small in comparison with the sulfate ion concentration, interference is corrected for as indicated in Sec. 4.4. Silica in excess of 500 mg/l will interfere, and, in waters containing large quantities of organic material, it may not be possible to precipitate barium sulfate satisfactorily.

There are no ions other than sulfate in normal waters that will form insoluble compounds with barium under strongly acid conditions. Determinations should be made at room temperature, which may vary over a range of 10°C without causing appreciable error.

1.3. *Minimum detectable concentration:* Approximately 1 mg/l sulfate.

2. Apparatus

2.1. *Magnetic stirrer:* It is convenient to incorporate a timing device to permit the magnetic stirrer to operate for exactly 1 min. The stirring speed should not vary appreciably. It is also convenient to incorporate a fixed resistance in series with the motor operating the magnetic stirrer to regulate the speed of stirring. If more than one magnet is used, they should be of identical shape and size. The exact speed of stirring is not critical, but it should be constant for each run of samples and standards and should be adjusted to about the maximum at which no splashing occurs.

2.2. *Photometer:* One of the following is required with preference in the order given:

a. *Nephelometer.*

b. *Spectrophotometer,* for use at 420 mμ, providing a light path of 4–5 cm.

c. *Filter photometer,* equipped with a violet filter having maximum transmittance near 420 mμ and providing a light path of 4–5 cm.

2.3. *Stop watch,* if the magnetic stirrer is not equipped with an accurate timer.

2.4. *Measuring spoon,* capacity 0.2–0.3 ml.

3. Reagents

3.1. *Conditioning reagent:* Mix 50 ml glycerol with a solution containing 30 ml conc HCl, 300 ml distilled water, 100 ml 95 per cent ethyl or isopropyl alcohol, and 75 g sodium chloride.

3.2. *Barium chloride,* crystals, 20–30 mesh.

3.3. *Standard sulfate solution:* Prepare a standard sulfate solution as described in *a* or *b*; 1.00 ml = 0.10 mg SO_4.

a. Prepare by diluting 10.41 ml of the standard $0.0200N$ H_2SO_4 titrant specified in Alkalinity, Sec. 3.2, to 100 ml with distilled water.

b. Dissolve 0.1479 g anhydrous sodium sulfate, Na_2SO_4, in distilled water, and dilute to 1,000 ml.

4. Procedure

4.1. Measure 100 ml of sample, or a suitable aliquot made up to 100 ml, into a 250-ml erlenmeyer flask. Add exactly 5.00 ml of conditioning reagent and mix in the stirring apparatus. While the solution is being stirred, add a spoonful of barium chloride crystals and begin the timing immediately. Stir for exactly 1 min at a constant speed.

4.2. Immediately after the stirring period has ended, pour some of the solution into the cell of the photometer and measure the turbidity at 30-sec intervals for 4 min. Maximum turbidity is usually obtained within 2 min and the readings remain constant thereafter for 3–10 min. Consider the turbidity to be the maximum reading obtained in the 4-min interval.

4.3. Estimate the sulfate concentration in the sample by comparing the turbidity reading with a standard curve

secured by carrying out the procedure with standard sulfate solutions. A suitable range of standards extends from 0 to 40 mg/l of sulfate ion in 5-mg/l increments. Above 40 mg/l the accuracy of the method decreases and the suspensions of barium sulfate lose stability.

4.4. Correction should be made for the apparent turbidity of the samples by running blanks in which no barium chloride is added. Stability of the conditions should be checked by running a standard sample with every three or four unknown samples.

5. Calculation

$$mg/l \; SO_4 = \frac{mg \; SO_4 \times 1,000}{ml \; sample}$$

6. Precision and Accuracy

Results are reproducible within ±5 per cent of the sulfate ion concentration when interferences are absent and the analyst's technique is uniformly good. The accuracy is estimated to be about ±10 per cent of the sulfate ion concentration, under the best analytical conditions, where the concentration is below 10 mg/l. Accuracy falls off rapidly for concentrations above 40 mg/l.

A synthetic unknown sample containing 259 mg/l sulfate was determined turbidimetrically by 19 laboratories with a standard deviation of ±28.5 mg/l. One-half of the reported results were within ±9 mg/l of the known sulfate concentration. The individual laboratories reproduced their own results within ±3.4 mg/l.

Bibliography

Gravimetric Method
1. KOLTHOFF, I. M. & SANDELL, E. B. *Textbook of Quantitative Inorganic*

Analysis. Macmillan Co., New York (3rd ed., 1952).

2. HILLEBRAND, W. F., ET AL. *Applied Inorganic Analysis.* John Wiley & Sons, New York (2nd ed., 1953).

Turbidimetric Method

3. SHEEN, R. T.; KAHLER, H. L.; & ROSS, E. M. Turbidimetric Determination of Sulfate in Water. *Ind. Eng. Chem., Anal. Ed.* 7:262 (1935).

4. THOMAS, J. F. & COTTON, J. E. A Turbidimetric Sulfate Determination. *Water & Sewage Works* 101:462 (1954).

5. GOLDMAN, E. Modification of the *Standard Methods* Procedure for Turbidimetric Determination of Sulfate (1958; unpublished).

6. ROSSUM, J. R. & VILLARRUZ, P. A. Suggested Methods for Turbidimetric Determination of Sulfate in Water. *J. AWWA* 53:873 (1961).

Other Methods

7. FRITZ, J. S. & YAMAMURA, S. S. Rapid Microdetermination of Sulfate. *Anal. Chem.* 27:1461 (1955).

8. FRITZ, J. S.; YAMAMURA, S. S.; & RICHARD, M. J. Titration of Sulfate Following Separation with Alumina. *Anal. Chem.* 29:158 (1957).

9. BERTOLACINI, R. J. & BARNEY, J. E. Colorimetric Determination of Sulfate with Barium Chloranilate. *Anal. Chem.* 29:281 (1957).

10. BERTOLACINI, R. J. & BARNEY, J. E. Ultraviolet Spectrophotometric Determination of Sulfate, Chloride, and Fluoride with Chloranilic Acid. *Anal. Chem.* 30:202 (1958).

Sulfide

Sulfide occurs in many well waters and sometimes is formed in lakes or surface waters, or even in distribution systems, as a result of bacterial action on organic matter under anaerobic conditions. Varying amounts may also be found in waters receiving sewage or wastes from tanneries, paper mills, oil refineries, chemical plants, and gas manufacturing works. Concentrations of a few hundredths of a milligram per liter cause a noticeable odor. Removal of sulfide odor is accomplished at the water treatment plant by aeration or chlorination.

In waters free from suspended solids, sulfide exists as a mixture of HS^- and H_2S, in proportions determined by the pH, as given in Table 27 (Part III). If the sample is not clear, insoluble metallic sulfides may also be present.

The colorimetric method of determination which is described in Part III (Sulfide, Method B) is applicable. Samples must be tested immediately after collection, unless preserved by the addition of zinc acetate, as specified in the following procedure.

Pretreatment of Low-Level Sulfide Samples

1. General Discussion

Many water supplies have only a few tenths or hundredths of a milligram of sulfide per liter. In these cases, it is advantageous to use zinc acetate in a procedure which, in addition to preserving the sample for up to 24 hr, causes zinc sulfide to be precipitated along with zinc hydroxide as a carrier precipitate. Upon settling, the sulfide content is concentrated into a smaller volume.

2. Reagents

2.1. *Zinc acetate,* 1*M.* Dissolve 22 g $Zn(C_2H_3O_2)_2 \cdot 2H_2O$ in enough distilled water to make a 100-ml solution.

2.2. *Sodium hydroxide,* 1*N.* Dissolve 40 g NaOH and dilute to 1 liter with distilled water.

3. Procedure

Place 1 ml zinc acetate solution in a bottle of 250-ml or 500-ml capacity. Collect the sample in this bottle, measuring the amount by a mark on the bottle. Add 1 ml NaOH. Stir the solution for a minute or two to coagulate the precipitate. Allow to stand until the supernatant water is clear. Siphon off most of this water, preferably 80–95 per cent of the sample taken, but with care to lose none of the precipitate. Pour the remaining water, with precipitate, into a graduated cylinder to measure the volume. Then, with the precipitate uniformly suspended in the water, withdraw a sample for sulfide determination as in Part III, Method B, Sec. 4.

The amount of zinc acetate added in the foregoing procedure may be varied according to the judgment of the analyst, the aim being to get a well-settling precipitate. The volume of sodium hydroxide solution should equal the volume of zinc acetate solution in order to insure a large excess of unprecipitated zinc, without which complete precipitation of the sulfide cannot be assured.

4. Calculation

$$\text{mg/l total sulfide} = \frac{T \times B}{A}$$

where A represents the volume of sample, B the volume of remaining sample with precipitate after decanting, and T the apparent total sulfide found in the colorimetric test.

Bibliography

1. POMEROY, R. Auxiliary Pretreatment by Zinc Acetate in Sulfide Analyses. *Anal. Chem.* 26:571 (1954).

Sulfite

Although sulfite may occur in certain industrial wastes and polluted waters, it is most commonly found in boiler and boiler feed waters to which sodium sulfite has been applied to reduce dissolved oxygen to a minimum and to prevent corrosion. The development of catalyzed sodium sulfite has extended its field of usefulness to the treatment of cooling, process, and distribution water systems at cold water temperatures.

1. General Discussion

1.1. *Principle:* An acidified water sample containing sulfite is titrated with a standardized potassium iodide-iodate titrant. Free iodine is released when the sulfite has been completely oxidized, resulting in the formation of a blue color in the presence of starch indicator.

1.2. *Interference:* The presence of other oxidizable substances in the water such as organic matter and sulfide will result in higher titration values for sulfite than are actually present. Nitrite, on the other hand, will combine with sulfite in the acid medium to destroy both, leading to low results. No interference occurs with the Dual-Purpose Dry Starch Indicator Powder because the sulfamic acid in this proprietary compound destroys the nitrite. Copper ion rapidly accelerates the oxidation of sulfite solution. Certain heavy metals may also react in a manner similar to copper. Proper sampling and immediate fixing by acid addition should minimize those difficulties.

1.3. *Minimum detectable concentration:* 2 mg/1 SO_3.

2. Reagents

2.1. *Sulfuric acid,* 1 + 1.

2.2. *Starch indicator:* Either the aqueous solution (*a*) or the dry powders (*b*) and (*c*) may be used.

a. To 5 g starch (potato, arrowroot, or soluble) in a mortar, add a little cold distilled water and grind to a paste. Pour into 1 liter of boiling distilled water, stir, and allow to settle overnight. Use the clear supernate. Preserve by adding either 1.3 g salicylic acid, 4 g zinc chloride, or a combination of 4 g sodium propionate and 2 g sodium azide to 1 liter of starch solution.

b. Soluble starch powder * provides a sharp endpoint change to blue when

0.1 g of the powder is used in the presence of free iodine.

c. A dual-purpose starch indicator powder † composed of cold-water-soluble starch in a sulfamic acid medium finds extensive use in control work. When this proprietary formulation is used, the sulfuric acid is omitted, and 3–4 drops phenolphthalein indicator solution are added to the water sample followed by sufficient dippers full (1 g) of indicator powder to discharge the alkaline red color of the sample. After a final dipperful in excess is added, the sample is titrated with standard potassium iodide-iodate titrant to the appearance of a permanent blue color in the sample.

2.3. *Standard potassium iodide-iodate titrant,* 0.0125*N.* Dissolve 0.4458 g anhydrous potassium iodate, KIO_3 (primary standard grade dried for several hours at 120°C), 4.35 g potassium iodide, KI, and 0.31 g sodium bicarbonate, $NaHCO_3$, in distilled water, and dilute to 1,000 ml. This titrant is equivalent to 0.500 mg SO_3 per 1.00 ml.

3. Procedure

3.1. Collect a fresh water sample with as little contact with air as possible. Cool hot samples to 50°C or below in the cooling apparatus depicted in Fig. 6. Do not filter the samples.

3.2. Add 1 ml H_2SO_4 (or 1 g dual-purpose starch indicator, Sec. 2.2c) to a 250-ml erlenmeyer flask or other titrating vessel, then measure 50 ml water sample in a graduated cylinder, and transfer to the flask. Add 1 ml starch indicator solution or 0.1 g starch

---

* The product known as Thyodene is imported by the Magnus Chemical Co. of Garwood, N.J., and is available from the Fisher Scientific Co. of Pittsburgh, Pa., and others.

† The use of this product, known as Dual-Purpose Dry Starch Indicator Powder, is covered by U.S. Patent No. 2,963,443 issued to E. T. Erickson.

powder b (omit this step if dual-purpose starch indicator powder, Sec. 2.2c, is used). Titrate with potassium iodide-iodate titrant until a faint permanent blue color develops in the sample, signaling the end of the titration. View the color changes against a white background.

4. Calculation

$$mg/l\ SO_3 = \frac{A \times N \times 40,000}{ml\ sample}$$

$$mg/l\ Na_2SO_3 = mg/l\ SO_3 \times 1.57$$

where A = ml titration for sample and N = normality of KI-KIO$_3$.

Surfactants (Anionic)*

The popularity of synthetic detergents (containing surface-active agents, or "surfactants") for general cleaning purposes has on occasion resulted in the frothing of some water supplies. Because 1 mg/l surfactant can cause a light froth in water, the limiting concentration has been set at 0.5 mg/l. As the single most widely used surfactant is alkyl benzene sulfonate (ABS), it is the one most likely to be present in raw water supplies. For this reason, ABS has been selected as the standard compound in the following two analytical methods (both tentative).

---

* In view of the soap and detergent industry's scheduled replacement of alkyl benzene sulfonate (ABS) surfactant with linear alkylate sulfonate (LAS) surfactant by the middle of 1965, a change in reference material will be required following the conversion to properly conduct both the methylene blue and infrared procedures. It is assumed that a linear alkylate sulfonate reference material for the preparation of the standard calibration solution will be available through The Soap and Detergent Association (40 E. 41st St., New York, N.Y. 10017) at that time. Alkyl benzene sulfonate surfactant and linear alkylate sulfonate surfactant are both methylene blue reactive substances, albeit not identically, thereby necessitating the preparation of an individual calibration curve from the appropriate surfactant.

Selection of method: It is recommended that the analyst who is interested in the ABS content of a raw water supply follow a two-step approach. He should first analyze the sample by the methylene blue method (A). If the result is low, 0.5 mg/l or so, no further analysis will generally be required, because the sum of the interferences (usually positive) plus true ABS is such that ABS is not a significant factor in the water. Experience has shown that the methylene blue procedure suffices when no problems are observed in a water supply. Should the methylene blue result be high, however, it becomes important to know how much represents true ABS and how much interferences. An infrared determination (B) is recommended in such a case, but if infrared equipment is not available, the analysis by Method B can be carried through to the recovery of the purified ABS and then completed colorimetrically by the methylene blue procedure. This alternative eliminates the need for expensive infrared equipment, which few laboratories have. The big drawback to the infrared method is that, compared to the methylene blue colorimetric process, it is fairly complicated and time consuming. On the other hand, if the problem is of sufficient importance, the local analyst is advised to seek the help of his state board of health in obtaining an infrared determination of ABS.

A. *Methylene Blue Method* (Tentative)

1. General Discussion

1.1. *Principle:* This method depends on the formation of a blue-colored salt when methylene blue reacts with anionic surfactants, which include not only ABS but also alkyl sulfates. The salt is soluble in chloroform, and the intensity of color is proportional to the concentration. The intensity is measured by making spectrophotometric readings in this solvent at a wavelength of 652 mμ. The method is applicable in the 0.025–100 mg/l (as ABS) range.

1.2. *Interference:* Both organic and inorganic compounds interfere with the determination of ABS. Some of the proven interferences can be predicted on the basis of chemical properties. Organic sulfates, sulfonates, carboxylates, phosphates, and phenols—which complex methylene blue—and inorganic cyanates, chlorides, nitrates, and thiocyanates—which form ion pairs with methylene blue—are among the positive interferences. Organic materials, especially amines, which compete with the methylene blue in the reaction, can cause low results. Positive errors are much more common than negative when determining anionic surfactants in water.

1.3. *Minimum detectable concentration:* 0.01 mg ABS.

2. Apparatus

2.1. *Spectrophotometer,* for use at 652 mμ, providing a light path of 1 cm or longer.

2.2. *Separatory funnels,* 500 ml, preferably with inert teflon stopcocks.

3. Reagents

3.1. *Standard alkyl benzene sulfonate (ABS) solution:* Weigh an amount of the reference material (obtain from The Soap and Detergent Assn.) equal to 1.000 g ABS on a 100 per cent active basis. Dissolve in distilled water and dilute to 1,000 ml. Dilute 10.00 ml of this stock solution to 1,000 ml with distilled water; 1.00 ml = 10.0 μg ABS.

3.2. *Phenolphthalein indicator solution:* Either the aqueous (*a*) or alcoholic (*b*) solution may be used.

a. Dissolve 5 g phenolphthalein disodium salt in distilled water and dilute to 1 liter. If necessary, add 0.02N NaOH dropwise until a faint pink color appears.

b. Dissolve 5 g phenolphthalein in 500 ml 95 per cent ethyl alcohol or isopropyl alcohol and add 500 ml distilled water. Then add 0.02N NaOH dropwise until a faint pink color appears.

3.3. *Sodium hydroxide,* 1N. Dissolve 40 g NaOH in distilled water and dilute to 1 liter.

3.4. *Sulfuric acid,* 1N. Cautiously dilute 28 ml conc H_2SO_4 to 1 liter with distilled water.

3.5. *Chloroform.*

3.6. *Methylene blue reagent:* Dissolve 0.1 g methylene blue * in 100 ml distilled water. Transfer 30 ml of this solution to a 1-liter flask. Add 500 ml distilled water, 6.8 ml conc H_2SO_4, and 50 g monosodium dihydrogen phosphate monohydrate, $NaH_2PO_4 \cdot H_2O$. Shake until dissolution is complete. Dilute to the 1-liter mark.

3.7. *Wash solution:* Add 6.8 ml conc H_2SO_4 to 500 ml distilled water in a 1-liter flask. Then add 50 g $NaH_2PO_4 \cdot H_2O$ and shake until dissolution is complete. Dilute to the 1-liter mark.

4. Procedure

4.1. *Preparation of calibration curve:* Prepare a series of ten separatory funnels with 0.00, 1.00, 3.00, 5.00, 7.00, 9.00, 11.00, 13.00, 15.00, and 20.00 ml of the standard ABS solution. Add sufficient water to make the total volume 100 ml in each separatory funnel. Treat each standard as described in Sec. 4.3 and plot a calibration curve of mg ABS versus absorbance.

4.2. *Volume of sample:* The volume of the water sample to be tested is based on the expected ABS concentration:

Expected ABS Concentration—mg/l	Sample Taken ml
0.025– 0.080	400
0.08 – 0.40	250
0.4 – 2.0	100
2 – 10	20.0
10 –100	2.00

If a sample of less than 100 ml is indicated, dilute to 100 ml with distilled water: if 100 ml or more is used, extract the entire sample.

---

* Eastman No. P573 or equivalent.

4.3. *Extraction and color development:*

a. Make the solution alkaline by adding NaOH, using phenolphthalein as the indicator. Then acidify with H_2SO_4 and transfer to a separatory funnel.

b. Add 10 ml chloroform and 25 ml methylene blue reagent. Rock vigorously for 30 sec and allow the phases to separate. Excessive agitation may cause emulsion trouble. Some samples require a longer period of phase separation than others.

c. Draw off the chloroform layer into a second separatory funnel. Rinse the delivery tube of the first separatory funnel with a small amount of chloroform. Repeat the extraction three times, using 10 ml chloroform each time. If the blue color in the water phase becomes faint and disappears, add 25 ml more methylene blue reagent.

d. Combine all extracts in the second separatory funnel. Add 50 ml wash solution and shake vigorously for 30 sec. Emulsions do not form at this stage. Allow to settle and draw off the chloroform layer through glass wool into a 100-ml volumetric flask. Repeat the washing twice more with 10 ml chloroform each time. Rinse the glass wool and the funnel with chloroform. Collect the washing in the volumetric flask, dilute to the mark with chloroform and mix well.

4.4. *Measurement:* Determine the absorbance of the solution at 652 mμ, against a blank of chloroform.

5. Calculation

$$\text{mg/l total apparent ABS} = \frac{\text{mg ABS} \times 1{,}000}{\text{ml sample}}$$

6. Precision and Accuracy

A synthetic unknown sample containing 0.40 mg/l ABS in distilled water was determined with a standard deviation of ± 0.06 mg/l in 57 laboratories using the methylene blue method. Half of the reported results were within ± 0.03 mg/l of the established ABS value. Fifty-seven analysts reproduced their own results within ± 0.03 mg/l.

A surface water unknown sample to which was added 2.60 mg/l ABS was determined with a standard deviation of ± 0.23 mg/l in 53 laboratories using the methylene blue method. Half of the reported results were within ± 0.15 mg/l of the added ABS value. Fifty-three analysts reproduced their own results within ± 0.10 mg/l.

A filtered domestic sewage sample containing 8.18 mg/l ABS was determined with a standard deviation of ± 1.04 mg/l in 57 laboratories using the methylene blue method. Half of the reported results were within ± 0.89 mg/l of the established ABS value. Fifty-seven analysts reproduced their own results within ± 0.25 mg/l.

B. Carbon Adsorption Method* (Tentative)

1. General Discussion

1.1. *Principle:* This method involves the collection and isolation of a few milligrams of ABS and its quantitative determination based on infrared absorption of an amine complex of ABS. Though lengthy, this method is specific and accurate for low ABS concentrations in water and it eliminates alkyl sulfates. When an infrared spectrophotometer is not available, a colorimetric determination can be substituted by recovering the purified ABS and applying the methylene blue method (*A*).

1.2. *Application:* This method is applicable to raw-water samples only, not to sewage or industrial wastes.

1.3. *Precaution:* Most samples contain both solid and liquid phases, and ABS is highly concentrated in the solid phase. For accurate analyses, it is

essential that the solids be either representatively sampled or excluded.

2. Apparatus

2.1. *Carbon adsorption tube:* The glass column, about 2×24 in., is charged with 100 g carbon. Screens of stainless steel or brass, about 30 mesh, divide the carbon into sections of 20, 30, 40, and 10 g (see Fig. 23).

2.2. *Buchner funnel,* 500 ml, medium porosity, sintered glass.

2.3. *pH meter.*

2.4. *Volumetric flasks,* either 2 or 5 ml.

2.5. *Separatory funnels,* 250 ml.

2.6. *Infrared spectrophotometer,* for use at 2–15 microns.

2.7. *Acid-washed glassware:* All glassware used in the infrared method must be free of contamination. A thorough rinse with $1 + 1$ HCl must be used to remove adsorbed ABS.

3. Reagents

3.1. *Standard alkyl benzene sulfonate*

---

* This method is identical in source and substance to that developed by the Subcommittee on Analytical Methods, Technical Advisory Committee, The Soap and Detergent Association.

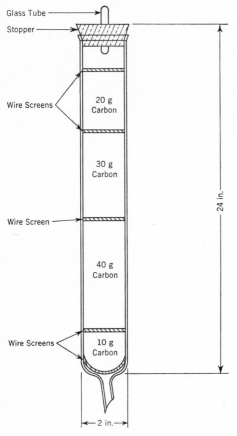

Glass Tube
Stopper
Wire Screens
20 g Carbon
30 g Carbon
Wire Screen
40 g Carbon
Wire Screens
10 g Carbon
24 in.
2 in.

Fig. 23. Carbon adsorption tube

(ABS), for calibration (obtain from The Soap and Detergent Assn.).

3.2. *Activated carbon,* unground, 30 mesh, for the carbon adsorption tube.†

Test for impurities in carbon: Extract 100 g carbon by boiling 1 hr with 1 liter of benzene-alcohol solution (Sec. 3.3). Filter the carbon, wash with 100 ml methyl alcohol, add the washings to the remainder of the solvent mixture, evaporate to dryness on a steam bath, and weigh. The residue consists of soluble organic impurities and should

be less than 10 mg, not including any residue from the solvent.

3.3. *Benzene-alcohol solution:* Mix 500 ml thiophene-free benzene, 420 ml methyl alcohol, and 80 ml 0.5N KOH.

3.4. *Methyl alcohol,* absolute.

3.5. *Hydrochloric acid,* conc.

3.6. *Sodium hydroxide,* 1N. Prepare as directed in Method A, Sec. 3.3.

3.7. *Petroleum ether,* boiling range 35°–60°C.

3.8. *Ethyl alcohol,* 95 per cent.

3.9. *Sulfuric acid,* 1N. Prepare as directed in Method A, Sec. 3.4.

3.10. *Buffer solution:* Dissolve 6.8 g monopotassium dihydrogen phosphate, KH_2PO_4, in 1 liter of distilled water. Adjust to pH 6.8–6.9 with 6N NaOH.

3.11. *1-methylheptylamine.**

3.12. *Solution for extracting ABS:* Dissolve 400 mg (20 drops) 1-methylheptylamine* in 400 ml chloroform. Prepare this solution daily.

3.13. *Chloroform.*

3.14. *Carbon disulfide or carbon tetrachloride.*

4. Procedure

4.1. *Preparation of calibration curve:* Place 25 mg standard ABS in a 5-gal glass vessel and dilute with about 4 gal distilled water. Mix thoroughly and, using synthetic rubberlike tubing, siphon the entire solution through the carbon column. Treat as described in Sec. 4.3. Repeat with 20, 15, 10, 5, and 0 mg ABS. Make two calibration curves by plotting the ABS added as the abscissa and the absorbances of the maxima at 9.6 and 9.9 microns as the ordinate. The baseline technique is best used in determining the absorbance of the maxima.

---

† Nuchar C190 (West Virginia Pulp and Paper Company) or equivalent.

* Eastman No. 2439 or equivalent.

4.2. *Volume of sample:* Estimate the concentration of ABS present in the sample. Calculate the volume of sample required to supply 10–25 mg ABS. If 2 liters or less, measure about 10 g granular activated carbon into a 2-liter glass-stoppered graduated cylinder, add the sample, and shake well for 2 min. Filter on a medium-porosity, sintered-glass Buchner funnel. If more than 2 liters of sample is required, pass through the carbon column at the rate of 10 gph or less.

4.3. *Extraction and measurement of ABS:*

a. Transfer the carbon from the Buchner funnel or column, treating the sections separately, to porcelain evaporating dishes and dry at 105°–110°C. Brush the dried carbon from each dish into separate 2-liter bottles or flasks with standard-taper necks and add 1 liter of benzene-alcohol solution. Add boiling chips and reflux under an air condenser for 1 hr. Filter with a vacuum through a Buchner funnel, draw off all liquid, release the vacuum, and add 100 ml methyl alcohol. Stir with a glass rod and draw off the wash with a vacuum. Wash a second time with another 100-ml portion of methyl alcohol. Return the carbon to the flask, add solvent as before, and reflux for 1 hr. While making this second extraction, evaporate the solvent from the first extract and washes. Carry out this evaporation in a 2-liter beaker on a steam bath. A gentle stream of nitrogen or air on the surface will hasten the evaporation.

b. Filter off the second extract and wash the carbon as before. Add the extract and washes to the beaker containing the first extract. Discard the carbon. Evaporate sufficiently to combine in one beaker the extracts from the 20-, 30-, and 40-g sections of the column. Treat the extracts of the 10-g section separately throughout the entire procedure. After the solvent has been removed, take up the residue in 50 ml warm distilled water. Transfer to a 250-ml standard-taper erlenmeyer flask. Rinse the beaker with 30 ml conc HCl and add slowly to the flask. Carbon dioxide is evolved. Rinse the beaker with 50 ml distilled water and combine with the other washings in the flask. Reflux under an air condenser for 1 hr.

c. Remove the condenser and continue boiling until the volume is reduced to 20–30 ml; transfer to a steam bath; and evaporate to near dryness. (A jet of air directed on the surface of the liquid will greatly aid evaporation.) Take the solids up in 100 ml distilled water and neutralize with NaOH solution to a pH of 8–9. Extract once with 50 ml petroleum ether. Up to 70 per cent ethyl alcohol may be added, if necessary, to break emulsions. Wash the petroleum ether twice with 25-ml portions of distilled water, discard the petroleum ether layer, and add the washes to the aqueous solution. Boil off any alcohol that was added.

d. Cool and transfer quantitatively to a 250-ml separatory funnel. Neutralize by adding H_2SO_4 until just acidic to litmus. Add 50 ml buffer solution (3.10) and 2 drops methylheptylamine (3.11) and shake vigorously. Add 50 ml ABS extracting solution and 25 ml chloroform. Shake for 3 min and allow the phases to separate. If an emulsion forms, draw off the lower (chloroform) phase, including any emulsion, and filter through a plug of glass wool wet with chloroform, using suction if necessary, into a 250-ml separatory funnel. Draw off the chloroform phase into a 400-ml beaker and return any aqueous solution to the first separatory funnel. Wash the glass wool plug with 10 ml chloroform and add to the chloroform extract.

e. Make an additional extraction with 50 ml ABS extracting solution and 25 ml chloroform. Shake 2 min and separate the phases (see 4.3d), if necessary. Extract a third time with 5 ml amine solution and 45 ml chloroform. Evaporate the combined chloroform extracts on a steam bath. With 10 ml chloroform, quantitatively transfer the residue to a 50-ml beaker, using three 5-ml portions of chloroform as rinses. Evaporate to dryness and continue heating on the steam bath for 30 min to remove excess amine. Take up the residue in about 1 ml carbon disulfide or carbon tetrachloride and filter through a plug of glass wool in a funnel stem (2-mm bore) into a 2- or 5-ml volumetric flask. Dilute to volume through the filter with several rinsings from the beaker.

f. Transfer a portion of the sample to an infrared cell without further dilution. Run the infrared absorption curve from 9.0 to 10.5 microns against a solvent blank. Measure the absorbance of the 9.6- and 9.9-micron peaks, using base lines from 9.5 to 9.8 and from 9.8 to 10.1 microns. From appropriate calibration curves calculate the ABS in the original sample. Report the values based on each wavelength separately. If infrared equipment is unavailable, a colorimetric finish can be used. The sulfonate-amine complex can easily be broken by boiling with aqueous alkali. After the amine has been boiled off (as indicated by a lack of amine odor) and suitable dilutions are made, colorimetric results should check well with infrared values.

g. Evaporate a 0.5–1.0-ml portion of the ABS solution on a sodium chloride flat. Record the absorption spectrum from 2 to 15 microns for positive qualitative identification of ABS.

Precaution: The carbon adsorption should be used on all samples. It separates the ABS from many of the other substances present and reduces emulsion difficulties.

NOTE: From 10 to 50 ml of water may be lost through a 60×1-cm air condenser during acid hydrolysis. This loss, while not affecting the hydrolysis, reduces the amount of water that needs to be boiled off after removal of the condenser.

Bibliography

General and Colorimetric Methods
1. BARR, T.; OLIVER, J.; & STUBBINGS, W. V. The Determination of Surface-Active Agents in Solution. *J. Soc. Chem. Ind. (London)* 67:45 (1948).
2. EPTON, S. R. New Method for the Rapid Titrimetric Analysis of Sodium Alkyl Sulfates and Related Compounds. *Trans. Faraday Soc.* 44:226 (1948).
3. EVANS, H. C. Determination of Anionic Synthetic Detergents in Sewage. *J. Soc. Chem. Ind. (London)* 69: Supplement 2:576 (1950).
4. DEGENS, P. N., JR., ET AL. Determination of Sulfate and Sulfonate Anion-Active Detergents in Sewage. *J. Appl. Chem. (London)* 3:54 (1953).
5. TASK GROUP REPORT. Characteristics and Effects of Synthetic Detergents. *J. AWWA* 46:751 (1954).
6. EDWARDS, G. P. & GINN, M. E. Determination of Synthetic Detergents in Sewage. *Sew. Ind. Wastes* 26:945 (1954).
7. LONGWELL, J. & MANIECE, W. D. Determination of Anionic Detergents in Sewage, Sewage Effluents, and River Water. *Analyst* 80:167 (1955).
8. MOORE, W. A. & KOLBESON, R. A. Determination of Anionic Detergents in Surface Waters and Sewage with Methyl Green. *Anal. Chem.* 28:161 (1956).
9. TASK GROUP REPORT. Determination of Synthetic Detergent Content of Raw

Water Supplies. *J. AWWA* 50:1343 (1958).

10. MAGUIRE, O. E., ET AL. Field Test for Analysis of Anionic Detergents in Well Waters. *J. AWWA* 54:665 (1962).

11. ABBOTT, D. C. The Determination of Traces of Anionic Surface-Active Materials in Water. *Analyst* 87:286 (1962).

12. ABBOTT, D. C. A Rapid Test for Anionic Detergents in Drinking Water. *Analyst* 88:240 (1963).

Carbon Adsorption Method

13. SALLEE, E. M., ET AL. Determination of Trace Amounts of Alkyl Benzenesulfonates in Water. *Anal. Chem.* 28:1822 (1956).

14. Ref. 9.

Synthetic Detergents

See Surfactants.

Tannin and Lignin

Lignin is a plant constituent which is often discharged as a waste during the manufacture of paper pulp. Another plant constituent, tannin, may enter the water supply through the process of vegetative degradation or the wastes of the tanning industry. Tannin is also applied in the so-called internal treatment of boiler waters, where it is said to reduce scale formation by causing the production of a more easily handled sludge.

Both lignin and tannin contain aromatic hydroxyl groups which react with tungstophosphoric and molybdophosphoric acids to form a blue color. However, the reaction is not specific for lignin or tannin, inasmuch as other reducing materials respond similarly.

The nature of the substance suspected in the water sample will dictate the choice of tannic acid or lignin for use in the preparation of the standard solution. This course is necessary because it is impossible to distinguish between hydroxylated aromatic compounds. Unless tannin or lignin is definitely known to be present in the water under examination, the results of this determination may logically be reported in the more general terms of "tannin-like," "lignin-like," or simply "hydroxylated aromatic" compounds.

1. General Discussion

1.1. *Principle:* Tannins and lignins reduce tungstophosphoric and molybdophosphoric acids to produce a blue color suitable for the estimation of concentrations up to at least 9 mg/l for tannic acid as well as lignin.

1.2. *Minimum detectable concentration:* Approximately 0.1 mg/l for tannic acid and 0.3 mg/l for lignin.

2. Apparatus

Colorimetric equipment: One of the following is required:

2.1. *Spectrophotometer,* for use at 700 mμ. A light path of 1 cm or longer yields satisfactory results.

2.2. *Filter photometer,* provided with a red filter exhibiting maximum transmittance in the wavelength range of 600–700 mμ. Sensitivity improves with increasing wavelength. A light path of 1 cm or longer yields satisfactory results.

2.3. *Nessler tubes,* matched, 100 ml, tall form, marked at 50-ml volume.

3. Reagents

3.1. *Tannin-lignin reagent:* Dissolve 100 g sodium tungstate dihydrate, 20 g molybdophosphoric acid (also called phosphomolybdic acid), and 50 ml 85 per cent phosphoric acid in 750 ml distilled water. Boil the liquid under reflux for 2 hr; cool and make up to 1 liter with distilled water.

3.2. *Sodium carbonate solution:* Dissolve 200 g Na_2CO_3 in 500 ml warm distilled water and dilute to 1 liter to form a saturated solution. Keep in a rubber-stoppered bottle.

3.3. *Stock solution:* Weigh 1.000 g of the tannic acid, tannin, or lignin compound which is being used for boiler water treatment or is known to be a contaminant of the water sample. Dissolve in distilled water and dilute to 1,000 ml.

3.4. *Standard solution:* Dilute 10.00 ml or 50.00 ml stock solution to 1,000 ml with distilled water to form a solution containing 0.010 mg or 0.050 mg active ingredient per 1.00 ml.

4. Procedure

Add 2 ml tannin-lignin reagent to 50.0 ml of clear sample and mix well. After 5 min add 10 ml sodium carbonate solution and mix thoroughly. Wait 10 min for color development. Compare visually against simultaneously prepared standards, or make photometric readings against a reagent blank prepared at the same time. The following guide can be used for the instrumental measurements in the wavelength region of 600–700 mμ:

Tannic Acid in 62-ml Final Volume *mg*	Lignin in 62-ml Final Volume *mg*	Light Path *cm*
0.05–0.60	0.10–1.5	1
0.01–0.15	0.03–0.40	5

Bibliography

1. BERK, A. A. & SCHROEDER, W. C. Determination of Tannin Substances in Boiler Water. *Ind. Eng. Chem., Anal. Ed.* 14: 456 (1942).

Taste and Odor

According to psychologists, there are only four true taste sensations: sour, sweet, salty, and bitter. All other sensations commonly ascribed to the sense of taste are actually odors, even though the sensation is not noticed until the material is taken into the mouth. Dissolved inorganic salts of iron, zinc, manganese, copper, sodium, and potassium can be detected by taste. Concentrations producing taste range from a few tenths to several hundred milligrams per liter. As these tastes are not accompanied by odor, the *taste* test must be used where they are involved. *(CAUTION: Be sure the sample being tested is safe to take into the mouth.)*

Odors occur in water because of the presence of foreign substances, usually organic. Some inorganic compounds, such as hydrogen sulfide, also cause odor. The contaminating materials may be of natural origin, may come from domestic and industrial waste discharges, or may be due to a combination of these. Because odorous materials are detectable when present in only a few micrograms per liter and are often complex, it is usually impractical and often impossible to isolate and identify the odor-producing chemical. Evaluation of odors is thus dependent on the sense of smell.

Odor tests are less fatiguing than taste tests; hence, an operator can conduct odor tests for a longer period. Higher temperatures can be used for odor evaluations than for the taste test, with a resultant increase in sensitivity on some samples. This section deals principally with odor, but the techniques can be applied to taste testing.

Taste and odor tests are useful as a check on the quality of raw and finished water; for control of odor through the plant and determination of treatment dosages; as a test of the effectiveness of different kinds of treatment; and as a means of tracing the source of contamination.

1. General Discussion

1.1. *Principle:* The organs of taste and smell are remarkably sensitive detectors, but they are not precise. People vary widely as to sensitivity, and even the same person will not be consistent in the concentrations he can detect from day to day. Panels of not less than five persons, and preferably ten or more, are recommended to overcome the deficiencies of using one observer, although useful data can be developed by one observer.

A calibrating standard is required

when it is necessary to depend on a single observer or to compare the sensitivity of different individuals. A chemical that can be used for odor calibration is n-butyl alcohol, but not at temperatures over 40°C.

To use the odor standard, make up various concentrations of the alcohol— a range of $\frac{1}{16}$ mg/l to 4 mg/l will include the threshold for most people. A large series of tests will establish the threshold detected most often. Suppose the concentration most frequently detected is $\frac{1}{8}$ mg/l. Each time samples are tested the observer also runs a threshold on the standard, and if the latter differs from $\frac{1}{8}$ mg/l, a proportionate correction is then applied to the threshold found on the sample. Table 17 illustrates the calculation. When large numbers of observers are testing the same sample at one location, panel procedures eliminate the necessity for a calibrating standard.

1.2. *Qualitative descriptions:* Suitable qualitative descriptions can be helpful in ascribing tastes and odors to the correct cause, and in dealing with consumer complaints. Taste and odor descriptions vary with the experience and background of the individual making the test. Table 18 is included here

TABLE 17—EXAMPLE OF ODOR CALIBRATION WITH ALCOHOL *

Day	Threshold on n-Butyl Alcohol mg/l	Threshold of Sample	Correction Factor	Corrected Threshold of Sample
1	$\frac{1}{8}$	16	1	16
2	$\frac{1}{4}$	8	2	16
3	$\frac{1}{2}$	16	4	64
4	$\frac{1}{16}$	32	$\frac{1}{2}$	16
5	$\frac{3}{4}$	8	6	48

* For this example, it is assumed that that observer's usual threshold on the alcohol is $\frac{1}{8}$ mg./l. Therefore, a threshold of $\frac{1}{4}$ mg/l on Day 2 indicates only 50 per cent sensitivity on that day, requiring a correction factor of 2.

TABLE 18—QUALITATIVE DESCRIPTIONS OF ODORS

Code	Nature of Odor	Description (Such as Odors of:)
A	Aromatic (spicy)	camphor, cloves, lavender, lemon
Ac	cucumber	*Synura*
B	Balsamic (flowery)	geranium, violet, vanilla
Bg	geranium	*Asterionella*
Bn	nasturtium	*Aphanizomenon*
Bs	sweetish	*Coelosphaerium*
Bv	violet	*Mallomonas*
C	Chemical	industrial wastes or treatment chemicals
Cc	chlorinous	free chlorine
Ch	hydrocarbon	oil refinery wastes
Cm	medicinal	phenol and iodoform
Cs	sulfuretted	hydrogen sulfide
D	Disagreeable	(pronounced, unpleasant)
Df	fishy	*Uroglenopsis, Dinobryon*
Dp	pigpen	*Anabaena*
Ds	septic	stale sewage
E	Earthy	damp earth
Ep	peaty	peat
G	Grassy	crushed grass
M	Musty	decomposing straw
Mm	moldy	damp cellar
V	Vegetable	root vegetables

to serve as a guide. Its usefulness is limited, but no suitable substitute is available. Consistency in naming odors is, of course, important if any interpretation is to be made.

1.3. *Sampling and storage:* Odor tests should be completed as soon as possible after collection of the sample. Glass bottles with glass stoppers should be used. If storage is necessary, collect 500 ml of sample in a glass container filled to the top; refrigerate, making sure no extraneous odors can be drawn into the sample when the water cools. Plastic containers should not be used for odor samples.

1.4. *Dechlorination:* Most tap waters are chlorinated. It is of value to run taste and odor tests on the water as delivered to the consumer. It is also useful to determine whether the chlorine in the water is producing an effect. The residual chlorine can be removed by using an equivalent amount of the sulfite or thiosulfate dechlorinating agents listed under Nitrogen (Ammonia), Method A, Sec. 3.7. *(CAUTION: Arsenic compounds should not be used as dechlorinating agents on samples to be tasted.)*

1.5. *Raw water:* The odor of raw water should be determined before any treatment has been applied. It is also of value in assessing raw-water quality to judge the influence of chlorination on the sample, because it is well known that taste and odor intensities of materials such as phenolic compounds are greatly increased by chlorination. By the same token, chlorination may mask the offensive odor of some natural materials. For this reason, chlorine dosages should be applied in stepwise fashion to cover a range from no residual to 1.0 mg/l. Observation of odors after 1 hr and after 24 hr will indicate chlorination effects. Dechlorination is necessary to ascertain the effect of the chlorine itself on the observation.

1.6. *Temperature:* Threshold values will vary with temperature. Taste tests should be made at 40°C, as this is near body temperature and no sensation of hot or cold will be encountered. On most tap waters and raw-water sources, a sample temperature of 60°C will permit the detection of odors that might otherwise be missed; 60°C should be considered the standard temperature for *hot threshold* tests. For some purposes, the hot odor may not be applicable; certain industrial materials may give lower thresholds at the higher temperature because of the volatilization of some components. A standard *cold threshold* test temperature of 40°C should be used on such samples. Always report the temperature at which observations are made.

2. Apparatus

All glassware, including pipets, cylinders, flasks, and sample bottles, must be freshly cleaned shortly before use. Thorough scrubbing with nonodorous cleansers or acid cleaning solution, followed by several rinses with odor-free water, is generally best. Rubber stoppers and corks should not be used. Narrow-mouth vessels are not suitable for running tests. If odor-free glassware is to be stored before use, it is helpful to keep it immersed in odor-free water.

2.1. *Odor flask:* The 500-ml glass-stoppered (¶ 32) erlenmeyer type is convenient.

2.2. *Thermometer,* 0°–110°C, chemical or metal-stem dial type.

2.3. *Pipets:* (a) transfer, volumetric —200, 100, 50, 25 ml; (b) measuring, 10 ml graduated in tenths.

2.4. *Glass-stoppered bottles,* 500 ml, to hold samples for testing.

2.5. *Erlenmeyer flasks,* 2 liter, to hold odor-free water.

2.6. *Odor-free water generator:* See Fig. 24.

2.7. *Large electrical hot plate or water bath.*

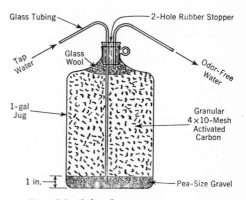

Fig. 24. Odor-free water generator

3. Reagents

Odor-free water: Odor-free water should be prepared as needed because it will absorb any odors that may be in the room. Most tap waters are suitable as sources for the preparation of the odor-free water. Highly mineralized waters or waters of unusually high or low pH may affect some odorous samples. The suitability of the water for odor tests should be determined. To prepare the odor-free water pass tap water through the odor-free generator (Fig. 24) at a rate of 0.1 liter/minute. Test the odor-free water at 40°C and 60°C before use. Collect the quantity needed for a test directly in a glass container. When the generator is first started, pass water through it for a short while to wash out carbon fines before collecting the odor-free water. The life of the carbon will vary with the condition and amount of the water filtered. Detection of odor in the water coming through the carbon indicates a change is needed. If residual chlorine appears in the odor-free water, renew the carbon in the generator.

4. Procedure

4.1. *Precautions:* Selection of persons to make taste or odor tests should be carefully made. Extreme sensitivity is not required, but insensitive persons should not be used. A good observer should have a sincere interest in the test. Smoking and eating should be avoided just prior to making the test. Odors associated with scented soaps, shaving lotions, and perfumes are likewise to be avoided. The flasks should not be touched at the neck. The room in which the tests are to be conducted should be free from distractions, draft, and odor. In certain industrial atmospheres, a special odor-free room may be required. "Odor-free" water and all glassware to be used should be checked for odor before the test. Tests should not be prolonged to the point of fatigue. Usually 15–30 min of rest will permit further examinations. To overcome psychological factors, it is best to have someone other than the observer code and prepare the dilutions. Start with the most dilute sample to avoid tiring the senses with a concentrated sample. The temperature of the samples during testing should be kept within 1° of the desired temperature for the test.

4.2. *Taste and odor quality:* Shake 200 ml of sample in a 500-ml glass-stoppered erlenmeyer flask kept at 40°C or at 60°C. Sniff the odor lightly and record the description in accordance with Table 18, or use some other term that best describes the odor. To

taste a sample, take 10–15 ml at 40°C into the mouth, hold it for several seconds, and discharge. It is not necessary to swallow the sample to taste it. Note the aftertaste, as well as the taste while the sample is in the mouth. *Do not taste samples if there is any doubt that they are safe to ingest.*

4.3. *Threshold measurement* *: The ratio by which the odor-bearing sample has to be diluted with odor-free water for the odor to be just detectable by the odor test is the "threshold odor number," designated by the abbrevia-

TABLE 19—THRESHOLD ODOR NUMBERS CORRESPONDING TO VARIOUS DILUTIONS

Sample Volume Diluted to 200 ml ml	Threshold Odor Number	Sample Volume Diluted to 200 ml ml	Threshold Odor Number
200	1	12	17
140	1.4	8.3	24
100	2	5.7	35
70	3	4	50
50	4	2.8	70
35	6	2	100
25	8	1.4	140
17	12	1.0	200

tion T. O. The total volume of sample and odor-free water used in each test is 200 ml. Table 19 gives the dilutions and the corresponding threshold numbers. If a total volume other than the 200 ml specified is used, the threshold number can be computed thus:

$$T. O. = \frac{A + B}{A}$$

---

* There are numerous methods for arranging and presenting samples for odor determinations. The methods offered here are believed to be practical and economical of time and personnel, and are adequate for the problems encountered at most water plants. If extensive tests are planned and statistical analysis of data is required, the experimenter should become familiar with the triangle test and the methods that have been used extensively by flavor and allied industries.[30]

where $A = $ ml of sample and $B = $ ml of odor-free water. The proper volume of odor-free water should be put into the flask first; the sample is then pipetted into the water. Then proceed as follows:

a. Determine the approximate range of the threshold number by adding 200 ml, 50 ml, 12 ml, 2.8 ml of the sample to separate 500-ml glass-stoppered erlenmeyer flasks containing odor-free water to make a total volume of 200 ml. A separate flask containing only odor-free water will serve as the reference for comparison. Heat the dilutions and the reference to the temperature desired for running the test.

b. Shake the flask containing the odor-free water, remove the stopper, and sniff the vapors. Test the sample containing the least amount of odor-bearing water in the same way. If odor can be detected in this dilution, more dilute samples must be prepared as described in Sec. 4.3e. If odor cannot be detected in the first dilution, repeat the above procedure using the sample containing the next higher concentration of the odor-bearing water, and continue this process until odor is clearly detected.

c. Based on the results obtained in the preliminary test, prepare a set of dilutions using Table 20 as a guide.

TABLE 20—DILUTIONS FOR VARIOUS ODOR INTENSITIES

Sample Volume in Which Odor First Noted			
200 ml	50 ml	12 ml	2.8 ml
Volume (*ml*) of Sample to Be Diluted to 200 ml			
200	50	12	
140	35	8.3	2.8
100	25	5.7	2.0
70	17	4.0	1.4
50	12	2.8	1.0

Two or more blanks may be inserted in the series, frequently in the vicinity of the expected threshold. The observer does not know which dilutions are odorous and which are blanks. He smells each flask in sequence, beginning with the least concentrated sample, until odor is detected with certainty.

d. Record the observations by indicating whether odor is noted in each test flask. For example:

ml sample diluted to 200 ml	12	0	17	25	0	35	50
Response	−	−	−	+	−	+	+

e. If the sample being tested requires more extensive dilution than is provided by Table 20, an intermediate dilution is prepared from 20 ml of sample diluted to 200 ml with odor-free water. Use this dilution for the threshold determination. Multiply the "T. O." obtained by ten to correct for the intermediate dilution. In rare cases more than one tenfold intermediate dilution step may be required.

5. Calculation

5.1. The threshold number is the dilution ratio at which taste or odor is just detectable. In the example above (Sec. 4.3d), the first detectable odor occurred when 25 ml of sample was diluted to 200 ml. Thus, the threshold is $200 \div 25 = 8$. Table 19 lists the threshold numbers that correspond to common dilutions.

5.2. Anomalous responses sometimes occur; a low concentration may be called positive and a higher concentration in the series may be called negative. In such a case, the threshold may properly be designated as that point of detection after which no further anomalies occur. For instance:

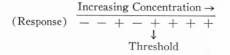

Increasing Concentration →

(Response) − − + − + + + +

↓

Threshold

5.3. Calculations from large numbers of panel results to find the most probable average threshold are best accomplished by appropriate statistical methods. For most purposes, the threshold of a group can be expressed as the geometric mean or the median of the individual thresholds.

6. Interpretation of Results

A threshold number is not a precise value. In the case of a single observer, it represents a judgment at the time of testing. Panel results are more meaningful because individual differences have less influence on the result. One or two observers can develop satisfactory data if they use calibration techniques or comparison with panels to check their sensitivity. Comparisons of data from time to time or place to place should not be attempted unless all test conditions have been carefully standardized and some basis for comparison of observer sensitivities exists.

Bibliography

1. WHIPPLE, G. C. The Observation of Odor as an Essential Part of Water Analysis. *APHA Public Health Papers & Repts.* 25:587 (1889).
2. ZWAARDEMAKER, H. Odoriferous Materials. In *International Critical Tables.* McGraw-Hill Book Co., New York (1926). Vol. 1, p. 358.
3. SPAULDING, C. H. The Quantitative Determination of Odor in Water. *A.J.P.H.* 21:1038 (1931).
4. BAYLIS, J. R. Procedure for Making Odor and Taste Determinations. *Water Works & Sewerage* 79:425 (1932).
5. FAIR, G. M. On the Determination of Odors and Tastes in Water. *J. New Engl. Water Works Assoc.* 47:248 (1933).

6. FAIR, G. M. & WELLS, W. F. The Air Dilution Method of Odor Determination in Water Analysis. *J. AWWA* 26:1670 (1934).
7. FAIR, G. M. & MOORE, E. W. Measurement of Intensity and Concentration of Odors Associated with Sewage Treatment Processes. *Sew. Works J.* 7:182 (1935).
8. CROCKER, E. C. Seeking a Working Language for Odors and Flavors. *Ind. Eng. Chem.* 27:1225 (1935).
9. BAYLIS, J. R. *Elimination of Taste and Odor.* McGraw-Hill Book Co., New York (1935).
10. GUILFORD, J. P. *Psychometric Methods.* McGraw-Hill Book Co., New York (1936).
11. HULBERT, R. & FEBEN, D. Studies on Accuracy of Threshold Odor Value. *J. AWWA* 33:1945 (1941).
12. SPAULDING, C. H. Accuracy and Application of Threshold Odor Test. *J. AWWA* 34:877 (1942).
13. THOMAS, H. A., JR. Calculation of Threshold Odor. *J. AWWA* 35:751 (1943).
14. CROCKER, E. C. *Flavor.* McGraw-Hill Book Co., New York (1945).
15. MONCRIEFF, R. W. *The Chemical Senses.* John Wiley & Sons, New York (1946).
16. CROCKER, E. C. & SJOSTROM, L. B. Odor Detection and Thresholds. *Chem. Eng. News* 27:1922 (1949).
17. McCORD, C. P. & WITHERIDGE, W. N. *Odors—Physiology and Control.* McGraw-Hill Book Co., New York (1949).
18. GERSTEIN, H. H. A Continuous Odor Monitor and Threshold Tester. *J. AWWA* 43:373 (1951).
19. BRAUS, H.; MIDDLETON, F. M.; & WALTON, G. Organic Chemical Compounds in Raw and Filtered Surface Waters. *Anal. Chem.* 23:1160 (1951).
20. CARTWRIGHT, L. C.; SNELL, C. T.; & KELLY, P. H. Organoleptic Panel Testing as a Research Tool. *Anal. Chem.* 24:503 (1952).
21. MIDDLETON, F. M.; BRAUS, H.; & RUCHHOFT, C. C. Fundamental Studies of Taste and Odor in Water Supplies. *J. AWWA* 44:538 (1952).
22. *Odors and the Sense of Smell—A Bibliography, 320 B.C.–1947.* Airkem Inc., New York (1952).

23. GELDARD, F. A. *The Human Senses.* John Wiley & Sons, New York (1953).

24. *Symposium on Odor.* Special Tech. Pub. 164, Am. Soc. Testing Materials, Philadelphia (1954).

25. Basic Odor Research Correlation. *Ann. N.Y. Acad. Sci.* 58: Art. 2:13 (1954).

26. LAUGHLIN, H. F. Palatable Level with the Threshold Odor Test. *Taste and Odor Control J.* 20:No. 8 (Aug. 1954).

27. AMAN, C. W. The Relation of Taste and Odor to Flavor. *Taste and Odor Control J.* 21:No. 10 (Oct. 1955).

28. ETTINGER, M. B. & MIDDLETON, F. M. Plant Facilities and Human Factors in Taste and Odor Contol. *J. AWWA* 48:1265 (1956).

29. BULLOCK, F. C., ET AL. Tastes and Odors in Water. *Proc. Soc. Water Treatment & Examination* 6:Part I:29 (1957).

30. *Flavor Research and Food Acceptance.* Reinhold, New York (1958).

31. MIDDLETON, F. M.; ROSEN, A. A.; & BURTTSCHELL, R. H. Taste and Odor Research Tools for Water Utilities. *J. AWWA* 50:21 (1958).

32. SHELLENBERGER, R. D. Procedures for Determining Threshold Odor Concentrations in Aqueous Solutions. *Taste and Odor Control J.* 24:No. 5 (May 1958).

33. SECHENOV, I. M. Problem of Hygienic Standards for Waters Simultaneously Polluted with Harmful Substances. *Gigiyena i Sanitariya* No. 10 (1956); No. 8 (1958) (Russian).

34. *Taste and Odor Control in Water Purification.* Industrial Chemical Sales Div., West Virginia Pulp & Paper Co., New York (2nd ed., 1959). Contains 1,063 classified references.

35. BAKER, R. A. Problems of Tastes and Odors. *J. WPCF* 33:1099 (1961).

36. ROSEN, A. A.; PETER, J. B.; & MIDDLETON, F. M. Odor Thresholds of Mixed Organic Chemicals. *J. WPCF* 34:7 (1962).

37. BAKER, R. A. Critical Evaluation of Olfactory Measurement. *J. WPCF* 34:582 (1962).

38. LAUGHLIN, H. F. Influence of Temperature in Threshold Odor Evaluation. *Taste and Odor Control J.* 28:No. 10 (Oct. 1962).

39. BAKER, R. A. Odor Effects of Aqueous Mixtures of Organic Chemicals. *J. WPCF* 35:728 (1963).

40. ROSEN, A. A.; SKEEL, R. T.; & ETTINGER, M. B. Relationship of River Water Odor to Specific Organic Contaminant. *J. WPCF* 35:777 (1963).

41. STAFF REPORT. The Threshold Odor Test. *Taste and Odor Control J.* 29:No. 6, 7, 8 (June, July, Aug. 1963).

Temperature

Temperature readings are used in the calculation of the various forms of alkalinity and in the saturation and stability studies with respect to calcium carbonate. In limnologic studies, water temperatures at different depths in reservoirs are required. Identification of the source of supply, such as deep wells, is often possible by temperature measurement alone. Industrial plants often require data on the temperature of water for process use or heat transmission calculations.

Normally, temperature measurements may be made with any good grade of mercury-filled centigrade thermometer, provided it is checked occasionally against a precision thermometer certified by the National Bureau of Standards.* Field instruments should be provided with a metal case to prevent breakage.

Depth temperature required for limnologic studies may be taken with

---

* Some commercial thermometers may be as much as 3° C in error.

a reversing thermometer, a thermophone, or a thermistor. The thermistor is considered to be the most convenient and also to be capable of the greatest accuracy. The reading should be made with the thermometer immersed in water, preferably flowing, after a period of time sufficient to permit a constant reading.

The temperature of the water at the sampling point should be expressed to the nearest degree centigrade, or closer if more precise data are required.

Bibliography

1. WARREN, H. E. & WHIPPLE, G. C. The Thermophone—A New Instrument for Determining Temperatures. *Mass. Inst. Technol. Quart.* 8:125 (1895).
2. *Standard Specifications for ASTM Thermometers—E1–58.* Am. Soc. Testing Materials, Philadelphia (1949).
3. REE, W. R. Thermistors for Depth Thermometry. *J. AWWA* 45:259 (1953).

Turbidity

A clear water is important in those industries where the product is destined for human consumption. Beverage producers, food processors, and treatment plants drawing upon a surface water supply commonly rely on coagulation, settling, and filtration measures to insure an acceptable effluent.

Turbidity in water is caused by the presence of suspended matter, such as clay, silt, finely divided organic matter, plankton, and other microscopic organisms. Turbidity should be clearly understood to be an expression of the optical property of a sample which causes light to be scattered and absorbed rather than transmitted in straight lines through the sample. Attempts to correlate turbidity with the weight concentration of suspended matter are impractical, as the size, shape, and refractive index of the particulate materials are of most importance optically but bear little direct relationship to the concentration and specific gravity of the suspended matter. The standard method for the determination of turbidity is the candle method. However, suspensions standardized by this method may be used, with or without dilution, in other instruments. Unfortunately, the results obtained using other instruments will not always agree closely with those obtained using the candle turbidimeter; and owing to fundamental differences in optical systems, the results obtained with different types of instruments will not always check closely with one another even if the instruments are precalibrated against the candle turbidimeter.

1. General Discussion

1.1. *Principle:* Turbidity measurements are based on the light path through a suspension which just causes the image of the flame of a standard candle to disappear—that is, to become indistinguishable against the general background illumination—when the flame is viewed through the suspension. The longer the light path, the lower the turbidity.

1.2. *Interference:* The determination of turbidity is applicable to any water sample that is free of debris and coarse sediments which settle out rapidly, although dirty glassware, the presence of air bubbles, and the effects of vibrations which disturb the surface visibility of the sample will lead to false results.

1.3. *Storage:* It is preferable to determine turbidity on the same day the sample is taken. If longer storage is unavoidable, however, samples may be stored in the dark up to 24 hr. For even longer storage, treat 1 liter of sample with 1 g mercuric chloride. All samples should be vigorously shaken before examination.

2. Apparatus

2.1. *Candle turbidimeter:* This is the standard instrument for making measurements of turbidity. It consists of a glass tube calibrated according to Table 21, a standard candle, and a support which aligns the candle and the tube. The glass tube and the candle are supported in a vertical position so that the centerline of the tube passes through the centerline of the candle. The candle support consists of a spring-loaded cylinder designed to keep the top of the candle pressed against the top of the support as the candle gradually burns away. The top of the support for the candle must be 7.6 cm (3 in.) below the bottom of the glass tube. The glass tube must have a flat, polished optical-glass bottom, and must conform to the specifications for nessler tubes as described in the General Introduction, A, Sec. 6. It must be kept clean and free from scratches. The glass tube is graduated to read directly in turbidity units. Most of the glass tube should be enclosed in a metal tube when observations are being made, both for the sake of protection against breakage and in order to exclude extraneous light.

2.2. *Candle,* made of beeswax and spermaceti, designed to burn within the limits of 114 to 126 grains per hour. To insure uniform results, the flame must be kept as near constant size and constant distance from the bottom of the glass tube as possible; this will require frequent trimming of the charred portion of the wick and frequent observations to see that the candle is pushed to the top of its sup-

TABLE 21—GRADUATION OF CANDLE TURBIDIMETER

Light Path * cm	Turbidity Units	Light Path * cm	Turbidity Units
2.3	1,000	11.4	190
2.6	900	12.0	180
2.9	800	12.7	170
3.2	700	13.5	160
3.5	650	14.4	150
3.8	600	15.4	140
4.1	550	16.6	130
4.5	500	18.0	120
4.9	450	19.6	110
5.5	400	21.5	100
5.6	390	22.6	95
5.8	380	23.8	90
5.9	370	25.1	85
6.1	360	26.5	80
6.3	350	28.1	75
6.4	340	29.8	70
6.6	330	31.8	65
6.8	320	34.1	60
7.0	310	36.7	55
7.3	300	39.8	50
7.5	290	43.5	45
7.8	280	48.1	40
8.1	270	54.0	35
8.4	260	61.8	30
8.7	250	72.9	25
9.1	240		
9.5	230		
9.9	220		
10.3	210		
10.8	200		

* Measured from inside bottom of glass tube.

port. All drafts must be eliminated during measurements to prevent the flame from flickering. The candle must burn for no more than a few minutes at a time, as the flame has a tendency to increase in size. Each time before the candle is lighted, such portions of the charred wick must be removed as can easily be broken off when manipulated with the fingers.

3. Reagents

3.1. *Turbidity-free water:* Pass distilled water through a membrane filter having a pore size no greater than 100 mμ if such filtered water shows a lower turbidity than the distilled water. Discard the first 200 ml collected. Otherwise, use the distilled water.

3.2. *Standard suspensions:* Use the instrumental standard with photoelectric turbidimeters as a common reference standard for comparison of turbidities of different treated waters. The visual standards are useful for checking a given water at various stages of the treatment process.

a. Instrumental standard: Add approximately 5 g kaolin to 1 liter distilled water, thoroughly agitate, and allow to stand for 24 hr. Withdraw the supernate without disturbing the sediment at the bottom. Determine the turbidity with the candle turbidimeter. Dilute portions of the suspension to the turbidity values desired, checking all above 25 units with the candle turbidimeter. Standard suspensions may be preserved by the addition of 1 g mercuric chloride to 1 liter of suspension. Suspensions must be well shaken before each reading, and must be checked at least once a month with the candle turbidimeter.

b. Visual comparison standards are best prepared using natural turbid water from the same source as that to be tested. Determine the turbidity with the candle turbidimeter, then dilute portions of the suspension to the turbidity values desired.

Suspensions of turbidities below 25 units cannot be checked directly; these must be made up at least once each month by dilution of a more concentrated suspension which has been freshly checked. Dilute suspensions calculated to contain 0.0, 0.2, 0.4, 0.6, 0.8, 1.0, etc., turbidity units should be made weekly by dilution of a 10-unit suspension. Store the suspensions in pyrex or other resistant-glass bottles.

4. Procedure

4.1. *Turbidities between 25 and 1,000 units:* Pour the sample into the glass tube until the image of the candle flame just disappears from view. At this stage the analyst should see a uniformly illuminated field with no bright spots. Addition of the sample should be carried out slowly toward the end. After the image has been made to disappear, the removal of 1 per cent of the sample should again make the flame image visible. It is convenient to employ a pipet to add or remove small amounts of the sample at the end. Care should be taken to keep the glass tube clean both inside and outside and to avoid scratching the glass. The accumulation of soot or moisture on the bottom of the tube may interfere with the accuracy of the results.

4.2. *Turbidities exceeding 1,000 units:* Dilute the sample with one or more volumes of turbidity-free water until the turbidity falls below 1,000 units. The turbidity of the original sample is then computed from the turbidity of the diluted sample and the dilution factor. For example, if 5 volumes of turbidity-free water were added to 1 volume of sample, and the diluted sample showed a turbidity of 500 units, then the turbidity of the original sample was 3,000 units.

4.3. *Turbidities between 5 and 100 units:* The candle turbidimeter has a lower limit of 25 units. In the range from 5 to 100 units, samples may be compared in sets of similar bottles with standard suspensions made by diluting more concentrated standard suspensions with turbidity-free water in known ratios. The sample and the standards are placed in bottles of the same size, shape, and type, enough empty space being left at the top of each bottle to allow adequate shaking before each reading. The comparison is made by viewing the sample and the standards through the sides of the bottles, looking through them at the same object, and noting the distinctness with which the object can be seen. Record the turbidity of the sample as that of the standard which produces the visual effect most closely approximating that of the sample. Readings may be made conveniently by viewing newsprint or a series of ruled black lines on white paper. It is preferable that artificial light be used, shining downward from above, so that no direct light reaches the eye. If a commercial turbidimeter is used, the manufacturer's instructions should be followed; calibration against the candle turbidimeter is necessary.

4.4. *Turbidities less than 5 units:* When the turbidity of a sample is less than 5 units, measurement of scattered light rather than transmitted light is employed. Visual instruments which operate on the scattering principle include the Baylis and the St. Louis tur-

bidimeters. Several photoelectric instruments, including nephelometers, are on the market. Detectors which receive forward-scattered light at a low angle from the transmitted beam measure a greater proportion of the total scattered light than do detectors mounted at 90 degrees from the transmitted beam. This results in higher sensitivity and better correlation between different suspensions standardized on the candle turbidimeter. The tubes to be used with the available instrument must be of clear, colorless glass. They should be kept scrupulously clean, both inside and out, and discarded when they become scratched or etched. They must not be handled at all where the light strikes them, but should be provided with sufficient extra length, or with a protective case, so that they may be handled. The tubes should be filled with samples and standards which have been thoroughly agitated, and sufficient time should be allowed for bubbles to escape. In visual instruments, record the turbidity as that of the most closely matching standard. In using commercial instruments, the manufacturer's instructions should be followed; calibration against the candle turbidimeter is necessary.

5. Interpretation of Results

5.1. Turbidity readings are recorded in accordance with the following:

Turbidity Range units	Record to Nearest:
0.0– 1.0	0.1
1 – 10	1
10 –100	5
100 –400	10
400 –700	50
700 or more	100

5.2. For comparison of water treatment efficiencies, it may be desirable to estimate more closely than is specified in the table; but, because of the uncertainties and discrepancies in turbidity measurements, it cannot be expected that two or more laboratories will duplicate results on the same sample more closely than specified.

Bibliography

1. WHIPPLE, G. C. & JACKSON, D. D. A Comparative Study of the Methods Used for the Measurement of Turbidity of Water. *Mass. Inst. Technol. Quart.* 13:274 (1900).
2. Report of Committee on Standard Methods of Water Analysis. *APHA Public Health Papers & Repts.* 27:377 (1901).
3. WELLS, P. V. Turbidimetry of Water. *J. AWWA* 9:488 (1922).
4. BAYLIS, J. R. Turbidimeter for Accurate Measurement of Low Turbidities. *Ind. Eng. Chem.* 18:311 (1926).
5. WELLS, P. V. The Present Status of Turbidity Measurements. *Chem. Revs.* 3:331 (1927).
6. BAYLIS, J. R. Turbidity Determinations. *Water Works & Sewerage* 80:125 (1933).
7. ROSE, H. E. & LLOYD, H. B. On the Measurement of the Size Characteristics of Powders by Photo-Extinction Methods. *J. Soc. Chem. Ind. (London)* 65:52 (Feb. 1946); 65:55 (Mar. 1946).
8. ROSE, H. E. & FRENCH, C. C. J. On the Extinction Coefficient: Particle Size Relationship for Fine Mineral Powders. *J. Soc. Chem. Ind. (London)* 67:283 (1948).
9. GILLETT, T. R.; MEADS, P. F.; & HOLVEN, A. L. Measuring Color and Turbidity of White Sugar Solutions. *Anal. Chem.* 21:1228 (1949).
10. JULLANDER, I. A Simple Method for the Measurement of Turbidity. *Acta. Chem. Scand.* 3:1309 (1949).
11. ROSE, H. E. Powder-Size Measurement by a Combination of the Methods of Nephelometry and Photo-Extinction. *J. Soc. Chem. Ind. (London)* 69:266 (1950).
12. ROSE, H. E. The Design and Use of Photo-Extinction Sedimentometers. *Engineering* 169:350, 405 (1950).
13. BRICE, B. A.; HALWER, M.; & SPEISER, R. Photoelectric Light-Scattering Photometer for Determining High Molecular Weights. *J. Opt. Soc. Am.* 40:768 (1950).
14. KNIGHT, A. G. The Measurement of Turbidity in Water. *J. Inst. Water Engrs.* 4:449 (1950).
15. HANYA, T. Study of Suspended Matter in Water. *Bull. Chem. Soc. Japan* 23:216 (1950).
16. JULLANDER, I. Turbidimetric Investigations on Viscose. *Svensk Papperstidn.* 22:1 (1950).
17. ROSE, H. E. A Reproducible Standard for the Calibration of Turbidimeters. *J. Inst. Water Engrs.* 5:310 (1951).
18. AITKEN, R. W. & MERCER, D. Comment on "The Measurement of Turbidity in Water." *J. Inst. Water Engrs.* 5:328 (1951).
19. ROSE, H. E. The Analysis of Water by the Assessment of Turbidity. *J. Inst. Water Engrs.* 5:521 (1951).
20. KNIGHT, A. G. The Measurement of Turbidity in Water: A Reply. *J. Inst. Water Engrs.* 5:633 (1951).
21. STAATS, F. C. *Measurement of Color, Turbidity, Hardness, and Silica in Industrial Waters.* Preprint 156, Am. Soc. Testing Materials, Philadelphia (1952).
22. PALIN, A. T. Photometric Determination of the Colour and Turbidity of Water. *Water & Water Engineering* 59:341 (1955).
23. CONLEY, W. R. & PITMAN, R. W. Microphotometer Turbidity Analysis. *J. AWWA* 49:63 (1957).

Zinc

Zinc is an essential and beneficial element in body growth. However, concentrations above 5 mg/l can cause a bitter astringent taste and an opalescence in alkaline waters. The zinc concentration of U.S. drinking waters has been reported to vary between 0.06 and 7.0 mg/l with a mean of 1.33 mg/l. Zinc most commonly enters the domestic water supply from the deterioration of galvanized iron and the dezincification of brass. In such cases the presence of lead and cadmium may additionally be suspected, because they are impurities of the zinc used in galvanizing. Zinc may also appear as a result of industrial waste pollution.

Selection of method: The dithizone method (*A*) is the method of choice for the determination of small zinc concentrations. The direct approach followed in the zincon method (*B*) makes it useful for control work. The

polarographic method (*C*) is valuable for screening the same sample for such metals as cadmium, copper, and nickel, which may interfere in the first two methods. Another polarographic method for scanning industrial wastes for metals is described in Part IV.

Sampling and storage: Samples should preferably be analyzed within 6 hr after collection. The addition of hydrochloric acid will preserve the metallic ion content, but requires that: (a) the acid be zinc-free; (b) the sample bottles be rinsed with acid before use; and (c) the samples be evaporated to dryness in silica dishes before they are analyzed to remove the excess HCl.

A. Dithizone Method

1. General Discussion

1.1. *Principle:* Nearly 20 metals are capable of reacting with diphenylthiocarbazone (dithizone) to produce colored coordination compounds. These dithizonates are extractable into organic solvents, such as carbon tetrachloride. Most interferences can be overcome in the zinc-dithizone reaction by adjusting the solution to pH 4.0 to 5.5 and by the addition of sufficient sodium thiosulfate. Zinc also forms a weak thiosulfate complex which tends to retard the reaction between zinc and dithizone, a reaction which is demonstrably slow and incomplete. For this reason, the determination is empirical and demands the use of an identical technique in both standardization and actual sample analysis. The duration and vigor of shaking, the volumes of sample, sodium thiosul-

fate, and dithizone, and pH should all be kept constant.

1.2. *Interference:* Interference from bismuth, cadmium, cobalt, copper, gold, lead, mercury, nickel, palladium, silver, and stannous tin in the small quantities found in potable waters is eliminated by complexing with sodium thiosulfate and by pH adjustment. Ferric iron, residual chlorine, and other oxidizing agents convert dithizone to a yellow-brown color. The zinc-dithizone reaction is extremely sensitive and unusual precautions must be taken to avoid contamination. Experience has shown that high and erratic blanks are often traceable to glass containing zinc oxide, surface-contaminated glassware, rubber products, stopcock greases, reagent grade chemicals, and distilled water. The extreme sensitivity of the reaction makes it desirable to prepare and segregate glassware especially for this determination, and to extract reagents with dithizone solution to remove all traces of zinc and contaminating metals. Dithizone and dithizonates decompose rapidly in strong light. Analyses should be performed in subdued light, and the solutions should not be exposed to the light of the photometer for a longer period than is necessary. Direct sunlight should also be avoided at all times.

1.3. *Minimum detectable concentration:* 1 μg Zn.

2. Apparatus

2.1. *Colorimetric equipment:* One of the following should be used, but it is also possible to make visual comparisons directly in separatory funnels:

a. Spectrophotometer, for use at either 535 or 620 mμ, providing a light path of 2 cm.

b. Filter photometer, providing a light path of 2 cm and equipped with either a green filter having maximum transmittance near 535 mμ or a red filter having maximum transmittance near 620 mμ.

c. Nessler tubes, matched.

2.2. *Separatory funnels,* capacity 125–150 ml, Squibb form, preferably with inert teflon stopcocks. If the funnels are of identical size and shape, visual color comparisons may be made directly in them.

2.3. *Glassware:* All glassware should be rinsed with $1 + 1$ HNO_3 followed by zinc-free water to avoid contamination errors.

2.4. *pH meter.*

3. Reagents

3.1. *Zinc-free water,* for rinsing of apparatus and preparation of solutions and dilutions. Redistill water in an all-pyrex apparatus; or pass distilled water through a mixed bed of ion-exchange resins—see General Introduction, A, Sec. 2, and Nitrogen (Ammonia), Method A, Sec. 3.1b.

3.2 *Stock zinc solution:* Dissolve 0.1000 g 30-mesh zinc metal in a slight excess of $1 + 1$ HCl; about 1 ml is required. Then dilute to 1,000 ml with zinc-free water; 1.00 ml = 0.100 mg Zn.

3.3. *Standard zinc solution:* Dilute 10.00 ml zinc stock solution to 1,000 ml with zinc-free water; 1.00 ml = 1.00 μg Zn.

3.4. *Hydrochloric acid,* 0.02N. Dilute 1.0 ml conc HCl to 600 ml with zinc-free water. If high blanks are traced to this reagent, dilute conc HCl with an equal volume of distilled water and redistill in an all-pyrex still.

3.5 *Sodium acetate,* 2N. Dissolve 68 g $NaC_2H_3O_2 \cdot 3H_2O$ and dilute to 250 ml with zinc-free water.

3.6. *Acetic acid,* $1 + 7$. Use zinc-free water.

3.7. *Acetate buffer solution:* Mix equal volumes of 2N sodium acetate solution and $1 + 7$ acetic acid solution. Extract with 10-ml portions of dithizone solution (I) until the last extract remains green; then extract with carbon tetrachloride to remove excess dithizone.

3.8. *Sodium thiosulfate solution:* Dissolve 25 g $Na_2S_2O_3 \cdot 5H_2O$ in 100 ml zinc-free water. Purify by dithizone extraction as in Sec. 3.7.

3.9. *Dithizone solution (I):* Dissolve 0.10 g diphenylthiocarbazone * in 1 liter carbon tetrachloride. Store in a brown glass-stoppered bottle in a refrigerator. If the solution is of doubtful quality or has been stored for a long time, the following test for de-

---

* Eastman No. 3092 or equivalent.

terioration can be applied: Shake 10 ml with 10 ml $1 + 99$ NH_4OH. If the lower, CCl_4, layer is only slightly yellow, the reagent is in good condition.

3.10. *Dithizone solution (II):* Dilute 1 volume of dithizone solution (I) with 9 volumes of CCl_4. If stored in a brown glass-stoppered bottle in a refrigerator, this solution is good for several weeks.

3.11. *Carbon tetrachloride.*

3.12. *Sodium citrate solution:* Dissolve 10 g $Na_3C_6H_5O_7 \cdot 2H_2O$ in 90 ml zinc-free water. Purify by dithizone extraction as in Sec. 3.7. This reagent is used in the final cleansing of glassware.

4. Procedure

4.1. *Preparation of colorimetric standards:* To a series of 125-ml Squibb separatory funnels, thoroughly cleansed as described in Sec. 1.2, add 0, 1.00, 2.00, 3.00, 4.00, and 5.00 ml standard zinc solution equivalent, respectively, to 0, 1.00, 2.00, 3.00, 4.00, and 5.00 μg Zn. Bring each volume up to 10.0 ml by adding zinc-free water. To each funnel add 5.0 ml acetate buffer and 1.0 ml sodium thiosulfate solution and mix. The pH should be between 4 and 5.5 at this point. To each funnel add 10.0 ml dithizone solution (II); stopper; and shake vigorously for 4.0 min. Allow the layers to separate. Dry the stem of the funnel with strips of filter paper and run the lower CCl_4 layer into a clean, *dry* colorimeter cell.

4.2. *Photometric measurement:* Either the red color of the zinc dithizonate can be measured at 535 mμ, or the green color of the unreacted dithizone at 620 mμ.

Set the photometer at 100 per cent transmittance with the blank, if the 535-mμ wavelength is selected; but if 620 mμ is used, set the blank at 10.0 per cent transmittance. Plot a calibration curve. A new calibration curve should be run with each set of samples.

4.3. *Treatment of samples:* If the zinc content is not within the working range, dilute the sample with zinc-free water or concentrate it in a silica dish. If the sample has been preserved with acid, an aliquot must be evaporated to dryness in a silica dish to remove the excess acid. It is not practical to neutralize with sodium or ammonium hydroxide, as these alkalis usually contain excessive amounts of zinc. Using a pH meter, and accounting for any dilution, adjust the sample to pH 2–3 with HCl. Transfer 10.0 ml to a separatory funnel. Complete the analysis as described in Sec. 4.1, beginning with the words "To each funnel add 5.0 ml acetate buffer," and continuing to the end of the paragraph.

4.4 *Visual comparison:* If a photometric instrument is not available, it will be necessary to run the samples and standards at the same time. The CCl_4 layers may be compared directly in the separatory funnels if these match in size and shape; otherwise transfer to matched test tubes or nessler tubes. The range of colors obtained with various amounts of zinc are roughly these:

Zinc μg	Color
0 (blank)	green
1	blue
2	blue-violet
3	violet
4	red-violet
5	red-violet

5. Calculation

$$\text{mg/l Zn} = \frac{\mu g \text{ Zn}}{\text{ml sample}}$$

6. Precision and Accuracy

A synthetic unknown sample containing 0.90 mg/l Zn, 1.80 mg/l Al, 0.42 mg/l Cu, 0.18 mg/l Cr, 0.62 mg/l Fe, and 0.25 mg/l Mn was determined in 14 laboratories with a standard deviation of ±0.24 mg/l by means of the dithizone mixed-color method. One-half of the reported results were within ±0.07 mg/l of the known zinc concentration. The individual laboratories reproduced their own results within ±0.02 mg/l.

B. Zincon Method*

1. General Discussion

1.1. *Principle:* Zinc forms a blue-colored complex with 2-carboxy-2'-hydroxy-5'-sulfoformazyl benzene (zincon) in a solution buffered to pH 9.0. Other heavy metals likewise form colored complexes. Heavy metals, including zinc, are complexed by cyanide. Chloral hydrate is added to specifically free the zinc from its cyanide complex. The zinc-zincon complex is measured before other heavy metal-cyanide complexes are destroyed by chloral hydrate. Sodium ascorbate reduces the interference of manganese. The final solutions are unstable and the procedure is designed to minimize the effects of color fading.

1.2. *Interference:* The following ions interfere in concentrations exceeding those listed:

Ion	mg/l	Ion	mg/l
Cd^{++}	1	Cr^{+++}	10
Al^{+++}	5	Ni^{++}	20
Mn^{++}	5	Cu^{++}	30
Fe^{+++}	7	Co^{++}	30
Fe^{++}	9	CrO_4^{--}	50

1.3. *Minimum detectable concentration:* 1 μg Zn.

* This method, with modifications, is identical in source and substance to ASTM D1691–59.

2. Apparatus

2.1. *Colorimetric equipment:* One of the following is required:

a. *Spectrophotometer,* for measurements at 620 mμ, providing a light path of 1 cm or longer.

b. *Filter photometer,* providing a light path of 1 cm or longer and equipped with a red filter having maximum transmittance near 620 mμ. Deviation from Beer's law occurs when the filter band pass exceeds 20 mμ.

3. Reagents

3.1. *Zinc-free water,* for rinsing of apparatus and preparation of solutions and dilutions. Prepare as directed in Method A, Sec. 3.1.

3.2. *Stock zinc solution:* Prepare as directed in Method A, Sec. 3.2.

3.3. *Standard zinc solution:* Dilute 10.00 ml stock zinc solution to 100 ml with zinc-free water; 1.00 ml = 10.0 μg Zn.

3.4. *Sodium ascorbate,* fine granular powder.†

3.5. *Potassium cyanide solution:* Dissolve 1.00 g KCN in 50 ml zinc-free water and dilute to 100 ml. This solution is stable for approximately 60

† Hoffman-LaRoche or equivalent.

days. CAUTION: POISON. *Potassium cyanide is extremely poisonous and more than customary precautions should be observed in its handling. Never use mouth pipets to deliver volumes of cyanide solution.*

3.6. *Buffer solution,* pH 9.0: Prepare 1*N* NaOH by dissolving 40 g NaOH in 500 ml zinc-free water and diluting to 1,000 ml. Dilute 213 ml 1*N* NaOH to approximately 600 ml with zinc-free water. Dissolve 37.8 g potassium chloride, KCl, and 31.0 g boric acid, H_3BO_3, in the solution and dilute to 1 liter.

3.7. *Zincon reagent:* Prior to use, grind the entire supply of zincon powder and mix well if it is not uniform as evidenced by the presence of different-colored particles. Dissolve 0.130 g powdered 2-carboxy-2'-hydroxy-5'-sulfoformazyl benzene (zincon) in 100 ml methyl alcohol (methanol). Let stand overnight to complete the dissolution of the zincon, or use a magnetic stirrer in a closed flask.

3.8. *Chloral hydrate solution:* Dissolve 10.0 g chloral hydrate in 50 ml zinc-free water and dilute to 100 ml. Filter if necessary.

3.9. *Hydrochloric acid,* conc.

3.10. *Sodium hydroxide,* 6*N*. Dissolve 240 g NaOH in 750 ml zinc-free water and dilute to 1,000 ml.

4. Procedure

4.1. *Preparation of colorimetric standards:* To a series of 50-ml erlenmeyer flasks, thoroughly cleansed, add 0, 0.25, 0.50, 1.00, 3.00, 5.00, and 7.00 ml standard zinc solution equivalent, respectively, to 0, 2.50, 5.00, 10.0, 30.0, 50.0, and 70.0 μg Zn. Bring each volume to 10.0 ml by adding zinc-free water. To each flask add in sequence, mixing thoroughly after each addition, 0.5 g sodium ascorbate, 1.0 ml KCN

solution, 5.0 ml buffer solution, and 3.00 ± 0.05 ml zincon solution. Add 3.0 ml chloral hydrate solution, note the time, and mix. Transfer to the photometer cell and measure the absorbance at 620 mμ *exactly* 5 min after adding the chloral hydrate solution. Use the treated blank as the reference solution for initial balancing of the photometer. Greater accuracy in the range below 10 μg Zn may be obtained by preparing a separate calibration curve for this range.

4.2. *Treatment of water samples:* If dissolved zinc is desired, filter the sample. If total zinc is desired, add 1 ml conc HCl to 50 ml thoroughly mixed sample and mix well to assure the dissolution of any precipitated zinc compound. Filter and adjust to pH 7 with 6*N* NaOH. Transfer a 10.0-ml aliquot of sample containing not more than 70 μg Zn to a 50-ml erlenmeyer flask. Complete the analysis as described in Sec. 4.1 beginning with the words "To each flask add in sequence . . .," and continue to the end of the paragraph.

Prepare as a reference solution a sample aliquot treated as above, except that 3.0 ml zinc-free water is substituted for the 3.0 ml chloral hydrate solution. This reference solution compensates for color, turbidity or interference not obviated by the procedure. It should be prepared as nearly simultaneously as possible with the sample aliquot.

5. Calculation

$$mg/l\ Zn = \frac{\mu g\ Zn}{ml\ sample}$$

6. Precision and Accuracy

The precision of this method is estimated at ±0.05 mg/l. Accuracy is of the same order of magnitude.

C. Polarographic Method (Tentative)

1. General Discussion

1.1. *Principle:* In common with many substances, zinc ions in aqueous solution can be reduced at the dropping mercury electrode if the potential of the mercury is kept sufficiently negative. The reduction process involves a transfer of electrons which constitutes an electric current. Under the proper conditions the magnitude of the current will be controlled by the rate at which the zinc ions reach the surface of the mercury drop by diffusion. The rate of diffusion will be proportional to the concentration of zinc in the solution and related to a number of other factors which can be kept essentially constant for any series of determinations. As a result, the polarographic or diffusion current associated with the zinc wave will be a linear function of the zinc concentration. The determination of zinc is made in an ammonia-ammonium chloride-ammonium carbonate solution. Zinc gives a good wave in this medium, and dissolved oxygen can be removed by the addition of sodium sulfite. Chromium and iron are reduced in the preliminary stages of the procedure. The chromium, and most of the iron, will be precipitated by the carbonate. The remaining iron, present as an ammonia complex, gives a wave which closely follows that of zinc, but the separation is sufficient to permit satisfactory zinc readings. Copper, cadmium, and nickel give well-separated waves which precede the zinc wave. They may be determined by this procedure with about the same order of precision and sensitivity as is zinc. The method is applicable to potable water, surface water, plating wastes, and sewage treatment plant effluents.

1.2. *Interference:* Cobalt gives a wave at the same potential as zinc. It should be absent, which is the usual case, or a correction factor, obtained from the determination of cobalt by an independent method, can be applied. Copper, cadmium, and nickel are reduced at more positive potentials than zinc, and should not be present in quantities much greater than zinc if very accurate results are to be obtained.

1.3. *Minimum detectable concentration:* 0.05 mg/l Zn.

2. Apparatus

2.1. *Polarograph:* Any commercially available polarograph may be used, or one may be constructed according to the directions given in any standard text on polarography. The galvanometer or recorder used should have a sensitivity of at least 0.01 microampere per millimeter of pointer deflection, and should not "load" the circuit. The electrodes should be arranged so that they can be immersed in the sample solution contained in a small beaker or vial.

2.2. *Glassware:* All glassware, including sample bottles, should be cleaned with 1 + 1 nitric or hydrochloric acids, and then rinsed thoroughly with tap water and zinc-free water.

3. Reagents

3.1. *Zinc-free water,* for preparation of solutions and dilutions. Prepare as directed in Method A, Sec. 3.1.

3.2. *Nitric acid,* conc, zinc-free.

3.3. *Hydrochloric acid,* conc, zinc-free.

3.4. *Ammonium hydroxide,* conc, zinc-free.

3.5. *Ammonium carbonate solution:* Dissolve 150 g $(NH_4)_2CO_3$ in zinc-free water and make up to 1 liter.

3.6. *Gelatin solution:* Dissolve 0.1 g gelatin in 10 ml warm, zinc-free water. Prepare daily.

3.7. *Sodium sulfite,* granular.

3.8. *Stock zinc solution:* Prepare as directed in Method A, Sec. 3.2; 1.00 ml = 100 μg Zn.

3.9. *Standard zinc solution:* Dilute 50.00 ml stock zinc solution to 100 ml with zinc-free water; 1.00 ml = 50 μg Zn.

4. Procedure

4.1. *Calibration of polarograph:*

a. When polarographic determinations are made in large numbers on a more or less daily basis, it is possible to calibrate the polarograph for any particular determination and provide temperature control or temperature correction factors. Inasmuch as polarographic response is almost always linear with concentration, a periodic analysis of a single standard will serve to check the instrument.

b. When determinations are made infrequently, a more satisfactory technique is to carry a blank and one or two standards along with each series of samples through all of the steps in the procedure. Frequently, it may be of value to add standard increments of zinc to portions of the sample itself, to check for recovery of zinc in the presence of extraneous salts.

c. Once a satisfactory wave form has been demonstrated, it is not always necessary to record the complete polarogram over the voltage range of interest. Voltage points at the foot of

the wave and on the plateau can be selected and readings taken at these points. For example, readings may be taken at −1.2 volts and −1.4 volts vs SCE (saturated calomel electrode). The reading at −1.4 volts minus the reading at −1.2 volts, when corrected for the increase in residual current corresponding to the increase in voltage, is the polarographic response for the sample or standard being read. The increase in residual current is obtained from the blank readings at the selected points and will automatically compensate for traces of zinc in the reagents.

4.2. *Sample pretreatment:*

a. Select a sample size, not to exceed 100 ml, that will contain not more than 0.1 mg Zn. Transfer to a 250-ml glass-stoppered erlenmeyer flask, add 3 ml conc nitric acid, and evaporate to dryness. If the sample is high in organic matter, add more acid and evaporate again. Repeat the treatment until the organic matter is destroyed. Finally, add about 2 ml conc hydrochloric acid and evaporate to dryness.

b. Treat the residue with exactly 0.5 ml conc hydrochloric acid. Add 7.5 ml zinc-free distilled water and a few crystals of sodium sulfite. Warm the flask under a hot-water tap, swirl the acid up the sides of the flask, stoppering if necessary to permit more vigorous agitation without loss of sample. Small amounts of silica may be present which will not dissolve, but treatment should be thorough enough to dissolve all of the zinc.

c. Add 1 ml conc ammonium hydroxide and mix. Add 1 ml ammonium carbonate solution, mix, and add 1 drop gelatin solution and 0.2 g solid sodium sulfite. Use a standardized scoop to measure the sodium sulfite. Swirl to dissolve the sulfite and decant into a suitable vessel for settling and for polarographing. Shell vials of 4-dram capacity are excellent. Allow the samples to stand for about 30 min, and polarograph without removal of the precipitate.

d. Water samples containing about 1 mg/l or more of zinc and relatively free of organic matter need not be evaporated. Transfer up to 7.5 ml sample to a 50-ml erlenmeyer flask and make the total volume 7.5 ml by the addition of zinc-free distilled water as necessary. Add exactly 0.5 ml conc hydrochloric acid, a few crystals of sodium sulfite, swirl, and continue the analysis as directed in Sec. 4.2c.

4.3. *Polarographic measurements:* Immerse the electrodes in the clear portion of the sample and polarograph over the range −1.1 to −1.5 volts vs the SCE (saturated calomel electrode). Compare the polarographic response of the sample to that obtained from a blank and from a standard containing 50 μg zinc. Treat both the blank and standard just as the sample was treated, using the same reagents in similar quantity.

5. Calculation

$$\text{mg/l Zn} = \frac{A \times 50}{B \times C}$$

where A = corrected reading for sample, B = corrected reading for 50-μg Zn standard, and C = ml sample taken.

6. Precision

This method will determine as little as 0.05 mg/l Zn with a precision of approximately ±0.01 mg/l. As the concentration increases, precision will be of the order of ±5 per cent.

Bibliography

Dithizone Method

1. HIBBARD, P. L. A Dithizone Method for Measurement of Small Amounts of Zinc. *Ind. Eng. Chem., Anal. Ed.* 9:127 (1937).
2. SANDELL, E. B. Determination of Copper, Zinc, and Lead in Silicate Rocks. *Ind. Eng. Chem., Anal. Ed.* 9:464 (1937).
3. HIBBARD, P. L. Estimation of Copper, Zinc, and Cobalt (With Nickel) in Soil Extracts. *Ind. Eng. Chem., Anal. Ed.* 10:615 (1938).
4. WICHMAN, H. J. Isolation and Determination of Traces of Metals: the Dithizone System. *Ind. Eng. Chem., Anal. Ed.* 11:66 (1939).
5. COWLING, H. & MILLER, E. J. Determination of Small Amounts of Zinc in Plant Materials: A Photometric Dithizone Method. *Ind. Eng. Chem., Anal. Ed.* 13:145 (1941).
6. ALEXANDER, O. R. & TAYLOR, L. V. Improved Dithizone Procedure for Determination of Zinc in Foods. *J. Assoc. Offic. Agr. Chemists* 27:325 (1944).
7. SNELL, F. D. & SNELL, C. T. *Colorimetric Methods of Analysis.* D. Van Nostrand Co., Princeton, N.J. (3rd ed., 1949). Vol. 2, pp. 1–7, 412–419.
8. BARNES, H. The Determination of Zinc by Dithizone. *Analyst* 76:220 (1951).
9. COOPER, S. S. & SULLIVAN, M. L. Spectrophotometric Studies of Dithizone and Some Dithizonates. *Anal. Chem.* 23:613 (1951).
10. SANDELL, E. B. *Colorimetric Determination of Traces of Metals.* Interscience Publishers, New York. (3rd ed., 1959). Chap. 49 and pp. 144–176.

Zincon Method

11. PLATTE, J. A. & MARCY, V. M. Photometric Determination of Zinc with Zincon. *Anal. Chem.* 31:1274 (1959).
12. *Manual of Industrial Water and Industrial Wastewater.* ASTM Special Tech. Pub. 148–F, Am. Soc. Testing Materials, Philadelphia (2nd ed., 1962).

Polarographic Method

13. KOLTHOFF, I. M. & LINGANE, J. J. *Polarography.* Interscience Publishers, New York (2nd ed., 1952).
14. ULLMANN, W. W., ET AL. Voltammetric Determination of Metals in Low Concentration. *Anal. Chem.* 34:213 (1962).

PART II

Methods for the Examination of
Water and Wastewater for Radioactivity

Introduction

The presence of radioactive contaminants in water supplies and in discharged wastes provides an immediate need for the formulation of techniques to assess the problem. With the development of nuclear science and its application to industrial operations, the seriousness of radioactive pollution is bound to increase.

An Advisory Committee of the U.S. Public Health Service recommended limits of radioactivity in drinking water.[4] The Federal Radiation Council criteria were observed in establishing limits in drinking water for radium-226 at 3 pc (picocuries) per liter and for strontium-90 at 10 pc/l. In the absence of all but a negligibly small fraction of strontium-90 and alpha emitters such as radium-226, the upper limit for gross beta activity is set at 1,000 pc/l. When the gross beta limit is exceeded, further radionuclide analysis is necessary. When considering radionuclides for which the Public Health Service or Federal Radiation Council have made no recommendations, reference may be made to the maximum permissible weekly concentration (168-hr week) guides recommended by the National Committee on Radiation Protection and Measurements [1] or the International Commission on Radiological Protection [2] after adjustment by a factor appropriate for exposure of the general population.

Radioactive isotopes provide a valuable new tool in research and technical investigations. They have already demonstrated their effectiveness in tracing dispersal of pollution in bodies of water, in determining flow patterns in streams, and in the study of many other problems.

It is essential that accepted methods be developed for the measurement of radioactivity in water and related materials, and for sampling and preparation of samples. The procedures given below are those which general experience to date has indicated to be most suitable. It is recognized that other techniques are in use and have proved satisfactory for certain specific purposes. As research and experience continue, many improvements will be developed.

The examination of aqueous environmental samples for gross alpha and beta radioactivity and select radionuclides embraces the examination of semisolid samples, such as sludge, plant and animal tissues, and airborne particulate radioactivity collected by filters or by other means.

Both natural and artificial sources of radiation from samples emitting alpha, beta, or gamma activity are included in the examination (to the exclusion of radiation external to the sample—i.e., cosmic, gamma, X-ray, and hard beta radiation in the environment). Because the rate of decay and the energy of radiation are unique characteristics of each radioelement, strict adherence to a standard procedure is essential to the proper interpretation of a radioactivity examination. Frequently, the procedure may have rigid timing requirements to discriminate between radioelements. For example, the rapid alpha analysis of airborne particulates usually consists of radon daughter products (largely radium C') from which the equilibrium parent radon concentration and each of its descendent products may be estimated. Subsequent alpha counting of the same sample could be designed to measure thoron daughter activity or long-lived alpha emitters. The beta activity of fresh rain a few minutes to several hours after collection may be significantly contaminated with radon daughter products. If the analysis is postponed for 6 hr, the radon daughters will disappear, along with some short-lived artificial radionuclides. The loss of activity resulting from delayed counting can be estimated by the extrapolation of decay data. During the concentration of water samples by evaporation, radionuclides such as elemental iodine or hydrogen iodide (in acid solution) may be lost by volatilization at temperatures below 105°C. If the sample is ignited the chance of volatilization is even greater. Radioactive substances such as carbon-14 and tritium may be present as volatile chemicals for the procedure of sample preparation used. Ground water usually contains nuclides of the uranium and thorium series. Special care in sampling and analyses is necessary because members of these series are often not in secular equilibrium. This is particularly true of gaseous radon, thoron and their daughter products, which may be present far in excess of the equilibrium concentration from radium in solution.

A. Collection of Samples

The introductory sections for each of Parts I, III, IV, V, and VII should be clearly understood as acceptable procedures for collecting representative samples. A few additional remarks peculiar to radioactive samples are in order.

The principles of representative sampling of water (Part I, Introduction, *A*, Sec. 3) and sampling of sewage and wastes (Part III, Introduction, *A*, Sec. 1) apply to sampling for radioactivity examinations.

Because a radioactive element is often present in submicrogram quantities, a significant fraction of it may be readily lost by adsorption on the surface of containers or glassware used in the examination. Similarly, a radionuclide may be largely or wholly adsorbed on the surface of suspended particles.

1. Sample Containers

When radioactive industrial wastes or comparable materials are sampled, care should be used to prevent the deposition of radioactivity on the walls and surfaces of glassware and equipment, causing loss of radioactivity and the possible contamination of subsequent samples due to reuse of inadequately cleansed glassware.

2. Preservation of Samples

The comments in Parts III and IV are particularly appropriate for all types of samples in Part II. Inasmuch as preservatives may alter the distribution of radioactivity in a sample, they should not be used until after the sample is separated into suspended and dissolved fractions. Formaldehyde or ethyl alcohol is suggested as a preservative for highly perishable samples such as food or foodlike samples. Preservatives and reagents should be tested for their radioactive content.

B. Counting Room

The design and construction of the counting room may vary widely according to the work to be accomplished. The room should be free of moisture and fumes which may affect the electrical stability of instruments. The background can be stabilized and lowered considerably by making the walls, floor, and ceiling out of several inches of concrete. Some shales, granites, and sands may contain sufficient natural activity to affect instrument background if used in the construction of a counting room.

A modern chemical laboratory can be used for processing routine environmental samples. It is generally better to segregate monitoring work from other laboratory operations when possible.

The need for air conditioning and humidity control depends on the number of instruments to be used and the prevailing climatic conditions. Generally electronic instruments perform best when the temperature remains constant within 3°C and does not exceed 30°C. The temperature inside the chassis of the instrument should be kept below that specified by the manufacturer.

Humidity affects instrument performance to an even greater extent than extremes of temperature because of moisture buildup on critical components. This causes leakage and arcing, and shortens the life of these components. A humidity of 80 per cent or less is usually satisfactory.

Most scalers are supplied with constant-voltage regulators suitable for controlling the usual minor fluctuations in line voltage. For unusual fluctuations, an auxiliary voltage regulation transformer should be used. A manually reset voltage-sensitive device in series with a voltage regulator placed in the main power line to instruments is suggested to protect them in case of power failure or a fluctuating line voltage.

Samples containing appreciable activity should be stored at a distance so as not to affect instrument background counting rate.

Floors and desk tops should be covered with a material that can be cleaned easily or replaced if necessary.

C. Counting Instruments

The operating principle of Geiger-Mueller and proportional counters is that the expenditure of energy by a radiation event causes ionization of counter gas and electron collection at the anode of the counting chamber. Through gas or electronic amplification, or both, the ion collection event triggers an electronic scaler recorder.

The principle of scintillation counters is similar in that quanta of light caused by the interaction of a radiation event and the detection phosphor is seen by a photomultiplier tube. The tube converts the light pulse into an amplified electrical pulse, which is recorded by an electronic scaler. Thallium-activated sodium iodide crystals and silver-activated zinc sulfide screens form useful scintillation detectors for counting gamma and alpha radioactivity, respectively.

Characteristic of most counters is a background or instrument counting rate usually due to cosmic radiation and the gamma radiation of natural radioactive contaminants of instrument parts and counting room construction material, and to the nearness of radioactive sources such as samples, fallout dust, and X-ray machines. In general, the background is roughly proportional to the size or mass of the counting chamber or detector, but it can be reduced by metal shielding such as several inches of lead.

Instrument "noise" or the false recording of radiation events may be caused by faulty circuitry, too sensitive a gain setting, effects of high humidity, and variable line voltage or transients. This problem is controlled by constant-voltage transformers with transient filters, proper adjustment of gain setting as specified by the manufacturer, and air conditioning of the counting room.

The internal proportional counter accepts counting pans within the counting chamber and thus at the beta operating voltage records all alpha, all beta, and little gamma radiation emitted into the counting gas. Theoretically, half of the radiation is emitted in the direction of the counting pan. Some of the beta radiation, but practically none of the alpha radiation, is backscattered into the counting gas by sample solids, the counting pan, or the walls of the counting chamber, so that, for substantially weightless samples, considerably more than 50 per cent of the beta radiation and slightly more than 50 per cent of the alpha radiation is counted. However, considerable care must be taken in sample preparation to prevent the sample or counting pan

from distorting the electrical field of the counter and thus depressing the counting rate. Nonconducting surfaces, airborne dusts, and vapor from moisture or solvents in particular interfere with counting.

The end-window Geiger-Mueller counting tubes are rugged and stable counting detectors. Usually the samples are mounted 5 to 15 mm from the window. Under these conditions, most alpha and weak beta radiations are completely stopped by the air gap and mica window and are not counted. Counting efficiencies for mixed fission products are frequently less than 10 per cent for substantially weightless samples having an area less than that of the window. Because most Geiger-Mueller tubes have diameters of about 2.5 cm, the pan size and, as a consequence, the water sample volume must be restricted. Under these conditions, the detectability is low and uncertain, particularly for unknown sources of radiation. On the other hand, the Geiger-Mueller tubes are excellent for counting samples of tracers or purified radionuclides. Usually, standard sample mounts can be prepared which yield reproducible counting efficiencies, and counting is not affected by the electrical conductance of sample pans.

Thin-window (Mylar) counting tubes approximately 5 cm in diameter provide counting efficiencies intermediate between conventional Geiger-Mueller tubes and internal counters. The thin windows and air gap from sample to window may absorb all of the weak alpha emissions, but 25 to 35 per cent of the beta activity of moderate energy is counted. The chamber diameter may be in excess of 60 mm, and sample mount diameters may be greater than 50 mm. The counting chambers have operational stability and less interference from nonconducting surfaces and moisture vapors than internal proportional counters. Their use as a substitute for the internal proportional beta counter is to be preferred over the more conventional small-diameter, thick-window counters.

1. Internal Proportional Counters

1.1. *Uses:* Internal proportional counters are suitable for determining alpha activity at the alpha operating plateau and alpha-plus-beta activity at the beta operating plateau. The alpha or beta activity, or both, can be in the form of gross activity or specific radionuclides.

The instruments usually consist of a counting chamber, a preamplifier, and a scaler with high-voltage power supply, timer, and register. Each instrument requires the use of a specified type of counting gas and accessories, the making of adjustments for sensitivity, and the carrying out of prescribed operating instructions.

1.2. *Plateau (alpha or beta):* It is necessary to find the operating voltage where the counting rate is constant— i.e., varies less than 3 per cent over a 150-v change in anode voltage.

a. With the instrument in operating order, place the alpha or beta standard (see Sec. 3 of *D* below) in the chamber, close, and flush the chamber with counter gas for 2–5 min.

b. Using the manufacturer's recommended operating voltage, count for a convenient time equal to an acceptable coefficient of variation, preferably 2 per cent. Repeat the test at voltages higher and lower than the suggested operating voltage in increments of 50 v. (CAUTION: *Instrument injury will result from prolonged continuous discharge at too high a voltage.*)

c. Plot the relative counting rate (ordinate) against anode voltage (abscissa). A plateau of at least 150 v in length with a slope of 3 per cent or less should result (see Fig. 25). Select an anode voltage near the center of this plateau for the operating voltage.

1.3. *Counter stability:* Before, during, and at the end of a series of sample counts, preferably three times a day, check instrument stability at the operating voltage by counting the plateau source (see Sec. 3 of *D* below). If the instrument reproduces the source count within two standard deviations of the count rate, proceed as in Sec. 1.4. If the source count is not so reproduced, replateau or service the instrument to correct inferior performance.

1.4. *Background:* Determine the background (with an empty counting pan in the counting chamber) after each test of counter stability. The total daily background counting time is preferably as long as the longest sample count each day.

1.5. *Sample counting:* Place the sample in the counting chamber. Be sure it is dry and adequately grounded to the chamber piston. (Thin aluminum metal pans can be grounded by impaling the pan wall on a pin mounted in the piston; heavier pans are self-grounded.) Flush with counter gas and count for a preset time (or preset count) to give the desired counting precision (see *F* below).

1.6. *Calibration of overall counter efficiency:* Because no instrument can detect all the radioactive disintegrations occurring in a sample, it is necessary to correct the observed counting rate for this inefficiency. Factors affecting efficiency are geometry, backscatter, self-absorption (sample absorption), and, in end-window counters, absorp-

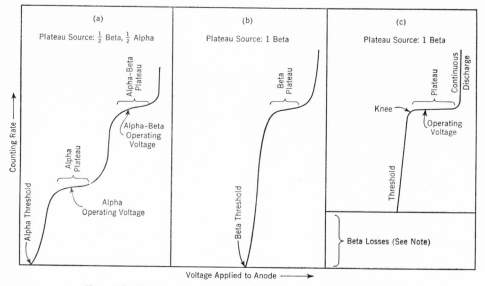

Fig. 25. Shape of counting rate—anode voltage curves

Key: (a) and (b) are for internal proportional counter with P-10 gas; (c) is for end-window Geiger-Mueller counter with Geiger gas (Note: Beta losses dependent on energy of radiation and thickness of window and air path).

tion by air gap and window. Although it is useful to know the variation in these factors, the overall efficiency can be determined for a fixed standard procedure by preparing standard sample sources and unknowns.

a. For measuring mixed fission products or beta radioactivity of unknown composition, use a standard solution of cesium-137 * for calibration of overall counter efficiency.

Prepare a standard (known disintegration rate) in an aqueous solution of sample solids similar in composition to that present in the unknown samples. Dispense increasing increments of solution in tared pans and evaporate.

Make a series of samples having a solid thickness of 1 to 10 mg/sq cm of bottom area in the counting pan. Use care in evaporation to obtain uniform solids deposition. Dry (103° C), weigh, and count. Calculate the ratio of counts per minute to disintegrations per minute (efficiency) for different weights of sample solids. Plot the efficiency as a function of sample thickness and use the resulting calibration curve to convert counts per minute (cpm) to disintegrations per minute (dpm).

b. If other radionuclides are to be tested, repeat the above procedure using certified solutions of each radionuclide. Unequal distribution of sample solids, particularly in the 0–3 mg/sq cm range, should be avoided in both calibration and unknown sample prep-

* For calibration standards and certification see *The Isotope Index*, J. S. Sommerville, ed., Scientific Equipment Co., P.O. Box 19086, Indianapolis 19, Ind.

aration; otherwise, inconsistent results will occasionally be obtained.

c. For alpha calibration, proceed as above, using uranyl acetate as a standard.

1.7. Calibration by use of known efficiency factors: This method of calibration is an alternative to Sec. 1.6.

For internal proportional counters the efficiency, *e,* in cpm/dpm, is:

$$e = G B T$$

where G is the geometry factor, B is the backscatter factor, and T is the transmission through the sample solids (self-absorption).

a. For beta activity from mixed fission products:

$G = 0.5$ for a small-diameter beta sample of weightless activity such as cesium-137 centered on a conducting pan in an internal counter. It remains substantially the same for weightless samples up to 5 cm in diameter.

$B = 1.36$ for stainless steel of infinite beta thickness and 1.25 for aluminum pans (bottle caps) on aluminum pistons.

T ranges from 1.0 for weightless samples to 0.6 for a sample thickness of 13.5 mg/sq cm (see Table 22).

TABLE 22—TRANSMISSION FACTORS FOR FISSION PRODUCTS (β) AND URANIUM (α)

T Value	Sample Thickness—*mg/sq cm*	
	Beta *	Alpha †
1.0	0	0
0.9	1.6	0.8
0.8	3.9	1.6
0.7	6.6	2.4
0.6	13.5	3.2
0.5		4.0

* For mixed fission product.
† For natural uranium.

Transmission factors for isotopes other than mixed fission products must be determined as in Sec. 1.6a. This

should be done by selecting radioisotopes with energy levels similar to those to be measured. This is particularly desirable in wastes where isotopes from research and industry are expected.

b. For samples of uranyl acetate, the alpha factors are: $G = 0.50$, $B = 1.02$, and T ranging from 1.0 for weightless samples to 0.5 for a sample thickness of 4 mg/sq cm (Table 22).

2. End-Window Counters

End-window counters may be used for beta-gamma and absorption examinations. Most alpha and soft beta radiations are stopped by the air gap and window. The sample pan should have a diameter less than that of the window and, for maximum efficiency, should be placed as close to the window as possible. Housing the detector inside a 2-in. thick lead shield will improve sensitivity of counting by decreasing the background by about 50 per cent. Associated equipment generally consists of a scaler having a timer, register, and high-voltage power supply.

2.1. Plateau and operating voltage: A beta plateau of about 200 v in length is determined in a manner similar to Sec. 1.2 above. (CAUTION: *Approach the high end of the plateau with care because continuous discharge will decrease the life of the tube.*) Select an operating voltage of ⅓ to ½ the length of the plateau above the knee (low-voltage end).

2.2. Counter stability: See Sec. 1.3 above. The problem is minor, but centering the sample pan or planchet in a given position is quite important.

2.3. Background: Proceed as in Sec. 1.4

2.4. Sample counting: Proceed as in Sec. 1.5 with the sample mounted close to the window.

2.5. *Calibration:* Calibrate the instrument by the procedure given in Sec. 1.6a.

2.6. *Coincidence correction:* Geiger-Mueller counters commonly have resolving times of 100 to 200 microseconds; therefore, data on samples of high counting rate must be corrected for loss in counts.

D. Laboratory Reagents and Apparatus

See the General Introduction, *A*, for basic standards for laboratory reagents and apparatus. The following special instructions are pertinent.

1. Reagents and Distilled Water

Make periodic checks on the background radioactivity of all solutions and reagents used in an examination. Discard those having a radioactivity which significantly interferes with the test.

2. Apparatus

Before reuse, thoroughly decontaminate apparatus and glassware with detergents and complexing agents, followed, if necessary, with acid and distilled-water rinses. Segregate equipment and glassware for storage and reuse on samples of comparable activity—i.e., keep apparatus for background and low-level studies separate from higher-level studies by the use of distinctive markings and different storage cabinets or laboratories. It is wise to adopt single-use counting pans, planchets, and auxiliary supplies. Slightly radiocontaminated glassware may be entirely satisfactory for use in chemical tests but unsatisfactory for radioanalysis.

3. Radioactivity Sources

3.1. Employ standard solutions whose calibration is traceable to sources of radioactivity certified by the National Bureau of Standards.

3.2. *Plateau sources:*

a. *Alpha:* Uranium oxide (U_3O_8), plated, not less than 45 mm in diameter, having an alpha activity of about 10,000 cpm.

b. *Beta:* Same as above except that the source is covered with 8–10 mg/sq cm of aluminum foil.

E. Expression of Results

Results of radioactivity analyses are reported preferably in terms of picocuries per liter (pc/1) at 20°C or, for samples of specific gravity significantly different from 1.00, picocuries per gram, where 1 picocurie = 10^{-12} curies = 2.22 dpm. For samples normally containing 1,000 to 1,000,000 pc per unit volume or weight, the nanocurie (nc) unit is preferred (1 nc = 10^{-9} curies = 1,000 pc). If the values are higher than 1,000 nc, the microcurie

(μc) unit is preferred. Ordinarily, the liter, kilogram, and square meter are preferred units of weight and measure.

It is important to report results in such a way that they will not imply greater or less accuracy than can be obtained by the method used. This matter is discussed in the General Introduction, *B*, Sec. 2 ("Significant Figures").

"Gross alpha" implies unknown alpha sources in which natural uranium salts have been used to determine self-absorption and efficiency factors.

"Gross beta" implies unknown sources of beta, including some gamma radiation, and calibration with Cs-137 as in *C*, Sec. 1.6, or application of correction factors as in *C*, Sec. 1.7.

F. Statistics

The General Introduction, *C*, Sec. 1, discusses the statistics of analytical problems as applied to chemical parameters. These remarks are also generally applicable to radioactivity examinations.

The variability of any measurement is measured by the standard deviation, which can be obtained from replicate determinations by well-known methods. There is an inherent variability in radioactivity measurements because the disintegrations occur in a random manner described by the Poisson distribution. This distribution is characterized by the property that the standard deviation of a large number of events, *N*, is equal to its square root or:

$$\sigma(N) = N^{\frac{1}{2}} \dots\dots\dots\dots (1)$$

Generally, the concern is not with the standard deviation of the number of counts but rather with the deviation in the rate (number of counts per unit time):

$$R' = \frac{N}{t} \dots\dots\dots\dots (2)$$

where *t* is the time of observation, which is assumed to be known with such high precision that its error may be neglected. The standard deviation

in the counting rate, $\sigma(R')$, can be calculated by the usual methods for propagation of error:

$$\sigma(R') = \frac{N^{\frac{1}{2}}}{t} = \left(\frac{R'}{t}\right)^{\frac{1}{2}} \dots (3)$$

In practice, all counting instruments have a background counting rate, *B*, when no sample is present. When a sample is present, the counting rate increases to R_0. The counting rate *R* due to the sample then is:

$$R = R_0 - B \dots\dots\dots\dots (4)$$

By propagation of error methods, the standard deviation of *R* can be calculated as follows:

$$\sigma(R) = \left(\frac{R_0}{t_1} + \frac{B}{t_2}\right)^{\frac{1}{2}} \dots\dots (5)$$

where t_1 and t_2 are the times over which the gross sample and background counting rates were measured, respectively. Practical counting times are often 30 min, or 2,500 total counts above background, whichever is the least in time. It is desirable to divide the counting time into two equal periods, so as to check the constancy of the observed counting rate. For low-level counting, t_2 should be about the same as t_1. The error thus calculated includes only the error caused by inherent variability of the radioactive disintegration process and should be reported as the "counting error."

A confidence level of 95 per cent or 1.96 standard deviations should preferably be selected and reported as the counting error.

Bibliography

Radiologic Health Standards and Recommendations

1. Maximum Permissible Body Burdens and Maximum Permissible Concentrations of Radionuclides in Air and Water for Occupational Exposure. *Natl. Bur. Standards Handbook* No. 69 (1959). pp. 1, 17, 37, 38, 93.
2. Recommendation of the International Commission on Radiological Protection, Revised Dec. 1, 1954, *Health Physics* 3:1 (1960).
3. FEDERAL RADIATION COUNCIL. Background Material for the Development of Radiation Protection Standards, Rept. No. 2 (Sept. 1961). U.S. Govt. Printing Office, Washington, D.C.
4. 1962 Public Health Service Drinking Water Standards. *Public Health Service Pub.* No. 956. U.S. Govt. Printing Office, Washington, D.C. (1963).

General Analytical Methods

5. JARRETT, A. A. Statistical Methods Used in the Measurement of Radioactivity (Some Useful Graphs). *U.S. Atomic Energy Comm. Documents* No. AECU-262 (June 17, 1946).
6. HULL, D. E. The Counting Method of Isotopic Analysis of Uranium. *U.S. Atomic Energy Comm. Documents* No. MDDC-387 (Oct. 18, 1946).
7. TAYLOR, D. *The Measurement of Radioisotopes.* John Wiley & Sons, New York (1951).
8. GRAF, W. L.; COMAR, C. L.; & WHITNEY, I. B. Relative Sensitivities of Windowless and End-Window Counters. *Nucleonics* 9:6, 22 (1951).
9. COWAN, F. P. Quantitative Summary of Natural Radiation and Naturally Occurring Isotopes. In *In-Service Training Course in Radiological Health.* Univ. of Michigan, Ann Arbor (Feb. 1951). pp. 56–59.
10. CORYELL, C. D. & SUGARMAN, N., ed. *Radiochemical Studies: The Fission Products.* McGraw-Hill Book Co., New York (1951).
11. NADER, J. S.; HAGEE, G. R.; & SETTER, L. R. Evaluating the Performance of the Internal Counter. *Nucleonics* 12:6, 29 (1954).
12. SAX, N. I., ET AL. Analysis for Long-Lived Fission Products in Soil. *U.S. Atomic Energy Comm. Repts.* No. NYO-4604 (1954).
13. KLEINBERG, J., ed. Collected Radiochemical Procedures. *U.S. Atomic Energy Comm. Repts.* No. LA-1721 (1954).
14. COMAR, C. I. *Radioisotopes in Biology and Agriculture.* McGraw-Hill Book Co., New York (1955).
15. FRIEDLANDER, G. & KENNEDY, J. W. *Nuclear and Radiochemistry.* John Wiley & Sons, New York (1955).

Gross Alpha and Gross Beta Radioactivity (Total, Suspended and Dissolved) *(Tentative)*

1. General Discussion

1.1. *Natural radioactivity:* Uranium, thorium, and radium are naturally occurring radioactive elements that have a long series of radioactive daughters which emit alpha or beta, and gamma, radiations until a stable end-element is produced. These naturally occurring elements, through their radioactive daughter gases, radon and thoron, cause an appreciable airborne particulate activity and contribute to the radioactivity of rain and ground waters. Additional naturally radioactive elements include potassium-40, rubidium-87, samarium-147, lutetium-176, and rhenium-187.

1.2. *Artificial radioactivity:* With the development and operation of nuclear reactors and other atom-smashing machines, large quantities of radioactive elements are being produced. These include almost all the elements in the periodic table.

1.3. *Significance of gross alpha and gross beta concentrations in water:* As stated in the Introduction to Part II, the 1962 Public Health Service Drinking Water Standards recommend limits for the concentration of radium-226 (3 pc/1) and strontium-90 (10 pc/1) in water. Furthermore, if alpha emitters and strontium-90 are known to be a negligible fraction of the above specified limits, the water supply would usually be regarded as radiologically acceptable, if the gross beta concentration does not exceed 1,000 pc/1.

By using the simpler techniques for routine measurement of gross beta activity, the presence of contamination may be determined in a matter of minutes, whereas hours or even days may be required to conduct the radiochemical analyses necessary to identify the particular radionuclides that are present in the sample.

Regular measurements of gross alpha and gross beta activity in water may be invaluable for early detection of radioactive contamination and indicate the need for supplemental data on the concentrations of the more hazardous radionuclides.

1.4. *Preferred counting instrument and calibration standard:* The internal proportional counter is the recommended instrument for counting gross

beta radioactivity because of its superior operating characteristics. These include a high sensitivity to detect and count a wide range of low- to high-energy beta radiation and a high geometry (2π) due to the introduction of the sample into the counting chamber. In this case the system of assay is calibrated by adding standard nuclide portions to media comparable to the samples and preparing, mounting and counting the standards identical to that of the samples.

When assaying gross beta activity in samples containing mixtures of naturally radioactive elements and fission products, the choice of a calibration standard may significantly influence the beta results because self-absorption factors and counting chamber characteristics are beta energy dependent.[4] Two radionuclides, cesium-137 and thallium-204, emit beta radiation having a maximum energy reasonably comparable to the average of maxima for fission products. Comparison of the transmission factor for these standards and fission products in Table 23 indicates that the difference in counting due to self-absorption is relatively

TABLE 23—TRANSMISSION FACTORS
(SELF-ABSORPTION)

Sample Thickness mg/sq cm	Transmission Factor			
	Cs-137	Tl-204	F.P. IPC *	F.P. E-W †
0.0	1.00	1.00	1.00	1.00
1.0	0.95	0.94	0.99	0.92
2.5	0.89	0.86	0.83	0.83
5.0	0.79	0.76	0.70	0.72
7.5	0.74	0.68	0.61	0.64
10.0	0.69	0.65	0.55	0.59

* Fission products in a 5.1-cm diameter dish and counted in an internal proportional counter.

† Fission products in a 5.1-cm diameter dish in a thin end-window counter 5.7 cm in diameter having a window thickness of about 0.8 mg/sq cm. The samples were positioned 0.8 cm below the window.

insignificant. The relatively short half-life (approx. 3.56 years) of thallium-204 precludes its use as a standard solution for extended periods (more than 12 months after absolute standardization). The use of cesium-137 (half-life about 30 years) as a calibration standard overcomes this disadvantage. Therefore, a standard solution of cesium-137, preferably certified by the National Bureau of Standards, is recommended for calibration of overall counter efficiency for gross beta determinations. The daughter products after beta decay of cesium-137 are stable barium-137 and metastable barium-137, which in turn disintegrates by gamma emission. For this reason, the standardization of cesium-137 solutions may be stated in terms of the gamma emission rate per milliliter or per gram. To convert gamma rate to equivalent beta disintegration rate multiply the calibrated gamma emission rate by 1.33.

1.5. *Radiation lost by self-absorption:* The radiation from alpha emitters having an energy of 8 mev and from beta emitters having an energy of 60 kev will not escape from the sample if they are covered by a sample thickness of 5.5 mg/sq cm. The radiation from a weak alpha emitter will be stopped if covered by only 4 mg/sq cm of sample solids. Consequently, for low-level counting it is imperative to evaporate all moisture and preferable to destroy organic matter before depositing a thin film of sample solids from which radiation may readily enter the counter. In counting water samples for gross beta radioactivity, a solids thickness of 10 mg/sq cm or less on the bottom area of the counting pan is recommended. For the most accurate results, the self-absorption

factor should be determined as outlined in Part II, Introduction, *C,* Sec. 1.6a.

2. Apparatus

2.1. *Counting pans,* of metal resistant to corrosion from sample solids or reagents, about 50 mm in diameter, 6–10 mm in height, and thick enough to be serviceable for one-time use. Stainless-steel or aluminum pans are satisfactory, depending on the kind of sample and reagents added.

2.2. *Internal proportional counting chambers,* capable of receiving and maintaining good electrical contact with counting pans, complete with preamplifier, scaler, timer, register, constant voltage supply, counting gas equipment, and counting gas (see Introduction, *B* and *C*).

2.3. *Membrane filter,** 0.45μ pore size.

2.4. *Gooch crucibles.*

3. Reagents

3.1. *Methyl orange indicator solution:* Dissolve 0.5 g methyl orange in 1 liter distilled water.

3.2. *Hydrochloric acid,* 1*N.* 1 + 11.

3.3. *Nitric acid,* 1*N.* Dilute 64 ml conc HNO_3 to 1 liter with distilled water.

3.4. *Lucite solution:* Dissolve 50 mg lucite in 100 ml acetone.

3.5. *Ethyl alcohol,* 95 per cent.

3.6. *Conducting fluid:* Anstac AC † or equivalent; prepare according to manufacturer's directions.

3.7. *Standard certified cesium-137 solution.*

---

* Type HA (Millipore Filter Corp., Bedford, Mass.) or equivalent.

† Chemical Development Corporation, Danvers, Mass.

3.8. *Reagents for wet-combustion procedure:*

a. Nitric acid, 6N. Dilute 380 ml conc HNO_3 to 1 liter with distilled water.

b. Hydrogen peroxide solution. Dilute 30 per cent H_2O_2 with an equal volume of water.

4. Procedure for Gross Alpha and Gross Beta Activity

4.1. For each 20 sq cm of counting pan area, take a volume of sample containing not more than 200 mg of residue for beta examination and not more than 100 mg of residue for alpha examination. The specific conductance test (Part I) helps to select the appropriate sample volume.

4.2. Evaporate by either of the following techniques:

a. Add the sample directly to a tared counting pan in small increments, with evaporation just below boiling temperature.

b. Place the sample in a pyrex beaker or evaporating dish, add a few drops of methyl orange indicator solution, add $1N$ HCl or $1N$ HNO_3 dropwise to pH 4–6, and evaporate on a hot plate or steam bath to near dryness. Avoid baking solids on the evaporation vessel. Transfer the residue to a tared counting pan with the aid of a rubber policeman and distilled water from a wash bottle. Thoroughly wet the walls of the evaporating vessel with a few drops of acid by means of a rubber policeman and transfer the acid washings to the counting pan. (Excess alkalinity or mineral acidity is corrosive to aluminum counting pans.)

4.3. Complete the drying in an oven at 103°–105°C, cool in a desiccator, weigh, and keep the sample dry until counted.

4.4. Sample residues having particles which tend to be airborne should be treated with lucite solution, then air and oven dried and weighed. The lucite acts as a binder to prevent counter contamination by such particles.

4.5. Count the alpha activity at the alpha plateau.

4.6. Count the beta-gamma activity at the beta plateau.

4.7. Store in a desiccator, and count for decay if necessary. Avoid heat treatment if ingrowth of gaseous daughter products is suspected.

5. Procedure for Gross Alpha and Gross Beta of Dissolved Matter

5.1. Proceed as in Sec. 4.1 with a sample volume containing the requisite maximum weight of dissolved matter.

5.2. Filter through a Gooch crucible or, if the suspended matter is to be examined, a membrane filter.

5.3. Process the filtrate as described in Sec. 4.2–4.6 above, and report the dissolved alpha activity and dissolved beta activity by Gooch or by membrane filtration as the case may be.

6. Procedure for Gross Alpha and Gross Beta of Suspended Matter

6.1. For each 10 sq cm of membrane filter area take a volume of sample not to exceed 50 mg of suspended matter for alpha assay and not to exceed 100 mg for beta assay.

6.2. Filter the sample through the membrane filter with suction; then wash the sides of the filter funnel with a few milliliters of distilled water.

6.3. Transfer the filter to a tared counting pan and oven dry.

6.4. Saturate the membrane with alcohol and ignite. When burning has stopped, direct the flame of a Meeker burner down on the partially ignited sample to fix the sample to the pan and obtain more complete ignition.

6.5. Cool, weigh, and count at the alpha and the beta plateaus.

6.6. If sample particles tend to be airborne, treat the sample with lucite solution, air dry, and count.

6.7. An alternate method of preparing membrane filters for counting consists of wetting the filters with conducting fluid, drying, weighing, and counting. (The weight of the membrane filter is then included in the tare.)

7. Alternate Procedure for Gross Alpha and Gross Beta of Suspended Matter

It is impractical to filter some sewage, highly polluted waters, and industrial wastes through membrane filters. In such cases it is necessary to proceed as follows:

7.1. Determine the total and dissolved activity by the procedures in Sec. 4 and 5.2 and estimate the suspended activity by difference.

7.2. Filter the sample through an ashless mat or filter paper of stated porosity. Dry, ignite, and weigh the suspended fixed residue. Transfer and fix a thin, uniform layer of sample residue to a tared counting pan with lucite solution. Dry, weigh, and count.

8. Procedure for Gross Alpha and Gross Beta of Nonfatty Semisolid Samples

The following procedure is applicable to samples of sludge, vegetation, soil, and the like:

8.1. Determine the total residue and fixed residue of representative samples according to Part III, Residue, Methods A and B, or Part V, Residue.

8.2. Reduce fixed residue of a granular nature to a fine powder with pestle and mortar.

8.3. Transfer a maximum of 100 mg fixed residue for alpha assay and 200 mg fixed residue for beta assay for each 20 sq cm of counting pan area (see Note below).

8.4. Distribute the residue to uniform thickness in a tared counting pan by (a) spreading a thick aqueous cream of residue which is weighed after oven drying, or (b) dispensing dry residue of known weight which is spread by means of lucite solution.

8.5. Oven dry at 103°–105°C, weigh, and count.

NOTE: The fixed residue of vegetation and similar samples is usually corrosive to aluminum counting pans. To avoid difficulty, use stainless-steel pans or treat a weighed amount of fixed residue with HCl or HNO_3 in the presence of methyl orange indicator to pH 4–6, transfer to an aluminum counting pan, dry at 103°–105°C, reweigh, and count.

9. Alternate Wet-Combustion Procedure for Biologic Samples

Some samples, such as fatty animal tissues, are difficult to process according to Sec. 8. An alternate procedure consists of acid digestion. Because the procedure creates a highly acid and oxidizing state, volatile radionuclides under these conditions would be lost.

9.1. To 2–10 g of sample in a tared silica dish or equivalent add 20–50 ml $6N$ HNO_3 and 1 ml 15 per cent H_2O_2 and digest at room temperature for a few hours or overnight. Heat gently and, when frothing subsides, heat more vigorously, but without spattering, until near dryness. Add two more $6N$ HNO_3 aliquots of 10–20 ml each, heat to near boiling, and continue gentle treatment until the sample is dry.

9.2. Ignite the sample in a muffle furnace for 30 min at 600°C, cool in a desiccator, and weigh.

9.3. Continue the test as described in Sec. 8.3–8.5.

10. Calculation and Reporting

10.1. *Counting error:* Determine the counting error, E (in picocuries per sample), at the 95 per cent confidence level from:

$$E = \frac{1.96 \ \sigma(R)}{2.22 \ e}$$

where $\sigma(R)$ is calculated from Eq 5 (Introduction, F), using $t_1 = t_2$ (in minutes); and e, the counter efficiency, is defined and calculated as in Introduction, C, Sec. 1.6 or 1.7 (for an internal counter).

10.2. *Alpha activity of water, biologic samples, or silts:* Report the alpha activity, in pc/l, by the equation

$$\text{Alpha} = \frac{\text{net cpm} \times 1,000}{2.22 \ e \ v}$$

where:

e = calibrated overall counter efficiency (see Introduction, C, Sec. 1.6 c), or
e = GBT (see Introduction, C, Sec. 1.7 b), and
v = volume of sample counted, in ml.

The counting error must also be expressed in terms of pc/l by dividing the picocuries per sample by the sample volume in liters. Similarly calculate and report the alpha activity in picocuries or nanocuries per kilogram of moist biologic material or per kilogram of moist and per kilogram of dry silt.

10.3. *Gross beta activity when alpha activity is insignificant:* For samples having an alpha activity less than one-half of the beta counting error, calcu-

late and report the gross beta activity and counting error in picocuries or nanocuries per liter of water or fluid, per kilogram of moist (live weight) biologic material, or per kilogram of moist and per kilogram of dry silt, according to Sec. 10.1 and 10.2, disregarding the slight amount of alpha activity.

For calculation of the pc/l of beta activity, the value of e in the above equation is determined as described in Introduction, C, Sec. 1.6b, or by using the calculated efficiency factor in Introduction, C, Sec. 1.7a.

10.4. *Beta activity when alpha activity is significant:* In samples containing an alpha activity (in cpm) which exceeds one-half the beta error (in cpm), deduct the net alpha cpm from the net beta cpm to give the net corrected beta cpm. Proceed as in Sec. 10.3 to calculate and report the beta radioactivity in picocuries or nanocuries per liter of water, per kilogram of moist biologic sample, or per kilogram of moist and per kilogram of dry silt. When the alpha activity represents a small fraction of the beta activity, a rough approximation of the beta counting error consists of the gross beta counting error. Where greater precision is desired, such as when the alpha activity is a substantial fraction of the gross beta activity, the beta counting error equals $(E_a^2 + E_b^2)^{1/2}$, where E_a is the alpha counting error and E_b the gross beta counting error.

10.5. *Miscellaneous information to be reported:* In reporting radioactivity data, it is important to identify adequately the sample, sampling station, date of collection, volume of sample, type of test, type of activity, type of counting equipment, standard calibration solutions used (particularly when standards other than natural uranium for alpha or cesium-137 for beta were used), time of counting (particularly if short-lived isotopes are involved), weight of sample solids, and kind and amount of radioactivity. As far as possible, the data should be tabulated for ease of interpretation, and repetitious items should be incorporated in the table heading or in footnotes. Unless particularly inconvenient, quantity units should not change within a given table. For low-level assays, where the counting error represents a significant fraction of the measurement, it should be reported to assist in the interpretation of results.

Bibliography

1. BURITT, B. P. Absolute Beta Counting. *Nucleonics* 5:8, 28 (1949).
2. GOLDIN, A. S.; NADER, J. S.; & SETTER, L. R. The Detectability of Low-Level Radioactivity in Water. *J. AWWA* 45:73 (1953).
3. SETTER, L. R.; GOLDIN, A. S.; & NADER, J. S. Radioactivity Assay of Water and Industrial Wastes with Internal Proportional Counter. *Anal. Chem.* 26:1304 (1954).
4. SETTER, L. R. Reliability of Measurements of Gross Beta Radioactivity in Water. *J. AWWA* 56:228 (1964).

Total Radioactive Strontium in Water *(Tentative)*

The important radioactive nuclides of strontium produced in nuclear fission are Sr-89 and Sr-90. Strontium-90, with its daughter, yttrium-90, is the most hazardous of all fission products. It decays slowly, with a half-life of about 28 years. Upon ingestion the strontium is concentrated in the bone; 10 per cent of the occupational maximum permissible concentration for Sr-90 in water is 100 pc/l, as compared to 10,000 pc/l for Sr-89, which has a half-life of only 53 days. The Federal Radiation Council intake guides for Sr-90 in ranges I, II, and III are 0–20, 20–200, and 200–2,000 pc per day per person, respectively, and for Sr-89 in ranges I, II and III the intake guides are 0–200, 200–2,000, and 2,000–20,000 pc per day per person, respectively. The 1962 Public Health Service Drinking Water Standards limit the concentration of Sr-90 in water to 10 pc/l.

1. General Discussion

1.1. *Principle:* The following method is designed to measure radioactive strontium in water. It is applicable to sewage and industrial wastes, provided steps are taken to destroy organic matter and eliminate other interfering ions. In this analysis, a known amount of inactive strontium ions, in the form of strontium nitrate, is added as a "carrier." The carrier, along with the radionuclides of strontium, is separated from other radioactive elements and inactive sample solids by precipitation as strontium nitrate from concentrated nitric acid solution. The strontium carrier, together with the radioactive isotopes of strontium, is finally precipitated as strontium carbonate, which is dried and weighed and the radioactivity measured. The activity in the final precipitate is due to radioactive strontium only, because all other radioactive elements are removed. A correction is applied to compensate for losses of carrier and activity during the various purification steps. A delay in the count will give an increased counting rate due to the ingrowth of Y-90 which, at equilibrium in three weeks, will be somewhat greater than the Sr-90 counting rate.

1.2. *Concentration techniques:* Because of the very low amount of radioactivity, a large-sized sample must be taken and the activity concentrated by precipitation. After the addition of strontium nitrate and barium nitrate carriers to the sample, sodium carbonate is added, which causes precipitation of alkaline earth carbonates along with other radioactive elements. The supernate is discarded and the precipitate is dissolved and reprecipitated to remove interfering radionuclides.

1.3 *Interference:* Radioactive barium (Ba-140–La-140) interferes in the determination of radioactive strontium, inasmuch as it precipitates along with the radioactive strontium. This interference is eliminated by adding inactive barium nitrate carrier and separating this from the strontium by precipitating barium chromate in acetate buffer solution.

In hard water, some calcium nitrate may be coprecipitated with strontium nitrate and cause errors in measuring the activity in the final precipitate. This interference is eliminated by repeated precipitations of strontium as the nitrate followed by leaching the $Sr(NO_3)_2$ with acetone.

The precipitate should be counted within 3–4 hr after the final separation, before much ingrowth of Y-90. (Recounting the precipitate after three weeks should give more than double the former count rate if all the strontium was Sr-90.)

2. Apparatus

2.1. *Counting instruments:* One of the following is required:

a. Internal proportional counter, gas flow, with scaler, timer, and register.

b. End-window Geiger-Mueller tube (mica), or other thin-window (Mylar) counter, with scaler, timer, register, and amplifier as needed.

2.2. *Hirsch funnel* or *membrane filter.**

2.3. *Filter paper,* Whatman No. 40 (or equal), cut to fit Hirsch funnel; or membrane filter.

2.4. *Watch glasses,* 25 mm, or *stainless-steel pans,* about 54 mm in diameter and 7 mm deep, for counting the precipitate.

3. Reagents

3.1. *Barium nitrate carrier:* Dissolve 42.1 g $Ba(NO_3)_2$ in distilled water and dilute to 1 liter.

3.2. *Strontium nitrate carrier:* Carefully add 48.31 g $Sr(NO_3)_2$ to a volumetric flask and dilute to 1 liter with distilled water.

3.3. *Nitric acid,* conc. Also 6N.

3.4. *Ammonium hydroxide,* conc. Also 5N, 1 + 2.

3.5. *Sodium carbonate solution:* Dissolve 124 g sodium carbonate monohydrate, $Na_2CO_3 \cdot H_2O$, in distilled water and dilute to 1 liter.

3.6. *Acetone,* anhydrous.

3.7. *Rare earth carrier, mixed:* Dissolve 12.8 g cerous nitrate hexahy-

---

* Type HA (Millipore Filter Corporation, Bedford, Mass.) or equal. Glass fiber filters mounted on nylon disc with ring (Control Molding Corp., Staten Island, N.Y.) with teflon filter holder (Flurolon Laboratory, Box 305, Caldwell, N.J.) make suitable sample mounts, the sample being covered by 0.25-mil Mylar film, (E. I. du Pont de Nemours, Wilmington, Del.).

drate, $Ce(NO_3)_3 \cdot 6H_2O$, 14 g zirconyl chloride octahydrate, $ZrOCl_2 \cdot 8H_2O$, and 25 g ferric chloride hexahydrate, $FeCl_3 \cdot 6H_2O$, in 600 ml distilled water containing 5 ml conc HCl, and dilute to 1 liter.

3.8. *Phenolphthalein indicator solution:* Either the aqueous (*a*) or alcoholic (*b*) solution may be used:

a. Dissolve 5 g phenolphthalein disodium salt in distilled water and dilute to 1 liter. If necessary, add $0.02N$ NaOH dropwise until a faint pink color appears.

b. Dissolve 5 g phenolphthalein in 500 ml 95 per cent ethyl alcohol or isopropyl alcohol and add 500 ml distilled water. Then add $0.02N$ NaOH dropwise until a faint pink color appears.

3.9. *Acetate buffer solution:* Dissolve 154 g ammonium acetate, $NH_4C_2H_3O_2$, in 700 ml distilled water, add 57 ml conc acetic acid, and dilute to 1 liter.

3.10. *Sodium chromate solution:* Dissolve 351 g sodium chromate tetrahydrate, $Na_2CrO_4 \cdot 4H_2O$, in distilled water and dilute to 1 liter.

3.11. *Ethyl alcohol,* 95 per cent.

3.12. *Diethyl ether.*

4. Procedure

4.1. To 4 liters of drinking water or a filtered sample of raw water in a beaker add 1.0 ml each of the barium and strontium carriers and mix. A smaller sample may be used if it contains at least 25 picocuries of radioactive strontium. The suspended matter that has been filtered off may be digested (see Gross Alpha and Gross Beta Radioactivity, Sec. 9.1), diluted, and analyzed separately.

4.2. Add 5 ml conc HNO_3, heat to boiling, then add 50 ml conc NH_4OH.

4.3. Add 50 ml sodium carbonate solution to the boiling solution. Stir and allow to simmer at 90°–95° C for about 1 hr.

4.4. Set the beakers aside and let stand until the precipitate has settled (about 1–3 hr).

4.5. Decant and discard the clear supernate. Transfer the precipitate to a 40-ml centrifuge tube and centrifuge. Decant the supernate.

4.6. Add conc HNO_3 dropwise (about 2 ml) to the precipitate until it is completely dissolved. Heat to boiling, add 1 ml distilled water, stir, then centrifuge. In the case of hard water (more than 250 mg/l $CaCO_3$) add 3 ml distilled water. Discard any residue such as SiO_2.

4.7. Transfer the clear supernate to a clean tube. If the volume of the solution exceeds 3 ml, it should be evaporated to 3 ml or less.

4.8. Add 30 ml conc HNO_3, cool, stir, and centrifuge. Discard the supernate. Invert the tube in a beaker for about 10 min to drain off most of the excess HNO_3.

4.9. Dissolve in 2 ml distilled water and repeat Sec. 4.8.

4.10. Repeat Sec. 4.9.

4.11. Repeat Sec. 4.9 again if more than 200 mg Ca was present in the water sample.

4.12. Add 20 ml anhydrous acetone, stir thoroughly, cool, and centrifuge. Discard the supernate.

4.13. Dissolve the precipitate of $Sr(NO_3)_2$ and $Ba(NO_3)_2$ in 3 ml distilled water, and heat to boiling for about 30 sec to remove any remaining acetone.

4.14. Add 20 ml conc HNO_3. Cool, stir, and centrifuge. Discard the supernate.

4.15. Dissolve the precipitate in 10 ml distilled water, add 1 ml mixed rare earth carrier, and precipitate by making the solution basic with 5N NH_4OH. Centrifuge and decant the supernate to a clean tube. Discard the precipitate.

4.16. Add a drop of phenolphthalein indicator, then add 6N HNO_3 dropwise, with stirring, until the solution is neutral. Add 5 ml acetate buffer solution. Heat to boiling; then add 1 ml sodium chromate solution with stirring. Continue stirring for 1 min, then centrifuge. Decant the supernate to a clean tube and use it for the determination of strontium in Sec. 4.17.

4.17. Add 2 ml con NH_4OH to the supernate, heat to boiling, and then add 10 ml sodium carbonate solution. Stir and filter by suction on a small weighed filter paper disc in a small Hirsch funnel or on a membrane filter. Wash three times with 5-ml portions of water, three times with 5-ml portions of 95 per cent ethyl alcohol, and three times with 5-ml portions of diethyl ether. Transfer the filter and precipitate to a watch glass or counting pan, dry 5 min at 90°–100° C in an oven, and weigh; then mount and count the precipitate ($SrCO_3$) in an internal or thin-window counter.

5. Calculation

5.1. *Correction for carrier loss:* It is assumed that any loss in carrier † causes a corresponding loss in activity; 1 ml strontium nitrate carrier (20 mg

---

† If desired, the carrier loss may be determined by flame photometry.

Sr per milliliter) is equivalent to 33.6 mg $SrCO_3$.‡

Correct count
$$= \text{observed count} \times \frac{33.6}{\text{mg final ppt}}$$

5.2. *Correction for counting efficiency:* To convert counts per minute to disintegrations per minute, the efficiency of the counter must be known. This is determined by counting a standard sample of known strontium activity under conditions identical with those of the unknown.

5.3 Calculate the strontium activity in pc/l by the following equation:

$$\text{Total Sr activity in pc/l} = \frac{h}{a \, d \, f \times 2.22}$$

where

a = beta counter efficiency;
$d = \dfrac{\text{wt of final } SrCO_3 \text{ ppt, in mg}}{33.6}$;
f = sample volume, in liters;
h = beta activity, in net counts per minute,
$\quad = (i/t) - k$;
i = total counts accumulated;
k = background, in counts per minute; and
t = time of counting, in minutes.

6. Precision and Accuracy

A precision of ±5.0 per cent can be expected between duplicate samples. The method is accurate to about ±15.0 per cent.

Bibliography

1. HAHN, R. B. & STRAUB, C. P. Determination of Radioactive Strontium and Barium in Water. *J. AWWA* 47:335 (1955).
2. GOLDIN, A. S.; VELTEN, R. J.; & FRISHKORN, G. W. Determination of Radioactive Strontium. *Anal. Chem.* 31:1490 (1959).

---

‡ Should more than traces of stable strontium be present in the original sample, it would behave as carrier and should be treated as such.

Strontium-90 in Water *(Tentative)*

1. Principle

Strontium-90 in a large sample of water is concentrated by carbonate precipitation at boiling temperature in the presence of carrier strontium. Much of the alkaline earth and polyvalent radionuclides also precipitate. The precipitate is dissolved in acid, and radiobarium is removed as a chromate at pH 5. Radioactive ions other than strontium are precipitated from acid solution as hydroxides by treating with ammonia in the presence of ferric iron. The purified strontium is again precipitated as carbonate and stored until ingrowth of the Sr-90 daughter, Y-90, is sufficient for its extraction and measurement (see Fig. 26).

2. Apparatus

The same as for Total Radioactive Strontium, Sec. 2, plus separatory funnels, capacity 60 ml.

3. Reagents

The following reagents listed under Total Radioactive Strontium, Sec. 3, are required: 3.1, 3.2, 3.4, 3.5, 3.7, 3.9, and 3.10; also:

3.1. *Hydrochloric acid, 6N.* 1 + 1.

3.2. *Methyl orange indicator solution:* Dissolve 0.5 g methyl orange in 1 liter distilled water.

3.3. *Ferric nitrate solution:* Dissolve 36.0 g ferric nitrate nonahydrate, $Fe(NO_3)_3 \cdot 9H_2O$, in distilled water containing 2 ml conc HNO_3 and dilute to 1 liter.

3.4. *Nitric acid, 14N, 6N, and 0.1N.*

3.5. *Nitric acid,* white fuming, 90 per cent minimum.

3.6. *Tributyl phosphate,* reagent grade. Shake with $14N$ HNO_3 to equilibrate.

3.7 *Yttrium carrier:* Dissolve 12.7 g yttrium oxide,* Y_2O_3, in 30 ml warm conc HNO_3, then add 20 ml conc HNO_3 and dilute to 1 liter with distilled water; 1 ml is equivalent to 10 mg Y, or approximately 34 mg $Y_2(C_2O_4)_3 \cdot 9H_2O$.

3.8. *Oxalic acid,* saturated solution. Approximately 11 g $H_2C_2O_4$ in 100 ml distilled water.

4. Procedure

4.1. Proceed as for Total Radioactive Strontium, Sec. 4.1–4.5.

4.2. Dissolve the precipitate in 2–3 ml $6N$ HCl, heat to drive off CO_2, and dilute to 15–20 ml with distilled water.

4.3. Add $5N$ NH_4OH dropwise to the methyl orange endpoint.

4.4. Add 1 ml sodium chromate solution and warm in a water bath.

4.5. Slowly add 5 ml acetate buffer solution and digest hot for 5–10 min.

4.6. Centrifuge, add 2–3 drops of barium nitrate carrier, stir without disturbing the precipitate, and recentrifuge. Save the supernate.

4.7. Make the supernate alkaline with $5N$ NH_4OH and precipitate strontium with 10 ml sodium carbonate solution.

4.8. Centrifuge, discard the supernate, and wash the precipitate with

---

* Yttrium oxide carrier, Code 1118, American Potash and Chemical Corp., West Chicago, Ill., or equivalent.

15–25 ml distilled water containing 1–2 drops sodium carbonate solution.

4.9. To remove rare earths, dissolve the precipitate in 2–3 ml 6N HCl, add 25 ml distilled water and 2–3 drops ferric nitrate solution, heat, and make alkaline with 5N NH$_4$OH.

4.10. Centrifuge, add 2–3 drops ferric nitrate solution, and recentrifuge.

4.11. Decant the supernate and add 0.5 ml mixed rare earth carrier. If a precipitate forms, add 6N HCl dropwise to dissolve it; then warm, make alkaline with 5N NH$_4$OH, centrifuge, add 0.5 ml mixed rare earth carrier, and recentrifuge.

4.12. Decant and note the time of the last rare earth precipitation, which is the start of the Y-90 ingrowth period.

4.13. Add 10 ml sodium carbonate solution to the supernate containing strontium, and centrifuge. Store the precipitate of strontium carbonate for up to two weeks, when Sr-90 and Y-90 are in secular equilibrium (see Fig. 26).

4.14. Dissolve the strontium carbonate in 2 ml 6N HNO$_3$.

4.15. Cool in an ice bath and add, with stirring, 10 ml fuming HNO$_3$.

4.16. Centrifuge and transfer the supernate into a 60-ml separatory funnel.

4.17. Dissolve the residue in 2 ml 6N HNO$_3$ and repeat Sec. 4.15 and 4.16. Note the time, which is the end of the Y-90 production and the beginning of its decay. Combine supernates in funnel (Sec. 4.16) and continue as in Sec. 4.18. Save residue for Sr yield determination (Sec. 4.28–4.30).

4.18. Add 6 ml 6N HNO$_3$ to the separatory funnel to bring the aqueous phase to 30 ml.

4.19. Add 5.0 ml tributyl phosphate reagent, shake thoroughly for 10 min, and transfer the aqueous layer to another 60-ml separatory funnel.

4.20. Repeat Sec. 4.19 twice. Combine the aqueous solution after the third organic extraction with the residue in Sec. 4.17.

4.21. Combine the three organic extracts and wash three times with 5-ml portions of 14N HNO$_3$. Combine the acid washings with the residue in Sec. 4.17.

4.22. Back-extract the combined organic phases with 10 ml 0.1N HNO$_3$ for 10 min.

4.23. Transfer the aqueous phase to a 50-ml beaker and reduce its volume on a hot plate.

4.24. Repeat Sec. 4.22 and 4.23 twice, combining the aqueous phases in the 50-ml beaker.

4.25. Evaporate the solution to about 10 ml, transfer it to a stainless-steel counting pan, and evaporate to dryness.

4.26. Wash the beaker with small portions of 0.1N HNO$_3$. Add the washings to the counting pan.

4.27. Count in an internal proportional or end-window counter.

4.28. Make the combined aqueous solution and washings in Sec. 4.21 alkaline with 5N NH$_4$OH and precipitate SrCO$_3$ with 10 ml sodium carbonate solution.

4.29. Centrifuge, discard the supernate, wash the precipitate with 15–25 ml distilled water containing 1–2 drops conc NH$_4$OH.

4.30. Transfer precipitate to a tared dish, dry (120°C), and weigh to determine strontium yield, or determine the yield with a flame photometer or with Sr-85 tracer (the latter technique overcomes fictitious yield from samples high in stable strontium).

5. Alternate Procedure by Oxalate Precipitation

5.1. Proceed as in Sec. 4.1–4.14, inclusive, then add 1 ml yttrium carrier.

5.2. Add conc NH_4OH dropwise to the methyl orange endpoint, then add 5 ml conc NH_4OH in excess. Note the time, which is the end of the Y-90 production and the beginning of its decay.

5.3. Centrifuge, save the supernate for Sec. 5.10. Wash the precipitate twice with 20-ml portions of hot distilled water, combining supernates for Sec. 5.10.

5.4. Dissolve the precipitate with $6N$ HNO_3 and repeat Sec. 5.2 and 5.3.

5.5. Dissolve the precipitate with $6N$ HNO_3 (about 2 drops) then add 25 ml distilled water and heat in a water bath at 90°C.

5.6. Gradually add 15–20 drops of saturated oxalic acid solution with stirring, followed by 2–3 drops of conc NH_4OH to adjust the pH at 2.0–3.0. Digest the precipitate for 5 min, then cool in an ice bath with occasional stirring.

5.7. Transfer the precipitate to a two-piece funnel with a weighed glass fiber filter. Allow the precipitate to settle by gravity, then apply suction. Wash the precipitate with hot distilled water, then three times with 95 per cent ethyl alcohol and three times with diethyl ether.

5.8. Air dry the precipitate with suction for 2 min, weigh, and mount on a nylon disc and ring with Mylar cover.

5.9. Count, preferably in an end-window counter.

5.10. Make the supernates from Sec. 5.3 and 5.4 alkaline with NH_4OH and proceed as in Sec. 4.28–4.30.

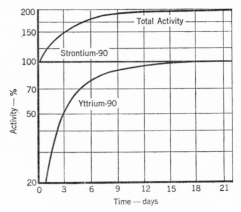

Fig. 26. Yttrium-90 vs strontium-90 activity as a function of time

6. Calculation

$$\text{pc/1 Sr-90} = \frac{\text{net cpm}}{a\,b\,c\,d\,f\,g \times 2.22}$$

where

a = counting efficiency;

b = chemical yield of extracting or precipitating Y-90;

c = ingrowth correction factor if not in secular equilibrium;

d = chemical yield of strontium determined gravimetrically or by flame photometry;

f = volume, in liters, of original sample;

g = Y-90 decay factor, calculated from
$$A = A_o e^{-\lambda t}$$

A = activity remaining after time interval;

A_o = activity of sample at some original time;

e = base of natural logarithms;

$\lambda = 0.693/T_{1/2}$, where $T_{1/2}$ for Y-90 is 64.2 hr; and

t = time, in hours, between separation and counting.

Bibliography

In addition to the references cited in the bibliography for the Total Radioactive Strontium method, the following also deserves attention:

GOLDIN, A. S. & VELTEN, R. J. Application of Tributyl Phosphate Extraction to the Determination of Strontium-90. *Anal. Chem.* 33:149 (1961).

Total Radium (Precipitation Technique) *(Tentative)*

There are four naturally occurring radionuclides—11.6-day radium-223, 3.6-day radium-224, 1,620-year radium-226, and 5.75-year radium-228. Radium-223 is a member of the uranium-235 series, radium-224 and radium-228 of the thorium series, and radium-226 of the uranium-238 series. The contribution of radium-228 (a beta emitter) to the radium alpha activity is negligible because of the 1.9-year half-life of its first alpha-emitting daughter product, thorium-228. The other three radionuclides are alpha emitters; each gives rise to a family of relatively short-lived daughter products, including three more alpha emitters. Because of the differences in half-lives of the nuclides in these series, the radionuclides of radium can be identified by the rate of ingrowth and decay of their daughters in a barium sulfate precipitate.[1, 2, 4] The activity of radium-226 increases at a rate governed by the 3.8-day half-life of radon-222. The ingrowth of alpha daughter activity in radium-223 is complete by the time a radium-barium precipitate can be prepared for counting. The ingrowth of the first two alpha-emitting daughters of radium-224 is complete within a few minutes and the third alpha daughter activity increases at a rate which is governed by the 10.6-hr lead-212. In the case of radium-224, the activity is also decreasing with a 3.6-day half-life of the parent, leading to a rather complicated ingrowth and decay curve.

The Federal Radiation Council has provided guidance for federal agencies conducting activities designed to limit exposure of people to radiation from nuclides deposited in the body as a result of their occurrence in the environment. The recommended radiation protection guides (RPG) for Ra-226 transient rates of intake are 0–2, 2–20, 20–200 picocuries per person per day for ranges I, II, and III, respectively. Range III calls for the application of control measures to reduce the intake to within Range II or below.

Inasmuch as these guides apply to total intake (from air, food, and water) the Public Health Service Advisory Committee on the 1962 Drinking Water Standards recommended a limit of 3 pc/l for Ra-226.

The standard specifies Ra-226 in particular, because other radium nuclides are much less important in causing internal radiation exposure.

The two principal methods of measuring radium are (a) the precipitation and purification of radium with barium as the sulfate for alpha counting and (b) the separation of radon from a concentrate of radium in an unknown. The former includes all radium nuclides, whereas the latter (emanation technique) is quite specific for Ra-226. At concentrations of total radium above the drinking water standard, the precipitation technique would require alpha measurement of the decay rate to resolve the Ra-226 content or, preferably, the measurement of Ra-226 by radon.

The total radium by precipitation is a screening technique applicable in particular to drinking water. As long as the concentration of total radium is less than the drinking water standard, the need for examination by a more specific method is minimal.

1. General Discussion

1.1. *Principle:* The following method is designed to measure radium in clear water. It is applicable to sewage and industrial wastes, provided steps are taken to destroy organic matter and eliminate other interfering ions (see Gross Alpha and Gross Beta Radioactivity, Sec. 9). However, ignition of sample ash should be avoided or a fusion will be necessary. Radium carried on barium sulfate is determined by alpha counting. Lead and barium carriers are added to the sample containing alkaline citrate, then sulfuric acid is added to precipitate Ra-Ba-Pb as sulfates. The precipitate is purified by washing with nitric acid, then dissolved in alkaline EDTA and reprecipitated as radium-barium sulfate by adjusting the pH to 4.5. This slightly acidic EDTA keeps other naturally occurring alpha emitters and the lead carrier in solution.

2. Apparatus

2.1. *Counting instruments:* One of the following is required:

(*a*) *Internal proportional counter,* gas flow, with scaler and register.

(*b*) *Alpha scintillation counter,* silver-activated zinc sulfide phosphor deposited on thin plastic (Mylar) with photomultiplier, scaler, timer, and register.

2.2. *Membrane filter holder or stainless steel (or Teflon) filter funnels* (Tracer Lab) with Fisher Filtrator or an equivalent vacuum source.

2.3. *Membrane filters* (Millipore type HA) *or glass fiber filters* (H. Reeve Angel & Co., No. 934-AH, diameter 2.4 cm).

3. Reagents

3.1. *Citric acid,* 1M. Dissolve 210 g citric acid, $H_3C_6H_5O_7 \cdot H_2O$, in distilled water and dilute to 1 liter.

3.2 *Ammonium hydroxide,* conc. Also 5N, 1 + 2.

3.3. *Lead nitrate carrier:* Dissolve 160 g $Pb(NO_3)_2$ in distilled water and dilute to 1 liter.

3.4. *Barium chloride carrier:* Dissolve 11.9 g $BaCl_2 \cdot 2H_2O$ in distilled water and dilute to 1 liter; 1 ml = 6.7 mg Ba.

3.5. *Methyl orange indicator solution:* Dissolve 0.5 g methyl orange in 1 liter distilled water.

3.6. *Sulfuric acid,* 18N. 1 + 1.

3.7. *Nitric acid,* conc.

3.8. *EDTA reagent,* 0.25M. Add 93 g disodium ethylenediaminetetraacetate dihydrate to distilled water, and dilute to 1 liter.

3.9. *Acetic acid,* conc.

3.10. *Ethyl alcohol,* 95 per cent.

3.11. *Acetone.*

3.12. *Lucite solution:* Dissolve 50 mg lucite in 100 ml acetone.

4. Procedure

4.1. To 1 liter of filtered sample in a 1,500-ml beaker add 5 ml 1M citric acid, 2.5 ml conc NH_4OH, 2 ml lead carrier, and 1.0 ml barium carrier.

4.2. Heat to boiling and add 10 drops methyl orange indicator.

4.3. While stirring, slowly add 18N H_2SO_4 to a permanent pink color, then add 0.25 ml acid in excess.

4.4. Boil gently 5 to 10 min.

4.5. Set the beaker aside and let stand until the precipitate is settled (3 to 5 hr or more).

4.6. Decant and discard the clear supernate. Transfer the precipitate to a 40-ml or larger centrifuge tube, centrifuge, decant, and discard the supernate.

4.7. Wash the precipitate three times with 10-ml portions of conc HNO_3, discarding the washings.

4.8. Dissolve the precipitate in the centrifuge tube with 10 ml distilled water, 10 ml EDTA, and 3 ml $5N$ NH_4OH.

4.9. Warm in steam bath to clear solution and add 2 ml conc acetic acid dropwise. Digest 5–10 min, cool, and centrifuge. Discard supernate. The quantity of acetic acid is approximately twice the amount needed to neutralize the NH_4OH, thus giving a pH of 4.5, which is sufficient to destroy the Ba-EDTA complex, but not the Pb-EDTA.

4.10. Wash the barium-radium sulfate precipitate with distilled water and mount it in a suitable manner for counting as given in Sec. 4.11, 4.12, or 4.13.

4.11. Transfer the Ba-Ra sulfate precipitate to a tared stainless-steel planchet with minimum of 95 per cent ethyl alcohol and evaporate under an infrared lamp. Add 2 ml acetone, 2 drops of lucite solution, disperse the precipitate evenly, and evaporate under an infrared lamp. Dry in oven at 110°C, weigh, and determine the alpha activity in an internal proportional counter.

4.12. Transfer the precipitate to a tared membrane filter in a holder and wash with 15–25 ml distilled water. Place the membrane in a counting dish with a weight (glass ring) and dry at 110°C. Weigh and count in an internal proportional counter or an alpha ZnS scintillation phototube counter.

4.13. Add 20 ml distilled water to the Ba-Ra sulfate precipitate, allow to settle in a steam bath, cool, and filter

using the special funnel * arrangement on a tared glass fiber filter paper. Dry the precipitate in the oven at 110°C to constant weight. Mount the precipitate on a nylon disc and ring with an alpha phosphor on Mylar,[3] and count with a bare phototube on a counter.

5. Calculation

$$pc/l\ radium = \frac{net\ cpm}{a\ b\ c\ d\ e \times 2.22}$$

where

$a =$ ingrowth factor (as shown in the following table) ;

Ingrowth hr	Alpha Activity from Ra-226
0	1.0000
1	1.0160
2	1.0363
3	1.0580
4	1.0798
5	1.1021
6	1.1238
24	1.4892
48	1.9054
72	2.2525

$b =$ efficiency factor for alpha counting;
$c =$ self-absorption factor ;
$d =$ chemical yield ; and
$e =$ sample volume, in liters.

The calculations are based on the assumption that the radium is radium-226. If the observed concentration approaches 3 pc/l it may be desirable to follow the rate of ingrowth and estimate the isotopic content [2, 4] or, preferably, to determine radium-226 by radon.

6. Precision and Accuracy

The quadruplicate results obtained from five laboratories reporting on

---

* Tracer Lab stainless steel two-piece funnel or equivalent.

each of two samples were analyzed statistically. The two samples contained 1.2 and 9.4 pc Ra-226 per liter, each with added contamination of Po-210 and U-238 alpha activity. The range of the mean values obtained by the laboratories was 1.20 to 1.33 with an average of 1.25 pc/l for the low concentration and 8.73 to 9.90 with an average of 8.97 pc/l for the high concentration. The standard deviation of precision was approximately 0.2 and 0.7 pc/l for the low and high concentrations, respectively.

Bibliography

1. KIRBY, H. W. Decay and Growth Tables for Naturally Occurring Radioactive Series. *Anal. Chem.* 26:1063 (1954).
2. SILL, C. Determination of Radium-226, Thorium-230, and Thorium-232. *U.S. Atomic Energy Comm. Rept.* No. TID 7616 (Oct. 1960).
3. HALLDEN, N. A. & HARLEY, J. H. An Improved Alpha-Counting Technique. *Anal. Chem.* 32:1961 (1960).
4. GOLDIN, A. S. Determination of Dissolved Radium. *Anal. Chem.* 33:406 (1961).

Radium-226 by Radon (Soluble, Suspended and Total) (Tentative)

1. General Discussion

Pertinent to the determination of radium-226 by radon is the discussion of the significance of radium, particularly in drinking water, as discussed under Total Radium (Precipitation Technique).

1.1. *Principle:* The radium in water is concentrated and separated from sample solids by coprecipitation with a relatively large amount of barium as the sulfate. The precipitate is treated to remove silicates and decompose insoluble radium complexes, fused with phosphoric acid to remove SO_3, and dissolved in HCl. The completely soluble radium is placed in a bubbler, which is then sealed and stored for several days to four weeks for ingrowth of radon-222. The bubbler is connected to an evacuated system and the radon gas is removed from the liquid by aeration, dried with a desiccant, and collected in a counting chamber. The counting chamber consists of a dome-shaped cylinder coated with silver-activated zinc sulfide phosphor, with a transparent window which rests on a photomultiplier tube during counting (Fig. 27). About 4 hr after radon collection, the alpha counting rate of Rn-222 and daughter products is at equilibrium and a count is obtained and related to known standards similarly treated.

The counting gas used to purge radon from the mother liquor to the counting chamber may be helium, nitrogen, or air. In each case, the gas should be free of radon, such as by aging. Although all of these gases are satisfactory, the yield and pulse height of scintillations are improved with the use of helium.

There is a variety of radium-by-radon techniques available. Some employ a minimum of chemistry, but utilize large Rn-counting gas chambers. Others involve more chemical separation, concentration and purification of

Ra-226 prior to de-emanation in counting cells of either the ionization or alpha scintillation types.

The selected method requires a moderate amount of chemistry coupled with a sensitive alpha scintillation count of radon plus daughter products in a small chamber.[2]

1.2. *Concentration techniques:* The chemical properties of barium and radium are similar; therefore, because barium does not interfere with de-emanation, as much as 100 mg may be used to aid in coprecipitating Ra from a sample to be placed in a single radon bubbler. However, radium is an impurity of barium salts, consequently reagent tests are necessary to account for added radium.

1.3. *Interferences:* Only gaseous alpha-emitting radionuclides Rn-219 (actinon) and Rn-220 (thoron) interfere with the test. Interference from them would be expected to be very rare in water not contaminated from industrial wastes such as uranium mill effluents.[3] The half-lives of these nuclides are only 3.92 and 54.5 sec, respectively, so that it is only their alpha-emitting decay products which interfere.

Interference from stable chemicals is limited. Small amounts of lead, calcium and strontium which are collected on barium sulfate do not interfere. However, lead may deteriorate the platinum ware. High dissolved solids and calcium at concentrations of 300 mg/l cause no difficulty.

The formation of precipitates in excess of a few milligrams during the radon ingrowth period is a warning that modifications[3] are necessary because radon recovery may be impaired.

1.4. *Minimum detectable concentration:* The minimum detectable concentration depends on scaler-photomul-

tiplier characteristics, background counting rate of the scintillation cell, length of counting period, radium contamination of reagents, and radium contamination of apparatus and environment. Without reagent purification, the overall reagent blank should be between 0.03 and 0.05 pc Ra-226, which may be considered the minimum detectable amount.

1.5. Where soluble radium-226 is of most significance some simplification may be achieved by performing an initial concentration of Ra-226 by barium coprecipitation as carbonate, solution of the carbonate by acidification with HCl, and transferral of the solution to a bubbler. The formation of any precipitate during the ingrowth period would tend to invalidate this or any method because radon occlusion in the precipitate may occur. Tests along these lines may prove satisfactory for many samples and would thus eliminate the need of platinum fusion vessels and the more involved chemical procedure.

2. Apparatus

2.1. *Scintillation counter* assembly with photomultiplier tube 2 in. or larger in diameter mounted in a light-tight housing.

2.2. *Scintillation cells,* Lucas type, preferably having a volume of 95–140 ml, made in laboratory[2, 3] or commercially available.*

2.3. *Radon bubblers,* capacity preferably 18–25 ml, as shown in Figure 27.† One is needed for standard ra-

---

* William H. Johnston Laboratories, 3617 Woodland Ave., Baltimore 15, Md.
† Available from Corning Glass Works, Special Apparatus Division, Corning, N.Y.

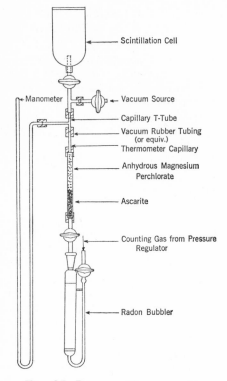

Scintillation Cell

Manometer

Vacuum Source

Capillary T-Tube

Vacuum Rubber Tubing (or equiv.)

Thermometer Capillary

Anhydrous Magnesium Perchlorate

Ascarite

Counting Gas from Pressure Regulator

Radon Bubbler

Fig. 27. De-emanation assembly

dium solution and one for each sample to be tested simultaneously.[3]

2.4. *Manometer,* open-end capillary tube or vacuum gage, 0–760 mm Hg.

2.5. *Gas purification* tube, 7–8 mm O.D. glass tubing, 100–120 mm long, constricted at lower end to hold glass wool plug (Fig. 27).

2.6. *Sample bottles,* polyethylene, 2- to 4-liter capacity.

2.7. *Membrane filters.*‡

2.8. *Gas supply:* Helium, nitrogen or aged air in high-pressure cylinder with two-stage pressure regulator.

2.9. *Silicone grease,* high-vacuum; *sealing wax,* "Pyseal," low-melting; and *paraffin.*

‡ Type HA (Millipore Filter Corp., Bedford, Mass.) or equivalent.

2.10. *Laboratory glassware:* All glassware must be decontaminated after use by heating for 1 hr in EDTA decontaminating solution at 90–100°C, then rinsed in water, $1 + 9$ HCl, and again in distilled water to dissolve barium-radium sulfate.

2.11. *Platinum ware:* Crucibles (20–30 ml) or dishes (50–75 ml), and a large dish (for flux preparation) with a platinum-tipped tongs (preferably Blair type). Platinum ware is cleaned by immersing and rotating in a molten bath of potassium pyrosulfate, cooling, rinsing in hot tap water, digesting in hot $6N$ HCl, rinsing in distilled water, and finally flaming over a burner.

3. Reagents

3.1. *Stock barium chloride solution:* Dissolve 35.6 g barium chloride, $BaCl_2 \cdot 2H_2O$, in distilled water and dilute to 1 liter.

3.2. *Dilute barium chloride solution:* Dilute 100 ml stock barium chloride solution to 1,000 ml as needed; 1 ml = 2 mg Ba.

3.3. *Acid barium chloride solution:* After standing 24 hr, filter the dilute barium chloride solution through a membrane filter. Acidify 980 ml of the filtrate with 20 ml conc HCl.

3.4. *Stock radium-226 solution:* Take every precaution to avoid unnecessary contamination of the working area, equipment, and glassware, preferably by preparing the radium standards in a separate area or room reserved for this purpose. Purchase a National Bureau of Standards gamma ray standard containing 0.1 μg radium-226. Cautiously break the neck of the ampoule which is submerged in 300 ml acid barium chloride solution in a 600-ml beaker. Chip the ampoule until it is broken or until the hole is large enough to obtain complete mixing. Transfer the solution with rinsing and dilute with acid barium chloride solution to 1 liter.

3.5. *Intermediate radium solution:* Dilute 100 ml stock radium solution to 1,000 ml with acid barium chloride solution; 1 ml = 10 pc Ra-226.

3.6. *Standard radium solution:* Dilute 30.0 ml intermediate radium solution to 100 ml with acid barium chloride solution; 1 ml = 3 pc Ra-226.

3.7. *Hydrochloric acid,* conc. Also 1 + 3 and 1 + 100.

3.8. *Sulfuric acid,* conc and 1 + 200.

3.9. *Hydrofluoric acid,* 48 per cent (in a dropping bottle).

3.10. *Ammonium sulfate solution:* Dissolve 10 g ammonium sulfate, $(NH_4)_2SO_4$, in distilled water and dilute to 100 ml.

3.11. *Solvent:* Mix equal volumes of acetone and 95 per cent ethyl alcohol.

3.12. *Phosphoric acid,* 85 per cent.

3.13. *Ascarite,* 8–20 mesh.

3.14. *Magnesium perchlorate,* anhydrous desiccant.

3.15. *EDTA decontaminating solution:* Dissolve 10 g disodium ethylenediaminetetraacetate dihydrate, also called (ethylenedinitrilo)tetraacetic acid sodium salt, and 10 g sodium carbonate in distilled water, and dilute to 1 liter.

3.16. *Special reagents for total and suspended radium:*

a. *Flux:* Add 30 mg barium sulfate, $BaSO_4$, 65.8 g potassium carbonate, K_2CO_3, 50.5 g sodium carbonate, Na_2CO_3, and 33.7 g sodium borate decahydrate, $Na_2B_4O_7 \cdot 10H_2O$, in a large platinum dish (500-ml capacity). Mix thoroughly and heat cautiously to expel water, then fuse and mix thoroughly by swirling. Cool and grind the flux in a porcelain mortar to pass a 10–12 mesh (or finer) screen, and store in an airtight bottle.

b. *Dilute hydrogen peroxide solution:* Dilute 10 ml 30 per cent H_2O_2 to 100 ml with distilled water as needed.

4. Calibration of Scintillation Counter Assembly

4.1. Test and select bubblers having a uniform flow over a fritted disc with a flow rate of 3–5 ml/min.

4.2. Apply silicone grease to stopcocks of a bubbler, and, with gas inlet stopcock closed, add 1 ml stock barium chloride solution, 10 ml (30 pc) standard radium solution, and additional acid barium chloride solution to fill the bubbler one-half to two-thirds full.

4.3. Dry the joint with lint-free paper or cloth, apply sealing wax, separately warm the joint parts and make connection with a twisting motion to uniformly spread wax. Allow joint to cool, then establish zero ingrowth time by purging liquid with counting gas for 15–20 min according to Sec. 4.10 and 4.14. Close stopcocks, record date and time, and store bubbler, preferably for three weeks or more before collecting and counting the radon. A partial Rn ingrowth period may be selected for the standard bubbler. Table 24 lists the ingrowth of the Rn from Ra-226, the Rn decay, and the correction factor accounting for Rn decay during the counting period.

4.4. Attach scintillation cell to vacuum train and slowly evacuate. Close stopcock from vacuum source and check manometer reading for 15–20 min to assure no leak in scintillation cell.

4.5. Cautiously admit counting gas to scintillation cell until atmospheric pressure is reached.

4.6. Place scintillation cell over photomultiplier tube, cover with light-tight hood and, after 10 min, obtain a background counting rate (preferably 100 to 1,000 min, depending on concentration of Ra-226 in unknown samples). Phototube *must not* be exposed to external light when energized with high voltage.

4.7. Repeat Sec. 4.4 to 4.6 for each scintillation cell.

4.8. If the performance and background are satisfactory, continue calibration.

4.9. With scintillation cell and standard bubbler (Sec. 4.3) on vacuum train, evacuate scintillation cell and purification system (Fig. 27).

4.10. Adjust gas regulator valve so that a very slow stream of gas will flow with the needle valve open. Attach gas supply to inlet of bubbler.

4.11. Very cautiously open bubbler outlet stopcock to equalize pressure and transfer all or most of the fluid in the inlet side arm to the bubbler chamber.

4.12. Close outlet valve and very cautiously open inlet valve to flush remaining fluid from side arm and fritted disc. Close inlet stopcock.

4.13. Repeat Sec. 4.11 to equalize pressure, and note the time.

4.14. With outlet stopcock fully open, cautiously open inlet stopcock so that the flow of gas produces a froth a few mm thick at the surface of bubbler solution. Maintain flow rate by carefully opening regulator valve and continue de-emanation for about 20 min, when the cell should be at atmospheric pressure. Note time of radon decay.

4.15. Close stopcocks to scintillation cell, close bubbler inlet and outlet, shut off and disconnect gas supply, and record the date and time of radon decay.

4.16. Store the bubbler for radon ingrowth and subsequent de-emanation, if desired (Table 24). The standard bubbler may be kept indefinitely.

4.17. Four hours after de-emanation, when daughter products are in virtual equilibrium with Rn, place scintillation cell on photomultiplier tube, cover with light-tight cover, let stand for about 10 min, then begin the count.

4.18. Correct the net counting rate for radon decay (Table 24) and relate it to the pc of Ra-226 in standard bubbler. Unless the scintillation cell is physically damaged, the calibration will remain essentially unchanged for years.

4.19. Repeat Sec. 4.8 through 4.19 on each scintillation cell.

4.20. Recondition used scintillation cells by evacuating and replacing the cell contents with counting gas. Three successive evacuations are preferred for cells having had high radon content.

5. Procedure for Soluble Radium-226

5.1. Filter at least 1 liter of sample or a volume containing up to 30 pc Ra-226 into a polyethylene bottle as soon after sampling as possible. Save the suspended matter for determination by the procedure described in Sec. 6.

5.2. Add 20 ml conc HCl per liter of filtrate and continue analysis when convenient.

5.3. Add 50 ml dilute barium chloride solution, with vigorous stirring, to 1,020 ml acidified sample (Sec. 5.2) in a 1,500-ml beaker. For each set of samples analyzed in parallel, run a reagent blank of distilled water.

5.4. Cautiously and with vigorous stirring add 20 ml conc H_2SO_4. Cover beaker and allow overnight precipitation.

5.5. Filter supernate through a membrane filter, use $1 + 200$ H_2SO_4 to transfer Ba-Ra precipitate to filter, wash precipitate twice with $1 + 200$ H_2SO_4.

5.6. Place filter with precipitate in a platinum crucible or dish, add 0.5 ml HF, 3 drops (0.15 ml) ammonium sulfate solution, and evaporate to dryness.

5.7. Wet membrane with several ml of acetone-alcohol solvent, ignite solvent with flame, ignite residue over a bunsen burner, and cool.

5.8. Add 1 ml H_3PO_4 with a calibrated dropper and heat on hot plate at 200°C; gradually raise and maintain a temperature of 300–400°C for 30 min.

5.9. Swirl vessel over a low bunsen flame adjusted so as to avoid spattering while covering the walls with hot H_3PO_4. Continue heat for a minute after precipitate fuses into a clear melt (just below redness) to insure complete removal of SO_3.

5.10. Fill cooled vessel one-half full with $1 + 3$ HCl, heat on steam bath, then gradually add additional $1 + 3$ HCl to within 2 mm of the vessel lip.

5.11. Evaporate on steam or hot water bath until there are no more vapors of HCl.

5.12. Add 4 ml $1 + 3$ HCl, swirl, and warm to dissolve $BaCl_2$ crystals.

5.13. Close gas inlet stopcock, add a drop of water to the fritted disc of the fully greased and tested radon bubbler, and transfer sample in platinum vessel to the bubbler by means of a medicine dropper. Use dropper to rinse the vessel with three 2-ml portions of distilled water.

5.14. Dry, wax if necessary, seal the joint, and establish zero ingrowth time as instructed in Sec. 4.3.

5.15. Close stopcocks, record date and time, and store bubbler for radon ingrowth, preferably for three weeks for low concentrations of Ra-226.

5.16. De-emanate and count Rn as instructed for calibrations in Sec. 4.9 through 4.18 with unknown sample replacing the standard bubbler.

5.17. The sample in bubbler may be stored for a second ingrowth or discarded and the bubbler cleaned for reuse. (A bubbler is readily cleaned while in an inverted position by attaching a tube from a beaker containing 100 ml $1 + 200$ HCl to the inlet, and another tube from outlet to a suction flask. By alternately opening and closing outlet and inlet stopcocks the acid rinse water is sequentially passed through the fritted disc, accumulated in the bubbler, and flushed into the suction flask. Drain bubbler dry with the aid of vacuum, heat the taper joint gently to melt the wax, and separate the joint. More extensive cleaning, as instructed in Sec. 2.11, may be necessary if the bubbler contained more than 10 pc Ra-226.)

6. Procedure for Ra-226 in Suspended Matter

6.1. Suspended matter in water usually contains earthy materials which require fusion, such as with an alkaline flux, to insure recovery of radium. The suspended matter of the sample (up to 1,000 mg of organic material) retained on the membrane filter in Sec. 5.1 from a known volume of water is dried in a tared platinum crucible and ignited as in Sec. 5.7.

6.2. Weigh crucible to estimate residue.

6.3. Add 8 g flux for each gram of residue, but not less than 2 g flux, and mix with a glass rod.

6.4. Heat over burner until reaction begins, then more carefully to prevent spattering. Continue heating over a Meeker burner for 20 min after bubbling stops, with an occasional swirl of the crucible to mix the contents and achieve a uniform melt. A clear melt is usually obtained only with samples of high silica or low residue content.

6.5. Remove crucible from burner and rotate as melt cools to distribute solids in a thin layer on crucible wall.

6.6. When cool, place crucible in a covered beaker containing 120 ml distilled water, 20 ml conc H_2SO_4, and 5 ml dilute H_2O_2 solution for each 8 g of flux. (Reduce acid and H_2O_2 in proportion to flux used.) Rotate beaker to dissolve solids if necessary.

6.7. When solids are dissolved, remove and rinse crucible. Add rinse water to beaker. Save crucible for Sec. 6.10.

6.8. Heat solution and slowly add 50 ml dilute $BaCl_2$ solution with vigorous stirring. Digest for 30 min, then cover beaker and allow overnight precipitation.

6.9. Add about 1 ml dilute H_2O_2 and, if yellow color (from titanium) deepens, add additional H_2O_2 until there is no further color change.

6.10. Continue analysis according to Sec. 5.5 through 5.16.

7. Procedure for Total Radium-226

7.1. Total Ra-226 in water is the sum of soluble and suspended radium previously described, or it may be determined directly by examining the original water sample which has been acidified with 20 ml conc HCl for each liter of sample and stored in a polyethylene bottle.

7.2. Thoroughly mix the acidified sample and take 1,020 ml or a volume containing not more than 1,000 mg of inorganic solids.

7.3. Add 50 ml dilute barium chloride solution and slowly, with vigorous stirring, add 20 ml conc H_2SO_4 per liter of sample. Cover and allow to precipitate overnight.

7.4. Filter supernate through membrane filter and transfer solids to filter as in Sec. 5.5.

7.5. Place filter and precipitate in tared platinum crucible and proceed as in Sec. 6.1 through 6.10, but omitting Sec. 6.8.

8. Calculations

8.1. The Ra-226 in a bubbler, including reagent blank, is as follows:

$$\text{Ra–226, in pc} = \frac{(R_s - R_b)}{R_e} \times \frac{1}{1-e^{-\lambda t_1}} \times \frac{1}{e^{-\lambda t_2}} \times \frac{\lambda t_3}{1-e^{-\lambda t_3}}$$

where

λ = decay constant for Rn–222, = 0.00755/hr;

t_1 = time interval allowed for ingrowth of Rn–222, in hours;

t_2 = time interval between de-emanation and counting, in hours;

t_3 = time interval of counting, in hours;

R_s = observed counting rate of sample in scintillation cell, c/hr;

R_b = (previously) observed background counting rate of scintillation cell with counting gas, c/hr;

R_e = calibration constant for scintillation cell (i.e., observed net count per hour corrected for radon equilibrium and decay (C/AB) per picocurie of Ra–226 in standard);

or:

$$\text{Ra–226, in pc} = \frac{(R_s - R_b)}{R_e} \times \frac{C}{AB}$$

where

A = factor for decay of radon (see Table 24);

TABLE 24—FACTORS FOR DECAY OF RADON, GROWTH OF RADON FROM RADIUM, AND CORRECTION OF RADON ACTIVITY FOR DECAY DURING COUNTING

Time	Factor for Decay of Radon*		Factor for Growth of Radon from Radium†		Factor for Correction of Radon Activity for Decay During Counting‡
	hr	days	hr	days	hr
0	1.000	1.000	—	0.000	1.000
¼	0.998	—	—	—	—
½	0.996	—	—	—	—
¾	0.994	—	—	—	—
1	0.992	0.834	—	0.166	1.004
2	0.985	0.696	—	0.304	1.007
3	0.978	0.581	—	0.419	1.011
4	0.970	0.484	—	0.516	1.015
5	0.963	0.404	—	0.596	1.019
6	0.956	0.337	—	0.663	1.023
7	0.948	0.281	—	0.719	1.027
8	0.941	0.235	—	0.765	1.030
9	0.934	0.196	—	0.804	1.034
10	0.927	0.163	0.082	0.837	1.038
11	0.920	0.136	—	0.864	1.042
12	0.913	0.114	0.091	0.886	1.046
13	0.906	0.095	—	0.905	1.050
14	0.900	0.079	0.100	0.921	1.054
15	0.893	0.066	—	0.934	1.058
16	0.886	0.055	0.114	0.945	1.062
17	0.880	0.046	0.120	0.954	1.065
18	0.873	0.038	0.127	0.962	1.069
19	0.866	0.032	0.134	0.968	1.073
20	0.860	0.027	0.148	0.973	1.077
21	0.853	0.022	—	0.978	1.081
22	0.847	0.019	—	0.981	1.085
23	0.841	0.015	—	0.984	1.089
24	0.834	0.013	0.166	0.987	1.093
25	0.828	0.011	—	0.989	1.097
26	0.822	—	—	0.991	1.101
27	0.816	—	0.184	0.992	1.105
28	0.809	—	—	0.994	1.109
29	0.803	—	—	0.995	1.113
30	0.797	—	0.201	0.996	1.117
31	0.791	—	—	0.996	1.122
32	0.785	—	—	0.997	1.126
33	0.779	—	0.221	0.997	1.130
34	0.774	—	—	0.998	1.134
35	0.768	—	—	—	1.138

TABLE 24—*Continued*

Time	Factor for Decay of Radon *		Factor for Growth of Radon from Radium †		Factor for Correction of Radon Activity for Decay During Counting ‡
	hr	days	hr	days	hr
36	0.762	—	0.239	—	1.142
37	0.756	—	—	0.999	1.146
38	0.751	—	—	—	1.150
39	0.745	—	0.256	—	1.154
40	0.739	—	—	—	1.159
41	0.734	—	—	—	1.163
42	0.728	—	0.272	—	1.167
43	0.723	—	—	1.000	1.171
44	0.717	—	—	—	1.175
45	0.712	—	0.288	—	1.180
46	0.707	—	—	—	1.184
47	0.701	—	—	—	1.188
48	0.696	—	0.304	—	1.192
49	0.691	—	—	—	1.196
50	0.686	—	—	—	1.201
51	0.680	—	0.320	—	1.205
52	0.675	—	—	—	1.209
53	0.670	—	—	—	1.213
54	0.665	—	0.335	—	1.218
55	0.660	—	—	—	1.222
56	0.655	—	—	—	1.226
57	0.650	—	0.350	—	1.231
58	0.645	—	—	—	1.235
59	0.640	—	—	—	1.239
60	0.636	—	0.365	—	1.244

* $e^{-\lambda t}$ based on radon half-life of 3.825 days.
† $1-e^{-\lambda t}$.
‡ $\lambda t/(1-e^{-\lambda t})$.

$B =$ factor for growth of radon from radium (see Table 24); and
$C =$ factor for correction of radon activity for decay during counting (see Table 24).

In calculating cell calibration constants, the same equation is used, but the pc of Ra-226 is known and R_c is the unknown.

8.2. Convert the activity into pc/l of soluble, suspended, or total radium-226 by the following equation:

$$\text{pc/l Ra-226} = \frac{(D - E) \times 1,000}{\text{ml sample}}$$

where

$D =$ pc Ra-226 found in sample; and
$E =$ pc Ra-226 found in reagent blank.

Bibliography

1. HURSH, J. B. Radium-226 in Water Supplies of the U. S. *J. AWWA* 46:43 (1954).

2. Lucas, H. F. Improved Low-Level Alpha Scintillation Counter for Radon. *Rev. Sci. Instr.* 28:680 (1957).

3. Rushing, D. E.; Garcia, W. J.; & Clark, D. A. The Analysis of Effluents and Environmental Samples from Uranium Mills and of Biological Samples for Radium, Polonium, and Uranium. *Radiological Health and Safety in Mining and Milling of Nuclear Materials* Vol. II:187 (1964) Internat. Atomic Energy Agency, Vienna, Austria.

PART III

Physical and Chemical Examination of Wastewater, Treatment Plant Effluents, and Polluted Waters

Introduction

The procedures described in Part III of this manual are intended for the physical and chemical examination of sewage, sewage treatment plant effluents, and polluted waters. Many of the procedures are applicable without change to industrial wastes resulting from the processing of foods, beverages, and biologic products. However, because of the wide variety of industrial wastes, both from physical and from chemical processes, their examination by methods in Part III must be carried out with judgment and caution, after consulting Part IV for procedures which are recommended as being particularly applicable to industrial wastes and effluents.

A. Collection of Samples

Only representative samples should be used for examination. The great variety of conditions under which collections must be made renders it impossible to prescribe a fixed procedure.

1. Method of Sampling Sewage, Effluents, and Wastes

The standard method prescribes the collection of a composite sample over a 24-hr period. In many cases it may be advisable to composite individual samples over a 1-hr, 2-hr, or 4-hr period; to divide the sample to represent shift work; or to extend it to cover the complete cycle of operation including all special, variable, or periodic discharges at irregular intervals, as well as Saturday and Sunday cleanups. This is particularly true with industrial wastes (see Part IV).

Individual portions should be taken in a wide-mouth bottle having a diameter of at least 35 mm at the mouth and a capacity of at least 120 ml. These portions should be collected each hour —in some cases each half hour or even every 5 min—and mixed at the end of the sampling period, or combined in a single bottle as collected. If preservatives are to be used, they should be added to the sample bottle initially, so that all portions of the composite are preserved as soon as collected. Analysis of individual samples may sometimes be necessary.

It is desirable, and often absolutely essential, to combine the individual samples in volumes proportionate to the volume of flow. A final volume of 2–3 liters is sufficient for sewage, effluents, and wastes.

Automatic sampling devices are available but should not be used unless the sample is preserved as described below. Sampling devices, including bottles, should be cleaned daily of all growths of sewage organisms.

2. Preservation of Samples

Samples of sewage, effluents, and wastes should be analyzed as soon as possible after collection. Determinations of substances such as dissolved oxygen, soluble sulfides, and residual chlorine should be made at the source.

365

No single method of preservation is entirely satisfactory, and the preservative should be chosen with due regard to the determinations that are to be made. All methods of preservation may be inadequate when applied to suspended matter. Formaldehyde affects so many of the determinations that its use is not recommended.

2.1. Dissolved oxygen: Samples for this determination are preserved as directed under Oxygen (Dissolved).

2.2. Biochemical oxygen demand: Samples must be free from all preservatives. When samples are composited, the individual or composite sample must be chilled immediately to 3°–4°C and kept at this temperature during the compositing period. In samples stored at room temperature, the BOD may drop 10–40 per cent in 6 hr, but in some instances it may rise.

2.3. Chemical oxygen demand: Samples for determining COD by the dichromate method should be preserved by adding sufficient H_2SO_4 to obtain a final acidity of pH 2–3.

2.4. Nitrogen balance: The nitrogen balance may be preserved for 24 hr by adding sufficient H_2SO_4 to produce 1,500 mg/l acidity in the sample, equivalent to pH 2–3. This treatment will lower the suspended matter and settleable matter, and will not preserve the nitrogen balance longer than 24 hr.

B. Methods Evaluation by the Committee

The Committee on Standard Methods of the Water Pollution Control Federation has attempted to establish the precision and accuracy of the methods in Parts III and IV. For most methods, results were obtained from ten replicate determinations on ten different days or, when necessary, from five replicate samples on 20 days.

Most methods studied were found to be statistically reliable, and the standard deviations given may be used with some confidence in statistical prediction. If a method has been found statistically unreliable, this is indicated in the statements on precision under the method. The standard deviations of unreliable methods cannot safely be used for statistical prediction, but may be of some value for indicating roughly the variation that may be expected.

In expressing the evaluation data on each test, the number of analysts and determinations is given in shorthand form; for example, "$n = 5$; 56×10," which means that 5 different analysts ran 56 separate sets of 10 determinations each, making a total of 560 determinations. Usually the precision is expressed as the standard deviation in original units of measurement—i.e., milligrams or milliliters. In a few instances, the precision is expressed as the coefficient of variation C_v (the ratio of the standard deviation to the average), expressed as a percentage:

$$C_v = \frac{100\,\sigma}{\bar{x}}$$

The standard deviation given with each method is based on careful laboratory examination. No attempt has been made to obtain the standard deviation under research conditions, or with the use of specially calibrated apparatus or glassware. The values given are to be regarded as provisional in nature and subject to change on further study. In general, the standard deviations given may be regarded as being too high rather than too low.

Bibliography

1. HATFIELD, W. D. & PHILLIPS, G. E. Preservation of Sewage Samples. *Water Works & Sew.* 88:285 (1941).

Acidity

The acidity of a water is the capacity of that water to donate protons. This includes the un-ionized portions of weakly ionizing acids, such as phosphoric acid, carbonic acid, fatty acids, and protein compounds, as well as hydrolyzing salts such as ferrous and/or aluminum sulfate. Mineral acids contribute to acidity when the sample has a low pH value.

The presence of a low pH with a high acidity in fresh domestic sewage generally indicates the discharge of acidic industrial wastes into the sewers.

Acidity may be determined by titration with an indicator (Method A) or by potentiometric titration (Method B). Where solutions are highly colored or turbid, Method B is recommended, as it is less likely to be affected by these factors.

A. Indicator Method

1. General Discussion

Acidity is determined by titration with a strong base to an endpoint given by an appropriate indicator. Titration to the methyl orange endpoint, pH 4.5, arbitrarily defined as "free acidity," for the most part measures only the relatively strong acids, such as mineral acids; whereas titration to the phenolphthalein endpoint, pH 8.3, defined as "total acidity," will include also the weak acids, acid salts and, with sufficient time for reaction between alkali additions, some acidity due to hydrolysis.

2. Reagents

2.1. *Phenolphthalein indicator solu-*tion: Either the aqueous (*a*) or alcoholic (*b*) solution may be used:

a. Dissolve 5 g phenolphthalein disodium salt in distilled water and dilute to 1 liter. If necessary, add 0.02N NaOH dropwise until a faint pink color appears.

b. Dissolve 5 g phenolphthalein in 500 ml 95 per cent ethyl alcohol or isopropyl alcohol and add 500 ml distilled water. Then add 0.02N NaOH dropwise until a faint pink color appears.

2.2. *Methyl orange indicator solution:* Dissolve 0.5 g methyl orange in 1 liter distilled water.

2.3. *Standard sodium hydroxide titrant,* 0.02N. Prepare as directed in Part I, Acidity, Sec. 3.1–3.3.

3. Procedure

3.1. *Phenolphthalein acidity:* The titration should be made in a glass cylinder, using a plunger-type stirring rod, to avoid loss of CO_2 and to improve the visibility of the endpoint. Pipet 50.0 or 100 ml of the settled sample into the cylinder placed on a white surface. Add 4 drops of phenolphthalein indicator solution. Use a glass rod of large diameter as a plunger to mix the solution during titration. The plunger should not be withdrawn completely from the solution while mixing; this avoids introduction of air bubbles. Titrate with 0.02N NaOH to the first appearance of a permanent pink color. Express the results as mg/l $CaCO_3$ or as me/l acid.

3.2. *Methyl orange acidity:* Determination of free acidity is made in a similar manner. Add 2 drops of methyl orange indicator solution to the sample and titrate with 0.02 N NaOH until the color changes from pink to yellow. It must be recognized that this determination may not yield a true value for the actual free acidity; titration to a methyl orange endpoint has been arbitrarily chosen to represent a satisfactory measure of free acidity. Alternative indicators having color changes in the same pH range as methyl orange may be substituted for it. Express the results as mg/l $CaCO_3$ or as me/l acid.

4. Calculation

$$\text{mg/l acidity as } CaCO_3 = \frac{A \times 1,000}{B}$$

$$\text{me/l acid} = \frac{A \times 20}{B}$$

where $A =$ ml standard sodium hydroxide titrant and $B =$ ml of sample.

Where solutions are strongly acidic, it is desirable to use a stronger titrating solution. If this is done, the results obtained should be multiplied by the normality of the stronger solution divided by 0.02.

5. Precision

The precision, expressed as the standard deviation, was found to be 0.08 ml ($n = 3$; 10×10).

B. *Potentiometric Titration Method*

1. Apparatus

Any of the commercial instruments for measuring pH with a glass electrode can be used as a potentiometer. Standardize the instrument according to the directions of the manufacturer.

2. Reagents

Standard sodium hydroxide titrant, 0.02N. Prepare as directed in Part I, Acidity, Sec. 3.1–3.3.

3. Procedure

Pipet 50.0 or 100 ml of the settled sample into a beaker. Titrate with 0.02N NaOH, with a minimum of stirring, until the instrument indicates the pH value selected as the endpoint. The endpoints may be selected to correspond to the methyl orange (pH 4.5) and phenolphthalein (pH 8.3) endpoints. Any other pH value may be selected if it seems to be advantageous with respect to the known acid components of the waste. The pH value used as the endpoint must be stated in reporting the results.

A potentiometric titration curve, wherein the amount of standard sodium hydroxide titrant is plotted against the pH, often gives additional information regarding the proper inflection points to use. However, mixtures of weak acids seldom produce curves with definite inflection points, and the arbitrary pH endpoints of 4.5 and 8.3 have been established as standard.

4. Calculation

Refer to Method A, Sec. 4.

5. Precision

The precision of the potentiometric titration has not been established.

Alkalinity

1. General Discussion

The alkalinity of a water is the capacity of that water to accept protons. It is usually imparted by the presence of salts of weakly ionized acids and the un-ionized portion of weakly ionized bases and/or free bases at high pH values.

Natural waters are generally neutral or slightly alkaline, because of the presence of bicarbonate, carbonate, hydroxide, and, occasionally, borate, silicate, sulfide, and phosphate. The alkalinity varies with the locality in which the water is found, and may range from a few milligrams per liter to several hundred. Domestic sewage usually has slightly greater alkalinity than the water from which it is derived. An abnormally high increase in alkalinity over that of the public water supply or stream involved indicates that a strongly basic industrial waste is being discharged into the sewer system or stream.

2. Procedure

Alkalinity is determined by titration with a strong acid. The different kinds of alkalinity are indicated by successive titration to the phenolphthalein and methyl orange endpoints, using $0.02N$ H_2SO_4, as directed in Part I, except that titration in glass cylinders improves the visibility of the endpoint. If solutions are strongly alkaline, it is desirable to use a smaller sample, or a stronger titrating solution, to avoid refilling burets. If this is done, the results must be multiplied by the appropriate dilution factor, or by the normality of the stronger solution divided by 0.02. In sewage and industrial wastes, it is generally not permissible to calculate hydroxide, carbonate, and bicarbonate from these titrations as is done in water analysis.

Where samples are highly colored or turbid, potentiometric titration should be used. The procedure in Acidity, Method B, should be followed, except that the titration is made with $0.02N$ H_2SO_4. The endpoints should be, arbitrarily, pH 8.3 and 4.5, to correspond to the phenolphthalein and methyl orange endpoints, unless the potentiometric titration curve indicates other proper inflection points.

3. Calculation

$$\text{Alkalinity} = \frac{A \times 1,000}{B}$$

where $A = $ ml H_2SO_4 solution and $B = $ ml sample.

4. Precision

The precision, expressed as the standard deviation, when using methyl orange or phenolphthalein as indicators in settled sewage was 0.07 ml ($n = 3$; 30×10). With filtered sewage, the standard deviation was 0.06 ml ($n = 3$; 30×10). No data are available on potentiometric titrations.

Chloride

Chloride, in the form of Cl ion, is one of the major inorganic anions which is increased in sewage over the raw water because sodium chloride is a common article of diet and passes unchanged through the digestive system. Along the sea coast, chloride may be present in high concentrations because of leakage of salt water into the sewer system. It may also be increased by industrial processes.

Selection of method: Three methods are presented for the determination of chlorides in sewage. The argentometric method (A) is suitable for use when 0.15–10 mg Cl is present in the portion of sample titrated. The mercuric nitrate method (B) is given for its easier endpoint. The tentative potentiometric method (C) is suitable for colored or turbid samples in which colored endpoints might be difficult to observe. The potentiometric method can also be used without a pretreatment step for solutions containing ferric (if not present in an amount greater than the chloride concentration), chromic, phosphate, ferrous, and other heavy metal ions.

A. Argentometric Method

If the sample contains sulfide, acidify an appropriate volume of sample, diluted if necessary to 50.0 ml, with H_2SO_4, and oxidize the sulfide by heating with H_2O_2 for a few minutes. Cool and neutralize with $NaHCO_3$, dilute to the original volume, and determine chloride by the argentometric method as in Part I.

B. Mercuric Nitrate Method

1. General Discussion

1.1. *Principle:* Chloride (halides) in sewage is titrated with a standard solution of mercuric nitrate to form mercuric chloride. At pH 2–3, the excess mercuric ion will produce a dark purple color with diphenylcarbazone indicator. The appearance of a light purple color (from a yellow solution) during the titration, indicates the approach of the endpoint. The endpoint is a definite change from a light purple to a deep purple color. Each analyst should acquaint himself with the endpoint by titrating several portions of the standard chloride solution and observing the change of colors.

1.2. *Interference:* Iodide and bromide are titrated with the mercuric nitrate, so this is actually a halide titration. Sulfate, chromate, and ferric ions interfere when present in excess of 10 mg/l.

2. Apparatus

Automatic buret: 5-ml capacity with reservoir and 0.02-ml subdivisions.

3. Reagents

3.1. *D.B. mixed indicator:* Dissolve 5 g diphenylcarbazone powder and 0.5 g bromophenol blue powder in 750 ml 95 per cent ethyl alcohol and dilute to 1 liter with ethyl alcohol.

3.2. *Standard sodium chloride solution:* Dissolve 0.8241 g predried NaCl in distilled water and dilute to 1 liter; 1.00 ml = 0.500 mg Cl.

3.3. *Standard mercuric nitrate titrant:* Dissolve 50 g mercuric nitrate in 1,500 ml distilled water containing 5.0 ml conc HNO_3, dilute to 2 liters, and standardize as follows:

a. Place 25 ml standard NaCl solution and 25 ml distilled water in a 150-ml beaker, titrate step by step according to the procedure given. Then calculate the strength of the $Hg(NO_3)_2$ solution as follows:

b. Calculation:

$$mg/l \text{ stand. } Hg(NO_3)_2 \text{ titrant} = \frac{12.5 \text{ mg}}{ml \ Hg(NO_3)_2 \text{ titrant used}}$$

c. The standard mercuric nitrate titrant should be standardized each time the buret reservoir is filled. The concentration (mg/ml) of the mercuric nitrate titrant should be marked on a label attached to the reservoir.

3.4. *Nitric acid,* 0.1N. Dilute 6.5 ml conc HNO_3 to 1 liter with distilled water.

3.5. *Sodium hydroxide,* 0.1N. Dilute 4 g NaOH to 1 liter with distilled water.

4. Procedure

4.1. Place 50.0 ml sewage sample in a 150-ml beaker (5 ml sample may be used when more than 5 ml of titrant are needed).

4.2. Add approximately 0.5 ml (one dropperful) D.B. indicator and mix well. The color should be purple. Add 0.2N HNO_3 dropwise until the color just turns yellow.

4.3. Titrate with standard mercuric nitrate titrant to the first permanent dark purple. Titrate a distilled water blank using the same procedure.

4.4. Record ml of titrant used.

5. Calculation

For 50-ml sample:

$$mg/l \ Cl = A \times B \times 20$$

For 5-ml sample:

$$mg/l \ Cl = A \times B \times 200$$

where A = ml titrant used, and B = mg/ml standard $Hg(NO_3)_2$ solution.

C. Potentiometric Method (Tentative)

1. General Discussion

1.1. *Principle:* Chloride is determined by potentiometric titration with silver nitrate solution using a glass and silver–silver chloride electrode system. During titration an electronic voltmeter is used to detect the change in potential between the two electrodes. The endpoint of the titration is that instrument reading at which the greatest change in voltage has occurred for a small and constant increment of silver nitrate added.

1.2. *Interference:* Iodide and bromide also are titrated as chloride. Ferricyanide causes high results and must be removed. Chromate and dichromate interfere and should be reduced to the chromic state or removed. Ferric iron interferes if present in an amount that is substantially higher than the amount of chloride. Chromic ion, ferrous iron, and phosphate do not interfere.

Grossly contaminated samples usually require pretreatment. Where contamination is minor, some contaminants can be destroyed simply by the addition of nitric acid.

2. Apparatus

2.1. *Glass and silver–silver chloride electrodes:* The latter is a silver electrode coated with silver chloride and may be prepared in the laboratory if desired, but can be purchased for use with particular instruments. Instructions on the use and care of the electrodes are supplied by the manufacturer.

2.2. *Electronic voltmeter,* to measure the potential difference between the electrodes. Many laboratories may find it possible to convert a pH meter to this use by substitution of the appropriate electrode.

2.3. *Mechanical stirrer,* with plastic-coated or glass impeller.

3. Reagents

3.1. *Standard sodium chloride solution,* 0.0141N. Dissolve 8.243 g NaCl, dried at 105°C, in distilled water and dilute to exactly 500 ml. Dilute 50.0 ml of this solution to exactly 1,000 ml. The final solution contains 0.500 mg Cl per 1.00 ml.

3.2. *Nitric acid,* conc.

3.3. *Standard silver nitrate titrant,* 0.014N. Dissolve 2.40 g $AgNO_3$ in distilled water and dilute to 1,000 ml. Standardize this solution by titrating exactly 10.0 ml standard NaCl solution using the procedure described in Sec. 4. Adjust the $AgNO_3$ titrant to the same normality as the NaCl solution; 1.00 ml = 0.500 mg Cl.

$$\text{Normality of } AgNO_3 = \frac{10.0 \times 0.0141}{\text{ml } AgNO_3}$$

3.4. *Special reagents for pretreatment:*

 a. *Sulfuric acid,* 1 + 1.

 b. *Hydrogen peroxide,* 30 per cent.

 c. *Sodium hydroxide,* 1N.

4. Standardization

4.1. Inasmuch as the various instruments that can be used in this determination differ in operating details, the manufacturer's instructions should be followed. Necessary mechanical adjustments should be made. Then, after allowing sufficient time for warmup (10 min), the internal electrical components are balanced to give an instrument setting of 0 mv or, if a pH meter is used, a pH reading of 7.0.

4.2. Place 10.0 ml standard NaCl solution in a 250-ml beaker, dilute to about 100 ml, and add 2.0 ml conc HNO_3. Immerse the stirrer and the electrodes in the solution.

there is the greatest change in instrument reading per unit addition of $AgNO_3$.

4.5. A differential titration curve should be plotted if the exact endpoint cannot be determined by inspection of the data. Plot the change in instrument reading for equal increments of $AgNO_3$ against the volume of $AgNO_3$ added, using the average of the buret readings

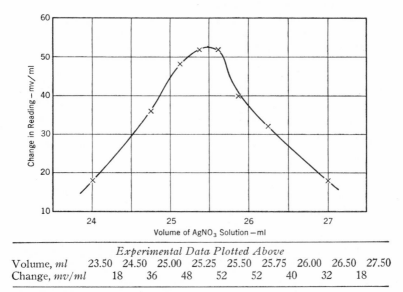

Experimental Data Plotted Above

Volume, *ml*	23.50	24.50	25.00	25.25	25.50	25.75	26.00	26.50	27.50
Change, *mv/ml*	18	36	48	52	52	40	32	18	

Fig. 28. Example of differential titration curve (endpoint is 25.5 ml)

4.3. Set the instrument to the desired range of millivolts or pH units. Start the stirrer.

4.4. Add standard $AgNO_3$ titrant, recording the scale reading after each addition. At the start, large increments of $AgNO_3$ may be added; then, as the endpoint of the reaction is approached, smaller and equal increments (0.1 or 0.2 ml) should be added at longer intervals, so that the exact endpoint can be determined. Determine the volume of $AgNO_3$ used at the point at which

before and after each addition. The procedure is illustrated in Fig. 28.

5. Procedure

5.1. Pipet exactly 100.0 ml of sample, or an aliquot containing not more than 10 mg chloride, into a 250-ml beaker. In the absence of interfering substances, proceed with Sec. 5.3.

5.2. In the presence of organic compounds, sulfite, or other interferences (such as large amounts of ferric iron or substantial amounts of cyanide or sulfide), acidify the sample with H_2SO_4, using litmus paper. Boil for 5 min to remove volatile compounds. Add more H_2SO_4, if necessary, to keep the solution acidic. Add 3 ml H_2O_2 and boil for 15 min, adding chloride-free distilled water to keep the volume above 50 ml. Dilute to 100 ml, add NaOH solution dropwise until alkaline to litmus, then 10 drops in excess. Boil for 5 min, filter into a 250-ml beaker, and wash the precipitate and paper several times with hot distilled water.

5.3. Add conc HNO_3 dropwise until acidic to litmus paper, then 2.0 ml in excess. Cool and dilute to 100 ml if necessary. Immerse the stirrer and the electrodes in the sample and start the stirrer. After making the necessary adjustments of the instrument according to the manufacturer's instructions, set the selector switch to the appropriate setting for measuring the difference of potential between the electrodes.

5.4. Complete the determination by titrating according to Sec. 4.4. If an endpoint reading has been established from previous determinations for similar samples and conditions, this predetermined endpoint can be used. For the most accurate work, a blank titration should be made by carrying chloride-free distilled water through the procedure.

6. Calculation

$$\text{mg/l Cl} = \frac{(A - B) \times C \times 35.45 \times 1,000}{D}$$

where $A =$ ml $AgNO_3$, $B =$ ml blank, $C =$ normality of titrant, and $D =$ ml sample.

7. Precision and Accuracy

In the absence of interfering substances, the precision and accuracy are estimated to be about 0.12 mg for 5 mg Cl, or 2.5 per cent of the amount present. When pretreatment is required for removal of interfering substances, the precision and accuracy are reduced to about 0.25 mg for 5 mg Cl, or 5 per cent of the amount present.

Bibliography

1. HAZEN, A. On the Determination of Chlorine in Water. *Am. Chem. J.* 11: 409 (1889).
2. KOLTHOFF, I. M. & FURMAN, N. H. *Potentiometric Titrations.* John Wiley & Sons, New York (2nd ed., 1931).
3. REFFENBURG, H. B. Colorimetric Determination of Small Quantities of Chlorides in Waters. *Ind. Eng. Chem., Anal. Ed.* 7:14 (1935).
4. CALDWELL, J. R. & MEYER, H. V. Chloride Determination. *Ind. Eng. Chem., Anal. Ed.* 7:38 (1935).
5. WALTON, H. F. *Principles and Methods of Chemical Analysis.* Prentice-Hall, New York (1952).
6. SERFASS, E. J. & MURACA, R. F. *Procedures for Analyzing Metal-Finishing Wastes.* Ohio River Valley Water Sanitation Commission, Cincinnati, Ohio (1954), p. 80.
7. WILLARD, H. H.; MERRITT, L. L.; & DEAN, J. A. *Instrumental Methods of Analysis.* D. Van Nostrand Co., Princeton, N.J. (3rd ed., 1958).
8. FURMAN, N. H., ed. *Standard Methods of Chemical Analysis.* D. Van Nostrand Co., Princeton, N.J. (6th ed., 1962). Vol. I.

Chlorine (Residual)

The determination of residual chlorine in sewage presents different problems than the determination in water. Because of the presence of organic compounds, particularly organic nitrogen, the residual chlorine exists in a combined state. A considerable amount of residual may exist in this form, and at the same time there may be appreciable unsatisfied chlorine demand. The addition of the reagents in the determination may change the relationships so that the residual chlorine is lost during the course of the procedure. In sewage, the differentiation of free available chlorine from combined available chlorine is not made. Sewage chlorination is seldom carried to the point necessary to produce free available chlorine.

The methods given below find a useful place in the determination of residual chlorine in sewage, although there are certain conditions which militate against the use of one or another of them for mixtures of wastes with sewage. With sewages containing particular wastes, certain precautions and modifications must be introduced for satisfactory results.

Selection of method: The iodometric method (*A*) may be used with either the amperometric or the starch-iodide endpoint. In the absence of interference, the two modifications give concordant results. The amperometric endpoint is inherently more accurate and is free of interference from color and turbidity, which can cause difficulty with the starch-iodide endpoint.

On the other hand, certain metals and complex anions are more troublesome in the amperometric endpoint than in the starch-iodide endpoint. These are discussed in more detail in Part IV, Chlorine (Residual), Method A. Regardless of the method of endpoint detection, either phenylarsine oxide or thiosulfate may be used as the standard reducing reagent, depending on convenience. The former is more stable and is to be preferred, other things being equal.

The orthotolidine method (*B*) consistently gives lower values than the iodometric method. The magnitude of the difference seems to depend on the concentration of organic matter. In pure water, both methods give essentially the same result. In ordinary settled sewage, the difference in residual chlorine can be of the order of 2–5 mg/l. In many sewage and waste mixtures, even greater differences may be found. The cause may be either more tightly combined chlorine which is unreactive to orthotolidine, or an actual loss of available chlorine by the activation effect when the pH is lowered in the orthotolidine determination. When nitrite nitrogen is present in amounts greater than 2 mg/l, the orthotolidine method should not be used. It may also be undesirable for use in the presence of manganic manganese.

Method C, a rapid spot plate test for field use, describes a technique which may also be applicable to plant control work.

A. Iodometric Method

1. General Discussion

1.1. *Principle:* Refer to Part I, Chlorine (Residual), Method A, Sec. 1.1, and Method F, Sec. 1.1. As used in sewage, the endpoint signal is reversed because the unreacted standard reducing agent remaining in the sample is titrated with standard iodine, rather than directly titrating the iodine released. This indirect procedure is necessary regardless of the method of endpoint detection, in order to avoid any contact between the full concentration of liberated iodine and the sewage.

1.2. *Interference:* Manganese, iron, and nitrite interference may be minimized by buffering to pH 4.0 before the addition of KI. An unusually high content of organic matter may cause some uncertainty in the endpoint. Whenever manganese, iron, and nitrite are definitely absent, this uncertainty can be reduced and precision improved by acidification to pH 1.0.

2. Apparatus

For a description of the amperometric endpoint detection apparatus and a discussion of its use, refer to Part I, Chlorine (Residual), Method F, Sec. 2.

3. Reagents

3.1. *Standard phenylarsine oxide solution, 0.00564N.* Dissolve approximately 0.8 g phenylarsine oxide powder in 150 ml 0.3N NaOH solution. After settling, decant 110 ml of this solution into 800 ml distilled water and mix thoroughly. Bring to pH 6–7 with 1 + 99 HCl and dilute to 1 liter with distilled water.

Standardization: Accurately measure 5–10 ml freshly standardized 0.0282N iodine solution into a flask and add 1 ml KI solution. Titrate with phenylarsine oxide solution, using starch solution as an indicator. Adjust to exactly 0.00564N and recheck against the standard iodine solution; 1.00 ml = 0.200 mg available chlorine. (CAUTION: *Toxic; take care to avoid ingestion.*)

3.2. *Standard sodium thiosulfate solution, 0.1N.* Dissolve at least 25 g $Na_2S_2O_3 \cdot 5H_2O$ in 1 liter freshly boiled distilled water. Bacterial decomposition may be avoided by the addition of 5 ml chloroform or 1 g NaOH per liter. Store for at least two weeks before standardizing.

Standardization: To 80 ml distilled water add, with constant stirring, 1 ml conc H_2SO_4, 10.0 ml of either 0.1N potassium biniodate solution containing 3.250 g/1 $KH(IO_3)_2$, or 0.1N potassium dichromate solution containing 4.904 g/1 $K_2Cr_2O_7$, and 15 ml KI solution. Allow to stand 6 min in subdued light at laboratory temperature and then dilute to 400 ml if $K_2Cr_2O_7$ was used and to 200 ml if biniodate was used. Titrate the liberated iodine with the thiosulfate solution being standardized, adding starch solution toward the end of the titration. Exactly 10.00 ml of thiosulfate should be required if the solutions under comparison are of equal strength.

3.3. *Standard sodium thiosulfate solution, 0.00564N.* Prepare by dilution of 0.1N sodium thiosulfate (Sec. 3.2). The stability of 0.00564N thiosulfate is improved if it is prepared by diluting an aged 0.1N solution, made as directed in the preceding section, with freshly boiled distilled water. (Boiled water is used because bacterial action decomposes $0.00564N$ thiosulfate.) The stability of the thiosulfate is greatly increased by adding 0.4 g NaOH per liter. This thiosulfate solution should be standardized daily, in accordance with the directions given above, using $0.00564N$ $K_2Cr_2O_7$ solution if desired. The use of an automatic buret of a type in which rubber does not come in contact with the solution is advisable; 1.00 ml = 0.200 mg available chlorine.

3.4. *Potassium iodide,* crystals.

3.5. *Acetate buffer solution,* pH 4.0. Dissolve 146 g anhydrous $NaC_2H_3O_2$, or 243 g $NaC_2H_3O_2 \cdot 3H_2O$, in 400 ml distilled water, add 480 g conc acetic acid, and dilute to 1 liter with distilled water.

3.6. *Standard arsenite solution,* $0.1N$. Accurately weigh a stoppered weighing bottle containing approximately 4.95 g arsenic trioxide, As_2O_3. Transfer without loss to a 1-liter volumetric flask and again weigh the bottle. Do not attempt to brush out the adhering oxide. Moisten the As_2O_3 with water, and add 15 g NaOH and 100 ml distilled water. Swirl the contents of the flask gently until the As_2O_3 is in solution. Dilute to 250 ml with distilled water and saturate the solution with CO_2, thus converting all the NaOH to sodium bicarbonate. Dilute to the mark, stopper the flask, and mix thoroughly. A solution thus prepared will preserve its titer almost indefinitely. (CAUTION: *Toxic; take care to avoid ingestion.*)

$$\text{Normality} = \frac{\text{g } As_2O_3}{49.455}$$

3.7. *Standard iodine solution,* $0.1N$. Dissolve 40 g KI in 25 ml distilled water, add 13 g resublimed iodine, and stir until dissolved. Transfer to a 1-liter volumetric flask and dilute to the mark.

Standardization: Accurately measure 40–50 ml $0.1N$ arsenite solution into a flask and titrate with the $0.1N$ iodine solution, using starch solution as indicator. To obtain accurate results, it is absolutely necessary that the solution be saturated with CO_2 at the end of the titration. A current of CO_2 may be passed through the solution for a few minutes just before the endpoint is reached, or a few drops of HCl may be added to liberate sufficient CO_2 to saturate the solution.

3.8. *Standard iodine titrant,* $0.0282N$. Dissolve 25 g KI in a little distilled water in a 1-liter volumetric flask, add the proper amount of $0.1N$ iodine solution exactly standardized to yield a $0.0282N$ solution, and dilute to 1 liter. For accurate work, this solution should be standardized daily in accordance with directions given in Sec. 3.7, using 5–10 ml of approximately $0.1N$ arsenite solution. Store in amber bottles or in the dark, protecting the solution from direct sunlight at all times and keeping it from all contact with rubber.

3.9. *Starch solution:* To 5 g starch (potato, arrowroot, or soluble) in a mortar, add a little cold water and grind to a thin paste. Pour into 1 liter of boiling distilled water, stir, and allow to settle overnight. Use the clear supernate. The solution should be preserved with 1.25 g salicylic acid or with 4 g zinc chloride per liter.

4. Procedure

4.1. *Amperometric endpoint:*

a. Volume of sample: For residual chlorine concentrations of 10 mg/1 or less, 200 ml should be titrated. For residual chlorine concentrations above this range, proportionately less of the sample should be used. It is preferable to use a sample of such size that not more than 10 ml phenylarsine oxide solution is required.

b. Preparation for titration: To a beaker suitable for use with the apparatus add 5.0 ml 0.00564N phenylarsine oxide solution or 0.00564N thiosulfate solution, KI in excess (approx. 1 g), and 4 ml acetate buffer solution, or sufficient to reduce the pH to between 3.5 and 4.2. Then add 200 ml of sample and mix thoroughly. Because 1 ml phenylarsine oxide reagent consumed by a 200-ml sample represents 1 mg/1 available chlorine, 5 ml reagent solution is sufficient for residual chlorine concentrations up to 5 mg/1. For residual chlorine concentrations of 5 to 10 mg/1, 10 ml reagent solution is required. The following is suggested as a possible dilution method: Add 10.0 ml reagent solution, excess KI (approx. 1 g), and 4 ml acetate buffer solution, or sufficient to reduce the pH to between 3.5 and 4.2, to the beaker or graduate. Dilute to 100 ml with distilled water and then add 100 ml of the sample for which the residual chlorine concentration is to be determined.

c. Titration: Add 0.0282N iodine titrant in small increments from a 1-ml pipet or a 1-ml buret. As iodine is added to the sample, the pointer remains practically stationary until the endpoint is approached. Just before the true endpoint, each increment of iodine titrant causes a temporary deflection of the microammeter, but the pointer drops back to about its original position. The true endpoint is reached when a small increment of iodine titrant gives a definite pointer deflection up-scale and the pointer does not return promptly to its original position. The volume of iodine titrant used to reach the endpoint is recorded.

4.2. *Starch-iodide endpoint:*

a. Volume of sample: The amount of sample to be taken for titration is governed by the concentration of chlorine in the sample. For residual chlorine of 10 mg/1 or less, 200 ml should be titrated; for greater residual chlorine concentrations, proportionately less of the sample should be used.

b. Titration: Place 5.00 ml 0.00564N phenylarsine oxide solution or 0.00564N thiosulfate solution in a flask or white porcelain casserole. Add excess KI (approx. 1 g), and 4 ml acetate buffer solution, or sufficient to reduce the pH to between 3.5 and 4.2. Pour in the sample and mix with a stirring rod. Just prior to titration with 0.0282N iodine, add 1 ml starch solution for each 200 ml of sample. Titrate to the first appearance of blue color which persists after complete mixing. Because 1 ml 0.00564N reagent solution consumed by a 200-ml sample represents 1 mg/1 available chlorine, 5 ml reagent is sufficient for residual chlorine concentrations up to 5 mg/1. For residual chlorine concentrations of 5–10 mg/1, 10 ml reagent solution is required.

5. Calculation

$$\text{mg/1 Cl} = \frac{(A - 5B) \times 200}{C}$$

where A = ml 0.00564N reagent, B = ml 0.0282N I, and C = ml sample.

B. Orthotolidine Method

1. General Discussion

The determination of residual chlorine in water by the orthotolidine method is discussed in Part I, Chlorine (Residual), Method B, which describes the many pitfalls of the test and the precautions to be observed. Particular attention is called to the importance of warming the sample to 20°C after the addition of orthotolidine, in order to complete the reaction. If the sample is warmed before the addition of orthotolidine, there will be further reaction between chlorine and organic matter, resulting in a low value for residual chlorine.

Permanent orthotolidine standards or commercial colorimeters are to be preferred to temporary standards. The technique for preparing standards is given in the section mentioned in the preceding paragraph, as is information on light sources. Directions for preparing the orthotolidine reagent are the same as for determinations in water (Part I, Chlorine (Residual), Method B, Sec. 5), but are repeated here for convenience. The concentration of acid in this reagent is such that it will produce a suitable pH in the sample even if the alkalinity is 1,000 mg/l. Higher alkalinities will require the addition of more orthotolidine reagent than is specified.

2. Apparatus

Comparator, turbidity compensating.

3. Reagent

Orthotolidine reagent: Dissolve 1.35 g orthotolidine dihydrochloride in 500 ml distilled water. Add this solution, with constant stirring, to a mixture of 350 ml distilled water and 150 ml conc HCl.

The orthotolidine reagent should be: (a) stored in amber bottles or in the dark; (b) protected at all times from direct sunlight; (c) used no longer than 6 months; (d) kept from contact with rubber; and (e) maintained at normal temperatures. At temperatures below 0°C the orthotolidine will precipitate from solution and cannot be redissolved easily. The use of a reagent from which part of the orthotolidine has precipitated may lead to errors due to a deficiency of orthotolidine.

4. Procedure

4.1. Add a 10-ml sample of chlorinated sewage to a cell or test tube containing 1 ml orthotolidine solution. If the temperature of the sample is less than 20°C, bring it to that temperature quickly after mixing it with orthotolidine. This may be done by placing the tube in hot water until the specified temperature is reached.

4.2. Place the treated sample in the dark during color development. Maximum color develops in less than 5 min and fading occurs thereafter. Therefore, to obtain maximum color intensity, the reading should be made within 5 min. In some cases, maximum color is attained immediately and the reading must be made before fading occurs.

4.3. Color comparison should be made in a turbidity-compensating comparator with color standards prepared as directed in Part I, Chlorine (Residual), Method B, Sec. 3 and 4. If permanent standards are used, note that the amount of sample is but 10 ml and the depth of liquid viewed is not the same as in Tables 6 and 7; adjustments may have to be made accordingly. The standards most commonly used represent 0.0, 0.10, 0.20, 0.40, 0.60, 0.80, and 1.00 mg/l Cl.

C. Orthotolidine-Arsenite Method

The orthotolidine-arsenite (OTA) test may be applied to sewage. The procedure is described in Part IV, Chlorine (Residual), Method D.

D. Spot Plate Test for Field Use

The following rapid spot plate technique offers simplicity and speed for plant control work and field use.

1. Apparatus

1.1. *Spot plates,* containing several depressions.

1.2 *Pipets,* large bore, 1 ml, fitted with pipet bulbs.

2. Reagents

2.1. *Orthotolidine reagent:* Prepare as directed in Method B, Sec. 3.

2.2. *Permanent standard solutions:* Prepare as directed in Part I, Chlorine (Residual), Method B, Sec. 4, and adjust color intensities and hues to match temporary standards in spot plates.

3. Procedure

Add 3 drops of orthotolidine reagent to a depression in the spot plate. By means of the pipet bulb, pipet 1 ml of the sample under examination directly and rapidly into the orthotolidine reagent, and stir with the tip of the pipet. The color will usually develop within 45 sec to 1 min and fade thereafter.

Compare the color developed with permanent standards pipeted into another spot plate. Temporary standards may be used. Several samples may be spotted at the same time. The minimum readable color is produced by a chlorine concentration between 0.05 and 0.1 mg/l.

Bibliography

1. LEA, C. Chemical Control of Sewage Chlorination: The Use and Value of Orthotolidine Test. *J. Soc. Chem. Ind.* (London) 52:245T (1933).
2. SYMONS, G. E. A Modification of the Chlorine Demand Test and the Orthotolidine Test for Residual Chlorine. *Sew. Works J.* 9:569 (1937).
3. COMMITTEE REPORT. Control of Chlorination. *J. AWWA* 35:1315 (1943).
4. MARKS, H. C.; JOINER, R.; & STRANDSKOV, F. B. Amperometric Titration of Residual Chlorine in Sewage. *Water and Sewage Works* 95:175 (1948).
5. STRANDSKOV, F. B.; MARKS, H. C.; & HORCHLER, D. H. Application of a New Residual Chlorine Method to Effluent Chlorination. *Sew. Works J.* 21:23 (1949).
6. NUSBAUM, I. & MEYERSON, L. A. Determination of Chlorine Demands and Chlorine Residuals in Sewage. *Sew. Ind. Wastes* 23:968 (1951).
7. MARKS, H. C. & CHAMBERLIN, N. S. Determination of Residual Chlorine in Metal Finishing Wastes. *Anal. Chem.* 24:1885 (1953).

Chlorine Requirement

"Chlorine demand," as defined in Part I, is of little significance in relation to the objectives of wastewater chlorination. "Chlorination requirement" is more applicable.

The chlorine requirement is defined as the amount of chlorine which must be added per unit volume to produce the desired result under stated conditions. The result (i.e., the purpose of chlorination) may be based on any of a number of criteria, such as a stipulated coliform density, a specified residual chlorine concentration, the destruction of a chemical constituent, or others. In each instance a definite chlorine dosage will be necessary. This dosage is the chlorine requirement.

In those cases where the desired result is a specified residual chlorine concentration, residuals may be determined by either the iodometric or the orthotolidine method. It is important that the same method be used for both laboratory testing and operational control.

In reporting results, the following information must be included: (1) the conditions of chlorination, such as pH, contact time, and temperature; (2) the result achieved; (3) the method used for determining the result; and (4) the chlorine dosage required to produce the desired result (i.e., the chlorine requirement).

A. Method for Control of Disinfection

1. General Discussion

For control of the disinfection process the chlorine requirement can be determined on either a plant or a laboratory scale. In plant tests the flow of sewage, quantity of chlorine used, contact time, residual chlorine concentration, and bacteriological results are determined. Sufficient replication will establish a correlation between bacteriological results and residual chlorine concentration. Operational control may then be based on residual chlorine determinations. Bacteriological tests should be performed periodically to verify the correlation.

In plant studies the test should be run with the minimum and average contact times corresponding to different flow conditions, to determine the average and the variations from the average of the number of coliform organisms in the effluent. Similarly, in laboratory studies more than one contact time should be used to establish minimum and average chlorine requirements compatible with the stipulated coliform densities and permissible variations.

It is to be understood that chlorine requirement is not an absolute value which can be used to compare the results from place to place and from time to time. It is rather a practical and realistic approach to the control of disinfection of sewage and to an estimate of the chlorine required.

The orthotolidine test may not be suitable for the determination of chlorine requirement in some cases, because often with no residuals, as determined by this method, substantial reductions in coliform organisms are obtained.

For a given sewage, the same amount of added chlorine will result in a higher residual value by the iodometric method than by the orthotolidine method.

2. Reagents

All of the reagents necessary for the determination of residual chlorine by the selected method are required and, in addition:

2.1. *Standard chlorine solution:* Pass chlorine gas through distilled water or tap water until the solution contains approximately 1.0 mg chlorine per ml. This solution is not stable and must be standardized each time it is used, or made up fresh daily. Standardization is accomplished according to directions in Part I, Chlorine (Residual), Method B, Sec. 3, using 5 ml chlorine water and 0.025N thiosulfate solution. The strength is calculated as follows:

$$\text{mg/ml Cl} = \frac{(A \pm B) \times N \times 35.45}{\text{ml sample}}$$

where $A =$ ml titration for sample, $B =$ ml titration for blank which may be positive or negative, and $N =$ normality of $Na_2S_2O_3$.

2.2. *Sodium sulfite solution:* Dissolve 10 g anhydrous Na_2SO_3 in 100 ml distilled water, and heat to boiling to sterilize. This solution should be prepared daily.

3. Procedure

3.1. *Measurement of samples:* In each of a series of 1-liter beakers, jars, or flasks, place a 500-ml portion of the sewage.

3.2. *Addition of chlorine:* While stirring gently and constantly, add increasing quantities of the chlorine solu-

tion to each of the vessels in suitable increments. Increments and dosages necessary will vary with the type and concentration of the waste as well as with the objective to be accomplished. A sufficient range should be used to include a dosage certain to produce the desired result.

3.3. *Determination of residual chlorine:* At the end of the stipulated contact times, residual chlorine is determined on each portion of the sewage by one or more of the procedures given in Part III, Chlorine (Residual), Method A, Sec. 4, or Method B, Sec. 4.

Note: In following Sec. 4 of Method A it is permissible, after completing preparations for titration, to set the samples aside until portions have been removed from the original sample for other tests.

3.4. *Determination of degree of disinfection:* Immediately after the aliquots have been removed for determination of residual chlorine, add 0.5 ml sodium sulfite solution to each of the sample portions and estimate the number of coliform organisms surviving, by the procedure given in Part VII, Tests for Presence of Members of Coliform Group by Multiple-Tube Fermentation Technique, A, Standard Tests. A series of dilutions of 1, 1/10, 1/100, and 1/1,000 will be sufficient in most instances to establish whether the stipulated effluent bacteriologic quality has been met. Triplicate planting of each dilution increases the accuracy of the coliform enumeration. The positive presumptive tubes should be confirmed on one of the confirmatory media as directed in the previously cited section. On the basis of the confirmed test, calculate the MPN.

4. Calculation

The chlorine requirement is the amount of chlorine that must be added per unit volume to produce the stipulated MPN.

5. Precision

The precision of the chlorine requirement as determined by this procedure is of a low order of magnitude on the basis of a single sample, because of the inaccuracies of the MPN determination. In order to establish the chlorine requirement for a given coliform density in the effluent with suitable precision, the test should be repeated at least ten times on different samples using otherwise identical conditions.

B. Methods for Purposes Other Than Disinfection Control

When chlorine is used for such purposes as odor control, BOD reduction, slime and insect control on trickling filters, and control of activated-sludge bulking, chlorine requirement is defined as the quantity of chlorine that must be added to produce the desired result. In most of the cases mentioned, chlorine requirement is best determined on a plant basis. Occasionally, laboratory tests may be more suitable, as in BOD reduction. If residual chlorine tests are to be used for control, either the iodometric or the orthotolidine method may be used. The procedure is analogous to the one given for disinfection control (Method A).

Color

Color is not normally determined on sewages, but is often an important constituent in industrial wastes. If color is to be determined in sewage, the methods given in Part IV should be used.

Detergents

See Surfactants.

Grease

In the determination of grease, an absolute quantity of a specific substance is not measured. Rather, groups of substances with similar physical characteristics are determined quantitatively, based on their mutual solubility in the solvent used. Grease, therefore, can be said to include fats, waxes, oils, and any other nonvolatile material extracted by hexane from an acidified sample of sewage or industrial waste. The deleterious effect these materials have on sewage treatment plant operation and digestion processes, as well as the offensive conditions they present on water surfaces, is well known. A knowledge of the quantity of grease present in a waste is helpful in overcoming difficulties in plant operation, in determining plant efficiencies, and in controlling the subsequent discharge of grease to receiving streams.

Two extraction methods are presented below—the Soxhlet method (A) and the tentative semiwet method (B). An elapsed time of 6 hr is required to complete a determination by Method

A, whereas Method B requires 2 hr. However, the personnel time ($1\frac{1}{2}$ hr) is the same for each. Of the two, Method A has the greater precision and accuracy. Both methods have been found to give reproducible results for grease concentrations up to 650 mg/l.

Sampling and storage: When possible, collect representative samples in a wide-mouth bottle calibrated to hold a measured volume, and perform the initial steps of the procedure in the sample bottle. When information is required concerning the average grease concentration of a waste over an extended period, the examination of individual portions collected at prescribed time intervals can be used to eliminate losses of grease on sampling equipment during the collection of a composite sample.

A. Soxhlet Extraction Method

1. General Discussion

1.1. *Principle:* Soluble metallic soaps are hydrolyzed by acidification. The solid or viscous grease is separated from the liquid sample by filtration. Grease is then extracted in a Soxhlet apparatus using hexane, and the residue remaining after evaporation of the hexane is weighed to determine the grease content of the sample. Compounds volatilized at or below 103°C will be lost when the filter is dried.

1.2. *Interference:* The method is entirely empirical, and duplicate results can be obtained only by strict adherence to all details. By definition, any material recovered is called grease and any filtrable hexane-soluble substances, such as elemental sulfur and certain organic dyes, will be extracted as grease. The

rate and time of extraction in the Soxhlet apparatus must be exactly as directed because of varying solubilities of different greases in hexane. In addition, the length of time required for drying and cooling the extracted grease cannot be varied. There may be a gradual increase in weight, presumably due to the absorption of oxygen, or a gradual loss of weight due to volatilization.

2. Apparatus

2.1. *Extraction apparatus,* Soxhlet.
2.2. *Vacuum pump,* or other source of vacuum.
2.3. *Buchner funnel,* 12 cm.

3. Reagents

3.1. *Hydrochloric acid,* conc.

3.2. *n-hexane,* boiling point 69°C.

3.3. *Filter paper,* Whatman No. 40, 11 cm.

3.4. *Muslin cloth discs,* 11 cm.

3.5. *Diatomaceous-silica filter aid suspension,** 10 g per liter distilled water.

4. Procedure

4.1. Collect 1 liter of sewage in a wide-mouth bottle marked at 1 liter. Acidify to pH 1.0; generally, 3 ml conc HCl is sufficient.

4.2. Prepare a filter consisting of a muslin cloth disc overlaid with filter paper. Wet the paper and muslin and press down the edges of the paper. Using a vacuum, pass 100 ml filter aid suspension through the prepared filter and wash with 1 liter distilled water. Apply a vacuum until no more water passes the filter.

4.3. Filter the acidified sample through the prepared filter. Apply a vacuum until no more water passes the filter.

4.4. Remove the filter paper to a watch glass with a forceps. Add the material adhering to the edges of the muslin cloth disc. Wipe the sides and bottom of the collecting vessel, the stirring rod, and the Buchner funnel with bits of filter paper soaked in hexane, taking care to remove all films due to grease and to collect all solid material. Add the bits of filter paper to the filter paper on the watch

* Hyflo Super-Cel (Johns-Manville Corp.) or equal.

glass. Roll the filter paper and the bits of filter paper and fit them into a paper extraction thimble. Add any bits of material remaining on the watch glass. Wipe the watch glass with a bit of filter paper soaked in hexane and place in the paper extraction thimble.

4.5. Dry the thimble with the filter paper in a hot-air oven at 103°C for 30 min. Fill the thimble with small glass beads. Weigh the extraction flask and extract the grease in a Soxhlet apparatus using hexane at a rate of 20 cycles per hour for 4 hr. Time from the first cycle.

4.6. Distill the solvent from the extraction flask in a water bath at 85°C (hexane may be reused if it is redistilled). Dry by placing the flask on a steam bath and draw air through the flask by means of a vacuum applied for 15 min.

4.7. Cool in a desiccator for 30 min and weigh.

5. Calculation

mg/l total grease

$$= \frac{\text{mg increase in weight of flask} \times 1,000}{\text{ml sample}}$$

6. Precision and Accuracy

Using synthetic samples containing various amounts of Crisco and Shell S.A.E. No. 20 oil, an average recovery of 98.7 per cent was obtained with a standard deviation of 1.86 per cent. Ten replicates each of two sewages yielded standard deviations of 0.76 mg and 0.48 mg.

B. Semiwet Extraction Method (Tentative)

1. General Discussion

1.1. *Principle:* The principle is the same as in Method A, except that contact between the solvent and grease is forced mechanically with a glass stirring rod.

1.2. *Interference:* Because of the variable composition of grease, it is impossible to say that a fixed, practicable, number of direct extractions removes a determinable percentage of the total grease in all types of sewage. If a limit is set on the number of extractions, even as high as ten, the more difficultly soluble fractions of grease may not be determined by this method. As in Method A, certain nongrease substances will be extracted by hexane. Also, strict adherence to all details must be observed if reproducible results are to be obtained.

2. Apparatus

2.1. *Buchner funnel,* 12 cm.

2.2. *Distilling flask,* 300 ml.

3. Reagents

Same as Method A, Sec. 3.

4. Procedure

4.1. Follow the same procedure as in Method A to the point in Sec. 4.4 where the filter paper has been removed from the Buchner funnel. Instead of placing it in an extraction thimble, place it in a 300-ml erlenmeyer flask. Also add the bits of filter paper used for wiping the flask.

4.2. Add 25 ml hexane to the flask. With the aid of a stirring rod of suitable length flattened at one end, stir the paper around in the solvent for 1 min. Occasionally squeeze the paper between the stirring rod and the wall of the flask. Allow the material to settle momentarily, then pour the solvent into a 12-cm funnel fitted with 18.5-cm Whatman No. 40 filter paper. Collect the solvent in a 300-ml distilling flask.

4.3. Repeat the above extraction nine more times, collecting all of the solvent in the one distilling flask.

4.4. Wash the filter paper in the funnel with hexane, using a glass rod to aid in dissolving the grease on the paper by rubbing the visible residues while applying a stream of solvent to the same spot. Add the washings to the contents of the flask.

4.5. Distill hexane from the distilling flask in a water bath at 85°C to a volume of approximately 25 ml. Transfer to a smaller tared flask using a 6-cm glass funnel, and rinse the larger flask and funnel with two small portions of hexane, adding the rinsings to the tared flask.

4.6. Distill hexane from the tared flask in a water bath at 85°C. Dry by placing on a steam bath and draw air through the flask by means of a vacuum applied for 15 min.

4.7. Cool in a desiccator for 30 min and weigh.

5. Calculation

See Method A, Sec. 5.

6. Precision and Accuracy

Using 100.0 mg Crisco as a standard grease, an average recovery of 98.2 per cent was obtained, with a standard deviation of ±4.0 mg. Analysis of ten replicate samples of a domestic sewage yielded a standard deviation of ±2.58 mg.

Bibliography

1. GEHM, H. W. Determination of Grease in Sewage. *Sew. Works J.* 13:927 (1941).
2. OKUN, D.; HURWITZ, E.; & MOHLMAN, F. W. Investigation of Methods for the Determination of Grease in Sewage

and Sludge. *Sew. Works J.* 13:485 (1941).
3. HATFIELD, W. D. & SYMONS, G. E. The Determination of Grease in Sewage. *Sew. Works J.* 17:16 (1945).
4. GILCREAS, F. W.; SANDERSON, W. W.; & ELMER, R. P. Two New Methods for the Determination of Grease in Sewage. *Sew. Ind. Wastes* 25:1379 (1953).
5. ULLMANN, W. W. & SANDERSON, W. W. A Further Study of Methods for the Determination of Grease in Sewage. *Sew. Ind. Wastes* 31:8 (1959).

Hydrocarbon and Fatty Matter Content of Grease

Grease is composed primarily of fatty matter resulting from kitchen wastes and hydrocarbons of petroleum origin. A knowledge of the percentage of each of these constituents in the total grease minimizes the difficulty in determining the major source of the grease and simplifies the correction of grease problems in sewage treatment plant operation and stream pollution abatement.

Using the method described, reproducible results have been obtained for concentrations up to 650 mg/l.

1. General Discussion

1.1. *Principle:* Activated alumina has the ability to adsorb polar materials. If a solution of grease dissolved in hexane is passed through a column of activated alumina, the grease will be adsorbed on the surface of the alumina. Further passage of pure solvent through the column will elute the nonpolar material that has been retained on the column. Because petroleum is composed chiefly of nonpolar hydrocarbons, and fatty acids and esters are polar, this procedure effects a separation.

1.2. *Interference:* The more polar hydrocarbons, such as the complex aromatic compounds and the hydrocarbon derivatives of chlorine, sulfur, and nitrogen, will be retained on the column and determined as fatty matter. Any compounds other than hydrocarbons and fatty matter recovered by the procedures for the determination of grease would also interfere.

2. Apparatus

2.1. *Vacuum pump,* or other source of vacuum.

2.2. *Buchner funnel,* 12 cm.

2.3. *Soxhlet extraction apparatus,* if Method A is to be used for grease determination.

3. Reagents

3.1. *Hydrochloric acid,* conc.

3.2. *n-hexane,* boiling point 69°C.

3.3. *Filter paper,* Whatman No. 40, 11 cm.

3.4. *Muslin cloth discs,* 11 cm.

3.5. *Diatomaceous-silica filter aid suspension,** 10 g per liter distilled water.

---

* Hyflo Super-Cel (Johns-Manville Corp.) or equal.

3.6. *Adsorption alumina,* 80–200 mesh.

4. Preparation of Adsorption Column

Take a piece of 30-cm glass tubing with a 1-cm inside diameter and draw out one end over a flame to an opening of 1-mm inside diameter. Pack the drawn end of the tube with glass wool to a depth of 4 cm. Fill the tube with adsorption alumina to an overall height of 16 cm (12 cm of alumina). Place a small plug of glass wool in the column on the surface of the alumina. The alumina in the column is capable of adsorbing about 700 mg of polar material and should be repacked with fresh alumina before this limit has been reached. Used alumina may be reactivated by ignition for 5 hr at 600°C in a muffle furnace.

5. Procedure

5.1. Dissolve in 10 ml of hexane the grease in the flask after completion of the grease procedure, and pass through the adsorption column. Collect the solvent in a tared flask.

5.2. Elute the nonpolar material in the column with seven 10-ml portions of hexane and collect the elute in the tared flask. Add each successive portion of hexane when the level of the preceding portion reaches the top of the alumina in the column.

5.3. Distill hexane from the flask in a water bath at 85°C. Dry by placing the flask on a steam bath and draw air through the flask by means of a vacuum applied for 15 min.

5.4. Cool the flask in a desiccator for 30 min and weigh.

6. Calculation

% hydrocarbon
$$= \frac{\text{mg increase in weight of flask} \times 100}{\text{mg total grease}}$$
% fatty matter $= 100 -$ % hydrocarbon

7. Precision and Accuracy

Using the hydrocarbon determination on 18 synthetic samples containing known amounts of Crisco and Shell S.A.E. No. 20 motor oil, an average of only 91.5 per cent of the oil was recovered, with a standard deviation of 2.68 mg. The low percentage recovery was due to the presence of polar material in the oil. Ten replicates each of two sewages yielded standard deviations of 0.26 mg and 1.06 mg, respectively.

For the determination of the fatty matter content of the grease, the analysis of 18 samples showed an average recovery of 103.9 per cent, with a standard deviation of 3.11 mg. The high results are related to the presence of polar material in the oil added. Ten replicates each of two sewages yielded standard deviations of 0.81 mg and 1.23 mg, respectively.

Bibliography

1. FIESER, L. F. & FIESER, M. *Organic Chemistry.* Reinhold Publishing Corp., New York (3rd ed., 1956). p. 109.
2. LEDERER, E. & LEDERER, M. *Chromatography: A Review of Principles and Applications.* D. Van Nostrand Co., Princeton, N.J. (2nd ed., 1957). p. 103.
3. ULLMANN, W. W. & SANDERSON, W. W. Methods for Measuring Grease in Sewage. *Sew. Ind. Wastes* 31:8 (1959).

Nitrogen (Ammonia)

The direct nesslerization of ammonia nitrogen in sewage (Method A) is satisfactory if a precision within 1–2 mg/l is sufficient. Distillation with nesslerization or titration (Method B) is more accurate and precise largely because 100-ml samples are distilled, thus reducing the volume ratio factor.

Sampling and storage: Because organic nitrogen is progressively ammonified by biologic activity, the determination of ammonia or organic nitrogen is best made on a fresh sample. If the analysis cannot be made immediately after collection, the nitrogen balance may be maintained with an excess of 1,500 mg/l H_2SO_4 (about 0.8 ml conc H_2SO_4 per liter).

A. Direct Nesslerization Method

1. General Discussion

1.1. *Principle:* After clarification with zinc sulfate and alkali, the sample is treated with nessler reagent, which produces a graduated series of yellow to brown colors.

1.2. *Interference:* A number of aliphatic and aromatic amines, organic chloramines, alcohols, aldehydes, and acetone, among other undefined organic compounds, cause trouble in direct nesslerization because they yield a yellowish or greenish off color or a turbidity with nessler reagent.

2. Apparatus

Colorimetric equipment: One of the following is required:

2.1. *Spectrophotometer,* for use at 400 to 425 mμ, providing a light path of 1 cm or longer.

2.2. *Filter photometer,* providing a light path of 1 cm or longer and equipped with a violet filter having maximum transmittance at 400 to 425 mμ.

2.3. *Nessler tubes,* matched, 50 ml, tall form.

3. Reagents

3.1. *Ammonia-free water:*

a. Ammonia-free water may be made by redistillation of distilled water that has been treated with bromine and allowed to stand overnight.

b. For most work, the ammonia may be removed from ordinary distilled water by shaking with a strong cation exchanger.* Traces of magnesium in some distilled water, however, cause cloudy nessler tubes.

3.2. *Zinc sulfate solution:* Dissolve 100 g $ZnSO_4 \cdot 7H_2O$ in ammonia-free distilled water and make up to 1 liter.

3.3. *Sodium hydroxide solution:* Dissolve 250 g NaOH in ammonia-free distilled water and make up to 1 liter.

3.4. *Stabilizer solution:* Either EDTA or Rochelle salt may be used to prevent calcium or magnesium precipitation following the addition of alkaline nessler reagent.

a. *EDTA solution:* Dissolve 50 g disodium dihydrogen ethylenediaminetetraacetate dihydrate in 60 ml am-

---

* Folin's ammonia permutit (a product of The Permutit Company) or equal.

monia-free water in which 10 g solid sodium hydroxide has been dissolved. Cool to room temperature and dilute to 100 ml.

b. Rochelle salt solution: Dissolve 50 g potassium sodium tartrate tetra-hydrate, $KNaC_4H_4O_6 \cdot 4H_2O$, which contains no ammonia as a contaminant, in ammonia-free water and dilute to 100 ml.

3.5. *Standard ammonium chloride solution:* For the stock solution dissolve 3.819 g NH_4Cl in ammonia-free water and dilute to 1,000 ml. From this stock solution prepare the standard solution by diluting 10.00 ml to 1,000 ml with ammonia-free water; 1.00 ml = 0.0100 mg N.

3.6. *Nessler reagent:* Dissolve 100 g anhydrous mercuric iodide, HgI_2, and 70 g anhydrous potassium iodide, KI, in a small quantity of ammonia-free water and add this mixture slowly, with stirring, to a cool solution of 160 g solid sodium hydroxide, NaOH, in 150 ml ammonia-free water. Dilute to 1 liter with ammonia-free water. Stored in pyrex glassware and out of the sun-light, this reagent is stable for periods up to a year under normal laboratory conditions. The reagent should give the characteristic color with ammonia within 10 min after addition and should not produce a precipitate with small amounts of ammonia within 2 hr. (CAUTION: *Toxic; take care to avoid ingestion.*)

4. Procedure

4.1. *Treatment of sample:* Add 1 ml zinc sulfate solution to 100 ml of sample. Mix thoroughly, add 0.4 to 0.5 ml NaOH solution to obtain a pH of 10.5; again mix; and clarify by centrifuging or filtering through filter paper, discarding the first 25 ml of filtrate.

4.2. Dilute 5.0 ml or less of the clarified liquor or filtrate to the mark in a 50-ml nessler tube with ammonia-free water. Add 1 or 2 drops of EDTA or Rochelle salt solution to prevent cloudy tubes. Nesslerize by adding 1 ml nessler reagent, and after 10 min compare with standards.

4.3. *Temporary standards:* Prepare a series of nessler tubes containing the following volumes of standard ammonium chloride solution, diluted to 50 ml with ammonia-free water: 0.0, 0.2, 0.4, 0.7, 1.0, 1.4, 1.7, 2.0, 2.5 ml. Add 1 ml nessler reagent to each tube and allow 10 min for color formation; 30 min may be required for very faint colors to form.

4.4. *Permanent standards:* Permanent standards may be prepared from potassium chloroplatinate and cobaltous chloride solutions as directed in Part I, Nitrogen (Ammonia), Method A, Sec. 4.7b, omitting such values as are not needed in sewage examination.

4.5. *Color measurement:* Colors may be compared visually in nessler tubes or measured by use of a photometer after a calibration curve has been established. For this purpose the aliquot portion may be diluted to 25 ml instead of 50, thus increasing the sensitivity of the method.

5. Calculation

$$\text{mg/l ammonia N} = \frac{\text{mg ammonia N} \times 1,000}{\text{ml sample}}$$

$$= \frac{\text{ml standard solution} \times 10}{\text{ml sample}}$$

6. Precision and Accuracy

The recovery of ammonia from sewage by direct nesslerization is 97–99 per cent. The precision in the color comparison, expressed as the standard deviation, is somewhat less than 0.001 mg ammonia nitrogen, or about 1 mg/l if a 1-ml sample is used for nesslerization ($n = 4$; 56×10).

B. Distillation Method

1. General Discussion

1.1. *Principle:* Free ammonia nitrogen can be quantitatively recovered by distillation when the distillation mixture is maintained at about pH 7.4. The distillate may be collected in a volumetric flask for nesslerization or the sample may be distilled into boric acid or standard sulfuric acid and the ammonia determined by titration.

1.2. *Interference:* Ammonia recovery will be low on samples containing more than 250 mg/l calcium unless sufficient phosphate buffer is added. The calcium and phosphate of the buffer react to precipitate calcium phosphate, releasing hydrogen ions and lowering the pH. A number of aliphatic and aromatic amines, organic chloramines, acetone, aldehydes, and alcohols, among other undefined organic compounds, yield a yellowish or greenish off color or a turbidity following the addition of nessler reagent to distillates collected from dechlorinated samples. Sulfide has also been reported to cause turbidity following nesslerization, a condition which may be avoided by adding lead carbonate to the flask prior to distillation. Volatile substances, such as formaldehyde, can be removed by boiling at low pH, after which the sample can be distilled and nesslerized in the normal way.

The titration procedure is also subject to amine interference because the standard acid can react with such alkaline substances. The titration process is free of interference from neutral organic compounds.

2. Apparatus

2.1. *Distillation apparatus:* A glass flask, 800 ml, with a condenser and adapter so arranged that the distillate can be collected either for nesslerization or in standard H_2SO_4 or H_3BO_3 solution for titration.

2.2. *Colorimetric equipment:* The same colorimetric equipment is required as for Method A.

3. Reagents

3.1. *Ammonia-free water:* Prepare as directed in Method A, Sec. 3.1.

3.2. *Phosphate buffer solution,* 0.5M. Dissolve 14.3 g anhydrous potassium dihydrogen phosphate, KH_2PO_4, and 68.8 g anhydrous dipotassium hydrogen phosphate, K_2HPO_4, in ammonia-free water and dilute to 1 liter.

3.3. *Standard sulfuric acid titrant,* 0.02N. Prepare as directed in Part I, Alkalinity, Sec. 3.2; 1.00 ml = 0.28 mg N. Other strengths of standard acid may be used.

3.4. *Indicating boric acid solution:* Prepare as directed under Nitrogen (Organic), Sec. 3.8.

3.5. *Standard ammonium chloride solution:* Prepare as directed in Method A, Sec. 3.5.

3.6. *Nessler reagent:* Prepare as directed in Method A, Sec. 3.6.

4. Procedure

4.1. *Distillation:* Steam out the still until free from ammonia. Place 100–400 ml of sample in an 800-ml kjeldahl flask. Neutralize to pH 7 if the sample is acid or alkaline. Add 25 ml phosphate buffer solution, which should keep the pH of the distillation mixture at 7.4 during the distillation. For samples containing more than 250 mg/l calcium, add up to 40 ml of buffer solution first and then adjust the pH to 7.4 with acid or base. Dilute to 400 ml with ammonia-free water and distill 200 ml into a 200-ml graduated flask for nesslerization or into standard H_2SO_4 or H_3BO_3 solution for titration as described in Nitrogen (Organic), Sec. 4.

4.2. *Nesslerization:* Dilute an aliquot of the distillate with ammonia-free water, nesslerize, and compare colors as directed in Method A, Sec. 4.5.

4.3. *Titration:* If the concentration of ammonia nitrogen is greater than 5 mg/l, collect the distillate in 50 ml indicating boric acid solution, and back-titrate with standard H_2SO_4 titrant as in Nitrogen (Organic), Sec. 4.3 and 4.4.

5. Calculation

For nesslerization:

$$\text{mg/l ammonia N} = \frac{R \times 2,000}{Sd}$$

where $R =$ ml standard solution, $S =$ ml sample, and $d =$ distillate nesslerized.

For titration:

mg/l ammonia N
$$= \frac{\text{ml } H_2SO_4 \text{ titration} \times 0.28 \times 1,000}{\text{ml sample}}$$

6. Precision and Accuracy

The distillation and titration procedure is more accurate than the direct nesslerization method. The recoveries are 99 to 100 per cent and the precision, over a range from 5 to 50 mg/l, may be expressed as a standard deviation of 0.18 ml H_2SO_4, or 0.5 mg/l when a 100-ml sample is used ($n = 3$; 5×5).

The distillation and nesslerization method is more precise for concentrations of 1 to 5 mg/l. Using a 100-ml sample and a 25-ml aliquot from the 200-ml distillate, the standard deviation was 0.0019 mg ammonia nitrogen or 0.15 mg/l ($n = 1$; 11×10).

Bibliography

1. PHELPS, E. B. A Critical Study of the Methods in Current Use for the Determination of Free and Albuminoid Ammonia. *APHA Public Health Papers & Repts.* 29:354 (1903) ; *J. Infectious Diseases* 1:327 (1904).

Nitrogen (Nitrate)

Nitrate nitrogen may be present in small amounts in fresh domestic wastewater. However, it is seldom found in influents to treatment plants because the nitrate serves as an oxygen source in the biologically unstable wastewater. On the other hand, nitrate is often found in the effluents of biological treatment plants, because it represents the final form of nitrogen from the oxidation of organic nitrogen compounds. Trickling filter and activated sludge treatment plant effluents may contain from 0 to 50 mg/l nitrate nitrogen, depending on the total nitrogen content of the influent, the degree of loading, and the temperature of the sewage.

The determination of nitrate nitrogen in domestic and industrial wastewaters is much more difficult than in natural waters because of higher concentrations of numerous interfering substances such as chlorides and organic matter. Consequently, four methods are presented as tentative; the brucine method (A), the phenoldisulfonic acid method (B), the diazotization method (C), and the polarographic method (D). These four methods cover a wide range of nitrate nitrogen concentrations and are adapted to eliminate a wide variety of interfering substances. Therefore, the analyst has a wide choice and may select the method most suitable to his own wastewater situation and the equipment in his laboratory.

Storage of sample: To prevent any change in the nitrogen balance through biological activity, the nitrate determination should be started promptly after sampling. If storage is necessary, samples should be kept at a temperature just above the freezing point. If acid preservation is employed, the sample should be neutralized to about pH 7 immediately before the analysis is begun.

A. *Brucine Method* (Tentative)

1. General Discussion

1.1. *Principle:* Brucine and nitrate react, under acid conditions, to form a sulfur-yellow color the intensity of which is proportional to the original nitrate concentration and is measured at 410 mμ. A fairly reproducible calibration curve is obtained when absorbance is plotted against nitrate concentration, although the Beer-Lambert relationship is not obeyed.

1.2. *Interference:* Domestic and industrial wastewaters will contain more and higher concentrations of interfering substances than will potable water supplies. The analyst should be aware of these interferences and how to eliminate them. Nitrite ion does not appreciably interfere up to a concentration of approximately 7.0 mg/l, although higher amounts may interfere. However, the brucine reagent contains sulfanilic acid, which should eliminate the concentrations of nitrite ion usually present in domestic and industrial wastewaters. Residual chlorine must be eliminated by the addition of sodium arsenite, provided the chlorine does not exceed 5 mg/l. A slight excess of sodium arsenite will not affect the determination. Organic matter may interfere by giving high absorbance readings at 410 mμ and by possible charring effects from the concentrated sulfuric acid reagent. If high concentrations of organic matter interfere, the sample must be clarified as described in Method B, Sec. 3.1.

Concentrations of other substances that do not interfere (in each case, the figures represent the highest concentration investigated) are 250 mg/l Fe, 85 mg/l OH as NaOH, 65 mg/l NH_4, 100 mg/l Ca, 60 mg/l Mg, 1,000 mg/l Cl as NaCl, 50 mg/l SO_3 as Na_2SO_3, 200 mg/l PO_4, and 200 mg/l SiO_2.

2. Apparatus

Same as Part I, Nitrogen (Nitrate), Method B, Sec. 2.

3. Reagents

Same as Part I, Nitrogen (Nitrate), Method B, Sec. 3.

4. Procedure

The procedure is described in detail in Part I, Nitrogen (Nitrate), Method B, Sec. 4.

Note: A modification of the color development (step 4.3 of the above method) may produce the desired Beer-Lambert relationship as follows: Cool all standards, reagents, and samples to ice temperature in an ice bath.

Place test tubes and rack in an ice bath and add reagents (cold) as follows: Carefully pipet 2.00 ml of sample containing not more than 10 mg/l N into the 50-ml pyrex test tube; add 1.0 ml brucine-sulfanilic acid reagent, using a safety pipet; add 10 ml H_2SO_4 and mix by quickly removing the test tube and tapping it with a finger; add 10 ml iced distilled water and mix as before. Transfer the rack with the samples to a boiling water bath and allow 10 min for color development. Cool samples and read transmittance at 410 mμ.

5. Calculation

Same as Part I, Nitrogen (Nitrate), Method B, Sec. 5.

6. Accuracy

An accuracy of 0.11 mg/l can be obtained in the range of nitrate concentration of 0 to 11 mg/l as nitrate nitrogen and in the absence of interfering substances.

B. *Phenoldisulfonic Acid Method* (Tentative)

1. General Discussion

1.1. *Principle:* A yellow color is produced by the reaction between nitrate and phenoldisulfonic acid. The intensity of this yellow color is proportional to the nitrate concentration and is measured at 410 mμ or 480 mμ. The Beer-Lambert relationship is obeyed up to 2 mg/l nitrate nitrogen when absorbance is measured at 410 mμ, the wavelength of maximum absorption, and up to 12 mg/l nitrate nitrogen when absorbance is measured at 480

mμ. These measurements are made in a light path of 1 cm.

1.2. *Interference:* Domestic and industrial wastewaters will contain more and higher concentrations of interfering substances than will potable water supplies. The analyst should be aware of these interferences and how to eliminate them. Chloride interferes at all concentrations and must be eliminated entirely. Silver sulfate is used to remove the chloride interference. Nitrite interferes in proportion to its concentration. Consequently, nitrite nitrogen must be determined and the amount subtracted from the total nitrate nitrogen concentration. Organic matter interferes from turbidity and from color that may absorb at 410 mμ or 480 mμ. Organic matter is eliminated by coagulation with aluminum hydroxide and color by adsorption with activated carbon.

2. Apparatus

Same as Part I, Nitrogen (Nitrate), Method A, Sec. 2.

3. Reagents

All the reagents of Part I, Nitrogen (Nitrate), Method A, Sec. 3 are required, and in addition:

3.1. *Activated carbon:* Any grade of highly adsorptive carbon will suffice. However, it must be checked for nitrate adsorption as follows: Prepare a nitrate standard containing 0.01 mg nitrate nitrogen per 100 ml of solution. To 50 ml of this standard, add 1 g of activated carbon and stir. Filter and compare the phenoldisulfonic acid color development with that of the untreated portion of the standard. If there is no reduction in nitrate concentration, the activated carbon is ready for use.

4. Procedure

4.1. *Removal of interferences:*
a. *Color and turbidity:* To 50 ml of the sample, add 0.5 g activated carbon and 1 ml Al(OH)$_3$ cream (floc), mix well, allow to stand for a few minutes, filter, and discard the first portion of the filtrate.

b. *Chlorides and nitrites:* Remove or convert as directed in Part I, Nitrogen (Nitrate), Method A, Sec. 4.2 and 4.3.

4.2. *Development of yellow color:* Proceed as directed in Part I, Nitrogen (Nitrate), Method A, Sec. 4.4.

5. Calculation

Same as Part I, Nitrogen (Nitrate), Method A, Sec. 5.

6. Precision and Accuracy

See Part I, Nitrogen (Nitrate), Method A, Sec. 6.

C. Diazotization Method (Tentative)

1. General Discussion

1.1. *Principle:* Under controlled conditions, nitrates may be reduced to nitrites with zinc, and the nitrites determined colorimetrically in the usual manner. The amount of zinc and the contact period for reduction are critical. The reaction is temperature-dependent, and all samples must be run at a temperature near that at which the calibration curve is prepared; the lower the temperature, the greater the slope of the calibration curve and the greater the accuracy. Nitrite originally present is destroyed by sodium azide in acid solution. Using a 2-cm light path, the color system obeys Beer's law to about 1.4 mg/l N or 6.2 mg/l NO$_3$.

1.2. *Interference:* Strong oxidizing and reducing substances should be absent. The following ions are known to interfere: ferric, mercurous, silver, bismuth, antimonous, lead, auric, chloroplatinate, and metavanadate. Cupric ions may cause low results. Colored ions which alter the color system should be absent.

1.3. *Minimum detectable concentration:* Using distilled water for sample preparation, the minimum detectable concentrations in a 50-ml sample are as follows: with a 10-cm light path, 0.002 mg/1 N; with a 5-cm light path, 0.005 mg/1 N; with a 2-cm light path, 0.01 mg/1 N; and with a 1-cm light path, 0.04 mg/1 N.

2. Apparatus

Colorimetric equipment: One of the following is required:

2.1. *Spectrophotometer,* for use at 520 mμ, providing a light path of 1 cm or longer.

2.2. *Filter photometer,* providing a light path of 1 cm or longer and equipped with a green filter having maximum transmittance near 520 mμ.

2.3. *Nessler tubes,* matched, 50 ml, tall form; or

2.4. *Test tubes,* 25 $\times$ 200 mm, Kimble No. 45048 or equal, fitted with cork stoppers (No. 4).

2.5. *Filter paper,* coarse, 15 cm, which will pass 50 ml of sample in 30 sec or less.

2.6. *Measuring spoon,* ¼-teaspoon capacity.

3. Reagents

3.1. *Zinc sulfate solution:* Dissolve 100 g $ZnSO_4 \cdot 7H_2O$ in distilled water and dilute to 1 liter.

3.2. *Sodium hydroxide solution:* Dissolve 240 g NaOH in 500 ml distilled water and dilute to 1 liter.

3.3. *Stock potassium nitrate solu-*tion: Dissolve 0.7218 g anhydrous KNO_3 in distilled water and dilute to 1,000 ml. This solution contains 100 mg/1 N.

3.4. *Standard potassium nitrate solution:* Dilute 50 ml stock potassium nitrate solution to 500 ml with distilled water; 1.00 ml = 0.01 mg N = 0.0443 mg NO_3.

3.5. *Sodium azide solution:* Dissolve 1.0 g NaN_3 in distilled water and dilute to 1 liter. (CAUTION: *Sodium azide is toxic; take care to avoid ingestion.*)

3.6. *Hydrochloric acid,* 1 + 4.

3.7. *Sulfanilic acid reagent:* Dissolve 0.60 g sulfanilic acid in 70 ml hot distilled water, cool, dilute to 100 ml with distilled water, and mix thoroughly.

3.8. *Zinc:* Add 1.000 g finely powdered zinc to 200 g sodium chloride, NaCl, in a bottle and mix thoroughly by shaking for several minutes. Each ml (¼ level teaspoon measure) contains 5.9 mg ($\pm$ 10 per cent) Zn. Shake the mixture vigorously each time before it is used.

3.9. *Naphthylamine hydrochloride reagent:* Dissolve 0.60 g 1-naphthylamine hydrochloride in distilled water to which 1.0 ml conc HCl has been added, dilute to 100 ml with distilled water, and mix thoroughly. The reagent becomes discolored, and a precipitate may form after one week, but it is still usable. It should be discarded when the sensitivity or reproducibility is affected. Store in refrigerator. Remove the precipitate by filtration.

3.10. *Sodium acetate solution, 2M:* Dissolve 16.4 g $NaC_2H_3O_2$ or 27.2 g $NaC_2H_3O_2 \cdot 3H_2O$ in distilled water and dilute to 100 ml. Filter if the solution is not clear.

4. Preparation of Calibration Curve

4.1. *For photometric measurements:* Prepare a suitably spaced series of standards by accurately pipeting calculated volumes of standard potassium nitrate solution into test tubes or nessler tubes. Tall-form 50-ml nessler tubes are recommended for convenience in mixing. These tubes, if used for reduction, will contain residual Zn and must be cleaned with dilute HCl before being used for visual comparison.

4.2. Add 1.0 ml 1 + 4 HCl and 1.0 ml sulfanilic acid reagent, dilute to about 40–45 ml, and mix thoroughly. Shake the Zn—NaCl mixture thoroughly and then add 1 ml ($\frac{1}{4}$ level teaspoon measure) to sample. Invert the sample 10 times, wait 2 min, and invert 10 times more. Then filter rapidly into 50-ml volumetric flasks. Time of contact with zinc is critical and the sample should be filtered 7 min after the addition of zinc.

4.3. Add 1.0 ml naphthylamine hydrochloride reagent to the filtrate and mix. Add 1.0 ml sodium acetate solution and mix. Allow 5 min for color development. Dilute to 50 ml and measure the reddish-purple color in a spectrophotometer at 520 mμ or in a filter photometer with a green filter having maximum transmittance near 520 mμ. Light path lengths suitable for various nitrate nitrogen ranges are as follows:

NO$_3$-N Range mg/l	Light Path cm
0.4 –14.0	1
0.2 –14.0	2
0.10–10.0	5
0.02– 3.0	10

4.4. Transmittance readings should be made against a blank to which all reagents (as directed under Sec. 4.2 and 4.3) have been added. Complete calibration curves should be determined following the preparation of new reagents.

4.5. Standards for visual comparison with nessler tubes are prepared as directed in Sec. 4.2 and 4.3.

5. Procedure

5.1. If the sample has been preserved with acid, it must be neutralized to about pH 7.

5.2. If the sample contains suspended solids and color, add 1 ml zinc sulfate solution to 100 ml of sample, mix thoroughly, add 0.4–0.5 ml sodium hydroxide solution to obtain a pH of 10.5 as determined with a pH meter and a high-pH glass electrode, and again mix thoroughly. Allow the treated sample to stand a few minutes, whereupon a heavy precipitate should fall, leaving the supernate clear and colorless. Clarify by centrifuging or filtering. Discard the first few ml of filtrate. Adjust the filtrate to about pH 7.

5.3. To destroy nitrites add 1.0 ml sodium azide solution to a 50.0-ml sample in a 150-ml beaker. Add 1.0 ml 1 + 4 HCl, and concentrate by gentle boiling, without spattering, to about 40 ml. Cool to room temperature and transfer to a test tube or nessler tube. Rinse the beaker with 1–2 ml distilled water, and add rinsings to the sample.

5.4. Add 1.0 ml sulfanilic acid reagent and mix thoroughly. Shake the Zn—NaCl mixture thoroughly, and then add 1 ml ($\frac{1}{4}$ level teaspoon measure) of the mixture to the sample. Invert 10 times, wait 2 min, invert 10 times, wait 2 min, and invert 10 times more. Then filter rapidly into a 50-ml volumetric flask. Time of contact with zinc is critical, and the sample should be filtered 7 min after the addition of zinc.

5.5. Add 1.0 ml naphthylamine hydrochloride to the filtrate and mix. Add 1.0 ml sodium acetate solution and mix. Allow 5 to 15 min for color development. Dilute to 50 ml and measure the reddish-purple color in a spectrophotometer at 520 mμ, in a filter photometer with a green filter having maximum transmittance near 520 mμ, or by comparison in nessler tubes.

5.6. Transmittance readings should be made against a sample blank to which all reagents except sulfanilic acid have been added. At least one check on the calibration curve should be run using known nitrate standards, preferably in the nitrogen range of the sample.

6. Calculation

$$\text{mg/l nitrate-N} = \frac{\text{mg nitrate-N} \times 1{,}000}{\text{ml sample}}$$
$$\text{mg/l NO}_3 = \text{mg/l nitrate-N} \times 4.43$$

7. Precision and Accuracy

On undiluted samples, and in the absence of interference, precision is estimated to be ± 0.02 mg/l N up to 1.4 mg/l, and accuracy is estimated to be 0.02 mg/l N in the range from 0.04 to 1.4 mg/l as nitrogen with a 2-cm light path.

D. Polarographic Method (Tentative)

1. General Discussion

1.1. *Principle:* The nitrate ion gives a polarographic wave at −1.2 volts versus the saturated calomel electrode in the presence of zirconyl chloride as the base electrolyte. A current reading is taken at −1.2 v before and after the addition of ferrous ammonium sulfate. The difference in current readings is applicable to nitrate nitrogen concentrations ranging from 0.0 to 25 mg/l.

1.2. *Interference:* The following precautions must be observed: (a) The stock solution of zirconyl chloride is sufficiently acid to reduce the pH of the sample to approximately 1.7, unless the sample has an extremely high pH and alkalinity. If this situation is suspected, it may be necessary to neutralize the sample before addition of the base electrolyte. (b) The ferric ion produces a slight current change in the base line as the ferrous ammonium sulfate reagent ages; consequently, the current reading after destruction of the nitrate ion must be corrected by means of a daily blank. (c) The nitrite ion also is reduced by the ferrous ion; consequently, nitrite must be determined and a correction factor applied to the total nitrate concentration. (d) Large concentrations of organic matter are known to suppress polarographic waves; therefore, such material as slime and zoogleal suspensions must be removed by aluminum hydroxide coagulation before analysis. (e) Various sulfides and mercaptans will contaminate the mercury in the polarographic cell and affect the results; sulfides must be absent or removed, if present, from the sample.

1.3. Minimum detectable concentration: A concentration of 0.1 mg/l nitrate nitrogen can be accurately determined in a 10-ml sample.

2. Apparatus

2.1. Polarograph: Almost any commercially available instrument with the dropping mercury electrode will suffice. The polarographic cell volume should be at least 25 ml.

2.2. Glassware: All glassware should be acid-washed and rinsed thoroughly in nitrate- and iron-free distilled water.

3. Reagents

3.1. Zirconyl chloride solution, 1.1N: Dissolve 17.7 g zirconyl chloride octahydrate $ZrOCl_2 \cdot 8H_2O$, in nitrate-free distilled water and dilute to 100 ml.

3.2. Ferrous ammonium sulfate solution, 0.5N: Dissolve 10.600 g of fresh ferrous ammonium sulfate hexahydrate, $Fe(NH_4)_2(SO_4)_2 \cdot 6H_2O$, in nitrate-free distilled water. Add 0.5 ml conc H_2SO_4 and dilute to 100 ml. Add to this reagent a piece of standard iron wire that has been cleaned with sandpaper and rinsed with dilute sulfuric acid.

3.3. Nitrogen gas: Commercial nitrogen gas requires purification by passing through 5 per cent pyrogallol in 25 per cent NaOH, and through two bottles of deoxygenated distilled water.

3.4. Mercury, triple distilled.

3.5. Standard nitrate solution: Prepare stock solution as directed in Part I, Nitrogen (Nitrate), Method A, Sec. 3.5. Prepare two standard solutions whereby 1 ml = 10 μg NO_3-N and 1 ml = 1.0 μg NO_3-N.

4. Procedure

4.1. Standardize the polarograph against the saturated calomel electrode in accordance with the manufacturer's directions.

4.2. Adjust the mercury drop rate to one drop every 3–4 sec.

4.3. Prepare the sample for analysis by elimination of known interferences or by determination of the nitrite ion. If organic matter must be removed, do so by aluminum hydroxide coagulation as directed in Method B, Sec. 4.1. Ordinarily, the activated carbon can be omitted.

4.4. Place 10.0 ml sample in the polarographic cell and add 1.0 ml 1.1N zirconyl chloride solution. Place the dropping mercury electrode in the sample about ½ in. above the mercury pool. Adjust the applied potential to −1.2 v versus the saturated calomel electrode.

4.5. Remove dissolved oxygen by bubbling nitrogen gas through the sample for 5 min. Because the pH of the sample and the base electrolyte is usually 1.7, this step should also remove sulfides.

4.6. Raise the outlet of the gas tube above the surface of the sample and note the current, I_1.

4.7. Add 0.5 ml ferrous ammonium sulfate solution, mix for 5 min with the nitrogen gas stream, and again read the current, I_2. (A dense white precipitate forms at this point, but does not affect the results.) The difference, ΔI $(= I_1 - I_2)$, is directly proportional to the nitrate concentration.

4.8. The current reading, I_2, must be corrected for the ferric ion interference from the ferrous ammonium sulfate. This must be done daily as follows: Prepare a solution (*a*) of 10.0 ml distilled water and 1.0 ml zirconyl chloride solution and another solution (b) of 10 ml distilled water, 1.0 ml zirconyl chloride solution, and 0.5 ml ferrous ammonium sulfate solution. Obtain current readings for these two solutions at −1.2 v. Subtract the current reading of solution a from that of solution b to obtain the correction factor that, in turn, must be subtracted from I_2.

5. Calculation

5.1. *Calibration curve:* If nitrates are determined routinely, a calibration curve of current change, $\triangle I$, versus nitrate concentration can be prepared from the standard nitrate solutions in Sec. 3.5. A straight line relationship can be obtained up to a concentration of 25.0 mg/l NO_3-N.

5.2. *Proportion technique:* If nitrates are determined infrequently, the unknown nitrate concentration can be determined in proportion to a known nitrate concentration. In this case prepare a standard nitrate solution approximately equal to the unknown. The unknown nitrate concentration is calculated as follows:

$$\text{mg/l } NO_3\text{-N} = \frac{\triangle I_x \times C_k}{\triangle I_k}$$

where $\triangle I_x$ is the current change in the unknown sample, and C_k and $\triangle I_k$ are the nitrate nitrogen concentration and current change of the known solution, respectively.

6. Precision

The standard deviation in ten replicates of domestic wastewater was ±0.032 around a mean concentration of 1.14 mg/l NO_3-N. The standard deviation in 30 replicates of domestic wastewater was ±0.226 around a mean concentration of 10.04 mg/l NO_3-N.

Bibliography

Brucine and Phenoldisulfonic Acid Methods

1. See Part I, Nitrogen (Nitrate), Bibliography.

Diazotization Method

2. EDWARDS, G. P., ET AL. Determination of Nitrates in Waste Water Effluents and Water. *J. WPCF* 34:1112 (1962).

Polarographic Method

3. RAND, M. C. & HEUKELEKIAN, H. Polarographic Determination of Nitrates in Sanitary Analysis. *Anal. Chem.* 25:878 (1953).

4. LAWRENCE, W. A. & BRIGGS, R. M. Polarographic Determination of Nitrate. *Anal. Chem.* 25:965 (1953).

Nitrogen (Nitrite)

1. General Discussion

1.1. *Interference:* This method is not interfered with by relatively large amounts, up to 1,000 times, of the alkaline earths, zinc, nickel, arsenate, benzoate, borate, bromide, chloride, fluoride, iodate, molybdate, nitrate, phosphate, sulfate, and thiocyanate. Numerous heavy metals such as gold, lead, bismuth, iron, or mercury interfere by precipitation and others because of colored salts. Aliphatic amines react with nitrites to liberate gaseous nitrogen. Ammonia does not interfere in the small concentrations usually encountered. Strong reducing or oxidizing agents should be absent.

1.2. Preservation of samples: Determination of the nitrite content must be made on fresh samples because conversion of nitrite into either nitrate or ammonia by biologic action proceeds uninterruptedly, unless the sample is temporarily preserved with 1,500 mg/l H_2SO_4 as directed in Part III, Introduction, A, Sec. 2.4.

2. Apparatus

Colorimetric equipment: One of the following is required:

2.1. Spectrophotometer, for use at 520 mμ, providing a light path of 1 cm or longer.

2.2. Filter photometer, providing a light path of 1 cm or longer and equipped with a green filter having maximum transmittance near 520 mμ.

2.3. Nessler tubes, matched, 50 ml, tall form.

3. Reagents

3.1. Sulfanilic acid solution: Dissolve 0.60 g sulfanilic acid in 70 ml hot distilled water, cool, add 20 ml conc HCl, dilute to 100 ml with distilled water, and mix thoroughly.

3.2. Naphthylamine hydrochloride solution: Dissolve 0.60 g 1-naphthylamine hydrochloride and 1 ml conc HCl in distilled water and dilute to 100 ml.

3.3. Sodium acetate solution, 2M. Dissolve 16.4 g $NaC_2H_3O_2$ or 27.2 g $NaC_2H_3O_2 \cdot 3H_2O$ in distilled water and dilute to 100 ml. Filter if the solution is not clear.

3.4. Stock sodium nitrite solution: Dissolve 0.493 g $NaNO_2$ in 1,000 ml nitrite-free distilled water.

3.5. Standard sodium nitrite solution: Dilute 100.0 ml stock sodium nitrite solution to 1,000 ml; then dilute 50.0 ml of this solution to 1.000 ml with sterilized nitrite-free distilled water, add 1 ml chloroform, and preserve in a sterilized bottle; 1.0 ml = 0.5 μg N or 1.6 μg NO_2.

3.6. Manganese sulfate solution: Prepare as directed under Oxygen (Dissolved), Method A, Sec. 2.1.

3.7. Potassium permanganate solution: Dissolve 0.4 g $KMnO_4$ in 1 liter distilled water.

3.8. Ammonium oxalate solution: Dissolve 0.9 g $(NH_4)_2C_2O_4 \cdot H_2O$ in 1 liter distilled water.

3.9. Nitrite-free water: Add 1 ml conc H_2SO_4 and 0.2 ml manganese sulfate solution to 1 liter distilled water and make pink with 1 to 3 ml potassium permanganate solution. After 15 min decolorize with ammonium oxalate solution.

4. Procedure

4.1. Place in a nessler tube or 50-ml volumetric flask 0.10–10.0 ml of sample —clarified, if necessary, with $ZnSO_4$ and NaOH as described under Nitrogen (Ammonia), Method A, Sec. 4.1— and dilute to 20–25 ml. If the sample is acid or alkaline, neutralize to pH 6.5–7.5 with a few drops of dilute HCl or NaOH.

4.2. Measure 1.0 ml sulfanilic acid solution into the diluted sample, mix, and allow to stand at least 3 min and not more than 10 min for diazotization. The pH of this solution should be about 1.4

4.3. Add 1.0 ml naphthylamine hydrochloride solution and 1 ml sodium acetate solution. This should buffer the system to a pH of 2.5. Dilute to 50 ml and mix well.

4.4. After 10 min, and before 30 min, measure the intensity of the reddish-purple color in a spectrophotometer, a filter photometer, or by comparison in nessler tubes as directed in Part I, Nitrogen (Nitrite), Sec. 4.3 or 4.4.

5. Calculation

$$\text{mg/l nitrite N} = \frac{\mu\text{g nitrite N}}{\text{ml sample}}$$

6. Precision and Accuracy

Although this color reaction is very sensitive, its accuracy in sewage and wastes analysis has not been determined. The precision, as standard deviation, on sewage effluents, using a filter photometer, is 0.05 μg nitrite N, which is equivalent to 0.1 ml standard solution ($n = 1$; 40×10). When

comparing with standard colors in nessler tubes, the standard deviation is 0.1 μg ($n = 1$; 10×10). The results are to be reported in terms of nitrogen equivalent.

Bibliography

1. ILOSVAY, M. L. Nitrous Acid in the Saliva and in Exhaled Air. *Bull. Soc. Chem. (Ser. 3)* 2:388 (1889).
2. WESTON, R. S. Notes on the Determination of Nitrogen as Nitrites in Waters. *J. Am. Chem. Soc.* 27:281 (1905).
3. REINDOLLAR, W. F. Nitrite Nitrogen Standards. *Ind. Eng. Chem., Anal. Ed.* 12:325 (1940).
4. RIDER, B. F. & MELLON, M. G. Colorimetric Determination of Nitrites. *Ind. Eng. Chem., Anal. Ed.* 18:96 (1946).

Nitrogen (Organic)

Organic nitrogen may be determined by digestion of the sample after removal of free ammonia, with subsequent distillation and titration with standard acid or as the difference between the value obtained for total kjeldahl nitrogen and that for free ammonia.

1. General Discussion

1.1. *Principle:* The kjeldahl method, using mercuric sulfate as a catalyst, converts organically bound nitrogen in the trinegative state to ammonium bisulfate by digestion with sulfuric acid to which potassium sulfate has been added to raise the boiling point to 345°–370°C. The temperature should not exceed 382°C or loss of nitrogen will result. After dilution, the solution is made alkaline with sodium hydroxide and the ammonia distilled into dilute boric acid solution, or the distillate is collected for nesslerization. The am-

monium borate is titrated with standard sulfuric acid, using a mixed indicator.

1.2. *Interference:* In the presence of large quantities of nitrogen-free organic matter, it is necessary to add an additional 50 ml of sulfuric acid–mercuric sulfate-potassium sulfate solution for each gram of solid material in the sample.

1.3. *Storage:* Because organic nitrogen in unsterilized sewage is continually ammonified, the determination must be made on a freshly collected sample. If the analysis cannot be made at once, the sample must be preserved with sufficient sulfuric acid to obtain a concentration of 1,500 mg/l H_2SO_4 or more.

2. Apparatus

2.1. *Digestion apparatus,* provided with a suction takeoff to remove water vapor and sulfur trioxide fumes.

2.2. *Distillation apparatus:* See Nitrogen (Ammonia), Method B, Sec. 2.1.

3. Reagents

3.1. *Ammonia-free water:* Prepare as directed in Nitrogen (Ammonia), Method A, Sec. 3.1.

3.2. *Phosphate buffer solution,* 0.5M. Dissolve 14.3 g anhydrous potassium dihydrogen phosphate, KH_2PO_4, and 68.8 g anhydrous dipotassium hydrogen phosphate, K_2HPO_4, in ammonia-free water and dilute to 1 liter.

3.3. *Mercuric sulfate solution:* Dissolve 8 g red mercuric oxide, HgO, in 50 ml 1 + 5 H_2SO_4 and dilute to 100 ml with distilled water.

3.4. *Sulfuric acid–mercuric sulfate–potassium sulfate solution:* Dissolve 267 g K_2SO_4 in 1,300 ml distilled water and add 400 ml conc H_2SO_4. Add 50 ml mercuric sulfate solution and dilute to 2 liters. This reagent crystallizes at temperatures lower than 14°C.

3.5. *Sodium hydroxide–sodium thiosulfate solution:* Dissolve 500 g NaOH and 25 g $Na_2S_2O_3 \cdot 5H_2O$ in distilled water and dilute to 1 liter.

3.6. *Phenolphthalein indicator solution:* Either the aqueous (*a*) or alcoholic (*b*) solution may be used.

a. Dissolve 5 g phenolphthalein disodium salt in distilled water and dilute to 1 liter. If necessary, add 0.02N NaOH dropwise until a faint pink color appears.

b. Dissolve 5 g phenolphthalein in 500 ml 95 per cent ethyl alcohol or isopropyl alcohol and add 500 ml distilled water. Then add 0.02N NaOH dropwise until a faint pink color appears.

3.7. *Mixed indicator:* Mix 2 volumes of 0.2 per cent methyl red in 95 per cent alcohol with 1 volume of 0.2 per cent methylene blue in 95 per cent ethyl alcohol. This solution must be made fresh every 30 days.

3.8. *Indicating boric acid solution:* Dissolve 20 g boric acid, H_3BO_3, in water, add 10 ml mixed indicator, and dilute to 1 liter with ammonia-free water. This solution must be made fresh every 30 days.

3.9. *Standard sulfuric acid titrant,* 0.02N. In this strength, 1.00 ml = 0.28 mg N. Other strengths of standard acid may be used.

3.10. *Sulfuric acid,* conc.

4. Procedure

4.1. Place a measured sample into an 800-ml kjeldahl flask. The sample size can be determined from the following table:

Organic Nitrogen in Sample mg/l	Sample Size ml
0–10	250
10–20	100
20–50	50.0
50–100	25.0

Dilute the sample to 300 ml, neutralize to pH 7, if necessary, and add 25 ml phosphate buffer solution. Boil or distill off the free ammonia. The residue from the free-ammonia determination—Nitrogen (Ammonia), Method B, Sec. 4.1—may also be used for this determination.

4.2. Add 50 ml acid-sulfate solution (Sec. 3.4; or 10 ml conc H_2SO_4, 6.7 g K_2SO_4, and 1.5 ml mercuric sulfate solution may be substituted). If large quantities of nitrogen-free organic matter are present, add an additional 50 ml acid-sulfate solution for each gram of solid material in the sample. Digest the mixture by boiling for 20 to 30 min after the solution has become clear.

Cool the residue and add 300 ml of ammonia-free water.

4.3. Make alkaline with the hydroxide-thiosulfate solution, using phenolphthalein as an indicator. Distill into 50 ml of the indicating boric acid solution until about 200 ml distillate has been collected. The tip of the condenser must extend well below the level of the boric acid solution, and the temperature in the condenser should not rise above 29°C.

4.4. Titrate the ammonia with 0.02N H$_2$SO$_4$ until the indicator turns a pale lavender.

4.5 Run a blank on the reagents used and make the necessary corrections.

5. Calculation

$$\text{mg/l organic N} = \frac{(A - B) \times 280}{C}$$

where $A =$ ml H$_2$SO$_4$ for sample, $B =$ ml H$_2$SO$_4$ for blank, and $C =$ ml sample.

6. Precision and Accuracy

For the range 1–5 mg/l organic nitrogen, 97.5–98.6 per cent was recovered, with a precision of $\pm$ 0.03 mg/l. In the range 5–50 mg/l, 98.5–99.5 per cent recovery was obtained, with a precision of ± 0.13 mg/l ($n = 1$; 4×10).

Bibliography

1. KJELDAHL, J. A New Method for the Determination of Nitrogen in Organic Matter. *Z. Anal. Chem.* 22:366 (1883).
2. PHELPS, E. B. The Determination of Organic Nitrogen in Sewage by the Kjeldahl Process. *J. Infectious Diseases* Suppl. 1:225 (1905).
3. MEEKER, E. W. & WAGNER, E. C. Titration of Ammonia in the Presence of Boric Acid. *Ind. Eng. Chem., Anal. Ed.* 5:396 (1933).
4. BRECHER, C. A New Method for Titrating Ammonia in the Micro-Kjeldahl Determination. *Wien. Klin. Wochschr.* 49:1228 (1936); *Chem. Abs.* 31:3818 (1937).
5. WAGNER, E. C. Titration of Ammonia in the Presence of Boric Acid. *Ind. Eng. Chem., Anal. Ed.* 12:771 (1940).
6. MACKENZIE, H. A. & WALLACE, N. S. The Kjeldahl Determination of Nitrogen: A Critical Study of Digestion Conditions. *Australian J. Chem.* 7:55 (1954).
7. MORGAN, G. B.; LACKEY, J. B.; & GILCREAS, F. W. Quantitative Determination of Organic Nitrogen in Water, Sewage, and Industrial Wastes. *Anal. Chem.* 11:833 (1957).

Nitrogen (Total Kjeldahl)

Total kjeldahl nitrogen includes ammonia and organic nitrogen, but does not include nitrite and nitrate nitrogen. The method is the same as that for organic nitrogen, except that the ammonia removal step (Sec. 4.1) is omitted. The procedure therefore begins with Sec. 4.2, using a measured volume of 100 ml or more of sample in an 800-ml kjeldahl flask.

Odor

The procedure for odor determination in sewage is the same as that given for industrial wastes in Part IV.

Oxygen (Dissolved)

Adequate dissolved oxygen (DO) is necessary for the life of fish and other aquatic organisms. The DO concentration may also be associated with corrosivity of water, photosynthetic activity, and septicity. The DO test is used in the biochemical oxygen demand (BOD) determination as carried out by the dilution method.

Selection of method: In the determination of DO, there are various ions and compounds which cause interference. To correct for these interferences, numerous modifications of the basic Winkler method have been proposed. These modifications are described below. (A tentative polarographic method for the determination of DO is given in Part IV.) The

choice of the exact procedure to be used will depend on the nature of the sample and the interferences present.

The azide modification (*A*) most effectively removes the interference caused by nitrite. This is the most common interference in biologically treated effluents and incubated BOD samples. The permanganate modification (*B*) is used in the presence of ferrous iron. When the sample contains 5 mg/l ferric iron salts or more, potassium fluoride is added as the first reagent in the azide modification or after the permanganate treatment for ferrous iron.

The alkali-hypochlorite modification (*C*) is used in the presence of sulfite, thiosulfate, polythionate, free chlorine,

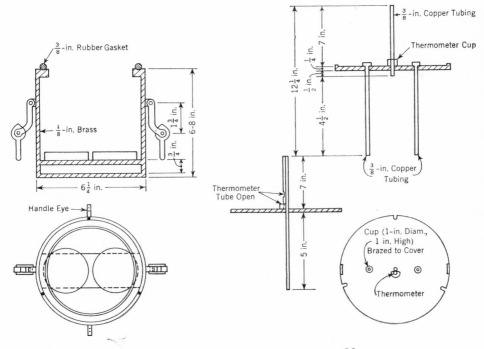

Fig. 29. DO and BOD sampler assembly

or hypochlorite. The precision and accuracy of this method leave much to be desired.

The alum flocculation modification (*D*) is used in the presence of suspended solids which cause interference. The copper sulfate–sulfamic acid flocculation modification (*E*) is used on activated-sludge mixed liquors.

The short modification (*F*) is used in the presence of organic matter which is easily oxidized at the pH of the alkaline-iodide treatment. This modification or the modification (*G*) should be used on undiluted domestic sewage samples. The latter modification is also used for waters which have been supersaturated with oxygen or those having a high organic content.

Collection of samples: Collect the sample in narrow-mouth, glass-stoppered bottles of 250–300-ml capacity. Special precautions are required to avoid entrainment or dissolution of atmospheric oxygen. In sampling from a line under pressure, a glass or rubber tube attached to the tap should extend to the bottom of the bottle. Allow the bottle to overflow two or three times its volume and replace the stopper, so that no air bubbles are entrained.

Samplers which permit collection of DO, BOD, and other samples from streams, ponds, or tanks of moderate depth are of the type shown in Fig. 29. Water from depth samples taken in a 1–3-liter Juday bottle is bled from the bottom through a tube extending to the bottom of a 250–300-ml DO bottle. In sampling from a reservoir at considerable depth, a sampler provided with a valve release should be used. The temperature of the sampled water should be recorded to the nearest degree centigrade, or more precisely, as desired.

Preservation of samples: There should be no delay in the determination of DO on all samples that contain an appreciable iodine demand. If modification A, or B, or G is to be used, preservation of samples for 4–8 hr is accomplished by adding 0.7 ml conc H_2SO_4 and 1 ml sodium azide solution (2 g NaN_3 in 100 ml distilled water) to the DO bottle. This will arrest biologic activity and maintain the DO if the bottle is stored at the temperature of collection or water sealed and kept at a temperature of 10°–20°C. As soon as possible, complete the procedure using 2 ml manganese sulfate solution, 3 ml alkali-iodide solution, and 2 ml conc H_2SO_4.

A. Azide Modification of Iodometric Method

1. General Discussion

The azide modification is used for most sewage, effluents, and streams, especially if they contain more than 0.1 mg/l nitrite nitrogen and not more than 1 mg/l ferrous iron. Other reducing or oxidizing materials should be absent. If 1 ml fluoride solution is added before acidifying the sample and there is no delay in titration, the method is also applicable in the presence of 100–200 mg/l ferric iron.

2. Reagents

2.1. *Manganese sulfate solution:* Dissolve 480 g $MnSO_4 \cdot 4H_2O$, 400 g

$MnSO_4 \cdot 2H_2O$, or 364 g $MnSO_4 \cdot H_2O$ in distilled water, filter, and dilute to 1 liter. When uncertainty exists regarding the water of crystallization, a solution of equivalent strength may be obtained by adjusting the specific gravity of the solution to a value of 1.270 at 20°C. The manganese sulfate solution should liberate not more than a trace of iodine when added to an acidified solution of potassium iodide.

2.2. *Alkali-iodide-azide reagent:* Dissolve 500 g sodium hydroxide, NaOH (or 700 g potassium hydroxide, KOH), and 135 g sodium iodide, NaI (or 150 g potassium iodide, KI), in distilled water and dilute to 1 liter. To this solution add 10 g sodium azide, NaN_3, dissolved in 40 ml distilled water. Potassium and sodium salts may be used interchangeably. This reagent should not give a color with starch solution when diluted and acidified.

2.3. *Sulfuric acid,* conc. The strength of this acid is about 36N. Hence, 1 ml is equivalent to about 3 ml of the alkali-iodide-azide reagent.

2.4. *Starch solution:* Prepare an emulsion of 5–6 g potato, arrowroot, or soluble starch in a mortar or beaker with a small quantity of distilled water. Pour this emulsion into 1 liter of boiling water, allow to boil a few minutes, and let settle overnight. Use the clear supernate. This solution may be preserved with 1.25 g salicylic acid per liter or by the addition of a few drops of toluene.

2.5. *Sodium thiosulfate stock solution,* 0.10N. Dissolve 24.82 g $Na_2S_2O_3 \cdot 5H_2O$ in boiled and cooled distilled water and dilute to 1 liter. Preserve by adding 5 ml chloroform or 1 g NaOH per liter.

2.6. *Standard sodium thiosulfate titrant,* 0.025N. Prepare either by diluting 250.0 ml sodium thiosulfate stock solution to 1,000 ml, or by dissolving 6.205 g $Na_2S_2O_3 \cdot 5H_2O$ in freshly boiled and cooled distilled water and diluting to 1,000 ml. Standard sodium thiosulfate solution may be preserved by adding 5 ml chloroform or 0.4 g NaOH per liter. Standard sodium thiosulfate solution, exactly 0.0250N, is equivalent to 0.200 mg DO per 1.00 ml.

Standardize with (a) biniodate or (b) dichromate:

a. Standard potassium biniodate solution, 0.025N. A stock solution equivalent in strength to 0.1N thiosulfate solution contains 3.249 g/l $KH(IO_3)_2$. The biniodate solution equivalent to the 0.025N thiosulfate contains 0.8124 g/l $KH(IO_3)_2$ and may be prepared by diluting 250 ml stock solution to 1 liter.

Standardization: Dissolve approximately 2 g KI, free from iodate, in an erlenmeyer flask with 100 to 150 ml distilled water; add 10 ml 1 + 9 H_2SO_4, followed by exactly 20.00 ml standard biniodate solution. Dilute to 200 ml and titrate the liberated iodine with the thiosulfate titrant, adding starch toward the end of the titration, when a pale straw color is reached. Exactly 20.00 ml 0.025N thiosulfate should be required when the solutions under comparison are of equal strength. It is convenient to adjust the thiosulfate solution to exactly 0.0250N.

b. Standard potassium dichromate solution, 0.025N. Potassium dichromate may be substituted for biniodate. A solution equivalent to 0.025N sodium thiosulfate contains 1.226 g/l $K_2Cr_2O_7$. The $K_2Cr_2O_7$ should be previously dried at 103°C for 2 hr. The solution should be prepared in a volumetric flask.

Standardization: Same as with biniodate, except that 20.00 ml standard dichromate solution is used. Place in the dark for 5 min, dilute to approximately 400 ml, and titrate with 0.025*N* thiosulfate solution.

2.7. *Special reagent—potassium fluoride solution:* Dissolve 40 g $KF \cdot 2H_2O$ in distilled water and dilute to 100 ml.

3. Procedure

3.1. To the sample as collected in a 250–300-ml bottle add 2 ml * manganese sulfate solution followed by 2 ml * alkali-iodide-azide reagent, well below the surface of the liquid; stopper with care to exclude air bubbles and mix by inverting the bottle several times. When the precipitate settles, leaving a clear supernatant above the manganese hydroxide floc, shake again. With sea water, a 10-min period of contact with the precipitate will be required. When settling has produced at least 100 ml clear supernate, carefully remove the stopper and immediately add 2.0 ml conc H_2SO_4 by allowing the acid to run down the neck of the bottle, restopper, and mix by gentle inversion until dissolution is complete. The iodine should be uniformly distributed throughout the bottle before decanting the amount needed for titration. This should correspond to 200 ml of the original sample after correction for the loss of sample by displacement with the reagents has been made. Thus, when a total of 4 ml (2 ml each) of the manganese sulfate and alkali-iodide-azide reagents is added to a 300-ml bottle, the volume taken for titration

should be $200 \times 300/(300 - 4) = 203$ ml.

3.2. Titrate with 0.025*N* thiosulfate solution to a pale straw color. Add 1–2 ml freshly prepared starch solution and continue the titration to the first disappearance of the blue color. If the endpoint is overrun, the sample may be back-titrated with 0.025*N* biniodate solution, which is added dropwise, or by an additional measured volume of sample. Correction for the amount of biniodate solution or sample should be made. Subsequent recolorations due to the catalytic effect of nitrite or to traces of ferric salts which have not been complexed with fluoride should be disregarded.

4. Calculation

4.1. Because 1 ml 0.025*N* sodium thiosulfate titrant is equivalent to 0.2 mg DO, each milliliter of sodium thiosulfate titrant used is equivalent to 1 mg/l DO if a volume equal to 200 ml of original sample is titrated.

4.2. If the results are desired in milliliters of oxygen gas per liter at 0°C and 760 mm pressure, multiply mg/l DO by 0.698.

4.3. To express the results as per cent saturation at 760 mm atmospheric pressure, the solubility data in Table 25 may be used. Equations for correcting the solubilities to barometric pressures other than mean sea level are given below the table.

4.4. The solubility of DO in distilled water at any barometric pressure, *P* (mm Hg), temperature, *t*°C, and saturated vapor pressure, *u* (mm Hg), for the given *t*, may be calculated between the temperature of 0° and 30°C by

$$\text{ml/l DO} = \frac{(P - u) \times 0.678}{35 + t}$$

---

* Although 2-ml quantities of the reagents insure better contact with less agitation, it is permissible to use 1-ml reagent quantities with 250-ml bottles.

TABLE 25—SOLUBILITY OF OXYGEN IN WATER EXPOSED TO WATER-SATURATED AIR *

Temp. °C	Chloride Concentration in Water—mg/l					Difference per 100 mg Chloride
	0	5,000	10,000	15,000	20,000	
	Dissolved Oxygen—mg/l					
0	14.6	13.8	13.0	12.1	11.3	0.017
1	14.2	13.4	12.6	11.8	11.0	0.016
2	13.8	13.1	12.3	11.5	10.8	0.015
3	13.5	12.7	12.0	11.2	10.5	0.015
4	13.1	12.4	11.7	11.0	10.3	0.014
5	12.8	12.1	11.4	10.7	10.0	0.014
6	12.5	11.8	11.1	10.5	9.8	0.014
7	12.2	11.5	10.9	10.2	9.6	0.013
8	11.9	11.2	10.6	10.0	9.4	0.013
9	11.6	11.0	10.4	9.8	9.2	0.012
10	11.3	10.7	10.1	9.6	9.0	0.012
11	11.1	10.5	9.9	9.4	8.8	0.011
12	10.8	10.3	9.7	9.2	8.6	0.011
13	10.6	10.1	9.5	9.0	8.5	0.011
14	10.4	9.9	9.3	8.8	8.3	0.010
15	10.2	9.7	9.1	8.6	8.1	0.010
16	10.0	9.5	9.0	8.5	8.0	0.010
17	9.7	9.3	8.8	8.3	7.8	0.010
18	9.5	9.1	8.6	8.2	7.7	0.009
19	9.4	8.9	8.5	8.0	7.6	0.009
20	9.2	8.7	8.3	7.9	7.4	0.009
21	9.0	8.6	8.1	7.7	7.3	0.009
22	8.8	8.4	8.0	7.6	7.1	0.008
23	8.7	8.3	7.9	7.4	7.0	0.008
24	8.5	8.1	7.7	7.3	6.9	0.008
25	8.4	8.0	7.6	7.2	6.7	0.008
26	8.2	7.8	7.4	7.0	6.6	0.008
27	8.1	7.7	7.3	6.9	6.5	0.008
28	7.9	7.5	7.1	6.8	6.4	0.008
29	7.8	7.4	7.0	6.6	6.3	0.008
30	7.6	7.3	6.9	6.5	6.1	0.008
31	7.5					
32	7.4					
33	7.3					
34	7.2					
35	7.1					
36	7.0					
37	6.9					
38	6.8					
39	6.7					
40	6.6					
41	6.5					
42	6.4					
43	6.3					
44	6.2					
45	6.1					
46	6.0					
47	5.9					
48	5.8					
49	5.7					
50	5.6					

* At a total pressure of 760 mm Hg. Under any other barometric pressure, P (mm; or P', in.), the solubility, S' (mg/l), can be obtained from the corresponding value in the table by the equation:

$$S' = S \frac{P - p}{760 - p}$$

in which S is the solubility at 760 mm (29.92 in.) and p is the pressure (mm) of saturated water vapor at the temperature of the water. For elevations less than 3,000 ft and temperatures below 25°C, p can be ignored. The equation than becomes:

$$S' = S \frac{P}{760} = S \frac{P'}{29.92}$$

Dry air is assumed to contain 20.90 per cent oxygen. (Calculations made by Whipple and Whipple.[4])

and between 30° and 50°C by

$$ml/l\ DO = \frac{(P - u) \times 0.827}{49 + t}$$

5. Precision and Accuracy

The DO in distilled water can be determined with a precision, expressed as a standard deviation, of 0.043 ml ($n = 3$; 6×10) of $0.025N$ sodium thiosulfate; and, in sewage and secondary effluents, of 0.058 ml ($n = 2$; 26×10). In the presence of appreci-able interference, even with the proper modification, the standard deviation may be as high as 0.1 ml. Still greater errors may occur in waters having organic suspended solids or heavy pollution. For many industrial wastes the tentative polarographic method given in Part IV may be desirable. Errors due to carelessness in collecting samples, prolonging the completion of the test, and selection of an unsuit-able modification should be avoided.

B. Permanganate Modification

1. General Discussion

The permanganate modification should be used only on samples containing ferrous iron.

High concentrations of ferric iron (up to several hundred milligrams per liter), such as may be present in acid mine water, may be overcome by the addition of 1 ml potassium fluoride and azide, if the final titration is made immediately upon acidification.

This modification is ineffective for the oxidation of sulfite, thiosulfate, polythionate, or the organic matter in sewage. The error with samples containing 0.25 per cent by volume of digester waste from the manufacture of sulfite pulp may amount to 7–8 mg/l DO. With such samples, a crude accuracy may be secured through preliminary treatment with the alkali-hypochlorite modification (Method C). At best, however, this procedure gives low results, amounting to 1 mg/l for samples containing 0.25 per cent of digester wastes.

2. Reagents

All the reagents required for Method A; and, in addition:

2.1. *Potassium permanganate solution:* Dissolve 6.3 g $KMnO_4$ in distilled water and dilute to 1 liter.

2.2. *Potassium oxalate solution:* Dissolve 2 g $K_2C_2O_4 \cdot H_2O$ in 100 ml distilled water; 1 ml of this solution is sufficient for the reduction of about 1.1 ml of the permanganate solution.

3. Procedure

3.1. To the sample collected in a 250–300-ml bottle add, below the surface, exactly 0.7 ml conc H_2SO_4 followed by 1 ml potassium permanganate solution and 1 ml potassium fluoride solution. Stopper and mix by inversion. It is essential to add not more than 0.7 ml conc H_2SO_4 as the first step of pretreatment. For this reason, it is best that the acid be added with a 1-ml pipet graduated to 0.1 ml. The amount of permanganate added should be sufficient to obtain a violet tinge which persists for 5 min. If the permanganate color is destroyed in a shorter time, add additional potassium permanganate solution, but avoid large excesses.

3.2. Remove the permanganate color completely by adding 0.5–1.0 ml potassium oxalate solution. Mix well and allow to stand in the dark (the reaction takes place more readily in the dark). Excess oxalate causes low results; add only an amount of oxalate which completely decolorizes the potassium permanganate without having an excess of more than 0.5 ml. Decolorization should occur in 2–10 min. If it is impossible to decolorize the sample without adding a large excess of oxalate, the DO result will be of little value.

3.3. From this point the procedure closely parallels Method A. Add 2 ml manganese sulfate solution, followed by 3 ml alkali-iodide-azide reagent. Stopper, mix, and allow the precipitate to settle. Remix for 20 sec and allow the precipitate to settle a second time; then acidify with 2 ml conc H_2SO_4.

When 0.7 ml acid, 1 ml potassium permanganate solution, 1 ml potassium oxalate solution, 2 ml manganese sulfate solution, and 3 ml alkali-iodide-azide (or a total of 7.7 ml of reagents) are used in a 300-ml bottle, the volume of the sample to be taken for titration is $200 \times 300/(300 - 7.7) = 205$ ml.

This correction is slightly in error because the potassium permanganate solution is near saturation in DO and 1 ml would add about 0.008 mg of oxygen to the DO bottle. However, since the precision of the method (standard deviation 0.06 ml of thiosulfate titration, or 0.012 mg oxygen) is 50 per cent greater than the error, it does not seem necessary to complicate the volume correction further by allowing for this small error. When substantially more potassium permanganate solution is used routinely, a solution several times more concentrated should be employed, so that 1 ml will generally satisfy the permanganate demand.

C. Alkali-Hypochlorite Modification (Tentative)

1. General Discussion

The alkali-hypochlorite modification is used on samples containing sulfite, thiosulfate, and polythionate. It can also be adapted to samples which contain appreciable quantities of free chlorine or hypochlorite. These are treated with sodium sulfite in the presence of potassium iodide and the first step in the modification is omitted, the oxidizing agents of the sample being reduced in acidic solution with sodium sulfite. However, this method cannot be relied upon to give accurate results.

2. Reagents

All of the reagents required for Method A; and, in addition:

2.1. *Alkali-hypochlorite solution, 2N* NaOCl. This solution may be prepared by passing chlorine gas through a 2.1N NaOH solution, with cooling, until a 1-ml test portion of the chlorinated solution requires about 20 ml of 0.1N thiosulfate for the neutralization of the iodine released upon acidification in the presence of an iodide. Use only the clear supernate after sedimentation. This solution may also be made by using commercial hypochlorite salts in place of pure sodium hypochlorite or from certain commercial hypochlorite solutions.* Its strength should be checked each week.

2.2. *Iodide solution, 1N.* Dissolve 17 g potassium iodide, KI, or 15 g sodium iodide, NaI, in distilled water and dilute to 100 ml. This solution should be preserved by the addition of 1 ml 1N NaOH for each 100 ml of solution.

2.3. *Sodium sulfite solution, 0.1N.* Dissolve 6.3 g Na_2SO_3 or 12.6 g $Na_2SO_3 \cdot 7H_2O$ in distilled water and dilute to 1 liter. This solution is rapidly oxidized by the air. Solutions more than a week old should not be used unless tests show that they have lost less than 20 per cent in strength.

2.4. *Sulfuric acid, 1 + 9.*

3. Procedure

To the sample collected in a 250–300-ml bottle add 0.2 ml or enough alkali-hypochlorite solution to oxidize the sulfite, avoiding a large excess. Mix by inversion for 20–30 sec. Add 1 ml iodide solution and acidify by the addition of 1 ml or more of $1 + 9$ H_2SO_4. Mix by inversion. Neutralize liberated iodine with 0.1N sodium sulfite solution, using 0.2 ml starch solution as an internal indicator. Restore the blue color with 0.1-ml portions of 0.1N potassium biniodate solution. Continue the treatment by the azide modification (*A*), adding 2 ml manganese sulfate solution and 3 ml alkali-iodide-azide, and, following the precipitation of manganese hydroxide, acidify with 2 ml conc H_2SO_4. Titrate a volume equivalent to 200 ml of the original sample.

D. *Alum Flocculation Modification*

1. General Discussion

Samples high in suspended solids may consume appreciable quantities of iodine in acid solution. This interference may be removed by alum flocculation.

2. Reagents

All the reagents required for Method A; and, in addition:

2.1. *Alum solution:* Dissolve 10 g aluminum potassium sulfate, $AlK(SO_4)_2 \cdot 12H_2O$, in distilled water and dilute to 100 ml.

2.2. *Ammonium hydroxide,* conc.

3. Procedure

Collect a sample in a glass-stoppered bottle of 500–1,000-ml capacity, using the same precautions as for regular DO samples. Add 10 ml alum solution, followed by 1–2 ml conc NH_4OH. Stopper and invert gently for about 1 min. Settle quiescently for about 10 min and then siphon the clear supernate into a 250–300-ml DO bottle until it overflows. Avoid aeration and keep the siphon submerged at all times. Continue the sample treatment by Method A, Sec. 3, or an appropriate modification.

---

* Such as Zonite (Zonite Products Corp.) or Clorox (Clorox Chemical Co.).

E. Copper Sulfate—Sulfamic Acid Flocculation Modification

1. General Discussion

This modification is used for biologic flocs, such as activated-sludge mixtures, which have high oxygen utilization rates.

2. Reagents

All the reagents required for Method A; and, in addition:

Copper sulfate–sulfamic acid inhibitor solution: Dissolve 32 g technical grade sulfamic acid, NH_2SO_2OH, without heat in 475 ml distilled water. Dissolve 50 g copper sulfate, $CuSO_4 \cdot 5H_2O$, in 500 ml water. Mix the two solutions together and add 25 ml conc acetic acid.

3. Procedure

Add 10 ml copper sulfate–sulfamic acid inhibitor to a 1-qt wide-mouth or 1-liter glass-stoppered bottle. Insert the bottle in a special sampler designed so that the bottle fills from a tube near the bottom and overflows only 25 to 50 per cent of the capacity of the bottle. Collect the sample, stopper, and mix by inversion. Allow the suspended solids to settle quiescently and siphon the relatively clear supernatant liquor into a 250–300-ml DO bottle. Continue the sample treatment as rapidly as possible by Method A, Sec. 3, or an appropriate modification.

F. "Short" Modification

1. General Discussion

The "short" modification is applicable to samples containing organic substances which are readily oxidized in a highly alkaline solution, or which are oxidized by free iodine in an acid solution, and to domestic sewage.

2. Reagents

All reagents required for Method A.

3. Procedure

To the sample collected in the usual manner add 2 ml manganese sulfate solution followed by 2 ml alkali-iodide-azide reagent. Stopper and mix by inversion for 20 sec. Immediately add 2 ml conc H_2SO_4 before the precipitate settles, mix, and titrate a volume equivalent to 200 ml of the original sample as directed in Method A, Sec. 3.2.

G. Modification for High DO or Organic Content

1. General Discussion

This modification is designed for samples containing more than 15 mg/l DO, or having a high organic content, such as in domestic sewage. The method uses an alkali-iodide-azide solution which is $6N$ in sodium iodide and $10N$ in sodium hydroxide. This is substantially a saturated solution of the two chemicals and provides sufficient iodide for oxygen-enriched samples. Potassium iodide cannot be used because of its limited solubility.

Additional advantages for this higher concentration of iodide in the reagent are diminished interference by organic matter, reduced loss of free iodine to the atmosphere, and a sharper endpoint in the titration.

2. Reagents

All the reagents required for Method A, except the alkali-iodide-azide reagent, which is replaced by:

Alkali-iodide-azide solution: Dissolve 400 g sodium hydroxide in 500 ml boiled and cooled distilled water, cool slightly, and then dissolve 900 g sodium iodide in the caustic solution. Dissolve 10 g sodium azide in 40 ml distilled water. Add the latter to the former and dilute, if necessary, to 1 liter. The final volume may be slightly over 1 liter owing to the very high concentrations of dissolved salts. The amount of sodium iodide is sufficient to determine up to 40 mg/l DO.

3. Procedure

To the sample collected in the usual manner, add 2 ml manganese sulfate solution followed by 2 ml alkali-iodide-azide solution. Stopper and mix by inverting the bottle. Allow the precipitate to settle and add 1.5 ml conc H_2SO_4, mix, and titrate a volume equivalent to 200 ml as directed in Method A, Sec. 3.2.

Bibliography

1. WINKLER, L. W. The Determination of Dissolved Oxygen in Water. *Ber.*
   Deut. Chem. Ges. 21:2843 (1888).
2. RIDEAL, S. & STEWART, G. G. The Determination of Dissolved Oxygen in Waters in the Presence of Nitrites and of Organic Matter. *Analyst* 26:141 (1901).
3. FOX, C. J. J. On the Coefficients of Absorption of Nitrogen and Oxygen in Distilled Water and Sea Water and Atmospheric Carbonic Acid in Sea Water. *Trans. Faraday Soc.* 5:68 (1909).
4. WHIPPLE, G. C. & WHIPPLE, M. C. Solubility of Oxygen in Sea Water. *J. Am. Chem. Soc.* 33:362 (1911).
5. GREENFIELD, R. E. & MICKLE, F. L. A New Sampler for Collecting Dissolved Oxygen Samples. *Illinois State Water Survey Bull.* 16:197 (1920).
6. BUSWELL, A. M. & GALLAHER, W. U. Determination of Dissolved Oxygen in the Presence of Iron Salts. *Ind. Eng. Chem.* 15:1186 (1923).
7. ALSTERBERG, G. Methods for the Determination of Elementary Oxygen Dissolved in Water in the Presence of Nitrite. *Biochem. Z.* 159:36 (1925).
8. THERIAULT, E. J. The Determination of Dissolved Oxygen by the Winkler Method. *Public Health Bull.* No. 151 (1925).
9. NICHOLS, M. S. Stabilized Starch Indicator. *Ind. Eng. Chem., Anal. Ed.* 1:215 (1929).
10. THERIAULT, E. J. & McNAMEE, P. D. Dissolved Oxygen in the Presence of Organic Matter, Hypochlorites, and Sulfite Wastes. *Ind. Eng. Chem., Anal. Ed.* 4:59 (1932).
11. COMMITTEE REPORT. The Determination of Dissolved Oxygen by the Winkler Method. *Sew. Works J.* 3:413 (1932).
12. MOORE, W. A. The Solubility of Atmospheric Oxygen in Sewage. *Sew. Works J.* 10:241 (1938).
13. RUCHHOFT, C. C.; MOORE, W. A.; & PLACAK, O. R. Determination of Dissolved Oxygen by the Rideal-Stewart and Alsterberg Modification of the Winkler Method. *Ind. Eng. Chem., Anal. Ed.* 10:701 (1938).
14. BARNETT, G. R. & HURWITZ, E. The Use of Sodium Azide in the Winkler Method for the Determination of Dissolved Oxygen. *Sew. Works J.* 11:781 (1939).
15. RUCHHOFT, C. C. & MOORE, W. A. The Determination of Biochemical Oxygen

Demand and Dissolved Oxygen of River Mud Suspensions. *Ind. Eng. Chem., Anal. Ed.* 12:711 (1940).

16. PLACAK, O. R. & RUCHHOFT, C. C. Comparative Study of the Azide and Rideal-Stewart Modifications of the Winkler Method in the Determination of Biochemical Oxygen Demand. *Ind. Eng. Chem., Anal. Ed.* 13:12 (1941).

17. RUCHHOFT, C. C. & PLACAK, O. R. Determination of Dissolved Oxygen in Activated-Sludge Sewage Mixtures. *Sew. Works J.* 14:638 (1942).

18. POMEROY, R. & KIRSCHMAN, H. D. Determinations of Dissolved Oxygen: Proposed Modification of the Winkler Method. *Anal. Chem.* 17:715 (1945).

Oxygen Demand (Biochemical)*

The oxygen demand of sewage, sewage plant effluents, polluted waters, or industrial wastes is exerted by three classes of materials: (a) carbonaceous organic material usable as a source of food by aerobic organisms; (b) oxidizable nitrogen derived from nitrite, ammonia, and organic nitrogen compounds which serve as food for specific bacteria (e.g., *Nitrosomonas* and *Nitrobacter*); and (c) certain chemical reducing compounds (ferrous iron, sulfite, and sulfide) which will react with molecularly dissolved oxygen. In raw and settled domestic sewage, most —and, for practical purposes, all—of the oxygen demand is due to the first class of materials and is determined by the biochemical oxygen demand (BOD) test described below. In biologically treated effluents, a considerable proportion of the oxygen demand may be due to oxidation of Class (b) compounds and will also be included in the BOD test. Class (c) materials present may not be included in the BOD test unless the test is based on a calculated initial dissolved oxygen. It should be understood that all three of these classes will have a direct bearing on the oxygen balance of the receiving water and must be considered in the

discharge of a waste to such a water.

If wastes consisted only of raw or treated domestic sewage, measurement of the oxygen load on a receiving water would be simple. Unfortunately, this is not always the case, because most wastes are complex in nature and may contain organic compounds not easily amenable to biologic oxidation. When such compounds are present, the usual methods of seeding and the standard incubation period of 5 days will fail to assess the effect these wastes may have at some point below their point of discharge.

Complete stabilization of a given waste may require a period of incubation too long for practical purposes. For this reason, the 5-day period has been accepted as standard. For certain industrial wastes, however, it may be advisable to determine the oxidation curve obtained. Conversion of data from one incubation period to another can only be made if such special studies are carried out. Studies in recent years have shown that the exponential rate of carbonaceous oxidation, k, at 20°C rarely has a value of 0.1, but may vary from less than one-half to more than twice this value. This fact usually makes it impossible to calculate the ultimate carbonaceous demand, L, of a sample from 5-day BOD values unless

---

* BOD, Biochemical Oxygen Demand.

the k value has been determined on the sewage, waste, or stream under consideration.

1. Apparatus

1.1. *Incubation bottles,* 250–300-ml capacity, with ground-glass stoppers. Bottles should be cleaned with a good detergent and thoroughly rinsed and drained before use. As a precaution against drawing air into the dilution bottle during incubation, a water seal is recommended. Satisfactory water seals are obtained by inverting the bottles in a water bath or adding water to the flared mouth of special BOD bottles.

1.2. *Air incubator or water bath,* thermostatically controlled at 20°C ± 1°C. All light should be excluded to prevent formation of DO by algae in the sample.

2. Reagents

2.1. *Distilled water:* Water used for solutions and for preparation of the dilution water must be of the highest quality, distilled from a block tin or all-glass still, contain less than 0.01 mg/l copper, and be free of chlorine, chloramines, caustic alkalinity, organic material, or acids.

2.2. *Phosphate buffer solution:* Dissolve 8.5 g potassium dihydrogen phosphate, KH_2PO_4, 21.75 g dipotassium hydrogen phosphate, K_2HPO_4, 33.4 g disodium hydrogen phosphate heptahydrate, $Na_2HPO_4 \cdot 7H_2O$, and 1.7 g ammonium chloride, NH_4Cl, in about 500 ml distilled water and dilute to 1 liter. The pH of this buffer should be 7.2 without further adjustment. If dilution water is to be stored in the incubator, the phosphate buffer should be added just prior to using the dilution water.

2.3. *Magnesium sulfate solution:* Dissolve 22.5 g $MgSO_4 \cdot 7H_2O$ in distilled water and dilute to 1 liter.

2.4. *Calcium chloride solution:* Dissolve 27.5 g anhydrous $CaCl_2$ in distilled water and dilute to 1 liter.

2.5. *Ferric chloride solution:* Dissolve 0.25 g $FeCl_3 \cdot 6H_2O$ in distilled water and dilute to 1 liter.

2.6. *Acid and alkali solutions,* 1N. For neutralization of waste samples which are either caustic or acidic.

2.7. *Sodium sulfite solution,* 0.025N. Dissolve 1.575 g anhydrous Na_2SO_3 in 1,000 ml distilled water. This solution is not stable and should be prepared daily.

2.8. *Seeding material:* The selection of the proper seed is an important factor in the BOD determination. In many cases, particularly in food-processing wastes, a satisfactory seed may be obtained by using the supernatant liquor from domestic sewage which has been stored at 20°C for 24–36 hr.

Many industrial wastes contain organic compounds which are not amenable to oxidation by domestic-sewage seed. In these cases the analyst may use seed prepared from soil, acclimated seed developed in the laboratory, or the receiving water collected below the point of discharge of the particular waste (preferably 2–5 miles below). The last two are the most likely possibilities. Receiving water used as a seed source will undoubtedly give the best estimate of the effect of a waste on such a water; but it must be collected at a point where there has been built up a biota capable of using for food the particular organic compounds present. In some cases this might entail the collection of a satisfactory seed many miles below the point of discharge of the waste, which might not be practical. With recurrent wastes not easily susceptible to biologic oxidation, it is usually more practical to build up an acclimated seed in the laboratory. This may be done by aerating and feeding sewage or receiving water with small daily increments of the particular waste, together with sewage, until a satisfactory seed is developed.

3. Procedure

3.1. *Preparation of dilution water:* The distilled water used should have been stored in cotton-plugged bottles for a sufficient length of time to become saturated with DO. The water may also be aerated by shaking a partially filled bottle or with a supply of clean compressed air. Situations may be encountered where it is desired to use stabilized river water to check stream performance with laboratory procedure. The distilled water used should be as near 20°C as possible and of the highest purity. Place the desired volume of distilled water in a suitable bottle and add 1 ml each of phosphate buffer, magnesium sulfate, calcium chloride, and ferric chloride solutions for each liter of water.

3.2. *Seeding:* If necessary, the dilution water is seeded by using the seed found to be the most satisfactory for the particular waste under study. Only past experience can determine the actual amount of seed to be added per liter. Seeded dilution water should be used the same day it is made.

3.3. *Pretreatment:*

a. *Samples containing caustic alkalinity or acidity:* Neutralize to about pH 7.0 with $1N$ H_2SO_4 or NaOH, using a pH meter or bromthymol blue as an outside indicator. The pH of the seeded dilution water should not be changed by the preparation of the lowest dilution of sample.

b. *Samples containing residual chlorine compounds:* If the samples are allowed to stand for 1 to 2 hr, the residual chlorine will often be dissipated. BOD dilutions can then be prepared with properly seeded standard dilution water. Higher chlorine residuals in neutralized samples should be destroyed by adding sodium sulfite. The appropriate quantity of sodium sulfite solution is determined on a 100–1,000-ml portion of the sample by adding 10 ml of $1 + 1$ acetic acid or $1 + 50$ H_2SO_4, followed by 10 ml potassium iodide solution (10 g in 100 ml) and titrating with $0.025N$ sodium sulfite solution to the starch-iodide endpoint. Add to a volume of sample the quantity of sodium sulfite solution determined by the above test, mix, and after 10–20 min test aliquot samples for residual chlorine to check the treatment. Prepare BOD dilutions with seeded standard dilution water.

c. *Samples containing other toxic substances:* Samples such as those from industrial wastes frequently require special study and treatment—for example, toxic metals derived from plating wastes.

d. *Samples supersaturated with DO:* Samples containing more than 9.17 mg/l DO at 20°C may be encountered during winter months or in localities where algae are actively growing. To prevent loss of oxygen during incubation of these samples, the DO should be reduced to saturation by bringing the sample to about 20°C in a partly filled bottle and agitating it by vigorous shaking or by aerating with compressed air.

3.4. *Dilution technique:* Make several dilutions of the prepared sample so as to obtain the required depletions. The following dilutions are suggested:

0.1–1.0 per cent for strong trade wastes, 1–5 per cent for raw and settled sewage, 5–25 per cent for oxidized effluents, and 25–100 per cent for polluted river waters.

a. Carefully siphon standard dilution water, seeded if necessary, into a graduated cylinder of 1,000–2,000-ml capacity, filling the cylinder half full without entrainment of air. Add the quantity of carefully mixed sample to make the desired dilution and dilute to the appropriate level with dilution water. Mix well with a plunger-type mixing rod, avoiding entrainment of air. Siphon the mixed dilution into two BOD bottles, one for incubation and the other for determination of the initial DO in the mixture; stopper tightly and incubate for 5 days at 20°C. The BOD bottles should be water sealed by inversion in a tray of water in the incubator or by using a special water-seal bottle. Prepare succeeding dilutions of lower concentration in the same manner, or by adding dilution water to the unused portion of the preceding dilution.

b. The dilution technique may be greatly simplified when suitable amounts of sample are measured directly into bottles of known capacity with a large-tip volumetric pipet and the bottle is filled with just sufficient dilution water so that the stopper can be inserted without leaving air bubbles. Dilutions greater than 1:100 should be made by diluting the waste in a volumetric flask before it is added to the incubation bottles for final dilution.

3.5 *Determination of DO:* If the sample represents 1 per cent or more of the lowest BOD dilution, determine DO on the undiluted sample. This determination is usually omitted on sewage and settled effluents known to have a DO content of practically zero. *With samples having an immediate oxygen demand, a calculated initial DO should be used, inasmuch as such a demand represents a load on the receiving water.*

3.6. *Incubation:* Incubate the blank dilution water and the diluted samples for 5 days at 20°C. Then determine the DO in the incubated samples and the blank, using the azide modification of the iodometric method (*A*). In special cases, other modifications may be necessary. Those dilutions showing a residual DO of at least mg/l and a depletion of at least mg/l should be considered the most reliable.

3.7. *Seed correction:* If the dilution water is seeded, determine the oxygen depletion of the seed by setting up a separate series of seed dilutions and selecting those resulting in 40–70 per cent oxygen depletions in 5 days. One of these depletions is then used to calculate the correction due to the small amount of seed in the dilution water. Do not use the seeded blank for seed correction because the 5-day seeded dilution water blank is subject to erratic oxidation due to the very high dilution of seed, which is not characteristic of the seeded sample.

3.8. *Dilution water control:* Fill two BOD bottles with unseeded dilution water. Stopper and water-seal one of these for incubation. The other bottle is for determining the DO before incubation. The DO results on these two bottles are used as a rough check on the quality of the unseeded dilution water. The depletion obtained should not be used as a blank correction; it should not be more than 0.2 ml and preferably not more than 0.1 ml.

3.9. *Glucose–glutamic acid check:* The BOD test is a bioassay procedure consequently, the results obtained are influenced greatly by the presence of toxic substances or the use of a poor seeding material. Experience has taught that distilled waters are frequently contaminated with toxic substances—most often copper—and that some sewage seeds are relatively inactive. The results obtained with such waters are always low.

The quality of the dilution water, the effectiveness of the seed, and the technique of the analyst should be checked periodically by using pure organic compounds on which the BOD is known or determinable. If a particular organic compound is known to be present in a given waste, it may well serve as a control on the seed used. There have been a number of organic compounds proposed, such as glucose or glutamic acid. For general BOD work a mixture of these (150 mg/l of each) has certain advantages. It must be understood that glucose has an exceptionally high and variable oxidation rate with relatively simple seeds. When used with glutamic acid, the oxidation rate is stabilized and is similar to that obtained with many municipal wastes (0.16–0.19 exponential rate). In exceptional cases, a given component of a particular waste may be the best choice to test the efficacy of a particular seed.

The standard glucose solution should show a BOD of 224 ± 10 mg/l; the standard glutamic acid solution should show a BOD of 217 ± 10 mg/l. Any appreciable divergence from these results raises a serious question concerning the quality of the distilled water or the viability of the seeding material. Further, if a variation greater than ± 20–22 mg/l occurs more frequently than 5 per cent of the time, the technique used is subject to improvement.

To check the dilution water, the seed material, and the technique of the analyst, prepare a standard solution containing 150 mg/l each of reagent grade glucose and glutamic acid which have been dried at 103°C for 1 hr. Pipet 5.0 ml of this solution into calibrated incubation bottles, fill with seeded dilution water, and incubate with seed control at 20°C for 5 days. On the basis of a mixed primary standard containing 150 mg/l each of glucose and glutamic acid, the 5-day BOD varies in magnitude according to the type of seed, and precision varies with the quality of seed, as shown in Table 26.

Excepting the oxidized river water and effluents, a low seed correction resulted in an appreciably higher value for the standard deviation. Each seed source should be checked to determine the amount required to obtain optimum precision. If results differ appreciably from those given in Table 26 after considering the seed source, the technique is questionable.

TABLE 26—EFFECT OF SEED TYPE AND QUALITY ON BOD RESULTS

Type of Seed	5-Day Seed Correction mg/l	Mean 5-Day BOD mg/l	Standard Deviation mg/l
Settled fresh sewage	>0.6	218	± 11
Settled stale sewage	>0.6	207	± 8
River water (4 sources)	0.05–0.22	224–242	± 7–13
Activated-sludge effluent	0.07–0.68	221	± 13
Trickling filter effluent	0.2–0.4	225	± 8

4. Immediate Dissolved Oxygen Demand

Substances oxidizable by molecular oxygen, such as ferrous iron, sulfite, sulfide, and aldehyde, impose a load on the receiving water and must be taken into consideration. The total oxygen demand of such a substrate may be determined by using a calculated initial DO or by using the sum of the immediate dissolved oxygen demand (IDOD) and the 5-day BOD. Where a differentiation of the two components is desired, the IDOD should be determined. It should be understood that the IDOD does not necessarily represent the immediate oxidation by molecular DO, but may represent an oxidation by the iodine liberated in the acidification step of the iodometric method.

The depletion of DO in a standard water dilution of the sample in 15 min has been arbitrarily selected as the IDOD. To determine the IDOD, the DO of the sample (which in most cases is zero) and the DO of the dilution water are determined separately. An appropriate dilution of the sample and dilution water is prepared, and the DO is determined after 15 min. The calculated DO of the sample dilution minus the observed DO after 15 min is the IDOD (mg/l) of the sample dilution.

5. Calculation

5.1. Definitions:

$D_0 = $ DO of original dilution water;
$D_1 = $ DO of diluted sample 15 min after preparation;
$D_2 = $ DO of diluted sample after incubation;
$S = $ DO of original undiluted sample;
$D_c = $ DO available in dilution at zero time
$= D_0 p + SP$;
$p = $ decimal fraction of dilution water used;

$P = $ decimal fraction of sample used;
$B_1 = $ DO of dilution of seed control before incubation;
$B_2 = $ DO of dilution of seed control after incubation;
$f = $ ratio of seed in sample to seed in control
$= \dfrac{\% \text{ seed in } D_1}{\% \text{ seed in } B_1}$; and
Seed correction $= (B_1 - B_2)f$.

5.2. Biochemical oxygen demand:

a. When seeding is not required:
$$\text{mg/l BOD} = \frac{D_1 - D_2}{P}$$

b. When using seeded dilution water:
$$\text{mg/l BOD} = \frac{(D_1 - D_2) - (B_1 - B_2)f}{P}$$

c. Including IDOD if small or not determined:
$$\text{mg/l BOD} = \frac{D_c - D_2}{P}$$

5.3. Immediate dissolved oxygen demand:

$$\text{mg/l IDOD} = \frac{D_0 - D_1}{P}$$

The DO determined on the unseeded dilution water after incubation is not used in the BOD calculations because this practice would overcorrect for the dilution water. In all of the above calculations, corrections are not made for small losses of DO in the dilution water during incubation. If the dilution water is unsatisfactory, proper corrections are difficult and the results are questionable.

6. Precision and Accuracy

There is no standard against which the accuracy of the BOD test can be measured. The precision of the DO determinations in the BOD test, expressed as the standard deviation in milliliters of $0.025N$ thiosulfate, is as follows:

DO in dilution water: 0.043 ml ($n = 3$; 6×10).

DO in sewage: 0.058 ml ($n = 2$; 26 ×10).

Incubated BOD samples, 1–20-day BOD (curve), glucose and glutamic acid: 0.079 ml ($n = 1$; 27 × 10).

Five-day BOD—
Raw sewage: 0.112 ml ($n = 3$; 38 × 10)
Settled sewage: 0.071 ml ($n = 1$; 20 × 5)
Activated-sludge effluent: 0.084 ml ($n = 3$; 30 × 10)
Trickling filter effluent: 0.075 ml ($n = 1$; 16 × 5)

These data indicate that, where interfering and toxic substances are absent, the standard deviation of the BOD test on sewages and effluents may range from 0.07 to 0.11 ml oxygen demand titrated. This should also hold true on wastes from food-processing industries or other organic nontoxic wastes.

Industrial wastes containing toxic materials or substances which interfere with the DO determination have not been studied statistically.

Bibliography

1. THERIAULT, E. J. The Oxygen Demand of Polluted Waters. *Public Health Bull.* No. 173 (1927).
2. MOHLMAN, F. W.; EDWARDS, G. P.; & SWOPE, G. Technique and Significance of the Biochemical Oxygen Demand Determination. *Ind. Eng. Chem.* 20: 242 (1928).
3. THERIAULT, E. J. Detailed Instructions for the Performance of the Dissolved Oxygen and Biochemical Oxygen Demand Tests. *Public Health Repts.* Suppl. 90 (1931).
4. THERIAULT, E. J.; McNAMEE, P. D.; & BUTTERFIELD, C. T. Selection of Dilution Water for Use in Oxygen Demand Tests. *Public Health Repts.* 46:1084 (1931).
5. LEA, W. L. & NICHOLS, M. S. Influence of Substrate on Biochemical Oxygen Demand. *Sew. Works J.* 8:435 (1936).
6. LEA, W. L. & NICHOLS, M. S. Influence of Phosphorus and Nitrogen on Biochemical Oxygen Demand. *Sew. Works J.* 9:34 (1937).
7. RUCHHOFT, C. C. & MOORE, W. A. Determination of Biochemical Oxygen Demand in River Mud and Suspensions. *Ind. Eng. Chem., Anal. Ed.* 12:711 (1940).
8. RUCHHOFT, C. C. Report on the Cooperative Study of Dilution Waters Made for the Standard Methods Committee of the Federation of Sewage Works Associations. *Sew Works J.* 13:669 (1941).
9. SAWYER, C. N. & BRADNEY, L. Modernization of the BOD Test for Determining the Efficiency of the Sewage Treatment Process. *Sew. Works J.* 18:1113 (1946).
10. RUCHHOFT, C. C.; PLACAK, O. R.; & ETTINGER, M. B. Correction of BOD Velocity Constants for Nitrification. *Sew. Works J.* 20:832 (1946).
11. HURWITZ, E., ET AL. Nitrification and BOD. *Sew. Works J.* 19:995 (1947).
12. RUCHHOFT, C. C., ET AL. Variations in BOD Velocity Constants of Sewage Dilutions. *Ind. Eng. Chem.* 40:1290 (1948).
13. GOTAAS, H. B. Effect of Sea Water on Biochemical Oxidation of Sewage. *Sew. Works J.* 21:818 (1949).
14. BUSWELL, A. M.; VAN METER, I.; & GERKE, J. R. Study of the Nitrification Phase of the BOD Test. *Sew. Ind. Wastes* 22:508 (1950).
15. MOHLMAN, F. W., ET AL. Experience with Modified Methods for BOD. *Sew. Ind. Wastes* 22:31 (1950).
16. SAWYER, C. N., ET AL. Primary Standards for BOD Work. *Sew. Ind. Wastes* 22:26 (1950).

Oxygen Demand (Chemical)

Determine chemical oxygen demand (COD) of sewage by the method given in Part IV.

pH Value

The pH value of a solution is the logarithm of the reciprocal of its hydrogen ion activity. It has little bearing on the strength of sewage, but it may be of considerable importance where industrial wastes are concerned. This is especially true of effluents from industrial-waste treatment plants, because state regulations frequently prescribe pH limits. Also, pH often provides a convenient control in chemical treatment processes.

pH should be determined by the glass electrode procedures described in Part I unless extremely accurate results are not required, as in plant control; if so, colorimetric methods may be used.

Standardization of electrodes and machines: The assembly should be checked at 20°C with two standard buffers, usually 0.01M borax buffer at pH 9.22 and 0.05M acid potassium phthalate buffer at pH 4.00, and the proper adjustments made. The electrodes should then be rinsed thoroughly and immersed in distilled water until used.

Care of electrodes: In the potentiometric determination of acidity, alkalinity, and pH, the glass and reference electrodes must be kept exceptionally clean. This is particularly true with sewages and industrial wastes, which often contain oils, greases, fats, and many other film-forming compounds that may inhibit the sensitivity of the electrodes. The proper care of electrodes includes:

a. Removing any film from the electrode with the proper solvent or a mild detergent, using soft tissue and being careful to wipe away all the film.

b. Repeated rinsing with distilled water and wiping with soft tissue to remove all solvent or detergent.

c. If necessary, restoring the glass electrode by immersing in 2 per cent HCl for 2 hr or more, then rinsing thoroughly with distilled water.

d. Always keeping both electrodes immersed in distilled water when not in use.

Precision

The standard deviation in determining the pH value of sewage with a glass electrode was found to be 0.03 ($n = 3$; 10×10). The precision in colorimetric methods is much lower. It cannot be given a definite value because of the variable effects of extraneous color and turbidity, and the effect of the indicator itself on poorly buffered solutions.

Residue

The results for total, volatile, and fixed residues are subject to considerable error because of losses of volatile compounds during evaporation and of carbon dioxide and volatile minerals during ignition, and because of the presence of calcium oxide in the ash.

Results for residues high in oil or grease content may be of questionable value, owing to the difficulty of drying to constant weight in a reasonable time.

In the interpretation of results, these possible sources of error must be recognized.

A. Residue on Evaporation

1. General Discussion

The determination of residue by evaporation may be of limited value for estimating the effect of an effluent on a receiving water, but it may be useful as a control in plant operation. A large number of solids crystallize as hydrates, which lose water at various temperatures and form decomposition products before all their water of hydration is given off. This also is true of various colloidal suspensions. In addition, volatile compounds are lost during evaporation and ignition. It is essential for the analyst to understand that the procedure given for residue on evaporation is quite arbitrary and the results generally will not represent the weight of actual dissolved and suspended solids. Because of the organic content of sewage, samples should be dried at 103°C. A more complete discussion of the temperature for drying residues may be found in Part I, Residue.

2. Procedure

Evaporate 100 ml of sample in an ignited and tared dish, dry to constant weight at 103°C, cool in a desiccator, and weigh. Drying for 1 hr at 103°C is usually sufficient. On samples with a pH below 4.3, NaOH is added and a pH of 4.3 maintained during evaporation. The amount of Na added is subtracted from the weight of residue.

3. Calculation

mg/l residue on evaporation

$$= \frac{\text{mg residue} \times 1{,}000}{\text{ml sample}}$$

4. Precision and Accuracy

The accuracy of all the solids determinations in sewage and industrial wastes is not measureable because there is no universal standard of comparison. When the residue from a 50–100-ml sample of raw sewage was weighed, the standard deviation of the weighing was found to be 1.9 mg ($n = 3$; 60×10), but these data are considered statistically unreliable because of sampling errors. On settled effluents, a standard deviation of 0.9 mg ($n = 1$; 5×20) was found and is statistically reliable.

B. Total Volatile and Fixed Residue

1. Procedure

Total volatile and fixed solids are determined by igniting the residue on evaporation (A) at 600° C in an electric muffle furnace to constant weight, usually requiring 10 to 15 min. The loss on ignition is reported as mg/l volatile solids and the residue as mg/l fixed solids. Calculate in the manner indicated above.

2. Precision and Accuracy

Using this procedure, the standard deviation of the weighing was found to be 1.5 mg ($n = 2$; 50×10), but these data are considered statistically unreliable because of sampling errors.

C. Total Suspended Matter (Nonfiltrable Residue)

1. General Discussion

Suspended matter is determined by filtration through a membrane filter or an asbestos mat in a Gooch crucible. However, for a rapid determination of suspended matter, particularly of aeration tank liquor or return sludge in activated-sludge plants, the aluminum dish method described in Part V, Tests on Activated Sludge, Method A, may be used.

2. Apparatus

2.1. *Membrane filter.*
2.2. *Gooch crucibles,* 25 ml.
2.3. *Suction apparatus.*

3. Reagent

Asbestos cream: Make a cream by adding 10 g acid-washed, medium-fiber asbestos prepared particularly for Gooch crucible determinations to 1 liter distilled water. Some asbestos sold for this purpose contains too much asbestos powder. This fine material should be removed by repeated decantations.

4. Procedure

4.1. The membrane filter should be used with its proper suction apparatus. The filter pore size should be chosen to include bacteria but large enough to pass a reasonable volume (100 ml) in 1 hr.

4.2. *Preparation of crucible:* The asbestos mat in the Gooch crucible should be prepared with care. The mat should weigh about 0.3 g and should be approximately 2 mm thick. To prepare the mat, the crucible is first filled with asbestos cream. Let stand 1–2 min to allow the heavier particles to settle, then apply suction. It is important that the suction used to prepare the mat be at least as great as that which will be used in filtering the sample. After the water has been drawn through the mat, the suction is left on and the crucible is filled with distilled water, which is likewise drawn through; then the mat is washed twice more with distilled water. The crucible with mat is dried in an oven at 103°C for 1 hr (30 min in a mechanical-convection oven). If the volatile matter is not to be determined, the crucible is cooled to room temperature in a desiccator and weighed.

If the volatile matter is to be determined by ignition, transfer the crucible from the oven to the muffle furnace and ignite at 600°C for 15–20 min. Remove the crucible from the furnace and, after partial cooling in the air, place it in a desiccator for 30–40 min and weigh.

Note: The amount of suspended matter removed during filtration depends on the thickness of the asbestos mat used in the Gooch crucible. Accordingly, a mat thickness of 2 mm is arbitrarily established in this procedure; the importance of uniform mat thickness should be recognized.

4.3. *Treatment of sample:* The volume of sample to be taken for filtration will depend on the concentration of suspended matter in the sample and should be as large as is practical. As a guide, 100-ml portions may be taken for sewages and industrial wastes having less than 200 mg/l suspended matter.

Measure out the well-mixed sample with a wide-tip pipet or a volumetric flask which has been cut down so that it will deliver the desired volume. Filter the sample through a weighed membrane filter or Gooch crucible, using suction. Leaving the suction on, wash with 10 ml distilled water to remove soluble salts. Dry the membrane filter or crucible and solids at 103°C for 1 hr (30 min in a mechanical-convection oven) and allow it to cool to room temperature in a desiccator before weighing.

5. Calculation

mg/l total suspended matter

$$= \frac{\text{mg suspended solids} \times 1{,}000}{\text{ml sample}}$$

6. Precision and Accuracy

The precision, expressed as standard deviation, was found to be as follows with the Gooch crucible: for sewage and some industrial wastes, 1.4 mg ($n = 3$; 65×10); for settled sewage, 0.4 mg ($n = 3$; 39×10).

D. Volatile and Fixed Suspended Matter

The volatilization of organic matter from sewage solids is subject to a great many errors. It should be done in an electric muffle furnace at 600°C.

1. Procedure

Ignite the crucible with the suspended matter for 15–20 min. Allow the crucible to cool partially in the air and then place it in a desiccator and allow it to cool 30–40 min before weighing. Report the weight lost on ignition as mg/l volatile suspended matter and the weight of ash remaining as mg/l fixed suspended matter.

2. Precision and Accuracy

On most of the samples of volatile and fixed suspended matter determined as above, the standard deviation was found to be 0.4 mg ($n = 3$; 49×10).

E. Dissolved Matter (Filtrable Residue)

Dissolved matter may be obtained by difference between the residue on evaporation (A) and total suspended matter (C) or by evaporating a filtered sample as directed for residue on evaporation (Method A, Sec. 2).

F. Settleable Matter

Settleable matter may be determined and reported on either a volume (ml/l) or a weight (mg/l) basis, as given in the following.

1. Procedure

1.1. *By volume:* Fill an Imhoff cone to the liter mark with a thoroughly mixed sample. Settle for 45 min, gently stir the sides of the cone with a rod or by spinning, settle 15 min longer, and record the volume of settleable matter in the cone as ml/l.

1.2. *By weight:* This technique defines settleable matter as that matter in sewage which will not stay in suspension during the settling period but either settles to the bottom or floats to the top.

a. Determine the suspended matter (in mg/l) in a sample of the sewage under investigation, as in Method C.

b. Pour a well-mixed sample of the sewage into a glass vessel not less than 9 cm in diameter, using a quantity of sample not less than 1 liter and sufficient to insure a depth of 20 cm. A glass vessel of greater diameter and a larger volume of sample may be used. Allow to stand quiescent for 1 hr and, without disturbing the settled material or that which may be floating, siphon 250 ml of sample from the center of the container at a point halfway between the surface of the settled sludge and the liquid surface. Determine the suspended matter (in mg/l) in all or in an aliquot portion of this supernatant liquor as directed under Method C. This is the nonsettling matter.

2. Calculation

mg/l settleable matter
= mg/l susp. matter — mg/l nonsettl. matter

Bibliography

1. THERIAULT, E. J. & WAGENHALS, H. H. Studies of Representative Sewage Plants. *Public Health Bull.* No. 132 (1923).
2. SYMONS, G. E. & MOREY, B. The Effect of Drying Time on the Determination of Solids in Sewage and Sewage Sludges. *Sew. Works J.* 13:936 (1941).
3. FISCHER, A. J. & SYMONS, G. E. The Determination of Settleable Sewage Solids by Weight. *Water Works & Sewerage* 91:37 (1944).
4. DEGEN, J. & NUSSBERGER, F. E. Notes on the Determination of Suspended Solids. *Sew. Ind. Wastes* 28:237 (1956).

Sulfide

In sewage analysis, determinations of three forms of sulfide are significant:

Total sulfide includes the dissolved H_2S and HS^-, as well as *acid-soluble* metallic sulfides present in the suspended matter. The ion S^{--} is not present in significant amount below a pH of 13. Acid-insoluble sulfides are not detected by the tests here given. Copper sulfide is the only common one in this class.

Dissolved sulfide is that remaining after the suspended solids have been removed by flocculation and settling.

Un-ionized hydrogen sulfide is calculated from the concentration of dissolved sulfide and the pH of the sample.

Selection of method: The titrimetric method *(A)* and the colorimetric method *(B)* may be used to determine all three forms and are applicable to water, sewage, and industrial wastes. Method A is more accurate, but it cannot be carried out directly in sewage because of interfering substances. It is necessary to evolve the sulfide in a stream of gas and collect it in zinc acetate solution before titration. The method can be applied only to solutions with sulfide concentrations above 1 mg/l. Method B is useful for the rapid determination of sulfide; it is especially recommended for low sulfide concentrations. The method is, however, designed for speed, sensitivity, and convenience rather than maximum accuracy. It is applicable to sulfide concentrations of 0.02–20 mg/l.

Sampling and storage: Samples must be taken with a minimum of aeration, for not only is sulfide volatilized by aeration, but also any oxygen which is taken up destroys it by chemical action. Samples to be used only for total-sulfide determination may be preserved by adding zinc acetate solution at the rate of 2 ml per liter. This precipitates sulfide as inert ZnS, and also prevents further sulfide generation. Determinations of dissolved sulfide, and analyses of samples not preserved with zinc acetate, must be commenced within 3 min of the time of sampling.

Samples to be used for determination of total sulfide must contain a representative proportion of suspended solids.

A. Titrimetric Method

1. Reagents

1.1. *Carbon dioxide:* Either a cylinder of CO_2 or a CO_2 generator can be used.

1.2. *Zinc acetate solution, 2N.* Dissolve 220 g $Zn(C_2H_3O_2)_2 \cdot 2H_2O$ in 870 ml water; this makes 1 liter of solution.

1.3. *Sulfuric acid,* conc.

1.4. *Iodine solution, 0.025N.* Dissolve 20–25 g potassium iodide, KI, in a little water and add 3.175 g iodine. After the iodine has dissolved, dilute to 1 liter and standardize against 0.025N sodium thiosulfate, using starch solution as indicator.

1.5. *Hydrochloric acid,* conc.

1.6. *Sodium thiosulfate titrant,* 0.025N. Prepare as directed in Oxygen (Dissolved), Method A, Sec. 2.6.

1.7. *Starch solution:* Prepare as directed in Oxygen (Dissolved), Method A, Sec. 2.4.

1.8. *Aluminum chloride solution,* 6N. Because of the hygroscopic and caking tendency of this chemical, it will be convenient to purchase 100-g or ¼-lb bottles of the hexahydrate, $AlCl_3 \cdot 6H_2O$. Dissolve the contents of a previously unopened 100-g bottle of this salt in 144 ml water, or the contents of a ¼-lb bottle in 164 ml water.

1.9. *Sodium hydroxide solution, 6N.* Dissolve 24 g NaOH pellets in distilled water and make up to 100 ml.

2. Procedure for Total Sulfide

2.1. Introduce a measured volume of sample, usually approximately 500 ml, into a 1-liter aeration cylinder equipped with an alundum filter disc in the bottom, or into a 1-liter wide-mouth bottle with a two-hole stopper carrying a fritted-glass diffuser tube and outlet tube. It is good practice to pass CO_2 gas through the apparatus, to displace oxygen, before introducing the sample and acidifying. To the outlet connect a ten-bulb absorption tube containing zinc acetate solution, or two 125-ml conical flasks, each containing about 5 ml zinc acetate solution diluted to

100 ml, and with suitable connections to pass the gas through them in series.

2.2. Acidify the sample with 10 ml conc H_2SO_4. Pass CO_2 or other inert gas (do not use air or oxygen) through the sample for 1 hr, or until suitable tests show that no more sulfide is coming over.

2.3. To the zinc acetate solution, add iodine solution well in excess of the amount necessary to react with the collected sulfide; 1.00 ml 0.025N iodine is equivalent to 0.400 mg sulfide.

2.4. Add 5 ml conc HCl, stopper, and shake. If two flasks are used, add nearly all of the iodine to the first flask, but half of the acid to each flask.

2.5. Transfer the liquid to a beaker and back-titrate with 0.025N sodium thiosulfate titrant, using starch solution as indicator. For accurate results a blank should be run on the reagents, especially if the sulfide content is low.

2.6. *Calculation:*

mg/l total sulfide as S
$$= \frac{(\text{ml iodine} - \text{ml Na}_2\text{S}_2\text{O}_3) \times 400}{\text{ml sample}}$$

3. Procedure for Dissolved Sulfide

Dissolved sulfide is determined on a sample from which the suspended solids have been removed by flocculating and settling.

3.1. Fill a 1-liter bottle with sample, flowing the liquid through the bottle after the manner of sampling for dissolved oxygen, in order to secure a sample which has had the least possible contact with air. Add 2 ml aluminum chloride solution and 2 ml NaOH solution, and stopper with no air bubbles under the stopper. Rotate back and forth about a transverse axis as vigorously as possible for at least 1 min in order to flocculate the contents thoroughly. The volumes of these

chemicals may be varied according to experience, the aim being to get good clarification without using excessively large amounts. Always use equal amounts of the two reagents.

3.2. Allow to settle for 15 min, or until the supernatant liquid is reasonably clear. Siphon a suitable portion of this liquid into the evolution apparatus as described under Sec. 2.1. Acidify, and proceed as for total sulfide.

4. Procedure for Un-Ionized Hydrogen Sulfide

Determine the pH of the original sample. Determine dissolved sulfide by the foregoing procedure. The concentration of un-ionized H_2S is found by multiplying the concentration of dissolved sulfide by a suitable factor as given in Table 27. These factors are

TABLE 27—HYDROGEN SULFIDE FACTORS

pH	Factor	pH	Factor	pH	Factor
5.0	0.98	6.8	0.44	7.7	0.091
5.4	0.95	6.9	0.39	7.8	0.073
5.8	0.89	7.0	0.33	7.9	0.059
6.0	0.83	7.1	0.29	8.0	0.048
6.2	0.76	7.2	0.24	8.2	0.031
6.4	0.67	7.3	0.23	8.4	0.020
6.5	0.61	7.4	0.17	8.8	0.0079
6.6	0.56	7.5	0.14	9.2	0.0032
6.7	0.50	7.6	0.11	9.6	0.0013

applicable at a temperature of 25°C. For temperatures below 20°C or above 30°C, or for sewages having a mineral-solids content exceeding 2,000 mg/l, suitable corrections should be made.

5. Precision and Accuracy

Precision and accuracy have not been determined, but it is known that the iodometric titration of zinc sulfide as described in Sec. 2.3–2.5 is quite accurate. The principal chance of error of the method is in the gaseous transfer of sulfide to the zinc acetate receiving solution. The analyst should check his technique for this by preparing a zinc sulfide suspension as directed in Sec. 3.7 under the colorimetric method (B), then determining the sulfide concentration by titrating one sample directly and another sample after gaseous transfer. Recovery should not be less than 95 per cent.

B. Colorimetric Method

1. General Discussion

1.1. *Principle:* The colorimetric method is based on the reaction which takes place, under suitable conditions, between paraaminodimethylaniline, ferric chloride, and sulfide ion, resulting in the formation of methylene blue. Ammonium phosphate is added prior to color comparisons to remove the color due to the presence of ferric ion.

1.2. *Interference:* Some strong reducing agents prevent the formation of the color or diminish its intensity. High sulfide concentrations—several hundred milligrams per liter—may completely inhibit the reaction, but dilution of the sample and subsequent analysis will eliminate this problem. Sulfite up to 10 mg/l SO_2 has no effect, although higher concentrations retard the reaction. Thiosulfate concentrations below 10 mg/l do not interfere seriously, but higher concentrations prevent color formation unless the thiosulfate is oxidized. The interference of sulfite and thiosulfate up to 40 mg/l of SO_2 or S_2O_3 can be eliminated by increasing the amount of $FeCl_3$ solution added from 2 drops to 6 drops, and extending the reaction time to 5 min. If present, sodium hydrosulfite, $Na_2S_2O_4$, will interfere by releasing some sulfide when the sample is acidified. Nitrite gives a pale yellow color at concentrations as low as 0.5 mg/l NO_2, but nitrite and sulfide are not likely to be found together, so that this possible interference is of little practical importance. To eliminate a slight interfering color, due to the reagent, which may be noticeable at sulfide concentrations below 0.1 mg/l, a dilute amine–sulfuric acid test solution is specified for concentrations of that order.

1.3. *Minimum detectable concentration:* 0.05 mg/l sulfide.

2. Apparatus

2.1. *Matched test tubes,* approximately 125 mm long and 15 mm in outside diameter, are most convenient for field use; 50-ml nessler tubes, with a corresponding increase in the amounts of sample and reagents, may also be used to give an increased depth of colored solutions, and therefore an increased sensitivity.

2.2. *Droppers,* delivering 20 drops per milliliter of the methylene blue solutions. In order to secure accurate results when measuring by drops, it is essential to hold the dropper in a vertical position and to allow the drops to form slowly, so that the outside of the dropper is thoroughly drained before the drop falls. For greater accuracy, the methylene blue solution may be measured with a 1-ml pipet graduated in 0.01 ml. Also, the tip of the dropper must be clean, so that water clings uniformly around the outside. If these precautions are followed, dropwise measurement is accurate; otherwise, it may be quite inaccurate.

2.3. *Glass-stoppered bottles,* capacity 100–300 ml. A BOD incubation bottle is recommended because its stopper is ground in such a way that it minimizes the possibility of entrapping air, and its specially designed lip provides a water seal.

3. Reagents

3.1. *Amine–sulfuric acid stock solution:* This solution may be purchased already prepared, or the paraaminodimethylaniline sulfate may be purchased and used without distillation, if tests show that its color formation qualities are satisfactory. To prepare, add 50 ml conc H_2SO_4 to 30 ml distilled water and cool. Add to this 20 g redistilled amine, or 27.2 g amine sulfate, stirring until dissolution is complete. Make up to 100 ml with distilled water. This stock solution will discolor somewhat on standing, but its usefulness remains unimpaired.

3.2. *Amine–sulfuric acid test solution (I):* Dilute 25 ml amine–sulfuric acid stock solution with 975 ml $1+1$ H_2SO_4. Use this solution for testing sulfide concentrations of 0.2–20 mg/l.

3.3. *Amine–sulfuric acid test solution (II):* Dilute 10 ml amine-sulfuric acid stock solution with 990 ml $1+1$ H_2SO_4. Cool the solution before using. This solution is preferable for low sulfide concentrations, giving better color matches. It must not be used for concentrations above 5 mg/l.

3.4. *Sulfuric acid solution,* $1+1$. Add, cautiously, 500 ml conc H_2SO_4 to 500 ml distilled water with continuous mixing. Cool the solution before using.

3.5. *Ferric chloride solution:* Dissolve 100 g $FeCl_3 \cdot 6H_2O$ in 39 ml water; this makes 100 ml of solution.

3.6. *Ammonium phosphate solution:* Dissolve 400 g $(NH_4)_2HPO_4$ in 805 ml distilled water; this makes 1 liter of solution.

3.7. *Methylene blue solution (I):* Use the USP grade of the dye, or one certified by the Biological Stain Commission. The percentage of actual dye content should be reported on the label and should be 84 per cent or more. Dissolve 1.0 g methylene blue powder in water and make up to 1 liter. This solution will be approximately the correct strength, but, because of variation between different lots of the dye, it must be standardized against sulfide solutions of known strength and adjusted; 1 drop (0.05 ml) of solution is equivalent to 1.0 mg/l sulfide.

Standardization: Prepare a suspension of zinc sulfide, ZnS, by adding 3 drops of $2N$ zinc acetate solution to 1 liter of distilled water. Bubble H_2S in for about 2 min. Bring to a boil, and boil for 2–5 min to remove the excess H_2S; then cool. Keeping the suspension well mixed, transfer just 200 ml to a flask. Determine the sulfide concentration in this by the titrimetric method (A), starting at Sec. 2.3, without first making the gaseous transfer. If 3 drops of zinc acetate solution was used, the initial addition of iodine solution should be in the neighborhood of 12 ml.

After making this analysis, run a test by the colorimetric procedure. If the apparent concentration by the colorimetric test is lower than by titration, dilute the methylene blue solution; if it is higher, add more dye to the solution, in proper proportion so that the result of the titrimetric test will be matched by the colorimetric test. After making an adjustment, repeat the colorimetric determination. With care, the result should now be within 5 per cent of the titrimetric results. If the difference exceeds 10 per cent, make further adjustments or refinements of technique until replicate tests are consistently within the 10 per cent limit.

The ZnS suspension may be used only on the day that it is prepared. The methylene blue solution is stable for a year if kept in the dark and tightly stoppered.

3.8. *Methylene blue solution (II):* This solution is prepared by diluting 10.0 ml of the adjusted methylene blue solution (I) to 100 ml; 1 drop (0.05 ml) of Solution II is equivalent to 0.1 mg/l sulfide.

3.9. *Zinc acetate solution, 2N.* Prepare as directed in Method A, Sec. 1.2.

4. Procedure for Total Sulfide

Sampling and testing should be carried out with all possible speed.

4.1. Taking care not to aerate the sample and to get a representative portion of any suspended matter that is present, pipet 7.5 ml of sample into each of two test tubes. If dilution is necessary, follow the procedure described in Sec. 4.4. To the first tube add 0.5 ml amine–sulfuric acid test solution (I or II). To the second tube add 0.5 ml $1 + 1$ H_2SO_4. Then to each tube add 0.1 ml (2 drops) ferric chloride solution. Close the tubes with the thumbs and mix by inverting slowly twice.

4.2. If sulfides are present, a blue color shows at once in the first tube; color development is complete in 1 min when Solution I is used. After 1–5 min add 1.6 ml ammonium phosphate solu-

tion to each tube and mix. When Solution II is used, wait not less than 5 min before adding ammonium phosphate. The color produced is stable for about 2 hr if the solution is kept out of strong light.

4.3. Add small portions of methylene blue solution, I or II (depending on the intensity of the color produced), to determine the volume or number of drops necessary to bring the color intensity of the solution in the second tube to that of the first tube. Color comparison when the sulfide concentration is less than 3 mg/l can be conveniently made by viewing down through the solutions against a white background. For concentrations from 3 to 20 mg/l, comparisons are made by viewing the tubes horizontally, after the volume in the first tube has been brought to that of the second tube with distilled water.

4.4. If the amine–sulfuric acid test solution used is Solution II and the color is greater than that which represents 5 mg/l sulfide, it is likely that the color will no longer be proportional to the amount of sulfide present. In this case, only a report of "5+" is permissible. If Solution I is used, a similar limit is imposed at 20 mg/l. Higher concentrations may be determined by dilution in the following manner: Measure 6 ml freshly boiled and cooled distilled water into a test tube; add 0.5 ml amine–sulfuric acid solution (I) and then 1.5 ml of sample; add 0.1 ml (2 drops) of ferric chloride solution; and continue as in the normal procedure, multiplying the final result by five. For other dilutions, up to fifteen times, the same procedure is used with different proportions of dilution water and sample, to total 7.5 ml. For dilutions still greater, use proportionally larger volumes of water and sample in order to eliminate the error inherent in measuring very small volumes of liquids.

4.5. *Calculation:* With methylene blue solution (I), adjusted so that 1 drop (0.05 ml) corresponds to 1.0 mg/l sulfide when 7.5 ml of sample is used:

mg/l sulfide = no. drops = ml × 20

With methylene blue solution (II), adjusted so that 1 drop (0.05 ml) corresponds to 0.1 mg/l sulfide when 7.5 ml of sample is used:

mg/l sulfide = no. drops × 0.1 = ml × 2

If dilution is used, multiply the result by the appropriate factor.

5. Procedure for Dissolved Sulfide

Removal of suspended matter by flocculating and settling leaves a sample in which dissolved sulfide can be determined by the colorimetric method, as well as by titrimetry. Follow the procedure in Method A, Sec. 3.1 and 3.2, except that, for convenience, a 100-ml bottle may be used instead of a 1-liter bottle. Reduce the amounts of $AlCl_3$ and NaOH to 4 drops, or to whatever volume accomplishes good clarification of the sample, always using the same volume of each.

6. Procedure for Un-Ionized Hydrogen Sulfide

Un-ionized hydrogen sulfide is calculated according to Sec. 4 of Method A. Be sure to use, in this calculation, the pH of the original sample—not the pH after adding any reagents.

7. Procedure for Very Low Sulfide Concentrations

The procedure given in Part I for very low sulfide concentrations in water can be applied to the determination of total sulfide in sewage.

8. Precision and Accuracy

The accuracy will be about ± 10 per cent if very careful technique is employed. The standard deviation has not been determined.

Bibliography

1. POMEROY, R. D. The Determination of Sulfides in Sewage. *Sew. Works J.* 8: 572 (1936).
2. POMEROY, R. D. Hydrogen Sulfides in Sewage. *Sew. Works J.* 13:498 (1941).
3. SANDS, A. E., ET AL. The Determination of Low Concentrations of Hydrogen Sulfide in Gas by the Methylene Blue Method. *US Bur. Mines Rept. Invest.* No. 4547 (1949).
4. BUDD, M. S. & BEWICK, H. A. Photometric Determination of Sulfide and Reducible Sulfur in Alkalis. *Anal. Chem.* 24:1536 (1952).

Surfactants (Anionic)

So many substances normally found in sewage and sewage effluents interfere with the determination of the surfactant component of synthetic detergents that it is very difficult to obtain an accurate value. An estimate of the concentration of anionic surfactants in sewage may be made using the methods in Part I.

Temperature

Temperature measurements may be made with any good grade of mercury-filled centigrade thermometer, provided it is checked occasionally against a precision thermometer certified by the National Bureau of Standards. Field instruments should be provided with a metal case to prevent breakage.

The temperature of sewages, effluents, and wastes at the time of sampling should be expressed in degrees centigrade to the nearest degree.

Turbidity

Turbidity is an expression of an optical property of the fine suspended matter in a sample. Measurement is based on comparison of interference in the passage of light rays through a sample with that in standard samples.

Turbidity may be determined by using a candle turbidimeter, provided the suspended matter is finely divided. The procedure to be followed is given in Part I. Turbidity may also be measured by a photometer or nephelometer that has been calibrated against prepared turbidity standards which, in turn, have been calibrated against a candle turbidimeter. Such determinations are subject to the limitations discussed in Part I.

PART IV

Physical and Chemical Examination
of Industrial Wastewaters

Introduction

The procedures described in Part IV of this manual are intended for use in the industrial-waste field. Because of the wide variety of industrial wastes, all the procedures may not be applicable to a specific waste or combination of wastes. Hence, some modification of a procedure may be necessary in specific instances. Whenever a procedure is modified, the nature of the modification must be plainly stated in the report of results.

A. Collection of Samples

The sampling and the analysis of industrial wastes usually require greater care and attention to details than sampling and analyzing sewage and sewage effluents. Industrial wastes are subject to rapid changes even within a few minutes, owing to breakdowns, spillovers, floor washing, evaporator entrainment, and numerous other causes.

The purpose of sampling and analysis may be to show the peak load concentration, the duration of peak loads, or the occurrence of variation throughout the day; for these purposes, samples should be taken at appropriate intervals—say every 5, 10, 15, or 60 min—and analyzed separately. On the other hand, if the purpose is to show the average loss during a shift or a 24-hr period, the individual samples which are collected every few minutes or hourly should be composited in proportion to the flow; preserved, if necessary; and analyzed as soon as possible.

Preservation of samples is difficult because almost all preservatives interfere with some of the tests. Immediate analysis is ideal. Storage at a low temperature ($4°C$) is perhaps the best way to preserve most samples until the next day. Chemical preservatives are to be used only when they are shown not to interfere with the examinations being made. When used, they should be added to the sample bottle initially, so that all portions of the composite are preserved as soon as collected. Care must be taken not to add too much sulfuric acid to the sample bottle before the addition of sample.

B. Expression of Results

Results may be expressed as milligrams per liter (mg/l) or as parts per million (ppm). If the concentration is less than 1 mg/l, the results may be expressed as micrograms per liter (μg/l) or parts per billion (ppb), where billion is understood to be 10^9. If the concentration is greater than 10,000 mg/l, the results should be expressed as per cent, 1 per cent being equivalent to 10,000 mg/l. In brines or wastes of high specific gravity, a cor-

437

rection must be made if the results are expressed as ppm or per cent by weight:

$$ppm \text{ by weight} = \frac{mg/l}{sp \text{ } gr}$$

$$\% \text{ by weight} = \frac{mg/l}{10,000 \times sp \text{ } gr}$$

In such cases, if the result is given in mg/l, the specific gravity must be stated.

Acidity and Alkalinity

The hydroxyl-carbonate-bicarbonate content of polluted waters may be determined by the usual titrations with methyl orange and phenolphthalein indicators or by potentiometric titrations to pH 4.5 and 8.3. If the concentration of some particular acid or alkali is desired in an industrial waste, the potentiometric method should be used and the endpoint or endpoints taken in the usual manner from the inflections shown on a plotted titration curve. If definite inflections are not obtained, the arbitrary endpoints of 4.5 and 8.3 should be used. Methods are those given in Part III.

Many wastes, such as iron pickle liquors and acidic mine effluents, are composed of the salts of ferrous and ferric iron and aluminum, with possibly some excess acid and other metallic salts. Alkaline receiving waters contain carbonate and bicarbonate, and the total alkalinity is dependent on the base element after evolution of carbon dioxide. The following procedures, suitable for mine waters and their receiving streams, give stoichiometrically equivalent values.

1. General Discussion

1.1. *Principle:* The total acidity of mine water is caused by the presence of mineral acids or the hydrolyzable salts of mineral acids. The amount of acidity, for control purposes, is deter-

mined by titration of a hot sample with a standard solution of a strong base to a predetermined endpoint. The alkalinity is determined by acidifying a hot sample with standard acid and back-titrating with standard alkali. Phenolphthalein is used as the endpoint indicator for both determinations. The solution is titrated hot in order to insure complete hydrolysis of the acid-producing salts.

1.2. *Interference:* The presence of ferrous or ferric iron produces precipitates of iron hydroxide varying in color from green through black to yellow. These precipitates may mask the endpoint, and extreme care is necessary to determine the color change. Aluminum is amphoteric and thus is soluble in alkali; large concentrations may give high results unless extreme care is exercised in determining the color change. A fleeting endpoint indicates the presence of aluminum.

1.3. *Sampling and storage:* The sampling procedure described above (Part IV, Introduction) can be used. The acidity and alkalinity values do not change when samples are stored in glass containers with the usual methods of closure.

2. Reagents

2.1. *Phenolphthalein indicator solution:* Either the aqueous (*a*) or alcoholic (*b*) solution may be used.

a. Dissolve 5 g phenolphthalein disodium salt in distilled water and dilute to 1 liter. If necessary, add 0.02*N* NaOH dropwise until a faint pink color appears.

b. Dissolve 5 g phenolphthalein in 500 ml 95 per cent ethyl alcohol or isopropyl alcohol and add 500 ml distilled water. Then add 0.02*N* NaOH dropwise until a faint pink color appears.

2.2. *Standard sodium hydroxide:* Various normalities may be used, such as 0.02*N*, 0.05*N*, or 0.10*N*, depending on the acidity or alkalinity of the waste water.

2.3. *Standard sulfuric acid,* normality equivalent to the sodium hydroxide used.

3. Procedure

3.1. *Phenolphthalein acidity* (at boiling temperature) :

a. Add several drops of phenolphthalein indicator solution to a sample of suitable size. The size of sample depends on the normality of the sodium hydroxide titrant and the concentration of the acid in the waste. The amount of reagent required should be between 10 and 25 ml. Boil the sample for 2 min and titrate the hot sample with sodium hydroxide to a pink endpoint.

b. Calculation:

Phenolphthalein acidity as mg/l $CaCO_3$

$$= \frac{CD \times 50,000}{E}$$

3.2. *Alkalinity* (at boiling temperature; pH 4.5 or above) :

a. The alkalinity determination requires the complete removal of carbonate and bicarbonate. Follow the same procedure as for acidity but add a measured volume of standard sulfuric acid until the solution remains colorless after boiling. Back-titrate with standard sodium hydroxide to a pink endpoint.

b. Calculation:

Alkalinity as mg/l $CaCO_3$

$$= \frac{(AB-CD) \times 50,000}{E}$$

where

$A = $ ml sulfuric acid added;
$B = $ normality of sulfuric acid;
$C = $ ml sodium hydroxide titrant used;
$D = $ normality of sodium hydroxide; and
$E = $ ml sample.

A negative value is acidity.

Cadmium

See Metals (Heavy), Method A.

Chloride

Chloride may be determined by the procedures for sewage in Part III, except that an appropriate size of sample should be taken.

Chlorine (Residual)

The determination of residual chlorine in industrial wastes is similar to the determination in sewage when a waste contains organic matter, but may be similar to the determination in water when the waste is low in organic matter.

Selection of method: The amperometric method (*A*), the iodometric method (*B*) with either amperometric or starch iodide endpoint determination, the orthotolidine method (*C*), and the orthotolidine-arsenite method (*D*) all find a useful place in determining residual chlorine in industrial wastes. For some industrial wastes, particularly those high in organic matter, the iodometric method as specified herein must be used to prevent contact between the full concentration of liberated iodine and the waste at any time. The method for sewage fulfills this requirement.

The iodometric method with amperometric endpoint is capable of giving a much more accurate endpoint and is free of interference from color and turbidity, which sometimes cause great difficulty with other procedures.

The determination of residual chlorine in water by the orthotolidine method is discussed in Part I, Chlorine (Residual), Method B. That section presents the limitations and precautions to be observed. Particular attention is called to the importance of warming the sample after the orthotolidine is added, in order to complete the reaction with minimum loss of chlorine due to consumption by organic matter. In any case, this method usually gives lower results than the iodometric when organic matter is present.

A. Amperometric Titration Method for Free Available Chlorine

Free available chlorine can be determined in an industrial waste, in the substantial absence of organic nitrogen, by the procedure in Part I, Chlorine (Residual), Method F. This method is not subject to interference from color, turbidity, iron, manganese, or nitrite nitrogen.

B. Iodometric Method for Total Residual Chlorine

Unless there is a specific need to know the free available chlorine, the iodometric method as given for sewage Part III, Chlorine (Residual), Method A, is used. Although manganese, iron, and nitrite may interfere with this method, the interference may be minimized by buffering to pH 4.0 before KI addition.

An unusually high content of organic matter may cause some uncertainty in the endpoint. Whenever manganese, iron, or nitrites are definitely absent, this uncertainty can be reduced and precision increased by buffering below pH 4.0—even as low as pH 3.0.

The amperometric method given for water should not be used to determine total residual chlorine.

C. Orthotolidine Method

The orthotolidine method is not applicable to wastes that are colored. When nitrite nitrogen is present in amounts greater than 2.0 mg/l, the orthotolidine method should not be used. Unless iron and manganese are present in the waste, the method is the same as in Part III, Chlorine (Resid-ual), Method B. The concentration of acid in the orthotolidine reagent is such that it will produce a suitable pH in the sample even if the alkalinity is 1,000 mg/l. Higher alkalinities will require the addition of more of the orthotolidine reagent than is otherwise specified.

D. Orthotolidine-Arsenite Method

The orthotolidine-arsenite (OTA) test is preferable to the orthotolidine method if iron and manganese are present in the waste and the organic nitrogen content is low.

1. Apparatus

The same apparatus is required as for the OTA test in water; see Part I, Chlorine (Residual), Method D, Sec. 2.

2. Reagents

The same reagents are required as for the OTA test in water; see Part I, Chlorine (Residual), Method D, Sec. 3.

3. Procedure

3.1. Label two comparator cells or French square bottles "A" and "B." Use 1 ml orthotolidine reagent in 10-ml cells, 1.5 ml in 15-ml cells, and the same ratio for other volumes of sample. Use the same volume of sodium arsenite solution as orthotolidine reagent.

3.2. To Cell A, containing sodium arsenite solution, add a measured volume of sample. Mix quickly, and immediately add orthotolidine reagent. Mix quickly and compare with color standards when maximum color develops—usually in less than 5 min. Record the result as the A value, which represents interfering color.

3.3. To Cell B, containing orthotolidine reagent, add a measured volume of sample. Mix quickly and compare with color standards when maximum color develops—usually in less than 5 min. Record the result as the B value, which represents the total amount of residual chlorine present and of interfering color.

3.4. More accurate readings may be obtained if both cells are placed in the comparator in such relative positions that the color compensation is made directly.

4. Calculation

If color compensation is not made directly:

$$mg/l \text{ total residual } Cl = B - A$$

where A is the result from Sec. 3.2 and B is the result from Sec. 3.3.

Bibliography

1. Gilcreas, F. W. & Hallinan, F. J. The Practical Use of the Orthotolidine-Arsenite Test for Residual Chlorine. *J. AWWA* 36:1343 (1944).
2. Marks, H. C.; Williams, D. B.; & Glasgow, G. U. Determination of Residual Chlorine Compounds. *J. AWWA* 43:201 (1951).

Chlorine Requirement

Many industrial wastes are chlorinated for the purpose of disinfection prior to discharge into streams and sewers with or without other types of treatment. They may also be chlorinated for such purposes as destruction of phenol, cyanide, color, or odor, reduction of BOD, and oxidation of iron.

A. Method for Control of Disinfection

The chlorine requirement for the disinfection of industrial wastes is defined as the amount of chlorine which must be added per unit volume of waste to produce the desired residual chlorine concentration after a definite contact time. Residual chlorine and contact time will have been chosen to give a stipulated result in terms of coliform density or other characteristic.

The results of such determinations may also be used for measuring the increase in chlorine requirement at the treatment plant due to the discharge of the waste into the sewer and for assessing the cost of chlorination attributable to the particular contributor to the plant.

When there are a number of contributors to a common treatment plant, the necessary value of residual chlorine will be based on the treatment plant effluent. The chlorine requirement for each contributor will then be the additional amount of chlorine necessary to produce the stipulated residual chlorine concentration after dilution of the waste with treatment plant effluent in the same volumetric ratio as actually occurs.

The procedures for determination of chlorine requirement in sewage, as given in Part III, Method A, are recommended.

B. Methods for Purposes Other Than Disinfection Control

When industrial wastes are to be chlorinated for such purposes as the destruction of chemicals or the reduction of undesirable qualities in effluents, the same general concept of chlorine requirement as developed for disinfection purposes can be applied. pH values may be varied according to the conditions and purposes of the chlorine treatment. Instead of using the remaining coliform organisms as the yardstick or endpoint for the chlorine requirement, the yardstick is based on the objective for which chlorine is applied. For example, if chlorine is applied for phenol destruction, the chlorine requirement is based on the actual phenol concentration desired. Contact times may be varied in conjunction with the quantity of chlorine applied, compatible with the accomplishment of the objective. All conditions of the test should be specified.

Chromium

See Metals (Heavy), Methods B and C.

Color

The color of an industrial waste is considered to be the color of the light transmitted by the waste solution after removing the suspended material, including the pseudocolloidal particles. It is recognized that the color characteristics of some wastes are affected by the light reflection from the suspended material in the wastes. However, until a suitable method is available for making solution reflectance determinations, the color measurements will be limited to the characteristics of light transmitted by clarified wastes. Suspended materials are removed by filtration through a standard filter aid medium. Color adsorption by calcined filter aids is practically negligible for the quantity of filter aid required. Centrifuging is not used because the results will vary with the size and speed of the centrifuge. Furthermore, particles with a specific gravity lower than that of water will tend to float or remain in suspension.

The color of the filtered waste is expressed in terms which describe the sensation realized when viewing the waste. The hue (red, yellow, green, etc.) of the color is designated by the term *dominant wavelength,* the degree of brightness by *luminance,* and the saturation (pastel, pale, etc.) by *purity.* These values are best determined from the light transmission characteristics of the filtered waste by means of a spectrophotometer (Method A). A rapid method which uses three color filters and a filter photometer is given as Method B. It is not as accurate as Method A but will give very satisfactory results. The light transmission data are converted to the color classification terms by using standards adopted by the International Commission on Illumination ("CIE"), and the selected-ordinate method.

A. Spectrophotometric Method

1. Apparatus

1.1. *Spectrophotometer,* having 10-mm absorption cells, a narrow (10 mμ or less) spectral band, and an effective operating range from 400 to 700 mμ.

1.2. *Filtration system,* consisting of the following (See Fig. 30):

a. Filtration flasks, 250 ml, with side tubes.

b. Walter crucible holder.

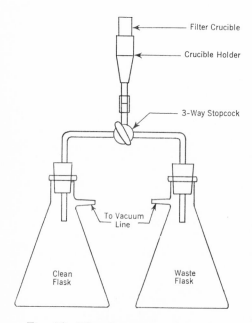

c. Micrometallic filter crucible, average pore size 40 microns.

d. Calcined filter aid.*

e. Vacuum system.

2. Procedure

2.1. *Preparation of sample:* Bring two 50-ml waste samples to room temperature. Use one sample at the original pH value of the waste; adjust the pH value of the other to 7.6 by using conc H$_2$SO$_4$ or NaOH, as required. A standard pH is necessary because of the variation of color with pH. Remove excessive quantities of suspended materials by centrifuging. Each sample is treated separately, as follows:

Thoroughly mix 0.1 g filter aid in a 10-ml portion of centrifuged waste sample and filter the slurry to form a precoat in the filter crucible. The filtrate is directed to the waste flask as in Fig. 30. Mix 0.04 g filter aid in a 35-ml portion of the centrifuged waste sample. While the vacuum is still in effect, filter through the precoat and pass the filtrate to the waste flask until clear; then direct the clear-filtrate flow to the clean flask by means of the three-way stopcock and collect 25 ml for the transmittance determination.

2.2. *Determination of light transmis-*

Filter Crucible

Crucible Holder

3-Way Stopcock

To Vacuum Line

Clean Flask

Waste Flask

Fig. 30. Filtration system for color determinations

---

* Celite No. 505 (Johns-Manville Corporation) or equal.

sion characteristics: Thoroughly clean the 10-mm absorption cells with detergent and rinse with distilled water. Rinse twice with filtered waste, clean the external surfaces with lens paper,

TABLE 28—SELECTED ORDINATES FOR SPECTRO-
PHOTOMETRIC COLOR DETERMINATIONS *

Ordinate No.	X	Y	Z
		Wavelength—$m\mu$	
1	424.4	465.9	414.1
2*	435.5*	489.5*	422.2*
3	443.9	500.4	426.3
4	452.1	508.7	429.4
5*	461.2*	515.2*	432.0*
6	474.0	520.6	434.3
7	531.2	525.4	436.5
8*	544.3*	529.8*	438.6*
9	552.4	533.9	440.6
10	558.7	537.7	442.5
11*	564.1*	541.4*	444.4*
12	568.9	544.9	446.3
13	573.2	548.4	448.2
14*	577.4*	551.8*	450.1*
15	581.3	555.1	452.1
16	585.0	558.5	454.0
17*	588.7*	561.9*	455.9*
18	592.4	565.3	457.9
19	596.0	568.9	459.9
20*	599.6*	572.5*	462.0*
21	603.3	576.4	464.1
22	607.0	580.4	466.3
23*	610.9*	584.8*	468.7*
24	615.0	589.6	471.4
25	619.4	594.8	474.3
26*	624.2*	600.8*	477.7*
27	629.8	607.7	481.8
28	636.6	616.1	487.2
29*	645.9*	627.3*	495.2*
30	663.0	647.4	511.2

Factors When 30 Ordinates Used

	0.03269	0.03333	0.03938

Factors When 10 Ordinates Used

	0.09806	0.10000	0.11814

* Insert in each column the transmittance value (per cent) corresponding to the wavelength shown. Where limited accuracy is sufficient, only the ordinates marked with an asterisk need be used.

and fill the cell with filtered waste.

Determine the transmittance values (in per cent) for the waste sample at each of the visible wavelength values presented in Table 28, using the ten ordinates marked with an asterisk for fairly accurate work and all 30 ordinates for increased accuracy. Use distilled water for the blank for 100 per cent transmittance and make all determinations with a narrow spectral band.

3. Calculation

3.1. Tabulate the transmittance values corresponding to the wavelengths shown in Columns X, Y, and Z in Table 28. Total each of the transmittance columns and multiply the totals by the appropriate factors (for 10 or 30 ordinates) shown at the bottom of the table, to obtain tristimulus values X, Y, and Z. The tristimulus value Y is the *per cent luminance* of the waste.

3.2. Calculate the trichromatic coefficients x and y from the tristimulus values X, Y, and Z by the following equations:

$$x = \frac{X}{X + Y + Z}$$

$$y = \frac{Y}{X + Y + Z}$$

Locate point (x, y) on one of the chromaticity diagrams in Fig. 31 and determine the dominant wavelength (in $m\mu$) and the purity (in per cent) directly from the diagram.*

Determine the hue from the dominant-wavelength value, according to the ranges in Table 29.

* If more accurate values are desired, larger charts are presented in Hardy's *Handbook of Colorimetry*.[1]

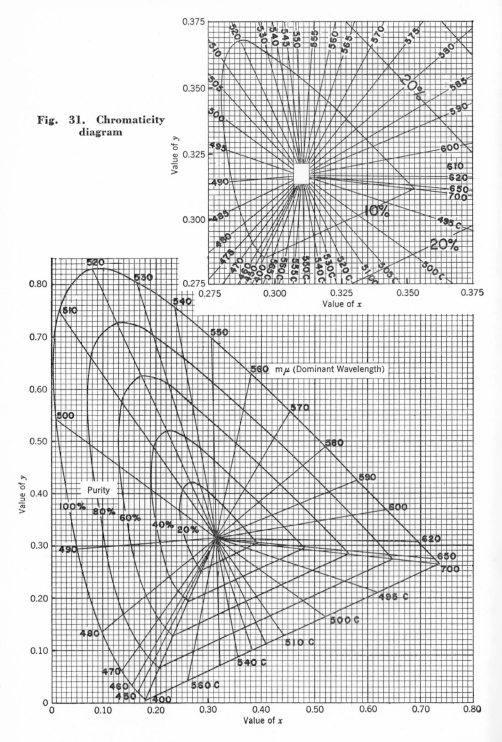

Fig. 31. Chromaticity diagram

TABLE 29—COLOR HUES FOR DOMINANT-WAVELENGTH RANGES

Wavelength Range mμ	Hue
400–465	violet
465–482	blue
482–497	blue-green
497–530	green
530–575	greenish-yellow
575–580	yellow
580–587	yellowish-orange
587–598	orange
598–620	orange-red
620–700	red
400–530c	blue-purple
530c–700	red-purple

4. Expression of Results

The color characteristics (at pH 7.6 and at the original pH) are expressed in terms of *dominant wavelength* (mμ, to the nearest unit), *hue* (e.g., "blue," "blue-green," etc.), *luminance* (per cent, to the nearest tenth), and *purity* (per cent, to the nearest unit).

The report should state the type of instrument (i.e., spectrophotometer), the number of selected ordinates (10 or 30), and the spectral band width (mμ).

B. Tristimulus Filter Method

1. General Discussion

A method for obtaining trichromatic color characteristics of solutions, suitable for routine control purposes, is to use three special tristimulus light filters, combined with a specific light source and photoelectric cell in a filter photometer. The percentage of tristimulus light transmitted by the waste solution is determined for each of the three filters. The transmittance values are then converted to trichromatic coefficients and color characteristic values.

2. Apparatus

2.1. *Filter photometer.*†

2.2. *Filter photometer light source:* Tungsten lamp at a color temperature of 3,000°K.‡

2.3. *Filter photometer photoelectric cells,* 1 cm.§

2.4. *Tristimulus filters:* Corning CS–3–107 (No. 1), CS–4–98 (No. 2), and CS–5–70 (No. 3).

2.5. *Filtration system:* See Method A, Sec. 1.2, and Fig. 30.

3. Procedure

3.1. *Preparation of sample:* See Method A, Sec. 2.1.

3.2. *Determination of light transmission characteristics:* Thoroughly clean (with detergent) and rinse the 1-cm absorption cells with distilled water. Rinse each absorption cell twice with filtered waste, clean the external surfaces with lens paper, and fill the cell with filtered waste.

Use distilled water as the blank for 100 per cent transmittance in another cell and determine the percentage of light transmission through the waste

---

† Fisher Electrophotometer or equivalent.
‡ General Electric lamp No. 1719 (at 6 v) or equivalent.

§ General Electric photovoltaic cell, Type PV–1, or equal.

for each of the three tristimulus light filters, with the filter photometer lamp intensity switch in a position equivalent to 4 v on the lamp.

4. Calculation

4.1. The luminance value is determined directly as the percentage transmittance value obtained with the No. 2 tristimulus filter.

4.2. The tristimulus values X, Y, and Z are calculated from the percentage transmittance (T_1, T_2, T_3) for filters No. 1, 2, 3, as follows:

$$X = T_3 \times 0.06 + T_1 \times 0.25$$
$$Y = T_2 \times 0.316$$
$$Z = T_3 \times 0.374$$

The trichromatic coefficients x and y, dominant wavelength, hue, and purity are calculated and determined in the same manner as in Method A, Sec. 3.2.

5. Expression of Results

The results are expressed in the same manner as in Method A, Sec. 4. Except for very exact referee work, this method gives results very similar to the more accurate Method A.

Bibliography

1. HARDY, A. C. *Handbook of Colorimetry.* Technology Press, Boston, Mass. (1936).
2. COMMITTEE REPORT. The Concept of Color. *J. Opt. Soc. Am.* 33:544 (1943).
3. RUDOLFS, W. & HANLON, W. D. Color in Industrial Wastes. I. Determination by Spectrophotometric Method. *Sew. Ind. Wastes* 23:1125 (1951).
4. JONES, H., ET AL. *The Science of Color.* Thomas Y. Crowell Co., New York (1952).
5. JUDD, D. D. *Color in Business, Science, and Industry.* John Wiley & Sons, New York (1952).

Copper

See Metals (Heavy), Method D.

Cyanide

In the examination of industrial wastes and other waters, "cyanide" refers to all of the CN groups in the cyanide compounds present that can be determined as the cyanide ion, CN^-, by the methods used. The cyanide compounds in which cyanide can be obtained as CN^- are classed as simple and complex cyanides.

The simple cyanides are represented by the formula $A(CN)_x$, where A is an alkali (sodium, potassium, ammonium) or a metal and x, the valence of A, is the number of CN groups. In the soluble compounds, particularly the simple alkali cyanides, the CN group is present as CN^-. In the metal-finishing industry, this is referred to as "free" cyanide, the cyanide that may be titrated directly with silver nitrate. In industrial wastes, free cyanide includes the soluble simple cyanides initially present plus those formed in any decomposition of complex cyanides.

The complex cyanides have a variety of formulas, but the alkali-metallic cyanides normally can be represented by $A_yM(CN)_x$. In this formula, A represents the alkali present y times, M the heavy metal (ferrous and ferric iron, cadmium, copper, nickel, silver, zinc, or others), and x the number of CN groups; x is equal to the valence of A taken y times plus that of the heavy metal. In these soluble alkali-metallic cyanides, the anion is not the CN groups but the radical, $M(CN)_x$.

The cyanides show varying degrees of chemical activity. The simple cyanides are readily changed to HCN during distillation with acid. Many of the metal cyanides, such as those of cadmium, copper, nickel, and zinc, react almost as readily. The iron cyanide complexes, under similar conditions, show greater resistance to decomposition to HCN, whereas those of cobalticyanides decompose very slowly.

The cyanide ion, CN^-, is very toxic. Because the simple alkali cyanides form CN^- when dissolved in aqueous solution, they, too, normally display intense toxicity. Many of the alkali-metallic cyanides are rather stable in aqueous solution and therefore normally have little or no toxicity. Under certain conditions, some not well defined, these complexes decompose to display varying degrees of toxicity, depending on the metal present and the proportion of the CN groups converted to the simpler alkali cyanides with their toxic CN^-.

The presence of cyanide in water has a significant effect on the biologic activity of the system. For example,

Dodge and Reams [3] report that the threshold limit of toxicity at infinite time for fish appears to be 0.1 mg/l as CN^-. Ludzack and colleagues [6] found that the microorganisms responsible for self-purification were inhibited by a CN^- content of 0.3 mg/l or above. The toxicity limits are affected by water quality, temperature, and type and size of organisms; hence, definite effects are difficult to establish, but the values quoted indicate the nature of the effects due to cyanides in water.

Selection of method: Procedures are given below for the removal of interfering substances and the conversion of all cyanides, except cobalticyanides, to the simple ion, CN^-, by preliminary treatment of the sample, and for the determination of the CN^- after such treatment.

The screening procedure selected for the preliminary treatment of the sample is applicable to many types of waters. The procedure was found effective on relatively pure water, river water, sewage, and several industrial wastes, including those from gas and coke operations, petroleum refining, and plating.

The preliminary screening procedure eliminates or reduces interference to a minimum. Such screening is subject to modification to conform to the nature of the interference. Distillation is an important part of the screening procedure because it not only isolates cyanide from most interferences, but converts most cyanide complexes into the simple CN^- that is readily measured by titration or color test. It is permissible to omit the distillation procedure when it is known that the sample contains only simple cyanides of the alkalis and is completely free of all interferences.

If all of the conditions for direct determination of CN^-, except turbidity, are met, it may be possible to extract the pyridine-pyrazolone color, thereby avoiding distillation. This procedure is similar to that of Nusbaum and Skupeko [5] and is very effective if turbidity is the principal interference. In such cases, the reliability of the test would be verified if the same results were obtained with and without distillation.

The concentration of the cyanide in the sample following the preliminary screening procedure can be determined by the modified Liebig titration method, Method A, using the rhodanine internal indicator of Ryan and Culshaw,[1] or by a colorimetric method, Method B, using pyridine-pyrazolone as outlined by Epstein.[2]

The proposal by Serfass and colleagues [8] that the titration method be used for samples with a cyanide concentration greater than 1 mg/l as CN and the colorimetric method below this level has been justified by the sensitivity and precision of the two methods at the respective cyanide levels. If the cyanide concentration is unknown, the colorimetric method is used only when titration of part of the distillate indicates a concentration of less than 1 mg/l as CN.

The titration method can be adapted for high concentrations of cyanide by increasing the strength of silver nitrate solution, by taking smaller samples and diluting before distillation, or by taking smaller aliquots of distillate and diluting before titration.

Preliminary Treatment of Samples

CAUTION: Due care should be exercised in the manipulation of cyanide samples because of the toxicity involved. They should be processed in a hood or other well-ventilated area. Avoid inhalation or ingestion of the sample or products of the sample. Do not attempt to acidify a sample unless liberated HCN can be trapped or controlled.

1. General Discussion

1.1. *Principle:* The nature of the preliminary treatment will vary according to the interfering substance present. Sulfide, fatty acids, and oxidizing agents are removed by special procedures that are more or less self-explanatory. Most other interfering substances are removed by distillation. The importance of the distillation procedure cannot be overemphasized. This step not only eliminates interference, but also results in the conversion of the cyanide into simple sodium cyanide, which may readily be measured by titration or color test.

The color test, in particular, is sensitive to variations in salt concentration. Although the pyridine-pyrazolone color reaction is reproducible through a pH range of 3 to 8, significant variations in salt concentration result in changes in the absorbance of the color. Therefore, it is essential to isolate these salts so that a controlled salt concentration may be used for all aliquots of the distillate and the standards, as provided in the colorimetric test.

Distillation of the sample in the presence of sulfuric acid readily converts the simple cyanides into HCN. Complex iron cyanides and a few others are not easily decomposed, but many, such as those of cadmium, copper, nickel, silver, and zinc, are also converted to HCN by boiling in the presence of acid. The conversion is hastened in the presence of magnesium and mercuric salts. These salts are extremely effective in reducing the ferrocyanides and ferricyanides to magnesium and mercuric simple cyanides, which, in turn, are readily decomposed by the acid to HCN. In spite of this favorable transition, an additional distillation period is required for conversion of all cyanide to HCN. Complete decomposition of the cobalticyanide complex does not occur even after distilling the sample under similar conditions for more than 24 hr.

The HCN gas and water vapor are evolved from the boiling sample. Through refluxing and use of an air stream, the water vapor is returned to the distilling flask and the HCN is swept over into a caustic solution, where it is converted to simple sodium cyanide for test.

1.2. *Interference:* Common interferences in the analysis for cyanide include: sulfide, heavy-metal ions, fatty acids, and other steam-distillable organic compounds which adversely affect the silver nitrate titration; thiocyanate, cyanate, glycine, urea, or other substances which may hydrolyze to form cyanide under analytical conditions; substances contributing color or turbidity, affecting both titration and color development; and oxidizing agents which are likely to result in the destruction of cyanide during manipulation, particularly during the distillation stage.

a. *Sulfide* is removed by treating the alkaline sample at pH 11.0 with small increments of powdered lead carbonate. Black lead sulfide precipitates in samples containing sulfide. Repeat this operation until no more lead sulfide forms. Filter and rinse the precipitate, add the rinse water to the filtrate, and use an aliquot for analysis. Avoid a large excess of lead carbonate and a long period of contact in order to minimize complexing or occlusion of the cyanide with the precipitated material.

b. *Fatty acids* form soaps under alkaline titration conditions and render it difficult or impossible to detect the endpoint. This type of interference may be removed by an extraction, as suggested by Kruse and Mellon.[7] The sample should be acidified with acetic acid to pH 6–7 and extracted with isooctane, hexane, or chloroform (preference in the order named). One extraction with a solvent volume equal to 20 per cent of the sample volume is usually adequate to reduce the fatty acids to a point below the interference level. Avoid multiple extractions or a long contact time at a low pH, in order to keep the loss of HCN at a minimum.

c. *Oxidizing agents* are removed by the procedure outlined by Serfass and colleagues.[8] If the sample tests positively with starch-iodide paper, titrate with sodium sulfite (12.6 g anhydrous Na_2SO_3 per liter of solution) until a negative test is obtained.

d. *Other interfering substances:* After the removal of sulfides, fatty acids, and oxidizing agents, if necessary, most other interferences can be removed by distillation.

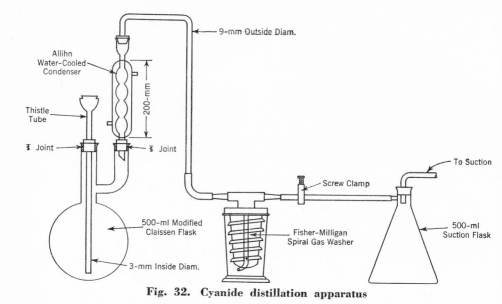

Fig. 32.   Cyanide distillation apparatus

1.3. Preservation of samples: Because most cyanides are very reactive and unstable, analysis should be made as soon as possible after sampling. If the sample cannot be analyzed immediately, add NaOH to raise the pH to 11.0 or above, and store in a cool place.

2. Apparatus

The following apparatus (see Fig. 32) is required:

2.1. Modified Claissen flask, 500 ml, having ⑤ joints, with side-arm delivery tube removed and opening sealed.

2.2. Air inlet, consisting of a thistle tube with ⑤ joint, having a glass tube (3-mm inside diameter) fused to the joint and extended to $\frac{1}{4}$ in. from the bottom of the modified Claissen flask.

2.3. Allihn-type condenser, with ⑤ joint to fit the modified Claissen flask.

2.4. Gas washer, spiral flow type, liquid capacity 100–250 ml (such as the modified Milligan washer), fitted

with a rubber tube with a pinch clamp in the bottom.

2.5. Suction flask, 500-ml capacity.

2.6. Water aspirator.

2.7. Heating element, for the modified Claissen flask.

2.8. Connecting tubing, rubber or glass as indicated.

3. Reagents

3.1. Sodium hydroxide solution, 1N. Dissolve 4 g NaOH in 100 ml distilled water.

3.2. Mercuric chloride solution: Dissolve 34 g $HgCl_2$ in 500 ml distilled water.   (CAUTION: *Toxic; take care to avoid ingestion.*)

3.3. Magnesium chloride solution: Dissolve 51 g $MgCl_2 \cdot 6H_2O$ in 100 ml distilled water.

3.4. Sulfuric acid, conc.

4. Procedure

4.1. Add the sample, containing not

more than 500 mg CN (diluted if necessary to 250–500 ml with distilled water), to the Claissen flask. Add exactly 50 ml 1N NaOH solution to the gas washer and dilute, if necessary, with distilled water to obtain an adequate depth of liquid in the absorber. Connect the train, consisting of boiling flask air inlet, flask, condenser, gas washer, suction flask trap, and aspirator. Adjust the suction so that approximately one bubble of air per second enters the boiling flask through the air inlet. This air rate will effectively act as a carrier for the HCN gas from flask to absorber and will usually prevent a reverse flow of HCN through the air inlet. If the air rate does not prevent the sample from backing up in the delivery tube, the air flow rate may be increased up to two bubbles per second without loss in efficiency. If the air rate becomes too high, the gas washer will not trap all of the HCN.

4.2. Add 20 ml mercuric chloride solution and 10 ml magnesium chloride solution through the air inlet tube. Rinse the tube with distilled water and allow the air flow to mix the flask contents for 3 min. Slowly add conc H_2SO_4 in an amount equal to 5 ml for each 100 ml of solution in the distilling flask, and rinse the air inlet once more.

4.3. Heat at a rate which will provide rapid boiling but will not flood the condenser inlet or permit vapors to rise more than halfway into the condenser. Reflux for 1 hr. Turn off the heat but continue the air flow. After 15 min of cooling, drain the gas washer contents into a separate container. Rinse the connecting tube from the condenser to the gas washer with distilled water, add the rinse water to the drained liquid, and dilute to 250 ml in a volumetric flask.

4.4. Determine the cyanide content by the titration method (A) if the cyanide concentration is greater than 1 mg/l as CN and by the colorimetric method (B) if the cyanide is below this level. If the cyanide concentration is unknown, it is recommended that 200 ml of the distillate be titrated by Method A. If the cyanide value is then found to be below the desired limit of 1 mg/l as CN, the remaining 50 ml of the distillate is diluted, if necessary, and examined as indicated in Method B.

4.5. Refill the gas washer with a fresh charge of 1N NaOH solution and repeat the reflux procedure.

4.6. If the sample includes only readily hydrolyzed cyanides, the absorber liquid from the first reflux will contain all of the available cyanide; if stable complex cyanides are present, a significant yield will appear in the absorber liquid from the second or from several successive periods, depending on the degree of stability.

A. *Titration Method*

1. General Discussion

1.1. *Principle:* The CN⁻ in the alkaline distillate from the preliminary screening procedure is titrated with a standard solution of $AgNO_3$ to form the soluble cyanide complex, $Ag(CN)_2^-$. As soon as all the CN⁻ has been complexed and a small excess of Ag^+ has been added, the excess Ag^+ is detected by the silver-sensitive indicator, para-dimethylaminobenzalrhodanine, which immediately turns from a yellow to a salmon color. The indicator is sensitive to about 0.1 mg/l Ag. If the titration shows the CN^- is below 1 mg/l, another aliquot is examined colorimetrically. The titration method can be adapted for high concentration as noted under selection of method.

1.2. *Interference:* All interferences are eliminated or reduced to a minimum by using only a distillate from the preliminary screening procedure.

1.3. *Minimum detectable concentration:* About 0.1 mg Ag, or about 0.05 mg CN. If all of the distillate from a 500-ml sample is used in the determination, the minimum detectable concentration approaches 0.1 mg/l CN.

2. Apparatus

Koch microburet, 5-ml capacity.

3. Reagents

3.1. *Sodium hydroxide solution, 1N.* Dissolve 4 g NaOH in 100 ml distilled water.

3.2. *Indicator solution:* Dissolve 0.02 g paradimethylaminobenzalrhodanine in 100 ml acetone.

3.3. *Standard silver nitrate titrant,* 0.0192N. Dissolve 3.27 g $AgNO_3$ in 1 liter distilled water. Standardize against standard NaCl solution using the argentometric method with K_2CrO_4 indicator, as directed in Part I, Chloride, Method A; 1.00 ml of this solution is equivalent to 1.00 mg CN.

4. Procedure

4.1. If preliminary treatment has included distillation, take an aliquot of the distillate without pH adjustment. If the sample has not been distilled, adjust the pH to 11.0 or above with 1N sodium hydroxide solution. Dilute the aliquot to 250 ml or some other convenient volume to be used for all titrations. Add 0.5 ml indicator solution.

4.2. Titrate with standard silver nitrate titrant to the first change in color from a canary yellow to a salmon hue. Titrate a blank containing the same amount of alkali and water.

It is advisable to adjust the sample size or the strength of $AgNO_3$ titrant so that the titration requires 2–10 ml. The analyst should use the amount of indicator that gives him the best result; the same amount should be used for all titrations. Most analysts find this titration difficult for the first few trials, and this is reflected in high blank values. As the analyst becomes accustomed to the endpoint, blank titrations decrease to 1 drop or less and precision improves accordingly.

5. Calculation

$$\text{mg/l CN} = \frac{(A - B) \times 1,000}{\text{ml original sample}} \times \frac{250}{\text{ml aliquot}}$$

where $A =$ ml standard $AgNO_3$ for aliquot, and $B =$ standard $AgNO_3$ for blank.

6. Precision and Accuracy

The modified Liebig titration when used at a cyanide level above 1 mg/l CN has a coefficient of variation * of 2.0 per cent for distilled samples or for relatively clear samples without significant interference. Extraction and removal of sulfide or oxidizing agents tend to increase the variation to

---

* See Part III, Introduction, B.

a degree determined by the amount of manipulation required and the type of sample. The limit of sensitivity is approximately 0.1 mg/l CN, but at this point the color change is indistinct. At 0.4 mg/l the coefficient of variation is four times that at a concentration level greater than 1.0 mg/l CN.

B. Colorimetric Method

1. General Discussion

1.1. *Principle:* The CN⁻ in the alkaline distillate from the preliminary screening procedure is converted to cyanogen chloride, CNCl, by reaction with chloramine-T at a pH less than 8 without hydrolyzing to the cyanate. After the reaction is complete, the CNCl forms a blue dye on the addition of a pyridine-pyrazolone reagent. If the dye is kept in an aqueous solution, the absorbance is read at 620 mμ. To obtain colors of comparable intensity, it is essential to have the same salt content in both the sample and the standards.

The above test, proposed by Epstein,[2] can be modified to improve sensitivity and precision by extracting the color with butyl alcohol and then reading the absorbance at 630 mμ. If the color is too intense, provision is made for using smaller aliquots for color development.

1.2. *Interference:* All interferences are eliminated or reduced to a minimum by using only a distillate from the preliminary screening procedure.

2. Apparatus

2.1. *Colorimetric equipment:* One of the following is required.

a. Spectrophotometer, for use at 620–630 mμ, providing a light path of 1 cm.

b. Filter photometer, providing a light path of 1 cm and equipped with a red filter having maximum transmittance at 620–630 mμ.

2.2. *Reaction tubes,* consisting of test tubes, approximately 1×8 in., fitted with rubber stoppers.

3. Reagents

3.1. *Sodium hydroxide solution,* 0.2N. Dissolve 8 g NaOH in 1 liter distilled water.

3.2. *Acetic acid,* conc and $1 + 4$.

3.3. *Stock cyanide solution:* Dissolve 2.51 g potassium cyanide, KCN, in 1 liter water. Standardize as directed in Method A, Sec. 4.2, against silver nitrate. The solution loses strength gradually and must be rechecked every week. Approximate strength, 1 ml = 1 mg CN. (CAUTION: *Toxic; take care to avoid ingestion.*)

3.4. *Standard cyanide solution:* Dilute 10 ml stock cyanide solution to 1,000 ml with distilled water, mix, and make a second dilution of 10 ml to 100 ml; 1.00 ml = 1.0 μg CN. This solution must be prepared daily. (CAUTION: *Toxic; take care to avoid ingestion.*)

3.5. *Chloramine-T solution:* Dissolve 1 g in 100 ml water. Prepare daily.

3.6. *1-phenyl-3-methyl-5-pyrazolone solution:* Prepare a saturated aqueous solution (approximately 0.5 g/100 ml) by adding the pyrazolone to water at approximately 75°C. Agitate occasionally as the solution cools to room temperature. If necessary, the pyrazolone (melting point 127°–128°C) can be purified by recrystallization from ethyl alcohol. Usually this is not required.

3.7. *Pyridine.*

3.8. *Bis-pyrazolone:* Dissolve 17.4 g of 1-phenyl-3-methyl-5-pyrazolone in 100 ml ethyl alcohol. Add 25 g phenyl hydrazine, freshly distilled, under reduced pressure. Reflux in an all-glass apparatus. Several hours of refluxing is necessary to produce the bis-pyrazolone, which is indicated by formation of crystals in the reflux mixture. A reflux of 6–8 hr, followed by standing at room temperature overnight, and a 1–2-hr reflux the following day are generally adequate for a good yield. Filter while hot, wash with hot 95 per cent ethyl alcohol, and air dry. The product (melting point greater than 320°C) is stable indefinitely in dry form.*

3.9. *Mixed pyridine-pyrazolone reagent:* Mix 125 ml of the filtered, saturated aqueous solution of pyrazolone with a filtered solution containing 0.025 g bis-pyrazolone dissolved in 25 ml pyridine. Several minutes of mixing is usually necessary to dissolve the bis-pyrazolone in pyridine. The mixed reagent develops a pink color on standing but, if used within 24 hr, this does not affect the color production with cyanide. Prepare daily.

3.10. *n-Butyl alcohol.*

3.11. *Disodium hydrogen phosphate solution:* Dissolve 5 g anhydrous Na_2HPO_4 in 100 ml water.

4. Procedure

4.1. Prepare one or more aliquots of the absorption liquid obtained from the

* Bis-pyrazolone may also be obtained commercially: Eastman No. 6969 or equal.

distillation procedure in reaction tubes which, together with their stoppers, have been carefully rinsed with distilled water. Dilute each to 15 ml with $0.2N$ NaOH, and neutralize with $1 + 4$ acetic acid to pH 6–7.

4.2. Prepare a blank by adding 15 ml $0.2N$ NaOH to a carefully rinsed reaction tube. Also prepare a series of standards containing 0.2, 0.4, 0.6, 0.8, and 1.0 μg CN. Neutralize blank and standards to pH 6–7 with $1 + 4$ acetic acid. The amount of the acid for all diluted aliquots, the blank, and the standards should be approximately the same.

4.3. Add 0.2 ml chloramine-T solution, stopper, and mix by inversion two or three times. Allow 1–2 min for the reaction.

4.4. Add 5.0 ml of mixed pyridine-pyrazolone reagent, stopper, and mix by inversion. Allow 20 min for color development.

4.5. If the aqueous color is to be measured, dilute all reaction tubes accurately to a definite volume—usually 25 ml—mix, and read absorbance at 620 mμ on all samples and standards. If the color of the distillate aliquot is too intense, repeat the test using a smaller sample or aliquot.

4.6. Greater sensitivity is possible if extracted color is used for the spectrophotometric reading, as follows: At the end of the color development period add 1 ml disodium hydrogen phosphate solution and 10 ml carefully measured butyl alcohol. Stopper and mix by inversion. If the emulsion formed by the two-phase system does not break within 1 to 3 min, add more of the phosphate solution and mix again. Withdraw an aliquot of the alcohol layer and measure the absorbance at 630 mμ. A large sample volume or trace quantities of cyanide may require a modified solvent volume.

The pyridine-pyrazolone color will not develop quantitatively in the alcohol layer if the phosphate is added before the color development is essentially complete in the aqueous phase.

5. Calculation

$$\mu g/1\ CN = \frac{\mu g\ CN\ in\ sample\ from\ calibration\ curve \times 1,000}{ml\ original\ sample\ representing\ colored\ sample}$$

6. Precision and Accuracy

The pyridine-pyrazolone sensitivity data given below are for a final volume of 25 ml after color development on the aqueous readings and in 10 ml of added solvent for extracted samples. The absorbances of the extracted samples were read in 1-cm cells. The color was extracted from a 25-ml volume in order to compare data with the aqueous readings, but no detectable difference in precision was obtained on extractions where 100 ml of sample was used.

For aqueous color readings, the coefficient of variation was 1.7 per cent, the sensitivity 0.5 μg, and the effective range 1–5 μg. For extracted color readings, the respective figures were 3.9 per cent, 0.1 μg, and 0.2–2.0 μg.

Sensitivity is defined as the amount of CN required to produce an absorbance of 0.05 or above with a precision not more than twice the coefficient of variation given. Effective range is the amount of CN present in the reaction tubes—containing 25 ml aqueous or 10 ml solvent—that results in an absorbance reading from 0.1 to 1.0.

The sensitivity of the extracted sample is determined by the ratio of water to solvent volume. The values given are for distilled samples. A turbid sample showed approximately the same precision on the extracted readings with a large increase in variation for the aqueous readings.

Bibliography

1. RYAN, J. A. & CULSHAW, G. W. The Use of *p*-Dimethylaminobenzylidene Rhodanine as an Indicator for the Volumetric Determination of Cyanides. *Analyst* 69:370 (1944).

2. EPSTEIN, J. Estimation of Microquantities of Cyanide. *Anal. Chem.* 19:272 (1947).

3. DODGE, B. F. & REAMS, D. C. Critical Review of the Literature Pertaining to Disposal of Waste Cyanide Solutions. *Am. Electroplaters' Soc. Research Repts.* 14:1 (1949).

4. RUCHHOFT, C. C., ET AL. *Tentative Methods for Analysis of Cadmium, Chromium, and Cyanide in Water.* U.S. Public Health Service, Environmental Health Center, Cincinnati, Ohio (1949).

5. NUSBAUM, I. & SKUPEKO, P. Determination of Cyanides in Sewage and Polluted Waters. *Sew. Ind. Wastes* 23:875 (1951).

6. LUDZACK, F. J., ET AL. Effect of Cyanide on Biochemical Oxidation in Sewage and Polluted Water. *Sew. Ind. Wastes* 23:1298 (1951).

7. KRUSE, J. M. & MELLON, M. G. Colorimetric Determination of Cyanides. *Sew. Ind. Wastes* 23:1402 (1951).

8. SERFASS, E. J., ET AL. Analytical Method for the Determination of Cyanides in Plating Wastes and in Effluents from Treatment Processes. *Plating* 39:267 (1952).

9. HUGHES, E. K. Suggested Nomenclature in Applied Spectroscopy. *Anal. Chem.* 24:1349 (1952).

10. LUDZACK, F. J., ET AL. Determination of Cyanides in Water and Waste Samples. *Anal. Chem.* 26:1784 (1954).

Grease

Grease in industrial wastes may be determined in the same manner as in sewage (see Part III).

Hydrocarbon and Fatty Matter Content of Grease

Hydrocarbon and fatty matter content of grease may be determined in the same manner as they are in sewage (see Part III).

Iron, Lead, Manganese

See Metals (Heavy), Methods E, F, and G, respectively.

Metals (Heavy)

Discharge of metallic wastes from electroplating plants and other metal-processing industries is a matter of serious concern because of their possible toxic properties or other adverse effects in receiving waters. The metals in question, collectively designated "heavy metals," include cadmium, chromium, copper, iron, lead, manganese, nickel, zinc, and possibly others for which standard methods have not yet been developed. They are conveniently considered as a group because it is not unusual to find several of them present in a single sample of polluted water or waste, because they exhibit similarities in their chemical reactions, and because the same sort of preliminary treatment is generally required for the sample. Many of the methods recommended for determination of these metals individually in water samples must be modified to eliminate the interference of other metals or anions likely to occur simultaneously in waste samples.

The colorimetric methods given, derived largely from the studies by Butts, Gahler, and Mellon and by Serfass and colleagues, are valid for the determination of any of the metals in the presence of ten-to-thousand-fold concentrations of the other metal ions and also of other ions that might be encountered. With the use of samples of appropriate size, the methods are applicable either to the relatively high concentrations anticipated in plant wastes or to the trace amounts of significance in sewage or receiving waters.

Polarography

The analysis of metal-bearing wastes and the receiving streams into which they are discharged is generally difficult and time consuming. Polarographic techniques are theoretically preferable to colorimetric methods because of the rapidity of analysis and because the method may be applied simultaneously to a variety of metals.

Two entirely different polarographic techniques are described. These methods differ in principle as well as sensitivity and it will be left to the discretion of the analyst as to which is used. The methods have been developed to permit the simultaneous determination of copper, lead, cadmium, zinc, and nickel.

A wide range of other elements can be determined polarographically with the selection of the proper supporting electrolyte. The sequence of supporting electrolytes used in these procedures was selected because it gives the maximum information for the least effort and with the least danger of contamination by reagents.

Preliminary Treatment of Samples

1. General Discussion

Iron, chromium, organic matter, turbidity, chlorides, oxidizing and reducing substances, and dissolved oxygen, are the major interferences that are likely to be encountered. The following procedure was designed to eliminate interference of this type and must be used prior to either of the two polarographic techniques described below. Deviation from the procedure, no matter how slight, may lead either to completely erroneous results or to polarograms which are impossible to interpret.

2. Apparatus

Sintered-glass filter, medium porosity, with holder.

3. Reagents

3.1. *Sulfuric acid,* conc.

3.2. *Nitric acid,* conc and $1 + 1$.

3.3. *Redistilled water:* Distilled water redistilled in all-glass apparatus.

3.4. *Ammonium hydroxide solution,* metal free: Pass tank ammonia gas through a glass-wool trap into chilled redistilled water until the concentration reaches about $7M$. Alternatively, distill 900 ml of conc NH_4OH in a 1,500-ml distilling flask into a 1-liter polyethylene bottle containing 250 ml of chilled redistilled water until the volume of liquid in the bottle has increased to 900 ml. Keep the tip of the condenser below the surface of the liquid during the distillation.

3.5. *Sodium sulfite,* crystal, reagent grade.

4. Procedure

4.1. Rinse all glassware with $1 + 1$ HNO_3, distilled water, and finally redistilled water.

4.2. Add 0.1 ml conc H_2SO_4 to 100 ml of sample in a pyrex erlenmeyer flask and evaporate to dense white fumes. Add conc HNO_3 to the fuming liquid drop by drop until the solution clears and becomes colorless. With some samples it is not possible to remove all of the color by this procedure; however, nitric acid is added until no further color change can be perceived. Wash down the sides of the flask with glass-distilled water to remove excess HNO_3 and again bring to fumes. Fuming also removes chlorides which interfere.

4.3. Neutralize the solution with the metal-free ammonia solution using pink litmus paper to indicate the completion of neutralization. The resultant solution is roughly $0.18M$ in $(NH_4)_2SO_4$. Boil to remove excess ammonia until the odor of ammonia disappears. Filter the solution through a sintered-glass filter and make up to 10 ml with redistilled water.

A. Polarography Using the Dropping Mercury Electrode

1. General Discussion

1.1. *Principle:* Conventional polarography is based on the unique properties displayed by an electrolytic cell consisting of a nonpolarizable reference electrode, a readily polarizable electrode in the form of a mercury drop falling from a capillary, and an electrolytic solution containing small amounts of electro-reducible or electro-oxidizable material. When an increasing electromotive force is impressed across such a cell and the resulting current is plotted as a function of the applied voltage, a curve is obtained whose extension along the current axis is directly related to the concentration of the trace material and whose inflection point is located at a voltage characteristic of that material.

1.2. *Interference:* When the recommended procedure is followed the only significant interferences would be from large quantities of other reducible species with half-wave potentials close to the metal of interest. The sequence of supporting electrolytes was selected,

however, to permit interpretation of the polarograms for each of the five metals of interest even in the presence of large quantities of one or more of these metals. The method was also tested in the presence of 100 mg/l of chromium, iron and organic matter with no detectable effect.

1.3. *Minimum detectable concentrations:* The lower limit of detection using ordinary equipment and the dropping mercury electrode is about $10^{-6}M$. Therefore, including a 10-to-1 concentration, the lower limits of detection are about 0.1 mg/l.

2. Apparatus

2.1. *Polarograph:* Any commercially available polarograph can be used that is capable of utilizing applied voltages of 0.00 to -2.0 v. Automatic voltage scanning and recording, although not required, is recommended.

2.2. *Polarographic cell:* Fig. 33 shows the conventional polarographic cell used with the dropping mercury electrode, including the mercury res-

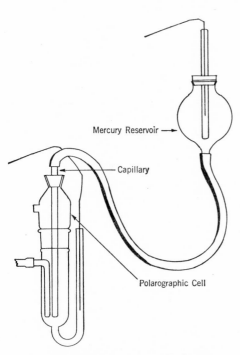

Fig. 33. Polarographic cell for use with dropping mercury electrode

ervoir. Cells of this type use the mercury pool as a reference electrode. The indicator electrode consists of small drops of mercury falling from a capillary attached to a reservoir of mercury. Other types of cells also available commercially permit the use of external standard reference electrodes. In general, selection of the type of cell to be used is left to the discretion of the analyst.

2.3. *De-aeration apparatus:* Oxygen is readily reduced at the dropping mercury electrode and must be removed from the solution to be analyzed. This is generally accomplished by bubbling nitrogen through the solution. Tank nitrogen, which is usually contaminated by traces of oxygen, can be purified by passing it over copper turnings

heated to 450°C. Equipment of this type is available commercially.

3. Reagents

3.1. *Mercury,* redistilled, National Formulary grade. Used mercury may be purified using commercially available oxidizers and gold adhesion filters.

3.2. *Ammonium   sulfate   solution,* saturated: Neutralize $7M$ metal-free ammonia solution with conc H_2SO_4, adding the acid slowly with extreme caution. Extract the neutralized solution with a solution of diphenylthiocarbazone   in   carbon   tetrachloride. Wash with carbon tetrachloride until all traces of color have been removed. Concentrate to a saturated solution by evaporation of excess water.

3.3. *Gelatin,* U.S.P. powder.

4. Procedure

4.1. Transfer the sample prepared according to the directions given under Preliminary Treatment of Samples to the polarographic cell. Add about 10 mg gelatin to suppress maxima which may interfere. A fritted-glass bubbler provides better dispersion of the nitrogen and more complete de-oxygenation. Place a small amount of purified mercury in the bottom of the cell to form the indicator electrode. Insert the dropping mercury electrode into the cell so that the tip dips into the upper part of the solution. Adjust the height of the mercury reservoir to give a drop time of 4 or 5 sec.

4.2. Connect the cell to the polarograph and run a polarogram at suitable sensitivity. Polarograms should be run from 0.00 v to about −1.6 v. While polarograms are being run, the nitrogen bubbler should be removed from the solution and held just above the surface to maintain an atmosphere of nitrogen and prevent surface absorption of oxygen.

4.3. After suitable curves have been run with $(NH_4)_2SO_4$ supporting electrolyte, add sufficient NH_4OH to make the solution about $0.4M$ in NH_3. Generally four or five drops of the ammonia solution as prepared in Preliminary Preparation of Samples, Sec. 3.4, is sufficient.

4.4. After curves have been run in the presence of free ammonia, add about 300 mg of ethylenediaminetetraacetate disodium salt and run suitable curves.

5. Interpretation of Polarograms

5.1. Half-wave potentials are read off at the half-way point of the rise as determined by inspection or by rough measurement. It is not necessary to correct for current resistance (IR) drop across the resistors in the measuring circuit for this type of work. Waveheights are measured vertically through the half-wave potential between straightline extrapolations of the sections of the polarogram immediately

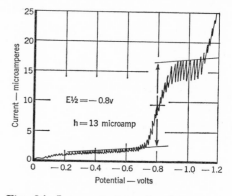

Fig. 34. Interpretation of polarograms obtained using the dropping mercury electrode

preceding and following the wave. This is illustrated in Fig. 34.

5.2. Half-wave potential and current concentration ratios of metals at the dropping mercury electrode are given in Table 30. These values will serve to identify the five metals—copper, nickel, lead, cadmium, and zinc—and will provide semiquantitative results which can be used to eliminate the necessity of analyzing for those metals that are absent and to determine sample size for wet analysis.

TABLE 30—HALF-WAVE POTENTIALS AND CURRENT CONCENTRATION RATIOS OF METALS AT THE DROPPING MERCURY ELECTRODE

| Metal | Supporting Electrolyte | | | | | |
| | 0.18M (NH$_4$)$_2$SO$_4$ | | 0.4M NH$_4$OH + 0.18M (NH$_4$)$_2$SO$_4$ | | 0.4M NH$_4$OH + EDTA + 0.18M (NH$_4$)$_2$SO$_4$ | |
	Half-Wave Potential v	Relative Wave Height [a]	Half-Wave Potential v	Relative Wave Height [a]	Half-Wave Potential v	Relative Wave Height [a]
Copper	0.02 to 0.05	0.0076	0.17 0.38 to 0.45	Often not seen 0.0040	0.47 to 0.51	0.0050
Lead	0.37 to 0.40	0.0010	0.43 to 0.47	0.0010	1.13 to 1.17	0.0010
Cadmium	0.57 to 0.59	0.0036	0.67 to 0.74	0.0036	No wave	......
Nickel	1.01 to 1.03	0.0083	0.91 to 0.95	0.0083	No wave	......
Zinc	0.98	0.0083	1.19 to 1.22	0.0083	No wave	......

[a] $\mu a/\mu g$ of element.

For quantitative results a similar table should be prepared by the analyst using his equipment and standard solutions of the metals of interest.

B. Polarography Using the Quiet Pool Electrode
(Tentative)

1. General Discussion

1.1. *Principle:* In polarography, the diffusion current due to a given concentration of reducible ion is dependent on the surface area of the indicator electrode. Because the surface area of the quiet pool electrode is many times the surface area of a drop of mercury, which serves as the indicator electrode in conventional polarography, higher diffusion currents are obtained. The surface area of the quiet pool electrode is constant; therefore, the residual current is small because it is not necessary to continually charge a new double layer as with the dropping mercury electrode. The large ratio of diffusion current to residual current is responsible for the greater sensitivity of the pool electrode.

The surface of the pool electrode is not continually renewed as is the surface of the dropping mercury electrode; therefore, as more of the reducible ions reach the surface of the electrode, the diffusion current increases. However, eventually the concentration of ions at the surface of the electrode will increase to a point where it will become increasingly more difficult for additional ions to penetrate. This phenomenon is reflected in the production of current peaks as polarograms are made, as opposed to plateaus obtained in conventional polarography. Because the buildup of ions at the surface of the electrode, as well as the resulting diffusion current, is time dependent, automatic scanning and recording is mandatory.

Peak currents obtained under properly standardized conditions are proportional to concentration. Peaks are characterized by half-peak potentials in the same manner as the plateaus obtained in conventional polarography are characterized by half-wave potentials.

1.2. *Interferences:* When the recommended procedure is followed the only significant interferences are from large quantities of other reducible species with half-wave potentials close to the metal of interest. In many cases, this type of interference can be eliminated by allowing the diffusion current of the interfering ion to decay before proceeding with the running of the polarogram. This procedure is described below. The method was also tested in the presence of 100 mg/l of chromium, iron and organic matter (tartaric acid) with no detectable effect.

1.3. *Minimum detectable concentrations:* The sensitivity of the pool electrode is such that the minimum detectable concentration is many orders of magnitude lower than the $10^{-6}M$ of the dropping mercury electrode. However, as sensitivity is increased, the effect of interferences is magnified. Therefore, it is suggested that sensitivity settings on the equipment used

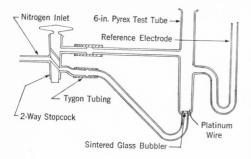

Fig. 35. Polarographic cell for use with the quiet mercury pool electrode

be selected to yield a sensitivity capable of detecting down to 0.01 mg/l. Under proper conditions, sensitivities can be increased.

2. Apparatus

2.1. *Polarograph:* Any commercially available polarograph, equipped with automatic voltage scanning and recording, and capable of utilizing voltages of +0.3 to −2.0 v may be used.

2.2. *Polarographic cell:* The cell recommended for use with this procedure is shown in Fig. 35. The fritted-glass bubbler projecting into the bottom of the cell may be made from 140–200-mesh borosilicate glass. The mercury pool lies in the annular space around the bubbler tube, which is sealed in such a way that the pool area, about 0.8 sq cm, is independent within limits of the volume of mercury added. A sealed-in platinum wire makes electrical contact with the pool. A three-way stopcock permits passing nitrogen either through the bubbler or over the surface of the solution. The volume of the cell from the top of the fritted bubbler to the top of the side-arm juncture should be 10 cc. The inside

of the cell is coated with a silicone preparation * to prevent penetration of the sample between the glass and the mercury.

2.3. *Reference electrode:* This consists of a small helix of No. 24 silver wire chloridized by brief anodic treatment in 10 per cent HCl and suspended in the U-shaped side-arm of the cell.

2.4. *Nitrogen purification train:* Because of the high sensitivity of quiet pool polarography, it is imperative that all traces of oxygen be removed from commercially available nitrogen before it is used. To accomplish this, tank nitrogen is led through a Vycor tube filled with copper turnings and heated to 450°C in an electric furnace, then successively through a trap, a bubbler to indicate flow rate, and finally the cell. The trap prevents backflow of the liquid into the Vycor heating tube.

2.5. *De-aeration apparatus:* A test tube (15-mm inside diameter) is graduated at 10 ml and provided with a side-arm about 15 mm above the graduation.

3. Reagents

3.1. *Mercury,* redistilled, National Formulary grade. Used mercury may be purified for reuse.

3.2. *Ammonium hydroxide solution:* Pass tank ammonia gas through a glass-wool trap into chilled redistilled water until the concentration reaches about $7M$. Alternatively, distill 900 ml conc NH_4OH in a 1,500-ml distilling flask into a 1-liter polyethylene bottle containing 250 ml of chilled redistilled water until the volume of liquid in the bottle has increased to

---

* Beckman Instruments, Inc., Desicote, or equivalent.

900 ml. Keep the tip of the condenser below the surface of the liquid during distillation.

3.3. *Ammonium sulfate solution,* saturated: Neutralize $7M$ metal-free ammonia solution with conc H_2SO_4, adding the acid slowly and with extreme caution. Extract the neutralized solution with a solution of diphenylthiocarbazone in carbon tetrachloride. Wash with carbon tetrachloride until all traces of color have been removed. Concentrate to a saturated solution by evaporation of excess water.

4. Procedure

4.1. Rinse all glassware, including the cell, with conc HNO_3, distilled water, and twice with redistilled water.

4.2. Place a fritted bubbler into the side-arm test tube to which has been added the sample as prepared according to directions given under Preliminary Treatment of Sample. Connect the nitrogen purification train to the bubbler and pass nitrogen through the sample for about 10 min before transferring to the polarographic cell.

4.3. Add saturated ammonium sulfate solution to the side-arm of the cell with a dropper to fill about half its height. Add carefully sufficient saturated potassium chloride solution to the outer end of the side-arm to force the ammonium sulfate just to the junction of the side-arm with the main body of the cell. The less dense potassium chloride solution forms a layer above the ammonium sulfate solution. Insert the chloridized silver wire into the potassium chloride solution to complete the silver–silver chloride reference electrode. Add redistilled water to the main section of the cell to a level just below the bottom of the side-arm juncture and add 10 drops of saturated ammonium sulfate solution. Connect the cell to the nitrogen train and bubble nitrogen through the solution for about 5 min. Add sufficient mercury from a buret to form an annular ring in the bottom of the cell surrounding the bubbler, making sure that the platinum wire is covered. Then add sufficient glass-distilled water to raise the level to the top of the side-arm juncture. Mercury should be allowed to stand in the buret for at least one day before use to allow certain impurities to rise to the surface.

Bubble nitrogen through the solution for an additional 3–5 min and then turn the stopcock to bypass it over the solution. Scan the voltage rapidly up and down several times manually and then make one or two automatic voltage scans from about $+0.3$ to -2.0 v. The first voltage scan with a freshly prepared mercury pool cathode usually gives an irregular curve with a high residual current. Basic salts, oxides of mercury, and traces of organic matter are probably responsible. This preconditioning process serves to smooth out these irregularities and does not affect the peak heights in the sample runs which follow.

4.4. Remove all of the blank solution from the cell by aspiration, taking care not to disturb the mercury surface. Transfer the sample through the side-arm of the de-aeration apparatus to the cell. Maintain a good current of nitrogen while the blank is being removed and the sample added to prevent the entrainment of oxygen. Bubble nitrogen through the sample for about 5 min. Meanwhile, make a few rapid manual up and down scans to further precondition the mercury. Bypass the nitrogen over the solution and make at least two automatic scans from $+0.2$

to —1.4 v at a rate of 0.15 v/min. By making more than one scan, the risk of mistaking an accidental and transitory peak for a significant one is reduced. After the peaks for the various metals in the sample have been located, re-scan the sample automatically as before, but hold the voltages stationary just beyond each peak until the current decays and then allow automatic scanning to proceed. In this manner, metals whose half-peak potentials lie close together may be evaluated without interference.

4.5. When satisfactory curves have been obtained in the ammonium sulfate medium, make the solution about 0.4 M with respect to NH_4OH. Bubble nitrogen through the solution to remove any oxygen which may have been introduced during the addition of the ammonia solution. Make at least two automatic scans from 0.0 to — 1.4 v at a rate of 0.15 v/min. After the solution has been made ammoniacal, it is essential not to allow the pool electrode to become positive because troublesome mercury-ammonia complexes may form. Finally, re-scan the sample, pausing just beyond each peak as described above.

5. Interpretation of Polarograms

5.1. Draw two parallel lines tangent to the curve at the turning points, marking the lower and upper limits of the excursion associated with the particular metal. The half-peak potential is then given by a point on the curve

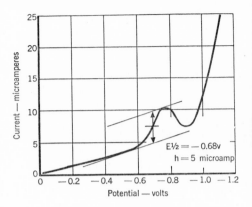

Fig. 36. Interpretation of polarograms obtained using the quiet mercury pool electrode

lying halfway between the lines and the peak height is the vertical distance between the lines. This is illustrated in Fig. 36.

5.2. Half-peak potentials and current concentration ratios of metals at the quiet pool electrode are given in Table 31. These values will serve to identify the five metals—copper, nickel, lead, cadmium, and zinc—and will provide semiquantitative results. Inasmuch as current concentration ratios are strictly dependent on rate of voltage application, any variation from the 0.15-v/min application rate used in the preparation of Table 31 will invalidate the results. For strictly quantitative results, a similar table should be prepared by the analyst using his cell and equipment with standard solutions of the metals of interest.

TABLE 31—HALF-PEAK POTENTIALS AND CURRENT CONCENTRATION RATIOS OF METALS AT THE QUIET POOL ELECTRODE

Metal	Supporting Electrolyte			
	0.18M (NH$_4$)$_2$SO$_4$		0.4M NH$_4$OH + 0.18M (NH$_4$)$_2$SO$_4$	
	Half-Peak Potential v	Relative Peak Height[a]	Half-Peak Potential v	Relative Peak Height[a]
Copper	+0.05 – 0.00	0.161 ± 0.008	−0.07 – −0.09	0.041 ± 0.005
Lead	−0.33 – −0.38	0.036 ± 0.006	−0.32 – −0.33	0.060 ± 0.003
Cadmium	−0.50 – −0.54	0.092 ± 0.006	− 0.38	0.022 ± 0.005
Nickel	No peak		−0.65 – −0.67	0.094 ± 0.006
Zinc	−0.96 – −1.02	0.180 ± 0.010	−0.88 – −0.93	0.097 ± 0.003
			−1.17 – −1.19	0.180 ± 0.028

[a] $\mu a/\mu g$ of element.

Colorimetry

Preliminary Treatment of Samples

1. General Discussion

1.1. Because all of the metals under consideration readily form complex ions and may do so with possible organic constituents of wastes or sewage, it is generally necessary that organic matter be destroyed in a preliminary treatment. The recommended treatment is digestion, either with a mixture of nitric and sulfuric acids or, when the organic matter is difficult to oxidize, with nitric and perchloric acids. Special perchloric acid procedures are included for samples of unusually high or refractory organic content.

Two approaches are provided. With the first, a single sample of suitable size is digested and aliquots of this are used for the determinations of the individual metals. With the second, separate samples are digested for each determination; appropriate volumes of sample for the latter approach are spec-ified under the individual determinations.

1.2. The acid digestion of the samples, by destroying organic matter, eliminates possible interference from this source. Interference from cyanide, nitrite, sulfide, sulfite, thiosulfate, and thiocyanate is also eliminated by oxidation or volatilization during the acid digestion.

1.3. Significant errors may be introduced during sampling and storage because of the tendency for many metal ions to be adsorbed on the walls of the sampling vessel. Errors arise in two ways: failure to remove previously adsorbed metal ions during cleaning leads to contamination of the sample and high results; adsorption of metal ions from the sample produces low results. To avoid these difficulties, sampling vessels should be carefully rinsed with 1 + 1 HNO$_3$ and then with water redistilled from an all-glass still or with distilled water passed through an ion-exchange column. Addition of 5 ml conc HNO_3 per liter of sample at the time of collection will help minimize subsequent adsorption of metals for samples that are not already strongly acid.

The volume of sample to be taken for digestion depends on the concentration of the metals to be determined, and is roughly as follows:

Concentration mg/l	Volume ml
<1	1,000
1–10	100
10–100	10
100–1,000	1

If one metal strongly predominates, its concentration should be ignored and the volume taken should be based on the concentration of the minor metals to be determined. A more exact estimate of the volume to be digested can be obtained by summing the volumes needed for determination of each of the constituents as given in the directions for the individual determinations.

2. Apparatus

2.1. *Sintered-glass or porcelain filter crucibles,* fine porosity, with holder; Gooch crucibles with glass fiber filter discs may be used.

2.2. *Conical flasks,* 125 ml.

All glassware should be cleaned thoroughly, then rinsed with $1 + 1$ HNO_3, and finally with glass-redistilled water.

3. Reagents

3.1. *Sulfuric acid,* conc.

3.2. *Nitric acid,* conc.

3.3. *Hydrogen peroxide,* 30 per cent.

3.4. *Redistilled water:* Distilled water redistilled in all-glass apparatus.

3.5. *Perchloric acid,* 60 per cent.

3.6. *Special reagent—ammonium acetate solution:* Dissolve 400 g $NH_4C_2H_3O_2$ in 600 ml redistilled water. This solution is required only if lead is to be determined in the presence of sulfate.

Total iron and heavy-metal impurities in the reagent acids should not exceed 0.0001 per cent. Blanks must be prepared in any event, but if the metallic impurities are greater than this the blanks will be too large and variable for precise determinations of small concentrations of the metals. When the amounts of acid specified are used, 0.0001 per cent of heavy-metal impurity will add about 0.03 mg of heavy metals to the sample.

4. Digestion with Sulfuric Acid

4.1. Agitate the sample to obtain a homogeneous suspension. Measure a suitable volume (as determined from Sec. 1.3) with a pipet or volumetric flask and transfer it to an evaporating dish or casserole. (If the volume required is greater than 250 ml, it may be transferred in portions as the sample evaporates.) Acidify the transferred sample or portion of sample to methyl orange with conc H_2SO_4, then add 5 ml conc HNO_3 and 2 ml 30 per cent H_2O_2 to reduce chromate. Evaporate on a steam bath or hot plate to 15–20 ml, covering the vessel with a watch glass, when necessary, to avoid loss of material by spattering. An infrared lamp may be placed over the sample to hasten the evaporation. (If the sample taken is 10 ml or less, it may be pipeted directly into the conical flask (Sec. 4.2) and boiled gently for 1 min after the addition of 5 ml conc HNO_3; then proceed with Sec. 4.2, beginning with "Add another 5 ml conc HNO_3.")

4.2. Transfer the evaporated solution, together with any solids remaining in the dish, to a 125-ml conical flask. Add another 5 ml conc HNO_3, which has been used to rinse the evaporating dish or casserole; 10 ml conc H_2SO_4; and a few glass beads, carborundum chips, or Hengar granules to minimize bumping. Evaporate on a hot plate (in a hood) until dense white fumes of SO_3 just appear in the flask, but do not continue heating beyond this point. If the solution is not clear, add another 10 ml HNO_3 and repeat the evaporation to fumes of SO_3. Be sure that all HNO_3 is removed, as indicated by the clarity of the solution and the absence of brownish fumes in the flask.

4.3. Cool the solution to room temperature and dilute carefully to about 50 ml with redistilled water. Heat nearly to boiling to dissolve slowly soluble salts, then filter through a sintered-glass or porcelain filter crucible into a thoroughly clean filter flask. Rinse the sample flask with two 5-ml portions of redistilled water, passing them through the crucible to wash any residue on the filter. (A filtering device which allows collection of the filtrate directly in a 100-ml volumetric flask may be used and, if available, is to be preferred.) Transfer the filtrate to a 100-ml volumetric flask and rinse the filter flask with two 5-ml portions of redistilled water, adding these rinsings to the volumetric flask. Finally dilute the solution in the volumetric flask to the 100-ml mark and mix thoroughly. The resulting solution is about $3N$ in H_2SO_4. Aliquots of this solution are taken for the determination of the metals; for the determination of lead, the solution obtained in the following section must also be used.

4.4. If the sample contains much lead, some of it will be present as $PbSO_4$ in the residue on the filter; this must be dissolved and measured as a part of the lead determination. Add 50 ml ammonium acetate solution to the conical flask in which the digestion was carried out, and heat to incipient boiling, rotating the flask occasionally to wet thoroughly all interior areas on which residue might have deposited. Reconnect the filter and draw the hot ammonium acetate solution through it slowly to dissolve the $PbSO_4$. Transfer the filtrate to a 100-ml volumetric flask, allow it to cool to room temperature, dilute to the mark, mix thoroughly, and set aside for the determination of lead.

5. Digestion with Nitric and Perchloric Acids

CAUTION: Heated mixtures of concentrated perchloric acid and organic matter may explode violently. To avoid this hazard the following precautions should be observed: (a) Do not add perchloric acid to a hot solution that may contain organic matter. (b) Always pretreat samples containing organic matter with HNO_3 prior to addition of $HClO_4$. (c) Use a mixture of nitric and perchloric acids in starting the digestion step. (d) Avoid repeated fumings of perchloric acid in ordinary hoods. Hoods for routine operations should be all stone or asbestos-cement. Glass fume eradicators * to be attached to a water pump are convenient for occasional work with $HClO_4$.

---

* Such as are obtainable from G. F. Smith Chemical Company, Columbus, Ohio.

5.1. Measure a sample, acidify to methyl orange with HNO_3, add another 5 ml conc HNO_3, and evaporate the sample as in Sec. 4.1.

5.2. Transfer the evaporated sample to a 125-ml conical flask as in Sec. 4.2, cool, and add 5 ml HNO_3 and 10 ml 60 per cent $HClO_4$. After adding a few boiling chips, heat on a hot plate and evaporate gently until dense white fumes of $HClO_4$ just appear. If the solution is not clear at this point, cover the neck of the flask with a watch glass and keep the solution just barely boiling until it clears. A further 10 ml HNO_3 may be added to aid the oxidation.

5.3. Cool the digested solution, dilute to about 50 ml with redistilled water, and boil to expel any chlorine or oxides of nitrogen. Then filter the sample as in Sec. 4.3, transfer the filtrate and washings to a 100-ml volumetric flask, cool, dilute to the mark, and mix thoroughly. The resulting solution is about $0.8N$ in $HClO_4$. Aliquots from this solution are taken for the determination of individual metals just as from the solution obtained in Sec. 4.

5.4. If lead is to be determined and if sulfate is present in the sample, the residue from the filtration must be treated as directed in Sec. 4.4.

6. Digestion of Sludges Having High or Refractory Organic Content

Transfer a sample, measured as in Sec. 4.1, to a suitable evaporating dish or casserole and evaporate to small volume on a steam bath. Then add 12 ml conc HNO_3 and evaporate on a hot plate to near dryness. Repeat the addition of HNO_3 and evaporation. Use 25 ml $1 + 1$ HNO_3 to transfer the residue to a 250-ml conical flask (add 10 ml to the residue to assist in the transfer and use the other 15 ml for rinsing the evaporating dish). Add 25 ml 60 per cent $HClO_4$ and boil until nearly dry, or until the solution is clear and white fumes of $HClO_4$ have appeared. Cool, add 50 ml redistilled water, and proceed with Sec. 5.3.

A. Method for Cadmium (Tentative)

1. General Discussion

1.1. *Principle:* Cadmium ions, like those of many other metals, form an intense red compound with diphenylthiocarbazone (dithizone) which can be extracted into carbon tetrachloride and used for the colorimetric determination of cadmium. When the extraction is carried out from a strongly basic solution, only a few substances—silver, mercury, copper, nickel, and cobalt—interfere and these can be removed by preliminary extractions.

After digestion of the sample with HNO_3-H_2SO_4 or with HNO_3-$HClO_4$ to decompose organic matter, any large amount of silver present is precipitated as AgCl. Copper and mercury, together with remaining silver, are then removed by an extraction with dithizone in chloroform at pH 2. The solution is adjusted to pH 9, and nickel is removed by addition of dimethylglyoxime and extraction with chloroform; any cobalt present is complexed with dimethylglyoxime so that it will not react with dithizone.

The solution is then made strongly basic and cadmium is extracted with dithizone in chloroform. Zinc extracted with the cadmium from this basic solution is removed by washing the chloroform solution with $0.5N$ NaOH. Finally, the cadmium is determined by measuring the absorbance of the cadmium-dithizone complex in chloroform at a wavelength of 515 mμ or with a suitable filter.

1.2. *Interference:* When the recommended procedure is used, the major interference is from massive amounts of zinc; if the zinc-cadmium ratio is large (greater than 500:1) it is difficult to extract the last traces of cadmium, and low results are obtained. Otherwise, quantities of cadmium from 2.5 to 25 μg can be determined readily in the presence of 0.25 mg each of copper, cobalt, and zinc, and 2.5 mg each of silver, mercury, lead, bismuth, arsenic, antimony, tin, chromium, aluminum, iron, manganese, nickel, cyanide, thiocyanate, phosphate, sulfite, thiosulfate, tartrate, acetate, and other common ions.

1.3. *Minimum detectable concentration:* The quantity of cadmium required to give a net absorbance of 0.01 (98 per cent transmittance) at 515 mμ in the final chloroform solution is about 0.5 μg when a 1-cm absorption cell is used. When 50 ml of initial sample is taken, this corresponds to 0.01 mg/l.

1.4. *Sampling and storage:* Because of the great sensitivity of the method and the ready adsorbability of cadmium ions on surfaces, great care should be used to see that sampling vessels are thoroughly clean. Polyethylene vessels are recommended. Glass vessels after normal cleaning should be washed with

$1 + 1$ HNO$_3$ and then rinsed with redistilled water.

Samples should be acidified with HNO$_3$ and an excess of 5 ml HNO$_3$ per liter of sample added at the time of collection.

2. Apparatus

2.1. *Volumetric pipets,* 5 ml.

2.2. *Photometric equipment:* One of the following, equipped with absorption cells providing a 1-cm light path and having lids for stoppers, is required:

a. Spectrophotometer, for use at 515 mμ.

b. Filter photometer, equipped with a green filter exhibiting maximum light transmission near 515 mμ.

2.3. *Separatory funnels,* 125 ml, Squibb form, with ground-glass or Teflon stopcocks and stoppers. Amber or low-actinic ware is convenient, but not essential. Wash with $1 + 1$ HNO$_3$ following normal cleaning and then rinse thoroughly with redistilled water.

2.4. *Volumetric flasks,* 25 ml, with ground-glass stoppers. Amber or low-actinic ware is desirable but not essential. Clean as described in Sec. 2.3.

3. Reagents

3.1. *Stock cadmium solution:* Dissolve 0.1000 g pure cadmium metal in 20 ml distilled water and 5 ml conc HCl, and dilute to 1,000 ml with redistilled water. Store this solution in a polyethylene container.

3.2. *Standard cadmium solution:* To 5.00 ml stock cadmium solution add 2 ml conc HCl, and dilute to 200 ml with redistilled water. Prepare as needed and use the same day; 1.00 ml = 2.5 μg Cd.

3.3. *Redistilled water:* Distilled water redistilled in all-glass apparatus.

3.4. *Potassium sodium tartrate solution:* Dissolve 50 g $KNaC_4H_4O_6 \cdot 4H_2O$ in 250 ml distilled water. Place in a separatory funnel and shake with 50-ml portions of dithizone solution (II) in carbon tetrachloride to purify from heavy-metal impurities. Remove the dithizone and its yellow oxidation product by extraction with portions of chloroform until the extracts remain colorless. Finally, extract with carbon tetrachloride to remove any chloroform. Store in a polyethylene bottle.

3.5. *Sodium hydroxide solution,* 2.5N. Dissolve 50 g NaOH in 450 ml redistilled water. Store in a polyethylene bottle.

3.6. *Carbon tetrachloride,* ACS grade or purified as follows: Reflux 500 ml CCl_4 with 100 ml 1.25N NaOH for 2 hr; separate the CCl_4 layer, wash it with 100 ml distilled water, dry it over anhydrous $CaCl_2$, and then distill over CaO. Avoid or redistill CCl_4 that comes in containers with metal or metal-lined caps.

3.7. *Hydrochloric acid,* conc.

3.8. *Dithizone solution (I):* Dissolve 0.1 g diphenylthiocarbazone in 100 ml chloroform.

3.9. *Dithizone solution (II):* Because even ACS grade dithizone may be contaminated by diphenylthiocarbodiazone, the oxidation product of dithizone, the following procedure should be used for preparing purified reagent:

Dissolve 100 mg ACS grade dithizone in 500 ml purified CCl_4. Keep this as a stock solution and store in a dark bottle in a cool place, preferably in a refrigerator.

Just before use, purify the stock solution as follows: Measure 75 ml into a 250-ml separatory funnel and add 75 ml distilled water plus 3 ml conc NH_4OH. Shake well, discard the CCl_4 layer, and then extract with fresh portions of CCl_4 until the organic layer remains colorless, discarding these organic extracts. Then add 75 ml of purified CCl_4, make the mixture acidic with $1 + 1$ HCl, and shake well. Draw off the CCl_4 layer, wash with 100 ml distilled water, separate, and dilute the CCl_4 layer to 150 ml. Use for only half a day.

3.10. *Chloroform:* Avoid or redistill material that comes in containers with metal-lined caps.

3.11. *Ammonium hydroxide,* conc. Place 660 ml redistilled water in a 1-liter polyethylene bottle and chill by immersion in an ice bath. Pass ammonia gas from a cylinder through a glass-wool trap into the chilled bottle until the volume of liquid has increased to 900 ml. As an alternate technique in preparing the ammonium hydroxide, place 900 ml conc reagent ammonium hydroxide in a 1,500-ml distillation flask and distill into a chilled 1-liter polyethylene bottle, containing initially 250 ml redistilled water, until the volume of liquid in the bottle has increased to 900 ml, keeping the condenser tip below the surface of the liquid.

3.12. *Dimethylglyoxime solution:* Dissolve 1 g dimethylglyoxime in 100 ml 95 per cent ethyl alcohol.

3.13. *Sodium hydroxide solution,* 0.5N. Dissolve 10 g NaOH in 490 ml redistilled water. Store in a polyethylene container.

4. Preparation of Calibration Curve

4.1. Pipet 1.00–10.00-ml portions of the standard cadmium solution into 125-ml separatory funnels (amber).

Dilute each to about 15–20 ml with re-distilled water and add 10 ml potassium sodium tartrate solution and 10 ml $2.5N$ NaOH. Then continue with Sec. 5.5 and 5.8 of the procedure.

4.2. Transfer a suitable portion of each final solution to a 1-cm absorption cell and measure its absorbance at 515 mμ or with a green filter having maximum transmission near this wavelength. As reference use either pure CCl_4 or a blank prepared by carrying 20 ml re-distilled water through the procedure employed for the standards. If pure CCl_4 is used as the reference, correct the absorbance readings of the standards by subtracting the absorbance of a blank prepared as described.

4.3. Construct a calibration chart by plotting corrected absorbance values against micrograms of cadmium.

5. Procedure

5.1. Pipet a measured aliquot containing 2.5–20 μg Cd from the digested sample, prepared according to directions given under Preliminary Treatment of Samples, into a 150-ml beaker. If a separate sample for cadmium is desired, measure a volume of sewage or waste containing 25–200 μg Cd, treat it according to Preliminary Treatment of Samples, and use a 10.00-ml aliquot of the final solution.

Add 0.2 ml conc HCl to precipitate silver, stir, and let stand 2 min. Filter, if necessary, and wash. To the combined filtrate and washings add 5 ml potassium sodium tartrate solution and adjust to pH 2.0 with conc HCl or NH$_4$OH.

5.2. Transfer the adjusted solution to a 125-ml separatory funnel and extract with 5-ml portions of dithizone solution (I) in chloroform until the dithizone layer remains green. Discard the extracts. Then wash with 10-ml portions of chloroform until the organic layer remains colorless, discarding the washings. Finally, wash with a 5-ml portion of CCl_4 and discard the washing.

5.3. Transfer the aqueous solution to a 150-ml beaker, add 5 ml potassium sodium tartrate solution, and adjust to pH 8.5–9.0 with conc NH$_4$OH. Return the solution quantitatively to the separatory funnel.

5.4. Add 5 ml dimethylglyoxime solution and shake vigorously for 30 sec. Extract with three or more 10-ml portions of $CHCl_3$ until any white precipitate of excess dimethylglyoxime has been removed. Discard the extract. Wash the aqueous layer with 5-ml CCl_4 and discard the washing.

NOTE: In the absence of copper, mercury, or silver, Sec. 5.2 may be omitted; in the absence of nickel or cobalt, Sec. 5.4 may be omitted.

5.5. Add 10 ml $2.5N$ NaOH to the aqueous layer in the separatory funnel and mix. Add 5 ml dithizone solution (II) in CCl_4 and shake thoroughly. Transfer the CCl_4 layer to a clean separatory funnel (amber) and reextract the aqueous layer with a second 5-ml portion of dithizone solution (II) in CCl_4. Combine the organic layer with the first one. Continue extracting with 3-ml portions of the dithizone in CCl_4 until the organic extracts remain colorless or only slightly yellow, adding these additional extracts to the previous ones.

5.6. Wash the combined organic extracts in succession with two 20-ml portions 0.5N NaOH and then with distilled water; discard the aqueous layer in each instance.

5.7. Filter the red solution of cadmium-dithizone complex through a small filter paper into a 25-ml volumetric flask. Wash the filter paper with a little CCl_4 and add the washing to the contents of the volumetric flask. Dilute to the mark with CCl_4 and mix well.

NOTE: During extraction of the cadmium (Sec. 5.5–5.7) it is advisable to darken the room unless amber or low-actinic glassware is used. Towels may be wrapped around the separatory funnels and volumetric flask to prevent sunlight from accelerating the light-sensitive decomposition of the solution.

5.8. Transfer a suitable portion of the CCl_4 solution to a 1-cm absorption cell and measure its absorbance within 15 min at a wavelength of 515 mμ or with a suitable green filter against a blank of pure CCl_4. From the observed absorbance subtract that of a reagent blank prepared by carrying 10 ml redistilled water through the entire procedure, including initial digestion. From the corrected absorbance determine the cadmium in the sample analyzed by reference to the calibration chart prepared according to Sec. 4.

6. Calculation

$$\text{mg/l Cd} = \frac{\mu\text{g Cd}}{\text{ml sample}} \times \frac{100}{\text{ml aliquot}}$$

B. Method for Total Chromium

1. General Discussion

1.1. *Principle:* Hexavalent chromium reacts with diphenylcarbazide in acidic medium to produce a red-violet coloration of unknown composition suitable for determination of low concentrations of chromium. The reaction is very sensitive, the absorbancy index per gram atom of chromium for the colored product being about 40,000 near 540 mμ. The colored product is not very stable; appreciable fading is noted after about 1 hr.

After the sample has been digested with HNO_3-H_2SO_4 or HNO_3-$HClO_4$ to decompose organic matter, the acidity is adjusted to $0.5N$, and the chromium is oxidized to the hexavalent state with potassium permanganate. Excess permanganate is reduced with sodium azide. Addition of an excess of diphenylcarbazide yields the red-violet product; its absorbance at 540 mμ is measured photometrically.

1.2. *Interference:* The reaction with diphenylcarbazide is nearly specific for chromium. Hexavalent molybdenum and mercury salts will react to form color with the reagent, but the intensities are much less than that for chromium at the specified pH. Concentrations of molybdenum and mercury up to 200 mg/l can be tolerated. Vanadium interferes to the greatest extent but can be present in a concentration up to ten times that of chromium without causing trouble. Potential interference from permanganate is eliminated by the prior reduction with azide. Of the remaining common elements only ferric iron in the form of yellow or yellow-brown compounds may interfere; in the absence of chlorides and with sulfuric and phosphoric acids present, the ferric ion color is not strong and no difficulty is encountered if the absorbance is measured photometrically at the appropriate wavelength. Large amounts of some metals cause low results by consuming the diphenylcarbazide reagent.

Interfering amounts of molybdenum, vanadium, iron, and copper can be removed by extraction of the cupferrates of these metals into chloroform. Procedure for this extraction is provided, but it should be included only when needed, for the presence of residual cupferron and chloroform in the aqueous solution complicates the later oxidation of chromium with permanganate.

1.3. *Minimum detectable concentration:* The quantity of chromium required to give a net absorbance of 0.01 (98 per cent transmittance) at 540 mμ is 1 μg with a 1-cm light path. When 100 ml of initial sample is taken, this corresponds to 10 μg/l.

1.4. *Sampling and storage:* In addition to the usual procedures and precautions for collection of samples of sewage or wastes, special care is needed to minimize adsorption of chromium on the walls of the sampling container. The sample should be acidified at the time of collection with HNO_3, and an excess 5 ml HNO_3 per liter of sample should be added.

2. Apparatus

2.1. *Photometric equipment:* One of the following is required:

a. Spectrophotometer, for use at 540 mμ, providing a light path of 1 cm or longer.

b. Filter photometer, providing a light path of 1 cm or longer and equipped with a greenish-yellow filter having maximum transmittance near 540 mμ.

2.2. *Separatory funnels,* 125 ml, Squibb form, with glass or Teflon stopcock and stopper.

3. Reagents

3.1. *Stock chromium solution:* Dissolve 0.1414 g $K_2Cr_2O_7$ in distilled water and dilute to 1 liter; 1.00 ml = 50.0 μg Cr.

3.2. *Standard chromium solution:* Dilute 10.00 ml stock chromium solution to 100 ml; 1 ml = 5 μg Cr.

3.3. *Nitric acid,* conc.

3.4. *Sulfuric acid,* 1 + 1.

3.5. *Perchloric acid,* 60 per cent.

3.6. *Methyl orange indicator:* Dissolve 0.5 g methyl orange in 1 liter distilled water.

3.7. *Hydrogen peroxide,* 30 per cent.

3.8. *Redistilled water:* Distilled water redistilled in all-glass apparatus.

3.9. *Ammonium hydroxide,* conc.

3.10. *Phosphoric acid,* 85 per cent.

3.11. *Potassium permanganate solution:* Dissolve 4 g $KMnO_4$ in 100 ml water.

3.12. *Sodium azide solution:* Dissolve 0.5 g NaN_3 in 100 ml water.

3.13. *Diphenlycarbazide solution:* Dissolve 0.25 g 1,5-diphenylcarbazide in 50 ml acetone. Store in a brown bottle. Discard when the solution becomes discolored.

3.14. *Chloroform:* Avoid or redistill material that comes in containers with metal or metal-lined caps.

3.15. *Cupferron solution:* Dissolve 5 g $C_6H_5N(NO)ONH_4$ in 95 ml distilled water.

3.16. *Sodium nitrite solution:* Dissolve 0.1 g $NaNO_2$ in 100 ml water.

4. Preparation of Calibration Curve

4.1. To compensate for possible slight losses of chromium during digestion or other operations of the analysis, the chromium standards are treated by the same procedure as the sample. Accordingly, pipet measured volumes of standard chromium solution ($5\mu g/ml$) ranging from 2.00 to 20.0 ml, to give standards for 10–100 μg Cr, into 250-ml beakers or conical flasks. Add either HNO_3 and H_2SO_4 (Sec. 5.2) or HNO_3 and $HClO_4$ (Sec. 5.3), depending on the method used for sample digestion, and proceed with digestion and subsequent treatment of the standards just as if they were samples, also carrying out cupferron treatment of the standards if this is required for the samples.

4.2. Transfer a suitable portion of each final solution to a 1-cm absorption cell and measure the absorbance at 540 mμ or with a filter for 540–560 mμ. As reference use either pure water or a reagent blank prepared by carrying 10 ml distilled water through the procedure employed for the standards. If pure water is used as the reference, the absorbance readings on the standards must be corrected by subtracting the absorbance of a reagent blank prepared as described.

4.3. Construct a calibration curve by plotting corrected absorbance values against micrograms of chromium.

5. Procedure

5.1. If a digested sample has been prepared according to directions given under Preliminary Treatment of Samples, pipet a measured aliquot containing 10–100 μg Cr into a 125-ml conical flask if treatment with cupferron can be omitted, or into a 125-ml separatory funnel if cupferron treatment is necessary. Proceed either with neutralization and subsequent treatment according to Sec. 5.5 or with the extraction of the cupferrates as in Sec. 5.4. If starting with an untreated sample, portions of the original sample can

be digested separately according to Sec. 5.2 or 5.3. The use of H_2SO_4 or $HClO_4$ is a matter of personal choice, although $HClO_4$, with HNO_3, is preferred for samples containing organic compounds which may be difficult to oxidize.

5.2. *Digestion with nitric–sulfuric acid:* If starting with an untreated sample, pipet a volume of sample containing 10–100 μg Cr into a 250-ml beaker. Add methyl orange indicator, followed by $1 + 1$ H_2SO_4, until the solution is acidic; then add 10 ml in excess. Add 1 ml H_2O_2 and heat to boiling. Cool somewhat and add 5 ml conc HNO_3 and a few carborundum boiling chips. Evaporate carefully on a hot plate to white fumes of SO_3, covering with a watch glass when the volume gets low. Do not fume to dryness. If the solution is not clear, add another 5 ml HNO_3 and repeat the evaporation to SO_3 fumes. Make further additions of HNO_3 and evaporate to fumes as necessary.

Cool the digestate nearly to room temperature, dilute to about 20 ml with water, and heat almost to boiling to dissolve slowly soluble salts. If the liquid is cloudy, filter it through a fine filter paper or sintered-glass filter, washing the residue with small portions of water. When separation of interfering substances with cupferron is not required, collect the filtrate in a 125-ml conical flask and proceed directly with Sec. 5.5; when cupferron treatment is necessary, collect the filtrate in a 125-ml separatory funnel or transfer it to the separatory funnel from the collecting vessel and proceed with Sec. 5.4.

5.3. *Digestion with nitric–perchloric acid:* If starting with an untreated sample, pipet a volume of sample containing 10–100 μg Cr into a 250-ml beaker.

Add methyl orange indicator; then add HNO_3 until the solution is acidic, plus 5 ml in excess. Add 1 ml H_2O_2 and heat on a hot plate. Evaporate to about 5 ml, covering the beaker with a watch glass when the volume gets low to avoid loss by spattering. Cool slightly; add 5 ml HNO_3 and 5 ml $HClO_4$. Evaporate on a hot plate to white fumes of $HClO_4$, but do not fume so strongly that no white fumes are visible within the beaker. If the digestate is not clear, add another 5 ml HNO_3 and again evaporate to fumes to assure complete decomposition of organic matter.

Cool slightly, dilute to about 20 ml with distilled water, and heat almost to boiling to dissolve slowly soluble salts. If the liquid is cloudy, filter it through a fine filter paper or a sintered-glass filter, washing the residue with small portions of water. When separation of interfering substances with cupferron is not required, collect the filtrate in a 125-ml conical flask and proceed directly with Sec. 5.5; when cupferron treatment is necessary, collect the filtrate in a 125-ml separatory funnel or transfer it to the separatory funnel from the collecting vessel and proceed with Sec. 5.4.

5.4. *Separation of molybdenum, vanadium, iron, and copper with cupferron:* Dilute the filtered digestate in the 125-ml separatory funnel to about 40 ml with distilled water and chill in an ice bath. Add 5 ml ice-cold cupferron solution, shake well, and allow to stand in the ice bath for 1 min. Extract the solution in the separatory funnel with three successive 5-ml portions of chloroform; shake each portion thoroughly with the aqueous solution, allow the layers to separate, and then withdraw and discard the chloroform extract. Transfer the extracted aqueous solution to a 125-ml conical flask, washing the separatory funnel with a small amount of distilled water and adding the wash water to the flask. Boil the solution in the flask for about 5 min to volatilize the chloroform, and cool.

5.5. Using methyl orange as indicator, add conc NH_4OH until the solution in the flask is just basic. Then add 1 + 1 H_2SO_4 dropwise until it is acidic, plus 1 ml (20 drops) in excess. Add 0.3 ml (5 drops) H_3PO_4. Adjust the volume of the solution to about 40 ml, add a boiling chip, and heat to boiling. Add 2 drops potassium permanganate solution to give a dark red color. If fading occurs, add additional drops of $KMnO_4$ to maintain an excess of about 2 drops. Boil the solution for 2 min longer (see note). Add 1 ml sodium azide solution and continue gently boiling. If the red color does not fade completely after boiling for approximately 30 sec, add another 1 ml sodium azide solution. Continue boiling for 1 min after the color has faded completely, then cool.

NOTE: Formation of a large amount of MnO_2 precipitate during the oxidation with permanganate may indicate incomplete decomposition of organic matter. On the other hand, slight browning may result from traces of cupferron not extracted by the chloroform. If oxidation of organic matter has not been complete, reduce the MnO_2 with 1 ml sodium nitrite solution, add HNO_3 and H_2SO_4 (or HNO_3 and $HClO_4$), and repeat the acid digestion procedure. Then proceed again with Sec. 5.5.

5.6. Transfer the cooled solution to a 100-ml volumetric flask, dilute to 100 ml, and mix. Add 2 ml diphenylcarbazide solution, mix, and allow to stand 5–10 min for full color development.

Then transfer an appropriate portion of the solution to a 1-cm absorption cell and measure its absorbance at 540 mμ or with a filter for 540–560 mμ. As reference use either pure water or a blank which has received the same treatment as the sample. If pure water is used as the reference, the absorbance reading of the sample must be corrected by subtracting the absorbance of a blank prepared as described (see also note below). From the measured or corrected absorbance, determine the milligrams of chromium present by reference to the calibration curve.

NOTE: If the solution is turbid after dilution to 100 ml in Sec. 5.6, an absorbance reading should be taken on it before the addition of the carbazide reagent, and a correction should be applied to the absorbance reading of the final colored solution by subtracting the absorbance measured previously.

6. Calculation

6.1. When the sample has been treated according to Sec. 5.1:

$$\text{mg/l Cr} = \frac{\mu\text{g Cr}}{\text{ml sample}} \times \frac{100}{\text{ml aliquot}}$$

6.2. When the sample has been treated according to Sec. 5.2. or 5.3:

$$\text{mg/l Cr} = \frac{\mu\text{g Cr}}{\text{ml sample}}$$

C. Method for Hexavalent Chromium

Soluble hexavalent chromium, in the absence of interfering amounts of substances such as molybdenum, vanadium, and mercury, may be determined colorimetrically by reaction with diphenylcarbazide in acid solution.

1. Apparatus

1.1. *Filter,* sintered glass or membrane.

1.2. *Photometric equipment,* as specified for Method B, Sec. 2.1.

2. Reagents

2.1. *Standard chromium solution:* Prepare as directed in Method B, Sec. 3.1 and 3.2.

2.2. *Redistilled water:* Distilled water redistilled in all-glass apparatus.

2.3. *Ammonium hydroxide,* conc.

2.4. *Sulfuric acid,* 1 + 1.

2.5. *Phosphoric acid,* 85 per cent.

2.6. *Diphenlycarbazide solution:* Prepare as directed in Method B, Sec. 3.13.

3. Preparation of Calibration Curve

Pipet measured volumes of the standard chromium solution (5 μg/ml) ranging from 2.00 to 20.0 ml into 100-ml volumetric flasks or nessler tubes. Add 2.5 ml 1 + 1 H_2SO_4 and dilute to 100 ml. Add 2 ml diphenylcarbazide solution, mix, and allow to stand for 5 min for full color development. Measure the absorbance at 540 mμ or with a filter for 540–560 mμ, and construct a calibration curve by plotting the absorbance values against micrograms of chromium.

4. Procedure

If necessary, filter a sample containing 10–100 μg Cr through a sintered-glass or membrane filter into a 125-ml conical flask. Adjust the solution until it is acidic to litmus paper by adding conc NH_4OH or conc H_2SO_4 as needed; then add 1.0 ml H_2SO_4 in excess and 0.3 ml H_3PO_4. Determine hexavalent chromium by completing the procedure according to Method B, Sec. 5.6.

If turbidity or color is present, the photometer should be balanced against a blank of the filtered sample containing the same amount of acid as the sample.

5. Calculation

$$mg/l\ Cr = \frac{\mu g\ Cr}{ml\ sample}$$

D. Method for Copper

1. General Discussion

1.1. *Principle:* Cuprous ion in neutral or slightly acidic solution reacts with 2,9-dimethyl-1,10-phenanthroline ("neocuproine") to form a complex in which 2 moles of the neocuproine are bound by 1 mole of Cu^+ ion. The complex can be extracted by a number of organic liquids, including a chloroform-methanol mixture, to give an orange-colored solution with a molar absorbancy index of about 8,000 at 457 mμ. The reaction is virtually specific for copper; the color system follows Beer's law up to a concentration of 0.2 mg Cu per 25 ml of organic solvent; full color development is obtained with the pH of the aqueous system between 3 and 9; the color system is stable in chloroform-methanol for several days.

After digestion of the sewage or waste with acid to destroy organic matter and to remove interfering anions (see Preliminary Treatment of Samples), the sample is treated with hydroxylamine-hydrochloride to reduce copper to the cuprous condition, and with sodium citrate to complex metallic ions which might give precipitates when the pH is raised. The pH is adjusted to 4–6 by the addition of ammonia, a solution of neocuproine in methanol is added, and the resultant complex is extracted into chloroform. After dilution of the chloroform to an exact volume with methanol, the absorbance of the solution is measured at 457 mμ.

1.2. *Interference:* Determination of copper by the recommended procedure is substantially free from interference by other metal ions. There have been reports that large amounts of chromium and tin may interfere. Potential interference from chromium can be avoided by addition of sulfurous acid to reduce chromate and complex chromic ion; in the presence of much tin or excessive amounts of other oxidizing ions, additional hydroxylamine—up to 20 ml —should be employed.

Cyanide and sulfide produce strong interference, but are removed during the digestion procedure, as are organic materials which might lead to difficulties.

1.3. *Minimum detectable concentration:* For the recommended procedure the minimum detectable concentration, corresponding to 0.01 absorbance or 98 per cent transmittance, is 3 μg Cu when a 1-cm cell is used and 0.6 μg Cu when a 5-cm cell is used. When the initial volume of sample corresponding to the aliquot taken is 100 ml, these concentrations become 30 and 6 μg/l Cu, respectively.

1.4. *Sampling and storage:* Precautions for sampling and storage described under Preliminary Treatment of Samples should be followed. Acidification, as described there, is especially important when the concentration of copper is less than 1 mg/l.

2. Apparatus

2.1. *Photometric equipment:* One of the following is required:

a. Spectrophotometer, for use at 457 mμ, providing a light path of 1 cm or longer.

b. Filter photometer, providing a light path of 1 cm or longer and equipped with a narrow-band violet filter having maximum transmittance in the range 450–460 mμ.

2.2. *Separatory funnels,* 125 ml, Squibb form, with glass or Teflon stopcock and stopper.

3. Reagents

3.1. *Redistilled water,* copper free. Most ordinary distilled water contains detectable amounts of copper. Redistilled water, prepared by distillation of singly distilled water in a resistant-glass still, or distilled water passed through an ion-exchange unit, should be used for the preparation of all reagents and for all dilutions or other operations in connection with copper determinations.

3.2. *Stock copper solution:* To 0.2000 g polished electrolytic copper wire or foil in a 250-ml conical flask, add 10 ml redistilled water and 5

ml conc HNO_3. After the reaction has slowed, warm gently to complete dissolution of the copper and then boil to expel oxides of nitrogen, using precautions to avoid loss of copper. Cool, add about 50 ml redistilled water, transfer quantitatively to a 1-liter volumetric flask, and dilute to the mark with redistilled water; 1 ml $=$ 200 μg Cu.

3.3. *Standard copper solution:* Dilute 50.00 ml stock copper solution to 500 ml with redistilled water; 1.00 ml $=$ 20.0 μg Cu.

3.4. *Sulfuric acid,* conc.

3.5. *Perchloric acid,* 60 per cent.

3.6. *Hydroxylamine - hydrochloride solution:* Dissolve 50 g $NH_2OH \cdot HCl$ in 450 ml redistilled water.

3.7. *Sodium citrate solution:* Dissolve 150 g $Na_3C_6H_5O_7 \cdot 2H_2O$ in 400 ml redistilled water. Add 5 ml hydroxylamine hydrochloride solution and 10 ml neocuproine reagent. Extract with 50 ml chloroform to remove copper impurities, and discard the chloroform layer.

3.8. *Ammonium hydroxide,* 6N. Dilute 400 ml conc NH_4OH (28–29 per cent) with 600 ml redistilled water. Store in a polyethylene bottle.

3.9. *Congo red paper,* or other pH test paper showing a color change in the pH range 4-6.

3.10. *Neocuproine reagent:* Dissolve 0.10 g 2,9-dimethyl-1,10-phenanthroline hemihydrate * in 100 ml methyl alcohol. This solution is stable under ordinary storage conditions for a month or more.

3.11. *Chloroform:* Avoid or redistill material that comes in containers with metal-lined caps.

3.12. *Methyl alcohol.*

---

* Such as is obtainable from G. F. Smith Chemical Company, Columbus, Ohio.

4. Preparation of Calibration Curve

4.1. Pipet accurately measured volumes of standard copper solution ranging from 1.00 to 10.00 ml (20.0–200 μg Cu) into 150-ml beakers, dilute to 10 ml with redistilled water, and add 1 ml of either H_2SO_4 or $HClO_4$, depending upon which acid is to be used for digestion of the samples. Add hydroxylamine-hydrochloride solution and sodium citrate solution, and then neutralize as described in Sec. 5.2; transfer to a 125-ml separatory funnel and carry through the extraction procedure as described in Sec. 5.3.

4.2. Transfer an appropriate portion of each final solution to a 1-cm absorption cell and measure the absorbance at 457 mμ or with a filter for 450–460 mμ. As reference use either pure chloroform or a reagent blank prepared by carrying 10 ml redistilled water plus 1 ml H_2SO_4 or $HClO_4$ through the procedure. If pure chloroform is used, the measured absorbance values must be corrected by subtracting the absorbance of a reagent blank carried through the procedure as described.

4.3. Construct a calibration curve by plotting absorbance value against milligrams of copper.

4.4. To prepare a calibration curve for smaller amounts of copper, dilute 10.0 ml of the standard copper solution to 100 ml. Then carry 1.00–10.00-ml volumes of this diluted standard through the previously described procedure, but use 5-cm cells for measurements of absorbance.

5. Procedure

5.1. If copper is the only heavy metal to be determined, take a sample of sewage or waste containing 0.1–1 mg Cu and treat it with the digestion procedure described under Preliminary Treatment of Samples. If several heavy metals are to be determined, the directions for size of sample given therein should be followed.

5.2. Pipet exactly 10.00 ml, or other suitable aliquot containing 4–200 μg Cu, from the solution for analysis obtained from preliminary treatment, into a 125-ml separatory funnel. Dilute to 10 ml with redistilled water, if a smaller aliquot has been used. Add 5 ml hydroxylamine-hydrochloride solution and 10 ml sodium citrate solution and mix thoroughly. Adjust the pH approximately to 4 by addition of 1-ml increments of ammonium hydroxide until congo red paper is just definitely red or other suitable pH test paper indicates a value between 4 and 6. (About 5 ml ammonium hydroxide is needed for each 10 ml of sample if digestion with H_2SO_4 was used, about 1.5 ml for each 10 ml if digestion with $HClO_4$ was used.)

5.3. Add 10 ml neocuproine reagent and 10 ml chloroform. Stopper and shake vigorously for 30 sec or more to extract the copper-neocuproine complex into the chloroform. Allow the mixture to separate into two layers and then withdraw the lower chloroform layer into a 25-ml volumetric flask, using care not to transfer any of the aqueous layer. Repeat the extraction of the water layer with an additional 10 ml chloroform and add this extract to the previous one. Dilute the combined extracts exactly to the 25-ml mark with methyl alcohol, stopper, and mix thoroughly.

5.4. Transfer an appropriate portion of the final organic solution to a suitable absorption cell (1-cm for 40–200 μg Cu; 5-cm for lesser amounts) and measure the absorbance at 457 mμ or with a filter for 450–460 mμ. As reference use either pure chloroform or a sample blank prepared by carrying 10 ml redistilled water through the complete digestion and subsequent procedure. If pure chloroform is used, the measured absorbance values must be corrected by subtracting the absorbance of a sample blank prepared as described.

5.5. From the measured or corrected absorbance determine the micrograms of copper in the final solution by reference to the appropriate calibration curve.

6. Calculation

$$\text{mg/l Cu} = \frac{\mu\text{g Cu}}{\text{ml sample}} \times \frac{100}{\text{ml aliquot}}$$

E. Method for Iron

1. General Discussion

1.1. *Principle:* Ferrous iron reacts with 1,10-phenanthroline in aqueous solution to form an orange-red complex, exhibiting maximum light absorption at a wavelength of 508 mμ. The absorbance of the colored solution is proportional to the concentration of iron; the intensity of color is independent of pH between 3 and 9; the color is stable indefinitely.

The sample is first digested with H_2SO_4 or $HClO_4$ to destroy organic matter, to remove interfering anions such as cyanide and nitrite, and to insure complete dissolution of the iron. The resulting solution is made $7N$–$8N$ in HCl, and the iron is separated from interfering substances by extraction of $FeCl_3$ into isopropyl ether. After reextraction of the iron into water, it is reduced with hydroxlyamine; the color complex is formed in acetate-buffered solution by the addition of a solution of phenanthroline. The absorbance of the resulting solution near 510 mμ is measured with a spectrophotometer or filter photometer.

1.2. *Interference:* Numerous metal ions, including those of chromium, copper, nickel, cobalt, zinc, cadmium, and mercury, may interfere with determination of iron by phenanthroline. Also, anions that complex iron, such as phosphate or polyphosphate, fluoride, citrate, tartrate, and oxalate, may retard or impair color development. All of these potential interferences are eliminated by the extraction procedure.

1.3. *Minimum detectable concentration:* The ferrous-phenanthroline complex has a molar absorbancy index equal to about 11,000 at 508 mμ. In a 100-ml final volume the method will detect 5 μg Fe if a 1-cm cell is used for photometric measurement and 1 μg Fe if a 5-cm cell is used (98 per cent light transmittance or 0.01 absorbance). If the volume of initial sample is 100 ml, the concentrations are 50 μg/l and 10 μg/l with the 1-cm and 5-cm cells, respectively.

1.4. *Sampling and storage:* Normal precautions for sampling and storage, as described in Preliminary Treatment of Samples, should be followed. Because procedures are given only for determination of total iron, no special precautions to prevent oxidation, reduction, solution, or precipitation of iron are necessary.

2. Apparatus

2.1. *Photometric equipment:* One of the following types of photometers, equipped with absorption cells providing light paths of 1 cm or longer, is required:

a. Spectrophotometer, for use at 510 mμ.

b. Filter photometer, equipped with a green filter having maximum transmittance near 510 mμ.

2.2. *Separatory funnels,* 125 ml, Squibb form, with ground-glass or Teflon stopcocks and stoppers.

3. Reagents

3.1. *Stock iron solution:* Dissolve electrolytic iron wire or "iron wire for standardizing" which has been rubbed with fine sandpaper to produce a bright surface, in 20 ml 1 + 5 H_2SO_4 and allow the reaction to proceed until the iron is completely dissolved. Then dilute to 1,000 ml with distilled water; 1 ml = 200 μg Fe. Prepare fresh at least every 6 months.

3.2. *Standard iron solution:* Prepare this solution the day it is to be used. Dilute 25.0 ml stock iron solution to 500 ml with iron-free distilled water; 1.00 ml = 10.0 μg Fe.

3.3. *Hydroxylamine–hydrochloride solution:* Dissolve 50 g $NH_2OH \cdot HCl$ in 450 ml distilled water. Prepare fresh every few days.

3.4. *Sodium acetate solution:* Dissolve 200 g $NaC_2H_3O_2 \cdot 3H_2O$ in 800 ml distilled water.

3.5. *Phenanthroline solution:* Dissolve 0.5 g 1,10-phenanthroline, $C_{12}H_8N_2 \cdot H_2O$, in 500 ml distilled water, warming to 80°–90°C to dissolve, as required. Alternatively, a few drops of conc HCl may be added to assist in dissolving the reagent.

3.6. *Hydrochloric acid,* conc, containing less than 0.00005 per cent of iron.

3.7. *Diisopropyl or isopropyl ether.*

3.8. *Sulfuric acid,* 1 + 5.

4. Preparation of Calibration Curves

4.1. *Range 0–100 μg Fe per 100 ml of final solution:* Pipet 2.0, 4.0, 6.0, 8.0, and 10.0 ml standard iron solution into 100-ml volumetric flasks. Add 1.0 ml $NH_2OH \cdot HCl$ solution and 1 ml sodium acetate solution to each flask. Dilute each to about 75 ml with distilled water, add 10 ml phenanthroline solution, dilute to volume, mix thoroughly, and let stand for 10 min. Then measure the absorbance of each solution in a 5-cm cell at 508 mμ or with a filter near 510 mμ against a reference blank prepared by treating distilled water with specified amounts of all reagents except the standard iron solution. Alternatively, distilled water may be used as a reference, but then the absorbance values for standard concentrations of iron must be corrected by subtracting the absorbance value for a reagent blank against distilled water. From the data obtained, construct a calibration curve for absorbance against milligrams of iron.

4.2. *Range 50–500 μg Fe per 100 ml of final solution:* Follow the procedure specified in Sec. 4.1, but use 10.0, 20.0, 30.0, 40.0, and 50.0 ml standard iron solution and measure the absorbance values in 1-cm cells.

5. Procedure

5.1. If a digested sample has been prepared according to the directions given in the section on Preliminary Treatment of Samples, pipet a 10.0-ml portion or other suitable aliquot containing 20–500 μg Fe into a 125-ml separatory funnel. If the volume taken is less than 10 ml, add distilled water to make up the volume to 10 ml. To the separatory funnel add 15 ml conc HCl for a 10-ml aqueous volume; or, if the aliquot taken was greater than 10.0 ml, add 1.5 ml conc HCl for every milliliter of sample used. Mix, cool, and proceed with Sec. 5.3.

5.2. To prepare a sample for specific determination of iron, measure a suitable volume of sewage or waste containing 20–500 μg Fe and carry it through either of the digestion procedures described under Preliminary Treatment of Samples. However, use only 5 ml H_2SO_4 or $HClO_4$ rather than the 10 ml specified there; also, the H_2O_2 may be omitted. When digestion is complete, cool the digested sample, dilute with just 10 ml distilled water, heat almost to boiling to dissolve slowly soluble salts, and, if the sample is still cloudy, filter through a glass fiber, sintered-glass, or porcelain filter, washing with 2–3 ml distilled water. Transfer the filtrate or the clear solution quantitatively to a 25-ml volumetric flask or graduate and make up to 25 ml with distilled water. Empty the flask or graduate into a 125-ml separatory funnel, rinsing with 5 ml conc HCl which is added to the funnel, and then add an additional 25 ml conc HCl measured with the same graduate or flask. Mix and cool to room temperature.

5.3. Extract the iron from the HCl solution in the separatory funnel by shaking for 30 sec with 25 ml isopropyl ether. Draw off the lower acid layer into a second separatory funnel. Extract the acid solution again with 25 ml isopropyl ether, drain the acid layer into

a suitable clean vessel, and combine the second portion of isopropyl ether with the first. Pour the acid layer back into the second separatory funnel and extract once more with 25 ml isopropyl ether. Withdraw and discard the acid layer, then add the ether layer to the previous ones in the original funnel. Persistence of a yellow color in the HCl solution after three extractions should not be taken as evidence of incomplete separation of iron. Copper, which is not extracted, gives a similar yellow color.

Shake the combined ether extracts with 25 ml distilled water to return the iron to the aqueous phase, and transfer the lower aqueous layer to a 100-ml volumetric flask. Repeat the extraction with a second 25-ml portion of distilled water, adding this to the first aqueous extract. Discard the ether layer.

5.4. Add to the volumetric flask containing the combined aqueous extract 1 ml $NH_2OH \cdot HCl$ solution, 10 ml phenanthroline solution, and 10 ml sodium acetate solution. Dilute to 100 ml with distilled water, mix thoroughly, and let stand for 10 min. Measure the absorbance at 510 mμ, using a 5-cm absorption cell for amounts of iron less than 0.1 mg or a 1-cm cell for quantities from 0.1 to 0.5 mg. As reference either distilled water or a sample blank prepared by carrying the utilized quantities of acids through the entire analytical procedure may be used. If distilled water is used as reference, the absorbance of the sample must be corrected by subtracting the absorbance of a sample blank prepared as described.

Determine the micrograms of iron in the sample used from the absorbance (corrected, if necessary) by reference to the calibration curve prepared according to Sec. 4.

6. Calculation

6.1. When the sample has been treated according to Sec. 5.1:

$$mg/l\ Fe = \frac{\mu g\ Fe}{ml\ sample} \times \frac{100}{ml\ aliquot}$$

6.2. When the sample has been treated according to Sec. 5.2:

$$mg/l\ Fe = \frac{\mu g\ Fe}{ml\ sample}$$

F. Method for Lead (Tentative)

1. General Discussion

1.1. *Principle:* The method is based on the fact that the elements which interfere with the extraction of lead at pH 8 to 9 in a cyanide medium can be removed by preliminary extraction at pH 2 to 3. The provisional equilibrium curves of Wichmann for metal dithizonates in chloroform have served as a guide for the development of the method described herein.

After the removal of the interfering elements, tartrate is added to prevent the formation of hydroxide, and the solution is brought to pH 8–9 with ammonium hydroxide and sodium cyanide. Lead is then extracted with a dilute solution of dithizone. Because an excess of dithizone is used, the pink color of the lead dithizonate is masked by the intense green color of the excess dithizone. This excess is removed from the carbon tetrachloride layer with alkaline cyanide solution, leaving the lead dithizonate in the organic solvent. The solution of lead dithizonate is diluted to a given volume and the color intensity determined by a colorimeter or spectrophotometer, or by comparison with standards.

The use of hydrazine acetate as the reducing agent may cause some difficulties, inasmuch as the reduction of ferric and stannic ions proceeds quite slowly. The preliminary reduction must be carried out carefully in accordance with the procedure.

1.2. *Interference:* The elements that interfere with the extraction of lead in cyanide medium at pH 8 to 9 are stannous tin, thallium, and bismuth. Thallium is so rarely encountered that its interference is hardly worth consideration. On the other hand, bismuth and, in particular, tin occur quite frequently; hence, special attention must be given to them.

The sample is first fumed with perchloric and nitric acids to remove organic compounds and then is reduced with hydrazine acetate to lower the oxidation state of those elements and compounds which are capable of oxidizing dithizone. The reduction assures that tin and iron exist in the lower valence state. At pH 2 to 3, dithizone forms complexes with copper, bismuth, tin, mercury, and silver. Thus, both bismuth and tin are removed so that they cannot interfere with the lead extraction at pH 8 to 9. Because there may be relatively large quantities of bismuth, tin, or copper, a strong solution of dithizone in chloroform must be used to extract these elements.

1.3. *Application:* The method was developed to determine 0–75 μg Pb in the presence of 100 μg of each of the following ions: Ag, Hg, Bi, Cu, Cd,

As, Sb, Sn, Fe, Al, Cr, Ni, Co, Mn, Zn, Ca, Sr, Ba, Mg, Na, K, and NH_4.

2. Apparatus

2.1. *Colorimetric equipment:* One of the following is required:

a. Spectrophotometer, for use at 520 mμ, providing a light path of 1 cm or longer.

b. Filter photometer, providing a light path of 1 cm or longer and equipped with a green filter having maximum transmittance near 520 mμ.

2.2. *pH meter.*

2.3. *Separatory funnels,* 125 ml, Squibb form, with ground-glass stoppers.

3. Reagents

3.1. *Redistilled water:* Distilled water redistilled in all-glass apparatus.

3.2. *Standard lead solution:* Dissolve 100 mg of the purest lead metal in a mixture of 2 ml conc HNO_3 and 2 ml distilled water. Heat gently if necessary. Dilute to 1,000 ml with distilled water. Store in polyethylene bottles; 1.00 ml = 100 μg Pb.

3.3. *Phenolphthalein indicator solution:* Either the aqueous (*a*) or alcoholic (*b*) solution may be used.

a. Dissolve 5 g phenolphthalein disodium salt in distilled water and dilute to 1 liter. If necessary, add 0.02N NaOH dropwise until a faint pink color appears.

b. Dissolve 5 g phenolphthalein in 500 ml 95 per cent ethyl alcohol or isopropyl alcohol and add 500 ml distilled water. Then add 0.02N NaOH dropwise until a faint pink color appears.

3.4. *Ammonium hydroxide,* conc. Prepare as in Method A, Sec. 3.11.

3.5. *Ammonium hydroxide,* 1 + 1.

3.6. *Hydrazine acetate solution:* Mix 15 ml lead-free hydrazine hydrate (64 per cent hydrazine)* with 50 ml conc acetic acid and dilute to 100 ml with distilled water.

3.7. *Sodium tartrate solution:* Dissolve 10 g $Na_2C_4H_4O_6 \cdot 2H_2O$ in 100 ml distilled water. To purify, shake with dithizone solution (II) in carbon tetrachloride until the organic solvent layer appears pure green in color. Wash away the traces of dithizone by extraction with pure $CHCl_3$ until the solution is water white. Then extract twice with CCl_4.

3.8. *Tartaric acid solution:* Dissolve 50 g $H_2C_4H_4O_6$ in 100 ml distilled water.

3.9. *Dithizone solution (I):* To remove the chief impurity, diphenylthiocarbodiazone, proceed as follows: The purification depends on the insolubility of diphenylthiocarbodiazone in basic aqueous solutions. Dissolve 250 mg dithizone crystals in 50 ml $CHCl_3$, filter through a small paper, and wash the filter with several small portions of $CHCl_3$. Transfer the filtrate to a separatory funnel and extract with portions of 1 + 99 NH_4OH until the $CHCl_3$ layer is nearly devoid of green color. Discard the $CHCl_3$ layer and wash the combined extracts with four 15-ml portions of $CHCl_3$. Discard the $CHCl_3$ extracts. Precipitate the dithizone by addition of 2 ml conc HCl; shake to completely neutralize the ammonia. Extract the precipitated dithizone with 25-ml portions of $CHCl_3$ and finally dilute the combined extracts with pure $CHCl_3$ to a volume of nearly 250 ml. The solution keeps well in the cold; it is preferably kept in the refrigerator or in cold running water.

---

* Such as is obtainable from Matheson Scientific, Inc.

In lieu of keeping the solution cold, it may be made up fresh as needed. The decomposition of this solution is evidenced by a gradual decrease in green color.

3.10. *Dithizone solution (II):* Dissolve 125 mg dithizone in 50 ml $CHCl_3$ and filter through a small filter paper. Wash the filter paper with small portions of pure $CHCl_3$ and combine all filtrates. Extract the filtrates with $1 + 99$ NH_4OH until the $CHCl_3$ layer is nearly devoid of green color. Wash the aqueous layer with pure CCl_4 to remove traces of $CHCl_3$ and any diphenylthiocarbodiazone. Reject the CCl_4 extracts. Neutralize the NH_4OH by shaking well with 2 ml conc HCl. Extract the precipitated dithizone with pure CCl_4. Dilute the extracts to 500 ml with pure CCl_4. This solution must be kept cool at all times in a refrigerator or, less desirably, in running water.

3.11. *Chloroform:* All chloroform, especially the reclaimed solvent, must be treated as follows: Drain off all water. Wash with conc H_2SO_4 until the solvent and the acid layers are clear and colorless. Use 50 to 100 ml acid per liter of solvent. Shake the solvent with a dilute solution of sodium bicarbonate and then wash thoroughly. Add calcium oxide to dry the solvent. Separate from the CaO and add 2 per cent of its volume of pure, absolute methyl alcohol. Distill the solvent slowly while keeping a pellet of CaO in the still. Reject the first 50 to 100 ml and do not allow the still to go to dryness.

3.12. *Carbon tetrachloride,* ACS grade. If not available, commercial grade and solvent to be reclaimed must be treated as follows: Shake 1,000 ml solvent with 50 ml 50 per cent aqueous solution of KOH. Repeat this extraction several times. Wash the CCl_4

with 25–50-ml portions of conc H_2SO_4 several times. The final washing with the acid should show no discoloration. Wash the CCl_4 with a dilute solution of sodium bicarbonate; wash repeatedly with water until the washings are perfectly neutral to litmus paper. Dry overnight with $CaCl_2$ and distill, or instead of drying overnight, distill about 10 per cent of the solvent and then collect the clear distillate. Do not distill the last 50 to 100 ml after collecting the main fraction.

3.13. *Thymol blue indicator solution:* Dissolve 0.4 g indicator in 100 ml distilled water.

3.14. *Potassium cyanide solution:* Dissolve 10 g KCN in 100 ml distilled water. (CAUTION: *Toxic; take care to avoid ingestion.*)

3.15. *Alkaline potassium cyanide solution:* To 175 ml pure conc NH_4OH add 15 ml potassium cyanide solution and 7.5 ml lead-free sodium sulfite solution (10 g in 100 ml water). Dilute to 500 ml with distilled water. To remove the lead from sodium sulfite, dissolve 10 g Na_2SO_3 in 100 ml distilled water and extract with dithizone solution (I) until the color of the organic layer is pure green. Remove traces of $CHCl_3$ by 4–5 extractions with pure CCl_4.

3.16. *Hydrochloric acid,* conc. If necessary, distill in a pyrex apparatus. The distillate will be approximately 22 per cent HCl.

4. Procedure

4.1. For the lead determination, the nitric acid–perchloric acid digestion is preferred. If the nitric acid–sulfuric acid digestion is used in the preliminary treatment, two determinations of lead are necessary, one on the solution resulting from the HNO_3-H_2SO_4 digestion and one on the ammonium acetate extract of the residue as described in Preliminary Treatment of Samples, Sec. 4.4.

4.2. Pipet an aliquot of the digested sample containing 10–100 μg Pb into a 125-ml beaker. Also run a blank, using lead-free distilled water.

4.3. A calibration curve is established using 1–10 ml of a standard lead solution made by diluting 10 ml of standard solution to 100 ml and carrying these quantities through the same procedure as the sample; 1.00 ml = 10 μg Pb.

4.4. Dilute the sample (Sec. 4.2) with 10 ml distilled water. Add 10–15 drops phenolphthalein indicator solution and nearly neutralize with 1 + 1 NH_4OH. Add 20 ml hydrazine acetate solution and heat to 90°–95°C in a water bath for at least 10 min. Cool.

NOTE: In the absence of tin and bismuth, Sec. 4.5–4.8 below may be omitted, thus considerably shortening the procedure.

4.5. Add 20 ml sodium tartrate solution. Adjust the pH to about 2.5, using a pH meter, by adding either 1 + 1 ammonium hydroxide or tartaric acid solution. Transfer to a separatory funnel.

4.6. Extract the solution in the funnel with 3-ml portions of dithizone solution (I) until the organic layer has a pure green color. Shake well each time and carefully drain off and discard the chloroform layer.

4.7. Extract the solution with two 5-ml portions of pure chloroform. This serves to remove the entrained dithizone. Discard the chloroform layers.

4.8. Remove the remaining chloroform by extracting with 5 ml CCl_4. Discard the CCl_4 layer.

4.9. Add 10 ml sodium tartrate solution and 5 drops thymol blue indicator solution. If necessary, add conc NH_4OH to make the indicator turn blue.

4.10. Add 10 ml potassium cyanide solution (Sec. 3.14). Adjust the pH to 8.5 by adding tartaric acid solution or 1 + 1 NH_4OH until the indicator turns green.

4.11. Extract with 5 ml dithizone solution (II) in CCl_4. Shake well and carefully transfer the solvent layer to another separatory funnel. Do not allow any of the aqueous phase to run into the CCl_4 extract.

4.12. Successively extract the aqueous phase with 2-ml portions of dithizone solution (II) until the green color of dithizone persists for at least two extractions. Combine all these extractions with the one from the previous step. When multiple samples are run, as with a calibration curve, be sure to use the same amount of dithizone solution for all extractions. The color of the blank increases somewhat as the number of extractions increases.

4.13. Extract the aqueous phase with 5 ml pure CCl_4 and add it to the other extracts.

4.14. To the combined CCl_4 extracts, add 20 ml alkaline potassium cyanide solution (Sec. 3.15) and shake well. The green coloration of dithizone will be replaced by the pink coloration of lead dithizonate; the alkaline aqueous solution will be yellowish owing to the formation of a salt of dithizone.

4.15. Drain off the CCl_4 layer into a 25- or 50-ml volumetric flask. Extract the aqueous phase with two 2-ml portions of pure CCl_4. Combine all the extracts and discard the aqueous layer.

4.16. Dilute the extracts in the volumetric flask to the mark by adding pure CCl_4 and shake well.

4.17. Filter the CCl_4 solution through small, dry papers to remove suspended droplets of water. Read the absorbance of this solution at 520 mμ using pure CCl_4 as a reference liquid. Blank corrections must be made by subtracting the absorbance of the blank from that of the sample readings.

5. Calculation

$$\text{mg/l Pb} = \frac{\mu\text{g Pb}}{\text{ml sample}} \times \frac{100}{\text{ml aliquot}}$$

G. Method for Manganese

1. General Discussion

1.1. *Principle:* Manganese is readily determined in small concentrations by oxidizing it in acidic solution to the intensely colored permanganate ion and measuring the absorbance of the resulting solution at a wavelength of 525 mμ. Either periodate or persulfate can be employed as the oxidizing agent; oxidation with persulfate is used in the method described here because of its greater speed, especially for traces of manganese. Oxidation with periodate can be carried out as described for the determination of manganese in water, using an appropriate aliquot of the digestate obtained according to the section on Preliminary Treatment of Samples.

After the sample has been digested with acid to oxidize organic matter and to volatilize chloride as HCl, phosphoric acid is added to form a colorless complex with ferric ion. Oxidation with the persulfate ion is carried out in hot, acidic solution in the presence of silver as a catalyst. The resulting permanganate color is stable for at least 24 hr if excess persulfate is present and the solution is kept from contact with organic matter, including dust.

1.2. *Interference:* The most impor-

tant interferences are organic matter, chloride ion, and other reducing substances, which may cause unstable colors by reducing permanganate. Chloride ion, by forming AgCl, also interferes with the catalytic action of silver and produces turbidity. Potential interference from all these substances is eliminated by proper performance of the acidic digestion and oxidation. Other colored ions, notably ferric iron, copper, nickel, and dichromate, interfere by contributing to the absorption of light at 525 mμ. The interference of iron is avoided by addition of phosphoric acid. That of the other ions is compensated by using as a photometric blank a portion of the sample from which the permanganate color has been bleached by reduction.

1.3. *Minimum detectable concentration:* The absorbancy index of permanganate per gram atom of manganese at 525 mμ is about 2,300. The minimum detectable quantity is 30 μg Mn when a 1-cm cell is used for photometric comparison, or 5 μg Mn when a 5-cm cell is used (98 per cent transmittance). If the volume of sample used is 100 ml, these quantities correspond to 300 and 50 μg/l, respectively.

1.4. *Sampling and storage:* Samples should be treated with HNO_3 at the time of collection to minimize adsorption or precipitation of manganese compounds on the surfaces of the container. Add sufficient HNO_3 to acidify and then add 5 ml excess conc HNO_3 for each liter of sample.

2. Apparatus

Photometric equipment: One of the following, equipped with suitable absorption cells providing light paths of 1 cm or longer, is required:

2.1. *Spectrophotometer,* for use at 525 mμ.

2.2. *Filter photometer,* equipped with a green filter exhibiting maximum transmittance near 525 mμ.

3. Reagents

3.1. *Stock manganese solution:* Dissolve 1.8 g potassium permanganate, $KMnO_4$, in about 450 ml distilled water in a 1-liter conical flask and heat for 4–5 hr at 70°–80°C, protecting the mouth of the flask against intrusion of dust. Filter while hot through a fritted-glass, glass fiber, or asbestos filter, collecting the filtrate in a thoroughly clean flask. Transfer the filtrate to a 500-ml volumetric flask, add 2 ml H_2SO_4, cool to room temperature, and dilute to the mark with distilled water.

Within 24 hr standardize oxidimetrically against sodium oxalate, following the procedure described in Part I, Calcium, Method B, Sec. 3.3, except that samples 0.2–0.4 g (weighed to 0.1 mg) should be used. (The standardization must be carried out promptly before any permanganate has decomposed or been reduced, so that the total

manganese content and the oxidimetric titer will correspond. As decomposition subsequent to the standardization will not change the manganese content of the acidified solution, diluted standards may be prepared at any time based on the initial oxidimetric titer, but not on any subsequent oxidimetric titer.)

3.2. *Standard manganese solution:* The volume of stock solution required to prepare 1 liter of a solution containing 50 mg/1 Mn is 4.55 divided by the normality of $KMnO_4$. Transfer exactly this volume, measured to 0.1 ml by means of a buret, to a 250-ml beaker or conical flask. Add 5 ml conc H_2SO_4 and then $NaHSO_3$ solution dropwise, with stirring, until the pink color of permanganate disappears. Heat the solution and boil gently for a few minutes to remove excess SO_2. Cool and transfer quantitatively to a 1-liter volumetric flask, rinsing the beaker or flask several times with distilled water. Dilute to 1,000 ml with distilled water; 1.00 ml = 50 μg Mn.

3.3. *Sulfuric acid,* conc.

3.4. *Nitric acid,* conc.

3.5. *Phosphoric acid, 6N.* Dilute 400 ml 85 per cent H_3PO_4 with 600 ml distilled water.

3.6. *Silver nitrate solution, 0.1N.* Dissolve 1.7 g $AgNO_3$ in 100 ml distilled water.

3.7. *Ammonium persulfate,* solid.

3.8. *Perchloric acid,* 60 per cent.

3.9. *Sodium nitrite solution:* Dissolve 5 g $NaNO_2$ in 95 ml distilled water.

3.10. *Special reagents for preparation of standard manganese solution:*

a. *Sodium bisulfite solution:* Dissolve 10 g $NaHSO_3$ in 90 ml distilled water.

b. *Sodium oxalate,* primary standard, $Na_2C_2O_4$.

4. Preparation of Calibration Curve

4.1. *Range 0–0.5 mg Mn per 100 ml of final solution:* Pipet 1.00, 2.00, 4.00, 6.00, and 10.00 ml standard manganese solution into 250-ml conical flasks. To each flask add 25 ml distilled water, 1 ml conc H_2SO_4, 0.5 ml conc HNO_3, 20 ml $6N$ H_3PO_4, 1 ml silver nitrate solution, and 1 g $(NH_4)_2S_2O_8$. Heat to boiling on a hot plate and boil gently for 1 min. Remove from the hot plate, add 0.2 g $(NH_4)_2S_2O_8$, and allow to stand for 1 min longer; then cool with running water. Transfer each solution quantitatively to a 100-ml volumetric flask, dilute to 100 ml with distilled water free of reducing substances, and mix thoroughly. Measure the absorbance of each solution in a 5-cm cell at a wavelength of 525 mμ or with a green filter for wavelengths near this value, using as reference a reagent blank prepared by carrying 25 ml distilled water through the procedure. Alternatively, distilled water may be used as a reference, but then the absorbance values for the standards must be corrected by subtracting the absorbance for the reagent blank compared to distilled water. Construct a calibration plot showing absorbance against milligrams of manganese.

4.2. *Range 0.2–2.0 mg Mn per 100 ml of final solution:* Follow the procedure specified in Sec. 4.1, but use 5.00, 10.00, 20.0, 30.0, and 40.0 ml standard manganese solution and measure the absorbance values in 1-cm cells.

5. Procedure

5.1. If a digested sample has been prepared according to the directions given in Preliminary Treatment of Samples, pipet a 10.0-ml portion or other suitable aliquot containing 0.05–2.0 mg Mn into a 250-ml conical flask. Add 25 ml distilled water, if the aliquot taken is less than 50 ml, and proceed with Sec. 5.3.

5.2. To prepare a solution for specific determination of manganese, measure a suitable volume of sewage or waste containing 0.02–2.0 mg Mn and carry it through either of the digestion procedures described under Preliminary Treatment of Samples. However, use only 5 ml H_2SO_4 or $HClO_4$ rather than the 10 ml specified there and omit the addition of H_2O_2. When digestion is complete, cool the digested sample, add 25 ml distilled water, and heat almost to boiling to dissolve slowly soluble salts. Filter through a glass fiber, sintered-glass, or porcelain filter to remove any cloudiness, washing the vessel and the filter with small portions of distilled water. Transfer the filtrate or clear solution quantitatively to a 250-ml conical flask and dilute to about 70 ml.

5.3. Add 20 ml $6N$ H_3PO_4, 1 ml silver nitrate solution, and 1 g $(NH_4)_2S_2O_8$ to the solution from Sec. 5.1 or 5.2. Heat to boiling on a hot plate and boil gently for 2 min. If the solution is brownish or turbid at this point because of incomplete oxidation of organic matter, add 1 g $(NH_4)_2S_2O_8$ more and continue boiling for 10 min. If, at the end of this time, the solution has still not cleared, add sodium bisulfite solution dropwise and reduce MnO_2 and MnO_4^-; then repeat the persulfate oxidation.

Remove the oxidized solution from the hot plate, add an additional 0.2 g $(NH_4)_2S_2O_8$, allow to stand for 1 min, then cool in running water to room temperature. Transfer the solution quantitatively to a 100-ml volumetric flask, dilute to the mark with distilled water, and mix thoroughly.

5.4. Pipet 50 ml of the solution from Sec. 5.3 into a second 100-ml volumetric flask to make the reference solution. To the transferred portion add sodium nitrate solution dropwise, mixing thoroughly after each drop, until the permanganate color is destroyed. No more than 2 drops should be required.

5.5. Transfer suitable portions of the sample solution and the bleached solution to absorption cells of appropriate optical path and determine the absorbance due to permanganate in one of two ways:

a. By measuring the absorbance of the sample solution against that of the bleached solution as reference at a wavelength of 525 mμ or with a green filter having maximum transmission near 525 mμ.

b. By measuring the absorbances of both sample solution and bleached solution against distilled water at the designated wavelength and subtracting absorbance of the bleached solution from that of the sample.

The former technique gives greater sensitivity and precision in the presence of large concentrations of other colored ions. However, it may be impossible to set the photometer at 0 absorbance or 100 per cent transmittance when the bleached solution contains large concentrations of colored ions. (The slit width of the spectrophotometer should not be changed from that used in preparing the calibration curve.) The latter technique must then be employed.

NOTE: The procedure described compensates for the interference of colored ions in the sample, but does *not* correct for manganous impurities in the reagents. Difficulties from this source are not likely. However, manganous impurities can be determined by carrying two portions of distilled water through the complete digestion and analytical procedure, except that one of them is not heated after the addition of ammonium persulfate. Measurement of the absorbance of the heated solution against the unheated one at 525 mμ gives a reagent correction to be applied to the absorbance of the sample.

Determine the milligrams of manganese in the final solution from the net absorbance by reference to the appropriate calibration curve prepared according to Sec. 4.

6. Calculation

6.1. When the sample has been treated according to Sec. 5.1:

$$\text{mg/l Mn} = \text{mg Mn} \times \frac{1,000}{\text{ml sample}} \times \frac{100}{\text{ml aliquot}}$$

6.2. When the sample has been treated according to Sec. 5.2:

$$\text{mg/l Mn} = \text{mg Mn} \times \frac{1,000}{\text{ml sample}}$$

H. Heptoxime Method for Nickel (Tentative)

1. Principle

Following preliminary digestion with the HNO$_3$-H$_2$SO$_4$ mixture, iron and copper are removed by extraction of the cupferrates with chloroform. The nickel is separated from other ions by extraction of the nickel heptoxime complex with chloroform, reextracted into the aqueous phase with hydrochloric acid, and determined colorimetrically in the acidic solution with heptoxime in the presence of an oxidant.

2. Apparatus

2.1. *Colorimetric equipment:* One of the following is required:

a. Spectrophotometer, for use at 445 $m\mu$, providing a light path of 1 cm or longer.

b. Filter photometer, providing a light path of 1 cm or longer and equipped with a violet filter with maximum transmittance near 445 $m\mu$.

2.2. *Separatory funnels,* 125 ml, Squibb form, with ground-glass stoppers.

2.3. *Electrodeposition apparatus,* for standardizing the nickel stock solution—desirable but not required.

3. Reagents

3.1. *Standard nickel sulfate solution:* Dissolve 0.4479 g $NiSO_4 \cdot 6H_2O$ in 1,000 ml distilled water; 1.00 ml = 100 μg Ni.

3.2. *Hydrochloric acid, 1.0N.* Dilute 85.5 ml conc HCl to 1 liter.

3.3. *Bromine water:* Saturate distilled water with bromine.

3.4. *Ammonium hydroxide,* conc.

3.5. *Heptoxime reagent:* Dissolve 0.1 g 1,2-cycloheptanedionedioxime * (heptoxime) in 100 ml 95 per cent ethyl alcohol.

3.6. *Ethyl alcohol,* 95 per cent.

3.7. *Sodium tartrate solution:* Dissolve 10 g $Na_2C_4H_4O_6 \cdot 2H_2O$ in 90 ml distilled water.

---

* Such as is obtainable from Hach Chemical Company, Ames, Iowa.

3.8. *Methyl orange indicator:* Dissolve 1 g of indicator in 1 liter distilled water.

3.9. *Sodium hydroxide solution, 6N.* Dissolve 240 g NaOH in 1 liter distilled water.

3.10. *Acetic acid,* conc.

3.11. *Cupferron solution:* Dissolve 1 g cupferron in 100 ml distilled water. Store in a refrigerator or make up fresh for each series of determinations.

3.12. *Chloroform.*

3.13. *Hydroxylamine - hydrochloride solution:* Dissolve 10 g $NH_2OH \cdot HCl$ in 90 ml distilled water. Make up daily.

4. Preparation of Calibration Curve

4.1. Pipet aliquots of the standard nickel sulfate solution into 100-ml volumetric flasks. The series should cover from 50 to 250 μg Ni, if 1-cm cells are used. Add 25 ml 1.0N HCl and 5 ml bromine water. Cool with cold running tap water and add 10 ml conc NH_4OH. Then immediately add 20 ml heptoxime reagent and 20 ml ethyl alcohol. Dilute to volume with distilled water and mix.

4.2. Measure absorbance at 445 $m\mu$ 20 min after addition of the reagent. The blank is prepared similarly except for omission of the nickel.

5. Procedure

5.1. *Separation of copper and iron:* Take an aliquot of the original sample (prepared by digesting with HNO_3-H_2SO_4 mixture as directed in Sec. 4 of Preliminary Treatment of Samples) containing from 50 to 250 μg Ni, place in a separatory funnel, and add 10 ml sodium tartrate solution, 2 drops methyl orange indicator, and enough 6N NaOH to make the solution basic to the indicator.

Add 1 ml acetic acid and cool by placing the separatory funnel under cold running tap water. Add 4 ml fresh cupferron reagent and extract any precipitate formed with 10 ml CHCl$_3$. Allow the layers to separate, and add more cupferron until a white, silky precipitate forms, which indicates that an excess of cupferron is present.

Shake the mixture, allow the layers to separate, and discard the CHCl$_3$ layer. Extract again with 10 ml CHCl$_3$ and discard the CHCl$_3$ layer. Add 1 ml fresh NH$_2$OH·HCl solution, mix, and let stand a few minutes.

5.2. *Separation of nickel:* Add 10 ml heptoxime reagent and extract the nickel complex with one 15-ml and then two 10-ml portions of CHCl$_3$. If the CHCl$_3$ layer is not colorless with the third extraction, continue until it is. Collect the CHCl$_3$ layers in a separatory funnel. Extract the nickel from the CHCl$_3$ by shaking with 15 ml 1.0N HCl. After allowing the layers to separate, draw off the CHCl$_3$ layer into another separatory funnel and rinse with 10 ml 1.0N HCl, which is added to the 15-ml portion of HCl.

5.3. Absorbance of the solution is determined as directed in Sec. 4.

6. Calculation

$$\text{mg/l Ni} = \frac{\mu\text{g Ni}}{\text{ml sample}} \times \frac{100}{\text{ml aliquot}}$$

I. Dimethylglyoxime Method for Nickel (Tentative)

If desired, dimethylglyoxime may be used instead of heptoxime to develop the color with nickel. The conditions of color formation are identical, but separate curves must be prepared. The rate of color development is slightly different for the two reagents, so that with dimethylglyoxime readings are taken exactly 10 min after addition of the reagent, whereas with heptoxime readings are taken exactly 20 min after addition of the reagent. Both systems are measured at 445 mμ. The heptoxime system is more stable. Dimethylglyoxime cannot be substituted for heptoxime in the extraction process, Method H, Sec. 5.2, under the conditions prescribed.

The calculation is the same as in Method H.

J. Method for Zinc (Tentative)

1. Principle

Zinc is separated from other metals by extraction with dithizone and is then determined by measuring the color of the zinc-dithizone complex in carbon tetrachloride. Specificity in the separation is achieved by extracting from a nearly neutral solution containing bis(2-hydroxyethyl)dithiocarbamyl ion and cyanide ion, which prevents moderate concentrations of cadmium, copper, lead, and nickel from reacting with dithizone. If excessive amounts of these metals are present, the special procedure given in Sec. 5.2 below must be followed.

The color reaction is extremely sensitive, and precautions must be taken to avoid introducing extraneous zinc during the analysis. Contamination may arise from water, reagents, and glassware, such as beakers and separatory funnels, on which zinc has been adsorbed during previous use. Appreciable blanks are generally found, and the analyst must satisfy himself that these blanks are representative and reproducible.

2. Apparatus

2.1. *Colorimetric equipment:* One of the following is required:

a. Spectrophotometer, for use at 535 $m\mu$, providing a light path of 1 cm or longer.

b. Filter photometer, providing a light path of 1 cm or longer and equipped with a greenish-yellow filter with maximum transmittance near 535 $m\mu$.

2.2. *Separatory funnels,* 125 ml, Squibb form, with ground-glass stoppers.

3. Reagents

3.1. *Standard zinc solution:* Dissolve 1.000 g zinc metal in 10 ml $1+1$ HNO_3. Dilute and boil to expel oxides of nitrogen. Transfer to a 1,000-ml volumetric flask and dilute to volume; 1.00 ml = 1.00 mg Zn.

3.2. *Redistilled water:* Distilled water redistilled from all-glass apparatus.

3.3. *Methyl red indicator:* Dissolve 0.1 g methyl red in 7.4 ml 0.05N NaOH

and dilute to 100 ml with distilled water.

3.4. *Sodium citrate solution:* Dissolve 10 g $Na_3C_6H_5O_7 \cdot 2H_2O$ in 90 ml water. Shake with 10 ml dithizone solution (I) to remove zinc, then filter.

3.5. *Ammonium hydroxide,* conc. Prepare according to Method A, Sec. 3.11.

3.6. *Potassium cyanide solution:* Dissolve 5 g KCN in 95 ml redistilled water. (CAUTION: *Toxic; take care to avoid ingestion.*)

3.7. *Acetic acid,* conc.

3.8. *Carbon tetrachloride,* zinc free.

3.9. *Bis(2-hydroxyethyl)dithiocarbamate solution:* Dissolve 4.0 g diethanolamine and 1 ml CS_2 in 40 ml methyl alcohol. Prepare every 3 or 4 days.

3.10. *Dithizone solution (I):* Dissolve 50 mg diphenylthiocarbazone in 500 ml CCl_4. Keep in the dark in a cool place.

3.11. *Dithizone solution (II):* Prepare a purified solution as follows: Measure 125 ml dithizone solution (I) into a 500-ml separatory funnel and add 100 ml distilled water followed by 3 ml conc NH_4OH. Shake well and discard the CCl_4 layer. Add 125 ml pure CCl_4, make just acidic with HCl, and shake. Draw off the CCl_4 layer and wash it twice by shaking with 50-ml portions of redistilled water; then dilute to 250 ml with pure CCl_4. Keep in a cool, dark place and do not use if more than 1 week old.

3.12. *Sodium sulfide solution (I):* Dissolve 3.0 g $Na_2S \cdot 9H_2O$ in 100 ml zinc-free water.

3.13. *Sodium sulfide solution (II):* Prepare just before use by diluting 4 ml sodium sulfide solution (I) to 100 ml.

3.14. *Nitric acid,* 6N.

3.15. *Hydrogen sulfide.*

4. Preparation of Calibration Curve

4.1. Prepare, just before use, a zinc solution containing 2.0 μg Zn per milliliter by diluting 5 ml standard zinc solution to 250 ml, then diluting 10 ml of the latter solution to 100 ml with redistilled water. Pipet 5.00, 10.00, 15.00, and 20.00 ml of the resulting solution, containing 10–40 μg Zn, into separate 125-ml separatory funnels and adjust the volumes to about 20 ml. Another funnel containing 20 ml zinc-free water is carried through as a blank.

4.2. Add 2 drops methyl red indicator and 2.0 ml sodium citrate solution to each funnel; if the indicator is not yellow at this point, add conc NH_4OH a drop at a time until the indicator just turns yellow. Next add 1.0 ml potassium cyanide solution and then acetic acid a drop at a time until the indicator just turns to a neutral peach color.

4.3. Extract the methyl red by shaking with 5 ml CCl_4 and discard the yellow CCl_4 layer. Then add 1 ml dithiocarbamate solution. Extract with 10 ml purified dithizone solution (II), shaking for 1 min.

4.4. Draw off the CCl_4 layer into another separatory funnel and repeat the extraction with successive 5-ml portions of dithizone solution (II) until the last one shows no change from the green dithizone color when viewed by transmitted light. Discard the aqueous layer.

4.5. Shake the combined dithizone extracts with a 10-ml portion of sodium sulfide solution (II), then separate the layers and repeat the washing with further 10-ml portions of Na_2S solution until the unreacted dithizone solution (II) has been completely removed, as shown by the aqueous layer remaining colorless or very pale yellow; usually three such washings are sufficient.

4.6. Finally, remove any water adhering to the stem of the funnel with a cotton swab and drain the pink CCl_4 solution into a dry 50-ml volumetric flask, using a few milliliters of fresh CCl_4 to rinse the last droplets from the funnel. Dilute to the mark with fresh CCl_4.

4.7. Determine the absorbance of the zinc dithizonate solutions at 535 mμ, and plot an absorbance-concentration curve after subtracting the absorbance of the blank. The calibration curve is linear if monochromatic light is used.

4.8. If large or erratic blanks are obtained despite the exercise of care in purifying water and reagents, they are probably caused by zinc adsorbed on the glass surface of the separatory funnels. These should be rinsed with HNO_3, then with distilled water, and finally shaken for several minutes with 5 ml sodium citrate and 5 ml dithizone. If possible, separatory funnels used for zinc analyses should be reserved for this purpose and not used for other determinations.

5. Procedure

5.1. After digestion of the sample as directed under Sec. 4.1 and 4.2 of Preliminary Treatment, take an aliquot containing 10–40 μg Zn, transfer to a clean 125-ml separatory funnel, and adjust the volume to about 20 ml. Determine the zinc in this solution exactly as described in Sec. 4 above for preparing the calibration curve.

Generally not more than 30 ml of dithizone solution (II) should be needed to extract the zinc completely; if more is required, the aliquot taken contains too much zinc or the quantity of other metals which react with dithizone exceeds the amount which can be withheld by the complexing agent. In the latter case, the procedure in Sec. 5.2 should be followed.

5.2. *Separation of excessive amounts of cadmium, copper, and lead:* This procedure should be followed when the quantity of these metals, separately or jointly, exceeds 2 mg in the aliquot taken. Place the aliquot in a 100-ml beaker, and adjust the volume to about 20 ml and the acidity to 0.4–0.5N,* by adding dilute HNO_3 or NH_4OH as necessary. Pass H_2S into the cold solution for 5 min. Filter off the precipitated sulfides using a sintered-glass filter, and wash the precipitate with two small portions of hot water. Boil the filtrate 3 to 4 min to remove H_2S; then cool, transfer to a separatory funnel, and determine the zinc as described in Sec. 5.1.

6. Calculation

$$\text{mg/l Zn} = \frac{\mu g\ Zn}{\text{ml sample}} \times \frac{100}{\text{ml aliquot}}$$

Bibliography

General

1. BUTTS, P. G.; GAHLER, A. R.; & MELLON, M. G. Colorimetric Determination of Metals in Sewage and Industrial Wastes. *Sew. Ind. Wastes* 22:1543 (1950).
2. SERFASS, E. J., ET AL. Determination of Impurities in Electroplating Solutions. *Plating* 35:156, 260, 458, 1019 (1948); 36:254, 818, 1034 (1949); 37:62, 166, 389, 495, 1057 (1950); 38:473 (1951).

3. CHRISTIE, A. A., ET AL. The Colorimetric Determination of Cadmium, Chromium, Copper, Iron, Lead, Manganese, Nickel, and Zinc in Sewage and Industrial Wastes. *Analyst* 82:336 (1957).

Cadmium

4. FISCHER, H. & LEOPOLDI, G. Determination of Small Quantities of Cadmium with Dithizone. *Mikrochim. Acta* 1:30 (1937).
5. SERFASS, E. J., ET AL. Determination of Impurities in Electroplating Solutions. *Plating* 35:458 (1948).
6. SHIRLEY, R. L.; BENNE, W. J.; & MILLER, E. J. Cadmium in Biological Materials and Foods. *Anal. Chem.* 21:300 (1949).
7. SANDELL, E. B. *Colorimetric Determination of Traces of Metals.* Interscience Publishers, New York (3rd ed., 1959).

Chromium

8. ROWLAND, G. P., JR. Photoelectric Colorimetry—Optical Study of Permanganate Ion and of Chromium-Diphenylcarbazide System. *Anal. Chem.* 11:442 (1939).
9. SALTZMAN, B. E. Microdetermination of Chromium with Diphenylcarbazide by Permanganate Oxidation. *Anal. Chem.* 24:1016 (1952).
10. URONE, P. F. Stability of Colorimetric Reagent for Chromium, *s*-Diphenylcarbazide, in Various Solvents. *Anal. Chem.* 27:1354 (1955).
11. ALLEN, T. L. Microdetermination of Chromium with 1,5-Diphenylcarbohydrazide. *Anal. Chem.* 30:447 (1958).
12. Ref. 7.

Copper

13. SMITH, G. F. & McCURDY, W. H. 2,9-Dimethyl-1,10-Phenanthroline, New Specific in Spectrophotometric Determination of Copper. *Anal. Chem.* 24:371 (1952).
14. LUKE, C. L. & CAMPBELL, M. E. Determination of Impurities in Germanium and Silicon. *Anal. Chem.* 25:1586 (1953).
15. GAHLER, A. R. Colorimetric Determination of Copper with Neocuproine. *Anal. Chem.* 26:577 (1954).
16. FULTON, J. W. & HASTINGS, J. Photometric Determinations of Copper in Aluminum and Lead-Tin Solder with Neocuproine. *Anal. Chem.* 28:174 (1956).

* The normalities of the solutions obtained in the preliminary treatment are approximately 3N for the HNO_3-H_2SO_4 digestion and approximately 0.8N for the HNO_3-$HClO_4$ digestion.

17. FRANK, A. J.; GOULSTON, A. B.; & DEA-CUTIS, A. A. Spectrophotometric Determination of Copper in Titanium. *Anal. Chem.* 29:750 (1957).

Iron

18. FORTUNE, W. B. & MELLON, M. G. Determination of Iron with *o*-Phenanthroline: a Spectrophotometric Study. *Ind. Eng. Chem., Anal. Ed.* 10:60 (1938).
19. RYAN, J. A. & BOTHAM, G. H. Iron in Aluminum Alloys: Colorimetric Determination Using 1,10-Phenanthroline. *Anal. Chem.* 21:1521 (1949).
20. REITZ, L. K.; O'BRIEN, A. S.; & DAVIS, T. L. Evaluation of Three Iron Methods Using a Factorial Experiment. *Anal. Chem.* 22:1470 (1950).
21. MORRIS, R. L. Determination of Iron in Water in the Presence of Heavy Metals. *Anal. Chem.* 24:1376 (1952).
22. Ref. 7.

Lead

23. WICHMANN, H. J. Isolation and Determination of Traces of Metals—Dithizone System. *Ind. Eng. Chem., Anal. Ed.* 11:66 (1939).
24. BRICKER, L. G. & PROCTOR, K. L. Application of Colorimetry to the Analysis of Corrosion-Resistant Steels: Determination of Lead. *Ind. Eng. Chem., Anal. Ed.* 17:511 (1945).
25. SERFASS, E. J. & LEVINE, W. S. *Monthly Rev. Am. Electroplaters Soc.* 33:1079 (1946).
26. *Official Methods of Analysis.* Assoc. Official Agricultural Chemists, Washington, D. C. (9th ed., 1960).

Manganese

27. WILLARD, H. H. & GREATHOUSE, L. H. Colorimetric Determination of Manganese by Oxidation with Periodate. *J. Am. Chem. Soc.* 39:2366 (1917).
28. MEHLIG, J. P. Colorimetric Determination of Manganese with Periodate. *Ind. Eng. Chem., Anal. Ed.* 11:274 (1939).
29. SERFASS, E. J. & LEVINE, W. S. Determination of Impurities in Electroplating Solutions. *Monthly Rev. Am. Electroplaters Soc.* 34:320 (1947).
30. SERFASS, E. J. & MURACA, R. F. *Procedures for Analyzing Metal Finishing Wastes.* Ohio River Valley Water Sanitation Commission, Cincinnati, Ohio (1954).
31. Ref. 7.

Nickel

32. Ref. 1.
33. FERGUSON, R. C. & BANKS, C. V. Spectrophotometric Determination of Nickel Using 1,2-Cycloheptanedionedioxime (Heptoxime). *Anal. Chem.* 23:448, 1486 (1951).
34. Ref. 30.

Zinc

35. SERFASS, E. J., ET AL. *Chemist Analyst* 36:55 (1947).
36. SERFASS, E. J., ET AL. Research Rept. Serial No. 3, Am. Electroplaters Soc., Newark, N.J. (1947), p. 22.
37. SERFASS, E. J., ET AL. Determination of Impurities in Electroplating Solutions. *Plating* 36:254, 818 (1949).
38. Ref. 1.
39. Ref. 30.
40. Ref. 7.

Nickel

See Metals (Heavy), Methods H and I.

Nitrogen (Ammonia)

For industrial wastes, use the ammonia distillation method given in Part III (Method B). If the wastes are acid or alkaline, neutralize with

$1N$ NaOH or $1N$ H_2SO_4 to a pH of 7.4 before adding the phosphate buffer. In dealing with certain wastes, it is desirable to determine the pH level following distillation. In case the pH has not been properly maintained in the range 7.2 to 7.6, greater amounts of buffer will usually suffice.

Nitrogen (Nitrate)

The determination of nitrates in industrial wastes is seldom significant. The methods given for sewage in Part III are applicable, although they are not very satisfactory and must be used with caution.

Nitrogen (Nitrite)

Nitrite nitrogen may be determined on a sample of clarified and neutralized waste by the method given for sewage in Part III.

Nitrogen (Organic)

Organic nitrogen is determined by the kjeldahl method given in Part III.

Nitrogen (Total Kjeldahl)

Total kjeldahl nitrogen may be run on the original sample, without first distilling the free ammonia, by following the procedure for organic nitrogen.

Odor (*Tentative*)*

Increased reuse of available water supplies has led to greater emphasis of the subjective quality criteria of water. Domestic consumers and process industries such as the food, beverage and pharmaceutical manufacturers require water essentially free of tastes and

---

* This method of test is identical to ASTM D1297.[5]

odors. Most organic and some inorganic chemicals contribute taste and odor. These may originate from municipal and industrial waste discharges, natural sources (such as decomposition of vegetable matter), or from associated microbiological activity. Taste tests are not generally needed and with few exceptions are not recommended for wastewaters or untreated effluents. Odor tests are important in measuring the intensity and nature of polluting sources. A combination of odor testing and instrumental analyses can be used to trace odor sources. In most cases it is necessary to make measurements of the odor in both the wastewater discharges and the receiving body if the actual relationship and effect is to be determined.

Odor effects resulting from a mixture of several chemicals are extremely complex. The blend of several odorants may produce an odor much greater in intensity than might be expected from the individual odors. There may also be the opposite effect; for example, the resulting odor may be of lesser intensity than expected. These complex effects have been demonstrated in laboratory and field studies.[1, 2, 3]

The ultimate odor testing device is the human nose. Because people vary in their response to different stimuli and from day to day or during a day for a given stimulus, extreme precision is not possible.[4] Consequently, odor results obtained by a number of persons are of greater meaning than a single tester's results. Whether 1 or 20 persons make the threshold test will depend on the ultimate purpose of the measurement or availability of personnel.

1. General Discussion

1.1. *Principle:* The sample of water is diluted with odor-free water until a dilution that is of the least definitely perceptible odor to the tester is found. At least two persons are necessary. One makes the dilutions and one or more determine the odor intensity. The odorous sample is selected from among three flasks, two of which contain odor-free water.

1.2. *Qualitative descriptions:* A satisfactory system for characterizing odor has not been developed. Table 18 (Part I, Odor) is presented as a guide; it has been used in the potable water field in lieu of a better system.

1.3. *Sampling and storage:* Odor tests must be made as soon as possible after sampling in glass-stoppered bottles. Fill the bottles completely and cool to 40°C if the temperature is greater. Storage may lead to changes in odor intensity or character through biological, chemical or physical reactions. If storage is necessary, the sample should be refrigerated. This will minimize but not necessarily eliminate changes. Precooling the samples in an ice bath before refrigeration will prevent contraction and subsequent absorption of refrigerator odors in the vapor space.

1.4. *Dechlorination:* Some waste waters which have been chlorinated may require odor testing as part of a control program. In such cases it often is advisable to determine odor of the chlorinated supply as well as of the dechlorinated water to determine the effect of chloroorganic derivatives. Dechlorination is achieved using arsenite or thiosulfate in exact stoichiometric quantity as described in Part III under Nitrogen (Ammonia), Method A, Sec. 3.7. It is important to check a blank to which a similar amount of dechlorinating agent has been added to determine if any odor has been imparted. Such odor usually disappears upon standing if excess reagent has not been added.

1.5. *Temperature:* The threshold odor results may vary as a function of temperature. The extent of this variation will depend on the chemical and physical characteristics of the odorous components. A temperature of 40°C, which approximates body temperature, is recommended for this test. Hot tests at 60°C have been used for testing drinking waters of very low threshold intensity, but this requires greater care. Many odor components readily volatilize at this temperature and the odor is frequently lost once the odor tester removes the stopper. In such cases the tester frequently cannot confirm initial response upon further inhalation. If temperatures other than 40°C are used, the results should bear this notation. It is good practice to report the sampling temperature also.

2. Apparatus

To assure reliable threshold measurements, it is necessary that all glassware be odor-free. Glassware must be thoroughly cleaned with nonodorous soap and acid cleaning solution, followed by rinsing with odor-free water. Glassware used in threshold testing should be reserved for that purpose only. Storage of glassware in clean areas does not assure an odor-free condition. Glassware must be recleaned prior to use. In no case must rubber, cork or plastic be used for the vessels or their stoppers.

2.1. *Water bath,* constant temperature, capable of temperature control of ± 1°C.

2.2. *Erlenmeyer flasks,* glass-stoppered, 500 ml, to hold sample dilutions during testing.

2.3. *Sample bottles,* glass-stoppered, to hold original samples.

2.4. *Pipets,* Mohr, 10 ml and 1 ml graduated in tenths; transfer, 25, 10, and 5 ml.

2.5. *Thermometer,* 0–110°C, chemical or metal-stem dial type.

3. Reagents

3.1. *Odor-free water:* Dilution water must be prepared fresh, as needed, by filtration through a bed of activated carbon. For precise work and where supplies are adequate, distilled water may be used as the source of water. If tap water is used, it is necessary to check the filtered water for chlorine residual to assure that no chlorinous residual exists. If chlorine is found, the water must be carefully dechlorinated (see Sec. 1.4).

The odor-free water generator may be made from a glass column 3 ft long and 2 in. in diameter packed with granular activated carbon between glass wool pulp in the column ends. Use all glass connections and tubing; no rubber or plastic is permissible. A convenient odor-free water generator may be made as shown in Fig. 24. When the generator is first started it should be flushed to remove carbon fines before the odor-free water is used.

The quality of water obtained from the odor-free water generator should be checked daily. This may be done by comparing the odor of this water against a sample prepared by filtration through a portion of fresh carbon packed in a small glass tube. Subtle odors of biological origin are often found if moist carbon filters are permitted to stand idle between test periods.

4. Precautions

4.1. *Atmosphere:* The area must be free of interfering odors. Background odor has been shown to affect threshold odor results.[3] Ideal control may be achieved by designating a separate area for sensory testing and providing activated-carbon filtered inlet air of controlled, constant temperature and humidity. A temperature of approximately 70°F and a relative humidity of approximately 50 per cent are recommended.

4.2. *Persons:* Testers should wash their hands and faces with odorless soap or detergent. They should refrain from smoking, spicy foods, or other substances that leave an aftertaste or odor for at least 30 min before making the tests. The testers should be free from colds or allergies that affect olfactory response. Testing frequency must not be so great as to induce olfactory fatigue. Frequent rests in an odor-free atmosphere are recommended.

The test should be conducted by at least two persons. The person making the odor measurement should not prepare the samples and should not know the dilution concentrations being evaluated. For precise work a panel of testers should be used. These persons should have been taught the testing procedure and their relative sensitivity determined to such standard chemicals as *n*-butanol and phenol. Some persons may not be suited as odor testers.

4.3. *Color and turbidity:* Many waste waters are colored or have a decided turbidity, which will bias the odor testing results. Use of a colored

lighting system will eliminate this bias in most cases. If turbidity is still a factor, it may be necessary to paint the exterior of the flasks to make them opaque.

5. Procedure

5.1. *Characterization:* A 200-ml sample in a 500-ml glass-stoppered erlenmeyer flask heated to 40°C in a water bath is checked by normal inhalation for odor characterization. Many wastewaters of complex composition will exhibit odors other than the sample odor if diluted. If such intermediate characterizations are desired, dilutions should be prepared according to the procedure described for the threshold odor test. The odor characteristic and the dilutions at which a distinct difference is noted should be recorded.

5.2. *Threshold odor units:* The threshold odor for wastewaters is reported in odor intensity index units * (OII), which is the number of times the original sample must be diluted in half with odor-free water for the odor to just be discernible.

5.3. *Preliminary threshold odor test:* The number of dilutions necessary during the threshold odor test may be minimized if the odor intensity is first estimated by a preliminary test. A sample aliquot of 25 ml is added by a pipet to 175 ml of odor-free water in a 500-ml erlenmeyer flask. The pipet transfer should be made with care.

---

* Threshold odor number (TO) defines the greastest dilution of the sample with odor-free water to yield the least definitely perceptible odor. These terms are related as follows:

$$TO = 2^{OII}$$

OII is used with wastewaters because of the complexity of the TON values if odorant concentration is high.

Sample solution should not touch the neck of the flask. The flask is stoppered and heated to 40°C in a water bath. The flask is then vigorously shaken or swirled, the cover removed and the presence of odor tested using normal inhalation. If no odor is found, lower dilutions are prepared until odor is detected. A range of such dilutions is generally made at the start to expedite testing. Odor testing, however, is always from the highest dilution toward lower dilutions. If odor is detected, greater dilutions are made, always being careful not to transfer less than 10 ml of the previous dilution. These pre-liminary tests will determine the approximate threshold level.

5.4. *Threshold odor test:* A range of sample dilutions of higher and lower odorant concentration than indicated by the preliminary test are prepared. Table 32 will facilitate this preparation. If only two persons are involved, the one making the preliminary odor test may prepare the sample dilutions for this series. Three clean, coded, odor-free flasks are presented for each test trial. Two contain 200 ml of odor-free water. For the first trial the person preparing the dilutions should use a flask containing less than half the sam-

TABLE 32—DILUTION OF SAMPLE AND REPORTING OF RESULTS

Dilution	Volume Transferred to Odor Flask ml [a]	Threshold Odor Number (Dilution Factor)	Odor Intensity Index, OII
Original sample	200	1	0
	100	2	1
	50	4	2
	25	8	3
	12.5	16	4
Dilution A (25 ml of original sample diluted to 200 ml)	50	32	5
	25	64	6
	12.5	128	7
Dilution B (25 ml of dilution A diluted to 200 ml)	50	256	8
	25	512	9
	12.5	1,024	10
Dilution C (25 ml of dilution B diluted to 200 ml)	50	2,050	11
	25	4,100	12
	12.5	8,200	13
Dilution D (25 ml of dilution C diluted to 200 ml)	50	16,400	14
	25	32,800	15
	12.5	65,500	16
Dilution E (25 ml of dilution D diluted to 200 ml)	50	131,000	17
	25	262,000	18
	12.5	534,000	19
	6.25	1,050,000	20

[a] Volume in odor flask made up to 200 ml with odor-free water.

ple concentration found to be the threshold level in the preliminary test. These flasks are heated to 40°C and offered in sets of three to the odor tester. The position of the odor-containing flasks and the two blanks should be randomized. The odor tester shakes each flask, removes the cover, and tests for odor. (Care should be exercised not to handle the neck of the flasks to prevent any odor transfer.) If no odor is detected, the tester shall decrease the dilution (increase concentration) and repeat the procedure until an odor is detected. The results are then recorded. During the testing procedure, dilutions are offered in generally increasing concentration. However, especially near threshold level, sets of three blanks and some repeat or lower dilutions should be inserted into the sequence. This discourages guessing.

The odor intensity index value for each tester is recorded, as well as the average and range of all tests.

6. Calculation

6.1. The odor intensity index is calculated as follows:

$$OII = 3.3 \log \frac{200}{A} + 3D$$

where A = ml of sample or ml of aliquot of the primary dilution used and D = number of 25:175 primary dilutions required to reach the determinable magnitude of odor intensity. The relationship between sample dilution and odor intensity is given in Table 32.

7. Interpretation

There is no precise odor value. Duplicate values for a tester with a specified odorant will agree within one OII value. The value will vary from person to person and from day to day. Person-chemical interactions exist. The results will differ by choice of panelists, panel size, and nature of chemical odorants.

Bibliography

1. ROSEN, A. A.; PETER, J. B.; & MIDDLETON, F. M. Odor Thresholds of Mixed Organic Chemicals. *J. WPCF* 34:7 (1962).
2. BAKER, R. A. Critical Evaluation of Olfactory Measurement. *J. WPCF* 34: 582 (1962).
3. BAKER, R. A. Odor Effects of Aqueous Mixtures of Organic Chemicals. *J. WPCF* 35:728 (1963).
4. ROSEN, A. A.; SKEEL, R. T.; & ETTINGER, M. B. Relationship of River Water Odor to Specific Organic Contaminants. *J. WPCF* 35:777 (1963).
5. *Manual on Industrial Water and Industrial Waste Water.* Amer. Soc. for Testing Materials, 2nd ed., 3rd printing (1963).

Additional References

6. INGOLS, R. S. & RIDENOUR, G. M. The Elimination of Phenolic Tastes by Chloro-Oxidation. *Water and Sewage Works* 95:187 (1948).
7. SILVEY, J. K. G.; RUSSELL, J. C.; REDDEN, D. R.; & McCORMICK, W. C. Actinomycetes and Common Tastes and Odors. *J. AWWA* 42:1018 (1950).
8. BRAUS, H.; MIDDLETON, F. M.; & WALTON, G. A Study of the Concentration and Estimation of Organic Chemical Compounds in Raw and Filtered Surface Waters. *Anal. Chem.* 23:1160 (1951).
9. ETTINGER, M. B. & RUCHHOFT, C. C. Effect of Stepwise Chlorination on Taste and Odor Producing Intensity of Some Phenolic Compounds. *J. AWWA* 43: 561 (1951).
10. MIDDLETON, F. M.; GRANT, W.; & ROSEN, A. A. Drinking Water Taste and Odor. *Ind. Eng. Chem.* 48:268 (1956).

11. SILVEY, J. K. G. & ROACH, A. W. Actinomycetes May Cause Tastes and Odors in Water Supplies. *Pub. Works* 87:103 (1956).

12. BEAN, E. L. Taste and Odor Control at Philadelphia. *J. AWWA* 49:205 (1957).

13. SIGWORTH, E. A. Control of Odor and Taste in Water Supplies. *J. AWWA* 49:1507 (1957).

14. BARTHOLOMEW, K. A. Control of Earthy, Musty Odors in Water by Treament with Residual Copper. *J. AWWA* 50:481 (1958).

15. BURTTSCHELL, R. H.; ROSEN, A. A.; MIDDLETON, F. M.; & ETTINGER, M. B. Chlorine Derivatives of Phenol Causing Taste and Odor. *J. AWWA* 51:205 (1959).

16. RYCKMAN, D. W. & GRIGAROPOULOS, S. G. Use of Chlorine and Its Derivatives in Taste and Odor Removal. *J. AWWA* 51:1268 (1959).

17. KINNEY, J. E. Evaluating the Taste and Odor Control Problem. *J. AWWA* 52:505 (1960).

Oxygen (Dissolved)

Various modifications of the iodometric titration for dissolved oxygen (DO), as discussed in Part III, are applicable to some industrial wastes. In such cases the titrimetric procedures are probably as accurate and precise as the polarographic techniques discussed below. However, in some wastes, even in 10 per cent concentrations, the titrimetric procedure, or any of its modifications, either is in serious error or is not applicable.

New polarographic instruments for determining DO have developed rapidly and numerous modifications are now available commercially. The dropping mercury electrode system is technically satisfactory, but the loss of mercury or the necessity of cleaning the mercury makes use of the instrument expensive and/or annoying. Most of the new DO instruments use solid metal electrodes with a plastic film cover and an electrolyte solution between the plastic film and the metal electrodes. Thus, the DO must diffuse through the plastic film and then through the electrolyte solution to the electrode surface. In most of the instruments, a current at a fixed potential is imposed across the electrodes. The variations in DO are correlated with the depolarizing activity of the oxygen of the gas and/or water sample. By a suitable choice of metals in the electrode pair, the electrochemical potential between the metals can provide the necessary voltage for electron flow, whereas the DO level can be indicated by its depolarizing effect. This system provides freedom from renewing batteries for intermittent observations and is particularly desirable for extended field observations.

In all of the instruments, the DO level is recorded as a factor of its "activity," or in other words as a percentage of the saturation value. Thus, the same instrument reading may indicate several different DO values if samples have different saturation values, as in an estuary with different saline concentrations, or in a stratified lake with water at different temperatures. The instruments are calibrated by readings against air and/or a water sample which has saturated oxygen, as well as in a sample with zero DO, preferably at the temperature of the samples to be studied.

The membrane over the electrodes must be tough or thick enough to withstand the mechanical shock of normal handling without rupturing, but should not be so thick as to require too much time for changes in the DO level to diffuse and reach equilibrium at the electrode surfaces. The membrane and electrolyte solution dimensions must be free of changes from different pressures or the diffusion rate, and hence the apparent DO, will change with the depth of submergence of the sensing elements without any DO change. Where the electrode system is used for indicating DO in temperature-stratified lakes, time must be allowed for equilibrium of the electrodes with the new temperatures, or the electrodes and their accessories must be designed to attain the new temperature quickly. This factor of rapid mixing is included in some instruments and not in others.

Where a group of samples has a constant temperature and conductivity, DO variations are readily obtained as the single variable. When certain industrial wastes are present that interfere with the titrimetric procedure, such as paper mill effluents, a polarographic DO instrument provides the only accurate technique.

Because of the limited time since the commercial introduction of the instruments, the Standard Methods Committee has not had time to evaluate or compare the various individual products. It is believed that if each analyst follows the manufacturer's directions carefully, the instrument can give the accuracy and precision of DO values claimed by the manufacturer.

Polarographic Method (Tentative)

1. General Discussion

The polarographic method is suggested as an alternative to the iodometric titration, for use especially under conditions where the titrimetric method and its modifications are subject to serious errors in the presence of high concentrations of industrial wastes.

1.1. *Interference:* Gaseous or volatile oxidants stronger than molecular oxygen will interfere in the technique described because they will be discharged at the voltage used. They will be removed by the nitrogen stream, so that their diffusion currents will not appear in the blank reading. The most frequently encountered substances of this class are free halogens.

Certain heavy-metal ions, and high concentrations of soaps or detergents, distort the current-voltage relationship characteristic of DO and may cause errors in the determination, when the operating voltage is not determined in their presence. These errors may be minimized or reduced by using the waste itself in determining the electrode voltage to be used.

1.2. *Sampling and storage:* In collecting samples for analysis, the same techniques should be employed as those described for the titrimetric procedures in Part III.

2. Apparatus

Any of the commercially available polarographs may be used, or one may be constructed in the laboratory, as described by Petering and Daniels,[2] Ingols,[7] Kolthoff and Lingane,[9] or Muller.[13]

3. Reagents

3.1. *Potassium chloride solution,* 0.01*N*. Dissolve 0.75 g KCl in distilled water and dilute to 1 liter.

3.2. *Methyl red solution:* Dissolve 100 mg methyl red in 7.4 ml 0.05*N* NaOH and dilute to 100 ml; 1 ml contains 1.0 mg methyl red.

3.3. *Nitrogen gas.*

4. Standardization

4.1. *Setup of instrument:* The instrument should be assembled, adjusted, and tested in accordance with the manufacturer's instructions.

4.2. *Determination of operating voltage:* Various authors have recommended the use of voltages from 0.3 to as high as 1.0. However, it is considered advisable for each laboratory to determine the best operating voltage for its particular instrument, conditions, and wastes.

A solution of KCl is aerated for a few minutes. Complete saturation is unnecessary. A sample is then introduced into the instrument, and the stock solution of methyl red is added to bring the final concentration of methyl red to approximately 15 mg/l. The voltage on the electrode is then varied in steps of 0.02 v from 0 to 2 v. At each voltage, the current, or galvanometer deflection, is read and recorded. It will be noted that the current increases as the mercury drop grows, then abruptly decreases when the drop falls. The maximum deflection is always taken as the reading.

A graph is then drawn, using voltage as the abscissa and current as the ordinate. The resulting curve will ordinarily have the form shown in Fig. 37.

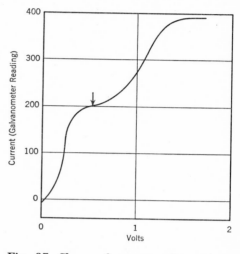

Fig. 37. **Shape of current-voltage curve for DO**

The center of the plateau between the two waves, indicated by the arrow in the figure, corresponds to the voltage which should subsequently be used.

When working with industrial wastes, the accuracy of the DO determination is improved by determining the optimum operating voltage in a sample of the waste itself. For this determination, an aerated sample of the waste is placed in the cell of the instrument, and current readings are taken at 0.02-v intervals from 0 to 3 v, or until the current becomes too great to be measured. The sample is then deoxygenated by bubbling nitrogen through it rapidly for 5 min. The gas tube is raised above the level of the liquid, and nitrogen is passed gently over the surface of the solution while a second set of readings is taken at the same voltages previously used. The graph of current versus voltage is now drawn, but the difference between the two readings at each voltage is the ordinate in this case. The curve may be found to be distorted from the form shown in Fig. 37. The voltage chosen for subsequent operation should lie at the midpoint of the best plateau in the curve. The use of "optimum operating voltages" which are far removed from the optimum voltage used in the preparation of the standard curve should be avoided unless proved by experimental work on the waste under consideration.

4.3. *Calibration:* A simple calibration method of sufficient accuracy is as follows: Several liters of $0.1N$ potassium chloride solution are prepared. A sample is removed by siphoning, and the DO is determined by the iodometric titration. A second sample is taken in a pipet and used to determine the current before and after deaeration, as described below in Sec. 5. The DO concentration in the stock solution is then changed by bubbling air, oxygen, or nitrogen through it, and samples are again taken for the two methods of analysis. This process is repeated until a set of points is obtained which covers the desired range of DO concentration in steps not greater than about 1 mg/l. The data are then corrected to a standard temperature as described in Sec. 6, and the corrected values are used for preparation of a standard curve. *When a new capillary is installed in the instrument, a new standard curve must be prepared.*

5. Procedure

5.1. Place the unknown sample in the cell of the instrument and add 0.15 ml methyl red solution for each 10 ml of sample. The predetermined voltage

is applied to the electrode, and the resulting current is noted. This part of the procedure should be executed rapidly to avoid changes in the DO content of the sample due to exposure to the air. Because the time actually required to obtain the initial galvanometer reading is only 30 to 40 sec, special precautions to protect the sample from air are not required. Aeration of the sample while it is being introduced into the cell should be held to a minimum.

5.2. A thermometer is inserted in the sample, and its temperature is read.

5.3. The DO is then removed by bubbling nitrogen through the sample rapidly for 5 min. The gas tube is lifted above the surface of the sample, and nitrogen is allowed to flow gently over the surface of the sample while a second current reading is taken.

5.4. The difference between the two readings is corrected for temperature as described in Sec. 6, then converted to DO concentration with the aid of the standard curve prepared as described in Sec. 4.3 above.

6. Calculation

The temperature coefficient of the diffusion current at 20°C has been reported as 1.6 per cent and as 1.4 per cent per degree centigrade in various types of solutions. The value 1.4 per cent per degree is closer to the true value for most industrial wastes. The formula for converting the observed difference in galvanometer reading, G, to a value, G_s, corresponding to a standard temperature, t_s, is:

$$G_s = G + 0.014G(t_s - t)$$

Using the corrected G_s, the DO concentration is read from the calibration curve.

7. Precision and Accuracy

The precision of the method in a 0.01N KCl solution containing 3.58 mg/l DO was represented by a standard deviation of 0.06 mg/l DO ($n = 1$; 1×10). The precision on industrial wastes has not been reported.

The following table indicates the probable accuracy of the method; the wastes were at dilutions of 1 to 25 per cent in BOD dilution water which had been saturated with DO:

Waste	Per Cent Recovery of Calculated DO
Penicillin	100–109
Titanium	107–122
Laundry waste	99–63
Dairy waste	100–93
Packinghouse waste	98–106
Metal plating waste	101–89

The use of single readings at one potential or the difference between the current readings at two potentials as the index of DO concentration cannot be applied to industrial wastes because of the frequent occurrence of materials which introduce serious errors in such readings. The difference between readings before and after deaeration, as described by Seaman and Allen [11] is much less subject to interferences.

Bibliography

1. VITEK, V. Polarographic Determination of Oxygen Contained in Industrial Gases and Waters. *Chim. & Ind. 29*: 215 (1933); *Coll. Czechoslov. Chem. Communs. 7*:537 (1935).
2. PETERING, H. G. & DANIELS, F. Determination of Dissolved Oxygen by Means of the Dropping Mercury Electrode, with Applications in Biology. *J. Am. Chem. Soc. 60*:2796 (1938).
3. BLINKS, L. R. & SKOW, R. D. The Time Course of Photosynthesis as Shown by a Rapid Electrode Method for Oxygen. *Proc. Natl. Acad. Sci. US 24*:420 (1938).
4. PETERING, H. G.; DUGGAR, D. M.; & DANIELS, F. Quantum Efficiency of Chlorella. *J. Am. Chem. Soc. 61*:3525 (1939).
5. BAUMBERGER, J. P. Relation Between Oxidation-Reduction Potential and Oxygen Consumption Rate of Yeast Cell Suspension. *Cold Spring Harbor Symposia Quant. Biol. 7*:195 (1939).
6. MANNING, M. A Method of Obtaining Continuous Records of Dissolved Oxygen in Lake Waters. *Ecology 21*:509 (1940).
7. INGOLS, R. S. Determination of Dissolved Oxygen by the Dropping Mercury Electrode. *Sew. Works J. 13*:1097 (1941).
8. GIGUERE, P. A. & LANGIER, L. Polarographic Determination of Dissolved Oxygen in Sea Water. *Can. J. Research 23B*:76 (1945); *Chem. Abs. 39*: 2264 (1945).
9. KOLTHOFF, I. M. & LINGANE, J. J. *Polarography*. Interscience Publishers, New York (1946).
10. MOORE, E. W.; MORRIS, J. C.; & OKUN, D. A. The Polarographic Determination of Dissolved Oxygen in Water and Sewage. *Sew. Works J. 20*:1041 (1948).
11. SEAMAN, W. & ALLEN, W. Polarographic Determination of Dissolved Oxygen in Water Containing Industrial Effluent. *Sew. Ind. Wastes 22*:912 (1950).
12. HIXSON, A. W. & GADEN, E. L. Oxygen Transfer in Submerged Fermentation. *Ind. Eng. Chem. 42*:1792 (1950).
13. MULLER, O. H. *The Polarographic Method of Analysis*. Chemical Education Co., New York (1951).
14. RAND, C. M. & HEUKELEKIAN, H. Determination of Dissolved Oxygen in Industrial Wastes by the Winkler and Polarographic Methods. *Sew. Ind. Wastes 23*:1141 (1951).

Oxygen Demand (Biochemical)

Most organic wastes from food processing and other sources, which are susceptible to biologic decomposition, may be analyzed for biochemical oxygen demand (BOD) by the dilution method described for sewage (Part III). Particular care should be taken in properly neutralizing the wastes, in seeding the dilution water with a good sewage seed or waste-polluted stream water, and in using the proper dilution so that toxicity is removed and the maximum BOD value is obtained. If increasing dilutions show increasing BOD values, the dilutions should be increased until the BOD levels off at a maximum figure.

Oxygen Demand (Chemical)

The chemical oxygen demand (COD) determination provides a measure of the oxygen equivalent of that portion of the organic matter in a sample that is susceptible to oxidation by a strong chemical oxidant. The values are an important, rapid parameter for stream and industrial-waste studies and control of waste treatment plants. In the absence of a catalyst, however, the method fails to include some organic compounds (such as acetic acid) which are biologically available to the stream organisms, while including some biologic compounds (such as cellulose) which are not a part of the immediate biochemical load on the oxygen assets of the receiving water. The carbonaceous portion of nitrogenous compounds can be determined, but there is no reduction of the dichromate by any ammonia in a waste or by any ammonia liberated from the proteinaceous matter (except in the presence of chlorides, as discussed later). With certain wastes containing toxic substances, this test may be the only method for determining the organic load. Where wastes contain only readily available, organic bacterial food and no toxic matter, the results can be used to approximate the ultimate carbonaceous BOD values.

The use of exactly the same technique each time is important because only a part of the organic matter is included, the proportion depending on the chemical oxidant used, the structure of the organic compounds, and the manipulative procedure.

The dichromate reflux method has been selected for the COD determination because it has advantages over other oxidants in reproducibility, applicability to a wide variety of samples, and ease of manipulation. The test will find its major usefulness in a plant for waste control purposes after many values have been obtained and correlated with some other important parameter or parameters.

1. General Discussion

1.1. *Principle:* Most types of organic matter are destroyed by a boiling mixture of chromic and sulfuric acids. A sample is refluxed with known amounts of potassium dichromate and sulfuric acid, and the excess dichromate is titrated with ferrous ammonium sulfate. The amount of oxidizable organic matter is proportional to the potassium dichromate consumed.

1.2. Interference and inadequacies: Straight-chain aliphatic compounds, aromatic hydrocarbons, and pyridine are not oxidized to any appreciable extent, although this method gives more nearly complete oxidation than the permanganate method. The straight-chain compounds are more effectively oxidized if silver sulfate is added as a catalyst; however, silver sulfate reacts with chlorides, bromides, or iodides to produce precipitates which are only partially oxidized by the procedure. There is no advantage in using the catalyst in the presence of aromatic hydrocarbons, but it is essential to the oxidation of straight-chain alcohols and acids.

The oxidation and difficulties caused by the presence of chlorides in the sample may be corrected by employing the following method, which is a complexing technique for the elimination of chlorides from the reaction. This is accomplished by adding mercuric sulfate to the samples before refluxing. This ties up the chloride ion as a soluble mercuric chloride complex which greatly reduces its ability to react further.

1.3. Application: The method can be used to determine COD values of 50 mg/l or more with the concentrated dichromate. With the dilute dichromate titrant, values below 10 mg/l are less accurate, but may be used to indicate an order of magnitude.

1.4. Sampling and storage: Unstable samples should be tested without delay, and samples containing settleable solids should be homogenized by means of a

blender to permit representative sampling. If there is to be a delay before analysis, the sample may be preserved by acidification with sulfuric acid. Initial dilutions in volumetric flasks should be made on wastes containing a high COD value in order to reduce the error which is inherent in measuring small sample volume.

2. Apparatus

Reflux apparatus, consisting of 250-ml erlenmeyer flasks with ground-glass 24/40 neck * and 300-mm jacket Liebig, West, or equivalent condensers ** with 24/40 ground-glass joint, and a hot plate with sufficient power to produce at least 9 watts/sq in. of heating surface, or equivalent, to insure an adequate boiling of the contents of the refluxing mixture.

3. Reagents

3.1. Standard potassium dichromate solution, 0.250N. Dissolve 12.259 g $K_2Cr_2O_7$, primary standard grade, previously dried at 103°C for 2 hr, in distilled water and dilute to 1,000 ml. Note: Nitrite nitrogen exerts a COD of 1.14 mg per mg nitrite N. To eliminate the interference of nitrites, sulfamic acid, in the amount of 10 mg for every 1 mg of nitrite N in the refluxing flask, may be added to the dichromate solution. Thus, 0.12 g of sulfamic acid per liter of dichromate solution will eliminate the interference of nitrites up to 6 mg/l in the sample.

3.2. Sulfuric acid reagent, conc. H_2SO_4 containing 22 g silver sulfate, Ag_2SO_4, per 9-lb bottle (1 to 2 days required for dissolution).

---

* Corning 5000 or equal.
** Corning 2360, 91548, or equal.

3.3. *Standard ferrous ammonium sulfate titrant, 0.25N.* Dissolve 98 g $Fe(NH_4)_2(SO_4)_2 \cdot 6H_2O$ in distilled water. Add 20 ml conc H_2SO_4, cool, and dilute to 1,000 ml. This solution must be standardized against the standard potassium dichromate solution daily.

Standardization: Dilute 10.0 ml standard potassium dichromate solution to about 100 ml. Add 30 ml conc H_2SO_4 and allow to cool. Titrate with the ferrous ammonium sulfate titrant, using 2 or 3 drops of ferroin indicator.

$$\text{Normality} = \frac{\text{ml } K_2Cr_2O_7 \times 0.25}{\text{ml Fe } (NH_4)_2 (SO_4)_2}$$

3.4. *Ferroin indicator solution:* Dissolve 1.485 g 1,10-phenanthroline monohydrate, together with 0.695 g $FeSO_4 \cdot 7H_2O$ in water and dilute to 100 ml. This indicator solution may be purchased already prepared.*

3.5. *Silver sulfate,* reagent powder. (See Sec. 3.2.)

3.6. *Mercuric sulfate,* analytical grade crystals.

3.7. *Sulfamic acid.* Note: Required only if the interference of nitrites is to be eliminated. (See Sec. 3.1.)

4. Procedure

4.1. Place 0.4 g $HgSO_4$, which may be measured conveniently in a Hach Company spoon No. 638 or equal, in a refluxing flask. Add 20.0 ml sample, or an aliquot diluted to 20.0 ml with distilled water, and mix. Then add 10.0 ml potassium dichromate titrant. Carefully add 30 ml conc H_2SO_4 containing Ag_2SO_4 with mixing. Pumice granules or glass beads

---

* G. F. Smith Chemical Company, Columbus, Ohio.

should be added to the reflux mixture to prevent bumping, which can be severe and dangerous. (CAUTION: *The reflux mixture must be thoroughly mixed before heat is applied. If this is not done, local heating occurs in the bottom of the flask, and the mixture may be blown out of the condenser.*)

The use of 0.4 g $HgSO_4$ is sufficient to complex 40 mg chloride ion, or 2 g/l when 20 ml of sample is used. If more chlorides are present, more $HgSO_4$ must be added to maintain a $HgSO_4$:Cl ratio of 10:1. If a slight precipitate develops, it does not adversely affect the determination.

4.2. Attach the flask to the condenser and reflux the mixture for 2 hr. A shorter reflux period may be used for particular wastes if it has been found to give the maximum COD. Cool and then wash down the condenser with distilled water.

4.3. Dilute the mixture to about 100 ml, cool to room temperature, and titrate the excess dichromate with standard ferrous ammonium sulfate, using ferroin indicator. Generally 2–3 drops of the indicator are used. Although the quantity of ferroin is not critical, it should not vary on sequential samples. This, however, depends on the individual analyst. The color change is sharp, going from blue-green to reddish-brown and should be taken as the endpoint although the blue-green color may reappear.

4.4. A blank consisting of 20 ml distilled water instead of the sample, together with the reagents, is refluxed in the same manner.

4.5. *Alternate procedure for other sample sizes:* For particular situations, a sample size ranging from 10.0 ml to 50.0 ml may be used, providing the volumes, weights, and normalities for the other reagents are adjusted accordingly. Typical examples are given in the following table:

volume increases, corresponding lower concentrations of chlorides will be complexed by 0.4 g of $HgSO_4$.

Sample Size ml	0.25N Stand. Dichromate ml	Conc H_2SO_4 with Ag_2SO_4 ml	$HgSO_4$ g	Normality of $Fe(NH_4)_2(SO_4)_2$	Final Vol. Before Titration ml
10.0	5.0	15	0.2	0.05	70
20.0	10.0	30	0.4	0.10	140
30.0	15.0	45	0.6	0.15	210
40.0	20.0	60	0.8	0.20	280
50.0	25.0	75	1.0	0.25	350

Satisfactory results will be obtained providing these ratios are maintained and the procedures outlined in Sec. 4.1 are followed through the entire procedure. If larger samples are used, 500-ml erlenmeyer refluxing flasks may be used to permit titration within the refluxing flask.

4.6. *Alternate procedure for dilute samples:* The standard procedure, Sec. 4.1 through 4.4, is followed with two exceptions: (1) 0.025N standard potassium dichromate is used and (2) the back-titration is performed with 0.01N ferrous ammonium sulfate. Extreme care must be taken with this procedure because a trace of organic matter in the glassware or the atmosphere may cause a gross error. If a further increase in sensitivity is required, it may be obtained by reducing a larger sample volume to 20 ml (final total volume 60 ml) by boiling in the refluxing flask on a hotplate in the presence of all the reagents. A blank should be carried through the same procedure. This technique has the advantage of concentrating without significant loss of easily digested volatile materials. Hard to digest volatile materials, such as volatile acids, are lost, but an improvement is gained over ordinary evaporative concentration methods. Also, as the sample

4.7. *Use of standard solution:* A standard solution of either glucose or potassium acid phthalate may be used to evaluate technique and the quality of the reagents. See Sec. 6, Precision and Accuracy, for reference to glucose. A 98 to 100 per cent recovery of the theoretical oxygen demand can be expected with potassium acid phthalate. The latter reagent has the advantage over glucose in that it can be chemically standardized. It is also stable over a period of time whereas glucose may be biologically decomposed quite rapidly.

5. Calculation

$$\text{mg/l COD} = \frac{(a - b)\,c \times 8{,}000}{\text{ml sample}}$$

where

COD = chemical oxygen demand from dichromate;
a = ml $Fe(NH_4)_2(SO_4)_2$ used for blank;
b = ml $Fe(NH_4)_2(SO_4)_2$ used for sample;
c = normality of $Fe(NH_4)_2(SO_4)_2$.

6. Precision and Accuracy

The method is quite precise and may be used on a wide variety of wastes even though the back titration is less than 1 ml. Using a 50-ml sample, this general method gave a standard deviation of 0.07 ml ($n = 1$; $2 \times$

10) on distillery wastes and averaged 0.095 ml on miscellaneous wastes ranging from 350 to 57,500 mg/l ($n = 1$; 6×10). With reagent grade glucose, the standard deviation was found to be ± 8.2 per cent of the mean, which was calculated to be 92 per cent of the theoretical oxygen demand.

The accuracy of this method has been determined by Ruchhoft and associates. For most organic compounds the oxidation is 95 to 100 per cent of theoretical value. Using the silver catalyst, short-straight-chain alcohols and acids are oxidized 85 to 95 per cent or more. Benzene, toluene, and pyridine are not oxidized by either procedure.

Bibliography

1. MUERS, M. M. Biological Purification of Whey Solutions. *J. Soc. Chem. Ind.* (London) 55:711 (1936).

2. MOORE, W. A.; KRONER, R. C.; & RUCHHOFT, C. C. Dichromate Reflux Method for Determination of Oxygen Consumed. *Anal. Chem.* 21:953 (1949).

3. MOORE, W. A.; LUDZACK, F. J.; & RUCHHOFT, C. C. Determination of Oxygen-Consumed Values of Organic Wastes. *Anal. Chem.* 23:1297 (1951).

4. MEDALIA, A. I. Test for Traces of Organic Matter in Water. *Anal. Chem.* 23:1318 (1951).

5. SUBRAHMANYAN, P.; SASTRY, C.; & PALLAI, S. Determination of the Permanganate Value for Waters and Sewage Effluent Containing Nitrite. *Analyst* 84:731 (1959).

6. SYMONS, J. M.; MCKINNEY, R. E.; & HASSIS, H. H. A Procedure for Determination of the Biological Treatability of Industrial Wastes. *J. WPCF* 32:841 (1960).

7. DOBBS, R. A. & WILLIAMS, R. T. *Elimination* of Chloride Interference in the Chemical Oxygen Demand Test. *Anal. Chem.* 35:1064 (1963).

pH Value

The glass electrode method as described in Part I is used to determine pH. Special attention must be paid to the directions given for the care and cleaning of electrodes as described therein (and also in Part III), because contaminating material may require special precautions.

Phenols

Phenols, defined as hydroxy derivatives of benzene and its condensed nuclei, may occur in domestic and industrial wastewaters and in drinking water supplies. Of the three procedures offered, each uses the 4-aminoantipyrine colorimetric method * that determines phenol, the ortho- and meta-substituted phenols, and, under the proper condition of pH, those para-substituted phenols in which the substitution is a carboxyl, halogen, methoxyl, or sulfonic acid group. Presumably, the 4-aminoantipyrine method does not determine those para-substituted phenols in which the substitution

---

* Similar in principle to, but different in detail from ASTM D1783.

is an alkyl, aryl, nitro, benzoyl, nitroso, or aldehyde group. A typical example of these latter groups is para-cresol, which may be present in certain industrial wastewaters and in polluted surface waters.

Selection of procedure: The 4-amino-antipyrine method is given in three forms: Method A, for extreme sensitivity, is adaptable for use in wastewaters containing less than 1 mg/l phenol and concentrates the color in a non-aqueous solution; Method B, used for phenol concentrations greater than 1 mg/l in which a high degree of sensitivity is not required, retains the color in the unconcentrated aqueous solution; Method C, a tentative procedure, is used where speed of analysis is required because it eliminates the distillation screening technique, and where a better estimation of para-substituted phenols is required because a different pH value is used for color development.

Interferences, Preservation, and Storage of Samples

1. Interferences

1.1. Domestic and industrial wastewaters may contain such interferences as phenol-decomposing bacteria, oxidizing and reducing substances, and alkaline pH values. Biological degradation is inhibited by the addition of $CuSO_4$ to the sample. Acidification with H_3PO_4 assures the presence of the copper ion and eliminates any chemical changes resulting from the presence of strong alkaline conditions.

1.2. Some of the treatment procedures used for the removal of interferences prior to analysis may result in an unavoidable loss of certain types of phenols. Consequently, some highly contaminated wastewaters may require specialized screening techniques for elimination of interferences and for quantitative recovery of the phenolic compounds. It is left to the analyst to meet these specialized situations.

1.3. Some of the major interferences can be eliminated as follows: (see Distillation Step, Sec. 3, for the required reagents.)

(a) *Oxidizing agents,* such as chlorine and as detected by the liberation of iodine upon acidification in the presence of potassium iodide, are removed immediately after sampling by the addition of an excess of ferrous sulfate or sodium arsenite. If oxidizing agents are not removed, the phenolic compounds will be partially oxidized and the results will be low.

(b) *Sulfur compounds* are removed by acidifying the sample to a pH of less than 4.0 with H_3PO_4, using methyl orange or a pH meter, and aerating briefly by stirring prior to the addition of $CuSO_4$. This should eliminate the interferences of H_2S and SO_2.

(c) *Oils and tars* contain phenols, so that an alkaline extraction is required prior to the addition of $CuSO_4$. The pH of the sample is adjusted to 12–12.5 by the addition of NaOH pellets. The oil and tar are extracted from the aqueous solution by CCl_4. Discard the oil- or tar-containing layer. Any excess CCl_4 in the aqueous layer is removed by warming on a water bath before proceeding with the distillation step.

2. Sampling

Sampling of domestic and industrial wastewaters should be done in accordance with the instructions of Part III, Introduction, A, Collection of Samples, Sec. 1, and Part IV, Introduction, A, Collection of Samples.

3. Preservation and Storage of Samples

3.1. Phenols in concentrations usually encountered in wastewaters are subject to biochemical and chemical oxidation.

Samples should be preserved and stored unless they will be analyzed within 4 hr after collection.

3.2. Acidify the samples to a pH of approximately 4.0 with H_3PO_4 using methyl orange or a pH meter. If H_2S or SO_2 are known to be present, briefly aerate or stir the sample with caution.

3.3. Biochemical oxidation of phenols is inhibited by the addition of 1.0 g $CuSO_4 \cdot 5H_2O$ per liter of sample.

3.4. The sample then should be kept cold (5°–10°C). Analyze preserved and stored samples within 24 hr after collection.

Distillation Step for Methods A and B

1. Principle

The phenols are distilled at a more or less constant rate from the non-volatile impurities. The rate of volatilization of the phenols is gradual, so that the volume of the distillate must equal that of the sample being distilled. The use of $CuSO_4$ during distillation of an acidic sample permits the formation of cupric sulfide without subsequent decomposition to H_2S. The acidic solution also prevents the precipitation of cupric hydroxide, which acts as an oxidizing agent toward phenols.

2. Apparatus

2.1. *Distillation apparatus,* all-glass, consisting of a 1-liter pyrex distilling apparatus with Graham condenser (Corning No. 3360 or equal) (see Fig. 17).

2.2. *pH meter.* Should conform to the requirements of Part I, pH Value, Glass Electrode Method, Sec. 2.

3. Reagents

All reagents must be prepared with distilled water free of phenols and chlorine.

3.1. *Copper sulfate solution:* Dissolve 100 g $CuSO_4 \cdot 5H_2O$ in distilled water and dilute to 1 liter.

3.2. *Phosphoric acid solution,* 1 + 9. Dilute 10 ml 85 per cent H_3PO_4 to 100 ml with distilled water.

3.3. *Methyl orange indicator:* Dissolve 0.5 g methyl orange in 1 liter distilled water.

3.4. *Chloroform or ether.*

4. Procedure

4.1. Measure 500 ml sample into a beaker, lower the pH to approximately

4.0 with the $1 + 9$ H_3PO_4 solution using the methyl orange indicator or a pH meter, add 5 ml copper sulfate solution, and transfer to the distillation apparatus. Use a 500-ml graduated cylinder as a receiver. The additions of H_3PO_4 and $CuSO_4$ may be omitted if the sample was preserved as described in Interferences, Preservation, and Storage of Samples, Sec. 3.2 and 3.3.

4.2. Distill 450 ml of sample, stop the distillation and, when boiling ceases, add 50 ml phenol-free distilled water to the distilling flask. Continue distillation until a total of 500 ml has been collected.

4.3. One distillation should prove sufficient for purification of the sample. Occasionally, however, the distillate is turbid. In this case, acidify the turbid distillate with $1 + 9$ H_3PO_4, add 5 ml copper sulfate solution, and distill as described in Sec. 4.2. If the second distillate is also turbid, the extraction process given in Method D, Sec. 4.1, should be attempted before the distillation.

A. Chloroform Extraction Method

1. General Discussion

1.1. *Principle:* The steam-distillable phenols react with 4-aminoantipyrine at a pH of 10.0 ± 0.2 in the presence of potassium ferricyanide to form a colored antipyrine dye. This dye is extracted from aqueous solution with chloroform and the absorbance is measured at 460 mμ. The concentration of phenolic compounds is expressed as $\mu g/l$ of phenol (C_6H_5OH). This method covers the phenol concentration range of 0.0 to 1,000 $\mu g/l$ with a sensitivity of 1 $\mu g/l$.

1.2. *Interference:* All interferences are eliminated or reduced to a minimum if the sample has been preserved and stored, and distilled in accordance with the foregoing instructions.

1.3. *Minimum detectable concentration:* The minimum detectable quantity is 0.5 μg phenol when a 25-ml $CHCl_3$ extraction with a 5-cm cell, or a 50-ml $CHCl_3$ extraction with a 10-cm cell, is used in the photometric measurement. The minimum detectable quan-

tity is 1 $\mu g/l$ phenol in a 500-ml distillate.

2. Apparatus

2.1. *Photometric equipment:* One of the following, equipped with absorption cells providing light paths of 1 to 10 cm (depending on the absorbance of the colored solutions and the individual characteristics of the photometer; in general, if the absorbance readings are greater than 1.0 in a given cell size, the next smaller size cell should be used), is required:

a. *Spectrophotometer,* for use at 460 mμ.

b. *Filter photometer,* equipped with a filter exhibiting maximum light transmission near 460 mμ.

2.2. *Funnels:* Buchner type with fritted disc (such as 15-ml Corning No. 36060 or equivalent).

2.3. *Filter paper:* An appropriate 11-cm filter paper may be used for filtration of the chloroform extracts in place of the Buchner-type funnels and anhydrous sodium sulfate.

2.4. *pH meter:* Should conform to the requirements of Part I, pH Value, Glass Electrode Method, Sec. 2.

2.5. *Separatory funnels,* 1,000 ml, Squibb form with ground-glass stoppers and teflon stopcocks. At least eight are required.

2.6. *Nessler tubes,* matched, 50 ml, tall form.

3. Reagents

All reagents must be prepared with distilled water free of phenols and chlorine.

3.1. *Stock phenol solution:* Dissolve 1.00 g reagent grade phenol in freshly boiled and cooled distilled water and dilute to 1,000 ml. Ordinarily this direct weighing of the phenol constitutes a standard solution. However, if extreme accuracy is required, standardize as directed in Sec. 4 below.

3.2. *Intermediate phenol solution:* Dilute 10.0 ml stock phenol solution to 1,000 ml with freshly boiled and cooled distilled water; 1 ml = 10.0 µg phenol. Prepare a fresh solution on each day of use.

3.3. *Standard phenol solution:* Dilute 50.0 ml intermediate phenol solution to 500 ml with freshly boiled and cooled distilled water; 1 ml = 1.0 µg phenol. Prepare this solution within 2 hr of use.

3.4. *Bromate-bromide solution,* 0.10N. Dissolve 2.784 g anhydrous potassium bromate, KBrO$_3$, in distilled water, add 10 g potassium bromide, KBr crystals, dissolve, and dilute to 1,000 ml.

3.5. *Hydrochloric acid,* conc.

3.6. *Standard sodium thiosulfate titrant,* 0.025N: Prepare and standardize as directed in Part III, Oxygen (Dissolved), Method A, Sec. 2.6.

3.7. *Starch solution:* Prepare as directed in Part III, Oxygen (Dissolved), Method A, Sec. 2.4.

3.8. *Ammonium chloride solution:* Dissolve 50 g NH$_4$Cl in distilled water and dilute to 1,000 ml.

3.9. *Ammonium hydroxide,* conc.

3.10. *Aminoantipyrine solution:* Dissolve 2.0 g 4-aminoantipyrine in distilled water and dilute to 100 ml. This solution should be prepared each day of use.

3.11. *Potassium ferricyanide solution:* Dissolve 8.0 g K$_3$Fe(CN)$_6$ in distilled water and dilute to 100 ml. Filter if necessary. Prepare fresh each week of use.

3.12. *Chloroform.*

3.13. *Sodium sulfate,* anhydrous, granular.

3.14. *Potassium iodide,* crystals.

4. Standardization of Phenol Solution

4.1. To 100 ml distilled water in a 500-ml glass-stoppered conical flask, add 50.0 ml stock phenol solution and 10.0 ml 0.1N bromate-bromide solution. Immediately add 5 ml conc HCl and swirl the stoppered flask gently. If the brown color of free bromine does not persist, add 10.0-ml portions of bromate-bromide solution until the color does persist. Keep the flask stoppered and allow to stand for 10 min; then add approximately 1 g KI. Usually, four 10-ml portions of bromate-bromide solution are required if the stock phenol solution contains 1,000 mg/l phenol.

4.2. Prepare a blank in exactly the same manner, using distilled water and 10.0 ml 0.1N bromate-bromide solution. Titrate the blank and sample with the

0.025N sodium thiosulfate titrant using starch solution as the indicator.

4.3. Calculate the concentration of the phenol solution as follows:

$$\text{mg/1 phenol} = 7.842 \, (A \, B - C)$$

where $A =$ ml thiosulfate for blank; $B =$ ml bromate-bromide solution used for sample divided by 10; and $C =$ ml thiosulfate used for sample.

5. Procedure

5.1. Place 500 ml of the distillate, or a suitable aliquot diluted to 500 ml, in a 1-liter beaker. If all 500 ml of distillate is used, it may not contain more than 50 μg (0.1 mg/1) phenol. If the sample is known to contain more than 50 μg phenol, a smaller aliquot must be used. Practically, the smallest aliquot would be 50 ml that contains not more than 50 μg (1 mg/1) phenol.

5.2. If the approximate phenol concentration of the original sample is not known, determine by a preliminary check the proper aliquot of the distillate and of the CHCl$_3$ to use for the final determination. This may be done without CHCl$_3$ extraction by carrying out the reaction in 50-ml nessler tubes and comparing against suitable phenol standards.

5.3. Prepare a 500-ml distilled water blank and a series of 500-ml phenol standards containing 5, 10, 20, 30, 40 and 50 μg phenol.

5.4. Treat sample, blank, and standards as follows: Add 10.00 ml ammonium chloride solution and adjust with conc NH$_4$OH to pH 10.0 ± 0.2. Transfer to the 1-liter separatory funnels, add 3.00 ml aminoantipyrine solution, mix well, add 3.00 ml potassium ferricyanide solution, again mix well, and allow the color to develop

for 3 min. The solution should be clear and light yellow.

5.5. Extract immediately with CHCl$_3$, using 25 ml for 1- to 5-cm cells and 50 ml for a 10-cm cell. Shake the separatory funnel at least 10 times, allow the CHCl$_3$ to settle, shake again 10 times, and allow the CHCl$_3$ to settle again.

5.6. Filter each of the chloroform extracts through the filter paper or through the fritted-glass funnels containing a 5-g layer of the anhydrous sodium sulfate. Collect the dried extracts in clean cells for the absorbance measurements; do not add more CHCl$_3$.

5.7. Read the absorbance of the sample and standards against the blank at a wavelength of 460 mμ. Plot absorbance against μg of standard phenol solutions for the calibration curve. Estimate the phenol concentration of the sample from the calibration curve. A separate calibration curve must be constructed for each photometer and each curve must be checked periodically to ensure reproducibility.

6. Calculation

$$\mu\text{g/1 phenol} = \frac{A}{B} \times 1{,}000$$

where $A = \mu$g phenol in sample, from calibration curve, and $B =$ ml original sample.

7. Alternative Procedure

7.1. If infrequent analyses for phenol are made, the analyst may prepare only one standard phenol solution instead of a series of solutions and a calibration curve.

7.2. In this case, prepare 500 ml of a standard phenol solution approximately equal to the phenolic content of the portion of the original sample used for final analysis. Also prepare a 500-ml distilled water blank.

7.3. Proceed as described in Sec. 5.4, 5.5, 5.6 and 5.7, except that the absorbances of the sample and the standard phenol solution are measured against the blank at 460 mμ.

7.4. Calculation of the phenol content of the original sample is:

$$\mu\text{g/l phenol} = \frac{C\,D}{E} \times \frac{1,000}{B}$$

where $C = \mu$g standard phenol solution, $D =$ absorbance reading of sample, E = absorbance of standard phenol solution, and $B =$ ml original sample.

8. Precision and Accuracy

The precision of this method is dependent on the skill of the analyst and on the interferences present after the distillation procedure. Because the "phenol" value is based on C_6H_5OH, this method can be regarded only as an approximation and as representing the minimum amount of phenols present. This is true because the phenolic value varies as the types of phenols vary within a given sample. Therefore, it is impossible to express the accuracy of the method.

B.   Direct Photometric Method

1. General Discussion

1.1. *Principle:* The steam-distillable phenols react with 4-aminoantipyrine at a pH of 10.0 ± 0.2 in the presence of potassium ferricyanide to form a colored antipyrine dye. This dye is kept in an aqueous solution and the absorbance is measured at 510 mμ. Because extreme sensitivity is not required in this method, smaller distillate volumes may be used for analysis. For example, this permits determination of 0.5 mg phenol, expressed as C_6H_5OH, in a 100-ml volume of distillate. Practically, the smallest distillate volume would be 10 ml. Consequently, this method covers the phenol concentration range of 0.0 to 50 mg/l with a sensitivity of 1 mg/l.

1.2. *Interference:* All interferences are eliminated or reduced to a minimum by using only the distillate from the preliminary distillation procedure.

1.3. *Minimum detectable concentration:* This method has considerably less sensitivity than Method A. The minimum detectable quantity is 0.1 mg phenol when a 5-cm cell is used in the photometric measurement and 100 ml distillate is used in the determination.

2. Apparatus

2.1. *Photometric equipment:* One of the following, equipped with absorption cells providing light paths of 1 to 5 cm, is required:

a. Spectrophotometer, for use at 510 mμ.

b. Filter photometer, equipped with a green filter exhibiting maximum light transmission near 510 mμ.

2.2. *Nessler tubes,* matched, 100 ml, tall form.

2.3. *pH meter.* See Method A, Sec. 2.5.

3. Reagents

The reagents are the same as for Method A, Sec. 3.

4. Procedure

4.1. Place 100 ml of the distillate, or a suitable aliquot diluted to 100 ml, in a 250-ml beaker. If all 100 ml of distillate is used it may not contain more than 0.5 mg (5.0 mg/1) phenol. If the sample is known to contain more than 0.5 mg phenol, a smaller aliquot must be used. Practically, the smallest aliquot would be 10 ml that contains not more than 0.5 mg (50 mg/1) phenol.

4.2. If the approximate phenol concentration of the original sample is not known, determine by a preliminary check the proper aliquot of the distillate to use for the final determination. This may be done by carrying out the reaction in 100-ml nessler tubes and comparing against suitable phenol standards.

4.3. Prepare a 100-ml distilled water blank and a series of 100-ml phenol standards containing 0.1, 0.2, 0.3, 0.4, and 0.5 mg phenol.

4.4. Treat sample, blank, and standards as follows: Add 2.00 ml ammonium chloride solution and adjust with conc NH_4OH to pH 10.0 ± 0.2. Add 2.00 ml aminoantipyrine solution, mix well, add 2.00 ml potassium ferricyanide solution, and again mix well.

4.5. After 15 min, transfer to cells and read the absorbance of the sample and standard against the blank at 510 mμ. Estimate the phenol content of the sample from the photometric readings as directed in Method A, Sec. 5.7. Visual comparison also can be made in 100-ml nessler tubes against the standard phenol solutions.

5. Calculation

$$\text{mg/1 phenol} = \frac{A}{B} \times 1,000$$

where A = mg phenol in sample, from calibration curve, and B = ml original sample.

6. Alternate Procedure

Refer to Method A, Sec. 7. Use the appropriate 100-ml aliquots of sample and standard phenol solutions. Proceed as described in Sec. 4.1, 4.2, 4.3, 4.4, and 4.5 above, except that the absorbances of sample and standard phenol solution are measured against the blank at 510 mμ. Calculation of the phenol content of the original sample is:

$$\text{mg/1 phenol} = \frac{C\,D}{E} \times \frac{1,000}{B}$$

where C = mg standard phenol solution, D = absorbance of sample, E = absorbance of standard phenol solution, and B = ml original sample.

7. Precision and Accuracy

Refer to Method A, Sec. 8.

C. Simplified Aminoantipyrine Method (Tentative)

1. General Discussion

1.1. *Principle:* This procedure involves a petroleum ether extraction of the phenols from an acidified sample, an alkaline aqueous extraction of the phenols from the petroleum ether, and color development with 4-aminoanti-pyrine and potassium ferricyanide at pH 7.9 ± 0.1. This method eliminates the distillation screening procedure required for Methods A and B.

1.2. *Interference:* Most of the organic and inorganic interferences are eliminated by the acid extraction of the sample with petroleum ether.

1.3. *Minimum detectable concentration:* The sensitivity depends on the size of the sample extracted. If 100 ml are extracted, the sensitivity is 70 $\mu g/1$; if 1,000 ml are extracted, the sensitivity is 7 $\mu g/1$.

2. Preservation and Storage of Sample

Refer to Interferences, Preservation, and Storage of Samples, Sec. 3.

3. Apparatus

3.1. *Spectrophotometer:* Any suitable spectrophotometer providing a light path of at least 2.3 cm for use at 500 mμ.

3.2. *Separatory funnels,* Squibb form, 250, 500, or 1,000 ml, glass-stoppered, with teflon stopcock.

4. Reagents

All reagents must be prepared with distilled water free of phenols and chlorine.

4.1. *Ammonium hydroxide,* $0.5N$. Dilute 35 ml conc NH_4OH to 1 liter with distilled water.

4.2. *Phosphate buffer solution:* Dissolve 104.5 g dipotassium hydrogen phosphate, K_2HPO_4, and 72.3 g potassium dihydrogen phosphate, KH_2PO_4, in distilled water and dilute to 1 liter. The pH of this buffer solution should be 6.8.

4.3. *Aminoantipyrine solution:* Refer to Method A, Sec. 3.10.

4.4. *Potassium ferricyanide solution:* Refer to Method A, Sec. 3.11.

4.5. *Petroleum ether,* 30°–60°C.

4.6. *Hydrochloric acid,* conc.

4.7. *Standard phenol solution:* Refer to Method A, Sec. 3.1, 3.2, 3.3.

5. Procedure

5.1. Place the appropriate volume of sample and an equal volume of a distilled water blank in separatory funnels. Add 10 ml conc HCl and mix.

5.2. Extract the phenols from the acidified sample with three 50-ml portions petroleum ether. Shake each extraction for 3 min. Place the combined extracts in a 250-ml separatory funnel.

5.3. Wash the combined petroleum ether extracts with two 50-ml portions distilled water to remove any emulsified HCl.

5.4. Extract the phenols from the washed petroleum ether with one 10.00-ml and two 5.00-ml portions $0.5N$ NH_4OH. Shake each extraction for 3 min.

5.5. Place the ammoniacal extracts in 50-ml volumetric flasks. Add 20 ml phosphate buffer solution and mix well. The pH of this solution should be 7.9 ± 0.1.

5.6. Add exactly 0.50 ml 4-amino-antipyrine solution and mix well.

5.7. Add exactly 0.50 ml potassium ferricyanide solution and mix well.

5.8. Bring the solution to 50.0 ml with distilled water and mix well.

5.9. Allow 15 min for maximum color to develop. Read the absorbance at 500 mμ against a reagent blank. Estimate the phenol concentration of the sample from the calibration curve.

6. Calculation

$$\mu g/l \text{ phenol} = \frac{A}{B} \times 1{,}000$$

where $A = \mu g$ phenol in sample, from calibration curve, and $B = $ ml original solution.

7. Preparation of Calibration Curve

7.1. Prepare a standard phenol solution, 1 ml $= 10$ μg, as directed in Method A, Sec. 3.1 and 3.2.

7.2. Add increasing volumes of the standard phenol solution to 20.00 ml $0.5N$ NH_4OH in 50-ml volumetric flasks so that the final concentrations are 0, 10, 30, 50, 70, and 100 μg.

7.3. Follow the directions in Sec. 5.5–5.9 above to develop color.

7.4. Construct the calibration curve by plotting absorbance against μg phenol. A separate calibration curve must be constructed for each photometer and checked periodically.

8. Precision and Accuracy

8.1. This method can be regarded only as an approximation and as representing the minimum amount of phenols present, because C_6H_5OH is used as the standard. Comparison of this method with Method A may indicate higher results. This is because more para-substituted phenols develop color at pH 7.9 than at pH 10.0.

8.2. The precision and accuracy of this method were determined for 2,4-dichlorophenol. For 99.7 per cent of the observations, the third standard error averaged ±0.501 about any mean percentage transmittance value.

This gave an average standard error of 0.75 per cent for five points on a calibration curve.

Bibliography

1. Scott, R. D. Application of a Bromine Method in the Determination of Phenols and Cresols. *Ind. Eng. Chem., Anal. Ed.* 3:67 (1931).
2. Emerson, E.; Beacham, H. H.; & Beegle, L. C. The Condensation of Aminoantipyrine. II. A New Color Test for Phenolic Compounds. *J. Org. Chem.* 8:417 (1943).
3. Ettinger, M. B.; Schott, S.; & Ruchhoft, C. C. Preservation of Phenol Content in Polluted River Water Samples Previous to Analysis. *J. AWWA* 35:299 (1943).
4. Ettinger, M. B. & Kroner, R. C. The Determination of Phenolic Materials in Industrial Wastes. *Proc. 5th Ind. Waste Conf.,* Purdue Univ. p. 345 (1949).
5. Ettinger, M. B.; Ruchhoft, C. C.; & Lishka, R. J. Sensitive 4-Aminoantipyrine Method for Phenolic Compounds. *Anal. Chem.* 23:1783 (1951).
6. Dannis, M. Determination of Phenols by the Aminoantipyrine Method. *Sew. Ind. Wastes* 23:1516 (1951).
7. Mohler, E. F., Jr. & Jacob, L. N. Determination of Phenolic-Type Compounds in Water and Industrial Waste Waters: Comparison of Analytical Methods. *Anal. Chem.* 29:1369 (1957).
8. Tallon, G. R. & Hepner, R. D. Determination of *p*-Cresol in Industrial Waste Waters. *Anal. Chem.* 30:1521 (1958).
9. Gordon, G. E. Colorimetric Determination of Phenolic Materials in Refinery Waste Waters. *Anal. Chem.* 32:1325 (1960).
10. Ochynski, F. W. The Absorptiometric Determination of Phenol. *The Analyst* 85:278 (1960).
11. Faust, S. D. & Aly, O. M. The Determination of 2,4-Dichlorophenol in Water. *J. AWWA* 54:235 (1962).

Residue

The procedures outlined under Residue in Part III are applicable to most industrial wastes. By definition, results will not include materials in the waste which are volatile under the conditions of the procedure. Deviations from the procedure may be made where conditions demand a change to include special ingredients. However, any deviations in the technique should be recorded and presented with the results.

A. Residue on Evaporation

The procedure and limitations of the determination of residue on evaporation are discussed in Part III, Residue, Method A.

B. Suspended Matter

Determine suspended matter as in Part III, Residue, Method C. In special cases where it is desired to exclude material such as oil, variations in the procedure to extract the oil from the suspended matter on the mat are allowable.

C. Volatile Matter

Volatile matter should be determined on the total residue or sussuspended matter according to the procedure given in Part III, Residue, Method D.

D. Settleable Matter

A determination of the amount of matter which will settle, and float, under certain prescribed conditions may be used to evaluate the efficiencies of settling tanks; the conditions may be varied to coincide more nearly with those in the process being studied. Procedures are given in Part III, Residue, Method F.

Sulfide

The procedure for sulfide determination in industrial wastes is the same as that for sewage in Part III.

Temperature

Temperature measurements may be made with any good grade of mercury-filled centrigrade thermometer, provided it is checked occasionally against a precision thermometer certified by the National Bureau of Standards. Field instruments should be provided with a metal case to prevent breakage. Temperature at time of collection should be recorded to the nearest degree centigrade.

Turbidity

Turbidity should be determined with a candle turbidimeter, or by photometric comparison against turbidity standards which have been calibrated by such a turbidimeter. Procedures to be followed are described in Part I.

Zinc

See Metals (Heavy) Method J.

Physical and Chemical Examination of Sludge and Bottom Sediments in Wastewater Treatment Processes and in Polluted Rivers, Lakes, and Estuaries

Introduction

The procedures described in Part V are intended for the physical and chemical examination of sludges and bottom sediment in sewage treatment processes and in polluted rivers, lakes, and estuaries. These methods have not been developed for and may not be applicable to chemical sludges or slurries.

In the following sections, wherever the words "sludge" and "sewage sludge" are used, the statement or direction is to apply to muds as well, unless otherwise stated.

Collection of Samples

Great care must be used in sampling sewage sludges, sludge banks, and muds. No definite procedure can be given, but every possible precaution should be taken to obtain a representative sample, whether from a tank, a sludge pile, or the bottom of a river. When analyses cannot be made immediately, samples may be preserved with 5 g sodium benzoate, or 1 ml conc H_2SO_4, for each 80 g of sample, provided that these preservatives do not interfere with the tests to be made. Sludge or mud samples cannot be preserved with chloroform or sodium benzoate when grease is to be determined.

Bibliography

1. JEWELL, M. E. Experiments on the Preservation of Mud Samples. *Illinois State Water Survey Bull.* 16:206 (1920).

Acidity

Acidity of sludges and muds is determined on the liquor that separates from them on standing. Titrations are made in a tall cylinder using a plunger as described in Part III, Acidity, Method A. When samples are highly colored or turbid, potentiometric titration (Part III, Acidity, Method B) should be used.

1. Reagents

1.1. *Standard sodium hydroxide titrant,* 0.05N. Prepare a stock solution of carbonate-free NaOH as directed in Part I, Acidity, Sec. 3.1, and determine its normality by titration with standard acid solution. Each week dilute the calculated volume of this stock solution to prepare the 0.05N solution, using recently boiled distilled water.

1.2. *Phenolphthalein indicator solution:* Either the aqueous (*a*) or alcoholic (*b*) solution may be used.

a. Dissolve 5 g phenolphthalein disodium salt in distilled water and dilute to 1 liter. If necessary, add 0.02N NaOH dropwise until a faint pink color appears.

b. Dissolve 5 g phenolphthalein in 500 ml 95 per cent ethyl alcohol or isopropyl alcohol and add 500 ml distilled water. Then add 0.02N NaOH dropwise until a faint pink color appears.

2. Procedure

Measure into a 90- or 100-ml cylinder or hydrometer jar 50 ml of supernatant liquor from the sample, taking care to minimize the loss of CO_2. Add 3 drops phenolphthalein indicator solution and titrate with $0.05N$ NaOH solution to the first permanent pink color. A plunger-type stirring rod is used.

3. Calculation

mg/l acidity as $CaCO_3$
$$= \text{ml } 0.05N \text{ NaOH} \times 50$$

me/l acidity $= \text{ml } 0.05N \text{ NaOH}$

Alkalinity

Alkalinity of sludges and muds is determined on the liquor that separates from them on standing. Titrations are made in a tall cylinder using a plunger as described in Part III, Acidity, Method A. When samples are highly colored or turbid, potentiometric titration should be used; Method B under Acidity in Part III should be followed, except that the titration is made with $0.05N$ H_2SO_4.

1. Reagents

1.1. *Standard sulfuric acid titrant,* $0.05N$. Prepare a stock solution of approximately this normality by diluting 1.5 ml conc H_2SO_4 to 1 liter with distilled water. Standardize against pure anhydrous Na_2CO_3. Dilute an exact quantity of this stock solution, depending on the normality, to 1 liter to prepare the $0.05N$ solution.

1.2. *Phenolphthalein indicator solution:* Either the aqueous (*a*) or alcoholic (*b*) solution may be used.

a. Dissolve 5 g phenolphthalein disodium salt in distilled water and dilute to 1 liter. If necessary, add $0.02N$ NaOH dropwise until a faint pink color appears.

b. Dissolve 5 g phenolphthalein in 500 ml 95 per cent ethyl alcohol or iso-propyl alcohol and add 500 ml distilled water. Then add $0.02N$ NaOH dropwise until a faint pink color appears.

1.3. *Methyl orange indicator solution:* Dissolve 0.5 g methyl orange in 1 liter distilled water.

2. Procedure

Measure into a 90- or 100-ml cylinder or hydrometer jar 50 ml of supernatant liquor from the sample, taking care to minimize the loss of CO_2. Add 3 drops phenolphthalein and titrate with $0.05N$ H_2SO_4 until the pink color has disappeared. Record milliliters of acid used as P. Add 3 drops methyl orange indicator and continue titration until the solution is a faint pink. Record the total milliliters of acid used, including that for the phenolphthalein titration, as T.

3. Calculation

When 50 ml of supernatant sludge liquor is used:

Phenolphthalein alkalinity as mg/l $CaCO_3$
$$= P \times 50$$
Methyl orange alkalinity as mg/l $CaCO_3$
$$= T \times 50$$

To express these results in milli-equivalents of alkalinity, use the factor 1 instead of 50 in the above calculations.

Appearance

The physical appearance of the sample, as well as the color and odor, should be recorded in terms which best describe the individual sample, no standard methods being recommended for describing these characteristics.

Color

There are no recommended terms for recording the color of the sample. It may be described by such color terms as seem suitable.

Density Index

See Tests on Activated Sludge, Method D.

Grease

Grease is defined as that material extracted by hexane from an acidified sample which would not be volatilized during the procedure; it includes soaps, fats, waxes, and oils. These materials are particularly resistant to digestion, cause excessive scum accumulation in digesters, clog the pores of filters, and deter the use of sludge as fertilizer. A knowledge of the amount of grease present in sludge can aid in the diagnosis of digestion and dewatering problems and indicate the suitability of a particular sludge for use as a fertilizer.

1. General Discussion

1.1. *Principle:* Drying of acidified sludges by heating leads to low results. Magnesium sulfate monohydrate is capable of combining with 75 per cent of its own weight in water in forming the heptahydrate. Magnesium sulfate monohydrate can be used to dry sludge. After drying, the grease can be extracted with hexane.

1.2. *Interference:* Refer to Part III, Grease, Method A, Sec. 1.2.

1.3. *Minimum detectable concentration:* The method has been found to give reproducible results for concentrations of grease up to 650 mg/l.

1.4. *Sampling and storage:* Every possible precaution must be taken to obtain a representative sample. When analysis cannot be made immediately, samples may be preserved with 1 ml conc H_2SO_4 for each 80 g of sample. Samples should never be preserved with chloroform or sodium benzoate when grease is to be determined.

2. Apparatus

2.1. *Extraction apparatus,* Soxhlet.

2.2. *Vacuum pump,* or other source of vacuum.

3. Reagents

3.1. *Hydrochloric acid,* conc.

3.2. *Magnesium sulfate monohydrate:* Prepare $MgSO_4 \cdot H_2O$ by drying overnight a thin layer of $MgSO_4 \cdot 7H_2O$ in an oven at 103°C.

3.3. *n-hexane,* boiling point 69°C.

3.4. *Grease-free cotton:* Nonabsorbent cotton after extraction with *n*-hexane.

4. Procedure

4.1. In a 150-ml beaker weigh a sample of wet sludge, 20 ± 0.5 g, of which the dry-solids content is known. Acidify to pH 2.0 (generally, 0.3 ml conc HCl is sufficient). Add 25 g magnesium sulfate monohydrate. Stir to a smooth paste and spread on the sides of the beaker to facilitate subsequent removal. Allow to stand until solidified, 15 to 30 min. Remove the solids and grind in a porcelain mortar. Add the powder to a paper extraction thimble. Wipe the beaker and mortar with small pieces of filter paper moistened with hexane and add to the thimble. Fill the thimble with small glass beads. Extract in a Soxhlet apparatus using hexane at a rate of 20 cycles per hour for 4 hr.

4.2. If any turbidity or suspended matter is present in the extraction flask, remove by filtering through grease-free cotton into another weighed flask. Rinse flask and cotton with hexane. Distill hexane from the extraction flask in water at 85°C. Dry by placing on a steam bath and drawing air through the flask with a vacuum for 15 min.

4.3. Cool in a desiccator for 30 min and weigh.

5. Calculation

Grease as % dry solids

$$= \frac{\text{gain in weight of flask (g)} \times 100}{\text{weight of wet solids (g)} \times \% \text{ dry solids}}$$

6. Precision and Accuracy

The examination of six replicate samples of sludge yielded a standard deviation of 4.6 per cent.

Bibliography

1. STEPHENSON, R. J. Estimation of Grease in Sewage Sludges. *Analyst* **74**:257 (1949).
2. GILCREAS, F. W.; SANDERSON, W. W.; & ELMER, R. P. Two New Methods for the Determination of Grease in Sewage. *Sew. Ind. Wastes* **25**:1379 (1953).
3. ULLMANN, W. W. & SANDERSON, W. W. A Further Study of Methods for the Determination of Grease in Sewage. *Sew. Ind. Wastes* **31**:8 (1959).

Hydrocarbon and Fatty Matter Content of Grease

The hydrocarbon and fatty matter content of grease in sludge is determined in the same manner as in sewage (Part III). Results are expressed as a percentage of the total grease in the sludge.

Nitrogen (Ammonia)

Rapidly weigh approximately 20 g wet sludge, containing approximately 5 per cent solids, to the nearest 0.1 g in a weighing bottle or crucible. Wash the sample into a 500-ml kjeldahl flask with ammonia-free distilled water, dilute to 250 ml, and determine nitrogen by distillation as directed in Part III, Nitrogen (Ammonia), Method B, except that 100 ml of distillate is collected in standard boric acid and titrated to the mixed-indicator endpoint with $0.02N$ H_2SO_4. A piece of paraffin added to the flask will prevent frothing. Calculate as mg/l N.

Nitrogen (Organic)

Using the residue from the ammonia determination, proceed as directed in Part III, Nitrogen (Organic), beginning with Sec. 4.2. Calculate as per cent N of the total dry solids. (A separate sample is used for the determination of the per cent solids.)

Nitrogen (Total Kjeldahl)

Dry a sample of sludge or mud in a drying oven at 103°C, grind thoroughly to a fine powder, and dry again for 30 min at 103°C.

Weigh accurately 1.0 g dried sludge or 1.0–5.0 g dried mud into a 500-ml kjeldahl flask. Add 20 ml conc H_2SO_4, 13.4 g K_2SO_4, 3 ml mercuric sulfate solution (Part III, Nitrogen [Organic], Sec. 3.3), and mix thoroughly. Digest slowly until frothing ceases, and for 30 min after the liquid becomes clear.

Cool, dilute to 350 ml with ammonia-free distilled water, and proceed as directed in Part III, Nitrogen (Organic), Sec. 4.3, distilling into boric acid solution.

Determinations by this method do not give an accurate measure of the total nitrogen of the wet sludge. At best it is kjeldahl nitrogen minus ammonium bicarbonate or carbonate lost on drying. A more rational method for determining the total kjeldahl nitrogen in wet sludge is to determine the ammonia nitrogen and organic nitrogen as above and add the results. The results are expressed as per cent N.

Odor

The odor of the sample may be recorded in any way that seems most descriptive, there being no standard terms for defining odors, although some of the terms recommended in Table 18 (Part I, Odor) may prove applicable.

Oxygen Demand (Biochemical)

The most accurate determination of biochemical oxygen demand (BOD) in sludges and muds involves a dilution method whereby:

a. The initial DO of the dilution is calculated.

b. The solids are maintained in suspension during the incubation period.

c. DO is determined on the incubated samples.

In incubated samples of muds the DO is determined by the alum flocculation method, whereas for activated sludges the copper sulfate–sulfamic acid method is used. Both are described in Part III, Oxygen (Dissolved), Methods D and E, respectively.

pH Value

The liquor which separates from sludge or mud is used for pH determinations. In normal sewage sludge, particularly digested sludge, the pH is dependent to a considerable extent on the carbon dioxide equilibrium. Any technique which allows a loss of carbon dioxide from the liquid will give results that are too high. The standard method for determining the pH value is the glass electrode procedure described in Part I. If extremely accurate results are not desired, colorimetric methods may be used.

Bibliography

1. Fair, G. M. & Moore, E. W. Determining the pH of Sewage Sludges. *Sew. Works J.* 1:3 (1930).
2. Hatfield, W. D. & Morkert, K. Determining the pH of Sewage Sludges. *Sew. Works J.* 6:246 (1934).

Residue

The determination of both total and volatile residue in sludge and muds, as in sewage, is subject to error due to the loss of ammonium carbonate and volatile organic matter while drying, making the results lower than they should be.

1. Procedure for Total Residue and Moisture

Weigh 25–50 g sludge to the nearest 0.01 g in a tared evaporating dish.

Evaporate to dryness on a water bath, dry at 103°C for 1 hr, cool in an individual desiccator containing fresh desiccant, and weigh. Dry sludge solids are very hygroscopic and absorb moisture rapidly. If the material contains 15 per cent solids or more, it may be necessary to dry for a longer period. This is particularly true if the material is high in organic or grease content. With samples of this type, evaporating in an oven at 103°C overnight or drying to constant weight may be necessary, but, by this prolonged heating in either technique, there will be loss of volatile organic matter and ammonium carbonates.

On elutriated sludge, 4–6 per cent solids, the standard deviation was found to be 0.02 per cent ($n = 1$; 4×10).

2. Procedure for Volatile Residue

Volatile residue, which includes volatile inorganic salts, is determined on the total residue obtained above by igniting it in an electric muffle furnace at 600°C for 60 min, avoiding loss of solids by decrepitation. Cool in a desiccator and reweigh. Report results as per cent ash and volatile solids.

On digested sludge, 42 per cent ash, the standard deviation was found to be 0.2 per cent ash ($n = 1$; 13×10). On elutriated sludge, 29 per cent ash, the standard deviation was found to be 0.2 per cent ash ($n = 1$; 4×10).

Settleability of Activated Sludge

See Tests on Activated Sludge.

Sludge Digester Gas

Gas Chromatographic Method (Tentative)

1. General Discussion

1.1. *Principle:* Gas chromatographic separation involves the transport of a sample of a gas mixture through a packed column. The column contains either a solid adsorbent or a liquid solvent coated over an inert solid support which provides a large surface for exchange. The solid adsorbent or liquid solvent constitutes the stationary phase. The sample is transported through the column by a carrier gas which constitutes the mobile phase. In a properly selected column, the stationary phase selectively retards the components of the sample, causing their movement through the column at different effective rates. The various components, therefore, tend to segregate into separate zones or bands, which are detected and measured quantitatively by a thermal conductivity cell at the exit of the column.

1.2. *Interference:* In the gas chromatographic method of analysis, the components of a sample can be identified and measured only after they are separated into different zones or bands by a chromatographic column. Therefore, the selection of a suitable column is all-important. When employing the gas-liquid partition columns recommended below, the only interference in the gas chromatographic analysis of methane is the presence of an excess amount of nitrogen or oxygen (more than 50 per cent, by volume, of either component). This interference may be eliminated by substituting the gas-liquid partition with a gas-solid adsorption column. The presence of an excessive amount of oxygen or nitrogen does not interefere with the analysis of carbon dioxide.

2. Apparatus

2.1. *Gas chromatograph,* with thermal conductivity detector and 10-mv full span recorder. If the detection of minor components, such as H_2S and H_2, is desired, a more sensitive recorder of 1-mv full span is required.

2.2. *Syringe,* 2 ml total capacity.

3. Reagents

3.1. *Gas-liquid partition column:* Dissolve 60 g silicone grease in 420 ml diethyl ether, then stir with 150 g ground and sieve-graded 28–48-mesh C-22 firebrick. After the slurry is air dried to remove the ether, pack it in a 3/16- to 1/4-in. I.D. stainless steel or plastic tubing; total length of column is 70 ft. Other liquid materials which may be substituted for silicone grease are: silicone oil 550, tetra-isobutylene, tri-meta-cresyl phosphate, and squalene. The gas-liquid partition column may separate air, CH_4, CO_2, and H_2S from each other. It does not separate N_2 from O_2, or from H_2.*

3.2. *Helium gas.*

4. Procedures

4.1. Coil the gas-liquid partition column to the desired shape and install it in the column oven of the gas chromatograph.

4.2. Open the valve of the helium gas tank and adjust the two-stage pressure gauge to the desirable pressure to maintain a constant gas flow rate, usually in the range of 60–80 ml/min.

4.3. Turn on the column oven heater and the detector current, and adjust them to the desired values. The column oven temperature is best maintained at 80°F for a gas-liquid partition column or a molecular sieve column. A higher temperature of 130°F is recommended when an activated charcoal or silica gel column is used.

4.4. Check rubber serum cap over the sample injection point against leakage by soap solution and replace it if any gas leakage is found. Ordinarily, a serum cap can withstand 200 to 300 sample injections, depending on the needle gauge used (usually 27).

4.5. Turn on the recorder approximately 30 min after the helium flow has started. Adjust the base line on the recorder chart to zero. Inject a 0.5–1.0-ml sample of sludge gas with a syringe after a stable base line is obtained on the recorder.

4.6. Sludge gas usually contains three components: N_2 (predominantly introduced from air leaks into the digester or during sampling), CH_4, and

---

* If appreciable amounts of O_2, N_2 or H_2 are present in the sample and their quantitative determination is desired, the gas-liquid partition column may be substituted by a *gas-solid adsorption column.* The latter column is prepared by grinding molecular sieve, type 5A, to 28–48 mesh, dried at 600°F for 2 to 3 hr, then packed into 3/16- to 1/4-in. I.D. tubing in the same manner as a partition column. The total length is 12 ft. The column completely separates H_2, O_2, N_2 and CH_4. It adsorbs CO_2 and H_2S irrevers-

ibly, hence is not suitable for the determination of these components.

If silica gel or activated charcoal is substituted for the molecular sieve, the adsorption column behaves much like a gas-liquid partition column. Either adsorbent separates air, CH_4, CO_2, but adsorbs H_2S irreversibly. It does not separate N_2, O_2 and H_2. The CO_2 peak is less sharp than that obtained from a gas-liquid partition column, therefore the accuracy is lower.

CO_2. Approximately 10 min after sample injection, N_2 appears as the first peak on the recorder when a 70-ft gas-liquid partition column is used with a helium flow rate of 85 ml/min at 80° F.

5. Calculation

5.1. When a gas-liquid partition column is used, and no appreciable amount (less than 5 per cent by volume) of H_2 is present in the sample gas, the percentage of each gas component may be computed according to:

$$\text{Volume} \% = \frac{A}{B} \times 100 \qquad (5.1)$$

where A = peak height of component and B = sum of peak height of all peaks.

5.2. When a high degree of accuracy is required, or when a gas-solid partition column is used, calibration curves of peak height, or peak area, versus sample volume for each component should be prepared by injecting pure gas of various volumes. The partial volume of each component in the sample can be read from the respective calibration curves by measuring the peak height, or peak area, of each individual peak.

$$\text{Volume} \% = \frac{C}{D} \times 100 \qquad (5.2)$$

where C = partial volume of the component (read from calibration curve) and D = volume of sample injected.

6. Precision and Accuracy

The precision and accuracy attainable will depend on the instrument employed and the technique of operation. A precision of ± 2 per cent can generally be achieved with proper care. The accuracy of the gas chromato-graphic method is within 5 per cent when the calculations are carried out in conformity with Eq. 5.1. A better result may be achieved if Eq. 5.2 is used and calibration curves of individual components are carefully prepared.

Bibliography

1. GRUNE, W. N.; CARTER, J. V.; & KEENAN, J. P. Development of a Continuous Gas Chromatographic Analyzer for Sludge Digestion Studies. *Sew. Ind. Wastes* 28:1433 (1956).
2. GRUNE, W. N.; PHILP, R. H.; & BORSH, R. J. Applications of Gas Chromatography, Conductivity and Potential Measurement in Sludge Digestion. *Biological Treatment of Sewage and Industrial Wastes,* Vol. II, pp. 80–96. Reinhold Publishing Co., New York (1958).
3. GRUNE, W. N.; COSSITT, R. E.; & PHILP, R. H. Anaerobic Process Automation by ORP, Conductivity and Gas Chromatography. *Proc. 12th Indus. Waste Conf.* Purdue Univ., pp. 604–635 (1958)
4. GRUNE, W. N. & PEEK, R. C. New Parameters for Improving Control of Sludge Digestion. *Wastes Eng.* 29: 354 (1958).
5. CHMIELOWSKI, J.; SIMPSON, J. R.; & ISAAC, P. C. Use of Gas Chromatography in Sludge Digestion. *Sew. Indus. Wastes* 31:1237 (1959).
6. GRUNE, W. N. & CHUEH, C. F. Gas Chromatography for Waste Treatment Control. *J. WPCF* 32:942–948 (1960).
7. GRUNE, W. N. Application of Gas Chromatography to Sludge Digestion Gas Analysis. *Water and Sewage Works* 107:396–399 (1960).
8. HENDERSON, W. L. Gas Analysis by Chromatography. *Water and Sewage Works* 107:312 (1960).
9. GRUNE, W. N. & CHUEH, C. F. Application of Gas Chromatography to Sludge Digestion Gas Analysis. *Internat. J. Air and Water Pollution,* Pergamon Press (1962).
10. GRUNE, W. N. & CHUEH, C. F. Application of Gas Chromatography to Sludge Digestion Gas Analysis. 5-Year Final Report to Nat. Inst. of Health, P.H.S., RG–4945 (May 30, 1962).

Volatile Acids (Total)

Column Partition Chromatography Method (Tentative)

1. General Discussion

1.1. *Principle:* Chromatographic columns are capable of a dynamic partition or distribution of dissolved or dispersed substances between two immissible phases, one of which is moving past the other. If an acidified aqueous sample containing organic fatty acids is adsorbed on a column of inert, granular material and an organic solvent is passed through the column, the organic acids will be extracted from the aqueous sample. Silicic acid is used as the adsorbent column, acidified aqueous solution as the stationary phase, and normal butanol in chloroform as the mobile phase.

The solvent system forces the organic acids through the column. Recovery of 95 per cent or better of the volatile fatty acids can be achieved. This method is reliable and rapid, requiring only 10 min per test, and can be readily employed in routine process control.

1.2. *Titration precaution:* Investigations have shown that the normalities of basic alcohol solutions decrease with time. These decreases usually are accompanied by the appearance of a white precipitate. The magnitudes of such changes are not normally significant in ordinary process control work if the tests are performed within a few days of standardization. For work in which more accurate results are required, the basic alcohol titrant should be standardized before each analysis.

2. Apparatus

2.1. *Centrifuge or filtering assembly.*

2.2. *Crucibles,* Gooch or fritted-glass, with filtering flask and vacuum source.

3. Reagents

3.1. *Silicic acid,* solid, 100-mesh: Remove fines by slurrying the acid in distilled water and decanting the supernate after settling for about 15 min. Repeat the process several times. Dry the washed acid in an oven at 103°C, then store in a desiccator.

3.2. *Chloroform-butanol reagent:* Mix 300 ml chloroform, 100 ml *n*-butanol, and 80 ml 0.5N H$_2$SO$_4$ in a separatory funnel and allow the water and organic layers to separate. Drain off the lower organic layer through filter paper into a dry bottle.

3.3. *Thymol blue indicator solution:* Dissolve 80 mg thymol blue in 100 ml absolute methanol.

3.4. *Phenolphthalein indicator solution:* Dissolve 80 mg phenolphthalein in 100 ml absolute methanol.

3.5. *Sulfuric acid,* 10N.

3.6. *Standard sodium hydroxide reagent,* 0.02N. Prepare in absolute methanol from conc NaOH stock solution in water.

4. Procedure

4.1. Centrifuge or filter enough sludge to obtain 10–15 ml of sample in a small beaker or test tube. Discard the residue. Add a few drops of thymol blue indicator solution, then 10N H$_2$SO$_4$, dropwise, until just red to thymol blue.

4.2. Place 10 g silicic acid in the

Gooch or fritted-glass crucible and apply suction to pack the column. With a pipet, distribute 5.0 ml acidified sample as uniformly as possible over the surface of the column. Apply suction momentarily to draw the sample into the silicic acid, releasing the vacuum as soon as the sample enters the column. Quickly add 50 ml chloroform-butanol reagent to the column and apply suction. Discontinue the suction just before the last of the reagent enters the column.

4.3. Remove the filter flask and add a few drops of phenolphthalein indicator solution to the eluate in the flask.

4.4. Titrate with $0.02N$ NaOH titrant in absolute methanol, taking care to avoid aerating the sample. Nitrogen or CO_2-free air delivered through a small glass tube may be used both to mix the sample and to prevent contact with atmospheric CO_2 during titration (CO_2-free air may be obtained by passing air through ascarite or equivalent).

4.5. In a similar manner, titrate a blank composed of 5.0 ml of acidified distilled water extracted with 50 ml of chloroform-butanol reagent.

5. Calculation

Organic acids in mg/l as acetic acid
$$= \frac{A \times 1,000 \times N \,(a - b)}{B}$$

where $A =$ equivalent weight of acetic acid ($=60$ mg/ml); $N =$ normality of the NaOH titrant; $a =$ titer of the sample, ml; $b =$ titer of the blank, ml; and $B =$ ml sample.

6. Precision and Accuracy

The method consistently yields average recovery efficiencies of about 95 per cent for organic acid concentrations in excess of 200 mg/l as acetic acid. Individual tests generally vary from the average by no more than 3 per cent if the tests are performed with reasonable care. A greater variation results when lower concentrations of organic acids are present in the sample.

Bibliography

1. MUELLER, H. F.; BUSWELL, A. M.; & LARSON, T. E. Chromatographic Determination of Volatile Acids. *Sew. Indus. Wastes* 28:255 (1956).
2. ETZEL, J. E. & POHLAND, F. G. Volatile Acid Formation During Sludge Digestion. *Pub. Works* 91:105 (July 1960).
3. WESTERHOLD, A. F. Organic Acids in Digester Liquor by Chromatography. *J. WPCF* 35:1431 (1963).
4. POHLAND, F. G. & DICKSON, B. H., JR. Organic Acids by Column Chromatography. *Water Works & Wastes Eng.* 1:54 (July 1964).

Sludge Volume and Density Indexes

See Tests on Activated Sludge.

Specific Gravity

Specific gravity is determined by comparing the weight of a volume of the sample of mud or sludge with that of an equal volume of distilled water.

Weigh to the nearest 0.1 g an empty, wide-mouth flask or bottle of about 250-ml capacity. Fill completely with distilled water and weigh again.

If the sample flows readily, fill the flask completely with the sample, weigh, and calculate the result:

$$\text{sp gr} = \frac{\text{weight of sample}}{\text{weight of distilled water}}$$

If the sample does not flow readily, add as much of it to the bottle as possible, without exerting pressure, and weigh. Fill the bottle containing the sample with water and weigh again, making sure that all entrained air bubbles have escaped. Determine the weight of added water by difference. Then:

$$\text{sp gr} = \frac{\text{weight of sample}}{\text{weight of water to fill bottle}}$$
$$- \text{weight of water added to sample}$$

Suspended Matter in Activated Sludge

See Tests on Activated Sludge.

Temperature

Temperature at the time of collection of the sample should be recorded to the nearest degree centigrade.

Tests on Activated Sludge

The activated-sludge process of sewage treatment is dependent on laboratory control through use of the procedures given below. These methods are presented as a group, because the sludge volume index (SVI) and the sludge density index (SDI) are calculated from suspended solids and the 30-min settleability test.

A. Suspended Matter

Suspended matter of sludges and aeration tank mixed liquors can be determined by the gravimetric method (Part III, Residue, Method C) or by he following aluminum dish method. If it is desirable to determine the volatile solids, the gravimetric method should be used.

1. Apparatus

1.1. *Aluminum dish,* with a perforated bottom similar to a Buchner funnel, inside diameter 92 mm, height 25 mm.

1.2. *Filter paper,* 90-mm diameter, Munktells No. 1F, Whatman No. 1, or equal.

1.3. *Sponge rubber ring,* 93-mm outside diameter, 75-mm inside diameter, thickness about 3 mm.

1.4. *Buchner funnel,* No. 2A, inside diameter at bottom 93 mm.

1.5. *Filter flask,* with side tube, 1,000-ml size.

2. Procedure

Dry the dish and filter paper in an oven. Cool in a desiccator and weigh. Wet the filter paper, place the dish with paper on a rubber ring in the Buchner funnel and apply about 20 in. of vacuum to the flask. Immediately add 20 to 100 ml sludge (which should yield 0.2 to 0.4 g dry solids) to the dish and, after the water has been extracted, dry in the oven for about 30 min at 103°–105°C. Cool in the desiccator and weigh.

The test is applicable to aeration tank liquor (for which the result is reported as mg/l) or to the heavier sludges, such as return sludge, for which the result may be reported as mg/l or as per cent dry sludge solids.

3. Precision and Accuracy

The standard deviation was 0.6 mg on a 100-ml sample ($n = 1$; 21×10).

B. Settleability

The settleability of activated sludge is determined by allowing 1,000 ml activated sludge to settle in a 1,000-ml graduated cylinder. Record the volume occupied by the sludge at various intervals of time—10, 20, 30, 45, 60 min; plot these volumes against time and obtain a curve indicating the rate of settling. For plant control a 30-min settling period is generally used.

C. Sludge Volume Index

The sludge volume index (SVI) is the volume in milliliters occupied by 1 g activated sludge after settling the aerated liquor for 30 min. A 1-liter sample is collected at the outlet of the aeration tanks, and settled for 30 min in a 1,000-ml graduated cylinder; the volume occupied by the sludge is reported as per cent or ml. The sample is thoroughly mixed, or an original sample taken, and the suspended solids are determined and reported in per cent by weight or mg/1.

$$SVI = \frac{\text{per cent settling by volume}}{\text{per cent suspended matter}}$$

$$SVI = \frac{\text{ml settled sludge} \times 1,000}{\text{mg/l suspended matter}}$$

The standard deviation of the sludge volume index was determined as 1.69 on an average index of 72—a coefficient of variation of 2.35 per cent ($n = 1$; 10×10).

D. Sludge Density Index

The sludge density index (SDI) is the reciprocal of the sludge volume index (SVI) multiplied by 100, and is calculated from the data determined by the methods described above.

$$SDI = \frac{\text{per cent suspended matter} \times 100}{\text{per cent settling by volume}}$$

$$= \frac{\text{mg/l suspended matter}}{\text{ml settled sludge} \times 10}$$

$$= \frac{100}{SVI}$$

The standard deviation of the sludge density index was found to be 0.033 on an average index of 1.40—a coefficient of variation of 2.35 per cent ($n = 1$; 10×10).

Bibliography

1. THERIAULT, E. J. & WAGENHALS, H. H. Studies of Representative Sewage Plants. *Public Health Bull.* 132:24 (1923).
2. DONALDSON, W. Some Notes on the Operation of Sewage Treatment Works. *Sew. Works J.* 4:48 (1932).
3. MOHLMAN, F. W. Editorial. *Sew. Works J.* 6:119 (1934).
4. SMITH, J. I. Investigation of Rapid Methods for Sludge Solids Estimation. *Sew. Works J.* 6:908 (1934).

PART VI

Bioassay Methods for the Evaluation of Acute Toxicity of Industrial Wastewaters and Other Substances to Fish

Introduction

The bioassay procedures described here are intended for use in industrial and other laboratories in evaluating the toxicity of wastes and other water pollutants to fish. These practical tests can be used to determine whether or not a waste or waste component is markedly toxic and, if toxic, the degree of toxicity. They will serve also as the basis for judging whether or not a waste can be discharged at a given rate without causing direct injury to fish and other organisms in the receiving water.

The value of such biologic tests of waste quality, in connection with the control of waste disposal and treatment, is being increasingly realized. Chemical examination of complex industrial wastes alone usually does not yield sufficient information. Many of their various toxic components cannot be readily detected, separated, and measured by chemical means. Moreover, the degree of toxicity of each of these numerous substances and mixtures of chemicals is not known. The toxicity of wastes can be greatly influenced by interactions between their individual components and the dissolved minerals present in widely varying amounts in receiving waters. Different kinds of fish are not equally susceptible to toxic substances, and much of the pertinent published information is based on experiments with hardy species only. Therefore, the toxicity of an industrial waste to local fish in their natural medium must be detected and evaluated directly through biologic tests under appropriate experimental conditions.

Death due to deficiency of dissolved oxygen (DO) in polluted water should be distinguished from death due to toxicity. To detect and evaluate the direct lethality of the wastes only, adequate DO must be maintained during toxicity tests.

Reasonable uniformity of experimental procedure and of the manner of presentation of results is essential; widespread adoption of uniform methods will promote the accumulation of comparable data. However, rigid standardization of experimental material and conditions is not desirable, for it would tend to defeat the purpose of practical tests. Strict comparability of test results could be achieved only by sacrificing much of their relevance and applicability to practical problems in specific localities. Experimental water (water used as a diluent) and test animals best suited to the purpose of each bioassay should be selected. With respect to other features, the tests can be more or less uniform. It is believed that the standardization of experimental conditions and procedures described here will insure adequate uniformity, reproducibility, and general usefulness of the bioassay results, without interfering unduly with the adaptability of the tests to local circumstances and problems.

Selection of method: The basic Routine Bioassay Method constitutes the simplest procedure. It is widely applicable, being suitable for the detection and evaluation of acute toxicity which is not associated with excessive oxygen demand and is due to substances that are relatively stable and are not extremely volatile. The Routine Bioassay Method is designed so that surface absorption of oxygen from the atmosphere plus some oxygen from the diluent generally provides an adequate amount of DO for the fish during the test period. Many industrial effluents and some chemicals have a high chemical or biochemical oxygen demand, which may cause oxygen depletion in test solutions. Although it is usually necessary to use artificial supplies of air or oxygen, DO must nevertheless be maintained at levels adequate for the test fish.

Uncontrolled aeration with compressed air has been generally unsatisfactory in bioassays of industrial effluents. Small additions of air will not ordinarily maintain the necessary quantities of DO, whereas vigorous aeration may drive off volatile toxicants and may greatly speed up biologic oxidation.

Three methods of maintaining adequate DO are described under Modifications of Routine Bioassay Method: (1) controlled artificial oxygenation of test solutions; (2) initial oxygenation of the diluent; and (3) renewal of test solutions.

Renewal of test solutions should also be employed whenever there is evidence or expectation of a rapid change of toxicity of test media. Such a change usually can be detected by testing solutions or waste dilutions which have stood in the test vessels for about 2 days and in which test animals exposed to the fresh media have died during this period. Serious volatility, instability, or detoxification of important constituents is indicated when the recorded average survival time of the test animals in a fresh medium is much less than the survival time in the corresponding older, used medium, if adequate DO is present throughout both tests.

Another modification of the routine bioassay method that may be useful in some instances is prolonging the test period beyond 96 hr. This is sometimes done when the material tested is of a low order of toxicity or when 24-, 48-, and 96-hr results indicate a major increase in mortality with time of exposure.

When the experimental data are reported, any deviation from the basic routine procedure should be described in order to facilitate interpretation of test results and their significance.

Routine Bioassay Method

1. General Discussion

1.1. *Principle:* The prescribed measure of acute toxicity is the median tolerance limit (TL_m) or the concentration of the tested material in a suitable diluent (experimental water) at which just 50 per cent of the test animals are able to survive for a specified period of exposure.* This exposure period may

---

* The TL_m corresponds to the median lethal dose or 50 per cent lethal dose (LD_{50}), which is frequently reported in toxicologic literature (commonly without specifying the duration of observation), and should not be confused with the "minimum lethal dose" (MLD). The expression "lethal dose" is not appropriate when designating a certain

be 24, 48, or 96 hr. At least the 24- and 48-hr TL_m values should be determined and recorded whenever the toxicity is sufficiently pronounced to permit their determination.

Concentrations of dilutions of liquid industrial wastes (aqueous solutions, suspensions, and emulsions of complex or unknown composition) are expressed as per cent by volume. For example, a 10 per cent dilution, or a TL_m of 10 per cent, equals 1 part of wastewater in 9 parts of diluent water. Concentrations of solutions of nonaqueous wastes and of individual chemicals (solids, liquids, or gases) are expressed in terms of milligrams per liter, or parts per million by weight of the substance added to the experimental water.*

To evaluate the toxicity, different concentrations are tested so that the concentration lethal to 50 per cent of the test animals within each prescribed test period can be found or estimated by interpolation. DO concentrations well above the minimum tolerable level are maintained throughout the course of each test, but unduly rapid reaeration of the test medium, which can result in speedy removal of important volatile constituents, is avoided.

1.2. Interference: Extreme volatility, instability, and rapid detoxification of waste components and chemicals tested, and also excessive oxygen demand, can render the routine bioassay method inapplicable, or can cause serious bias of the results. (See "Selection of Method" above and Sec. 9.2 below.)

1.3. Sampling and storage: Samples of industrial or other effluents which are not constant in their composition should be collected at different times and should not be unnecessarily combined to make composite samples, because knowledge of the maximal toxicity of a variable effluent often is required in connection with the control of waste disposal in flowing waters, rather than knowledge of the average toxicity.†

Samples of industrial or other effluents should be stored in completely filled, stoppered bottles at a fairly uniform temperature not greatly exceeding the initial temperature. If the waste may contain organic matter subject to bacterial decomposition, the samples should be refrigerated (without freezing) and held at a temperature between 0° and 4°C. Duration of storage prior to testing should be kept to a minimum.

---

concentration in an external medium, inasmuch as a dose, strictly speaking, is a measured quantity administered. Unlike "lethal dose" and "lethal concentration" (LC), the term "tolerance limit" is universally applicable in designating the effective level of any measurable lethal agent, including high and low temperatures, pH, and the like. For this and other reasons, the term "median tolerance limit" and the symbol TL_m are recommended.

* The inclusion of any water of hydration as part of the weight of the solute (e.g., $CuSO_4 \cdot 5H_2O$) should be clearly indicated.

† Extensive damage to the aquatic life of

a receiving stream can result from brief, intermittent discharges of a highly toxic waste, even if the toxicity of the effluent at other times and its average toxicity are negligible. Therefore, if the composition and toxicity of an effluent vary considerably, it is necessary to test a number of individual (grab) samples taken at times when the effluent is likely to be most toxic, in order to determine the maximal toxicity. A composite sample of an effluent consisting of portions collected at regular time intervals can be useful only when average toxicity is to be evaluated.

2. Apparatus

2.1. *Test containers:* The size and shape of the vessels or aquaria, hereafter referred to as test containers, in which fish are exposed to the test media, have not been standardized. The size depends on the required volume of test medium, which in turn depends on the number and size of fish used in each test (Sec. 5.6). However, the depth of the vessels must be more than 6 in. (Sec. 5.2). Test containers should be of glass and should be chemically clean. For tests with fish of ordinary size, 2 to 3 in. in length, the containers may be wide-mouth glass bottles or cylindrical glass jars 10 to 12 in. in diameter, 12 in. or more high, with a capacity of about 4.5 to 5 gal (17 to 19 liters). Smaller or larger glass jars, or rectangular aquarium tanks, may be more suitable for tests with smaller or larger fish.

Six to twelve test containers often are needed for performing a bioassay most efficiently.

2.2. *Testing laboratory:* An ordinary heated or air-conditioned laboratory room with thermostatic controls suitable for maintaining prescribed test temperatures (Sec. 5.1) will generally suffice for the conduct of bioassays with warm-water fish. A specially insulated constant-temperature room or a large water bath equipped for precise temperature control and good circulation of air or water is usually preferable, and such a facility may be necessary for conducting bioassays with cold-water fishes.

2.3. *Acclimatizing tank:* The aquarium in which the test animals are acclimatized and prepared for use in toxicity tests (Sec. 3.6) usually is a rectangular tank with glass sides and a capacity of 15 to 50 gal, its size de-

pending on the size and number of fish to be used. Because the water in the acclimatizing tank must approximate the test temperature, this tank must be placed in a room with suitable, constant temperature, or it must be equipped with thermostatic devices. Thermostatic equipment must be selected with care to avoid contact of the water with harmful metals, such as copper and copper alloys, zinc, and cadmium. Facilities must be provided also for adequate aeration with compressed or pumped air released near the bottom of the tank from several air diffusion stones or dispersers.

3. Selection and Preparation of Test Animals

3.1. *Kinds of fish to be used:* The test fish should be a species adaptable to the laboratory conditions of temperature, feeding, and handling. Availability of an adequate supply of healthy fish of desirable uniform size may be the major factor governing selection of the species to be used. Information on species which have been used successfully is given in the literature.[1, 9, 12]

If available, fish species which are deemed important locally should be given preference. If circumstances necessitate the use of some other kind, such as one of the common aquarium fishes (guppies, goldfish, etc.), for routine bioassays, or if one of these aquarium fishes is chosen in order to insure uniformity of test animals at all times with respect to age, size, nutritional and temperature history, etc., comparative tests should be performed, using appropriate toxicants, to relate the sensitivity of the selected species to those of locally important game and food fishes.

Although any fresh-water or marine fish species that suits the purpose of the investigation may be used, species belonging to any of the following widely distributed and important fresh-water families are particularly recommended, and one or more of these should be selected unless there is good reason for making a different choice:

Centrarchidae (sunfishes, basses, crappies)
Salmonidae (trouts, charrs, salmons)
Cyprinidae (true minnows)
Catostomidae (suckers)

For tests relating to estuarine pollution problems and some others, some species belonging to the families Gasterosteidae (sticklebacks) and Cyprinodontidae (killifishes, top minnows) can be outstandingly suitable test animals, because of their tolerance of wide variations of water salinity, their abundance in many coastal waters, their small size, etc. However, species of the family Cyprinodontidae may be much more resistant to many toxicants than most of the other recommended forms. Marine species of the genus *Fundulus* have been widely used as experimental material.

3.2. *Identification:* Fish used for each individual toxicity evaluation must all be of the same species. They should be identified at least as to genus, and preferably as to species. The correct scientific name should be stated when the test results are reported.*

3.3. *Source:* Test fish may be obtained from any single, common source (hatchery, lake, stream). They should all be collected and brought to the

---

* A list of species published by the American Fisheries Society [2] is a helpful guide to proper, widely approved nomenclature of fishes.

laboratory for acclimatization at about the same time.

3.4. *Size:* The largest fish in an individual bioassay should be not more than 1.5 times the length of the smallest specimen used. Small specimens, averaging less than 3 in. in length, generally are the most convenient and desirable test animals.

3.5. *Stocks:* Stocks of test fish may be kept initially in any suitable enclosures or containers (small ponds, liveboxes, screened pens, concrete or wooden tanks, or glass aquaria) and in any water of suitable quality and temperature in which they remain in good condition until needed. Care and feeding of stock animals are discussed by Doudoroff and colleagues.[5]

3.6. *Acclimatization and feeding:* The test animals should be acclimatized for at least 1 week (preferably 10 days or longer) to laboratory conditions similar to those under which the tests are to be performed, with regard especially to the temperature and chemical properties (or source) of the water.

The fish should be fed at fairly regular intervals, at least three times a week and preferably daily, during the acclimatization period, but should not be fed for a period of about 2 days before they are used in a test.

3.7. *Fitness:* The incidence of specimens dying or becoming seriously diseased in the acclimatizing aquarium during a period of 4 days immediately preceding a test must be less than 10 per cent. Otherwise, the test animal lot should be deemed unfit for use until the incidence of disease and the mortality rate decline sufficiently. Test specimens must show no symptoms of disease or abnormalities of appearance or behavior at the time of their transfer to test containers.

4. Selection and Preparation of Experimental Water (Diluent)

4.1. *Usual source of experimental water:* The experimental water to be used as a diluent and acclimatizing medium should be obtained from the body of water which receives the waste under investigation. When the toxicity of a waste alone is to be determined, the water should be obtained at a point where there is no pollution or contamination with waste from any source.

When a stream water receiving the waste to be tested is subject to previous contamination with other wastes, the toxicity of the test waste in conjunction with previous contaminants must be considered in judging safe rates of discharge. For evaluation of this resulting toxicity, it is necessary to use experimental water obtained immediately upstream from the point of discharge of the waste to be tested, but outside the zone of its influence. Such an evaluation is possible only when the test animals can be held successfully in the diluent water.

4.2. *Substituted water:* If uncontaminated experimental water cannot be supplied from the body of water under consideration, water of similar quality, with respect to its dissolved-mineral content, should be obtained from another source, or else prepared by adding appropriate chemicals to a natural water of suitable quality, which may first be diluted, if necessary, with distilled or demineralized water of assured purity. As a general rule, the calcium, magnesium, sulfate, and dissolved-solids content of this substituted water should not differ by more than 25 per cent from that of the water receiving the waste tested. It is advisable to adjust the pH, alkalinity, and hardness of the substituted water to match those of the receiving water as closely as practicable. This is especially necessary when effluents are known to contain metal salts, cyanide complexes, ammonium compounds, or other chemicals the toxicity of which is known to be greatly affected by changes in these characteristics. When wide variations occur in quality characteristics of receiving waters, it is desirable to determine the toxicity of the waste material at the upper and lower limits of the range.

4.3. *Modification of water for use as diluent:* When uncontaminated water is used as a diluent it should be adjusted to the test temperature and well aerated with dispersed compressed air. Excessive amounts of noncolloidal suspended matter should be removed by settling or filtration.

When a contaminated water is employed as a diluent, delay of its use, unnecessary aeration, and other treatment which can result in serious alteration or removal of the pollutants present, should be avoided.

5. Other Prescribed Experimental Conditions

5.1. *Test temperatures:* The tests should be performed at a uniform temperature between 20° and 28°C when so-called warm-water fish (e.g., Centrarchidae and most Cyprinidae) are used as test animals, or between 12° and 18°C when cold-water fish (e.g., Salmonidae) are used.

It is desirable to hold the temperature as closely as possible to the selected and reported value. For reliable results the overall range should not exceed 4°C.

5.2. *Depth of liquid in test containers:* The average depth of the liquid should be uniform in all parallel tests and should never be less than 6 in. The purpose of the latter restriction is to limit the rate of escape of any gaseous or other volatile components, which varies with the ratio of the exposed surface area to the volume of the liquid.

5.3. *Dissolved oxygen content of liquids tested:* The DO content of test solutions, or dilutions, should not fall below 4 mg/l when warm-water fish are used as test animals, or 5 mg/l when cold-water fish are used.

5.4. *Aeration and oxygenation of liquids tested:* Reaeration of the liquid in a test container occurs at the still surface exposed to the atmosphere. When the rate of absorption of oxygen from the air is not great enough to maintain the prescribed DO concentration, other methods for regulation or maintenance of the oxygen content must be employed (see Modifications of Routine Bioassay Method). Unregulated artificial aeration of waste samples, and dilutions, by dispersed compressed air or other means, is not permissible unless no gaseous or volatile components, which may be driven rapidly out of solution, are present. Thorough aeration is an approved treatment for some wastes before discharge, but the toxicity of a waste or waste dilution which has been aerated is often less than that of an unaerated sample.

5.5. *Number of test animals:* At least ten animals should be used for testing each experimental concentration of the substance or waste under investigation, if final conclusions are to be based on the outcome of the test. These animals may be divided equally among two or more test containers with solutions, or waste dilutions, of the same concentra-

tion. Indeed, duplication of each test is desirable. Fewer than ten animals may be used in preliminary tests (Sec. 6.1a), to determine the range of concentrations which should be tested with the larger number of fish in the routine test procedure (Sec. 6.1b).

5.6 *Total animal weight and liquid volume:* The weight of all fish in a test container should not exceed 2 g per liter of liquid medium. Preferably, it should be about 1 g, or less, per liter of liquid, especially when the average weight of the fish is not much more than 2 g each. Sometimes the weight of fish which can be held successfully in a given volume of liquid may be further restricted by the available oxygen supply and related requirements.

6. Procedure

6.1. *Procedural elements:* The concentration of a test waste or other substance fatal to 50 per cent of the test animals in a specified exposure period, under the prescribed experimental conditions, sometimes can be found directly by experiment, but such direct determination of the TL_m is not often practicable or advantageous. It is sufficient to record the percentages of test animals surviving at concentrations somewhat higher and lower than the TL_m, so that it can be estimated by interpolation.

a. *Exploratory tests:* When testing effluents of completely unknown toxicity, much time and effort may be saved by conducting small-scale exploratory bioassays to determine the approximate range of concentration of the waste which should be covered in the full-scale tests. In these preliminary tests, solutions are prepared over a wide range of concentrations; for example, 100, 10, 1, and 0.1, or 100, 32, 10, and 3.2 per cent of the effluent by volume.

An industrial effluent or a saturated solution of a chemical of uncertain toxicity can be tested without any dilution only if it has an adequate DO content. If found to be deficient in DO, it must be diluted with well-aerated experimental water until the required persistent DO concentration (Sec. 5.3) is attained, before introduction of the test animals. If at least half of the test animals die during the test while the DO concentration remains adequate, and all or nearly all controls (Sec. 6.3) survive, measurable acute toxicity of the pollutant is indicated. If no fish are killed in 24 hr, the test should be continued for 48 or 96 hr. If toxicity cannot be demonstrated and evaluated by the routine method, a modification may have to be tried before concluding that no acute toxicity can be detected and measured.

In the exploratory tests two or more fish are placed in an appropriate volume of each of the test solutions. For two average-size test fish (2–3 in. long) 2 liters of test solution in 1-gal wide-mouth glass bottles are usually adequate. The duration of the exploratory tests depends on the results obtained. Usually observations overnight or for 24 hr will indicate the percentages between which the concentrations for the full-scale tests should be selected. When the test materials have low toxicity or act slowly, or when the waste must be diluted to insure adequate oxygen, it may be necessary to continue the test for 48 or 96 hr to demonstrate toxicity and to determine the concentration range to be tested. Usually the test range to be used in the full-scale routine tests falls between the highest concentration at which all fish survive for 24 hr and the lowest concentration at which all or most fish die in the same period.

Exploratory tests can also indicate whether excessive oxygen depletion or loss of toxicity in test solutions is such that modifications of the routine bioassay method are necessary.

b. Full-scale tests for toxicity evaluation: When the range in concentration or test range to be covered by the full-scale tests has been determined by exploratory bioassays, the toxicity of the pollutant is measured by testing several concentrations within the limits of this range. A series of at least 4–6 such concentrations should be tested in order to make possible a sufficiently precise estimation of the TL_m.

6.2. Choice of concentrations to be tested: Although TL_m may be determined by using any appropriate concentrations of the substance or waste to be assayed, it has been found best and most convenient to use the logarithmic series of concentration values given in Table 33. These values can represent concentrations expressed as per cent by volume, as milligrams per liter, or as parts per million by weight. They may be multiplied or divided, as necessary, by any power of 10. For example, the two values in the first column may be 10.0 and 1.0 as shown, or they may be 100 and 10, or 1.0 and 0.1, with the values in the other columns changed accordingly. The series of values, 10.0, 5.6, 3.2, 1.8, and 1.0 per cent, are evenly spaced when plotted on a logarithmic scale. Generally five such points are adequate for obtaining the desired information on the variable effluents from most industries. A higher degree of precision

TABLE 33—GUIDE TO SELECTION OF EXPERIMENTAL CONCENTRATIONS, BASED ON PROGRESSIVE BISECTION OF INTERVALS ON LOGARITHMIC SCALE

Col. 1	Col. 2	Col. 3	Col. 4	Col. 5
10.0				
				8.7
			7.5	
				6.5
		5.6		
				4.9
			4.2	
				3.7
	3.2			
				2.8
			2.4	
				2.1
		1.8		
				1.55
			1.35	
				1.15
1.0				

can often be obtained by using the intermediate concentrations listed in Col. 4; namely, 7.5, 4.2, 2.4, and 1.35 per cent. The concentrations in Col. 5 are used only in very unusual circumstances.

Some investigators prefer other, similar series of concentrations, such as that presented in Table 34. The

TABLE 34—GUIDE TO SELECTION OF EXPERIMENTAL CONCENTRATIONS, BASED ON DECILOG INTERVALS

Concentrations		Log of Concentration
Col. 1	Col. 2	
10.0		1.00
	7.94 (or 7.9)	0.90
6.31 (or 6.3)		0.80
	5.01 (or 5.0)	0.70
3.98 (or 4.0)		0.60
	3.16 (or 3.15)	0.50
2.51 (or 2.5)		0.40
	1.99 (or 2.0)	0.30
1.58 (or 1.6)		0.20
	1.26 (or 1.25)	0.10
1.00		0.00

values shown in Col. 1 usually are used first. If additional tests are deemed advisable for reducing the intervals between the test concentrations, the appropriate values from Col. 2 may be used. The reason for selection of these concentration values will be apparent when their logarithms, given in the right-hand column, are considered. Other series of test concentrations can be equally satisfactory, but a logarithmic series is always advantageous and should be approximated. A more detailed description of the use of logarithmic series of concentrations is given by Doudoroff, et al.[5]

The magnitude of suitable intervals between the test concentrations used for establishing a TL_m by interpolation cannot be definitely prescribed. It depends on the required degree of precision (which varies with the planned use of the test results) and on the nature of the experimental data. When two test concentrations, one above and one below the TL_m, have proved unquestionably lethal to some (about 20 per cent or more) but not to all of the test animals, determination of survival percentages at intermediate concentrations generally is not essential. Otherwise, the estimate of TL_m can often be markedly improved by reducing the intervals between the test concentrations. However, the testing of more concentrations may not be justifiable when the increased reliability of the estimate thus achieved can have no practical import. The intervals between the concentrations included in the first column of Table 34, and those included in the first three columns of Table 33, are believed to be sufficiently small for most industrial effluents. Narrower and wider intervals are recommended only when they are clearly advantageous and adequate.

TABLE 35—DILUTIONS FOR VARIOUS TEST SOLUTION CONCENTRATIONS

Test Solution Concentration Desired			Strength of Stock Solution—g/l				
			100	10	1	0.1	0.01
per cent	ppm or mg/l	ppb or µg/l	Volume (ml) to Be Diluted to 1 Liter				
1.0	10,000		100				
0.56	5,600		56				
0.32	3,200		32				
0.18	1,800		18				
0.10	1,000		10	100			
0.056	560		5.6	56			
0.032	320		3.2	32			
0.018	180		1.8	18			
0.010	100		1.0	10	100		
0.0056	56			5.6	56		
0.0032	32			3.2	32		
0.0018	18			1.8	18		
0.0010	10			1.0	10	100	
0.00056	5.6				5.6	56	
0.00032	3.2				3.2	32	
0.00018	1.8				1.8	18	
0.00010	1.0	1,000			1.0	10	100
0.000056	0.56	560				5.6	56
0.000032	0.32	320				3.2	32
0.000018	0.18	180				1.8	18
0.000010	0.10	100				1.0	10
0.0000056	0.056	56					5.6
0.0000032	0.032	32					3.2
0.0000018	0.018	18					1.8
0.0000010	0.010	10					1.0

In preparing test solutions of highly toxic compounds, it may not be feasible to add measured quantities directly to the test aquaria. Table 35 is useful in determining suitable quantities of dilutions to be added.

6.3. *Control tests:* With each test of any concentration of the substance assayed, or with each series of tests of different concentrations tested simultaneously, a concurrent control test must be performed in exactly the same manner as the other tests, using the experimental water (diluent) alone as the medium in which the fish (controls) are held. The DO content of the water in the control test containers is subject to the restrictions applicable to other tests. There should be no more than 10 per cent mortality among the controls during the course of any test, and at least 90 per cent must remain in apparently good health. Otherwise, the test results cannot be deemed reliable and every simultaneous test should be repeated.

6.4. *Preparation of test dilutions of wastes:* All dilutions required for a single toxicity bioassay should be prepared with the same sample of waste, portions of which may be stored until needed in completely filled, tightly stoppered bottles at a temperature of 0° to 4°C (without freezing). Duration of storage should be held to a minimum and should be reported, along with the source and nature of the sample. Any undissolved material present in a waste sample should be uniformly dispersed by agitation before a measured portion of the sample is withdrawn for addition to a measured quantity of water in a test container. The waste then should be mixed thoroughly with the diluent by gentle stirring to insure good dispersion and solution of any undissolved soluble matter. Unnecessary exposure of the waste samples and dilutions to the atmosphere, through violent agitation or otherwise, should be carefully avoided.

6.5. *Transfer of test animals:* Test animals should be transferred from the acclimatizing aquarium to the test containers as soon as possible but at most within 30 min after preparation of the experimental solutions or waste dilutions. This time interval should be uniform and should be recorded. Test animals should be transferred from one container to another only with small-mesh dip nets of soft material or with wet hands, and should not be allowed to rest on any dry surface or be held out of water longer than necessary. Any specimen accidently dropped or otherwise mishandled during transfer should be rejected and not used for test purposes until its health and freedom from injury have been established. All the test animals should be selected and graded in advance according to size to avoid unnecessary handling just before the test.

6.6. *Duration of tests:* Duration of all tests should be at least 48 hr, and preferably 96 hr. In the event that more than half of the test animals survive for 48 hr at the highest concentration that can be tested properly, the test must be continued for 96 hr. The substance or waste under investigation may be reported as having no acute toxicity only when it has been shown that most of the test animals survive for 96 hr at this maximal test concentration. If toxicity cannot be demonstrated or evaluated by the routine procedure, modifications should be employed before concluding that no significant acute toxicity can be detected and measured.

6.7. *Observations during tests:* The number of fish which have died in each test container should be observed and recorded exactly 24 and 48 hr after their introduction, and also after 96 hr if the tests are continued beyond the minimum (48-hr) period. The number of fish which are alive but show pronounced symptoms of intoxication and distress, such as loss of equilibrium and other markedly abnormal behavior, also should be noted and recorded. Close observations of the reactions of the fish during the first 4 to 8 hr may give an indication of the nature of the toxicant and serve as a guide for further tests. Test animals should be deemed "dead" at the time of observation only if respiratory and other movements, either spontaneous or in response to mild mechanical stimulation (prodding the animal or pressing its tail with a glass rod), cannot be readily detected during an observation period of about 5 min. Dead fish should be removed as soon as observed.

Minimum required quantities (samples) of the liquids tested should be removed from the test containers as often as necessary for determination of DO or other instructive chemical tests. To maintain the liquid surface at a uniform level, such samples may be replaced with equal volumes of similar solutions or dilutions, prepared at the same time as those tested and stored in separate containers.

6.8. *Feeding of test animals during tests:* The fish should not be fed during tests of limited duration (96 hr or less). Feeding tends to increase the rate of respiratory metabolism and increases excretory or other waste products which may influence the toxicity of test solutions.

7. Physical and Chemical Determinations

Determinations that should be made are temperature, DO, and pH. Others, such as alkalinity, acidity, and hardness, may be useful, depending on the nature of the effluent.

Determination of DO is necessary to detect any fish mortality caused by oxygen depletion and to assure control of oxygen during the bioassays. High or low pH values which may cause fish mortality can be readily determined. Changes in pH and other water quality characteristics may have a definite bearing on the toxicity of many substances. Chemical tests may also give indications of the nature of the major toxicants and may help greatly in the application of bioassay results.

Physical and chemical determinations are normally made on test solutions before adding fish and after fish mortality or at the termination of the bioassay. Some determinations, especially for DO, may be needed more frequently. Samples may be siphoned directly from the test aquaria into small DO bottles and other containers.

8. Calculation (Estimation of TL_m)

A TL_m reported may be a concentration at which 50 per cent survival actually was observed in a test (if higher and lower percentages have been recorded for the next lower and higher test concentrations, respectively); or it may be a value obtained by interpolation, based on observed percentages of test animals surviving at concentrations lethal to more than half and to less than half of the test subjects.

The derivation of the median value by interpolation involves merely plotting the experimental data on semilogarithmic coordinate paper, with test concentrations laid off on the logarithmic scale and survival percentages on the arithmetic scale. Then a straight line is drawn between the two points representing survival percentages at two successive concentrations of the test series which were lethal to more than half and to less than half of the test animals. From the point at which this line intersects the 50 per cent survival line a perpendicular drawn to the concentration ordinate indicates the TL_m concentration. This method is referred to as straight-line graphical interpolation.

Figure 38 illustrates the estimation of TL_m values by the straight-line graphical interpolation method. Hypothetical experimental data are presented in the accompanying table, which shows the numbers of animals used for testing different dilutions of a liquid industrial

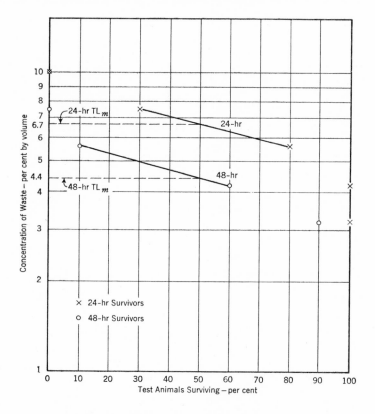

Experimental Data (Hypothetical) Plotted Above

Concentration of Waste % by vol.	No. of Test Animals	No. of Test Animals Surviving	
		After 24 Hr	After 48 Hr
10.0	10	0	0
7.5	10	3	0
5.6	10	8	1
4.2	10	10	6
3.2	10	10	9

Fig. 38. Estimation of median tolerance limits by straight-line graphical interpolation

waste or effluent, and the numbers surviving after exposure periods of 24 hr and 48 hr. These experimental results are plotted in the figure. The 24-hr and 48-hr median tolerance limits are shown to be about 6.7 and 4.4 per cent waste, respectively.

If the difference, or interval, between the two important test concentrations is not much more than 25 per cent of the higher value, a rough estimate of the TL_m sufficient for most practical purposes can be obtained even when the observed survival percentages at these concentrations are 0 and 100 per cent. At least one higher and one lower concentration always should be included in the series tested, in order to obtain confirmatory data.

Other widely accepted and often more satisfactory procedures include graphical methods which involve fitting a smooth, signoid curve to data plotted in the manner described above, or fitting a straight line to data plotted on logarithmic probability paper,[4] as well as the more refined methods of probits, logits, or angles.[7]

Sometimes the observed survival percentages change little or erratically with progressively increasing concentration of the test substance, even rather large changes of concentration having but little effect on its lethality, for one reason or another. Under these circumstances it may be necessary to resort to one of the above methods of TL_m estimation rather than the straight-line graphical interpolation method in order to make full use of the available experimental data to achieve satisfactory precision.

9. Precision and Accuracy

9.1. *Precision:* The precision of toxicity bioassay results obtained by the routine method cannot be explicitly stated. It depends on the degree of uniformity of the test animals with respect to their resistance to the particular toxicant assayed, and on the number of animals used in each test. It is influenced also by the number of concentrations within the test range which are bioassayed and, to some extent, by the method of interpolation (estimation

of TL_m) employed. None of these factors has been rigidly standardized, inasmuch as the required precision varies widely with the purpose of the bioassay or the planned use of the test results.

The normal biologic variation of individuals of a species limits the precision of any bioassay method. All individuals do not react identically to a toxicant, and minor differences in their metabolism may, in replicate tests, cause slight changes in test solution characteristics, such as pH, carbon dioxide, and DO. A precision within 10 per cent is the greatest that can be expected under carefully standardized conditions when using ten uniform fish in solutions of a toxicant whose action is not greatly affected by changes in characteristics of test solutions. The precision with toxicants (e.g., metal salts) whose action is greatly affected by changes in test solution characteristics is much less. The use of additional replicate tests and a larger number of test fish may increase the precision.

9.2. *Accuracy and interpretation of bioassay results:* It should be understood that a routine toxicity bioassay yields only a measure of the toxicity of a substance to a particular, selected group of fish of a certain kind, size, age, and physiologic condition, at a certain time or season, and when the substance is added to water with specific characteristics. The TL_m determined may or may not closely approximate the true median tolerance limit for an entire population of fish under average conditions to be found in their natural habitat. The test animals used in a bioassay usually are not truly representative of an entire population with respect to size, age, environmental history, and physiologic condition; the

TL_m obtained consequently differs, more or less, from the median tolerance limit for the population. However, such "inaccuracy" of a bioassay is not usually to be deplored. In most instances, it is indeed desirable to determine a TL_m for sensitive fish under the most adverse conditions likely to be encountered in their natural habitat, and at a time in their life when they are highly susceptible to the toxicant tested.

The toxicity of a test medium can change in the course of a test, owing to the gradual escape, decomposition, or detoxification of some constituents, to the accumulation of metabolic products, and to other causes. The ensuing bias of the bioassay result can be serious. The toxicity of a waste determined by the routine bioassay procedure can be less than its actual toxicity in a receiving stream if the potency of the sample declines during the test. In a receiving stream the fish maintain their position and are therefore continually exposed to fresh waste. Results more applicable to situations of this kind can be obtained by the use of modifications of the routine method involving renewal of test solutions, such as continuous-flow bioassay.

10. Reporting and Application of Bioassay Results

10.1. *Reporting of experimental data and results:* A report of a toxicity bioassay always should include information on the kind of fish used as test animals, their source and average size, the test temperature, and also the source of the experimental water and its composition (mineral content), or at least its more important characteristics, such as the total alkalinity, pH, hardness, any pronounced turbidity or considerable salinity, and the known or possible presence of any unusual natural constituents or contaminants. Other pertinent data, such as the volume and depth of the liquid medium and the number and total weight of fish in each test container, and a summary of the results of chemical determinations made in the course of the tests (particularly the recorded DO and pH values), also can be instructive and helpful.

A complete report should include, in addition to the TL_m values determined, a concise statement or table of the experimental data on which these values are based; that is, the number of fish used and the recorded percentages of survival at each tested concentration.

10.2. *Significance and practical application of bioassay results:* The TL_m values are useful measures of the acute toxicity of the tested substances under certain experimental conditions, but they obviously do not represent concentrations which may be deemed safe, or harmless, in fish habitats subject to pollution. Concentrations of wastes which are not demonstrably toxic to fish within 96 hr may be very toxic under conditions of continuous exposure in a receiving water. Under stream conditions and with prolonged exposure, toxic levels may be only a small fraction of the determined 48-hr or 96-hr TL_m values. Therefore, when estimating safe discharge rates or dilution ratios for industrial effluents or other pollutants on the basis of acute-toxicity evaluations, one must make use of liberal "safety factors," more properly termed "application factors." Even the provision of an apparently ample margin of safety can fail to accomplish its purpose when there is accumulative toxicity which cannot be predicted from acute-toxicity bioassay results, and when the choice of test animals, of experimental water, or of experimental procedure, or the sampling of wastes for bioassay, has been improper or unfortunate.

No single, simple application factor can be valid for all wastes or toxicants. The constituents of a complex waste that are responsible for the acute toxicity of the waste may be, but are not necessarily, the constituents responsible for such chronic or cumulative toxicity as may be demonstrable when the waste has been diluted enough so that it is no longer acutely toxic. The chronic toxicity may be lethal after a long time, or it may cause only non-lethal impairment of functions or performance of the animals, such as their ability to swim, their appetite and growth, their resistance to disease, their reproductive capacity, and their ability to compete with other forms in the natural environment. The acute toxicity bioassays cannot be expected to reveal such effects, nor to indicate reliably at what waste concentrations they will or will not occur. Nevertheless, knowledge of the acute toxicity of a waste often can be very helpful in predicting or anticipating and preventing delayed damage to aquatic life in receiving waters, as well as in regulating toxic waste discharges so as to avoid rapid mortality of fish exposed to the toxicants for relatively short periods of time.

Formulas for the estimation of waste concentrations compatible with indefinite survival and well-being of various fish and other valuable aquatic organisms in receiving waters need to be developed and widely tested. Such formulas have been tentatively proposed and procedures for their derivation and verification have been described or suggested and discussed elsewhere.[1, 8–10, 12] A review article [11] on the water quality requirements of fish can serve as a general introduction to physiologic, toxicologic, and ecologic fundamentals.

Modifications of Routine Bioassay Method

1. Controlled Artificial Oxygenation of Test Solutions

Artificial oxygenation of test solutions may be employed when excessive biochemical or other oxygen demand of a waste is found to interfere with the evaluation of its toxicity by the routine method. Vigorous aeration with compressed air has not generally proved satisfactory in work with industrial wastes because of rapid losses of toxicity that often result.

A method for controlled oxygenation without accelerating the rate of escape of volatile substances has been de-scribed in detail by Doudoroff et al.[5] This method consists of using a partially closed vessel and carefully regulating the release of bubbles of air and oxygen so that the required oxygen concentration can be maintained without loss of volatile material in excess of the loss during tests by the routine method. The rate of escape of free carbon dioxide in water is used for calibrating the bubbling rate in the test container. Bubbles of air and oxygen are introduced at the predetermined rate, through glass tubing, near the bottom of the test container.

A similar method of controlled release of oxygen has been used successfully for bioassays with many types of industrial effluents in open test aquaria. In many instances, the addition of pure oxygen in the form of large bubbles at a slow rate (30 to 180 bubbles per minute) to the open test containers used in the routine bioassay method is quite satisfactory for maintaining oxygen concentrations without excessive loss of volatile materials or toxicity. An oxygen cylinder, a pressure reduction valve, necessary tubing, and three-way air valves described by Henderson and Tarzwell [9] are satisfactory for this purpose. Oxygen can be introduced into test solutions by means of glass tubing (a 5-mm inside diameter has been satisfactory with numerous industrial effluents) and the rate of application adjusted as necessary. Careful regulation is necessary to maintain adequate dissolved oxygen and avoid any considerable supersaturation.

Another method of oxygenating test solutions in open test jars has been described by Hart, Weston, and De-Mann.[3] An interface of adjustable area between the liquid tested and oxygen gas is maintained inside a submerged, inverted funnel with perforations near the base. A small impeller inside the funnel gently agitates the liquid, accelerating the absorption and diffusion of oxygen.

Sometimes it may be satisfactory simply to maintain an oxygen-enriched atmosphere over the still surface of the test solutions in large partially-filled bottles or other suitable test containers.

2. Initial Oxygenation of the Diluent

Another modification of the routine bioassay procedure is the addition of oxygen to the dilution water. An industrial effluent can be free of oxygen, and it also can have a considerable immediate (chemical) oxygen demand, which must be satisfied. The DO content of each test dilution must be adequate at the beginning of the test; however, excessive supersaturation during the test should be avoided. In order to introduce the required amount of oxygen without recourse to artificial aeration or excessive dilution of the test waste, additional oxygen may be dissolved in the diluent water before it is mixed with the waste. This can be done by bubbling compressed oxygen gas (released from a disperser) through the water in a tall container. The oxygen content or the immediate oxygen demand of the waste sample should be determined. The required oxygen content of the diluent to be added, or the minimum degree of dilution with well-oxygenated (supersaturated) water of known oxygen content that will insure an adequate initial DO level, can then be estimated.

3. Renewal of Test Solutions

A third modification of the routine procedure involves renewal of the liquids tested, for the purpose of maintaining more or less uniform concentrations of any volatile and unstable toxic components and adequate DO content. This modification is recommended especially when there are reasons for believing that the toxicity of the liquids declines rapidly during the course of a test. Rapid reduction of toxicity can result from extreme volatility of important dissolved substances. It can also be due to destruction or removal from solution of toxic constituents by oxidation, hydrolysis, or precipitation, or by their combination with metabolic products or with mucus of the test animals, accumulation or metabolic destruction within the tissues of the test animals, and so forth. Accumulation of metabolic products sometimes may cause an increase of the toxicity of the liquids tested.

Constant-flow systems, in which the diluted wastes or test solutions are renewed continually (that is, replaced with fresh mixtures flowing constantly into the experimental containers), have proved very useful in research laboratories. With such apparatus, constancy of the composition and oxygen content of the test liquids can be insured. For practical reasons, however, the use of constant-flow apparatus cannot be generally recommended for routine application at this time.

Periodic renewal of the liquid tested, at daily or other convenient intervals, presents fewer difficulties. This can be accomplished by transferring the test animals quickly, by means of a dip net, to a test container with fresh liquid. Renewal of the test medium at intervals of 24 hr is often both convenient and sufficient, but renewal at shorter intervals, such as 12 or 8 hr, sometimes is necessary or advisable. When the oxygen demand of the substance tested is great, artificial oxygenation of the test solutions may also be needed in order to maintain an adequate DO concentration This is not often necessary, however, if the liquids are renewed at intervals of 24 hr or less.

4. Tests of Prolonged Duration

The duration of routine tests has been more or less arbitrarily limited to 96 hr. More prolonged tests sometimes are deemed desirable, inasmuch as even acute toxicity does not always cause death within the 96-hr test period.

When some test animals are still alive but dying or evidently affected after a 96-hr exposure to some concentrations of a toxic material, the advisability of prolonging the tests is indicated. Median tolerance limits for longer exposure periods (e.g., 10 days) thus can be determined. If tests are continued for periods longer than 10 days, the test fish may have to be fed.

Bibliography

1. HART, W. B.; DOUDOROFF, P.; & GREENBANK, J. The Evaluation of the Toxicity of Industrial Wastes, Chemicals, and Other Substances to Fresh-Water Fishes. Waste Control Lab., Atlantic Refining Co., Philadelphia (1945).
2. CHUTE, W. H., ET AL. A List of Common and Scientific Names of the Better Known Fishes of the United States and Canada. Trans. Am. Fisheries Soc. 75:353 (1948).
3. HART, W. B.; WESTON, R. F.; & DeMANN, J. G. An Apparatus for Oxygenating Test Solutions in Which Fish Are Used as Test Animals for Evaluating Toxicity. Trans. Am. Fisheries Soc. 75:228 (1948).
4. LITCHFIELD, J. T. & WILCOXON, F. A Simplified Method of Evaluating Dose-Effect Experiments. J. Pharmacol. Exp. Therap. 96:99 (1949).
5. DOUDOROFF, P., ET AL. Bioassay Methods for the Evaluation of Acute Toxicity of Industrial Wastes to Fish. Sew. Ind. Wastes 23:1380 (1951).
6. DOUDOROFF, P. Biological Observations of Industrial Waste Disposal. Proc. 6th Ind. Waste Conf., Purdue Univ. (Eng. Extension Bull. No. 76), p. 88 (1951).
7. FINNEY, D. J. Statistical Method in Biological Assay. Hafner Publishing Co., New York (1952).
8. COMMITTEE REPORT. Aquatic Life Water Quality Criteria. Sew. Ind. Wastes 27:321 (1955).
9. HENDERSON, C. & TARZWELL, C. M. Bioassays for Control of Industrial Effluents. Sew. Ind. Wastes 29:1002 (1957).

10. HENDERSON, C. Application Factors to Be Applied to Bioassays for the Safe Disposal of Toxic Wastes. In *Biological Problems in Water Pollution* (C. M. Tarzwell, ed.). Robert A. Taft Sanitary Eng. Center, Cincinnati, Ohio (1957). pp. 31–37.

11. DOUDOROFF, P. Water Quality Requirements of Fishes and Effects of Toxic Substances. In *The Physiology of Fishes* (M. E. Brown, ed.). Academic Press, New York (1957). Vol. 2, pp. 403–430.

12. WARREN, C. E. & DOUDOROFF, P. The Development of Methods for Using Bioassays in the Control of Pulp Mill Waste Disposal. *TAPPI* 41:8:211A (1958).

PART VII

Routine Bacteriologic Examinations of Water to Determine Its Sanitary Quality

Introduction

The following sections describe the procedures to be employed in making routine bacteriologic examinations of samples of water to determine the sanitary quality of the water and its suitability for general use. The limitations of the procedures must be thoroughly understood. The methods hereinafter described are intended to indicate the degree of contamination of the water with wastes from human or animal sources. Although there have been some recorded instances of the isolation of specific pathogenic bacteria from polluted water, sewage, and sewage sludge, these have been the result of extensive laboratory studies based on the use of specialized procedures for the collection of pertinent samples. Attempts to isolate such organisms on a routine basis have not proved fruitful and may prove confusing.

The isolation of pathogenic bacteria or other microorganisms from water and sewage cannot be recommended as a routine practice, inasmuch as the techniques available at present are tedious and complicated. The results are not of major significance and may be confusing in a particular study of pollution.

For many years the coliform group of bacteria, as defined below, has been used to indicate the pollution of water with wastes and thus the suitability of a particular water supply for domestic and dietetic uses. The cultural reactions and characteristics of the coliform group have been studied extensively. Full discussions can be found in many texts on bacteriology and particularly on the bacteriology of water and sanitation.

Experience has established the significance of coliform group densities as criteria of the degree of pollution shown by the bacteriological results and thus of the sanitary quality of the sample under examination. Developments in bacteriologic techniques and culture media have increased the sensitivity of the multiple-tube fermentation test, resulting in the acceptance of this test as a major standard method. The significance of the tests and the interpretations of the results are well authenticated and have been used as a basis of standards of bacteriologic quality of water supplies.

The membrane filter technique, which provides a direct plating for the detection and estimation of coliform densities in a given volume of water, is an effective method for the detection of bacteria of the coliform group and thus for the presence of pollution. Modification of the details of this method, particularly the culture medium recommended, has resulted in rendering the results of this test comparable with those given by the multiple-tube fermentation procedure. There are still limitations in the application of the membrane filter technique for the examination of all types of water. When used with strict adherence to these limitations and to the specified technical details, the membrane filter can be used as an equivalent method to the multiple-tube fermentation procedure. It has thus been included as an alternative standard method for the detection of bacteria of the coliform group.

It has become the custom to report the results of the coliform test by the multiple-tube fermentation procedure as a "most probable number" (MPN) index. It should be realized that this is merely an index of the number of coliform bacteria which, more probably than any other number, would give the results shown by the laboratory examination. It is not an actual enumeration of the coliform bacteria in any given volume of sample. It is, however, a valuable tool for appraising the sanitary quality of water and the effectiveness of water treatment processes.

Direct plating methods such as the membrane filter procedure permit a direct count of coliform colonies as the number per 100 ml. Use of this technique necessitates adjustment in the interpretation of the results of bacteriological examinations as indicative of the degree of pollution of the water supply.

Increasing attention to the potential value of fecal streptococci as indicators of significant pollution of water has prompted the inclusion in this edition of tentative methods for the detection and enumeration of such microorganisms. Improvements in the technical details of these procedures, based on current research, have been incorporated.

Although methods have been proposed for the detection of enteric viruses in water, to date such methods have not been studied sufficiently to warrant their inclusion in this edition, even as tentative. When subsequent editions are prepared, these techniques will doubtless be sufficiently well established to permit their inclusion.

Past editions have not included additional standard methods for the differentiation of coliform bacteria indicative of contamination often designated as of fecal origin as contrasted to coliform bacteria indicative of pollution by organisms not of fecal origin. Such differentiation has in the past been considered of limited value in assessing the suitability of water for human consumption, because the presence of either type of coliform bacteria renders the water potentially unsatisfactory and of unsafe sanitary quality. Recent investigations strongly indicate that the portion of the coliform group which is present in the gut or the feces of warm-blooded animals generally includes organisms which are capable of producing gas from lactose in a suitable culture medium at $44.5° \pm 0.5°C$. Inasmuch as organisms from other sources cannot generally produce gas in this manner, this criterion may be used to define the fecal section of the coliform group. Both the multiple-tube dilution technique and the membrane filter procedure have been modified to include incubation of confirmatory tests at $35°C$ and $44.5°C$ to provide estimates of the density of both fecal and non-fecal organisms, as defined, in the sample under consideration. The investigations cited suggest that this differentiation will yield valuable information relative to the possible source of pollution in water, and especially the remoteness of this pollution, inasmuch as the *non-fecal* members of the coliform group may be expected to survive longer than the *fecal* members, again as defined above, in the unfavorable environment provided by the water.

Methods for the determination of the standard plate count in water are retained as optional procedures because experience indicates that an approximate enumeration of total numbers of bacteria multiplying at a temperature of $35°C$ and $20°C$ may yield useful information concerning the quality of the water and may provide supporting data regarding the significance of the results of the coliform test. The standard plate count is useful in judging the efficiency in operation of various water treatment processes.

Experience accumulated during recent years in the shipment of un-iced samples by mail indicates that changes in types or numbers of bacteria during such storage for limited periods of time are negligible. Therefore, requirements concerning the storage and shipment of samples to a laboratory for bacteriological examination have been continued as given in the previous (11th) edition. These eliminate the necessity for refrigeration during transportation but recommend maintaining the temperature of the samples as closely as possible to the temperature of the source at the time of sampling.

The results of the examination of routine bacteriologic samples of water cannot be regarded as providing complete or final information concerning the quality of the water. Bacteriologic results must be considered in the light of information available concerning the sanitary conditions surrounding the source of any particular sample. Precise evaluation of the quality of a water supply can be made only when the results of laboratory examinations of the water are interpreted in the light of such sanitary survey data.

In particular, the inadequacy of the results of the examination of a single sample from a given source must be appreciated. When possible, evaluation of the quality of a water supply must be based on the examination of a series of samples collected over a known and protracted period of time.

The rapidly increasing attention being given to problems of pollution of tidal estuaries and other bodies of saline water has focused attention on necessary modification of existing bacteriological techniques in order that they may be used effectively in the examination of samples from such sources. In the following section, the application of the specific techniques to saline water has not been discussed because the available experience suggests that these procedures can be used satisfactorily with either saline or fresh waters.

The various bacteriological methods outlined in Part VII, developed primarily to permit the prompt and rapid examination of samples of water, have frequently been considered to apply only to routine examinations. These same methods, however, are the basic techniques required for research investigations in problems of sanitary bacteriology and water treatment. Their value in routine studies must not overshadow or limit their even greater value in research studies. Similarly, all of these techniques should be the subject of experimental investigations to establish their specificity, improve their details, and expand their application to the measurement of the sanitary quality of water supplies.

USPHS Standards of Drinking-Water Quality

In the United States the quality of public water supplies has generally been judged in terms of the 1962 US Public Health Service Drinking Water Standards,[1, 3] which are prescribed for water supplies to be certified for use on carriers subject to the federal quarantine regulations. These standards provide definite minimums as to number of samples examined and also establish the maximum number of coliform organisms allowable per 100 ml of finished water.

Sampling

Bacteriologic examinations should be carried out on samples collected at representative points throughout the distribution system. The frequency of sampling and the location of sampling points should be such as to determine properly the bacteriologic quality of the treated water supply and may be controlled in part by the known quality of the untreated water and, thus, by the need for treatment. The minimum number of samples to be collected and examined each month should be based on the population * served by the supply. Proportionately larger numbers of samples should be examined from supplies serving small populations than from supplies serving relatively large communities. It is important to examine repetitive samples from a designated point, as well as samples from a number of well-distributed sampling points. Daily samples collected following an unsatisfactory sample should be considered special samples and should not be included in totaling the number of samples examined monthly.

Application

The maximum number of allowable coliform organisms is prescribed in

* In communities having large commuting populations, the basis should be the total population of users rather than the resident population. Other unusual supply demands may require modification of minimum numbers examined.

terms of standard portion volume (10 ml and 100 ml) and the number of portions examined. The absence of gas in all tubes, when five 10-ml portions are examined by the fermentation tube method (less than 2.2 coliforms per 100 ml) is generally interpreted to indicate that the single sample meets the standards. A positive confirmed test for coliform organisms in three or more tubes (10-ml portions) or the presence of 4 or more coliform organisms in 100-ml samples established by (direct enumeration methods) M.F. tests [2] indicates the need for immediate remedial action and additional examinations. Daily samples from the sampling point should be collected and examined promptly until the results obtained from at least two consecutive samples show the water to be of satisfactory quality.

These Standards also include limiting concentrations of chemical and physical constituents of water as related to its safety and potability.

The World Health Organization has established International Standards of Drinking Water Quality.[4] These are similar to the US Public Health Service Standards, but have been modified and liberalized to apply to water supply conditions in all parts of the world. Although permitting other densities of bacteria of the coliform group, these International Standards—if employed in the control of water selection and treatment—will provide a water supply safe and acceptable for dietetic and domestic uses.

Bibliography

1. Public Health Service Drinking Water Standards, 1962. *U.S. Pub. Health Service Publ.* No. 956 (1963).
2. Public Health Service Drinking Water

Standards, 1946. *Public Health Repts.* 61:371 (1946) ; Reprint 2697.
3. Public Health Service, Department of Health, Education, and Welfare: Interstate Quarantine Drinking Water Stand-

ards—Miscellaneous Amendments. *Federal Register,* pp. 1271–2 (Mar. 1, 1957).
4. *International Standards of Drinking Water Quality.* World Health Organization (1961).

Laboratory Apparatus

1. Incubators

Incubators must maintain a uniform and constant temperature at all times in all areas and must not vary more than $\pm 1\,°C$ in the areas used. This can be accomplished by the use of a water-jacketed or anhydric type with thermostatically controlled low-temperature electric heating units properly insulated and located in or adjacent to the walls or floor of the chamber and preferably equipped with mechanical means of circulating air.

Incubators equipped with high-temperature heating units are unsatisfactory, because such sources of heat, when improperly placed, frequently cause localized overheating and excessive drying of the media, with consequent inhibition of bacterial growth. Incubators so heated may be used to operate satisfactorily by replacing the high-temperature units with suitable wiring arranged to operate at a lower temperature and by installation of mechanical air circulation. It is desirable, where ordinary room temperatures vary excessively, that laboratory incubators be kept in special rooms maintained at a few degrees below the recommended incubator temperature.

Special incubating rooms, well insulated and equipped with properly distributed heating units and with forced air circulation, may be used, provided they conform to desired tempera-

ture limits. When such rooms are used, the daily range in temperature in areas where plates or tubes are incubated shall be recorded. Incubators shall be provided with shelves so spaced as to assure uniformity of temperature throughout the chamber. The inside dimensions of the chamber shall be adequate to accommodate, without crowding, 160 to 200 petri dishes or an equivalent mass of fermentation tubes. A 1-in. space shall be provided between walls and stacks of dishes or baskets of tubes.

An accurate thermometer (checked against one certified by the National Bureau of Standards) with the bulb continuously immersed in liquid (glycerine, water, or mineral oil) shall be maintained on each shelf within the incubator and daily readings of the temperatures recorded. In addition, it is desirable to maintain a maximum and minimum registering thermometer within the incubator on the middle shelf to record the range in temperature variations over a 24-hr period. Temperature variations within the incubator when filled to maximum capacity should be determined at intervals. It is recommended that a recording thermometer be installed in every incubator whenever possible, so that a permanent record of temperature variations within the incubating chamber may be maintained.

2. Hot-Air Sterilizing Ovens

Hot-air sterilizing ovens shall be of sufficient size to prevent crowding of the interior, constructed to give uniform and adequate sterilizing temperatures, and equipped with suitable thermometers capable of registering accurately in the range 160°–180°C. The use of a temperature-recording instrument is optional.

3. Autoclaves

Autoclaves shall be of sufficient size to prevent crowding of the interior; constructed to provide uniform temperatures within the chambers (up to and including the sterilizing temperature of 121°C); equipped with accurate thermometers with the bulb properly located on the exhaust line so as to register minimum temperature within the sterilizing chambers (temperature-recording instrument is optional); having pressure gages and properly adjusted safety valves connected directly with saturated-steam power lines or directly to a suitable special steam generator; and capable of reaching the desired temperature within 30 min. In emergencies, where results have been demonstrated to be satisfactory, a pressure cooker may be substituted for an autoclave, provided it is equipped with an efficient pressure gage and with a thermometer whose bulb is 1 in. above the water level.

4. Gas Sterilizers

The sterilizer shall be equipped with automatic controls capable of carrying out a complete sterilization cycle according to present directions. Ethylene oxide diluted to 10 to 12 per cent with an inert gas shall be used. The automatic control cycle shall consist of evacuation of the sterilizing chamber to at least 25 in. of vacuum, which shall be held for 30 min, adjustment of humidity and temperature, charging with the ethylene oxide mixture to a pressure dependent on the mixture used, holding such pressure for at least 4 hr, venting of the gas, evacuation to 25 in. of vacuum, and finally bringing to atmospheric pressure with sterile air. The humidity, temperature, pressure and time of sterilizing cycle depend on the gas mixture used.

If sample bottles packaged for shipment are sterilized, they shall be stored overnight before being shipped to allow the last traces of the gas mixture to dissipate.

In general, mixtures of ethylene oxide with chlorinated hydrocarbons such as freon are deleterious to plastics, although with temperatures below 130°F, gas pressure not over 5 psi, and time of sterilization less than 6 hr, the effect is minimal. Carbon dioxide as a diluent of the ethylene oxide is preferable for plastic but the exposure time and pressure required are greater, depending on the temperature and humidity that can be used.

The proper cycle and gas mixture shall be determined for the particular objects to be sterilized, and confirmed by sterility tests of the object.

5. Colony Counters

Standard apparatus, such as a Quebec colony counter, dark-field model preferred, or one providing equivalent magnification (1.5 diameters) and satisfactory visibility, shall be used.

6. pH Equipment

Electrometric pH meters shall be used for accurate determination of pH values of media.

7. Balances

Balances providing a sensitivity of at least 2 g at a load of 150 g shall be used, with appropriate weights. An analytical balance having a sensitivity of 1 mg under a load of 10 g shall be used for weighing small quantities (less than 2 g) of materials.

8. Media Preparation Utensils

Borosilicate glass or other suitable noncorrosive equipment, such as stainless steel, shall be used. Glassware must be clean and free from foreign residues or dried particles of agar, and also from toxic or foreign materials which may contaminate media, such as chlorine, copper, zinc, antimony, chromium, and detergents.

9. Pipets

Pipets may be of any convenient size, provided it is found by actual test that they deliver accurately and quickly the required amount in the manner in which they are used. The error of calibration must not exceed 2.5 per cent. Pipets with unbroken tips and with graduations distinctly marked shall be used. For satisfactory work relative to enforcement of regulations of water quality, bacteriologic transfer pipets calibrated and marked may be required. Pipets conforming to the APHA standards given in the latest edition of *Standard Methods for the Examination of Dairy Products* [9] may be used. It is recommended that the mouth end of all pipets be protected— e.g., by a cotton plug—to eliminate hazards to the worker or possible contamination by saliva of the sample being pipeted.

10. Pipet Containers

Boxes of aluminum or stainless steel, end measurement 2–3 in., cylindrical or rectangular, length about 16 in., shall be used. When these are not available, paper wrappings may be substituted. To avoid excessive charring during sterilization, best-quality sulfate pulp (kraft) paper should be used. *Copper cans or boxes should not be used as containers.*

11. Dilution Bottles or Tubes

Bottles or tubes of resistant glass, preferably borosilicate, closed with glass stoppers or screw caps equipped with liners that do not produce toxic or bacteriostatic compounds in appreciable amounts on sterilization, shall be used. Cotton plugs must not be used as closures. Graduation levels shall be indelibly marked on the side of the dilution bottle or tube. Plastic bottles constructed of nontoxic materials and of acceptable size may be substituted for glass.

12. Petri Dishes

Petri dishes 100 mm in diameter with the side wall of the bottom at least 15 mm high, with glass or porous tops as preferred, shall be used. The bottom of the dish shall be free from bubbles and scratches and shall be flat so that the medium will be of uniform thickness throughout the plate. Plastic petri dishes when found to be satisfactory and when presterilized by the manufacturer may be substituted for glass dishes for single use only. Petri dishes may be sterilized and stored in metal cans (aluminum or stainless steel, but not copper), or may be wrapped in paper—preferably best-quality sulfate pulp (kraft)—prior to sterilization.

13. Fermentation Tubes

A fermentation tube of any type may be used, provided it permits conformance to the requirements for concentration of nutritive ingredients as described subsequently.

14. Sample Bottles

A bottle of glass or other material resistant to the solvent action of water, capable of being sterilized, and of any suitable size and shape may be used for a sample intended for bacterial examination. It shall hold a sufficient volume of sample for all the required tests, permit proper washing, and maintain the sample uncontaminated until the examinations are completed. Ground-glass stoppered bottles, preferably widemouthed, of resistant glass are recommended. Plastic bottles of suitable size, widemouthed, and manufactured of nontoxic materials have been found satisfactory as sample containers

and eliminate hazards due to breakage during shipment.

Metal or plastic screw-cap closures may be used on sample bottles provided no volatile compounds are produced on sterilization and they are equipped with liners that do not produce toxic or bacteriostatic compounds on sterilization.

The tops and necks of sample bottles with glass closures shall be covered with metal foil, rubberized cloth, heavy impermeable paper, or milk bottle cover caps, before sterilization.

Many plastic sample bottles are available. These should not be used for repetitive sampling unless it has been demonstrated that they can be sterilized. Some may be autoclaved once or twice at 121°C for 10 min, but only a few do not distort and leak when repeatedly autoclaved. Generally, the neck of the bottle shrinks faster than the thicker cap and the threads no longer make a watertight seal. Resistance to distortion is dependent not only on the type of plastic but also is markedly affected by the method of molding.

Washing and Sterilization

All glassware must be thoroughly cleansed using a suitable detergent and hot water (160°F), rinsed with hot water (180°F) to remove all traces of residual washing compound, and finally rinsed with distilled water.

Inhibitory Residues on Glassware—Test Procedure

Certain wetting agents or detergents used in washing glassware may contain bacteriostatic or inhibiting substances

which require 6 to 12 successive rinsings to remove all traces from the glass surface and insure freedom from residual bacteriostatic action. The following test procedure is recommended for the biological examination of glassware where bacteriostatic or inhibitory residues may be present.

1. *Procedure for test*

1.1. Wash six petri dishes according to usual laboratory practice and designate as group A.

1.2. Wash six petri dishes as above and rinse 12 times with successive portions of distilled water and designate as group B.

1.3. Rinse six petri dishes with the detergent wash water (in use concentration), dry without further rinsing, and designate as group C.

1.4. Sterilize the dishes in groups A, B, and C by usual procedure.

1.5. Add a water sample yielding 20 to 60 colonies, pour plates in triplicate, and proceed according to the procedure described for the Standard Plate Count.

2. Interpretation of results

2.1. Difference in average number of colonies of less than 15 per cent on plates of groups A, B, and C indicates that the detergent has no toxicity or inhibitory characteristics.

2.2. Difference in colony count of 15 per cent or more between groups A and B demonstrates inhibitory residue left on plates, etc., by routine washing procedure.

2.3. Disagreement in averages of less than 15 per cent between groups A and B, and greater than 15 per cent between groups A and C, indicates that the detergent has inhibitory properties but is removed during routine washing process.

Sterilization

Glassware, except when in metal containers, shall be sterilized for not less than 60 min at a temperature of 170°C, unless it is known from recording thermometers that oven temperatures are uniform, under which exceptional condition 160°C may be used. Glassware in metal containers should be heated to a temperature of 170°C for not less than 2 hr.

Sample bottles other than of plastic may be sterilized as above or in an autoclave at 121°C for 15 min.

For those plastic bottles that distort on autoclaving, low-temperature ethylene oxide gas sterilization should be used.

Bibliography

1. HILL, H. W. Porous Tops for Petri Dishes. *J. Med. Research* 13:93 (1904).
2. COLLINS, W. D. & RIFFENBURG, H. B. Contamination of Water Samples with Material Dissolved From Glass Containers. *Ind. Eng. Chem.* 15:48 (1923).
3. CLARK, W. M. *The Determination of Hydrogen Ion Concentration.* Williams & Wilkins Co., Baltimore (3rd ed., 1928).
4. PRICKETT, P. S. & MILLER, N. J. A Modified APHA Milk Dilution Pipette. *A.J.P.H.* 21:1374 (1931).
5. STARK, C. N. & TERRY, C. W. *The Construction of a Reliable Bacteriological Incubator.* Dairy Dept., Cornell Univ., Ithaca, N.Y. (1934).
6. ARCHAMBAULT, J.; CUROT, J.; & McCRADY, M. H. The Need of Uniformity of Conditions for Counting Plates (With Suggestions for a Standard Colony Counter). *A.J.P.H.* 27:809 (1937).
7. RICHARDS, O. W. & HEIJN, P. C. An Improved Dark-Field Quebec Colony Counter. *J. Milk Technol.* 8:253 (1945).
8. COHN, B., ET AL. The Determination of pH and Titratable Acidity. *Manual of Methods for Pure Culture Study of Bacteria.* Soc. Am. Bacteriologists, Geneva, N.Y. (1945). Leaflet 9.
9. *Standard Methods for the Examination of Dairy Products.* Am. Public Health Assoc., New York (11th ed., 1960).

Preparation of Culture Media

A. General Procedures

1. Storage of Culture Media

Culture media may be stored in any clean, dry space where excessive evaporation and danger of contamination have been eliminated. The dehydrated media shall be stored tightly in the dark at less than 30°C in an atmosphere of low humidity and shall not be used if they become discolored or caked so as not to be free-flowing powders. It is advisable to purchase dehydrated media in small quantities that will be used within six months after opening. Culture media should be prepared in batches such that the entire batch will be used in less than 1 week.

Liquid media in fermentation tubes, if stored at refrigeration or even at moderately low temperatures, may dissolve sufficient air to produce, upon incubation at 35°C, a bubble of air in the tube. It is imperative, therefore, that fermentation tubes which have been at a low temperature be incubated overnight before use and those tubes containing air discarded.

Fermentation tubes may be stored at approximately 25°C; but because evaporation may proceed rapidly under these conditions, resulting in marked changes in concentration of the ingredients, storage at this temperature shall not exceed a period of 1 week.

2. Adjustment of Reaction

The reaction of culture media should be stated in terms of hydrogen ion concentration, expressed as pH.

The increase in the hydrogen ion concentration (decrease in pH) during sterilization will vary slightly with the individual sterilizer in use, and the initial reaction required to obtain the correct final reaction will have to be determined. The decrease in the pH reading will usually be 0.1 to 0.2 but may occasionally be as great as 0.4. When buffering salts such as phosphates are present in the media, the decrease in pH value as determined will be negligible.

2.1. *Potentiometric method:* Tests to control the adjustment to the required hydrogen ion concentration should preferably be made with a pH meter.

2.2. *Colorimetric method:* This method depends on the use of an indicator whose color in solution is characteristic of the pH value of the solution.

a. *Preparation of indicator solutions:* Weigh out carefully 0.1 g of each indicator * and grind, preferably in an agate mortar, with the volume of 0.05N NaOH given in the tabulation below:

Indicator	pH Range	NaOH ml
Bromcresol purple	5.2–6.8	3.7
Bromthymol blue	6.0–7.6	3.2
Phenol red	6.8–8.4	5.7
Cresol red	7.2–8.8	5.3
Thymol blue	8.0–9.6	4.3

When solution is complete, make up to 25 ml. This is the stock solution; for use, dilute 1 ml stock solution of bromthymol blue or bromcresol purple

---

* The indicator powders are also commercially available as the sodium salts, which are soluble, therefore need not be triturated with 0.05N NaOH in a mortar.

with 9 ml distilled water; for other indicators, dilute 1 ml stock solution with 19 ml water.

b. Color standards: Color standards of the required pH may be purchased commercially, or may be prepared by adding 0.5 ml indicator solution to buffer solutions of the proper pH prepared according to Clark and Lubs.[3]

c. Procedure: Place 5 ml distilled water in each of two clean test tubes, similar in size, shape, and color to the tubes used for the color standards; 150 × 16-mm tubes are recommended. Withdraw 10 ml of the medium to be adjusted and add 5 ml to each of the two tubes. To one of these add 0.5 ml of a solution of an indicator which will adequately cover the desired pH range. The amount of indicator in the test solution must be the same as in the standard. This is usually 0.5 ml. Commercial comparators for colorimetric pH determinations may be used in this procedure.

Using a comparator block, place the tube containing the diluted medium plus the indicator in front of a tube of distilled water and place the tube of diluted medium without indicator in front of the color standard of the pH desired.

Titrate the tube of diluted medium plus indicator with an accurate 1 + 9 dilution of 1N NaOH solution until the color viewed through the distilled-water tube matches the color of the pH standard as observed through the diluted medium without the indicator.

Calculate the amount of the NaOH solution which must be added to the bulk of the medium to reach this reaction. After addition and thorough mixing, check the reaction and adjust if necessary. The required final reaction is given in the directions for preparing each medium. If a specific reaction is not prescribed, adjustment is not necessary.

3. Sterilization

All media, except sugar broths or those with other specifications, must be sterilized in an autoclave at 121°C for 15 min after the temperature has reached 121°C. When the pressure reaches zero, the medium must be removed from the autoclave and cooled quickly to avoid decomposition of sugars by prolonged exposure to heat. To permit uniform heating and rapid cooling, materials should be packed loosely and in small containers.

Carbohydrate liquid media may usually be sterilized in the autoclave at 121°C for 10 min; the autoclave temperature shall never exceed 121°C.

It is sometimes preferable to prepare a 10–20 per cent solution of the carbohydrate in distilled water and to sterilize this solution as above, or by filtration through a diatomaceous candle, a Seitz filter pad, or a membrane filter. The sterile solution is then added, with aseptic precautions, to media previously sterilized in the autoclave.

4. Clarification

Use any method of clarification which yields a medium suitable for detection of all bacterial colonies and which at the same time will not remove or add nutritive ingredients; clarification may be accomplished by centrifugation, by sedimentation, or, in the case of melted agar, by filtration through coarse paper, cotton, cheesecloth, or towels. Do not clarify with egg albumen. Necessity for clarification depends on intended use, or inherent cloudiness, or preference of the individual worker.

B. Materials

1. Water

Only distilled water or demineralized water which has been tested and found free from traces of dissolved metals and bactericidal and inhibitory compounds may be used for preparation of culture media and reagents. Bactericidal compounds may be measured by a biologic test procedure as outlined in the following. Residual chlorine or chloramines will be found in distilled water prepared from chlorinated water supplies. The possible presence of these compounds should always be determined by a suitable quantitative procedure such as a starch-iodide titration. If chlorine compounds are found in the distilled water they should be neutralized by addition of the equivalent amount of sodium thiosulfate or sodium sulfite. In this way, the presence of these compounds can be eliminated from the distilled water used in the preparation of dilution waters.

1.1. *Test for bactericidal properties of distilled water—Principle:* The test is based on the growth of *Aerobacter aerogenes* in a chemically defined minimal growth medium. The addition of a toxic agent or a growth promoting substance will alter the 24-hr population by an increase or decrease of 20 per cent or more, when compared to a control.

1.2. *Apparatus and Materials:*

a. Glassware: All glassware must be rinsed in freshly redistilled water from a glass still. The sensitivity of the test depends on the cleanliness of the sample containers, flasks, tubes, and pipet. Use only borosilicate glassware.

b. Culture: Any strain of coliform IMViC type $--++$ (*A. aerogenes*).

This can be obtained easily from any polluted river or sewage sample.

1.3. *Reagents:* Use only reagents of the highest purity. Some brands of potassium dihydrogen phosphate, KH_2PO_4, have large amounts of impurities. The sensitivity of the test is controlled in part by the purity of the reagents employed.

a. Sodium citrate solution: Dissolve 0.29 g sodium citrate, $Na_3C_6H_7O_7 \cdot 2H_2O$ in 500 ml redistilled water.

b. Ammonium sulfate solution: Dissolve 0.26 g ammonium sulfate, $(NH_4)_2SO_4$, in 500 ml redistilled water.

c. Salt mixture solution: Dissolve 0.26 g magnesium sulfate, $MgSO_4 \cdot 7H_2O$, 0.17 g calcium chloride, $CaCl_2 \cdot 2H_2O$, 0.23 g ferrous sulfate, $FeSO_4 \cdot 7H_2O$, and 2.50 g sodium chloride, NaCl, in 500 ml redistilled water. Do not sterilize by heat in the autoclave because heat causes decomposition of the salt mixture. Turbidity appears in 3–5 days. Store in the dark at 5°C because sunlight converts the ferrous salt to ferric.

d. Phosphate buffer solution: Stock phosphate buffer solution (see C, Media Specifications, Sec. 1.1) diluted 1 to 25.

e. Sterilization of reagents: The reagents shall be sterilized as follows: Unknown distilled water sample, boil for 1 min; prepare reagents with redistilled water heated to boiling; phosphate buffer solution may be sterilized by microfilter filtration or boiling.

1.4. *Procedure:*

a. Collect 150–200 ml of water sample in a sterile borosilicate glass flask and heat for 10 min at 80°–90°C. Label

5 flasks or tubes, A, B, C, D, and E. Add water samples and redistilled water to each flask as indicated in the following protocol:

film with the pipet, being careful not to tear the agar, and pour the contents back into the original 99-ml water blank.

Media Reagents	Control Test—*ml*		Optional Tests—*ml*		
	Control A	Unknown Dist. Water B	Food Available C	Nitrogen Source D	Carbon Source E
Sodium citrate solution	2.5	2.5	—	2.5	—
Ammonium sulfate solution	2.5	2.5	—	—	2.5
Salt mixture solution	2.5	2.5	2.5	2.5	2.5
Phosphate buffer (7.3 ± 0.1)	1.5	1.5	1.5	1.5	1.5
Unknown water	—	21.0	21.0	21.0	21.0
Redistilled water	21.0	—	5.0	2.5	2.5
Total volume	30.0	30.0	30.0	30.0	30.0

b. Add a suspension of *Aerobacter aerogenes* (IMViC type $--++$) of such density that each flask will contain 25–75 cells per ml. Make an initial bacterial count by plating replicate 1-ml samples in plate count agar. Incubate tests A–E at 32° or 35°C for 20–24 hr. Make plate counts using dilutions of 1, 0.1, 0.01, 0.001 and 0.0001 ml.

1.5. *Preparation of a bacterial suspension:*

a. Bacterial growth: On the day prior to performing the distilled water suitability test, inoculate a strain of *Aerobacter aerogenes* onto a nutrient agar slant with a slope of approximately 2½ in. in length contained in a 125 × 16-mm screw-cap tube. Streak the entire agar surface to develop a continuous growth film and incubate 18–24 hr at 35°C.

b. Harvesting of viable cells: Pipet 1–2 ml sterile dilution water from a 99-ml water blank onto the 18–24-hr culture. Emulsify the growth on the slant by gently rubbing the bacterial

c. Dilution of bacterial suspension: Make a 1-to-100 dilution of the original bottle into a second water blank, and a further 1-to-100 dilution of the second bottle into a third water blank, shaking vigorously after each transfer. Then pipet 0.1 ml of the third dilution (1:1,000,000) into each of the flasks A, B, C, D, and E. This procedure should result in a final dilution of the organisms to a range of 25–75 viable cells for each ml of test solution.

d. Verification of bacterial density: Variations among strains of the same organism, different organisms, media and surface area of agar slopes will possibly necessitate adjustment of the dilution procedure to arrive at a specific density range between 25–75 viable cells. To establish the growth range numerically for a specific organism and medium, make a series of plate counts from the third dilution to determine the bacterial density. Then choose the proper volume from this third dilution, which when diluted by the 30 ml in the flasks A, B, C, D, E, will contain 25–75 viable cells per ml. If the procedures are standardized as to surface area of the slant and laboratory technique, it is possible to reproduce results on repeated experiments with the same strain of microorganism.

e. Procedural difficulties:

1. Unknown water sample stored in soft-glass containers or glass containers without liners for metal caps.

2. Contamination of reagent by distilled water with a bacterial background.

3. Correct dilution of *A. aerogenes* to get 25–75 cells per ml.

4. Spread of dilutions used in the 24-hr counts. Make plate counts using dilutions of 1.0, 0.1, 0.01, 0.001, and 0.0001 ml.

5. The initial colony count before incubation is made to rule out gross contamination of the sample.

f. Calculation:

1. For growth-inhibiting substances:

$$\text{Ratio} = \frac{\text{colony count per ml flask B}}{\text{colony count per ml flask A}}$$

A ratio of 0.8 to 1.2 (inclusive) shows no toxic substances; a ratio of less than 0.8 shows growth-inhibiting substances in the water sample.

2. For nitrogen and carbon sources that promote growth:

$$\text{Ratio} = \frac{\text{colony count per ml flask C}}{\text{colony count per ml flask A}}$$

3. For nitrogen sources that promote growth:

$$\text{Ratio} = \frac{\text{colony count per ml flask D}}{\text{colony count per ml flask A}}$$

4. For carbon sources that promote bacterial growth:

$$\text{Ratio} = \frac{\text{colony count per ml flask E}}{\text{colony count per ml flask A}}$$

Do not attempt to calculate ratios 2, 3 or 4 when ratio 1 indicates a toxic reaction. For ratios 2, 3 or 4, a ratio in excess of 1.2 indicates an available source for bacterial growth.

g. Interpretation of results:

1. The colony count from flask A after 20–24 hr at 35°C will depend on the number of organisms initially planted in flask A and on the strain of *A. aerogenes* used in the test procedures. This is the reason the control, flask A, must be run for each individual series of tests. However, for a given strain of *A. aerogenes* under identical environmental conditions, the terminal count should be reasonably constant when the initial plant is the same. The difference in the initial plant of 25 and 75 will be about 3-fold larger for the 75 organisms initially planted in flask A, providing the growth rate remains constant. Thus, it is essential that the initial colony count on flask A and flask B should be approximately equal to secure accurate data.

2. When the ratio exceeds 1.2, it may be assumed that growth-stimulating substances are present. However this procedure is an extremely sensitive test and ratios up to 3.0 would have little significance in actual practice. Therefore, Tests C, D, and E do not appear necessary except in special circumstances, when the ratio is between 1.2 and 3.0.

3. Usually flask C will be very low and tubes D and E will have a ratio of less than 1.2 when the ratio of flask B/flask A is between 0.8 and 1.2. The limiting factors of growth in flask A are the nitrogen and organic carbon present. An extremely large amount of ammonia nitrogen with no organic carbon could increase the ratio in flask D above 1.2 or the absence of nitrogen with high carbon concentration could

give ratios above 1.2 in flask E with a B/A ratio between 0.8 and 1.2.

4. A ratio below 0.8 indicates the water contains toxic substances and this ratio includes all allowable tolerances. As indicated in item 2 (above), the 1.2 ratio could go as high as 3.0 without any undesirable results.

5. Specific corrective measures in specific cases of defective distillation apparatus cannot be recommended. However, careful inspection of the distillation equipment and a review of production and handling of the distilled water should enable local laboratory personnel to correct the cause of the difficulty.

2. Beef Extract

Any brand of beef extract known to give satisfactory results may be used. Meat infusion must not be used.

3. Yeast Extract

Any yeast extract known to yield satisfactory results may be used.

4. Peptone

Any peptone which comparative tests have shown to give satisfactory results may be used.

5. Sugar

All sugars used for the preparation of culture media must be chemically pure and suitable for bacteriologic purposes.

6. Agar

The agar used, either granular or chopped, must be of bacteriologic grade.

7. General Chemicals

All general chemicals employed as ingredients in culture media must be ACS or reagent grade.

8. Dyes

Only dyes certified by the Biological Stain Commission for use in the preparation of media may be employed.

C. Media Specifications

The use of dehydrated media is recommended to provide uniformity of culture media. In preparing media from the basic ingredients, follow the directions given below.

Note: The term "per cent solution" as used in these directions is to be understood to mean "grams of solute per 100 ml of solution."

1. Dilution Water

1.1. *Buffered water:* To prepare stock phosphate buffer solution, dissolve 34.0 g potassium dihydrogen phosphate, KH_2PO_4, in 500 ml distilled water, adjust to pH 7.2 with $1N$ NaOH, and dilute to 1 liter with distilled water.

Add 1.25 ml stock phosphate buffer solution to 1 liter distilled water. Dispense in amounts that will provide 99 ± 2.0 ml or 9 ± 0.2 ml, after autoclaving for 15 min.

1.2. *Peptone dilution water:*
Prepare a 10 per cent solution of peptone in distilled water. Dilute a

measured volume to provide a final 0.5 per cent solution.

Dispense in amounts to provide 99 ± 2.0 ml or 9 ± 0.2 ml after autoclaving for 15 min.

2. Nutrient Broth

Add 3 g beef extract and 5 g peptone to each liter distilled water. Heat slowly on a water bath, stirring until dissolved. Adjust the reaction so that the pH reading after sterilization will be between 6.8 and 7.0.

Bring to a boil, cool to 25°C, make up lost weight with distilled water, and clarify as desired. Distribute in test tubes or other containers of size and volume desired. Sterilize as directed in Sec. 3 of A above.

3. Lactose Broth

To nutrient broth prepared as above, add 0.5 per cent lactose. Adjust the reaction so that the pH reading after sterilization will be between 6.8 and 7.0, preferably 6.9. Place in fermentation tubes and sterilize in an autoclave as directed in Sec. 3 of A above, provided that the total time of exposure to any heat is not more than 30 min. Cool rapidly after removal from the autoclave.

If the above condition of exposure to heat cannot be fulfilled, prepare a 10–20 per cent solution of lactose in distilled water and sterilize by heating at 121°C for 10 min as directed in Sec. 3 of A. Add this solution to sterile nutrient broth in an amount sufficient to make a 0.5 per cent lactose solution, and tube with proper precautions for preserving its sterility. It is permissible to add, by means of a sterile pipet, directly to a tube of sterile nutrient broth, enough of the sterile lactose solution to make the required 0.5 per cent concentration. The tubes so prepared must be incubated at 35°C for 24 hr as a test for sterility before they are used.

When volumes of lactose broth less than 100 ml are to be prepared, pipet sufficient lactose solution to yield the required 0.5 per cent concentration.

When fermentation tubes or other containers for the examination of 10-ml or 100-ml portions of sample are prepared, the lactose broth medium must be of such strength that the addition of that volume of sample to the medium in the fermentation tube will not reduce the concentration of ingredients in the mixture below that in the standard medium. Where dehydrated medium is used, the proper concentration of ingredients may be obtained by using the following table:

Inoculum ml	Amount of Medium in Tube ml	Volume of Medium + Inoculum ml	Dehydrated Lactose Broth Required g/l
1	10 or more	11 or more	13
10	10	20	26.0
10	20	30	19.5
100	50	150	39
100	35	135	50.1
100	20	120	78

4. Lauryl Tryptose Broth

To each liter of cold distilled water add 20 g tryptose, 5.0 g lactose, 2.75 g dipotassium hydrogen phosphate, K_2HPO_4, 2.75 g potassium dihydrogen phosphate, KH_2PO_4, 5.0 g sodium chloride, and 0.1 g sodium lauryl sulfate. Dissolve the ingredients, distribute into fermentation tubes, and autoclave as directed previously. The final pH should be approximately 6.8.

As with lactose broth, the lauryl tryptose broth must be of such strength that the addition of 100-ml or 10-ml portions of the sample to the medium will not reduce the concentrations of the various ingredients below that of the standard medium. When the dehydrated material is used, prepare in accordance with the following table:

6. Plate Count Agar (Tryptone Glucose Yeast Agar)

To each liter of distilled water add 5.0 g peptone-tryptone, 2.5 g yeast extract, 1.0 g glucose (dextrose), 15.0 g agar, bacteriological grade. Adjust the final pH to 7.0 ± 0.1. This medium also can be used in the preparation of slants.

7. Endo Medium

7.1. Formula I:

a. Preparation of stock agar: Add 5 g beef extract, 10 g peptone, and 30 g agar to each liter of distilled water. Boil until the agar is dissolved and make up lost weight with distilled water. Adjust the reaction so that the pH reading after sterilization is 7.4. Clarify if desired, add 10 g lactose per

Inoculum ml	Amount of Medium in Tube ml	Volume of Medium + Inoculum ml	Dehydrated Lauryl Tryptose Broth Required g/l
1	10 or more	11 or more	35.6
10	10	20	71.2
10	20	30	53.4
100	50	150	106.8
100	35	135	137.1
100	20	120	213.6

5. Tryptone Glucose Extract Agar

To each liter of distilled water add 3.0 g beef extract, 5.0 g tryptone, 1.0 g glucose, 15.0 g agar. Heat to boiling until all ingredients are dissolved. Adjust so that the pH reading after sterilization will be between 6.8 and 7.0. Make up lost weight with hot distilled water and clarify. Distribute to the desired containers and sterilize as previously directed.

liter of medium, and dissolve. Place in small flasks or bottles, 100 ml to each, and sterilize in an autoclave as directed previously.

b. Preparation of plates: Prepare a 3 per cent solution of certified basic fuchsin in 95 per cent ethyl alcohol. Allow to stand 24 hr and filter.

Melt lactose agar prepared as above. To each 100 ml add 1 ml basic fuchsin solution and 0.125 g anhydrous sodium sulfite dissolved in 5 ml distilled water.

(The sulfite solution must be freshly prepared.) Mix thoroughly. Pour plates with the usual precautions against contamination, and allow to harden.

The medium should be light pink when hot and almost colorless when cool. As batches of fuchsin differ somewhat in dye content, it is possible that the medium made according to this formula may be too highly colored before inoculation or may not give the proper reaction when seeded with coliform organisms. If so, the strength of the basic fuchsin solution may be varied.

7.2. Formula II: As an alternative to the composition given above, add to 1 liter of distilled water 3.5 g dipotassium hydrogen phosphate, K_2HPO_4, 10.0 g peptone, 20.0 g agar (washed and dried), and 10.0 g lactose. Boil, adjust, and clarify as in Sec. 7.1a. Then, to each 100 ml of this solution add 0.25 g sodium sulfite (anhydrous), and 1.0 ml basic fuchsin, certified (filtered 5 per cent alcoholic solution).

8. Eosin Methylene Blue Agar

Add 10 g peptone, 2 g dipotassium hydrogen phosphate, K_2HPO_4, and 20 g agar to each liter of distilled water. Heat to boiling until all ingredients are dissolved and make up loss due to evaporation with distilled water. Adjustment of reaction is not necessary. Place measured quantities, usually 100 or 200 ml, in flasks or bottles and sterilize in an autoclave as directed previously.

To prepare plates, melt agar medium; to each 100 ml add 5 ml sterile 20 per cent aqueous lactose solution, 2 ml 2 per cent aqueous solution of eosin, and 1.3 ml 0.5 per cent aqueous solution of methylene blue. Mix thoroughly, pour into petri dishes, and allow to harden.

It is permissible to add all of the ingredients to the stock agar at the time of preparation, place in tubes or flasks, and sterilize. Plates may be prepared from this stock. Decolorization of the medium occurs during sterilization, but the color returns after cooling.

9. Brilliant Green Lactose Bile Broth

Dissolve 10 g peptone and 10 g lactose in not more than 500 ml distilled water. Add 20 g dehydrated oxgall dissolved in 200 ml distilled water. The solution of dehydrated oxgall should have a pH between 7.0 and 7.5.

Make up with distilled water to approximately 975 ml. Adjust the reaction to a pH reading of 7.4. Add 13.3 ml 0.1 per cent solution of brilliant green in distilled water. Then add sufficient distilled water to make the volume 1 liter. Filter through cotton. Distribute in fermentation tubes and sterilize as directed previously.

10. EC Medium

Add 20 g tryptose or trypticase, 5 g lactose, 1.5 g bile salts mixture or bile salts No. 3, 4 g dipotassium hydrogen phosphate, K_2HPO_4, and 5 g sodium chloride, NaCl, to each liter of distilled water. Heat to boiling until all ingredients are dissolved and make up lost volume with distilled water. Distribute into fermentation tubes, and autoclave as directed previously. No adjustment of pH is required.

11. Boric Acid Lactose Broth

Add 10 g proteose peptone, 5 g lactose, 12.2 g anhydrous dipotassium hydrogen phosphate, K_2HPO_4, 4.1 g anhydrous potassium dihydrogen phosphate, KH_2PO_4, and 3.5 g boric acid to each liter of distilled water. Heat to boiling until all ingredients are dissolved and make up lost volume with distilled water. Distribute into fermentation tubes, and autoclave as directed previously. No adjustment of pH is required.

12. M-Endo Medium

Dissolve the following ingredients * in 1 liter distilled water to which 20 ml 95 per cent ethyl alcohol has been added:

	g
Tryptone or polypeptone	10.0
Thiopeptone or thiotone	5.0
Casitone or trypticase	5.0
Yeast extract	1.5
Lactose	12.5
Sodium chloride	5.0
Dipotassium hydrogen phosphate .	4.375
Potassium dihydrogen phosphate .	1.375
Sodium lauryl sulfate	0.050
Sodium desoxycholate	0.10
Sodium sulfite	2.10
Basic fuchsin	1.05

Bring the medium to the boiling point and stop heating. Do not boil and do not submit to steam under pressure. The pH of the finished medium should be between 7.1 and 7.3.

The finished medium should be stored at 2°–10°C and any unused medium discarded after 96 hr.

13. LES MF Holding Medium—Coliform

Dissolve the following in 1 liter distilled water:

	g
Tryptone	3.0
M-Endo broth MF	3.0
Dipotassium hydrogen phosphate	3.0
Sodium benzoate	1.0
Sulfanilamide	1.0
Para aminobenzoic acid	1.2
Acti-dione	0.5

Heat to boiling until all ingredients are dissolved and make up lost volume with distilled water. Distribute into fermentation tubes and autoclave as directed previously. No pH adjustment is required.

14. LES Endo Agar Medium

Dissolve the following * in 1 liter cold distilled water to which 20 ml 95 per cent ethyl alcohol has been added:

	g
Yeast extract	1.2
Casitone or trypticase	3.7
Thiopeptone or thiotone	3.7
Tryptose	7.5
Lactose	9.4
Dipotassium hydrogen phosphate ...	3.3
Potassium dihydrogen phosphate ...	1.0
Sodium chloride	3.7
Sodium desoxycholate	0.1
Sodium lauryl sulfate	0.05
Sodium sulfite	1.6
Basic fuchsin	0.8
Agar	15.0

Heat to boiling to complete solution. Cool to 45°–50° and dispense in 4-ml quantities into the lower section of 60-mm glass or plastic dishes. If dishes of any other size are used, adjust the quantity to give an equivalent depth. Plates may be stored up to two weeks in the refrigerator. Do not expose to direct sunlight.

---

* Dehydrated Difco M-Endo broth MF (No. 0749–02), dehydrated BBL M-coliform broth MF (No. 01–494), or equivalent, may be used as a substitute for M-Endo medium as described.

---

* Dehydrated Difco Bacto-M-Endo LES agar (No. 0736) may be used as a substitute for M-Endo LES agar medium as described.

15. Azide Dextrose Broth

To each liter of distilled water add 4.5 g beef extract, 15.0 g tryptone or polypeptone, 7.5 g glucose, 7.5 g sodium chloride, 0.2 g sodium azide. Heat minimally, with stirring, until all ingredients are dissolved. Make up lost weight with distilled water. Adjust the reaction so that the pH reading after sterilization will be about 7.2. Distribute to the desired tubes and sterilize as directed under Preparation of Culture Media, A, Sec. 3.

16. M-Enterococcus Agar Medium

Dissolve in 1 liter distilled water 20 g tryptose, 5 g yeast extract, 2 g glucose, 4 g dipotassium hydrogen phosphate, K_2HPO_4, and 0.4 g sodium azide. Adjust the pH to 7.2, add 1 per cent agar, and heat sufficiently to dissolve the agar. Heat above 100°C is not recommended. After cooling slightly, add 1 ml 1 per cent sterile solution of 2,3,5-triphenyltetrazolium chloride per 100 ml of medium.

A dehydrated product can be purchased and is preferred. If used, follow the manufacturer's directions for preparation, and sterilize by bringing to a boil. Cool to 50°C before pouring.

17. Ethyl Violet Azide Broth Medium

To each liter of distilled water add 20 g tryptone or biosate, 5 g glucose, 5 g sodium chloride, 2.7 g dipotassium hydrogen phosphate, K_2HPO_4, 2.7 g potassium dihydrogen phosphate, KH_2PO_4, 0.4 g sodium azide, 0.83 mg ethyl violet. Heat minimally, with stirring, until all ingredients are dissolved. Sterilize as directed in Preparation of Culture Media, A, Sec. 3.

The reaction after sterilization should be about pH 7.0.

18. Tryptophane Broth

To 1 liter distilled water add 10 g tryptone or trypticase. Heat, with stirring, to obtain complete solution. Distribute in 5-ml portions into test tubes and sterilize in an autoclave as directed under Preparation of Culture Media, A, Sec. 3.

19. Buffered Glucose Broth

To 800 ml distilled water add 5 g proteose peptone or other peptone giving equivalent results, 5 g glucose, and 5 g dipotassium hydrogen phosphate, K_2HPO_4. Heat gently, with occasional stirring, until ingredients are dissolved. Filter, cool to 20°C, and dilute to 1 liter with distilled water. Distribute in 5-ml portions in test tubes and sterilize in an autoclave at 121°C for 12–15 min, making sure that the total time of exposure to heat is not longer than 30 min.

20. Salt Peptone Glucose Broth

To 1 liter distilled water add 10 g polypeptone or proteose peptone, 5 g sodium chloride, and 10 g glucose. Adjust the pH to 7.0–7.2. Tube in 5-ml amounts and sterilize in an autoclave at 121°C for 12–15 min, making sure that the total time of exposure to heat is not longer than 1 hr.

21. Koser's Citrate Broth

In 1 liter distilled water dissolve 1.5 g sodium ammonium hydrogen phosphate, $NaNH_4HPO_4 \cdot 4H_2O$ (microcosmic salt), 1 g dipotassium hydrogen phosphate, K_2HPO_4, 0.2 g magnesium sulfate heptahydrate, and

3.0 g sodium citrate dihydrate crystals. Distribute in 5-ml portions in test tubes and sterilize as directed under Preparation of Culture Medium, A, Sec. 3.

22. Simmon's Citrate Agar

In 1 liter distilled water dissolve 0.2 g magnesium sulfate heptahydrate, 1.0 g ammonium dihydrogen phosphate, 1.0 g dipotassium hydrogen phosphate, K_2HPO_4, 2.0 g sodium citrate dihydrate, 5.0 g sodium chloride, 15.0 g agar, 0.08 g bromthymol blue. Tube for long slants and sterilize as directed under Preparation of Culture Medium, A, Sec. 3.

23. Tryptone Glucose Extract Broth

To each liter of distilled water add 3 g beef extract, 5 g tryptone, and 1 g dextrose (glucose). Dissolve the ingredients, distribute into tubes, and adjust the reaction so that the pH after autoclaving will be 7.0. Autoclave as directed previously.

24. Brain-Heart Infusion

To each liter distilled water add 200 g infusion from calf brains, 250 g infusion from beef heart, 10 g proteose peptone, 2 g dextrose, 5 g sodium chloride, and 2.5 g disodium hydrogen phosphate. Dissolve the ingredients, adjust the reaction so that the pH after autoclaving will be 7.4, distribute into tubes, and autoclave as directed previously.

25. Brain-Heart Infusion Agar

To each liter distilled water add 200 g infusion from calf brains, 250 g infusion from beef heart, 10 g proteose peptone, 2 g dextrose, 5 g sodium chloride, 2.5 g disodium hydrogen phosphate, and 15 g agar. Heat to boiling until all ingredients are dissolved, adjust the reaction so the pH after sterilization will be 7.4, distribute into tubes (slant tubes), and autoclave as previously directed.

Bibliography

1. WHITTAKER, H. A. The Source, Manufacture, and Composition of Commercial Agar-Agar. *A.J.P.H.* 1:632 (1911).
2. NOYES, H. A. Agar-Agar for Bacteriological Use. *Science* 44:797 (1916).
3. CLARK, W. M. & LUBS, H. A. The Colorimetric Determination of Hydrogen Ion Concentration and Its Application in Bacteriology. *J. Bacteriol.* 2:1, 109, 191 (1917).
4. LEVINE, M. Differentiation of *B. coli* and *B. aerogenes* on a Simplified Eosine Methylene Blue Agar. *J. Infectious Diseases* 23:43 (1918).
5. LEVINE, M. A Simplified Fuchsin Sulphite (Endo) Agar. *A.J.P.H.* 8:864 (1918).
6. LEVINE, M. Further Observations on the Eosine Methylene Blue Agar. *J. AWWA* 8:151 (1921).
7. LEVINE, M. Bacteria Fermenting Lactose and Their Significance in Water Analysis. *Iowa State Coll. Agr. Mech. Arts Bull.* 62:117 (1921).
8. BUNKER, G. C. & SCHUBER, H. The Reaction of Culture Media. *J. AWWA* 9:63 (1922).
9. DUNHAM, H. G.; McCRADY, M. H.; & JORDAN, H. E. Studies of Differential Media for Detection of *Bacterium coli* in Water. *J. AWWA* 14:535 (1925).
10. JORDAN, H. E. Brilliant Green Bile for the Detection of the Coli-Aerogenes Group. *J. AWWA* 18:337 (1927).
11. JORDAN, H. E. Brilliant Green Bile for Coli-Aerogenes Group Determinations. *J. AWWA* 24:1027 (1932).
12. RUCHHOFT, C. C. Comparative Studies of Media for the Determination of the Coli-Aerogenes Group in Water Analysis. *J. AWWA* 27:1732 (1935).
13. BOWERS, C. S. & HUCKER, G. J. The Composition of Media in the Bacteriological Analysis of Milk. *N.Y. State*

Agr. Expt. Sta. Tech. Bull. p. 228 (1935).

14. RUCHHOFT, C. C. & NORTON, J. F. Study of Selective Media for Coli-Aerogenes Isolations. *J. AWWA* 27:1134 (1935).

15. McCRADY, M. H. A Practical Study of Procedures for the Detection of the Presence of Coliform Organisms in Water. *A.J.P.H.* 27:1243 (1937).

16. McCRADY, M. H. A Comparison of Mac-Conkey's Broth and Standard Lactose Broth as Media for Detection of Coliform Organisms in Water. *A.J.P.H.* 29:1250 (1939).

17. DARBY, C. W. & MALLMANN, W. L. Studies on Media for Coliform Organisms. *J. AWWA* 31:689 (1939).

18. KELLY, C. B. Brilliant Green Lactose Bile and the *Standard Methods* Completed Test in Isolation of Coliform Organisms. *A.J.P.H.* 30:1034 (1940).

19. RICHEY, D. Relative Value of 2 Per Cent and 5 Per Cent Brilliant Green Bile Confirmatory Media. *J. AWWA* 33:649 (1941).

20. HOWARD, N. J.; LOCHHEAD, A. G.; & McCRADY, M. H. A Study of Methods for the Detection of the Presence of Coliform Organisms in Water. *Can. Public Health J.* 32:29 (1941).

21. MALLMANN, W. L. & DARBY, C. W. Uses of a Lauryl Sulphate Tryptose Broth for the Detection of Coliform Organisms. *A.J.P.H.* 31:127 (1941).

22. MALLMANN, W. L. & BREED, R. S. A Comparative Study of Standard Agars for Determining Bacterial Counts in Water. *A.J.P.H.* 31:341 (1941).

23. WYNNE, E. S.; RODE, L. J.; & HAYWARD, A. E. Mechanism of the Selective Action of Eosine Methylene Blue Agar on the Enteric Group. *Stain Technol.* 17:11 (1942).

24. HOWARD, N. J.; LOCHHEAD, A. G.; & McCRADY, M. H. Report of the Committee on Bacteriological Examination of Water and Sewage. *Can. Public Health J.* 33:49 (1942).

25. ARCHAMBAULT, J. & McCRADY, M. H. Dissolved Air as a Source of Error in Fermentation Tube Results. *A.J.P.H.* 32:1164 (1942).

26. WATTIE, E. Coliform Confirmation from Raw and Chlorinated Waters with Brilliant Green Bile Lactose Broth. *Public Health Repts.* 58:377 (1943).

27. McCRADY, M. H. A Practical Study of Lauryl Sulfate Tryptose Broth for Detection of the Presence of Coliform Organisms in Water. *A.J.P.H.* 33:1199 (1943).

28. LEVINE, M. The Effect of Concentration of Dyes on Differentiation of Enteric Bacteria on Eosin Methylene Blue Agar. *J. Bacteriol.* 45:471 (1944).

29. FIFIELD, C. W. & SCHAUFUS, C. P. Improved Membrane Filter Medium for the Detection of Coliform Organisms. *J. AWWA* 50:193 (1958).

30. *Standard Methods for the Examination of Dairy Products.* Am. Public Health Assoc., New York (11th ed., 1960).

31. McCARTHY, J. A.; DELANEY, J. E.; & GRASSO, R. J. Measuring Coliforms in Water. *Water & Sewage Works* 108:238 (1961).

32. DELANEY, J. E.; McCARTHY, J. A.; & GRASSO, R. J. Measurement of *E. coli* Type I by the Membrane Filter. *Water & Sewage Works* 109:289 (1962).

Samples

1. Collection

1.1. *Containers:* Samples for bacteriologic examination must be collected in bottles which have been cleansed with great care, rinsed in clean water and sterilized as directed under Laboratory Apparatus, Washing and Sterilization.

1.2. *Dechlorination:* A dechlorinating agent should be added to bottles intended for the collection of water containing residual chlorine unless they contain broth for direct planting of the sample therein. Sodium thiosulfate is a satisfactory dechlorinating agent. Its presence in a sample from a chlorinated supply at the instant of collection will neutralize any residual chlorine and will prevent a continuation of the bactericidal action of the chlorine during the time the sample is in transit to the laboratory. The bacteriologic examination will then indicate more probably the true bacterial content of the water at the time of sampling.

The sodium thiosulfate should be added to the clean sample bottle before sterilization in an amount to provide an approximate concentration of 100 mg/l in the sample. This can be accomplished by adding to a 4-oz bottle 0.1 ml of a 10 per cent solution of sodium thiosulfate. The bottle is then stoppered, capped, and sterilized by either dry or moist heat as directed previously.

1.3. *Sampling procedures:* When the sample is collected, ample air space shall be left in the bottle to facilitate mixing of the sample by shaking, preparatory to examination. Care must be exercised to have the samples representative of the water to be tested and to assure that no contamination of the sample occurs at the time of collection or prior to examination.

The sampling bottle shall be kept unopened until the moment at which it is required for filling. The stopper and hood shall be removed as a unit with care to eliminate soiling, and during sampling the stopper and neck of the bottle shall not be handled and shall be protected from contamination. The bottle shall be held near the base, filled without rinsing, the stopper replaced immediately, and the hood secured around the neck of the bottle.

If a sample of water is to be taken from a distribution system tap without attachments, it should be ascertained that the tap chosen is supplying water from a service pipe directly connected with the main, and is not, for instance, served from a cistern or storage tank. The tap should be opened fully and the water allowed to run to waste for 2 or 3 min or a sufficient time to permit clearing the service line. The flow from the tap should then be restricted to permit filling the bottle without splashing. Leaking taps which allow water to flow over the outside of the tap must be avoided as sampling points.

In collecting samples directly from a river, stream, lake, reservoir, spring, or shallow well, the aim must be to obtain a sample that is representative of the water which will be the source of supply to consumers. It is therefore undesirable to take samples too near the bank or too far from the point of drawoff, or at a depth above or below the point of drawoff. In a stream, areas of relative stagnation should be avoided.

Samples from a river, stream, lake, or reservoir can often be taken by holding the bottle in the hand near its base and plunging it, neck downward, below the surface. The bottle should then be turned until the neck points slightly upwards, the mouth being directed toward the current. If no current exists, as in a reservoir, a current should be artificially created by pushing the bottle horizontally forward in a direction away from the hand. If it is not possible to collect samples from these situations in this way, a weight may be attached to the base of the bottle, which can then be lowered into the water. In any case damage to the bank must be guarded against; otherwise, fouling of the water may occur. Special apparatus which permits mechanical removal of the stopper of the bottle below the surface is required to collect samples from the depths of a lake or reservoir.

If the sample is to be taken from a well fitted with a hand pump, water should be pumped to waste for about 5 min before the sample is collected. If the well is fitted with a mechanical pump, the sample should be collected from a tap on the discharge. If there is no pumping machinery, a sample can be collected directly from the well by means of a sterilized bottle fitted with a weight at the base; in this case care should be taken to avoid contamination of the samples by any surface scum.

1.4. *Size of sample:* The volume of a sample should be sufficient for carrying out all of the tests required, preferably not less than 100 ml for water samples intended for bacteriologic examination.

1.5 *Identifying data:* All samples should be accompanied by complete and accurate identifying and descriptive data. Samples not so identified shall not be accepted for examination. Typical required essential data are indicated as follows:

PUBLIC WATER SUPPLIES

(Submit a card for each bottle filled)

Laboratory number _____ Date collected _____ Date received in laboratory _____

Samples from { City / Village _____ / Hamlet / Township } County _____

Supply owned by _____
(Company, municipality, or institution)

Other municipalities supplied _____

DESCRIPTION OF SAMPLE: Sampling point _____
(Do not state "tap" only)

If chlorination has been interrupted, state for how long _____

Have there been recent heavy rains _____ Fires _____ Repairs to main _____

Indicate amounts (lb/mil gal) of chlorine _____ used on day of sampling

Indicate ppm RESIDUAL CHLORINE at sampling point _____ OT/OTA; at point of

treatment _____ OT/OTA

Are there complaints regarding taste _____ odor _____ appearance _____

sanitary quality _____ corrosion _____.

Remarks: Other information concerning sample.

Signed _____ Title _____

PLEASE ANSWER ALL QUESTIONS PERTINENT TO SAMPLE

GROUND WATER
(Submit a card for each bottle filled)

Laboratory number _____ Date collected _____ Date received in laboratory _____

Samples from $\begin{cases}\text{City} \\ \text{Village} \\ \text{Township}\end{cases}$ _____ County _____

Owner of water supply _____ Tenant of property _____

Sampling point _____

Is a separate chemical (or bacteriologic)   Date of last previous
sample being submitted from this source? Yes _____ No _____ sample _____

_____

WELL: Dug _____ Drilled _____ Driven _____ Depth _____ Diameter _____

Type of cover _____ Curb _____ Casing _____ Depth of casing _____ Type of pump _____

Are cover, curb and casing tight _____

SPRING: Location: Steep slope _____Level ground _____Type of cover_____ Type of curb_____

Are curb and cover tight _____

Supply chlorinated when sampled Yes _____ No _____ Residual chlorine _____

Can surplus water pumped or surface drainage enter the water supply _____

Recent $\begin{cases}\text{repairs} \\ \text{construction}\end{cases}$ _____

State geologic character of surrounding soil _____

Name all possible sources of pollution and indicate distance of each from the water supply ____

_____

(Include privies, cesspools, septic tanks, tile fields, barnyards, fertilized areas)

Is water supply involved in reported illness _____ Explain _____

Signed _____ Title _____

PLEASE ANSWER ALL QUESTIONS PERTINENT TO SAMPLE

2. Preservation and Storage

The bacteriologic examination of a water sample should be initiated immediately after collection. However, such a requirement is seldom practical and more realistic arrangements must be established. Therefore, it is recommended that the technical procedures be started preferably within 1 hr after collection; the time elapsing between collection and examination should in no case exceed 30 hr.

During the period elapsing between collection and examination, the temperature of the sample should be maintained as close as possible to that of the source of the sample at the time of sampling. The time and temperature of storage of all samples should be recorded and should be considered in the interpretation of the laboratory results.

When local conditions necessitate delays in receipt of sample longer than 24 hr, consideration should be given to providing for a field examination of such samples, by making use, for example, of the membrane filter technique or of temporary laboratory facilities at the site.

Bibliography

1. McCarthy, J. A. Storage of Water Sample for Bacteriological Examinations. *A.J.P.H.* 47:971 (1957).

Standard Plate Count

1. Preparation and Dilution

The sample bottle shall be shaken vigorously 25 times, and the required portion shall be withdrawn at once with a standard sterile pipet to the petri dish, dilution bottle, or tube. If dilutions are made, the dilution bottle shall be likewise shaken 25 times before portions are removed.

The water used for dilution must be prepared as directed under Preparation of Culture Media, C, Media Specifications, Sec. 1. Tap or distilled water must not be used.

2. Plating

A 1-ml, 0.1-ml, or other suitable volume of the sample or dilution to be used for plating should be placed in the petri dish first. It is recommended that dilutions be used in preparing volumes less than 1 ml; in the examination of sewage or turbid water, a 0.1-ml inoculum of the original sample shall not be measured but an appropriate dilution should be prepared.

Not less than 10 ml of liquefied agar medium at a temperature of 43° to 45°C should be added to the water in the petri dish. The agar may be stored in a melted condition in a container providing maintenance of the proper temperature for no longer than 3 hr and shall not be remelted.

Tryptone glucose extract agar (or plate count agar) shall be used.

The cover of the dish should be lifted just enough for the introduction of the pipet or the culture medium. The agar and the sample shall be thoroughly mixed and uniformly spread over the bottom of the dish by tilting and rotating the dish.

The plates shall be solidified as rapidly as possible after pouring, and placed immediately in the appropriate incubator. Not more than 20 min should elapse between plating and pouring.

3. Incubation

Incubation for the standard plate count using an agar medium shall be at a temperature of 35° ± 0.5°C for 24 ± 2 hr or at 20° ± 0.5°C for 48 ± 3 hr. In the examination of chlorinated supplies where chlorination has not been effective and where the chlorine in the sample has been neutralized by the addition of sodium thiosulfate, coliform bacteria may not develop sufficiently to be detected in 24 hr, although in 48 hr the count may be appreciable. Glass-covered dishes and plastic dishes shall be inverted in the incubator. Plates are to be packed as directed under Laboratory Apparatus, Sec. 1. Any deviation from this method must be stated in the report of examination.

4. Counting

In preparing plates, such amounts of water should be planted as will give from 30 to 300 colonies on a plate. The aim should be always to have at least two plates giving the numbers between these limits, except as provided below.

Ordinarily, it is not desirable to plant more than 1.0 ml in a plate; therefore, when the total number of colonies developing from 1.0 ml is less than 30, it is obviously necessary to disregard the rule above and to record the result as observed. With this exception, only plates showing 30 to 300 colonies should be considered in determining the standard plate count. The result as reported shall be the average of all plates falling within the limits.

Counting shall be done with an approved counting aid, such as the Quebec colony counter. If such equipment is not available, counting may be done with one providing equivalent magnification and illumination.

To avoid fictitious accuracy and yet to express the numerical results by a method consistent with the precision of the technique employed, the recorded number of bacteria per milliliter shall not include more than two significant figures. For example, a count of 142 is recorded as 140, and a count of 155 as 160, whereas a count of 35 is recorded as 35.

Counts shall be designated as "standard plate count at 35°C," or "standard plate count at 20°C."

Bibliography

Dilution

1. BUTTERFIELD, C. T. The Selection of Dilution Waters for Bacteriological Examinations. *Public Health Repts.* 48:681 (1933) ; Reprint 1580.

Plating

2. BOWERS, C. S. & HUCKER, G. J. The Composition of Media in the Bacteriological Analysis of Milk. *N.Y. State Agr. Expt. Sta. Tech. Bull.* p. 228 (1935).
3. MALLMANN, W. L. & BREED, R. S. A Comparative Study of Standard Agars for Determining Bacterial Counts in Water. *A.J.P.H.* 31:341 (1941).
4. HOWARD, N. J.; LOCHHEAD, A. G.; & McCRADY, M. H. Report of the Committee on Bacteriological Examination of Water and Sewage. *Can. Public Health J.* 33:49 (1942).

Incubation

5. WHIPPLE, G. C. On the Necessity of Cultivating Water Bacteria in an Atmosphere Saturated with Moisture. *Mass. Inst. Technol. Quart.* 12:276 (1899).
6. *Standard Methods for the Examination of Dairy Products.* Am. Public Health Assoc., New York (11th ed., 1960).

Counting

7. ARCHAMBAULT, J.; CUROT, J.; & McCRADY, M. H. The Need of Uniformity of Conditions for Counting Plates. *A.J.P.H.* 27:809 (1937).
8. JENNISON, M. W. & WADSWORTH, G. P. Evaluation of the Errors Involved in Estimating Bacterial Numbers by the Plating Method. *J. Bacteriol.* 39:389 (1940).

Tests for Presence of Members of Coliform Group

The coliform group includes all of the aerobic and facultative anaerobic, Gram-negative, nonspore-forming, rod-shaped bacteria which ferment lactose with gas formation within 48 hr at 35°C.*

---

* The "coliform group" as defined above is equivalent to the "B. coli group" as used in the third, fourth, and fifth editions of this manual, and to the "coli-aerogenes group" as used through the eighth edition.

The standard test for the coliform group may be carried out either by the multiple-tube fermentation technique (Presumptive Test, Confirmed Test, or Completed Test) described herein or by the membrane filter technique described under a separate heading, each technique being applicable within the limitations specified and with due consideration of the purpose of the examination.

Multiple-Tube Fermentation Technique

It has been adequately demonstrated that, even after the prescribed shaking, the distribution of bacteria in water is irregular. It is entirely possible to divide a given volume of water into portions and after testing find that the number of organisms in any portion may be none, or at least less than the arithmetic average based on examination of the total volume might indicate. It is also quite probable that the growth in a fermentation tube may result not from one but from many organisms. It is reasonable, however, to assume that growth develops from a single individual.

It is convenient to express the results of the examination of replicate tubes and dilutions in terms of "most probable number." This term is actually an estimate based on certain probability formulas. Theoretical considerations and large-scale replicate determinations indicate that this estimate tends to be greater than the actual number, and that this disparity tends to diminish with increasing numbers of tubes in each dilution examined.

The accuracy of any single test will depend, then, on the number of tubes used. The most satisfactory information will be obtained when the largest portion examined shows gas in some or all of the tubes, and the smallest portion shows no gas in all or a majority of the tubes. The numerical value of the estimation of the bacterial content is largely determined by that dilution which shows both positive and negative results. The number of portions, especially in the critical dilution, will be governed by the desired accuracy of the result. The increased interest in and the numerous investigations into the precision of the multiple-tube technique and the expression of the results as MPN should not be permitted to confuse the issue to the extent that these methods are regarded as a statistical exercise rather than a means of estimating the coliform density of a water and thereby aiding in establishing its sanitary quality. The best assessment of such quality still must depend on the interpretation of the results of the multiple-tube technique or of other methods, possibly more precise, which may be developed, and of all other information regarding a water which may be obtained by surveys or otherwise.

Water of drinking-water quality: When examining water for evidence of acceptability under the standards of the US Public Health Service, only media and methods specified in the latest edition of those standards may be used. It is necessary to use a minimum of five fermentation tubes of the chosen presumptive medium, each containing 10 ml or 100 ml of the water sample. Practical considerations generally militate against the use of larger portions. The Confirmed Test or the Completed Test shall be employed.

For water examined frequently, or even daily, the common practice of inoculating five 10-ml or five 100-ml portions and one tube each in one or more lesser amounts generally provides sufficient definite information. In the examination of other waters presumed to be of drinking-water quality, the use of at least five tubes in each dilution is necessary to provide acceptable precision and reasonably satisfactory information; in no case shall less than three tubes per dilution be used.

For the routine examination of most potable water supplies, particularly those that are disinfected, the object of the test is to determine the presence or absence of coliform organisms as a measure of either the efficiency of operation or the presence of bacterial contamination. The safety of the water is generally judged by a knowledge of the sanitary condition of the supply and monitored by the number of samples yielding positive or negative

results. It is expected that greater than 95 per cent of all samples examined yield negative results. An occasional positive result, unless repeated from the same sampling point, or unless it is one yielding three or more positive tubes when five tubes are inoculated, is generally of limited significance. What is important is an increase in the number of positive samples over a period of time or an abrupt increase in a short period of time. Both indicate a change in the quality of the water, the significance of which should be studied and correction made if necessary.

Water of other than drinking-water quality: In the examination of waters of other than drinking-water quality, a series of lactose broth or lauryl tryptose broth tubes should be inoculated with decimal quantities of the water, the selection of the size of the portions depending on the probable coliform density as indicated by the experience of the bacteriologist and the extent of knowledge of the character of the water. The object of the examination of nonpotable water is generally to estimate the density of bacterial contamination or determine a source of pollution. This definitely requires a numerical value for reporting results. The multiple-tube fermentation technique may be used, but to obtain statistically valid MPN values a minimum series of three, but preferably five tubes, each inoculated with decimal quantities of samples, should be made. A sufficient number of samples must be examined to yield representative results for the sampling station. Generally, the log average or median value of the results of a number of samples will be a value in which the effect of individual extreme values is minimized. The membrane filter technique may prove the better procedure to accomplish this objective, although in many wastes and polluted waters the membrane filter technique may not be applicable and the multiple-tube technique will be required, as discussed under the membrane filter technique.

A. Standard Tests

1. Presumptive Test

Lactose broth or lauryl tryptose broth may be used in the Presumptive Test.

1.1. *Procedure:*

a. Inoculate a series of fermentation tubes ("primary" fermentation tubes) with appropriate graduated quantities (multiples and submultiples of 1 ml) of the water to be tested. The concentration of nutritive ingredients in the mixture of medium and added portion of sample must conform to the requirements given under Media Specifications, C, Sec. 2, 3, and 4. The portions of the water sample used for inoculating the lactose broth fermentation tubes will vary in size and number with the character of the water under examination, but in general should be decimal multiples and submultiples of 1 ml. These should be selected in accordance with the above discussion of the multiple-tube test.

b. Incubate the fermentation tubes at 35° ± 0.5°C. Examine each tube at the end of 24 ± 2 hr and, if no gas has formed, again at the end of 48 ± 3 hr. Record the presence or absence of gas formation at each examination of the tubes, regardless of the amount. More detailed records of the amount of gas formed, though desirable for the purpose of study, are not necessary for performing the standard tests prescribed.

1.2. *Interpretation:* Formation within 48 ± 3 hr of gas in any amount in the inner fermentation tubes constitutes a positive Presumptive Test.

The appearance of an air bubble must not be confused with actual gas production. If the gas formed is a result of fermentation, the broth medium will become cloudy and active fermentation may be shown by continued appearance of small bubbles of gas throughout the medium outside of the inner fermentation tube when gently shaken.

The absence of gas formation at the end of 48 ± 3 hr of incubation constitutes a negative test. An arbitrary limit of 48 hr for observation doubtless excludes from consideration occasional members of the coliform group which form gas very slowly; but for the purpose of a standard test based on the definition of the coliform group, exclusion of these occasional slow gas-forming organisms is satisfactory.

2. Confirmed Test

The use of confirmatory brilliant green lactose bile broth fermentation tubes or of Endo or eosin methylene blue agar plates is permitted.

2.1. *Procedure:* Submit all primary fermentation tubes showing any amount of gas at the end of 24-hr incubation to the Confirmed Test. If active fermentation appears in the primary fermentation tube before the expiration of the 24-hr period of incubation, it is preferable to transfer to the confirmatory medium without waiting for the full 24-hr period to elapse. If additional primary fermentation tubes show gas production at the end of 48-hr incubation, these too shall be submitted to the Confirmed Test.

2.2. *Alternative procedure:* Where three or more multiple portions of a series of three or more decimal dilutions of a given sample are planted, submit to the Confirmed Test all tubes of the two highest dilutions (smallest volumes) of the original samples showing gas formation in 24 hr.

All tubes producing gas in 24 hr that have not been submitted to the Confirmed Test must be recorded as containing organisms of the coliform group, even though all the Confirmed Tests made yield negative results.

Submit to the Confirmed Test all tubes of all dilutions of the original sample in which gas is produced only at the end of 48 hr.

If less than three portions of any dilution (volume), or if a series of less than three decimal dilutions of the original sample, are planted, submit all tubes producing gas at 24 or 48 hr to the Confirmed Test.

2.3. *Procedure with brilliant green lactose bile broth:*

a. Use a sterile metal loop 3 mm in diameter to transfer one loopful of medium from the primary fermentation tube showing gas to a fermentation tube containing brilliant green lactose bile broth. When making such transfers, gently shake the tube first, or mix by rotating.

b. Incubate the inoculated brilliant green lactose bile broth tube for 48 ± 3 hr at 35°C ± 0.5°C.

c. Interpretation: The formation of gas in any amount in the inverted vial of the brilliant green lactose bile broth fermentation tube at any time within 48 ± 3 hr constitutes a positive Confirmed Test.

2.4. *Procedure with Endo or eosin methylene blue agar plates:*

a. Streak one or more plates from each of the selected primary fermentation tubes showing gas formation; it is essential that the plates be so streaked as to insure the presence of some discrete colonies, separated by at least 0.5 cm from one another. Careful attention to the following details, when streaking plates, will result in a high proportion of successful isolation if coliform organisms are present:

(1) Employ an inoculating needle slightly curved at the tip.

(2) Tap and incline the primary fermentation tube to avoid picking up any membrane or scum on the needle.

(3) Insert the end of the needle into the liquid in the tube to a depth of approximately 5.0 mm.

(4) Streak the plate by bringing only the curved section of the needle in contact with the agar surface, so that the latter will not be scratched or torn.

b. Incubate the plate (inverted, if with glass cover) at 35°C ± 0.5°C for 24 ± 2 hr.

c. Interpretation: The colonies developing on Endo or eosin methylene blue agar may be described as: (1) *typical*—nucleated, with or without metallic sheen; (2) *atypical*—opaque, unnucleated mucoid after 24-hr incubation, pink; (3) *negative*—all others.

If typical coliform colonies have developed on the plate within the incubation period of 24 ± 2 hr, the result of the Confirmed Test may be considered positive.

If only atypical colonies have developed within 24 ± 2 hr, the result cannot yet be considered definitely negative, because many coliform organisms fail to form typical colonies on Endo or eosin methylene blue plates, or the colonies develop slowly. In such a case it is always necessary to complete the test as directed in Sec. 3 below.

If no colonies, or only noncoliform-type colonies, have developed within 24 ± 2 hr, the results of the Confirmed Test may be considered negative.

3. Completed Test

The Completed Test is used as the next step following the Confirmed Test. It may be applied to the brilliant green lactose bile broth fermentation tubes showing gas in the Confirmed Test, or to typical or atypical colonies found on the plates of solid differential medium used for the Confirmed Test.

3.1. *Procedure:*

a. If the brilliant green lactose bile broth tubes used for the Confirmed Test are to be employed for the Completed Tests, streak one or more Endo or eosin methylene blue plates from each tube showing gas, as soon as possible after the appearance of gas. Incubate the plates at $35°C \pm 0.5°C$ for 24 ± 2 hr.

b. From each of these plates, or from each of the plates used for the Confirmed Test (Sec. 2), fish one or more typical coliform colonies or, if no typical colonies are present, fish two or more colonies considered most likely to consist of organisms of the coliform group, transferring each fishing to a lactose broth fermentation tube or a lauryl tryptose broth fermentation tube and to a nutrient agar slant.

The use of a colony counter is recommended to provide optimum magnifica-

tion to assist in fishing colonies from the plates of selective medium.

When transferring colonies, take care to choose, if possible, well-isolated colonies separated by at least 0.5 cm from other colonies, and barely to touch the surface of the colony with the needle in order to minimize the danger of transferring a mixed culture.

The agar slants and secondary broth tubes incubated at $35°C \pm 0.5°C$ for 24 ± 2 or 48 ± 3 hr, and Gram-stained preparations (see Sec. 4) from those corresponding to the secondary lactose broth tubes that show gas are examined microscopically.

3.2. *Interpretation:* The formation of gas in the secondary lactose broth tube and the demonstration of Gram-negative, nonspore-forming, rod-shaped bacteria in the agar culture may be considered a satisfactory Completed Test, demonstrating the presence of a member of the coliform group in the volume of sample examined.

If, after 48 ± 3 hr, gas is produced in the lactose and no spores on the slant, the test may be considered "completed" and the presence of coliform organisms demonstrated.

4. Gram Stain Technique

The Completed Test for coliform group organisms includes the determination of Gram-stain characteristics of the organisms isolated, as discussed above.

According to the American Society for Microbiology [7]:

A word of caution is necessary as to the interpretation of the Gram stain. The test is often regarded with unjustified finality because organisms are generally described as being either Gram positive or Gram negative. Many organisms, however, actually are Gram variable. Hence, one should never give the Gram reaction of an unknown organism on the basis of a single test. He should repeat the procedure on cultures having different ages and should use more than one staining technique in order to determine the constancy of the organism toward the stain.

There are a large variety of modifications of the Gram stain, many of which have been listed by Hucker and Conn.[2, 4] The following modification by Hucker is valuable for staining smears of pure cultures.

4.1. *Reagents:*

a. Ammonium oxalate–crystal violet: Dissolve 2 g crystal violet (85 per cent dye content) in 20 ml 95 per cent ethyl alcohol; dissolve 0.2 g ammonium oxalate monohydrate in 20 ml distilled water; mix the two solutions, ordinarily in equal parts. It is sometimes found, however, that this gives so concentrated a stain that Gram-negative organisms do not properly decolorize. To avoid this difficulty, the crystal violet solution may be diluted as much as ten times, and the diluted solution mixed with an equal quantity of ammonium oxalate solution.

b. Lugol's solution, Gram's modification: Dissolve 1 g iodine crystals and 2 g potassium iodide in 300 ml distilled water.

c. Counterstain: Dissolve 2.5 g safranin dye in 100 ml 95 per cent ethyl alcohol. Add 10 ml of the alcoholic solution of safranin to 100 ml distilled water.

d. Ethyl alcohol, 95 per cent.

4.2. *Procedure:* Stain the smear for 1 min with the ammonium oxalate-crystal violet solution. Wash the slide in water; immerse in Lugol's solution for 1 min.

Wash the stained slide in water; blot dry. Decolorize with ethyl alcohol for 30 sec, using gentle agitation. Blot and cover with counterstain for 10 sec; then wash, dry, and examine as usual.

Cells which decolorize and accept the safranin stain are Gram negative. Cells which do not decolorize but retain the crystal violet stain are Gram positive.

5. Test for Section I Coliform Group (Fecal Coliform)

Elevated temperature tests for the separation of organisms of the coliform group of fecal origin from those derived from nonfecal sources have been used in many parts of the world and with various modifications. Recent modifications in technical procedures, standardization of methods, and detailed studies of the coliform group found in various warm-blooded animal feces compared with the coliform group from other environmental sources have established the value of elevated temperature *confirmatory* test procedures to indicate the fecal or nonfecal origin of the strains. The two following procedures yield adequate information as to the fecal or nonfecal source of the coliform group when used as a confirmatory test procedure. These procedures cannot be used in the primary isolation (presumptive test method) for the coliform group. They are applicable to a positive standard presumptive test or coliform colony from solid medium.

Elevated temperature tests for differentiation of coliforms are applicable to evaluation of pollution in raw water sources for treatment procedures, estimation of pollution in streams and surface waters, interpretation of questionable coliform data which has doubtful significance, and for special investigations. It is not recommended for examination of untreated water supplies being considered for potable water.

5.1. *Fecal coliform test (EC medium):* This procedure, used as described, may be expected to differentiate between coliforms of fecal origin (intestine of warm-blooded animal) and coliforms from other sources with a reasonable accuracy. Use EC medium as described under Media Specifications, C, Sec. 10.

a. Procedure: Inoculate a fermentation tube of medium with a 3-mm loop of broth from a positive presumptive tube and incubate in a water bath at 44.5° ± 0.5°C for 24 hr. Cultures from selective medium (brilliant green bile lactose broth, membrane filter test, eosin methylene blue agar, etc.) should be inoculated in lactose broth (or lauryl tryptose broth) and incubated at 35°C until gas is produced; then proceed with inoculation of the EC fermentation tube. All EC tubes must be placed in the water bath within 30 min after planting.

b. Interpretation: Gas production in the fermentation tube within 24 hr or less is considered a positive reaction indicating fecal origin. Tubes which fail to produce gas (growth sometimes occurs) are a negative reaction indicating derivation from a source other than the intestinal tract of warm-blooded animals.

5.2. Fecal coliform test (boric acid lactose broth): Boric acid lactose broth selectively inhibits essentially the same group of coliforms as the above described EC medium when used according to the provisions of the test procedure and can be considered reasonably accurate. Use boric acid lactose broth as described under Media Specifications, C, Sec. 11.

a. Procedure: Inoculate a fermentation tube of the medium with a 3-mm loop of broth from a positive presumptive tube and incubate at 43° ± 0.5°C

for 24–48 hr. Inoculate cultures from selective medium (brilliant green bile lactose broth, membrane filter test, eosin methylene blue agar, etc.) in lactose broth (or methylene blue agar, etc.) and incubate at 35°C until gas is produced within 48 hr; then proceed with inoculation of the boric acid lactose broth fermentation tube. All tubes must be placed in the water bath within 30 min after planting.

b. Interpretation: Gas production in the fermentation tube within 48 hr is considered a positive reaction indicating fecal origin. Tubes which fail to produce gas (growth sometimes occurs) are a negative reaction indicating derivation from a source other than the intestinal tract of warm-booded animals.

Bibliography

1. PERRY, C. A. & HAJNA, A. A. A Modified Eijkman Medium. *J. Bacteriol.* 25:419 (1933).
2. PERRY, C. A. & HAJNA, A. A. Further Evaluation of EC Medium for the Isolation of Coliform Bacteria and *Escherichia coli. A.J.P.H.* 34:735 (1944).
3. VAUGHN, R. H., ET AL. A Buffered Boric Acid Lactose Medium for Enrichment and Presumption Identification of *Escherichia coli. Food Research* 16:10 (1951).
4. LEVINE, M., ET AL. Simultaneous Determination of Coliform and *Escherichia coli* Indices. *Appl. Microbiol.* 3:310 (1955).
5. CLARK, H. F., ET AL. The Coliform Group. I. The Boric Acid Lactose Broth Reaction of Coliform IMViC Types. *Appl. Microbiol.* 5:396 (1957).
6. GELDREICH, E. E., ET AL. The Coliform Group. II. Reactions in EC Medium at 45°C. *Appl. Microbiol.* 6:347 (1958).
7. GELDREICH, E. E., ET AL. Type Distribution of Coliform Bacteria in the Feces of Warm-Blooded Animals. *J. WPCF* 34:295 (1962).

B. Application of Tests to Routine Examinations

The following basic considerations apply to the selection of the Presumptive Test, the Confirmed Test, or the Completed Test in the examination of any given sample of water or wastewater.

1. Presumptive Test

The Presumptive Test may be applied to the examination of:

a. Any sample of waste, sewage, sewage effluent (except chlorinated effluent), or water known to be heavily polluted, the fitness of which for use as drinking water is not under consideration.

b. Any routine sample of raw water in a treatment plant, provided records indicate the Presumptive Test is not too inclusive for the production of pertinent data.

2. Confirmed Test

The Confirmed Test should be applied in the examination of:

a. Any water to which the Presumptive Test is known, from previous records, to be inapplicable.

b. Routine samples of drinking water, water in process of treatment, and finished waters.

c. Chlorinated sewage effluents.

d. Bathing water.

3. Completed Test

The Completed Test should be applied in the examination of water samples where the results are to be used for the control of the quality of raw or finished waters; or if not applied to all samples, then to such a proportion of them as to establish beyond reasonable doubt the value of the Confirmed Test in determining the sanitary quality of such water supplies.

NOTE: Schematic outlines of the Presumptive, Confirmed, and Completed Tests are shown in Fig. 39.

A. *Presumptive Test*

Inoculate lactose or lauryl tryptose broth fermentation tubes and incubate 24 ± 2 hr at
35° C ± 0.5° C

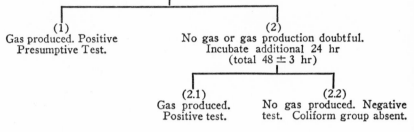

(1)
Gas produced. Positive
Presumptive Test.

(2)
No gas or gas production doubtful.
Incubate additional 24 hr
(total 48 ± 3 hr)

(2.1)
Gas produced.
Positive test.

(2.2)
No gas produced. Negative
test. Coliform group absent.

B. *Confirmed Test*

Inoculate lactose or lauryl tryptose broth fermentation tubes and incubate 24 ± 2 hr at
35° C ± 0.5° C

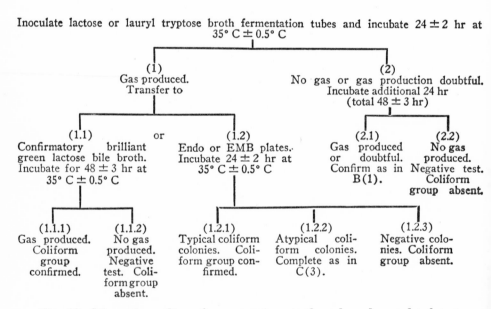

(1)
Gas produced.
Transfer to

(2)
No gas or gas production doubtful.
Incubate additional 24 hr
(total 48 ± 3 hr)

(1.1)
Confirmatory   brilliant
green lactose bile broth.
Incubate for 48 ± 3 hr at
35° C ± 0.5° C

or

(1.2)
Endo or EMB plates.
Incubate 24 ± 2 hr at
35° C ± 0.5° C

(2.1)
Gas produced
or   doubtful.
Confirm as in
B(1).

(2.2)
No gas
produced.
Negative test.
Coliform
group absent.

(1.1.1)
Gas produced.
Coliform
group
confirmed.

(1.1.2)
No gas
produced.
Negative
test. Coli-
form group
absent.

(1.2.1)
Typical coliform
colonies.   Coli-
form group con-
firmed.

(1.2.2)
Atypical   coli-
form   colonies.
Complete as in
C(3).

(1.2.3)
Negative colo-
nies. Coliform
group absent.

Fig. 39. Schematic outline of presumptive, confirmed, and completed tests

C. Completed Test

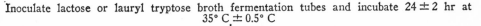

Inoculate lactose or lauryl tryptose broth fermentation tubes and incubate 24 ± 2 hr at 35° C ± 0.5° C

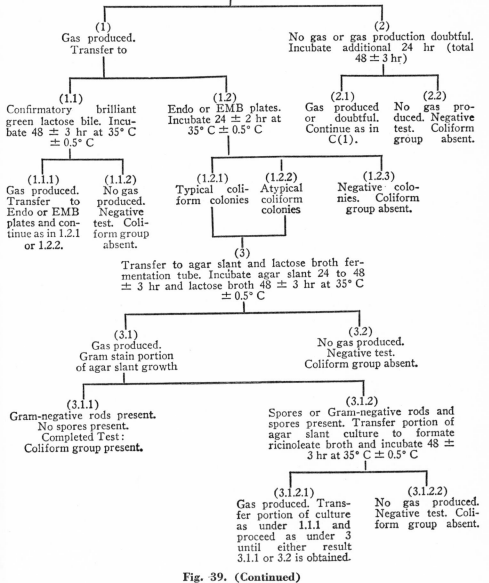

(1)
Gas produced.
Transfer to

(2)
No gas or gas production doubtful. Incubate additional 24 hr (total 48 ± 3 hr)

(1.1)
Confirmatory brilliant green lactose bile. Incubate 48 ± 3 hr at 35° C ± 0.5° C

(1.2)
Endo or EMB plates. Incubate 24 ± 2 hr at 35° C ± 0.5° C

(2.1)
Gas produced or doubtful. Continue as in C(1).

(2.2)
No gas produced. Negative test. Coliform group absent.

(1.1.1)
Gas produced. Transfer to Endo or EMB plates and continue as in 1.2.1 or 1.2.2.

(1.1.2)
No gas produced. Negative test. Coliform group absent.

(1.2.1)
Typical coliform colonies

(1.2.2)
Atypical coliform colonies

(1.2.3)
Negative colonies. Coliform group absent.

(3)
Transfer to agar slant and lactose broth fermentation tube. Incubate agar slant 24 to 48 ± 3 hr and lactose broth 48 ± 3 hr at 35° C ± 0.5° C

(3.1)
Gas produced.
Gram stain portion of agar slant growth

(3.2)
No gas produced.
Negative test.
Coliform group absent.

(3.1.1)
Gram-negative rods present.
No spores present.
Completed Test:
Coliform group present.

(3.1.2)
Spores or Gram-negative rods and spores present. Transfer portion of agar slant culture to formate ricinoleate broth and incubate 48 ± 3 hr at 35° C ± 0.5° C

(3.1.2.1)
Gas produced. Transfer portion of culture as under 1.1.1 and proceed as under 3 until either result 3.1.1 or 3.2 is obtained.

(3.1.2.2)
No gas produced. Negative test. Coliform group absent.

Fig. 39. (Continued)

C. Estimation of Coliform Group Density

1. Precision of Fermentation Tube Test

It is desirable to keep in mind the fact that, unless a large number of portions of sample are examined, the precision of the fermentation tube test is rather low. For example, even when the sample contains one coliform organism per milliliter, about 37 per cent of 1-ml tubes may be expected to yield negative results because of irregular distribution of the bacteria in the sample. When five tubes, with 1 ml of sample in each, are employed under these conditions, a completely negative result may be expected less than 1 per cent of the time.

Even when five fermentation tubes are employed, the precision of the results obtained is not of a high order. Consequently, great caution must be exercised when interpreting, in terms of sanitary significance, the coliform results obtained from the use of a few tubes with each dilution of sample.

2. Computing and Recording of MPN

The number of positive findings of coliform group organisms (either presumptive, confirmed, or completed) resulting from multiple-portion decimal dilution plantings should be computed and recorded in terms of the "most probable number" (MPN). The MPN for a variety of planting series and results is given in Tables 36 through 41. Included in these tables are the 95 per cent confidence limits for each MPN value determined.

The quantities indicated at the heads of the columns relate more specifically to finished waters. The values may be used in computing the MPN in larger or smaller portion plantings in the following manner: if instead of portions of 10, 1.0, and 0.1 ml, a combination of portions of 100, 10, and 1 ml is used, the MPN is recorded as 0.1 times the value in the table.

If, on the other hand, a combination of corresponding portions of 1.0, 0.1, and 0.01 ml is planted, record 10 times the value in the table; if a combination of portions of 0.1, 0.01, and 0.001 ml is planted, record 100 times the value in the table.

When more than three dilutions are employed in a decimal series of dilutions, the results from only three of these are significant. To select the three dilutions to be employed in determining the MPN index, using the system of five tubes of each dilution as an example, the highest dilution which gives positive results in all of the five portions tested (no lower dilution giving any negative results) and the two next succeeding higher dilutions should be chosen. The results of these three

TABLE 36—MPN INDEX AND 95 PER CENT CONFIDENCE LIMITS FOR VARIOUS COMBINATIONS OF POSITIVE AND NEGATIVE RESULTS WHEN FIVE 10-ML PORTIONS ARE USED

Number of Tubes Giving Positive Reaction Out of 5 of 10 Ml Each	MPN Index per 100 Ml	95% Confidence Limits	
		Lower	Upper
0	<2.2	0	6.0
1	2.2	0.1	12.6
2	5.1	0.5	19.2
3	9.2	1.6	29.4
4	16.0	3.3	52.9
5	Infinite	8.0	Infinite

TABLE 37—MPN INDEX AND 95 PER CENT CONFIDENCE LIMITS FOR VARIOUS COMBINATIONS
OF POSITIVE AND NEGATIVE RESULTS WHEN FIVE 10-ML PORTIONS,
FIVE 1-ML PORTIONS AND FIVE 0.1-ML PORTIONS ARE USED

Number of Tubes Giving Positive Reaction Out of			MPN Index per 100 Ml	95% Confidence Limits		Number of Tubes Giving Positive Reaction Out of			MPN Index per 100 Ml	95% Confidence Limits	
5 of 10 Ml Each	5 of 1 Ml Each	5 of 0.1 Ml Each		Lower	Upper	5 of 10 Ml Each	5 of 1 Ml Each	5 of 0.1 Ml Each		Lower	Upper
0	0	1	2	<0.5	7	4	2	1	26	9	78
0	1	0	2	<0.5	7	4	3	0	27	9	80
0	2	0	4	<0.5	11	4	3	1	33	11	93
1	0	0	2	<0.5	7	4	4	0	34	12	93
1	0	1	4	<0.5	11	5	0	0	23	7	70
1	1	0	4	<0.5	11	5	0	1	31	11	89
1	1	1	6	<0.5	15	5	0	2	43	15	114
1	2	0	6	<0.5	15	5	1	0	33	11	93
2	0	0	5	<0.5	13	5	1	1	46	16	120
2	0	1	7	1	17	5	1	2	63	21	150
2	1	0	7	1	17	5	2	0	49	17	130
2	1	1	9	2	21	5	2	1	70	23	170
2	2	0	9	2	21	5	2	2	94	28	220
2	3	0	12	3	28	5	3	0	79	25	190
3	0	0	8	1	19	5	3	1	109	31	250
3	0	1	11	2	25	5	3	2	141	37	340
3	1	0	11	2	25	5	3	3	175	44	500
3	1	1	14	4	34	5	4	0	130	35	300
3	2	0	14	4	34	5	4	1	172	43	490
3	2	1	17	5	46	5	4	2	221	57	700
3	3	0	17	5	46	5	4	3	278	90	850
4	0	0	13	3	31	5	4	4	345	120	1,000
4	0	1	17	5	46	5	5	0	240	68	750
4	1	0	17	5	46	5	5	1	348	120	1,000
4	1	1	21	7	63	5	5	2	542	180	1,400
4	1	2	26	9	78	5	5	3	918	300	3,200
4	2	0	22	7	67	5	5	4	1,609	640	5,800

TABLE 38—MPN INDEX AND 95 PER CENT CONFIDENCE LIMITS FOR VARIOUS COMBINATIONS OF POSITIVE AND NEGATIVE RESULTS WHEN ONE 50-ML PORTION, FIVE 10-ML PORTIONS AND FIVE 1-ML PORTIONS ARE USED

Number of Tubes Giving Positive Reaction Out of			MPN Index per 100 Ml	95% Confidence Limits		Number of Tubes Giving Positive Reaction Out of			MPN Index per 100 Ml	95% Confidence Limits	
1 of 50 Ml Each	5 of 10 Ml Each	5 of 1 Ml Each		Lower	Upper	1 of 50 Ml Each	5 of 10 Ml Each	5 of 1 Ml Each		Lower	Upper
0	0	1	1	<0.5	4	1	2	1	7	1	17
0	0	2	2	<0.5	6	1	2	2	10	3	23
0	1	0	1	<0.5	4	1	2	3	12	3	28
0	1	1	2	<0.5	6	1	3	0	8	2	19
0	1	2	3	<0.5	8	1	3	1	11	3	26
0	2	0	2	<0.5	6	1	3	2	14	4	34
0	2	1	3	<0.5	8	1	3	3	18	5	53
0	2	2	4	<0.5	11	1	3	4	21	6	66
0	3	0	3	<0.5	8	1	4	0	13	4	31
0	3	1	5	<0.5	13	1	4	1	17	5	47
0	4	0	5	<0.5	13	1	4	2	22	7	69
1	0	0	1	<0.5	4	1	4	3	28	9	85
1	0	1	3	<0.5	8	1	4	4	35	12	100
1	0	2	4	<0.5	11	1	4	5	43	15	120
1	0	3	6	<0.5	15	1	5	0	24	8	75
1	1	0	3	<0.5	8	1	5	1	35	12	100
1	1	1	5	<0.5	13	1	5	2	54	18	140
1	1	2	7	1	17	1	5	3	92	27	220
1	1	3	9	2	21	1	5	4	16	39	450
1	2	0	5	<0.5	13						

TABLE 39—MPN Index and 95 Per Cent Confidence Limits for Various Combinations of Positive and Negative Results When Five 50-Ml Portions, Five 10-Ml Portions and Five 1-Ml Portions Are Used

Number of Tubes Giving Positive Reaction Out of			MPN Index per 100 Ml	95% Confidence Limits		Number of Tubes Giving Positive Reaction Out of			MPN Index per 100 Ml	95% Confidence Limits	
5 of 50 Ml Each	5 of 10 Ml Each	5 of 1 Ml Each		Lower	Upper	5 of 50 Ml Each	5 of 10 Ml Each	5 of 1 Ml Each		Lower	Upper
0	0	1	1	<0.5	2	4	1	1	4	1	9
0	1	0	1	<0.5	2	4	1	2	4	1	9
0	1	1	1	<0.5	2	4	2	0	4	1	9
0	2	0	1	<0.5	2	4	2	1	4	1	9
0	3	0	1	<0.5	2	4	2	2	5	2	12
1	0	0	1	<0.5	2	4	3	0	5	2	12
1	0	1	1	<0.5	2	4	3	1	5	2	12
1	1	0	1	<0.5	2	4	3	2	6	2	14
1	1	1	1	<0.5	2	4	4	0	6	2	14
1	2	0	1	<0.5	2	4	4	1	7	3	17
1	2	1	2	<0.5	4	4	5	0	7	3	17
1	3	0	2	<0.5	4	4	5	1	8	3	19
2	0	0	1	<0.5	2	5	0	0	4	1	9
2	0	1	1	<0.5	2	5	0	1	4	1	9
2	1	0	1	<0.5	2	5	0	2	6	2	14
2	1	1	2	<0.5	4	5	1	0	5	2	12
2	2	0	2	<0.5	4	5	1	1	6	2	14
2	2	1	2	<0.5	4	5	1	2	7	3	17
2	3	0	2	<0.5	4	5	2	0	6	2	14
2	3	1	3	1	7	5	2	1	8	3	19
2	4	0	3	1	7	5	2	2	10	4	23
3	0	0	2	<0.5	4	5	2	3	12	4	28
3	0	1	2	<0.5	4	5	3	0	9	3	21
3	1	0	2	<0.5	4	5	3	1	11	4	26
3	1	1	2	<0.5	4	5	3	2	14	5	34
3	1	2	3	1	7	5	3	3	18	6	53
3	2	0	3	1	7	5	4	0	13	6	31
3	2	1	3	1	7	5	4	1	17	6	47
3	2	2	4	1	9	5	4	2	22	7	70
3	3	0	3	1	7	5	4	3	28	9	85
3	3	1	4	1	9	5	4	4	35	11	100
3	4	0	4	1	9	5	5	0	24	8	75
3	4	1	4	1	9	5	5	1	35	11	100
4	0	0	2	<0.5	4	5	5	2	54	18	140
4	0	1	3	1	7	5	5	3	92	27	220
4	0	2	3	1	7	5	5	4	161	39	420
4	1	0	3	1	7						

TABLE 40—MPN INDEX AND 95 PER CENT CONFIDENCE LIMITS FOR VARIOUS COMBINATIONS OF POSITIVE AND NEGATIVE RESULTS WHEN THREE 10-ML PORTIONS, THREE 1-ML PORTIONS AND THREE 0.1-ML PORTIONS ARE USED

Number of Tubes Giving Positive Reaction Out of			MPN Index per 100 Ml	95% Confidence Limits	
3 of 10 Ml Each	3 of 1 Ml Each	3 of 0.1 Ml Each		Lower	Upper
0	0	1	3	<0.5	9
0	1	0	3	<0.5	13
1	0	0	4	<0.5	20
1	0	1	7	1	21
1	1	0	7	1	23
1	1	1	11	3	36
1	2	0	11	3	36
2	0	0	9	1	36
2	0	1	14	3	37
2	1	0	15	3	44
2	1	1	20	7	89
2	2	0	21	4	47
2	2	1	28	10	150
3	0	0	23	4	120
3	0	1	39	7	130
3	0	2	64	15	380
3	1	0	43	7	210
3	1	1	75	14	230
3	1	2	120	30	380
3	2	0	93	15	380
3	2	1	150	30	440
3	2	2	210	35	470
3	3	0	240	36	1,300
3	3	1	460	71	2,400
3	3	2	1,100	150	4,800

TABLE 41—MPN INDEX AND 95 PER CENT CONFIDENCE LIMITS FOR VARIOUS COMBINATIONS OF POSITIVE AND NEGATIVE RESULTS WHEN FIVE 10-ML PORTIONS, ONE 1-ML PORTION AND ONE 0.1-ML PORTION ARE USED

Number of Tubes Giving Positive Reaction Out of *			MPN Index per 100 Ml	95% Confidence Limits	
5 of 10 Ml Each	1 of 1 Ml Each	1 of 0.1 Ml Each		Lower	Upper
0	0	0	0	0	5.9
0	1	0	2	0.050	13
1	0	0	2.2	0.050	13
1	1	0	4.4	0.52	14
2	0	0	5	0.54	19
2	1	0	7.6	1.5	19
3	0	0	8.8	1.6	29
3	1	0	12	3.1	30
4	0	1	15	3.3	46
4	0	0	20	5.9	48
4	1	0	21	6.0	53
5	0	0	38	6.4	330
5	0	1	96	12	370
5	1	0	240	12	3,700

* Includes only 15 of the 24 combinations of positive tubes. The other 9 are inherently unlikely to occur with any degree of frequency. If they occur in more than 1 per cent of the tests, it is an indication of faulty technique or that the assumptions underlying the MPN estimate are not being fulfilled.

When a case such as shown below, in *d,* arises, where a positive occurs in a dilution higher than the three chosen according to the rule, it should be included in the result of the highest chosen dilution, making the result read as in *e:*

	1 ml	0.1 ml	0.01 ml	0.001 ml
(d)	5/5	3/5	1/5	1/5
(e)	5/5	3/5	2/5	0/5

A desirable procedure for obtaining a single MPN value for a series of samples is to express the results of the examination of each sample in terms of its MPN value and strike a geometric average of these values. In some instances, it may be advantageous to compute an arithmetic average of the results of a series of samples in order

volumes should then be used in the computation of the MPN index. In the examples given below, the significant dilution results are shown in boldface (the number in the numerator represents positive tubes; that in the denominator, the total tubes planted):

	1 ml	0.1 ml	0.01 ml	0.001 ml
(a)	5/5	5/5	2/5	0/5
(b)	5/5	4/5	2/5	0/5
(c)	0/5	1/5	0/5	0/5

In *c,* the first three dilutions should be taken, so as to throw the positive result in the middle dilution.

to emphasize the significance of a single high MPN value.

Bibliography

Standard Tests

1. MEYER, E. M. An Aerobic Spore-Forming Bacillus Giving Gas in Lactose Broth Isolated in Routine Water Examination. *J. Bacteriol.* 3:9 (1918).
2. HUCKER, G. J. & CONN, H. J. Methods of Gram Staining. *N.Y. State Agr. Expt. Sta. Tech. Bull.* No. 93 (1923).
3. NORTON, J. F. & WEIGHT, J. J. Aerobic Spore-Forming Lactose Fermenting Organisms and Their Significance in Water Analysis. *A.J.P.H.* 14:1019 (1924).
4. HUCKER, G. J. & CONN, H. J. Further Studies on the Methods of Gram Staining. *N.Y. State Agr. Expt. Sta. Tech. Bull.* No. 128 (1927).
5. PORTER, R.; MCCLESKEY, C. S.; & LEVINE, M. The Facultative Sporulating Bacteria Producing Gas From Lactose. *J. Bacteriol.* 33:163 (1937).
6. COWLES, P. B. A Modified Fermentation Tube. *J. Bacteriol.* 38:677 (1939).
7. *Manual of Methods for Pure Culture Study of Bacteria.* Soc. Am. Bacteriologists, Geneva, N.Y. (1946). Leaflet 4.
8. BREED, R. S., ET AL., ed. *Bergey's Manual of Determinative Bacteriology.* Williams & Wilkins Co., Baltimore (7th ed., 1957).

Numerical Interpretation

9. MCCRADY, M. H. The Numerical Interpretation of Fermentation Tube Results. *J. Infectious Diseases* 17:183 (1915).
10. GREENWOOD, M. & YULE, G. U. On the Statistical Interpretation of Some Bacteriological Methods Employed in Water Analysis. *J. Hyg.* 16:36 (1917).
11. WOLMAN, A. & WEAVER, H. L. A Modification of the McCrady Method of the Numerical Interpretation of Fermentation Tube Results. *J. Infectious Diseases* 21:287 (1917).
12. MCCRADY, M. H. Tables for Rapid Interpretation of Fermentation Tube Results. *Can. Public Health J.* 9:201 (1918).
13. REED, L. J. *B. coli* Densities as Determined From Various Types of Samples. *Public Health Repts.* 40:704 (1925); Reprint 1029.
14. HOSKINS, J. K. The Most Probable Number of *B. coli* in Water Analysis. *J. AWWA* 25:867 (1933).
15. HOSKINS, J. K. Most Probable Numbers for Evaluation of Coli-Aerogenes Tests by Fermentation Tube Method. *Public Health Repts.* 49:393 (1934); Reprint 1621.
16. HOSKINS, J. K. & BUTTERFIELD, C. T. Determining the Bacteriological Quality of Drinking Water. *J. AWWA* 27:1101 (1935).
17. HALVORSON, H. O. & ZIEGLER, N. R. Application of Statistics to Problems in Bacteriology. *J. Bacteriol.* 25:101 (1933); 26:331, 559 (1933); 29:609 (1935).
18. SWAROOP, S. Numerical Estimation of *B. coli* by Dilution Method. *Indian J. Med. Research* 26:353 (1938).
19. DALLA VALLE, J. M. Notes on the Most Probable Number Index as Used in Bacteriology. *Public Health Repts.* 56:229 (1941).
20. THOMAS, H. A., JR. Bacterial Densities from Fermentation Tube Tests. *J. AWWA* 34:572 (1942).
21. Public Health Service Drinking Water Standards, 1946. *Public Health Repts.* 61:371 (1946); Reprint 2697.
22. *Standard Methods for the Examination of Water, Sewage, and Industrial Wastes.* APHA, AWWA & FSIWA, New York (10th ed., 1955).
23. WOODWARD, R. L. How Probable Is the Most Probable Number? *J. AWWA* 49:1060 (1957).
24. MCCARTHY, J. A.; THOMAS, H. A.; & DELANEY, J. E. Evaluation of Reliability of Coliform Density Tests. *A.J.P.H.* 48:12 (1958).

Tests for Presence of Members of Coliform Group by Membrane Filter Technique

The membrane filter technique was presented as a tentative procedure in the 10th Edition. The information obtained by its use following this edition led to the adoption of the technique as standard procedure in the 11th Edition, with a proviso that it should be used for determining the potability of drinking waters only after parallel testing had shown that it afforded information equivalent to that given by the standard multiple-tube test. Certain limitations were noted, especially with regard to waters high in turbidity and in noncoliform bacteria.

Since publication of the 11th Edition, widespread use of the technique has shown its value, especially in its high degree of reproducibility, the possibility of using relatively larger volumes of sample, and the obtaining of definite results more rapidly than with standard tube procedure. The method has proved particularly valuable in the routine analysis of a given water after its applicability has been established. The US Public Health Service has approved its use for certain water supplies. It has also been shown to be extremely useful in emergencies, and in the examination of waters not used for drinking. However, it is still necessary to permit the use of the technique in drinking water examination only after adequate parallel testing to show its applicability.

It still must be recognized, as well, that turbidity due to algae or other material may not permit testing of sample volume sufficient to produce significant results, and that low coliform estimates may be caused by high numbers of noncoliforms or the presence of substances toxic to the procedure. Experience indicates that the membrane filter technique is applicable in the examination of saline waters.

A. Standard Test

1. Laboratory Apparatus

All glassware and other apparatus used in bacteriologic analyses with the membrane filter should be composed of material free from agents having unfavorable effects on bacterial growth. Any deviation from recommendations presented below must be carefully noted. Quantitative tests to demonstrate that the deviations in question do not introduce agents or factors resulting in conditions less favorable for growth are required.

Glassware should be sterilized as directed under Laboratory Apparatus, Washing and Sterilization.

1.1. *Sample bottles:* Sample bottles should be of the type described in Laboratory Apparatus, Sec. 14.

1.2. *Dilution bottles:* Dilution bottles should be of the type described in Laboratory Apparatus, Sec. 11.

1.3. *Pipets and graduated cylinders:*

Pipets and graduated cylinders may be of any convenient size or shape, provided it is found by actual test that they deliver accurately the required amount in the manner in which they are used. The error of calibration must in no case exceed 2.5 per cent.

It is recommended that the mouth end of all pipets be protected with a cotton plug.

The opening of graduated cylinders should be covered with metal foil or a suitable paper substitute prior to sterilization.

1.4. *Containers for culture medium:* Containers for culture medium should be of glass. They may be of any size or shape convenient for storage and adequate mixing of the medium contained. Screw-cap tubes, 25×150 mm, are recommended, although cotton-stoppered tubes, metal-cap tubes, or dilution bottles are acceptable.

1.5. *Culture dishes:* Culture dishes of the petri dish type should be used. The bottom of the dish should be flat and should be 5 to 6 cm in diameter so that the absorbent pad for nutrient will lie flat. The glass should be borosilicate or equivalent grade. Clean culture dishes may be wrapped singly or in convenient numbers, in metal foil or a suitable paper substitute, prior to sterilization.

Glass petri dishes are preferable for use in routine laboratory analyses. The optional containers described below are recommended for field use or under other conditions not favorable for cleaning, sterilization, and reuse. *Disposable plastic dishes,* or their equivalent, may be used. Sterilization should be accomplished by exposure of the opened culture dishes to ethyl alcohol, ethylene oxide, ultraviolet radiation, or other appropriate chemical or physical agents. Choice of means of sterilization should be governed not only by convenience but also by actual tests demonstrating the effectiveness of such means of sterilization. The freedom of the culture containers from residual growth-suppressive effects resulting from the methods of sterilization must be demonstrated. After sterilization and removal of the agent of sterilization, the containers should be closed, employing sterile techniques, and stored in a dustproof container until used. Suitable sterile plastic dishes can be purchased.

1.6. *Filtration units:* The filter-holding assembly (Fig. 40) should consist of a seamless funnel which fastens to a receptacle bearing a porous plate for support of the filter membrane. The parts should be so designed that the funnel unit can be attached to the receptacle by means of a convenient locking device. The construction should be such as to insure that the membrane filter will be securely held on the porous plate of the receptacle without mechanical damage and that all the fluid will pass through the membrane in the filtration of the sample. The filter-holding assembly may be constructed of glass, porcelain, or any noncorrosive bacteriologically inert metal. It is recommended that the two parts of the assembly be wrapped separately in heavy wrapping paper for sterilization and storage until use.

For filtration the receptacle of the filter-holding assembly is mounted in a 1-liter filtering flask with a side tube, or other suitable device such that pressure differential can be drawn on the filter membrane. The filter flask should be connected by the side arm to an electric vacuum pump, filter pump operating on water pressure, hand aspirator, or other means of securing a pressure differential.

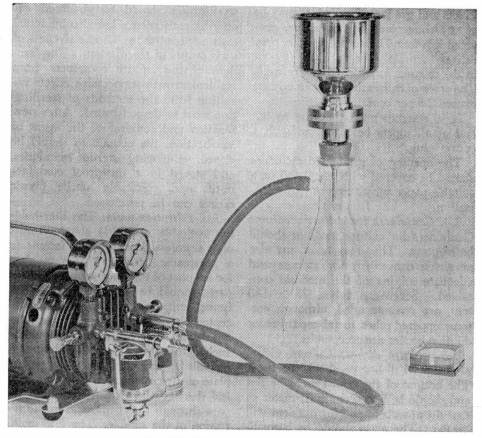

Fig. 40. Membrane filter assembly

1.7. Filter membranes: Only those filter membranes may be employed which have been found by complete laboratory tests certified by the manufacturer to provide full bacterial retention, stability in use, freedom from chemicals inimical to the growth and development of bacteria, and satisfactory speed of filtration. They should preferably be grid marked. Several different brands of membrane filters meeting these specifications can be obtained from manufacturers and suppliers of laboratory equipment.

Filter membranes must be sterilized prior to use, preferably by autoclave. The paper separators, but not the absorbent paper pads, should be removed from the packaged filters. The filters should be divided into groups of 10–12, or other convenient units, and placed in 10-cm petri dishes or wrapped in heavy wrapping paper. The membranes are then autoclaved 10 min at 121°C (15 psi). At the end of the sterilization period, the steam is allowed to escape rapidly to minimize the accumulation of water of condensation on the filters. Suitable packaged sterile filters can be purchased.

1.8. *Absorbent pads:* Absorbent pads for nutrients should be discs of filter paper or other material known to be free of agents that inhibit bacterial growth. They should be approximately 48 mm in diameter and of such thickness that they will absorb 1.8 to 2.2 ml of nutrient. The pads should be wrapped in heavy wrapping paper or packaged in 10-cm petri dishes in convenient numbers for sterilization. Sterilization in an autoclave is recommended.

1.9. *Forceps:* Forceps should be round tipped, without corrugations on the inner sides of the tips. They may be sterilized before use by dipping in 95 per cent ethyl or absolute methyl alcohol and then igniting the fluid.

1.10. *Incubators:* Facilities for incubation of membrane filter cultures must provide a temperature of $35°C \pm 0.5°C$ with constant saturated humidity.

1.11. *Microscopes:* Use of a binocular wide-field dissecting microscope giving magnification of 10 to 15 diameters is recommended for help in the differentiation and counting of colonies. Other optical devices may be acceptable, provided they permit use of a light source above and approximately perpendicular to the plane of the filter membrane.

2. Materials and Culture Media

Refer to Preparation of Culture Media, A, B, and Sec. 12 of C.

3. Samples

Samples should be collected and stored as directed previously under Samples.

4. Definition

All organisms which produce a dark colony (generally purplish-green) with a metallic sheen within 24 hr of incubation are considered members of the coliform group. The sheen may cover the entire colony or appear only in a central area or on the periphery (Fig. 41). The coliform group thus defined is not necessarily the same as that defined as the "coliform group" described in the multiple-tube fermentation technique, but it probably has the same sanitary significance, particularly if suitable studies have been made to establish the relationship between the results obtained by the filter and by the standard tube dilution procedure.

Coliform organisms may occasionally produce colonies which are not typical in color or sheen. If only atypical forms are found, their identity should be established.

5. Procedure

Generally speaking, the highest numbers, and therefore the safest assessment of the quality of drinking waters, may be obtained only by the use of an enrichment procedure. This step may be eliminated in the routine examination of drinking water where repeated determinations have shown that sufficiently adequate results are obtained by a single-step technique. Enrichment is generally not necessary in the examination of nonpotable waters or sewages.

In the following sections, methods are offered with and without enrichment, and providing for the use of the agar-based medium or the M-Endo medium without agar. It is advisable to state which method is used in the reporting of results.

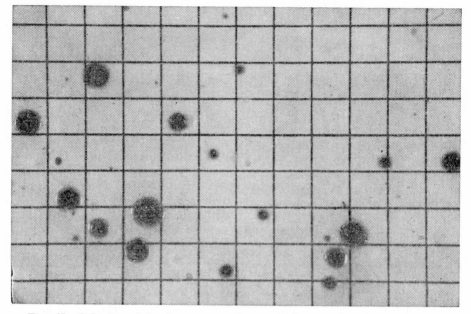

Fig. 41. Colonies of fecal streptococci on membrane filters incubated on M-enterococcus agar; 100 ml of polluted river water was filtered

5.1. *Selection of sample size:* The size of sample will be governed by the expected bacterial density; in finished-water samples it will be limited only by the degree of turbidity. An ideal quantity will result in the growth of about 50 coliform colonies and not more than 200 colonies of all types. Finished waters may be examined by the filtration of duplicate portions of the same volume, such as 100 to 500 ml or more, or by filtration of two aliquot volumes. All other waters should be examined by the filtration of three aliquot volumes depending on the expected bacterial density. When less than 20 ml is to be filtered, the portion should be diluted to a minimum volume of 30 ml before filtration.

5.2. *Filtration of sample:* Using sterile forceps, place a sterile filter over the porous plate of the apparatus, grid side up. Carefully place the matched funnel unit over the receptacle and lock it in place. The filtration is then accomplished by passing the sample through the filter under partial vacuum. The filter should be rinsed by the filtration of three volumes of 20–30 ml of sterile buffered water. Unlock and remove the funnel, and remove the filter by sterile forceps and place it on the sterile pad or agar with a rolling motion to avoid the entrapment of air.

5.3. *Preparation of culture dish:* If the agar-based medium is used, the culture dish is prepared as directed under Preparation of Culture Media, C, Media Specifications, Sec. 14. An absorbent sterile pad is placed in the larger half of the dish and saturated with approximately 1.8 ml of lauryl tryptose broth. Carefully remove any surplus liquid. The prepared filter is then placed on the pad as described above.

5.4. *Enrichment incubation:* The filters are incubated in an inverted position for 1½–2 hr at 35°C ± 0.5°C. Membrane filters should always be incubated in 100 per cent humidity.

If no enrichment is to be used, the prepared filter is placed directly on the agar and incubated for 22–24 hr.

5.5. *Transfer:* The dishes are removed from the incubator, and the filters are stripped from the pad and rolled onto the surface of the agar. Incorrect placement of the filter is at once obvious, because patches of unstained membrane indicate entrapment of air. If this appears, the filter must be carefully realigned. The used pad is left in the dish to aid in maintaining humidity.

5.6. *Final incubation:* The transferred filters are incubated for 20–22 hr at 35°C ± 0.5°C.

Alternate Method:

5.7. *Preparation of culture dish:* If the agar-based medium is not used, place a sterile absorbent pad in each culture dish, and pipet enough enrichment medium, such as lauryl tryptose broth, to saturate the pad. Remove any surplus liquid. The prepared filter is then placed on the pad as described above.

5.8. *Enrichment period:* The filters are incubated for 1½–2 hr at 35°C ± 0.5°C in an inverted position.

If no enrichment is to be used, a sterile pad is placed in the culture dish and saturated with the final M-Endo medium. The prepared filter is then placed directly on the pad and incubated for 22–24 hr at 35°C ± 0.5°C.

5.9. *Transfer:* The cultures are removed from the incubator and the tops of the dishes are removed. With sterile forceps the pad and filter are together lifted to the top of the dish. Place a new sterile pad in the bottom of the dish and saturate with the final M-Endo medium. Transfer the filter with the same precautions as above. The used pad may be discarded.

5.10. *Final incubation:* The transferred filters are incubated for 20–22 hr at 35°C ± 0.5°C.

5.11. *Counting:* All dark colonies, as described above, are counted as coliform colonies. The count is best made with the aid of a low-power (15–20 magnifications) stereomicroscope or other optical device, using a light source above and approximately perpendicular to the plane of the filter. The counting of noncoliform colonies may at times offer useful information.

6. Estimation of Coliform Density

The estimated coliform density is reported in terms of coliforms per 100 ml. The computation is made by use of the following equation:

coliform colonies/100 ml

$$= \frac{\text{coliform colonies counted} \times 100}{\text{ml sample filtered}}$$

B. *Delayed Incubation Test* (Tentative)

A proposed modification of the membrane filter technique will permit shipment of the filter pad after filtration to a distant laboratory for incubation and completion of the test. This delayed incubation test for coliform bacteria in water may be used for a coliform approximation where it is impossible to apply conventional procedures. It may be used where it is not practical to maintain the desired temperature during shipment of the sample; where the elapsed time would exceed 24 hr; in instances where it is necessary to have the sample processed in a central laboratory; or for other reasons which may prevent the analysis of the sample at or near the collection location. The applicability of the delayed incubation test for a specific water source can be determined by comparative test procedures with conventional methods. Limited data secured by the delayed incubation test have yielded consistent results in a series of samples. This gives the test promise of considerable value in the estimation of the comparative changes in pollution levels in surface waters located in remote areas from routine laboratory services.

The procedure offered for delayed incubation consists of filtration of the sample on a membrane filter in the field, placement of the filter on the holding medium, shipment to the laboratory, and completion of the coliform examination by transfer of the filter to a final medium and incubation. The holding medium contains nutrients barely sufficient to maintain bacterial life with a minimum of growth, and a mixture of inhibiting substances which have been found effective in affording an even suppression of the growth of all the members of the coliform group without interfering later with normal growth on the LES M-Endo agar which is used as a final medium.

Directions for the preparation of this holding medium and for the procedure for the examination follow. Two alternative procedures are given.

Method A

1. Materials and Culture Media

1.1. *M-Endo medium:* Prepare as described in Media Specifications, Sec. 12.

1.2. *Sodium benzoate solution:* Dissolve 12 g sodium benzoate (USP grade) in sufficient distilled water to make 100 ml. Do not autoclave this solution. Discard the solution after 3 months.

1.3. *Preservative medium:* Prepare by adding 3.2 ml sodium benzoate solution to 100 ml of M-Endo medium.

1.4. *Culture dishes:* Disposable, sterile, moisture-tight plastic petri dishes are recommended for use where samples are shipped. Such containers are low in weight and do not break in transit. In an emergency, glass petri dishes wrapped in plastic or similar material may be used. Specifications for culture dishes are described in Sec. 1.5 of *A* above.

2. Procedure

2.1. *Filtration:* Observe the same procedure and precautions as prescribed under *A* above.

2.2. *Sample preservation and shipment:* Remove the filter from the filtration unit with sterile forceps, and roll it, grid side up, on the surface of an absorbent pad saturated with preservative medium. Protect the membrane from moisture loss. Transfer the culture dish containing the membrane to a shipping container and send it to the laboratory for completion of the examination.

2.3. *Incubation:* At the laboratory,

transfer the membrane from the culture dish to a second culture dish containing an absorbent pad saturated with M-Endo medium and incubate at 35°C for 20 ± 2 hr as directed under *A* above. (A fresh culture dish is used in this step to avoid any residues of sodium benzoate.)

2.4. *Counting:* Count typical colonies as directed under Sec. 5.5 of *A* above.

3. Estimation of Coliform Density

Proceed as under Sec. 6 of *A* above. Record times of collection, filtration, and laboratory examination, and calculate the elapsed time.

Method B

1. Materials and Culture Media

1.1. *LES MF Holding Medium— Coliform:* Prepare as in Media Specifications, Sec. 13. No heating is necessary. Final pH 7.1 ± 0.1.

1.2. *Culture dishes:* Disposable, sterile, moisture-tight plastic petri dishes (50 × 12 mm) are recommended. Such containers are low in weight and do not break in transit.

2. Procedure

2.1. *Filtration:* The membrane filter is prepared in the same fashion as when used for immediate incubation.

2.2. *Sample preservation and shipment:* Place an absorbent pad in the petri dish and saturate with LES MF coliform holding medium; 2 ml are sufficient to saturate most absorbent pads. Permit the pad and medium to stand for a few minutes before pouring off the excess. Remove the membrane filter from the filtration unit with sterile forceps, and roll it, grid side up,

onto the surface of the saturated pad. The humidity is preserved by the tight closure afforded by the plastic petri dish. The culture dish is then transferred to a shipping container and sent to the laboratory for completion of the examination procedure. The sender must use discretion at this step of the procedure, in order to assure that during the first hours of storage the membrane is not exposed to extreme cold or excessively hot temperature conditions.

2.2. *Incubation:* At the laboratory, the membrane filter is transferred from the holding environment to LES Endo agar (growth and indicator medium). At the time of transfer, if distinct colony formation is observed on the membrane surface without the aid of magnification, it is recommended that the transfer be made and the petri dish then refrigerated until late in the day, when it is incubated at 35°C for a 16-hr period. All other membranes after transfer are incubated for 20 hr. This manipulation of the incubation time will permit the bacteriologist to exert a measure of control on the problems of overgrowth and the dissipation of sheen that interfere with coliform colony count.

2.4. *Counting:* All dark colonies having a metallic-appearing surface luster are counted as coliform colonies. The counts are made with the aid of a low-power (10–15 magnification) microscope or other suitable optical device, using a light source above and approximately perpendicular to the plane of the filter membrane.

Bibliography

1. CLARK, H. F., ET AL. The Membrane Filter in Sanitary Bacteriology. *Public Health Repts.* 66:951 (1951).

2. GOETZ, A. & TSUNEISHI, N. Application of Molecular Filter Membranes to Bacteriological Analysis of Water. *J. AWWA* 43:943 (1951).

3. VELS, C. J. Graphical Approach to Statistics. IV. Evaluation of Bacterial Density. *Water & Sewage Works* 98:66 (1951).

4. TASK GROUP REPORT. Technique of Bacterial Examination of Water. *J. AWWA* 45:1196 (1953).

5. TAYLOR, E. W.; BURMAN, N. P.; & OLIVER, C. W. Use of the Membrane Filter in the Bacteriological Examination of Water. *J. Appl. Chem.* (London) 3:233 (1953).

6. KABLER, P. W. Water Examinations by Membrane Filter and MPN Procedures. *A.J.P.H.* 44:379 (1954).

7. GELDREICH, E. E., ET AL. A Delayed Incubation Membrane Filter Test for Coliform Bacteria in Water. *A.J.P.H.* 45:1462 (1955).

8. THOMAS, H. A. & WOODWARD, R. L. Use of Molecular Filter Membranes for Water Potability Control. *J. AWWA* 48:1391 (1956).

9. CLARKE, N. F.; KABLER, P. W.; & GELDREICH, E. E. Advantages and Limitations of the Membrane Filter Procedure. *Water & Sewage Works* 104:385 (1957).

10. FIFIELD, C. W. & SCHAUFUS, C. P. Improved Membrane Filter Medium for the Detection of Coliform Organisms. *J. AWWA* 50:193 (1958).

11. McCARTHY, J. A. & DELANEY, J. E. Membrane Filter Media Studies. *Water & Sewage Works* 105:292 (1958).

12. McCARTHY, J. A.; DELANEY, J. E.; & GRASSO, R. J. Measuring Coliforms in Water. *Water & Sewage Works* 108:238 (1961).

Test for Presence of Fecal Streptococcal Group *(Tentative)*

The terms "fecal streptococcus" and "enterococcus" have been used somewhat synonymously by many authors in recent years and there have been varying opinions as to what species, varieties or biotypes of streptococci are included when these terms are employed.

On the basis of newer concepts of speciation of the fecal streptococci it is suggested that the terms "fecal streptococcus," and "Lancefield's group D Streptococcus" be considered as synonymous and that the use of these terms be restricted to denote the following species or their varieties used as indicators of fecal contamination: *S. faecalis, S. faecalis* var. *liquefaciens, S. faecalis* var. *zymogenes, S. durans, S. faecium, S. bovis,* and *S. equinus.* Other varieties or biotypes of *S. faecalis* and *S. faecium* have been reported, but their nomenclature and taxonomic position in the fecal streptococcal group must await further investigation.

The streptococci in the fecal streptococcal group are indicators of fecal pollution of water, inasmuch as the normal habitat of these organisms is generally the intestine of man and animals. Therefore, fecal streptococcal determinations may be of particular value for stream pollution surveys, and for determining the sanitary quality of waters from shallow lakes, bathing areas, and wells. Because recent studies indicate that streptococci similar to organisms in the fecal streptococcal group may be found on certain plants or plant products, wastes from food processing industries discharged into a body of water might be the source of some of these bacteria.

The membrane filter technique or the multiple-tube technique may be used for the fecal streptococcal determinations. The membrane filter tech-nique affords direct counts of fecal streptococci, is easy to perform, and is efficient for most types of water samples.

A. Membrane Filter Technique

1. Laboratory Apparatus

Refer to membrane filter assembly and laboratory apparatus under Tests for Presence of Members of Coliform Group by Membrane Filter Tech-niques, A, Standard Test, Sec. 1.

2. Materials and Culture Media

2.1. *Filters:* Because the filters are incubated on an agar medium, they can be purchased without the absorbent pads. If thin paper separates the filter, stack in desired numbers, place an ab-sorbent pad on each end of the stack, wrap tightly in suitable paper, and sterilize by autoclaving at 121°C for 10 min. At end of sterilization period, allow steam to escape rapidly to mini-mize accumulation of water of conden-sation on filters.

2.2. *Culture medium (M-enterococcus agar):* Refer to Preparation of Cul-ture Media A, B, and C, Sec. 12.

3. Procedure

3.1. Pour approximately 10 ml M-enterococcus agar into 60-mm petri plates; flame the surface, if necessary, to eliminate bubbles.

3.2. Filter samples of water through the sterile membrane to attain 40 to 100 colonies on the membrane surface. Amounts varying from 100 to 10, 1, 0.1, or 0.01 ml may be necessary, depending on the amount of pollution in the water sample (refer to Membrane Filter Coli-form Tests, A, Sec. 5.1). Transfer the filter directly to the agar medium in the petri plates, avoiding air bubbles. In-vert and incubate at 35°C ± 0.5°C for 48 hr under normal conditions of hu-midity.

3.3. Count all red and pink colonies with stereomicroscope magnifying 10X. Express as number of fecal streptococci per 100 ml of water.

4. Confirmed Test

In the examination of samples of water from sources other than swim-ming pools, results reported to date indicate that practically 100 per cent of the red and pink colonies that grow on filters placed on the M-enterococcus agar are fecal streptococci. If further confirmation is indicated:

(a) Fish selected typical colonies from membrane, inoculate into brain-heart infusion broth or tryptose glucose broth and into brain-heart infusion agar slant. Incubate at 35° ± 0.5°C for 24–48 hr. If growth is detected, continue as in (b) and (c).

(b) Subculture from tube showing growth into either brain-heart infusion broth or tryptose glucose broth, incu-bate at 45°C for 48 hr, and note growth results.

(c) Transfer a loopful of growth from the brain-heart infusion agar slant to a clean glass slide and add a few drops of freshly tested hydrogen peroxide to the smear. The absence of bubbles constitutes a negative catalase test indicating a probable streptococcus culture and confirmation should be continued as stated in the following paragraphs. The presence of bubbles constitutes a positive cata-

lase test which indicates the presence of non-streptococci species and confirmation need not be continued.

(d) Growth at 45°C in 40 per cent bile broth constitutes a positive test for fecal streptococci.

References in the bibliography should be consulted if further confirmatory tests are desired.

B. Multiple-Tube Technique

1. Presumptive Test

1.1. *Procedure:*

a. Inoculate a series of tubes of azide dextrose broth with appropriate graduated quantities of the water to be tested. Use 10 ml of single-strength broth for inocula of 1 ml or less, and 10 ml of double-strength broth for 10-ml inocula. The portions of the water sample used will necessarily vary in size and number with the character of the water and should be decimal multiples of 1 ml. Refer to the section on tests for the presence of members of the coliform group for suggestions concerning amounts of inocula, in order to have some negative tubes in the higher dilution.

b. Incubate inoculated tubes at 35°C ± 0.5°C. Examine each tube at the end of 24 ± 2 hr for the presence of turbidity. If no definite turbidity is present, reincubate and read again at the end of 48 ± 3 hr.

2. Confirmed Test

All azide dextrose broth tubes showing turbidity after 24- or 48-hr incubation must be subjected to the Confirmed Test.

2.1. *Procedure:*

a. Transfer 3 loopfuls of growth from each azide dextrose broth tube to a tube containing 10 ml ethyl violet azide broth. The wire loop should have a minimum diameter of 3 mm.

b. Incubate the inoculated tubes for 48 hr at 35°C ± 0.5°C. The presence of enterococci is indicated by the formation of a purple button at the bottom of the tube, or occasionally by a dense turbidity.

3. Computing and Recording of MPN

Refer to Tables 36–41 and to the section on estimation of coliform group density.

Bibliography

1. SHERMAN, J. M.   The Streptococci. *Bacteriol. Rev.* 1:3 (1937).
2. SKAUDHAUGE, K. *Studies on Enterococci with Special Reference to the Serological Properties.* Einar Munksgaards, Copenhagen (1950).
3. MALLMANN, W. L. & SELIGMANN, E. B. A Comparative Study of Media for the Detection of Streptococci in Water and Sewage. *A.J.P.H.* 40:286 (1950).
4. LITSKY, W.; MALLMANN, W. L.; & FIFIELD, C. W. A New Medium for

the Detection of Enterococci in Water. *A.J.P.H.* 43:873 (1953).

5. LITSKY, W.; MALLMANN, W. L.; & FIFIELD, C. W. Comparison of the Most Probable Number of *Echerichia coli* and Enterococci in River Waters. *A.J.P.H.* 45:1049 (1955).

6. SHATTOCK, P. M. F. The Identification and Classification of *Streptococcus faecalis* and Some Associated Streptococci. *Ann. Inst. Past.*, Lille, 7:95–100 (1955).

7. COOPER, K. E. & RAMADAN, F. M. Studies in the Differentiation Between Human and Animal Pollution by Means of Faecal Streptococci. *J. Gen. Microbiol.* 12:180 (1955).

8. LAKE, D. E.; DIEBEL, R. H.; & NIVEN, C. F., JR. The Identity of *Streptococcus faecium*. *Bacteriol. Proc.* p. 13 (1957).

9. BARNES, E. M. Reduction as a Means of Differentiating *Streptococcus faecalis* from *Streptococcus faecium*. *J. Gen. Microbiol.* 14:57 (1957).

10. SLANETZ, L. W. & BARTLEY, C. H. Numbers of Enterococci in Water, Sewage, and Feces Determined by the Membrane Filter Technique with An Improved Medium. *J. Bacteriol.* 74:591 (1957).

11. BREED, R. S., ET AL., ed. *Bergey's Manual of Determinative Bacteriology.* Williams and Wilkins Co., Baltimore (7th ed. 1957).

12. MORELIS, P. & COLOBERT, L. Un milieu Selectif Permettant l' Identification et le Denombrement Rapides de *Streptococcus faecalis*. *Ann. Ins. Past.* 95:667 (1958).

13. SUREAU, P. Isolation and Enumeration of Faecal Streptococci in Waters by Means of Filtering Membranes. *Ann. Inst. Past.* 95:6 (1958).

14. MEDREK, T. F. & LITSKY, W. Comparative Incidence of Coliform Bacteria and Enterococci in Undisturbed Soil. *Appl. Microbiol.* 8:60 (1959).

15. CROFT, C. C. A Comparative Study of Media for Detection of Enterococci in Water. *A.J.P.H.* 49:1379 (1959).

16. BARTLEY, C. H. & SLANETZ, L. W. Types and Sanitary Significance of Fecal Streptococci Isolated from Feces, Sewage and Water. *A.J.P.H.* 50:1545 (1960).

17. KENNER, B. A.; CLARK, H. F.; & KABLER, P. W. Fecal Streptococci. II. Quantification of Streptococci in Feces. *A.J.P.H.* 50:1553 (1960).

18. NIVEN, C. F., JR. Microbial Indices of Food Quality: Fecal Streptococci. *Proc. of Conf. on Microbiological Quality of Foods,* Academic Press (1963).

19. SHATTOCK, P. M. F. *Enterococci: Chemical and Biological Hazards in Food.* Iowa University Press. p. 303 (1963).

20. MUNDT, J. C. Occurrence of Enterococci on Plants in a Wild Environment. *Appl. Microbiol.* 11:141 (1963).

Differentiation of Coliform Group of Organisms *(Tentative)*

The methods previously given for the detection and estimation of the coliform group of bacteria provide full information on the pollution and sanitary quality of the water supply under examination. Differentiation of the fecal coliform organisms as a group has been de-scribed in the previous test procedure.

Occasionally, it is of value to differentiate the coliform strains and identify them according to genera and species for research or special study purposes. Tentative methods for such differentiation are presented.

A. Culture Purification

It is well known that the accuracy of the completed test and differential tests is at times impaired by failure to purify cultures. It is essential that a pure culture be obtained. This may be accomplished by streaking the culture obtained from the completed lactose broth tube to an eosin methylene blue agar plate, which is then incubated at 35°C for 24 hr. A single, well-isolated colony fished to an agar slant is incubated at 35° ± 0.5°C for 24 hr and a Gram stain is made to confirm the presence of Gram-negative, nonspore-forming rods.

Variation in organisms of the coliform group, particularly the "unstable" variation characteristic of the *mutabile* type, is occasionally encountered. It is advisable, therefore, when attempting purification of cultures, to be on the lookout for this phenomenon. An apparent mixture of organisms may, in reality, consist of a single strain that is showing variation. However, persistent ± reactions may very well indicate inadequate purification of the culture.

B. Differential Tests

The differentiation of the coliform group into the *E. coli, A. aerogenes,* and *E. freundii* (or intermediate) species has been carried out on the basis of the results of four tests (indole, methyl red, Voges-Proskauer, and sodium citrate) often referred to collectively as the "IMViC tests." These tests are tentatively recommended for differential determination. If further tests are added to these, the real and apparent variety of strains within the coliform group may be correspondingly increased, as has been done in the classical systems of MacConkey,[14, 15] Clemesha,[16] and Levine.[23] Although such complete differentiation may be desirable from a research standpoint, it does not appear to be warranted in routine water work.

A simplified grouping of the reaction combinations is given in Table 42.

The significance of finding various types of coliform organisms in water samples has been and still is a subject

TABLE 42—INTERPRETATION OF IMViC
REACTIONS

Organism	Indole	Methyl Red	Voges-Proskauer	Citrate
Escherichia coli				
Variety I	+	+	−	−
Variety II	−	+	−	−
Escherichia freundii (Intermediates)				
Variety I	−	+	−	±
Variety II	+	+	−	+
Aerobacter aerogenes				
Variety I	−	−	+	±
Variety II	±	−	+	+

of considerable study. It must be remembered that all types of coliform organisms may occur in feces. Although *E. coli* will nearly always be found in fresh pollution derived from several sources, some other type or types of coliform organisms, not accompanied by *E. coli,* may occasionally be found in fresh pollution from a particular source.

On the other hand, there is little or no evidence that coliform bacteria multiply on fresh grasses or grains; nor is there evidence that they multiply in soil. Consequently, it is at least debatable whether grasses, grains, and soils can be considered normal habitats of any of the coliform organisms. Much more study of a quantitative character is needed before the practical value of routine differentiation in the coliform group can be demonstrated.

It is well to keep in mind, however, the possibility of occasional multiplication of coliform organisms on leather washers, wood, swimming pool ropes, or jute packing, as well as in slime formation in pipes. In fact, differentiation of coliform types finds one of its most practical applications in the study of unexpected coliform densities that may be explained by multiplication on or in organic materials. The presence of a large number of coliform organisms of the same type in water from a well or spring, or from a single tap on a distribution system, for example, is very suggestive of such multiplication.

1. Indole Test

1.1. *Reagents:*

a. Medium: Use tryptophane broth as described under Preparation of Culture Media, C, Media Specifications, Sec. 18.

b. Test reagent: Dissolve 5 g paradimethylaminobenzaldehyde in 75 ml isoamyl (or normal amyl) alcohol, ACS grade, and add 25 ml conc HCl. The reagent should be yellow. Some brands of paradimethylaminobenzaldehyde are not satisfactory, and some good brands become unsatisfactory on aging.

The amyl alcohol solution should have a pH value less than 6.0. Both amyl alcohol and benzaldehyde compound should be purchased in as small amounts as consistent with the volume of work to be done.

1.2. *Procedure:* Inoculate 5-ml portions of medium from a pure culture and incubate at $35° \pm 0.5°C$ for 24 ± 2 hr. Add 0.2–0.3 ml test reagent and shake. Let the tube stand for about 10 min and observe the results.

A dark red color in the amyl alcohol surface layer constitutes a positive indole test; the original color of the reagent, a negative test. An orange color probably indicates the presence of skatole and may be reported as a $\pm$ reaction.

2. Methyl Red Test

2.1. *Reagents:*

a. Medium: Use buffered glucose broth as described under Preparation of Culture Media, C, Media Specifications, Sec. 19.

b. Indicator solution: Dissolve 0.1 g methyl red in 300 ml alcohol and dilute to 500 ml with distilled water.

2.2. *Procedure:* Inoculate 10-ml portions of medium from a pure culture. Incubate at 35°C for 5 days. To 5 ml of the culture add 5 drops methyl red indicator solution.

Record a distinct red color as methyl red positive and a distinct yellow color as methyl red negative. A mixed shade should be recorded as questionable and possibly indicative of incomplete culture purification.

3. Voges-Proskauer Test

3.1. *Reagents:*

a. Media: This test may be carried out using the medium as described for the methyl red differential test or if desired, an alternative salt peptone glucose medium may be used as described under Preparation of Culture Media, C, Media Specifications, Sec. 20.

b. Naphthol solution: Dissolve 5 g purified *a*-naphthol (melting point 92.5°C or higher) in 100 ml absolute alcohol. This solution should be prepared fresh each day.

c. Potassium hydroxide solution: Dissolve 40 g KOH in 100 ml distilled water.

3.2. *Procedure:* Inoculate 5 ml of either culture medium and incubate at 35°C for 48 hr. To 1 ml of culture add 0.6 ml naphthol solution and 0.2 ml KOH solution. Development of a pink to crimson color in the mixture from 2 to 4 hr after adding the reagents constitutes a positive test. Results should not be read after this period of time.

4. Sodium Citrate Test

4.1. *Reagents:*

a. Medium: Use either Koser's citrate broth as described under Preparation of Culture Media, C, Media Specifications, Sec. 21, or Simmon's citrate agar as described under the same heading, Sec. 22.

4.2. *Procedure:*

a. Inoculation into the liquid medium may be made only with a straight needle and a light inoculum should be made. A pipet should never be used, because of the danger of invalidating

the result by introduction of nutrient material with the transfer. Incubate at 35° ± 0.5°C for 72 to 96 hr. Record visible growth as positive, no growth as negative.

b. Inoculate the agar medium with a straight needle, using both a stab and a streak. Incubate 48 hr at 35° ± 0.5°C. Growth on the medium with (usually) a blue color is a positive reaction; the absence of growth is recorded as negative.

Bibliography

Broths

1. DOMINICK, J. F. & LAUTER, C. J. Methylene Blue and Brom Cresol Purple in Differentiating Bacteria of the Colon-Aerogenes Group. *J. AWWA* 21:1067 (1929).
2. SALLE, A. J. A System for the Bacteriological Examination of Water. *J. Bacteriol.* 20:381 (1930).
3. RITTER, C. The Presumptive Test in Water Analysis. *J. AWWA* 24:413 (1932).
4. PERRY, C. A. & HAJNA, A. A. A Modified Eijkman Medium. *J. Bacteriol.* 26:419 (1933).
5. HAJNA, A. A. & PERRY, C. A. A Comparison of the Eijkman Test With Other Tests for Determining *E. coli.* *J. Bacteriol.* 30:479 (1935).
6. HAJNA, A. A. & PERRY, C. A. Comparative Study of Presumptive and Confirmative Media for Bacteria of the Coliform Group and for Fecal Streptococci. *A.J.P.H.* 33:550 (1943).
7. PERRY, C. A. & HAJNA, A. A. Further Evaluation of EC Medium for the Isolation of Coliform Bacteria and *Escherichia coli.* *A.J.P.H.* 34:735 (1944).

Agars

8. MACCONKEY, A. T. Bile Salt Media and Their Advantages. *J. Hyg.* 8:322 (1908).
9. Ref. 2.
10. TONNEY, F. O. & NOBLE, R. E. The Interpretation of Direct Differential Counts of Colon-Aerogenes Organisms in Well Waters. *J. Bacteriol.* 23:473 (1932).

11. NOBLE, R. E. & TONNEY, F. O. A Solid Brilliant Green Lactose Bile Medium for Direct Plating. *J. AWWA* 27:108 (1935).

12. SCHULHOFF, H. B. & HEUKELEKIAN, H. A Direct Plating Method for the Determination of the Potability of Water. *J. AWWA* 28:1963 (1936).

Differential Tests

13. EIJKMAN, C. Die Garungsprobe bei 46 C. als Hilfsmittel bei der Trinkwasseruntersuchung. *Zentr. Bakteriol. Parasitenk., I., Orig.* 37:742 (1904).

14. MacCONKEY, A. Lactose-Fermenting Bacteria in Feces. *J. Hyg.* 5:333 (1905).

15. MacCONKEY, A. Further Observations on the Differentiation of Lactose-Fermenting Bacteria with Special Reference to Those of Intestinal Origin. *J. Hyg.* 5:86 (1909).

16. CLEMESHA, W. W. *The Bacteriology of Surface Waters in the Tropics.* Thacker, Spink & Co., Calcutta & London (1912).

17. ROGERS, L. A.; CLARK, W. M.; & DAVIS, B. J. The Colon Group of Bacteria. *J. Infectious Diseases* 14:411 (1914).

18. ROGERS, L. A.; CLARK, W. M.; & EVANS, A. C. The Characteristics of Bacteria of the Colon Type Found in Bovine Feces. *J. Infectious Diseases* 15:99 (1915).

19. ROGERS, L. A.; CLARK, W. M.; & EVANS, A. C. The Characteristics of Bacteria of the Colon Type Occurring on Grains. *J. Infectious Diseases* 17:137 (1915).

20. CLARK, W. M. The Final Hydrogen Ion Concentrations of Cultures of *Bacillus coli*. *Science* 42:71 (1915).

21. CLARK, W. M. & LUBS, W. A. The Differentiation of Bacteria of the Colon-Aerogenes Family by the Use of Indicators. *J. Infectious Diseases* 17:160 (1915).

22. LEVINE, M. On the Significance of the Voges-Proskauer Reaction. *J. Bacteriol.* 1:153 (1916).

23. LEVINE, M. Notes on *Bact. coli and Bact. aerogenes. A.J.P.H.* 11:21 (1921).

24. LEVINE, M. Bacteria Fermenting Lactose and Their Significance in Water Analysis. *Iowa State Coll. Agr. Mech. Arts Bull.* 62:117 (1921).

25. KOSER, S. A. Correlation of Citrate Utilization by Members of the Colon-Aerogenes Group with Other Differential Characteristics and with Habitat. *J. Bacteriol.* 9:59 (1924).

26. KOSER, S. A. Differential Tests for Colon-Aerogenes Group in Relation to Sanitary Quality of Water. *J. Infectious Diseases* 35:14 (1924).

27. MELLON, R. R. Studies in Microbic Heredity. II. The Sexual Cycle of *B. coli* in Relation to the Origin of Variants with Special Reference to Neisser and Massini's *B. coli mutabile*. *J. Bacteriol.* 10:579 (1925).

28. KOSER, S. A. Cellobiose Fermentation by the Coli-Aerogenes Group. *J. Infectious Diseases* 38:505 (1926).

29. SIMMONS, J. S. A Culture Medium for Differentiating Organisms of Typhoid-Colon-Aerogenes Groups and for Isolation of Certain Fungi. *J. Infectious Diseases* 39:209 (1926).

30. KOVACS, N. A Simplified Method for Detecting Indol Formation by Bacteria. *Z. Immunitatsforsch.* 56:311 (1928); *Chem. Abs.* 22:3425 (1928).

31. GREER, F. E., ET AL. The Sanitary Significance of Lactose-Fermenting Organisms Not Belonging to the *B. coli* Group. *J. Infectious Diseases* 42:556 (1928).

32. RUCHHOFT, C. C., ET AL. Coli-Aerogenes Differentiation in Water Analysis. *J. Bacteriol.* 21:407 (1930); 22:125 (1931).

33. PERRY, C. A. & HAJNA, A. A. A Modified Eijkman Medium. *J. Bacteriol.* 26:419 (1933).

34. EPSTEIN, S. S. & VAUGHN, R. H. Differential Reactions in the Coli Group of Bacteria. *A.J.P.H.* 24:505 (1934).

35. HAJNA, A. A. & PERRY, C. A. A Comparison of the Eijkman Test with Other Tests for Determining *E. coli*. *J. Bacteriol.* 30:479 (1935).

36. LEVINE, M. Effect of Temperature and Boric Acid on Gas Production in the Colon Group. *J. Bacteriol.* 29:24 (1935).

37. VAUGHN, R. H. Selectivity of Boric Acid Media in the Colon Group. *Iowa State Coll. J. Sci.* 10:103 (1935).

38. EDSON, F. G. & WITT, N. F. A Study of Boric Acid-Bile Medium for Water Analysis. *Univ. Colo. Studies* 23:281 (1936).

39. BARTRAM, M. T. & BLACK, L. A. Reaction of *Escherichia, Aerobacter,* and *Citrobacter* Strains in Boric Acid and Hexamine Media. *J. Bacteriol.* 31:24 (1936).

40. BARRITT, M. W. The Intensification of the Voges-Proskauer Reaction by the Addition of Alpha-Naphthol. *J. Pathol. Bacteriol.* 42:441 (1936).

41. PARR, L. W. Viability of Coli-Aerogenes Organisms in Culture and in Various Environments. *J. Infectious Diseases* 60:291 (1937).

42. FOOTE, H. B. The Possible Effects of Wild Animals on the Bacterial Pollution of Water. *J. AWWA* 24:72 (1937).

43. STUART, C. A.; GRIFFIN, A. M.; & BAKER, M. E. Relationships of Coliform Organisms. *J. Bacteriol.* 36:391 (1938).

44. *The Bacteriological Examination of Water Supplies.* Public Health Rept. 71, Ministry of Health of Great Britain, London (revised 1939).

45. PARR, L. W. Coliform Bacteria. *Bacteriol. Rev.* 3:1 (1939).

46. VAUGHN, R.; MITCHELL, N. B.; & LEVINE, M. The Voges-Proskauer and Methyl Red Reactions in the Coli-Aerogenes Group. *J. AWWA* 31:993 (1939).

47. HAJNA, A. A. & PERRY, C. A. Optimum Temperature for Differentiation of *Escherichia coli* from Other Coliform Bacteria. *J. Bacteriol.* 38:275 (1939).

48. McCRADY, M. H. Slow Lactose Fermenters in Water Analysis. *A.J.P.H.* 29:261 (1939).

49. STUART, C. A.; MICKLE, F. L.; & BORMAN, E. K. Suggested Grouping of Slow Lactose-Fermenting Organisms. *A.J.P.H.* 30:499 (1940).

50. LEVINE, M. Determination and Characterization of Coliform Bacteria from Chlorinated Waters. *A.J.P.H.* 31:351 (1941).

51. BORMAN, E. K.; ROBINTON, E. D.; & STUART, C. A. A Study of Standard Methods for the Detection of Coliform Organisms in Raw and Treated Waters. *A.J.P.H.* 31:557 (1941).

52. STUART, C. A., ET AL. Eijkman Relationships of the Coliform and Related Bacteria. *J. Bacteriol.* 43:447 (1942).

53. PARR, L. W. & FRIEDLANDER, H. Studies on Aberrant Coliform Bacteria. *A.J.P.H.* 32:381 (1942).

54. STUART, C. A., ET AL. Biochemical and Antigenic Relationships of the Paracolon Bacteria. *J. Bacteriol.* 45:101 (1943).

55. BORMAN, E. K.; STUART, C. A.; & WHEELER, K. M. Taxonomy of the Family Enterobacteriaceae. *J. Bacteriol.* 48:351 (1944).

56. WOLFORD, E. R. & BERRY, J. A. Condition of Oranges as Affecting Bacterial Content of Frozen Juice with Emphasis on Coliform Organisms. *Food Research* 13:172 (1948).

57. POE, C. F. & CHARKEY, L. W. A Study of Boric Acid Media for the Separation of *Escherichia* and *Aerobacter*. *J. Bacteriol.* 57:386 (1948).

58. BEISEL, C. G. & TROY, V. S. The Vaughn-Levine Boric Acid Medium as a Screening Presumptive Test in the Examination of Frozen Concentrated Orange Juice. *Fruit Prods. J.* 28:356 (1949).

59. VAUGHN, R. H.; LEVINE, M.; & SMITH, H. A. A Buffered Boric Acid Lactose Medium for Enrichment and Presumptive Identification of *Escherichia coli.* *Food Research* 16:10 (1951).

60. LEVINE, M., ET AL. Simultaneous Determination of Coliform and *Escherichia coli* Indices. *Appl. Microbiol.* 3:310 (1955).

61. CLARK, H. F., ET AL. The Coliform Group. I. The Boric Acid Lactose Broth Reaction of Coliform IMViC Types. *Appl. Microbiol.* 5:396 (1957).

62. LEVINE, M. & MINETTE, H. P. Observations on Procedures and Media for Expediting Detection of *Escherichia coli* in Water. *Bacteriol. Proc. Soc. Am. Bacteriologists* p. 32 (1958).

63. GELDREICH, E. E., ET AL. The Coliform Group. II. Reactions in EC Medium at 45°C. *Appl. Microbiol.* 6:347 (1958).

Test for Presence of Enteric Viruses in
Water and Wastewater

Routine examination of water and wastewater for enteric viruses is not practical at the present time. The term "enteric virus," as used herein, includes all viruses known to be excreted in quantity in the feces of man. The group includes the Polioviruses, the Coxsackie viruses, the ECHO (enteric cytopathogenic human orphan) viruses, the adenoviruses, and the virus(es) of infectious hepatitis. The total number of such viruses approaches 100, with new types being discovered continually.

The enteric virus group, in the broadest sense, could be utilized as indicators of fecal pollution, inasmuch as most of them appear to be infectious only for humans and are excreted in feces. However, it must be recognized that although nearly everyone discharges coliform bacteria and streptococci in feces, excretion of enteric viruses by apparently healthy persons is largely confined to individuals under 15 years of age. It has been calculated that the relative enteric virus density to coliform density in sewage is about 1 to 65,000,[1] a ratio which makes coliform detection considerably easier than virus detection. Thus, viruses cannot at present be used as a measure of water quality, because it is possible to have fecal pollution, with associated enteric pathogenic bacteria, in the absence of viruses. However, it is also possible to have viral agents present in the absence of bacterial indicators of pollution, inasmuch as viruses and bacteria react differently to various changes in their environment.[1, 2]

Because all of the enteric viruses are discharged in quantity in the feces of infected individuals, there is obvious opportunity for these agents to contaminate water sources. The detection of these agents in sewage or water thus becomes a matter of importance and a number of techniques have been devised for this purpose. All of these techniques have been developed with the primary objective of concentrating the viruses in sewage or water to a point where they can be detected without testing impossibly large sample volumes. It is now well documented[3, 4, 5] that the "swab" technique of sample collection is superior to the "grab sample" technique. Further concentration of the liquid expressed from the gauze swab is desirable. This can be accomplished by the resin or ultracentrifuge method.[4] Available information indicates that the ultracentrifuge method is superior and yields a higher percentage of positive samples.

The examination of sewage or water for enteric viruses is still largely limited to specific research problems. Although it is relatively easy to obtain positive isolations from sewage, particularly during late summer and early fall, it is usually difficult to detect viruses in surface waters because of the dilution afforded any entering sewage. Detection of virus in these waters must await improved methods of concentrating small numbers of viruses from relatively large volumes of water.

The sanitary and epidemiological significance of enteric viruses in water and sewage is unknown. The mere presence of a viral agent in sewage does not necessarily mean that a significant health hazard is present. A problem might be created only when the density of such agents became high enough for some to survive whatever treatment might be applied to the sewage, so that large numbers of viable organisms entered the receiving waters. These agents may gain access to the water supply of a community and, if they survive the treatment process, initiate an epidemic such as occurred with the virus of infectious hepatitis.[6] From an epidemiological viewpoint, the qualitative demonstration of viruses in sewage could partially indicate the type of infection present in the community, not only in an epidemic, but also in a surveillance program.[7]

Enteric viruses have not been demonstrated in treated urban water in the United States, either because they are not present or because current techniques are not sufficiently efficient to detect them. Epidemiological evidence also indicates that fully treated water is not now an important vehicle in the transmission of these agents. Increasing reuse of water may change this situation in the future.

Bibliography

1. MELNICK, J. L.; EMMONS, J.; OPTON E. M.; & COFFEY, J. H. Coxsackie Viruses from Sewage: Methodology, Including an Evaluation of the Grab Sample and Gauze Pad Collection Procedures. *Am. J. Hyg.* 59:185 (1954).
2. KELLEY, S. M.; CLARK, M. E.; & COLEMAN, M. B. Demonstration of Infectious Agents in Sewage. *A.J.P.H.* 45:1438 (1955).
3. CLARKE, N. A.; STEVENSON, R. E.; & KABLER, P. W. Survival of Coxsackie Virus in Water and Sewage. *J. AWWA* 48:677 (1956).
4. CLARKE, N. A. & CHANG, S. L. Enteric Viruses in Water. *J. AWWA* 51:1299 (1959).
5. GRAVELLE, C. R. & CHIN, T. D. Enterovirus Isolations from Sewage: A Comparison of Three Methods. *J. Inf. Diseases* 109:205 (1961).
6. WILEY, J. S.; CHIN, T. D.; GRAVELLE, C. R.; & ROBINSON, S. Enterovirus in Sewage During a Poliomyelitis Epidemic. *J. W.P.C.F.* 34:168 (1962).
7. CLARKE, N. A.; BERG, G.; KABLER, P. W.; & CHANG, S. L. Human Enteric Viruses in Water: Source, Survival and Removability (To be published).

PART VIII

Methods for Detection and Isolation of Iron and Sulfur Bacteria

Introduction

The tenth edition of this manual contained a tentative section dealing with so-called nuisance bacteria. These included slime-forming, iron, sulfur, and sulfate-reducing bacteria. Some of these organisms are important in water treatment and distribution systems, and may be especially bothersome in industrial use, as in cooling and boiler water. They may cause odor, taste, frothing, color, increases in turbidity, and tuberculation in pipe. (This last is partly instrumental in causing a decrease in carrying capacity, although today it appears that corrosion and deposition are more due to physicochemical phenomena than to iron bacteria.) Their food supply may be wholly or partly inorganic and they may extract it, if attached or in a gelatinous substrate, from a low concentration in flowing water. This seems quite important in the case of sulfur bacteria using small amounts of hydrogen sulfide. Temperature, light, pH, and oxygen supply all affect the growth of these organisms in some way.

The term "slime-forming organisms" may well be omitted from this section, for a double reason. Some of them, species of *Sphaerotilus* for example, are related to either the sulfur or the iron bacteria. Actually, the term "bacterial slimes," which seems to be gaining in popularity, is used to denote a mixture of bacteria, other organisms, and debris, the bacteria and fungi being attached filamentous forms. However, if by slime-forming is meant a secretion of mucilaginous or viscous material, then a very heterogenous group of bacteria is incriminated, much more widely classified than the group included here. One of the worst offenders is a bacillus active in the formation of dextran, or a similar substance, in the industrial treatment of citrus wastes. The iron bacteria especially are noticeable in this regard. Therefore, it seems appropriate to deal only with the iron and sulfur bacteria in this section.

Iron Bacteria

1. General Characteristics

"Iron bacteria" are considered to be capable of withdrawing iron present in their aqueous habitat, and of depositing it in the form of hydrated ferric hydroxide on or in the mucilaginous secretions. A somewhat similar mechanism exists for bacteria using manganese. The large amount of brown slime so produced will impart a reddish tinge and an unpleasant odor to drinking water and may render the supply unsuitable for domestic or industrial purposes. Included in undesirable effects may be pitting and tuberculation of bacterial origin. Bacteria of this type, to obtain energy, oxidize ferrous to ferric iron, which is precipitated as ferric hydrate. In water mains the frictional loss is greatly increased thereby. Iron may be obtained from the pipe itself, or from the water being carried. The amount of ferric hydrate deposited is very large in comparison to the enclosed cells.

Some bacteria which do not oxidize ferrous iron may, nevertheless, indirectly cause it to be dissolved or deposited. In their growth, they either liberate iron by utilizing organic radicals to which the iron is attached, or alter environmental conditions to permit solution or deposition of iron. Less ferric hydrate may be produced, but taste, odor, and fouling may be encouraged.

2. Classification

There are a large number of organisms which either utilize iron as a source of energy or cause its deposition. These include protozoa and algae. No classification of iron bacteria based on cultural characteristics is possible at this time. Any classification based on morphology is certain to include widely divergent taxonomic types. Thus, *Bergey's Manual*[7] includes three genera, *Sphaerotilus, Leptothrix,* and *Toxothrix* in the Chlamydobacteriales, while *Crenothrix* is placed in a family by itself. These are the filamentous forms which deposit iron in their sheaths. Not all of these classifications have been accepted by Pringsheim,[2] but on the morphological bases shown in Bergey, they seem valid. There is, however, a real question as to the propriety of the term iron bacteria for *Sphaerotilus natans,* which Skerman[8] and Waitz[11] have shown can accumulate elemental sulfur in the presence of low oxygen and small amounts of hydrogen sulfide (Fig. 42).

Gallionella is placed in the family Caulobacteraceae, and five species are listed; *G. ferruginea* is the species usually referred to. This family consists of stalked bacteria, and besides *Gallionella* includes other members not usually thought of as iron bacteria—for instance, *Siderophacus* and *Nevskia.* The latter often contains globules "of fat or sulfur," which again brings up the question raised above.

The family Siderocapsaceae includes ten genera whose cells are usually surrounded by a thick, mucilaginous capsule containing iron or manganese compounds. These genera are: *Siderocapsa, Siderosphaera, Sideronema, Ferribacterium, Sideromonas, Naumaniella, Ochrobium, Siderococcus, Siderobacter,* and *Ferrobacillus.* Until recently these

Fig. 42. Habit sketch of *Sphaerotilus*
(Sphaerotilus *species may be related to either iron or sulfur bacteria*)

have not been widely considered in North America except by bacteriologists; only one species, *Ferrobacillus ferrooxidans,* has been isolated and cultured. However, as they are widely distributed in European iron-bearing waters, the North American records probably will be amplified, and their economic aspects more fully defined.

3. Enumeration

The lack of definitive culture media prevents enumeration by this method. Generally, only presence or absence may be noted; direct examination of field samples, or examination of slides which have been suspended in waters supposedly containing iron bacteria, is recommended. Removal of ferric hydrate with dilute hydrochloric acid is helpful, and staining by Lugol's iodine solution, carbol fuchsin, and gentian violet may be useful.

4. Cultivation and Enrichment

Iron bacteria sometimes may be cultivated by passing a slow stream of water over glass slides. A suitable medium suggested by Duchon and Miller may be made as follows: Dissolve dextrose in distilled water to give a 10 mg/l concentration. Distribute 50-ml portions into 125-ml erlenmeyer flasks, sterilize in an autoclave, and add from a freshly prepared stock solution sufficient ferrous sulfate to give a concentration of 10 mg/l. Inoculate 8 ml of the test sample into this medium. Incubate at 20°C for 3 to 4 weeks. Examine the growths microscopically.

Only with rare exceptions have any of the iron bacteria been grown in pure culture. Leathen, McIntyre, and Braley[3] have reported successfully growing some of the autotrophic iron bacteria which oxidize ferrous iron to the ferric state in water with an acid pH on the following medium: To 1 liter distilled water add 0.15 g ammonium sulfate, 0.05 g potassium chloride, 0.50 g magnesium sulfate heptahydrate, 0.05 g dipotassium hydrogen phosphate, and 0.01 g calcium nitrate. Sterilize at 15 psi for 15 min.

Prepare a stock solution of 10.0 g ferrous sulfate heptahydrate in 100 ml distilled water. Sterilize the solution with a Berkefeld or Fisher-Jenkins filter.

After the autoclaved basic medium cools, add 10 ml of the ferrous iron solution per liter of base. The final pH is approximately 3.5.

Sphaerotilus can be cultivated on a wide variety of media. A common one is 2 per cent agar made up with filtered raw sewage or settled sewage. Stokes[5] gives a different procedure, and many others are available.

Leptothrix apparently has been cultured by Sartory and colleagues.[10] Their medium consists of the following, added to 1 liter of spring water: 1.0 g ammonium sulfate, 0.5 g magnesium sulfate heptahydrate, 0.1 g dipotassium hydrogen phosphate, and 0.02 g calcium nitrate.

A special erlenmeyer flask containing 100 ml of this medium is sterilized. The flask contains a lateral opening, permitting introduction of 0.05 g iron filings, also sterilized. The flask is stoppered to allow entering air to be sterilized. Flasks are kept at room temperature and examined 3 days after inoculation, at which time the carbon dioxide in air and medium is in equilibrium, as indicated by the formation of iron carbonate on the surface of the filings.

To isolate *Leptothrix,* add 20 g of

the above solution to 1 liter of gelatin or agar medium. Repick and culture. After 3 days a brownish or blackish culture is obtained. This medium was also used for *Gallionella*.

Wolfe [9] has recently grown *Gallionella* in isolation culture. His method is to prepare agar slants from sterile ferrous sulfide precipitate and 3 per cent sterile melted water agar at 45°C. This mixture is slanted in screw-cap tubes. Then a liquid medium is added, consisting of: ammonium chloride, 1.0 g/l; dipotassium hydrogen phosphate, 0.5 g/l; magnesium sulfate heptahydrate, 0.2 g/l; and calcium chloride, 0.1 g/l. Carbon dioxide is bubbled through this medium for 10–15 sec before it is added to the test tubes. The tubes may then be inoculated with a drop of a suspension of a *Gallionella* deposit from a water main, aeration tray, filter bed, or other natural source. *Gallionella* grows well at room temperatures, and colonies usually appear in 18–36 hr after inoculation.

These appear to be the only methods used up to the present for the iron bacteria. Obviously, much research is needed for this group.

Sulfur Bacteria

1. General Characteristics

Sulfur bacteria are rather difficult to group because of wide diversity in their sulfur relationships. One group comprises the green bacteria, which grow in an environment containing hydrogen sulfide. For them hydrogen sulfide is a hydrogen donor and is oxidized only to free sulfur. Another group, the sulfur purple bacteria, oxidizes various inorganic sulfur compounds. Still another group, mostly filamentous, oxidizes hydrogen sulfide independently of light (which the sulfur purple bacteria do not) and stores elemental sulfur. Most of them are autotrophs, and they all reduce carbon dioxide to obtain energy, although other substances are also used. They are considered nuisance bacteria primarily because some of them produce hydrogen sulfide, and because they may be destructive to concrete or other structures.

2. Classification

Bergey's Manual [7] includes five families, 29 genera, and 80 species of organisms which might be considered sulfur bacteria. Not all of them are recognizable as such by microscopic examination. In addition, some others (*Sphaerotilus*, for example) may be transferred to the sulfur group. Also included are a few genera (*Vitreoscilla*, *Bactoscilla*, and *Microscilla*), as well as an occasional blue-green alga, whose ecologic relationships relative to sulfur are not well known. Some of these species are not important in the context of this manual—for example, predominantly marine forms and the green sulfur bacteria (Chlorobacteriaceae), although the development of saline water conversion may change this evaluation.

The first important family of colorless sulfur bacteria in Bergey is the Thiobacteriaceae. There are five genera with 17 species, all but about four being poorly known. The three species of *Thiobacterium* are known principally from work in Europe; they deposit free sulfur either within or without the short rods. *Macromonas* cells are large and slow moving, and contain calcium carbonate crystals as well as sulfur. *Thiovulum* is found in both marine and fresh-water environments and its spherical cells attain a size of 20 microns; it spins rapidly on an axis, and is aerobic or microaerophilic. *Thiospira* is also large, a swimming spiral with very evident sulfur granules.

Only one of the Athiorhodaceae might properly be called a sulfur bacterium—*Rhodopseudomonas palustris,* which oxidizes thiosulfate. It is hardly known except to research workers.

The family Chlorobacteriaceae contains green bacteria. The six genera are rarely encountered, except under special conditions. Although several members are unmistakably sulfur bacteria, the group at present merits little attention here.

The genus *Thiobacillus* is autotrophic. *T. concretivorus,* a short rod, is quite important because it corrodes concrete sewers and other concrete structures. It precipitates sulfur. *T. coproliticus* oxidizes free sulfur to sulfate; *T. denitrificans* oxidizes thiosulfate; *T. thiooxidans* can start with thiosulfate, oxidizing it to sulfur, and this, in turn, to sulfuric acid. Altogether, the genus, or at least seven of the nine species, are important to man, and are in the sulfur cycle. This is the best known genus of the family, largely because of the work of Starkey, Lipman, and their colleagues.

All the above bacteria occur singly, but cells of *Thiobacterium* may be embedded in a jelly, and there are some unusual pseudoaggregates in the Chlorobacteriaceae. The Thiorhodaceae, or sulfur red bacteria family, contains 13 genera of purple to pale pink bacteria. Nine occur in some sort of colony—a gelatinous mass or capsule. All contain sulfur granules, difficult to see at times, but all are easily classified as to family on the basis of color and sulfur granules. They are not usually a nuisance, and generic separations are too tenuous for further discussion here.

The remaining sulfur bacteria, with one exception, are filamentous. The family Beggiatoaceae is best known, its genera being *Beggiatoa* and *Thiothrix.* The former contains six species, all free, moving by gliding and containing sulfur granules. *B. gigantea,* a marine species, is up to 50 microns in diameter, and may be several millimeters in length. *Thiothrix* has seven species, is attached and nonmotile. Its filaments tend to become attenuated at the ends. A recently discovered genus [12] is nonfilamentous, much like *Zooglea* in appearance except for sulfur (Fig. 43a and 43b).

The family Achromatiaceae contains a single genus, *Achromatium,* poorly known, whose cells are spherical to oval and may reach a length of 95 microns. They normally contain crystals of calcium carbonate as well as sulfur, are single, and have a peculiar gliding movement. Usually a mud-water interface organism, it is not at present of great importance here.

3. Enumeration

There is no satisfactory method of enumerating Chlorobacteriaceae, Thiorhodaceae, and Athiorhodaceae at present. However, culture methods for some of them are available and others

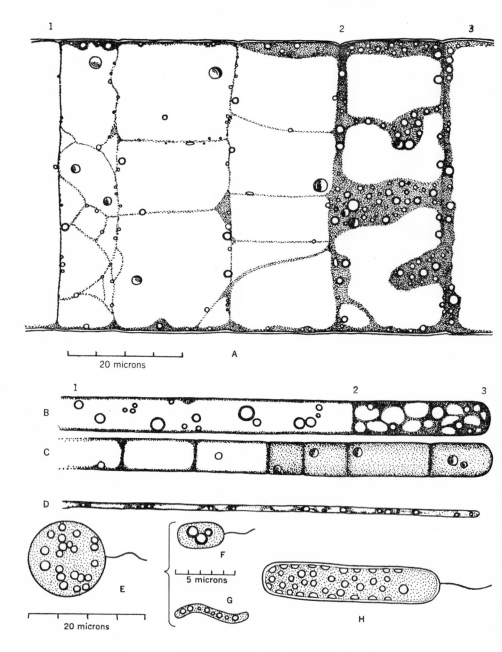

Fig. 43a. Sulfur bacteria

Key: A—*Beggiatoa gigas;* B—*Beggiatoa alba;* C—*Beggiatoa alba* (sulfur granules practically absent) ; D—*Beggiatoa leptomitiformis* (views A–D are same scale; 1–2 is optical section, 2–3 is surface view) ; E—*Thiovulum;* F—*Chromatium;* G—*Thiospirillum;* H—*Chromatium.*

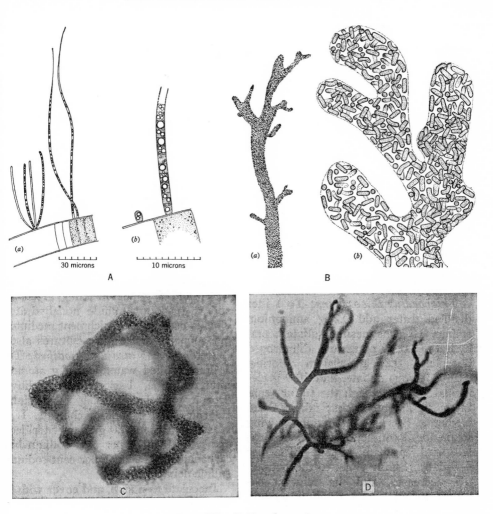

Fig. 43b. Sulfur bacteria

In A(a), the sulfur bacterium *Thiothrix* is shown attached to a blue-green alga; in A(b), *Thiothrix* has been greatly enlarged to show sulfur granules. Though not a sulfur bacterium, *Zooglea ramigera* is shown in B (habit sketch at left, cells in jelly at right) to illustrate its similarity to the sulfur bacterium *Thiodendron* below (D). View C is a photograph of *Thiodictyon*, a red sulfur bacterium.

can be worked out. *Beggiatoa, Thiothrix, Thiospirillopsis, Thioploca, Achromatium,* and possibly *Thiovulum* are amenable to direct counting as so many filaments or so many cells. In addition, *Beggiatoa alba* can now be cultured [4, 13] and may be counted. Drummond and Postgate [6] have developed a method for enumerating sulfate reducers, which depends on their use of, and blackening of, a cysteine medium.

4. Cultivation and Enrichment

Media are now available for pure culture isolation of *Thiobacillus thioparus, Thiobacillus thiooxidans, Chromatium okenii, Beggiatoa alba,* and perhaps others. Starkey's media [1] for the first two are described below.

Thiobacillus thioparus: To 1 liter of water add 10.0 g sodium thiosulfate pentahydrate, 2.0 g dipotassium hydrogen phosphate, 0.1 g magnesium sulfate heptahydrate, 0.1 g calcium chloride, 0.1 g ammonium chloride, 0.02 g ferric chloride hexahydrate, and 0.02 g manganese sulfate monohydrate. Inoculate and incubate for 2–3 days. The surface becomes covered with sulfur from autotrophic oxidation of thiosulfate.

Thiobacillus thiooxidans: To 1 liter distilled water add 0.2 g ammonium sulfate, 0.5 g magnesium sulfate heptahydrate, 3.0 g potassium dihydrogen phosphate, 0.25 g calcium chloride, 0.01 g ferrous sulfate, and 10.0 g elemental sulfur. Weigh the sulfur separately in 250-ml flasks; add 100 ml medium. Sterilize 30 min in flowing steam for 3 consecutive days. Inoculate and incubate at 25°–30°C for 4–5 days. Sulfur sinks to the bottom, pH decreases, and the solution becomes turbid. The dilution method allows enumeration.

Beggiatoa was grown by Scotten [4] on a variety of media; his solid media were kept in an atmosphere containing 0.03 per cent by volume of hydrogen sulfide. Calaway [13] has modified some of Scotten's media. He grows the organism in an enrichment medium, using 0.8 g hay (which has been dried after being triply extracted by boiling 36 hr) plus 5.7 g sewage sludge extract. This is prepared like soil extract. After good cultures of *B. alba* have appeared, masses are washed and transferred to beef extract agar. Migrating strands are then cut loose and replated. After two or three replatings, pure cultures are obtained. These are then grown in abundance in a liquid medium containing 5 mg dipotassium hydrogen phosphate, 7 mg potassium chloride, 15 mg sodium chloride, 7 mg calcium chloride, 5 mg magnesium sulfate heptahydrate, 1,000 mg gelysate, 10 mg yeast extract, 500 mg sodium acetate, 10 mg trickling filter sludge extract, 2 mg ferric chloride, and distilled water to make 1 liter.

Chromatium okenii, and probably others, has been isolated and grown by Waitz [11] on the following media:

Molisch, modified: To 1 liter spring water add 5 g peptone, 5 g glycerol, and 1 g sodium sulfide nonahydrate. This is used as an enrichment medium, but supports dense pure cultures also.

Breggoff stab medium, modified: To 1 liter distilled water add 1 g ammonium chloride, 1 g potassium dihydrogen phosphate, 0.5 g magnesium chloride, 0.03 g sodium chloride, 1 g yeast extract, and 20 g agar. Sterilize, and add 40 ml 5 per cent sodium bicarbonate and 20 ml 5 per cent sodium sulfide nonahydrate.

Inoculate as a stab, and cover with 1 in. of paraffin.

Bibliography

1. STARKEY, R. L. Isolation of Some Bacteria Which Oxidize Thiosulfate. *Soil Sci.* 39: (1935).
2. PRINGSHEIM, E. G. The Filamentous Bacteria *Sphaerotilus, Leptothrix, Cladothrix* and Their Relation to Iron and Manganese. *Phil. Trans. Roy. Soc. London, Ser. B* 233:453 (1949).
3. LEATHEN, W. W.; McINTYRE, L. D.; & BRALEY, S. A. A Medium for the Study of the Bacterial Oxidation of Ferrous Iron. *Science* 114:280 (1951).
4. SCOTTEN, H. L. The Isolation and Study

of Pure Cultures of *Beggiatoa* Species. Unpublished thesis, Univ. of Indiana, Bloomington (1951).

5. STOKES, J. L. Studies on the Filamentous Sheathed Iron Bacterium *Sphaerotilus natans*. *J. Bacteriol.* 67:278 (1954).

6. DRUMMOND, J. P. M. & POSTGATE, J. R. A Note on the Enumeration of Sulfate-Reducing Bacteria in Polluted Water and Their Inhibition by Chromate. *J. Appl. Bacteriol.* 18:307 (1955).

7. BREED, R. S., ET AL., ed. *Bergey's Manual of Determinative Bacteriology*. Williams and Wilkins Co., Baltimore (7th ed., 1957).

8. SKERMAN, V. B. D.; DEMENTJEVA, G.; & CAREY, B. J. Intracellular Deposition of Sulfur by *Sphaerotilus natans*. *J. Bacteriol.* 73:509 (1957).

9. WOLFE, R. S. Cultivation, Morphology, and Classification of the Iron Bacteria. *J. AWWA* 50:1241 (1958).

10. SARTORY, A.; SARTORY, R.; & MYER, J. In *Microbiologie Pratique*. Librairie Maloine, Paris. pp. 273–276.

11. WAITZ, S. & LACKEY, J. B. Morphological and Biochemical Studies on the Organisms *Sphaerotilus natans*. *Quart. J. Fla. Acad. Sci.* 21:335 (1959).

12. LACKEY, J. B. & LACKEY, E. W. The Habitat and Description of a New Genus of Sulfur Bacterium. *J. Gen. Microbiol.* 26:29 (1961).

13. LACKEY, J. B.; LACKEY, E. W.; & MORGAN, G. B. Taxonomy and Ecology of the Sulfur Bacteria. *Univ. Fla. Bull. Series* (in press).

PART IX

Biologic Examination of Water, Wastewater Sludge, and Bottom Materials

Introduction

The biologic examination of water, wastewater sludge, or bottom materials embraces a qualitative analysis of the kinds of plankton and bottom organisms present, a quantitative estimate of their number or bulk, and a brief survey of the particulate inorganic and amorphous matter. Such information is important in gaging water quality and may serve one or several of the following purposes:

a. To explain the cause of color and turbidity and the presence of objectionable odors, tastes and visible particulates in water and to indicate possible methods for their prevention or removal.

b. To aid in the interpretation of the various chemical analyses, as, for example, in relating the presence of biologic forms to oxygen deficiency or supersaturation in natural waters.

c. To identify the source of a water that is mixing with another.

d. To explain the clogging of pipes, screens and filters and to aid in the design and operation of waterworks.

e. To indicate pollution by sewage or industrial wastes.

f. To indicate the progress of the self-purification of streams and other bodies of water.

g. To aid in explaining the mechanism of biologic sewage treatment methods or to serve as an index to the effectiveness of the treatment.

h. To aid in the study of the ecology of fish, shellfish, and other aquatic organisms. To obtain information on food, parasites, and other factors affecting the well-being of these forms.

i. To determine whether or not ground water is contaminated by unfiltered surface water.

j. To determine optimum times for treatment of raw surface water with algicides and to check on the effectiveness of such treatment.

k. To determine, within the water plant, the effectiveness of various stages in the treatment of water and to aid in determining effective chlorine dosage as it is related to organic materials in water.

The term "plankton" will be used in a broad sense to designate not only microscopic and near-microscopic free-floating forms, but also those minute attached organisms which ordinarily grow along the shore or on the bottom. However, the term applies to the latter only when they are detached and are found floating freely in the water. Bacteria are excluded.

Included with the plankton, for example, are such groups among the plants as the Chrysophyta (diatoms and related forms), the Chlorophyta (green algae), the Cyanophyta (blue-green algae), and the Eumycophyta (fungi). Among the animals, the Protozoa, the

Rotifera, the Crustacea, the Porifera, the Bryozoa, and small worms and immature insects, when free-floating, are also considered as plankton.

"Total plankton" as here used refers to all of the plankton obtained by simple sedimentation of a sample. The term "net plankton" refers to that portion of total plankton retained by a net as described under Equipment for the Collection and Examination of Water, A, Devices for Collecting Samples of Total Plankton, Sec. 2.

The organisms associated with bottom materials of lakes and streams or with sludge and deposits in trickling filters may be divided into two groups on the basis of size. Organisms retained by a 30-mesh sieve are referred to as "benthic macroorganisms," while those which pass a 30-mesh sieve and are retained by a 100-mesh sieve are designated as "benthic microorganisms." Annelid worms, mollusks, and immature insects are examples of the macroorganisms. Ostracods, nematodes, protozoans, rotifers, and small aquatic crustaceans are typical microorganisms found in bottom materials.

Clumps of organic matter, decaying vegetation, silt, cast molts of water organisms, and headless stalks of such organisms as *Carchesium* are considered amorphous matter, in studies of water and sediment samples. The prevailing type and the primary characteristics of this material should be recorded, for this information can be valuable in making the final evaluation of the data being collected.

Equipment for Collection and Examination of Water

A. *Devices for Collecting Samples of Plankton*

1. Total Plankton

For obtaining samples of total plankton, use a wide-mouth, glass-stoppered 2-liter glass bottle or special samplers which will collect water at any desired depth.

Such samplers, which include the Kemmerer water bottle, Hale's sampler, Irwin's sampler, and the pump sampler, are illustrated and described in Whipple[8] and Welch.[18] In situations where it can be used, the modified Kemmerer sampler (Fig. 44.) is preferred. In very deep water the Nansen water bottle (Fig. 45) is employed.

2. Net Plankton

2.1. *Wisconsin plankton net:*

a. Materials: A part of the plankton may be collected by passing the water through any fine-mesh cloth. This process removes only a fraction of the total population; the organisms which are collected are known as net plankton (macroplankton). Certain fine-

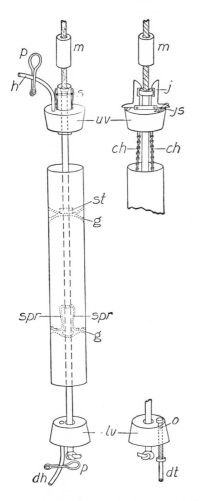

Fig. 44. Modified Kemmerer sampler

Left: view of complete sampler with valves open. Top right: another type of construction of upper valve and tripping device. Bottom right: another type of construction of lower valve and drain tube. Key: ch—chain which anchors upper valve to upper interior guide; dh—rubber drain tube; dt—brass drain tube; g—interior guide fastened to inner surface of body of sampler; h—rubber tube; j—jaw of release; js—jaw spring; lv—lower valve; m—messenger; o—opening into interior of drain tube; p—pinch cock; s—upper release spring operating on horizontal pin, one end of which fits into

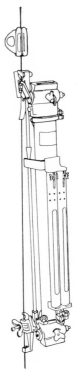

Fig. 45. Nansen reversing water bottle

meshed materials are superior to others and, except in emergencies, only those particularly suited to net construction should be used. The materials which have been used by limnologists include silk bolting cloth, linen, and wire cloth. India linen is often used, but any good grade of thin linen not too tightly woven is suitable. It is the least desirable material, however, for it lacks uniformity of mesh. Wire cloths are made very precisely, although in the past they have been considered impractical for

groove on central rod; spr—spring fastened to lower internal guide and operating in groove on central rod to provide lower release; st—stop on central rod; uv—upper valve. (From Welch.[18])

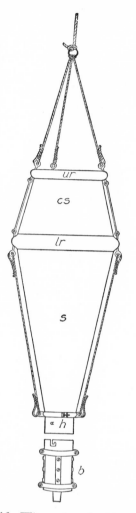

Fig. 46. Wisconsin plankton net

Key: b—detachable bucket, shown detached
from headpiece; cs—canvas sleeve between
upper and lower rings; lr—lower ring; h—
headpiece; s—sleeve of silk bolting cloth
between lower ring and headpiece; ur—upper
ring. The third supporting cord, extending
from lower ring to headpiece, and the third
supporting wire, connecting upper and lower
rings, are not shown in the figure. (From
Welch.[18])

the construction of plankton nets for
ordinary purposes. However, silk
bolting cloth is the material commonly
used in fresh water. It is manufactured
in a number of grades and with a large
range of mesh sizes. Size 25 is recommended as the type most suitable. This
cloth, when properly shrunk, has 200
meshes to the linear inch—40,000
meshes per square inch or 6,200 meshes
per square centimeter. Nylon of
equivalent mesh may also be used as a
net material and is now coming into
general use in marine studies.

   b. Construction of nets: Most plankton nets are constructed in the form of a
truncated cone. Several types of nets
may be used. A very useful type is
held partly submerged in the water
while measured quantities of the sample
are poured in at the top. There are
also tow nets, which are pulled through
the water, simultaneously collecting and
concentrating the sample. The Birge
cone net and the Wisconsin plankton
net (Fig. 46) are examples of the latter type. Detailed descriptions of tow
nets of this kind are presented in Whipple [8] and Welch.[18]

3. Other Methods

   Other special devices have been designed by oceanographers and limnologists. Representative samplers of this
type include the Juday plankton trap
(Fig. 47), Clarke's modification of the
Juday plankton trap, and Clarke's
plankton sampler. These rather complex samplers may be admirably suited
to special problems. Welch [18] gives detailed descriptions. It should be remembered that only net plankton can be
collected by these devices.

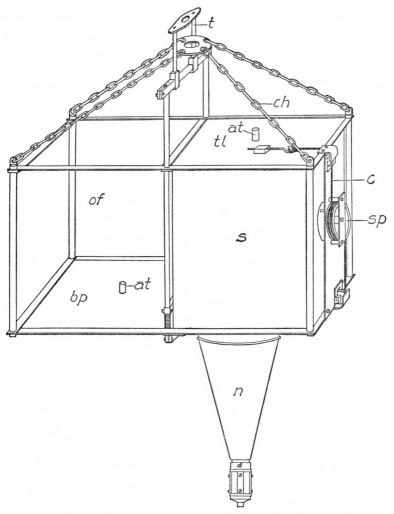

Fig. 47. Juday plankton trap (side view, closed position)

Key: at—air tube; bp—bottom plate; c—operating cord; ch—one of four supporting chains; n—plankton net; of—open frame; s—side plate; sp—operating spring; t—top part of tripping device; tl—top lid. (From Welch.[18])

B. Collection and Storage of Water Samples

Sampling points should be carefully selected to obtain representative samples. Special precautions should be taken to obtain a sample containing a typical dispersion of organisms free from floating debris, mud, or extraneous material. The actual sites selected for collection should correspond as nearly as possible to those used in bacteriological and chemical studies in order to permit reasonable correlations.

1. Collection of Samples

Samplers of the special types mentioned under Equipment, A, may be used to obtain samples. In many instances, the plankton sample is taken simultaneously with samples intended for biochemical or chemical analysis and in the same sampler. If no sampler is available and a surface sample will be adequate, an ordinary glass bottle may be used. For this purpose a clean 2-liter bottle, not necessarily sterile, having a wide mouth and a glass stopper is ideal. Smaller samples can be collected and, according to some workers, as little as 200 ml may suffice. It is generally agreed, however, that a large sample is advantageous. In making the collection, the bottle, with stopper removed, is thrust as far as possible, mouth downward, into the water. It is then inverted and allowed to fill.

If the sample is to be examined while organisms are still alive—and this is often advisable in special studies where the greatest accuracy is desired—it should be kept at its original temperature or iced to lower the temperature until the examination can be made. The bottle should not be placed in sunlight even on a cold day, and exhaustion of dissolved oxygen should be prevented by taking care not to fill the sample bottle completely. Such care is essential, as plankton organisms are very sensitive to environmental changes. One investigator, for example, reports that a rise of 10° C in 30 min is lethal to many of the common plankton species and that frequently the lamp heat reach-

ing the slide on the stage of a microscope is quickly fatal. The chilling which occurs when samples are iced appears to be relatively harmless.

2. Preservation and Storage

Unless the sample is to be examined fresh as indicated above, it should be preserved immediately after collection by the addition of formalin. This is accomplished by adding 5 ml of commercial formalin * to each 100 ml of water. In routine sampling practice, 40 ml of formalin is added to each liter of sample.

Because colors fade rapidly, the preserved plankton must be stored in the dark. Under favorable conditions, although carotenes and xanthophyll are said to break down, chlorophyll retains its color rather well; it has been found that an expert can identify most organisms in a preserved sample even after several years of storage. For practical purposes a preserved sample has many advantages, but it should be remembered that the plankton organisms in a preserved concentrate have been subjected to sudden immersion in a fluid which often produces severe contraction and distortion of body form. No ideal preservative has yet been found. The microscopist, therefore, must always be on the alert for misleading effects produced by the preservative. Comparison with an occasional live sample from the same source will aid the investigator to recognize forms

---

* Commercial formalin contains 37–42 per cent formaldehyde. This type of formalin is usually acid (pH approximately 4) and it may be desirable to render it neutral or basic. A slightly basic formalin is much to be preferred if specimens are kept for long periods of time. This adjustment can be provided by adding household borax, hexamine, or a concentrated ammonia solution to the formalin.

which may be distorted in routine pre-served samples. (See Lackey [13].)

3. Concentration of Water Samples

If organisms are numerous in the original sample, no concentration is necessary. In some instances, where a "water bloom" prevails, dilution of the water sample may actually be needed before enumeration can take place. There is no general agreement among workers in the field relative to the number of organisms needed per unit volume of sample to provide a basis for an accurate count, although it is hoped that current statistical research studies in this field may eventually provide a basis for agreement. However, for practical purposes it is neces-sary to set some arbitrary limit. In doing so, it can be agreed that organisms are too numerous for an accurate count when they overlap one another in a standard counting cell. Conversely, organisms are too scarce when the average per Whipple field, under standard procedure, is less than one. It is suggested, therefore that the ideal sample should contain a concentration of organisms which will produce a count of not less than ten organisms per field when a Whipple micrometer and a standard counting cell are used. If this count is not attained, the sample should be concentrated. If other methods of counting are employed, the corresponding limit can be determined for the particular procedure.

C. Apparatus for Examination of Plankton Samples

1. Microscopes

1.1. *Compound microscope:* Although most workers prefer the binocular compound microscope (Fig. 48), the monocular type can be used. Either type should be equipped with a mechanical stage capable of moving all parts of a counting cell past the aperture of the objective. Standard equipment should consist of $10\times$ oculars (paired when a binocular microscope is used) and the following objectives:

Type of Objective	Overall Magnification With $10\times$ Ocular
16 mm (low power).........	$100\times$
8 mm (medium power).....	$200\times$–$210\times$
4 mm (high power, dry)....	$430\times$–$450\times$
1.8 mm (oil immersion).....	$900\times$–$980\times$

Unlike the higher powers, the medium-power or 8-mm objective with a working distance of approximately 1.6 mm can be used with a standard plankton counting cell 1 mm deep. Providing twice the magnification of the low-power objective ordinarily used in enumerating plankton, this medium-power lens is useful in several ways. For example, small organisms can be examined more carefully during the process of counting by shifting momentarily to the 8-mm objective, and if allowances are made for the reduction in field area, it will be found that plankton counts can be made with this objective.

1.2. *Low-power stereoscopic microscope:* The stereoscopic microscope (Fig. 49) is essentially two complete

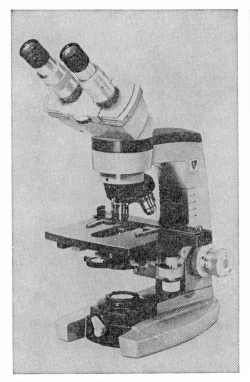

Fig. 48. Binocular compound microscope   **Fig. 49. Stereoscopic microscope**

microscopes assembled into a binocular instrument to give a stereoscopic view and an erect rather than an inverted image. This microscope is indispensable for the study of organisms which occur in bottom sediments and for counting large organisms such as crustacea in plankton samples. The optical equipment of this microscope should include 9× or 10× and 12× or 15× paired oculars in combination with 1×, 4× and 8× objectives. This combination of lenses bridges the gap between the hand lens and the compound microscope, making available magnifications ranging from 9× to 120×.

1.3. *Inverted compound microscope:* In Europe the inverted compound microscope (Fig. 50) is used routinely for plankton counting because it enables the technician to bypass time-consuming concentration techniques. This instrument is unique in that the objectives are below a movable stage and the illumination comes from above. Workers employing this instrument place their samples directly into a 10-, 15-, or 20-ml glass cylinder with a clear glass bottom. After a suitable period of setting, usually 6 hr, the preserved samples are examined and counted directly. If a 10-ml sample is used, the concentration is automatically 10:1. This instrument is recommended for research investigations and for use in the larger water plants.

Fig. 50. Unitron binocular inverted biological microscope
(with 35-mm camera back)

2. Counting Cell

A counting cell is used to provide a known volume and area for microscopic examination and enumeration of organisms. It consists of a brass or glass rim closely cemented to a plate of optical glass or plate glass. The depth of this cell should be 1 mm. It is recommended that a cell of 1-ml capacity (inside dimensions 20×50 mm) be used. The inner portion of the rim of this cell must form a right angle with the bottom. There can be no cove or rounded junction either at the base of the vertical wall or at the corners of the counting cell. Such rounded construction will interfere with the accuracy of a count by affecting the uniformity of distribution of the organisms. A No. 3 cover glass 0.25 to 0.50 mm thick is also needed. It should be of such size as to cover the entire cell and its rim (Fig. 51). Where a magnification of 430–450× is desired, a counting cell of less depth is required. The Palmer cell [25] is 0.4 mm deep and can be used with the highpower, dry, 43–45× (4 mm) objective. A counting cell of this type is not required for the Lackey drop-sedimentation procedure.

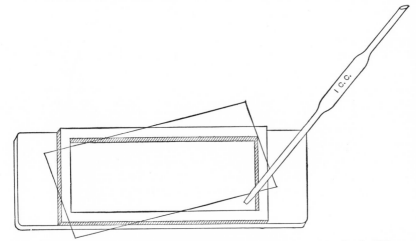

Fig. 51. Counting cell (Sedgwick-Rafter), showing method of filling
(From Whipple [8])

3. Micrometers

3.1. *Ocular micrometer:* For field limitation the microscope should be fitted with a Whipple disc micrometer. This ocular micrometer, placed in the eyepiece of the microscope, is an accurately ruled square subdivided into 100 squares. One of the small squares near the center is further subdivided into 25 still smaller squares (Fig. 52). Dimensions of the entire square are such that, with a 16-mm (10×) objective, a 10× ocular, and a correctly adjusted tube length, the area delimited on the stage of the microscope is exactly 1 sq mm. This combination is determined accurately by reference to a stage micrometer, and exact adjustment may be attained by a change in the drawtube length of the microscope. In many modern microscopes, the tube length is not an adjustable feature and exact coincidence cannot be obtained; thus,

it is necessary to establish the exact coverage obtained at the tube length which has been set by the manufacturer. If the square exceeds or falls below 1 sq mm, a factor must be used to convert the results obtained to those represented by a standard area.

When the outside limits of the Whipple micrometer cover exactly 1 sq mm on the stage, the very smallest square will cover an area of 20 × 20 microns, or 400 square microns. This is known as the "areal standard unit." If this unit also has a thickness or depth of 20 microns, it becomes a "volumetric standard unit" or "cubic standard unit." Its volume is 8,000 cubic microns.

If the Whipple micrometer does not exactly coincide with 1 sq mm on the stage, the volumetric enumeration method may still be used by applying a factor to the cubic standard unit or

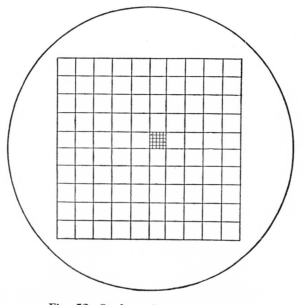

Fig. 52. Ocular micrometer ruling
(A Whipple micrometer reticule is illustrated)

by changing the counting technique as indicated in Reporting of Results, B, Sec. 1.

If the Whipple micrometer is transferred to another ocular or the ocular is moved to another microscope, recalibration is necessary. This is also true if objectives are changed.

3.2. *Measuring eyepiece:* A measuring eyepiece is also needed by the microscopist to determine the exact size of specimens which are being examined. A glass disc or reticule bearing a linear scale of arbitary divisional size and total length is placed engraved side down on the diaphragm of an ordinary ocular to convert it to a measuring device. In stereoscopic and binocular microscopes, the measuring reticule is placed in the right eyepiece. If a considerable amount of measurement is done, an eyepiece with a permanent factory-mounted reticule or a screw micrometer with a shifting scale may be desirable.

3.3. *Stage micrometer:* A stage micrometer is needed for the calibration of the Whipple micrometer and the ocular measuring micrometer, and to establish the diameter of the micro-

scope field for each ocular and objective combination. This micrometer is a standardized, accurately ruled scale mounted on a glass slide. Use a stage micrometer in which the finest engraved lines are designated as being 0.01 mm apart. Calibration of an ocular micrometer, for example, is accomplished by superimposing the images of the stage and the ocular micrometers and noting the point of correspondence of graduations (Fig. 53).

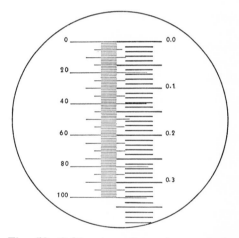

Fig. 53. Calibration of eyepiece reticule

Calibration of Microscope

Microscope eyepieces to be used in counting plankton are fitted with glass discs (reticules) bearing parallel, engraved, equidistant lines or engraved, subdivided squares which are designed to measure microscopic objects or accurately delimit microscope fields (Fig. 52). Before these ocular micrometers can be used, they must be carefully

calibrated in combination with each objective.

The ocular micrometers are calibrated by measuring an object of known dimensions, thus determining the value of each subdivision by reference. A stage micrometer or glass slide, on which an accurately ruled scale has been engraved, is placed on the microscope stage and serves as the object of known dimensions.

The procedure consists of determining the number of intervals on the ocular micrometer required to cover one or several intervals on the scale of the stage micrometer. With the ocular and stage micrometers parallel and in part superimposed, a line at one end of the eyepiece scale is selected and matched with a similar line of the stage micrometer scale. If the two scales are then carefully examined along their entire length, it will be observed that the lines also correspond at another point (Fig. 53).

Inasmuch as the exact distance between lines on the stage micrometer is known, the linear value of each ocular division can now be determined by reference. For example, if the smallest interval on the stage micrometer is 0.01 mm and 25 of these 0.01-mm divisions are equal to 75 divisions on the ocular scale, 1 ocular division = 0.25 mm/

75 = 0.0033 mm = 3.3 microns. When this ocular is used for measurement, the result is a direct reading of length in microns. Thus an object covering 5 ocular divisions is 16.5 microns long.

When high-power objectives are calibrated, the stage micrometer lines are magnified to a point where they have appreciable width. As a result, the calibration procedure must be modified by placing an ocular line alongside of, rather than end to end with, the stage micrometer lines. The ocular lines used for calibration should both lie on the same side of their stage micrometer counterparts.

Single observations will not suffice to establish a true calibration of ocular micrometers. The average of a large number of observations must be used. The data obtained will be more readily available if a graph such as shown in Fig. 54 is prepared, in which the ocular scale dimensions are plotted against the

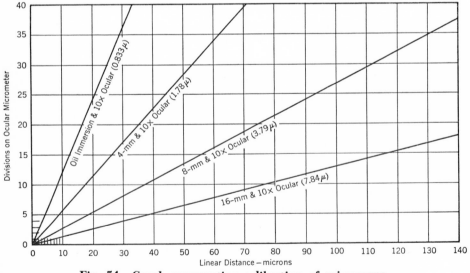

Fig. 54. Graph representing calibration of microscope
A calibration curve must be prepared for each individual microscope.

linear distances they represent on the stage. By reference to this chart, the length in microns of any given object examined may be determined quickly.

If the same eyepiece and objectives are used and no change is made in the microscope tube length, there will be no need to recalibrate an ocular micrometer.

The Whipple micrometer is usually calibrated by adjusting the tube length of the microscope at low power (10×, 16-mm objective) in such a way that the outer lines of the square coincide exactly with the 0.0-mm and 1.0-mm lines on the stage micrometer. At higher powers and where the tube length cannot be adjusted, the calibration is carried out in the same manner as for ocular measuring micrometers.

Reporting of Results

A. Forms

Although it is difficult to design a "bench sheet" that will fit all situations in plankton counting, most workers find forms of this type useful. Where repeated examinations are made of one sampling point or a series of similar sampling areas, a very satisfactory sheet can be prepared. Because there can be considerable latitude in the preparation of such forms, no exact specifications are given. Instead, a sample bench sheet is presented as a typical example in Fig. 55.

It will be noted that the form shown provides spaces for information on the identity and history of each sample. Included are such items as the exact place and time of collection, the name of the collector, the time of arrival in the laboratory, the laboratory serial number, the date of examination, and the name of the examiner.

The manner of ruling the sheet may vary widely. In the sample shown, the sheet is ruled to facilitate entries when five or ten fields are examined. Obviously, a form of this kind will vary slightly with the counting procedure adopted and the type of work being carried on. The form can be fitted to the requirements of the laboratory concerned, its chief function being to assure an immediate, accurate, and uniform recording of results. In preparing bench sheets, it is suggested that the general plan of Fig. 55 be followed, inasmuch as this form has been developed by practical workers in the field and is based on long experience.

LIMNOLOGY BENCH SHEET
Plankton Enumeration

Location _____

Serial No. _____ Date _____ Concentration _____ L. to _____ cc.

Factors: Survey to Liter/100 L. _____ Strip to Liter/100 L. _____ Field to Liter/100 L. _____

Collected by _____ Date _____ Method of Counting _____

ORGANISMS	Survey Count	SR Strip Count	SR Field Strip		Count			Totals	Volume Per Liter Per 100 L.	Numbers Per Liter Per 100 L.
			1	2	3	4	5			

(Continued on other side)

Date Received _____ Date Examined _____ By _____

Continued

ORGANISMS	Survey Count	SR Strip Count	SR Field Strip		Count			Totals	Volume Per Liter Per 100 L.	Numbers Per Liter Per 100 L.
			1	2	3	4	5			

SPECIAL INFORMATION
General Character of Sample

As collected   As concentrated

Color _____

Nature of turbidity _____

Odor if detectable _____

Remarks: _____

Fig. 55. Sample bench sheet for use with centrifuge method
On this form, numbers rather than cubic standard units are reported.

B.   *Reporting of Observations*

1.   **Reporting in Terms of Numbers of Organisms**

Reporting the number of organisms of each species is a straightforward procedure and requires much less time than a method which is based on the volume of each plankton species. In many instances, a simple count of this kind is entirely adequate for the practical problems involved and may be used without modification. In other instances, where a fairly uniform plankton prevails and the same locality is examined repeatedly, the direct count can be converted into volume units by applying factors. For example, each species may be assigned a volumetric factor which for practical purposes represents the average volume of any organism within the group. By applying this factor to the numerical count, the final report can be given in terms of volume. If desired, this figure can then be converted to its equivalent in cubic standard units. Some workers have stated that cubic standard units is a poor way to give volumetric reports and prefer to report their counts of living cellular matter as parts per million or milligrams per liter. In the latter procedure, the specific gravity of the organisms must be known. Ordinarily, the practical worker assumes this value is 1.0, the same as that of water, and proceeds accordingly to report the plankton organisms in terms of mg/l.

When colonial or filamentous forms are counted, they should be reported in terms of standardized units. *Melosira* or *Oscillatoria,* for example, may be reported as units or fractions of units 100 microns in length. In some colonial forms, the number of cells may be enu-merated; more often it is desirable to report the number of colonies. In the latter procedure, especially where colony size may vary considerably, the volume of each colony should be estimated by reference to the Whipple micrometer guide lines while the count is being made. The report can then be rendered in terms of an equivalent number of standardized medium-sized colonies. The size of colony chosen as a standard may be arbitrary but should fall near the median. Such a procedure facilitates comparison of samples and, if desired, provides an easy basis for converting a numerical count into volumetric equivalent.

In enumerating the organisms, the field count is usually made first, counting all organisms which lie within the limits determined by the Whipple disc. This count is carried out with an 8-mm or 16-mm objective and 10× oculars.

It is followed by the strip count and survey count, which include organisms too scarce for accurate counting by the random field technique. These counts are made as directed under Continuous Centrifuge Method for Estimation of Total Plankton, Sec. 4.1–4.4.

In recording the count, a bench sheet is very useful; the results are simply entered in their proper columns as the enumeration is carried out and are then ready for summation. Certain modifications in the use of a form may be made to fit the situation at the time a count is made. For example, if the form shown in Fig. 55 is used and ten rather than five fields are examined, a double entry may be made in each square, above and below the diagonal line. When standard lengths of filaments and standard-size colonies are reported, suitable entries are conveniently made within parentheses following the name of the organism.

2. Reporting in Terms of Volumetric Units

The cubic standard unit has been used for many years and is preferred by some workers as a method for the quantitative expression of results. Where records of long standing have all been in terms of this type of unit, it may be desirable to continue its use, although it is more time consuming than the simple numerical count and not as easily understood as reporting in terms of ppm or mg/l. It is essentially an extension of the areal standard unit method, the third dimension being measured and volume expressed in terms of a cube rather than a square 20 microns on a side.

In practical work, it is well to obtain a value for the average volume of organisms which occur repeatedly and are fairly uniform in size. The plane dimensions of the organisms in the view presented under the microscope are measured directly; the thickness is estimated from a knowledge of the shape of the organisms on the basis of past measurements. This value may be in volumetric standard units for spherical, cubical, and some irregularly shaped species, or it may be in areal units (the product of two dimensions) for organisms that have a widely varying third dimension. Representatives of species that are not uniform in size must have their bulk estimated as they appear in the count.

The thickness of large forms can be determined, approximately, by the movement of the body tube of the microscope. The fine-adjustment

drum on most microscopes has a scale the divisions of which represent known vertical movements of the objective. Successive readings will establish thickness if the upper and lower surfaces of the object are brought into sharp focus. The reading obtained must be multiplied by the index of refraction of the medium in which the object is suspended. The index of refraction of water is 1.33.

Inasmuch as a cubic standard unit represents a cube measuring 20 microns on each side, it will have a volume of 8,000 cubic microns, and the volume of each organism in terms of cubic standard units is obtained as follows:

$$\text{volume in cubic units} = \frac{\text{volume in cubic microns}}{8,000}$$

If the product of only two dimensions (areal units) is given, designate this. The third dimension must be estimated at the time of counting in such cases. In species lacking uniformity of size, the bulk is estimated when seen.

Proceed with the survey. After its completion, record each genus or species, showing the total number of volumetric standard units observed. A record of the number of individual organisms or cells may be kept simultaneously by noting this number on the count sheet as the numerator of a fraction, the measurements of the cells being recorded as the denominator; thus, "4/3," 4 being the number of cells and 3 representing the dimensional values, such as volumetric standard units or linear units.

Proceed with the total count for ten random fields. Record each genus or species and for each, as in the survey, the total number of volumetric units observed.

A record of the number of individual organisms or cells may be kept simultaneously (again as in the survey) by noting this number on the counting sheet as the numerator of a fraction, the measurements of the cells being recorded as the denominator.

A record of amorphous matter in volumetric standard units may also be made for each of the ten fields of the survey examination.

The computation of volumetric standard units from the individual measurements and estimates is facilitated by the use of a chart like Fig. 56

TABLE 43—AREA OF CIRCLE AND VOLUME OF SPHERE AND CUBE FOR GIVEN DIAMETER

Diameter	Area of Circle	Volume of Sphere	Volume of Cube
0.5	0.196	0.065	0.125
1.0	0.785	0.524	1.000
2.0	3.142	4.189	8.000
3.0	7.069	14.137	27.000
4.0	12.566	33.510	64.000
etc. (to 30 or 40)			

or by data such as given in Table 43, which are commonly included in engineers' and other handbooks.

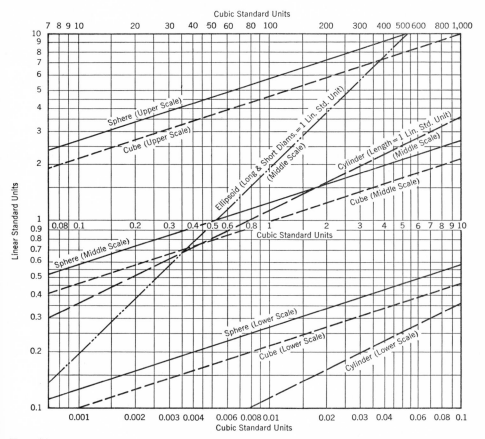

Fig. 56. Determination of cubic standard units from linear dimensions of organisms
Chart gives volume-linear relationship for organisms of different shapes (From Whipple [8])

Continuous Centrifuge Method for Estimation of Total Plankton

1. Equipment for Concentration

1.1. *Continuous centrifuge:* A continuous electric centrifuge similar to the Foerst type is required (Fig. 57). Without a load this centrifuge should have a speed of approximately 20,000 rpm and should be light enough to be portable.

1.2. *Automatic feeding funnel:* An ordinary glass funnel with a maximum diameter of 6 in. is needed. This funnel should be drawn out into a tip which allows a liter of water to pass in 6 or 7 min, or a tip may be attached. The integral tip is highly desirable inasmuch as it facilitates cleaning of the apparatus between samples.

1.3. *Support for sample bottle and feeding funnel:* A heavy ring stand and three rings are needed. One ring with a diameter of 7.5 to 10 cm serves as a support for the feeding funnel; another, of size depending on the type of sample bottle being used and incomplete for one-fourth of its circumference, serves as a support for the sample bottle, which rests on it in an inverted position with its neck and mouth below the upper edge of the funnel. The removal of a sector of this supporting ring facilitates the insertion of a full sample bottle. The third ring is slipped over the base of the inverted bottle to keep it in position and prevent tipping. For details of assembly see Fig. 57.

2. Concentration of Sample

Because water samples may be quickly concentrated by the continuous centrifuge method, larger samples are frequently used than with other procedures. A 2-liter sample is usually concentrated unless organisms are extremely abundant. If the sample contains highly buoyant organisms which tend to float at the surface as a scum, the centrifuge may remove only a portion of such forms at the first centrifugation. Juday [7] states that, in the case of *Aphanizomenon*, only one-half of the organisms are removed the first time but substantially all that remain are taken out by a second centrifuging. He states further that the first centrifuging removes approximately 98 per cent of the organisms that are usually considered in a plankton catch. When time permits, another means for the concentration of highly buoyant organisms may be employed. The sample is allowed to stand until a scum forms. The scum is removed by skimming, and the remainder of the sample is centrifuged. The centrifuge concentrate and the scum are then combined.

Samples may be fed into the centrifuge by means of a hand-operated control valve, but the semiautomatic feeding apparatus shown in Fig. 57 saves time and is usually more satisfactory than hand feeding. To assemble the apparatus, first insert the calibrated tip of the funnel slightly below the upper rim of the central collar or inlet tube of the centrifuge, centering the tip of the funnel over the rotor cup of the centrifuge so that even distribution is assured; then move the incomplete ring down to within 1 or 1½ in. of the top of the funnel. The centrifuge is then set in motion and the sample bottle, from which the stopper has

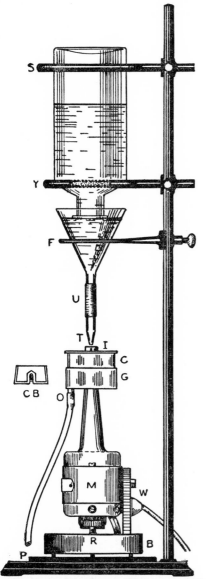

Fig. 57. Funnel and centrifuge assembly for concentrating organisms

Key: P—pad, rubber or felt; B—base; M—motor; R—rheostat; W—motor terminals; G—guard; C—cover; CB—cross section of bowl; I—inlet tube; O—outlet tube; T—tip regulating flow; U—rubber tubing; F—funnel support; Y—incomplete ring for bottle support; S—guard ring.

been removed, is quickly inverted and slipped into position above the funnel in such a manner that the neck of the bottle is below the upper edge of the funnel. The sample is thus fed into the funnel at a rate equivalent to that of the discharge of the calibrated tip. When the third or supporting ring has been slipped into place, the apparatus may be left to itself until the entire sample has been centrifuged.

For maximum efficiency, the rate of flow through the centrifuge must be controlled. Too rapid delivery slows the machine and leads to imperfect results. Too slow delivery unduly prolongs the running time although it does no harm. The optimum rate is usually 6 to 7 min per liter, and the funnel tip is calibrated to deliver water at this rate. The centrifuge should be kept operating at full speed for at least 1 min after the water disappears from the funnel tip. This will insure the smallest possible volume of the final concentrate within the bowl.

After the centrifuge run has been completed, the bowl is removed and the organisms are gently dislodged from its sloping sides to resuspend them in the 4 or 5 ml of water remaining in the bowl. If the suspension is too heavy, algae-free water (e.g., centrifuge effluent from the same sample) or buffered water (Part VII, Preparation of Culture Media, C, Sec. 1) may be used for dilution. The dilution is usually made in such a way that a definite, easily remembered, ratio to the original sample is obtained; some multiple of 5 is convenient.

If the concentrate cannot be examined while fresh, it may be preserved at this point by using 5 per cent formalin solution as a diluting medium in place of the algae-free water referred to in the preceding paragraph. A concentrate derived from an original sample preserved in the field is treated in the same manner. The 5 per cent formalin preservative is prepared by adding 5 ml full-strength commercial formalin (37–42 per cent formaldehyde) to 95 ml distilled water.

The preserved sample is next transferred to a suitable bottle that has been properly labeled to establish the identity of the sample and its concentration. Such samples, if stored in the dark, will keep well and may be examined at the convenience of the investigator. The final dilution is usually made at the time of microscopic examination.

All parts of the centrifuge and self-feeding arrangement which come in actual contact with a water sample must be thoroughly cleaned before another sample is processed.

3. Selection of Aliquot Portion

The portion taken from the concentrated sample should be representative and the examination should include a sufficient number of organisms to insure accuracy.

Shake the concentrated sample gently but in such a manner that complete mixing will occur. Place the cover glass obliquely across the counting cell. By means of a pipet, withdraw 1 ml of material from the sample bottle before the motion of the sample induced by mixing has ceased. Introduce one-half at each open corner of the counting cell (Fig. 51). Carefully done, this will cause the cover slip to rotate automatically into a position completely covering the cell. After a 4–5 min settling period the sample is ready for the enumeration procedure. During this interval most organisms settle toward the bottom and a few rise to the surface, coming to rest against the cover slip.

4. Differential Count of Organisms

4.1. *Differential count:* A differential count may be defined as the enumeration of some or all of the different kinds of plankton organisms, distinguishing them qualitatively. It involves identifying, counting, and recording the numbers of individuals of each kind. In contrast, the total count has been defined as an enumeration of all the plankton forms without any attempt to distinguish between different kinds.

In making a differential count, the contents of the cell should be examined under the microscope in three ways. First, the most abundant forms are counted by examining a number of standard fields; next a strip extending the whole length of the cell is examined for organisms which are less numerous; and, finally, the whole cell is examined for large forms and those very limited in number. In all cases, examine the full depth of the cell to include floating forms.

General rules or suggestions for counting which are applicable to any of the three procedures listed are as follows:

a. It is ordinarily impractical to count bacteria.

b. Include in the count the remains of organisms living before the sample was preserved, but if it is difficult to discrimininate positively, do not count the doubtful specimens.

c. Objects near the limit of vision of a given ocular and objective combination cannot be adequately counted. Examine them under higher powers.

d. Detritus and objects other than plankton are recorded if this information can be of any use in the final interpretation of results. For example, counts of wood fibers from paper mills may be of value in pollution surveys.

e. If a plankton organism lies on the boundary line of the field, count only that portion lying inside and record as a fraction. Another common system is to designate two adjacent sides of the field as "counters" and the opposing sides as "noncounters"; any organisms touching the "counters" are counted, while those touching the opposite sides are ignored.

f. The length of filamentous forms should be estimated and reported in units of a selected standard length. Some workers report filaments in terms of 100-micron units.

g. Other forms having irregular colonies may be reported in terms of estimated units of volume, selecting arbitrarily a volume which approximates a medium-size colony.

h. Except as indicated in *f* and *g*, individual organisms should be reported whenever possible unless colonial groups have a fairly constant number of cells. When a species of the latter type is reported in terms of colony units, it is well to indicate in the record the number of cells considered representative.

4.2. Field count: The field count is made with the 16-mm objective and a 10× ocular equipped with a Whipple micrometer. When the distribution of organisms in the sample is uniform and organisms are relatively abundant, conditions are ideal for counting and relatively few fields need to be examined.

The exact number of fields which must be examined will vary considerably, depending on the accuracy required and the characteristics of the sample. Careful statistical work is currently being carried on to ascertain, on a mathematical basis, the exact number of fields that must be examined in any given sample to attain a preselected degree of accuracy.

For routine work it is recommended that, in samples which are adequately concentrated to provide at least ten organisms per field, not less than ten standard fields should be examined in making a plankton count. When special studies are being made, it may be necessary to increase the number of fields tenfold. Also, when an 8-mm objective is substituted for the 16-mm objective, the number of fields examined must be increased from ten to 40.

The fields selected should be taken at random and should be well separated from one another. In order that certain parts of the cell may not be inadvertently avoided, some workers divide the area of the counting cell into four sectors by diagonal lines connecting opposite corners. Fields are then selected at random from each of the general areas so delimited.

In making a differential count, certain forms will be too scarce to appear in satisfactory numbers in each field examined—that is, less than one per field on the average. Such organisms must be counted by strip counts or survey counts.

4.3. Strip count: This count is made when a species is not abundant enough to be accurately enumerated by the Whipple field count. It is also suited to the enumeration of organisms which are too small to be identified or counted properly under the low magnification available in the basic field count method. The strip count is essentially the enumeration of a selected group of organisms as they occur within an area represented by the full length of a Sedgwick-Rafter cell (50 mm) and the width of a microscopic field (approximately 0.7 mm). The microscopic-field width generally used is that produced by a combination of a 10× ocular and an 8-mm objective. The exact width of this strip varies with individual lenses and must be determined by reference to a stage micrometer. In a fully calibrated microscope where the field diameter is known, it is a simple matter to convert strip counts into units which correspond with other methods.

In the actual count, enumeration is begun at one end of the cell and all organisms which are to be recorded are counted as the slide is moved past the objective by the mechanical stage. Usually one trip is made along the long axis of the cell. In some instances, it may be desirable to count several strips to obtain the accuracy desired.

4.4. *Survey count:* Large plankton forms, such as microcrustaceans and rotifers, which can be identified rather readily at low magnifications and are less numerous than the smaller organisms, should be counted by the survey method. This involves enumeration of all organisms of this type which are present in an entire cell volume of 1 ml. Ideally, this count is made with a low-power stereoscopic microscope using its highest power. In routine work, however, most microscopists use the low-power objective, 16 mm, in combination with a 10× ocular.

By means of the mechanical stage, the entire contents of the counting cell are moved past the objective for recognition and enumeration of the organisms being counted. In making this traverse, it is possible to include smaller plankton organisms if these have special significance and cannot be accurately counted by the other procedures.

If the total number of organisms is still too small for accurate reporting, several cells may be counted or the following supplementary procedure adopted: the entire sample is poured into a petri dish, which is then examined under a stereoscopic microscope. Guide lines or squares should be ruled on the petri dish for the purpose of orientation.

The survey count is the method generally applied to silk net collections, although the field or strip count may also be used.

5. Calculation of Results

5.1. *Cubic standard units:* The following calculation is an example of the procedure followed when reporting in terms of cubic standard units. (Results may also be reported in terms of the number of organisms per unit volume of sample by a slight change in procedure.)

a. Record the total number of organisms, or standard units, or both, found by examination of the ten fields or by mechanical-stage traverses.

b. Convert into terms of volumetric standard units the totals recorded for each species. This computation is not necessary where the bulk of a species has been estimated, whenever seen, in terms of volumetric standard units.

c. As each value of volumetric units is obtained, convert this into volumetric standard units per milliliter of original unconcentrated sample. The latter value is obtained by multiplying the volumetric units by suitable factors secured in the following way:

$$\text{factor} = \frac{a}{b} \times \frac{c}{d}$$

where

$a =$ number of fields in 1-ml counting cells 1 mm deep;
$b =$ number of fields counted;
$c =$ ml concentrate; and
$d =$ ml original sample.

If, for example, there are 1,000 fields in the counting cell, 10 fields are examined in the field count, 250 ml water is filtered, 15 ml is the volume of the concentrate, and the cell holds 1 ml and is 1 mm deep, the equation becomes:

$$\text{field count factor} = \frac{1,000}{10} \times \frac{15}{250} = 6$$

In the survey count, the entire cell is examined. If the conditions are the same as those above, 1,000 fields are covered and the equation becomes:

$$\text{survey factor} = \frac{1,000}{1,000} \times \frac{15}{250} = 0.06$$

Multiplication of the results of the field count and survey by the respective factors gives the approximate actual volume of each organism in 1 ml water. This can be converted into cubic standard units per liter by multiplying by 1,000.

d. Record the volumetric standard units per milliliter of sample for each species observed in the survey and field count. Total the items in each column; then add the two sums to obtain the final result, which is expressed as total volumetric standard units or organisms per milliliter of sample. The volume of amorphous matter may be computed and recorded in similar fashion.

5.2. *Number of organisms:* The following calculation is used when reporting in terms of number of organisms per unit volume. (Results may also be reported in terms of cubic standard units by a slight change in procedure.)

For illustrative purposes, the bench sheet shown in Fig. 55 is used here, and the calculation is designed to give the number of organisms per liter rather than per milliliter as in the above example.

a. Record the field count total in the column designed for this purpose. Inasmuch as it is recommended that ten fields be examined, this is the total number of organisms found in ten fields.

b. Calculate the factors needed to convert the survey count, strip count, and field count into number of organisms per liter of original unconcentrated sample. This can be converted into number per 100 liters by multiplying by 100, or into number per milliliter by dividing by 1,000.

(1) *Survey count:* The entire area of a Sedgwick-Rafter counting cell or of several cells is examined. If the contents of one cell are examined and counted, then:

$$\text{factor} = \frac{c}{d} \times 1,000$$

(2) *Strip count:* One or several strips may be examined. If one strip is used, then:

$$\text{factor} = \frac{\text{area of cell}}{\text{area of strip examined}} \times \frac{c}{d} \times 1,000$$

(3) *Field count:* The total number of organisms in ten fields is multiplied by a factor obtained as follows:

$$\text{factor} = \frac{a}{b} \times \frac{c}{d} \times 1,000$$

The Drop-Sedimentation Method

1. Equipment for Concentration

The drop-sedimentation method is essentially a rapid sedimentation by centrifugation of the plankton organisms in a selected volume of water, followed by a withdrawal of all but a few drops of the supernatant liquid. The sediment is resuspended in these drops and an aliquot examined microscopically.

1.1 *Clinical centrifuge:* The centrifuge considered most adequate for this procedure is a small, electric, enclosed, clinical type, equipped with a head which will take two 50-ml tubes. Fully loaded, this centrifuge should be able to maintain a speed of 2,500–3,500 rpm under constant operation. Under these conditions the relative centrifugal force will range from 350 to 2,000 times gravity, depending on the radius from the center of rotation.

1.2. *Centrifuge tubes:* Centrifuge tubes must be tapered and should have a working capacity of 50 ml, but need not be graduated. Resistant glass is preferred. This type of tube is described by some vendors as a "long cone point centrifuge tube" and may be obtained as a regular stock item.

1.3. *Drawoff pipet:* This pipet, utilized in drawing off the supernatant liquid, is simply a straight glass tube long enough to reach the bottom of the centrifuge tube, with a 50–60-ml rubber bulb at one end and a gradual taper at the other. The diameter of the orifice is not specified, but it is suggested that the opening be adjusted to deliver 14–18 drops per milliliter.

1.4. *Dropping pipet:* This pipet is used in handling the final concentrate. It is usually a drawn-out piece of glass tubing with an ordinary medicine dropper bulb slipped over one end; an 8-mm tube may be used. The full diameter is maintained for 120 mm, about half the length of the pipet, and the remaining portion is drawn in a flame to a gradual taper. The inside diameter of the tip should be approximately 1.5 mm. Such an orifice delivers 14–18 drops per milliliter and offers no serious interference to large or long plankton organisms. Calibration is unnecessary, for the whole process of selecting an aliquot of the sample is relative.

The catch is gently drawn into the pipet tube, then expelled again, and the drops are counted. If, for example, 20 drops are desired as the final volume and only 18 drops are available, then 2 drops of the discarded supernatant must be returned to the sample. The same pipet is also used in measuring the sample, which is examined and counted on the microscope stage.

2. Concentration of Sample

The sample is subdivided into 50-ml portions, and each of these is placed in a centrifuge tube of the type described in Sec. 1.2. Thus, if the initial sample is 1,000 ml (200-ml samples are used by some investigators) and the entire amount is concentrated, ten runs will be necessary if a two-place centrifuge is used. The centrifuge is operated at 2,500–3,500 rpm for a period of 5–10 min. After centrifugation the supernatant liquid is removed cautiously by sucking out the upper portion of the sample with a pipet equipped with a 50-ml rubber bulb or by a suction device attached to a vacuum line and equipped with a trap. With practice, the operator can suck up all but the last 5 or 6 drops without disturbing the small sedimented catch which lies at the tip of the centrifuge tube.

It is advantageous at this point to plan the volume of the catch so that the number of drops remaining in the tube will have a definite, easily calculated ratio to the original sample. Thus, in the example just given, where 1,000 ml constitutes the original sample and 10 centrifuge runs are made, let it be assumed that each 50-ml centrifuge tube has all but 5 drops of its contents removed after centrifugation. Because 20 tubes are employed, the total number of drops will be 100 and each drop will represent 10 ml of the original sample. If plankton organisms are abundant, the number of drops in the catch should be increased, possibly to 10 drops per 50-ml centrifuge tube. The exact final dilution must be determined as indicated elsewhere, but microscopic inspection will indicate the concentration most suited to an accurate count.

Following the procedure just outlined, the sample is ready for microscopic examination and enumeration. If the sample is not preserved, it should be examined immediately. The method is particularly suited to examination of live material, and no delay which will alter the sample should be incurred if this advantage is to be retained.

3. Selection of Aliquot Portion

Mix the sample thoroughly by stirring, then transfer 1 drop to a clean 1 × 3-in. microslide. Cover with a clean 25-mm square No. 1 cover glass (0.13 to 0.18 mm in thickness). Thicker, and therefore heavier, cover glasses squeeze out too much sample at the edges. With practice, a fairly even distribution of organisms can be obtained under the cover. Count immediately.

4. Differential Count of Organisms

Place the slide, prepared in the manner outlined in Sec. 3, on the mechanical stage of the microscope and count the organisms in one path across the middle of the cover from left to right; then count a similar path crossing the middle of the cover slip at right angles.

A 25-mm square cover glass, when a 10× ocular and 16-mm objective are used, has approximately 16.5 paths including the amount squeezed out along the edges. This can be verified for the microscope concerned by moving step by step along the rough edge of the cover, one diameter of the field at a step. There are approximately 65 paths when a 4-mm objective is used. Computations of the number of organisms per unit volume are based on this information. The magnifications with these combinations of lenses range from 100 diameters at low power to 430 or 440 diameters at high power.

A plankton worker can readily identify and count organisms as small as 20 microns at low power and as small as 3 or 4 microns at high power. None is missed because of the depth of the medium.

If all species are to be enumerated, several slides must be prepared; for after two paths have been examined, it is frequently necessary to discard that drop and count a second, third, and so on. This may be necessary for the following reasons:

a. Many organisms when examined while alive—*Rhodomonas lacustris*, for example—die quickly and disintegrate completely. This is especially true if quick and extensive rises occur in the temperature.

b. Many organisms in live samples migrate to or from the edges of the cover glass in response to light conditions or oxygen depletion.

c. Evaporation may occur, leaving dry areas under the cover glass.

d. Some species of organisms may be so abundant that dilution of the sample is essential to count them.

e. In order to count rapid swimmers such as *Euglena* spp., it may be necessary to kill them. (A drop of Lugol's solution in 20 to 40 drops of catch will do so but leave them recognizable for counting.)

5. Calculation of Results

A worker utilizing the drop-sedimentation method can identify and count organisms down to 20 microns at 100 diameters. Those only 3 to 4 microns in length can be examined and counted at high power, such as 440×. Results are usually reported in terms of numbers of organisms, but can be converted to volume in the manner outlined in Reporting of Results, B, Sec. 2.

After enumerating and recording the organisms occurring in the concentrate, the computation of numbers actually present in the raw water is easily accomplished. The following example will illustrate the method, assuming an original sample of 100 ml (larger samples should be used in most instances):

a. Centrifuge 100 ml and remove the supernatant liquid, leaving 12.5 drops after decanting.

b. Calculate the ratio of the entire sample to the number of drops: 100/12.5 = 8, or 1 drop = ml of sample.

c. When 1 drop is placed on the microscope slide and covered with a 25-mm square cover slip, there will be 16 paths (microscope field traverses) with a 10× objective, 64 paths with a 44× objective. The exact number of paths must be determined for each individual microscope.

d. On the basis that 1 drop = 8 ml and that it also represents 16 or 64 paths, 1 ml of the raw water will be represented by a count of organisms occurring in 2 paths at low power or in 8 paths at high power.

e. The recommended procedure for counting based on the foregoing is as follows: Count 2 paths in each of 5 drops at a magnification of 100× and 2 paths in each of 4 of these drops at 440×. Simply switch from low to high power for the higher magnification.

f. If, for example, in the 10 paths examined under low power, *Euglena oxyuris* occurred in the following sequence: 1, 0, 1, 1, 2, 0, 1, 1, 0, 1, making a total of 8, the average path contains 0.8 organisms. Inasmuch as 2 paths are equivalent to 1 ml, there are 2× 0.8 = 1.6 organisms per milliliter of raw water.

g. If *Euglena pisciformis* is to be counted in the same sample, it may be desirable to use 440× because this species is too small to identify certainly at low power. When the count obtained is 18, 24, 21, 11, 23, 19, 14, 26, the total is 156 in 8 paths (4 drops, 2 paths each). On this basis, the number of *E. pisciformis* per milliliter of raw water will also be 156, for 8 paths are equivalent to 1 ml. Several species can be counted at one time if the procedure is rapid and the preparation is not allowed to dry out.

Sand Filtration Method for Estimation of Total Plankton

1. Equipment for Concentration

1.1. *Filtering funnels:* A cylindrical funnel of 500-ml capacity is required with dimensions as follows: top diameter approximately 2 in., with straight side for about 9 in., narrowing over a distance of about 3 in. to a bore of 0.5-in. diameter, terminated by a straight portion 0.5 in. in diameter and 2.5 in. long. The funnel is closed at the bottom by a tightly fitting, one-hole rubber stopper containing a small glass U-tube whose outer arm extends 1 in. above the short end in the stopper. The U-tube prevents complete drainage of water from the filter sand after filtration (Fig. 58).

1.2. *Cloth discs:* Cloth discs, about $\frac{3}{8}$ in. in diameter, are needed to support the sand in the funnel. These are cut preferably from silk bolting cloth having about 200 meshes to the inch, although nylon or linen cloth may be used.

1.3. *Filter sand:* White sand is required as the filtering medium. This may be Berkshire or Ottawa sand, ground quartz, or white beach sand. It should be washed and screened, only that portion being used which passes a U.S. Series No. 60 screen and is retained on a No. 120 screen.

2. Concentration of Sample

Filtration should be carried out as soon as possible after collection of the sample. If the sample is kept cool, 3 or 4 hr may safely intervene; but, for longer periods and at high summer temperatures, it is desirable to preserve the sample as directed in Equipment for Collection and Examination of Water, B, Collection and Storage of Water Samples, Sec. 2.

Prepare the sand filter (Fig. 58) for use, first inserting the glass U-tube in the large end of the rubber stopper; then cover the moistened small end with a disc of bolting cloth and place the whole firmly in the lower end of the funnel. The latter should be perfectly clean on the inside.

Pour sand into the funnel to form a layer $\frac{1}{2}$ in. deep on top of the disc. Add 5 to 10 ml distilled water to wash down any sand on the walls of the funnel and to drive the air from the sand. As the distilled water filters through the sand, tilt the funnel from side to side to permit the escape of air.

Mix the sample well, but do not shake violently. Measure out 250-1,000 ml, according to the density of the microscopic organisms in the sample, in a graduate and pour slowly into the funnel, holding the latter in a slanting position and taking care to leave the sand undisturbed.

Allow the water to filter through the sand. Moderate suction may be used to hasten filtration. Wash down the side occasionally with the waste filtrate water from the sample. If living organisms are being concentrated, keep the temperature of the sample uniform during filtration to avoid the lethal effect of heat. After the water has reached the level of the outer arm of the U-tube, disconnect the suction, if employed; carefully remove the U-tube from the stopper to allow most of the remaining water to drain through the sand.

As soon as the sand has drained, transfer the funnel to a horizontal pos-

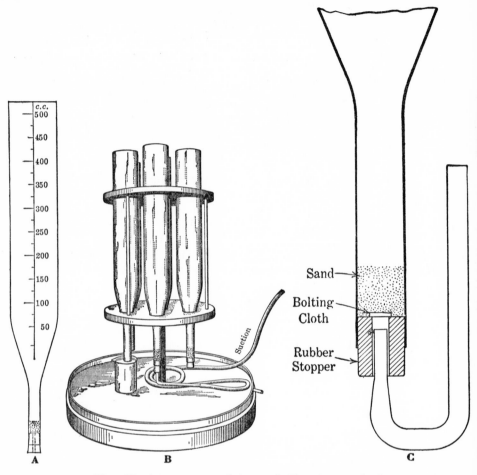

Fig. 58. Apparatus used in sand filtration method

A—cylindrical funnel; the graduations are commonly omitted except on funnels that are to be used in the field. B—revolving stand for filter funnels. C—concentrating attachment, showing U-tube in place. (From Whipple.[8])

ition and remove the stopper slowly with a twisting movement; then raise the funnel to a vertical position inside a small beaker. The plug of sand usually falls into the beaker. Wash down the walls of the funnel with 5–20 ml waste filtrate water, the amount varying with the final concentration of sample desired. The water should be measured with a pipet and is finally col-

lected in the beaker containing the sand and organisms. The container is then shaken gently to detach organisms from the sand grains.

Allow a moment for the coarse sand to settle, then decant promptly into a beaker. A second washing, with an additional 5 ml water, is usually necessary. If the mixing has been thorough, any water remaining in the sand will have the same concentration of organisms as the decanted water of the second washing.

If the concentrated sample is to be preserved for future examination, a 5 per cent solution of formalin (5 ml in 95 ml distilled water) may be used to wash down the funnel, or the formalin may be added to the concentrate and the latter made up to a definite volume; some multiple of 5 is convenient.

3. Selection of Aliquot Portion

Refer to Continuous Centrifuge Method, Sec. 3.

4. Differential Count of Organisms

Refer to Continuous Centrifuge Method, Sec. 4.

5. Calculation of Results

Refer to Continuous Centrifuge Method, Sec. 5.

Alternative Methods

Other forms of plankton concentration are allowable if their accuracy under the conditions used is as great as that of the methods already described. Also, under very special conditions and in emergencies, methods applicable to a specific problem may have to be devised. Several plankton concentration methods of this type, and the equipment required for each, are described in the following sections.

A. Settling Method

This procedure is based on the gravity settling of the organisms which occurs in water after a preserving agent has been added to the sample. Sufficient formalin (30 to 50 ml commercial formalin per liter sample) to produce quick killing and preservation of all organisms is added to the sample bottle, which is then stoppered to prevent evaporation and the entry of dust, and set aside in the dark for approximately two weeks, when most of the plankton will have settled to the bottom. Water is then carefully siphoned off until the upper five-sixths or more of the water column has been removed. Care is taken not to disturb the bottom sediment or the surface film, for organisms may be found in both of these layers. If the resulting sample is not sufficiently concentrated, repeat the process, using a glass tube as a settling device. Frequently three or four settlings and transfers of this kind must be used. Inasmuch as a 2-week period of settling must be allowed each time, it is readily understood that this method is very time consuming.

B. Filter Paper Method

This method is suited more for qualitative than quantitative work. If organisms are very numerous, a quantitative estimate may be obtained. However, for the rare forms it is impractical because the catch is likely to contain too few individuals to make possible a dependable enumeration. The method consists of filtering water samples through a hard-surface filter paper fitted in a glass funnel. The collected plankton is then washed off the paper. Even though the method may be slightly accelerated by application of suction to the collecting flask, it is very slow, and small plankton forms either adhere very closely to the paper or become caught in its meshes, thus making their removal difficult or impossible. Hard-surface filter papers equivalent to No. 575 Schleicher and Schuell or No. 50 Whatman may be employed.

Bottom-Fauna Methods

The examination of bottom materials or sludges involves a qualitative and usually a quantitative determination of the organisms which they contain, as well as a general consideration of the nature of amorphous matter or debris which may be present. Such examinations are made for a number of purposes; for example:

a. To indicate the effect of pollution by domestic sewage or industrial wastes on the body of water receiving such materials.

b. To indicate the progress of self-purification of streams and other bodies of water.

c. To aid in the study of problems relating to shellfish, fish, or other aquatic organisms of importance to man.

d. To aid in the interpretation of data obtained in chemical, bacteriological, and plankton studies carried on as a part of stream pollution or water supply surveys.

e. To aid in explaining the mechanism of biologic sewage treatment methods.

The fauna and flora associated with bottom materials of lakes and streams, or with sludge and deposits in trickling filters, may be divided into two groups —namely, macroorganisms and microorganisms. Procedures for the collection, separation and handling of macroorganisms differ from the methods used for the microscopic forms. Procedures used for both include collection, concentration, separation, identification, and enumeration. The type of collecting apparatus used is dependent on the collection site. For the macroorganisms, materials collected are strained and washed and the individual animal or plant is picked from the debris retained on the sieve. These organisms are then examined microscopically for identification. The volume of organisms is usually determined by displacement methods. In studies of the micro bottom fauna and flora a variety of collecting methods may also be used, depending on the sampling site. However, samples so secured are handled by methods similar to those used for plankton or fine-mesh sieves may be used for the separation of materials. When the latter method is used, microscopic organisms are defined as those which pass through a U.S. Series No. 30 sieve, but are retained by a No. 100 sieve.

The qualitative and, when possible,

the quantitative estimation of organisms which commonly grow on submerged surfaces such as stones, wood, aquatic plants, or other objects requires special technique. These organisms, forming more or less continuous slimy or woolly felted coatings on submerged objects, have been designated the "periphyton," although this term is not truly accurate in view of the fact that both plants and animals contribute to the mass.

A. Apparatus for Collection and Concentration of Bottom-Fauna Samples

1. Collecting Devices

Methods and apparatus needed in a study of bottom fauna will vary with the nature of the bottom deposit which is to be sampled, and no single sampler has been devised which will function under all conditions. If extensive surveys are to be undertaken, several types of samplers should be available, some suited to hard bottoms and stone-strewn riffles, others to soft mucky deposits.

1.1. *Dredge for soft-bottom deposits:* The Ekman dredge, modified from the original design by the provision of a messenger-type tripping device for closing, has been very successful and is now considered standard equipment. Two sizes are available, one having a cross-sectional area of 36 sq in. (6 × 6 in.) and the other 81 sq in. (9 × 9 in.).

The dredge is a rectangular or square brass box closed at its lower opening by strong spring-operated jaws and at its upper end by two thin, hinged, over-

lapping lids that are held shut by water pressure when the dredge is drawn to the surface. The details of construction are shown in Fig. 59. This sampler works well in finely divided mud, marl, or muck, but only moderately well in sand, as fine sand grains tend to jam the closing mechanism.

1.2. *Dredge for hard-bottom deposits:* In sampling hard sand, gravel, clay, and similar bottom sediments, the Petersen dredge has received wide approval. This dredge is fairly heavy; ordinary models weigh approximately 35 lb and additional weights are available to bring the total to 70 lb or more. The weight of the dredge, added to the leverage developed by its closing mechanism, causes the sampler to bite deeply into the bottom material even though it is hard. The exact bite taken by a dredge varies with its size. A dredge having a sampling area of 100 to 110 sq in. is convenient. The principal features of its construction are shown in Fig. 60.

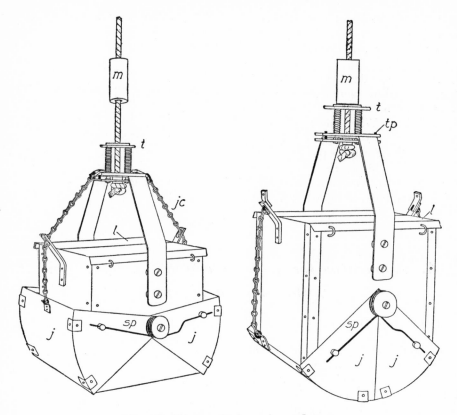

Fig. 59. Ekman dredge of usual type

Left: in open form and ready to be lowered into water. Right: in closed form after messenger
has released trip mechanism and jaws have closed. Key: j—jaw; jc—jaw chain; l—top lid;
m—messenger; sp—spring which operates jaws; t—trip mechanism; tp—trip pin. (From
Welch.[18])

1.3. Samplers for rocky, gravelly bottoms:

a. Surber stream bottom sampler: The Surber sampler (Fig. 61) is a convenient, lightweight device for procuring quantitative samples from shallow rock-strewn streams. Essentially it consists of an extraheavy silk bolting cloth net, No. 000 XXX, 27 in. long, having an opening of 1 sq ft. The net is held open by a metal frame hinged at one side to another frame of equal size. In use, the frame which supports the net is placed in a vertical position and the other is locked into position at right angles, thus limiting the collection area when the sampler is placed on the stream bottom.

Triangular cloth wings fill the side spaces between the horizontal and vertical metal frames. Some workers in constructing this type of net use XX grit gauze having 38 meshes to the inch in place of the No. 000 XXX silk bolting cloth. In operation, the opening of the net is placed upstream, allowing the current to hold the net open; the device is then let down to the bottom, working the lower edge of the 1-sq ft metal frame into the bottom material. Rocks and bottom deposits are dug up within the frame area to a depth of at least 2 in., allowing organisms to be carried into the open net. In some instances, it may be necessary to rub or brush the organisms or their cases from the rocks so that they may

drift back into the net, or it may even be desirable to place pebbles in the net or other suitable container so that organisms can be removed later in the laboratory. When the collection has been removed from the net, the sampler may be folded into a small, compact bundle easily transported to the next sampling point.

b. The Hess sampler: The Hess device, circular with a 1-sq ft area, is suited to similar bottom deposits and overcomes some of the difficulties occasionally encountered with Surber's sampler. However, it is more compli-

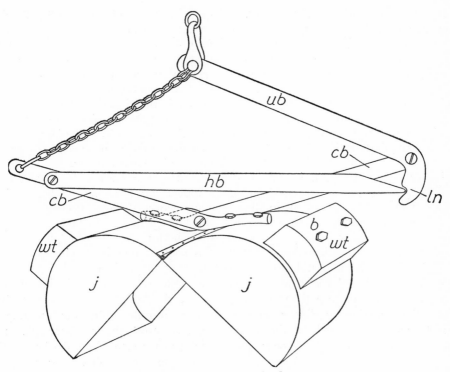

Fig. 60. Petersen dredge

Key: b—stud bolt for fastening weight to jaw of dredge; cb—cross bar; hb—horizontal locking bar; j—semicylindrical jaw of dredge; ln—locking notch; ub—upper bar; wt—weight bolted to dredge jaw. (From Welch.[18])

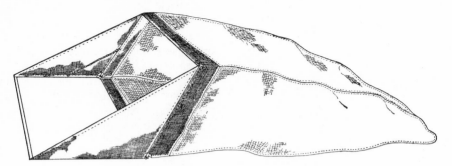

Fig. 61. Surber stream bottom sampler

The cloth net is held open by a hinged metal frame (From Whipple [8])

cated in construction and has not received wide acceptance. It prevents the escape of larger organisms which are strong swimmers and keeps rocks from falling in. It can also be used in quiet backwater areas. For a more detailed description, see Welch [18].

c. Modified Wilding sampler: Where rocky or pebbly bottoms exist and the other sampling devices listed are not entirely satisfactory, the 1-sq ft bottom sampler shown in Fig. 62 may be used. It consists of a 14-gage copper-bearing black-steel cylinder, 13½ in. in diameter and 30 in. high. The lower end is armed with curved sickle blades, which penetrate the deposit when the sampler is forced into it by a rotary motion. Water and rocks, as well as the finer sediments, are then removed from the cylinder by dipper and by hand and concentrated in the usual manner by scraping the rocks and straining the water and sediment through the standard sieves. This device can be used only in relatively shallow water, and is very helpful in small streams. It can be used both in

quiet water and in rapidly flowing streams. Because this cylinder sampler fully encloses the area being studied, practically all organisms except extremely minute forms will be recovered. The only serious objection to the device is that it has considerable bulk.

1.4. *Special samplers:* For unusual situations or problems, adaptations of existing samplers or specialized equipment may be necessary.

a. Modified Ekman dredge: Where samples can be procured by wading, some workers have successfully used the Ekman dredge to take samples on firm bottoms. To accomplish this a 5-ft piece of pipe is attached as a handle and a rod is extended down its center to release the tripping device. In use, the dredge so modified is pushed firmly into the sediment; the trip is released after the operator places a heel on each side of the dredge on the upper edge (back) of each jaw. While the jaws are thus being pushed down, a strong upward pull is exerted on the handle, forcing the jaws shut.

b. Ooze sucker: When a sample of

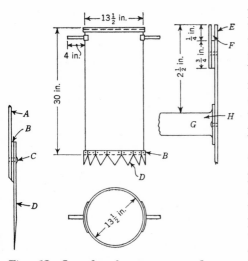

Fig. 62. Sampler for use on rocky or pebbly bottoms

Key: A—tube made of 14-gage copper-bearing black steel; B—rim between tube and sickle teeth; C—rivet; D—sickle teeth curved to fit around tube and riveted in place; E—detail of top rims and handle; F—slot for future extension tube; G—handle (¾-in. pipe); H—handle welded to strap, and strap riveted to tube.

the uppermost part of the bottom deposit is desired, an ooze sucker may be used. A device of this kind is described by Welch [18] from an original design by Rawson as modified by Moore in 1939. It consists of a large, horizontal brass ring, which stops the sampler in the upper layer of the sedimentary deposit. Within this ring is a large rubber bulb, which is attached to a funnel tube and is mounted vertically with the shallow funnel extending just below the ring. When the sampler is lowered, the bulb is compressed between two flat plates. By means of a messenger, the plates are released at the proper moment and the bulb is allowed to expand, sucking in the surface ooze through a 20-mesh screen mounted at the mouth of the collecting funnel. The instrument is very delicate and must be carried in a protecting case. It is more adaptable to qualitative than to quantitative work and finds its greatest usefulness in the former type of sampling.

c. Young's hollow-square sampler: Quantitative samples of the so-called periphyton may be obtained without special equipment by cutting off portions of plants, sections of roots, dead leaves, or submerged wood. However Young's sampler, consisting of sheet brass bent to form a hollow square enclosing an area of 1–2 sq cm (depending on the size of sample required), is a very useful device. One end of the sampler (Fig. 63) is sharpened by beveling the brass. In operation, the sharpened end of the sampler is pressed against the surface covered by the periphyton until it cuts through and encloses a portion of the growth. The surrounding material is scraped away,

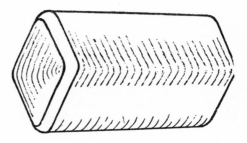

Fig. 63. Hollow-square sampler

Designed by Young, this device is intended for securing quantitative samples of periphyton from hard objects having large areas. (From Welch.[18])

leaving an isolated square of organisms. These are collected in a container after the sampler is removed. Short sections of any metal tubing may be used in the same way by beveling the edge at one end. A correction factor is readily applied to convert the results to a standard area if desired.

d. Screen-dipper surface sampler: In studying the effects of insecticides on organisms which live near the surface film of a body of water, Hess and Tarzwell [15, 17] utilized a method which may be useful in other types of surveys. Because this sampler collects material from a portion of the aquatic environment untouched by the other devices which have been described, it is believed that it may be valuable in surveys requiring an assay of all possible phases of an ecologic association.

The sampler is a square copper dipper, 4 × 4 in., with an adjustable handle attached to one of its sides. A copper or brass screen having approximately 40 meshes to the inch is soldered to the bottom of the dipper. This allows the water to pass through the sampler as it is slowly skimmed sideways along the surface. A mark placed 2 in. above the skimming edge of the dipper serves as a guide so that the collector can take a sample at the proper depth. Inasmuch as a sample ⅓ ft wide is collected over a distance of 3 ft and includes a water depth of 2 in., the area sampled represents 1 sq ft, and the volume strained is ⅙ cu ft. The contents of the dipper are washed into a strainer pan having the same screen mesh as that used for the bottom of the dipper. The material is next poured into a special concentrator to remove the excess water, after which the catch is transferred to a suitable container and preserved for subsequent study in the laboratory. The

details of construction and operation are set forth in Hess and Tarzwell.[15, 17]

e. Tile box sampler: Increased interest in recent years in the occurrence of biologic slimes in polluted rivers has resulted in the development of methods for their study. Where industrial wastes of high carbohydrate content are encountered, the slime bacterium, *Sphaerotilus* sp., and associated organisms, may be stimulated to such an extent that a serious nuisance will result at places of growth, as well as at points sometimes far downstream where detached growths may be transported in suspension.

For years the technique of submerging glass microscope slides or similar materials has been practiced to determine occurrence and distribution of attached growths.[26] Utilizing the same principle, the tile box sampler (Fig. 64) is suggested for the larger streams to provide a suitable attachment surface for slimes and a means for their quantitative determination.

The box is made of marine plywood, with side members extended backward at a slight angle to serve as fins. The device is oriented in the current so that the water passes freely through it and past the tiles, which are held in a vertical position edgewise to the axis of flow. Provision may also be made for holders to suspend microscope slides to provide for direct fixing, staining and examination of growth *in situ*. The tiles are of unglazed ceramic material, either 4½ or 6 in. square.

In large rivers, samplers should, if possible, be tied to fixed structures such as floats at boat moorages. However, if representative sampling requires that samplers be located where fixed structures are unavailable, buoys and anchors may be used. Chain of at

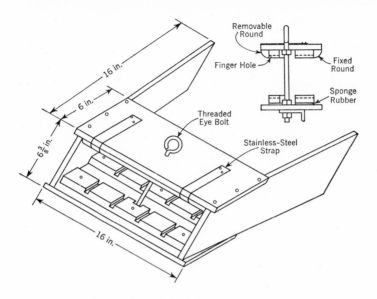

Fig. 64. Wilson tile box sampler

least 1,200-lb test has been found successful, along with 10-gal can buoys and anchors of 100-lb minimum weight.

After the box has been held in the stream for the desired period—usually 1 week in summer and 2 weeks in winter—the device is lifted slowly to the surface, two of the tiles are carefully removed, and growths are thoroughly scraped from their smooth surfaces (one side of the tile is usually ribbed, the other smooth) into a wide-mouth bottle of about ½-pt capacity. A medium-size steel spatula is satisfactory as a scraper. To rinse the tile, a 3 per cent solution of formalin (3 ml plus 97 ml distilled water) is applied by means of a plastic squeeze bottle. Growth caught on the leading edge of the tile is disregarded. A small amount of slime from the reverse side of a tile is placed in a separate bottle for microscopic examination and qualitative determination of the living material.

After removal of the sample, the tiles are thoroughly cleaned with a scrub brush and cleaning powder, rinsed, and immersed for 1 min or more in a strong chlorine solution for disinfection. They may then be reinserted in the tile box.

The material removed from the tile is centrifuged in two stages. This reduces the volume to the point where the entire sample may be transferred to a tared 35-ml evaporating dish. Determinations of dry weight and loss on ignition are then made to differentiate between total organic matter and ash content. The latter also includes inorganic solids and silt adhering to the slime.

Microscopic examinations of the living or fixed and stained material which is collected from the reverse side of the tiles or from glass microscope slides attached to the tile boxes provides other useful information. Estimates of percentages by volume of *Sphaerotilus* sp., fungi, algae, protozoa, and general amorphous matter, including silt and wood fibers, can be made rapidly and are an important guide to full interpretation of the quantitative results.

f. Reighard tow net: Slimes can also be collected by a net. The Reighard tow net (Fig. 65) as described in Welch [18] is provided with a net of 16-mesh silk bolting cloth which has a circular opening 1 sq ft in area (13.6-in. diameter). Steel rods serve as framework and runners to protect the net where the device is used as a bottom drag.

The Reighard tow net may be used

ume of water passing through the net is calculated.

In the laboratory, the total quantity of slime and associated material is determined by 1-hr sedimentation in an Imhoff cone. Microscopic examination and percentage differentiation by volume of slimes versus other organisms and debris may be accomplished, just as with the samples from tile boxes.

1.5. *Qualitative samplers:* Any of the samplers mentioned above may also be used to obtain qualitative samples. There are, however, specially designed

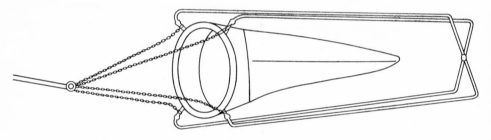

Fig. 65. Reighard tow net
(J. N. Wilson modification)

for either qualitative or quantitative samples. In the former instance, the net may be towed from a boat or, where the current is sufficiently swift, tied to a dock for a period of time to check the presence of suspended slimes. If quantitative samples are desired, the net is tied to a dock or boat anchored in a stream and weights or floats are used where necessary to regulate the depth of the net. The duration of sampling is timed and the current velocity is measured by meter, pitot tube, or similar device. The volume of water passing through the net is thus determined. The usual collection period is 5 min, after which the catch is washed from the net into a container and preserved by the addition of formalin to a final concentration of 3 per cent. The vol-

exploratory samplers which may be used for this purpose.

a. Sounding weight sampler: This is a combined sounding weight and exploratory sampling device. It consists of a heavy lead sounding weight, usually 5 lb, to the lower end of which a conical collecting cup has been attached by a rod which extends through its center. A sliding cover is provided which leaves the cone receptacle open on the way down but drops in place as the weight is pulled to the surface (Fig. 66).

b. U. S. Public Health Service scoop sampler: This is a cone-shaped metal cup with a sharp cutting edge which has been fastened to an elongated strap-iron handle (Fig. 67). When a rope has been attached to this handle, the

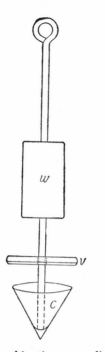

Fig. 66. Combination sounding weight and reconnaissance bottom sampler

Key: w—lead weight; v—sliding cover; c—collecting cup (From Welch [18])

sampler can be thrown into the water and dragged along the bottom until a suitable sample has been obtained.

c. Hand screen: One of the most useful single tools for collecting small animals from rapid streams consists of a sheet of wire screening 2 or 3 ft long and 24 to 30 in. wide. The ends are fastened in slots sawed in two handles approximately 5 ft long. This sampler is held in the current while the bottom upstream is vigorously stirred. The dislodged organisms are caught by the screen, from which they may be dumped into a sorting tray. (See Taxonomic References, Needham.[1])

The same equipment and methods may be used in concentrating qualitative samples as in quantitative work.

2. Sieves

Two screen sieves of standard mesh are needed for the concentration of samples. One of these, a relatively coarse screen, is a U.S. Standard Sieve Series No. 30, having openings of 0.589 mm. The other is a No. 100, having openings of 0.149 mm.

3. Containers

A small tub and a 3-gal pail are needed for proper manipulation of the sample. Gallon pails, with double friction cover, or 1-gal glass bottles with mouths 4 in. wide or more, equipped with screw caps, may be used for storage of preserved samples or to carry concentrated live samples to the labo-

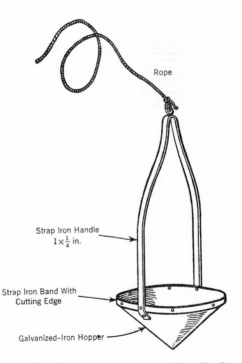

Rope

Strap Iron Handle
$1 \times \frac{1}{4}$ in.

Strap Iron Band With
Cutting Edge

Galvanized-Iron Hopper

Fig. 67. Mud sampler devised by U. S. Public Health Service
(From Whipple [8])

ratory. Squat wide-mouth glass bottles of 100-ml capacity, or ½-pt fruit jars, may be used for the microorganisms sample retained by the 100-mesh sieve. These containers may also be used for storage of specimens after final sorting and counting. Ordinarily, however, small glass vials are used for the sorted specimens.

4. Microscopes

A stereoscopic microscope is essential, and for careful work a compound microscope must also be available. The microscopes listed as equipment for plankton examination will also fit the needs for bottom sediment work. In addition, it is suggested that a special lamp suited to the stereoscopic microscope be provided. This lamp should be readily adjustable to furnish direct rather than transmitted illumination of the object from a number of angles, and it is desirable that the intensity of the light be variable at the will of the operator.

B. Collection of Bottom Sediment or Sludge Samples

1. Sampling Points

Sampling points should be carefully selected to assure the collection of samples which represent the prevailing condition of the environment being studied. The exact location and number of samples taken must be left to the judgment of the individual investigator. However, it is self-evident that there should be a spread of samples throughout the area being studied and that more than one sample should be taken at each station during the course of a study. Samples may be taken at irregularly scattered or random points, or collected along ranges which cross an area. Often it is feasible to collect three samples at each station, arranging them at equidistant points along a cross section. One sample is taken at the center, and the other two at points to the left and right of center and halfway to the bank. In this method of sampling, nontypical microenvironments along the bank are excluded. In pollution surveys, the near-shore area is frequently unrepresentative, for it may be influenced readily by minute and often unimportant local situations. Trout, for example, have been taken from heavily polluted sections of streams where oxygen in the channel was exhausted much of the time. In one instance of this kind, the fish lived fairly comfortably within the sphere of influence of a spring which entered the stream. Immature insects, as well as other bottom-dwelling organisms, may be affected similarly. It is evident, therefore, that the selection of a sampling point is very important and that it should be based on a first-hand knowledge of the stream or other aquatic environments involved. An exploratory or reconnaissance survey prior to final selection of the sampling station is very desirable as an aid to proper sampling.

2. Collection Procedures

2.1. *Dredge sampling method:* If a dredge sampler is used, proceed as follows:

a. See that the dredge is in working order, that the tripping mechanism operates, and that the messenger is in place if the sampler is actuated by such a device.

b. Lower the dredge vertically and very slowly to the bottom so that water currents are not set up. Such currents may displace the soft, flocculent upper layers.

c. Upon its arrival at the bottom allow the dredge to settle; then trip the closing mechanism. If the Petersen dredge is used, this is accomplished by slackening the cord. The Ekman dredge is tripped by releasing a brass messenger which slides down the line readily if sufficient tension is exerted to keep it straight.

d. Draw the dredge up to the surface, and slip it into a tub. Neither type of dredge should be lifted above the water surface for any considerable distance before it is placed in the tub which is to receive the sample.

e. Empty the dredge. The Ekman dredge is discharged by pulling up each jaw chain two or three times as the sampler is held mouth downward. The Petersen dredge is emptied by prying the jaws apart and scooping out the sediments with the hand or some convenient scraping device. Before the Ekman dredge is emptied, the upper flaps may be opened to ascertain whether or not a suitable sample has been taken.

2.2. Other sampling methods: Methods to be employed when other collecting devices are used have been presented in a general way in Sec. 1 of *A* above, which describes the equipment. Additional details may be found in Welch [18].

C. Concentration of Samples

1. Macroorganisms

1.1. General considerations: Although it is possible to convey the entire dredge sample to the laboratory for concentration—and this may be the procedure of choice in freezing weather—the best procedure consists of washing and screening the catch in the field immediately following collection.

The screening of dredge samples may be done over the side of the boat used in collecting the samples, or, if the water is rough, this work may be carried out near the bank or shore in protected water, such as a dock area. If screening is done near shore, precautions should be taken to avoid contamination of the sample by organisms belonging to this environmental niche.

1.2. Screening and decanting: In concentrating the bottom sediment samples, the initial step is screening. The material, which has been discharged from the sampler into a tub, is stirred vigorously to suspend the fine sediment. The cloudy supernatant liquid is then drained off quickly by pouring it through a No. 30 sieve into a 3-gal pail or other suitable container. If water free of bottom-dwelling organisms is added to the sample, the process may be repeated several times. Organisms and debris collecting on the screen are removed and stored in a suitable container.

1.3. Combined washing-screening process: The residue remaining after the decanting procedure is further reduced in volume and cleaned by a combined washing-screening process. This is accomplished by lowering the No. 30 sieve containing a portion of the sample into water until it is half submerged. Next, the sieve is given a vigorous circular motion at the same time that it is raised and lowered slightly. Such agitation produces a swirling movement which turns the sample over and over while a current of water passes alternately up and down through the screen. When the water is no longer clouded by its passage through the sample, and in the opinion of the operator all of the fine sediment has been removed, the sample is ready for examination. The residue is a clean, washed concentrate containing a mixture of animal and vegetable debris, coarse sand and gravel, and the organisms to be identified and enumerated. It is combined with the residue obtained in the decanting procedure and placed in 1-gal glass or metal containers for transportation to the laboratory.

1.4. *Samples in transit:* In transit,

the concentrate must be kept cool. If the distance is great and final examination may be delayed, the sample should be preserved by the addition of formalin to make a 5 to 10 per cent solution (10 ml of commercial formalin added to 90 ml water constitutes a 10 per cent solution) or by adding alcohol (final concentration 80–90 per cent).

2. Microorganisms

If the investigator wishes to extend his studies to the micro fauna of the bottom sediments, the material passing through the No. 30 sieve into the 3-gal pail in the initial decanting procedure is strained through a No. 100 sieve. The residue remaining on the No. 100 screen contains the organisms belonging to this group and it should therefore be removed from the screen and stored or preserved in wide-mouth, 100-ml bottles or other suitable containers. This material is examined by a special technique described in the next section.

D. Examination of Sediment Concentrates

1. Macroorganisms

The macro fauna of the bottom sediment is found in the material retained by the No. 30 sieve. If this concentrate is preserved in the field, it should be subjected to another washing process prior to laboratory examination. Formalin vapors, which are extremely irritating to most individuals, can be removed by this procedure. In addition, the washing process is an aid in sorting, for the water stream brings about a separation of the various portions of the concentrate. The recommended procedure is as follows:

A strong stream of water is directed into the pail containing the sample until it is filled. The supernatant water is quickly poured from the container and strained through the No. 30 sieve. After this process has been repeated several times, it will be found that almost all the organisms and most of the vegetable material have been deposited on the screen.

The material collected on the screen is washed into a shallow dish, where it can be spread out in a thin layer. With the aid of a pair of forceps, the organisms may be separated from the debris by hand picking. A white, flat-bottom dish or pan is recommended for this sorting. If the washing has been thorough, very few or no organisms at all will be found in the heavier residue left in the sample pail, and this portion of the sample can be examined very quickly in spite of its bulk. Again, the method of examination consists in spreading the material thinly over the flat bottom of a white pan or dish in such a manner that all organisms may be readily recognized and removed. The catch should be preserved at once in 5 to 10 per cent formalin or 80 to 90 per cent alcohol if the final identification of the specimens is postponed.

2. Microorganisms

The material retained on the No. 100 sieve after passing the coarse screen is much finer in texture than the macro fauna sample and therefore requires a somewhat different treatment. Inasmuch as the organisms are rather minute, the sample must be examined microscopically to determine the identity of the specimens and the number of individuals present. A low-power stereoscopic microscope is required for this procedure, and it will be found that a magnification of 20× is convenient for most work.

The identification and counting procedure is similar to that employed in the examination of silk net plankton. An aliquot portion of the sample is placed in a Syracuse watch crystal or a square glass dish similar to a petri dish. The bottoms of these dishes should be ruled off in parallel guide lines, the distance between these guide lines being slightly less than the width of field characteristic of the microscope at the magnification used in making the count. Organisms within the dish are identified and counted as it is moved past the objective of the microscope. The guide lines are used for orientation as the sample is moved from right to left, or vice versa, in covering the entire area of the dish. As the dish is moved past the objectives, all organisms lying between the lines are counted.

To obtain the accuracy desired, it may be necessary to examine several aliquot portions. The amount of material which is placed in a dish for examination is related to the physical nature of the sample. For example, if the sample contains very little silt or debris, the visibility will be good and relatively large portions may be used. Conversely, a sample heavily laden with debris must be examined in a very thin layer and in many portions. The total amount of material examined must further be based on such factors as uniformity of sample, total volume of sample, types of organisms present, a knowledge of the character of the sampling point, and the objectives of the study. Usually the examination of one-tenth of the entire volume of the sample will suffice.

E. Calculation and Reporting of Results

1. Forms

Bench sheets of the type used in plankton counting will also be useful in bottom sediment studies. Various workers may differ in their opinions relating to the information which should be included in such a form, and it is therefore suggested that each worker develop his own. However, for the purpose of reference and as a working model, the sample form shown in Fig. 68 is recommended.

identification, when it can be made with assurance, is desirable. Space does not permit a discussion of the principles of taxonomy for the identification of plankton or bottom-dwelling organisms. This information, as well as dis-

BIOLOGICAL EXAMINATION OF SEDIMENT

Location_____

Serial No._____ Date_____ Collecting Device_____

Factor: Number of Organisms per Square Yard/Meter _____

ORGANISMS	Per Sample	Per Square Yd. Square M.	POLLUTIONAL STATUS		
			Pollut.	Facult.	Cleaner

SPECIAL INFORMATION   Totals_____

                              %_____

General character of sample as collected_____

After sifting_____Sieve used_____

Depth_____Odor_____

Temp. of material_____Water movement_____

Received_____Examined_____By_____

Remarks:_____

Fig. 68. Sample bench sheet for bottom sediment records

2. Identification of Organisms

Whenever possible, the species of an organism should be determined. It is recognized that identification to genus or to a more generalized group may suffice in some instances, but specific

cussions relating to the use of living organisms as indexes of pollution, are presented by various authors whose publications are listed in the bibliography. As a matter of orientation, illustrations of some of the more common plankton and bottom-dwelling organisms are shown in Plates I-XXXIX.

3. Quantity of Organisms

The results of a bottom sediment study can be expressed in various ways, such as number of organisms per square yard or square meter, number per volumetric unit of sample, volume per unit area or unit volume of sample, or weight of organisms per unit area or unit volume. In stream pollution surveys, it is customary to report the number of organisms per square yard or per square meter, and this method is adopted here for the purpose of illustrating the necessary calculations. When the identity and the number of organisms in a given sample have been determined, the results can be converted from the number of organisms per sample to the number per square yard by applying a factor obtained as follows:

$$\text{factor} = \frac{1,296}{\text{dredge sampling area (sq in.)}}$$

When the sampling area of the dredge is 36 sq in., the factor is $1,296/36 = 36$.

In the case of a sample retained on the No. 100 sieve, only a part of the sample is examined critically under the microscope. In order to express the results on the same basis as given above, the calculation is modified as follows:

$$\text{factor} = \frac{V \times 1,296}{S \ A}$$

where V = total volume of sample, in ml;
S = volume of sample examined, in ml; and
A = dredge sampling area, in sq in.

Where the original volume of the sample is 100 ml, the amount examined 10 ml, and the sampling area of the dredge 36 sq in., the factor becomes $100/10 \times 1,296/36 = 360$.

All results should be carefully recorded and entered on a standard form of the type shown in Fig. 68.

Bibliography

1. CALKINS, G. N. The Microscopical Examination of Water. *Mass. State Board of Health Repts.* 23:397 (1891).
2. CALKINS, G. N. A Study of Odors Observed in Drinking Water. *Mass. State Board of Health Repts.* 24:355 (1892).
3. RAFTER, G. W. *The Microscopical Examination of Potable Water.* D. Van Nostrand Co., Princeton, N.J. (1892).
4. STUDENT. On the Error of Counting With a Haemacytometer. *Biometrika* 5:351 (1907).
5. NEEDHAM, J. G. & LLOYD, J. T. *The Life of Inland Waters.* Comstock Publishing Associates, Ithaca, N.Y. (1915).
6. PURDY, W. C. Pollution and Natural Purification of the Ohio River. *Public Health Bull.* No. 131 (1922).
7. JUDAY, C. A Third Report on Limnological Apparatus. *Trans. Wisconsin Acad. Sci.* 22:299 (1926).
8. WHIPPLE, G. C.; FAIR, G. M.; & WHIPPLE, M. C. *The Microscopy of Drinking Water.* John Wiley & Sons, New York (1927).
9. BAYLIS, J. R. & GERSTEIN, H. H. Microorganisms in Lake Michigan Water. *Munic. News & Water Works* 76:291 (1929).
10. MORGAN, A. H. *Field Book of Ponds and Streams.* G. P. Putnam's Sons, New York (1930).
11. ABDERHALDEN, E., ed. *Handbuch der Biologischen Arbeitsmethoden.* Urban & Schwarzenberg, Berlin (1936).
12. OLSON, T. A. Microscopic Methods Used in Biological Investigation of Lake and Stream Pollution and Interpretation of Results. *Sew. Works J.* 8:759 (1936).
13. LACKEY, J. B. The Manipulation and Counting of River Plankton and Changes in Some Organisms Due to Formalin Preservation. *Public Health Repts.* 53:2080 (1938).
14. TIFFANY, L. H. *Algae, the Grass of Many Waters.* C. C. Thomas, Publisher, Springfield, Ill. (1938).
15. HESS, A. D. & TARZWELL, C. M. The Feeding Habits of *Gambusia affinis*

affinis, With Special Reference to the Malaria Mosquito, *Anopheles quadrimaculatus. Am. J. Hyg.* 35:142 (1942).

16. PHELPS, E. B. *Stream Sanitation.* John Wiley & Sons, New York (1944).

17. TARZWELL, C. M. The Effects on Surface Organisms of the Routine Hand Application of DDT Larvicides for Mosquito Control. *Public Health Repts.* 62:525 (1947).

18. WELCH, P. S. *Limnological Methods.* Blakiston Co., Philadelphia (1948).

19. BARTSCH, A. F. Biological Aspects of Stream Pollution. *Sew. Works J.* 20:292 (1948).

20. MACAN, T. T. & WORTHINGTON, E. B. *Life in Lakes and Rivers.* Collins, London (1951).

21. LIEBMANN, H. *Handbuch der Frishwasser und Abwasserbiologie—Biologie des Trinkwassers, Badewassers, Fischwassers, Vorfluters, und Abwassers.* Munich (1951). Vol. 1, p. 539.

22. GAUFIN, A. R. & TARZWELL, C. M. Aquatic Invertebrates as Indicators of Stream Pollution. *Public Health Repts.* 67:57 (1952).

23. MOORE, E. W. The Precision of Microscopic Counts of Plankton in Water. *J. AWWA* 44:208 (1952).

24. CLARKE, G. L. *Elements of Ecology.* John Wiley & Sons, New York (1954).

25. PALMER, C. M. & MALONEY, T. E. A New Counting Slide for Nannoplankton. *Amer. Soc. Limnol. & Oceanog. Spec. Pub.* No. 21 (1954).

26. COOKE, W. B. Colonization of Artificial Bare Areas by Microorganisms. *Botan. Rev.* 22:613 (1956).

27. USINGER, R. L. *Aquatic Insects of California.* Univ. of California Press, Berkeley (1956).

28. HUTCHINSON, G. E. *A Treatise on Limnology.* John Wiley & Sons, New York (1957). Vol. 1.

29. TARZWELL, C. M., ed. *Biological Problems in Water Pollution (Transactions Water Pollution Seminar, 1956).* Robert A. Taft Sanitary Eng. Center, Cincinnati, Ohio (1957).

30. MOORE, H. B. *Marine Ecology.* John Wiley & Sons, New York (1958).

31. NEEDHAM, G. W. *The Practical Use of the Microscope, Including Photomicrography.* C. C. Thomas, Springfield, Ill. (1958).

32. KUTKUHN, J. T. Notes on The Precision of Numerical and Volumetric Plankton Estimates from Small-Sample Concentrates. *Limnology & Oceanog.* 3:69 (1958).

33. LUND, J. W. G.; KIPLING, C.; & LECREN, E. D. The Inverted Microscope Method of Estimating Algal Numbers and the Statistical Basis of Estimation by Counting. *Hydrobiologica* 11:143 (1958).

34. BARNES, H. *Oceanography and Marine Biology.* Macmillan Co., New York (1959).

Taxonomic References

When taxonomic references of wide geographic coverage do not exist, publications of a more limited nature are listed. For taxonomic groups not listed, see general references.

General

1. PRATT, H. S. *A Manual of the Common Invertebrate Animals Exclusive of Insects.* Blakiston Co., Philadelphia (1935).

2. FASSET, N. C. *A Manual of Aquatic Plants.* McGraw-Hill Book Co., New York (1940).

3. MUENSCHER, W. C. *Aquatic Plants in the United States.* Comstock Publishing Associates, Ithaca, N.Y. (1944).

4. PENNAK, R. W. *Fresh-Water Invertebrates of the United States.* Ronald Press, New York (1953).

5. EDMONDSON, W. T., ed. *Ward and Whipple's Fresh-Water Biology.* John Wiley & Sons, New York (2d ed., 1959).

6. EDDY, S. & HODSON, A. C. *Taxonomic Keys to the Common Animals of the North Central States Exclusive of the Parasitic Worms, Insects, and Birds.* Burgess Publishing Co., Minneapolis, Minn. (1962).

7. NEEDHAM, J. G. & NEEDHAM, P. R. *Guide to the Study of Fresh-Water Biology.* Comstock Publishing Associates, Ithaca, N.Y. (1962).

Algae

8. ELMORE, C. J. *The Diatoms (Bacillarioideae) of Nebraska.* Univ. of Nebraska, Lincoln (1921).

9. SMITH, G. M. Phytoplankton of the

Inland Lakes of Wisconsin. Parts I and II. *Wisconsin Univ. Geol. & Nat. Hist. Survey Bull.* No. 57 (1924).

10. PASCHER, A., ed. *Die Susswasser Flora Deutschlands, Osterreichs, und der Schweiz. Heft 4. Volvocales—Phytomonadinae.* G. Fischer, Jena, Germany (1927).

11. PASCHER, A., ed. *Die Susswasser Flora Mitteleuropas. Heft 10. Bacillariophyta (Diatomeae).* G. Fischer, Jena, Germany (1930).

12. SMITH, G. M. *The Fresh-Water Algae of the United States.* McGraw-Hill, New York (1950).

13. PRESCOTT, G. W. *Algae of the Western Great Lakes Area.* Bull. 31, Cranbrook Inst. of Science, Bloomfield Hills, Mich. (1951).

14. TIFFANY, L. H. & BRITTON, M. E. *The Algae of Illinois.* Univ. of Chicago Press, Chicago (1952).

15. DROUET, F. & DAILY, W. A. Revision of the Coccoid Myxophyceae. *Butler Univ. Botan. Studies* 12:1 (1956).

16. PALMER, C. M. *Algae in Water Supplies.* Pub. 657, US Public Health Service, Washington, D.C. (1959).

Annelid Worms

17. GALLOWAY, T. W. The Common Fresh-Water Oligochaeta of the United States. *Trans. Am. Microscop. Soc.* 30:285 (1911).

18. NACHTRIEB, H. F.; HEMINGWAY, E. E.; & MOORE, J. P. The Leeches of Minnesota. *Minn. Geol. & Nat. Hist. Survey, Zoological Ser.* No. 5 (1912).

19. WELCH, P. S. The Genera of Enchytraeidae (Oligochaeta). *Trans. Am. Microscop. Soc.* 39:25 (1920).

20. MILLER, J. A. *The Leeches of Ohio.* Contribution No. 2, Franz Theodore Stone Lab., Ohio State Univ., Columbus (1929).

21. STEPHENSON, J. *The Oligochaeta.* Oxford Univ. Press, London (1930).

22. BERE, R. Leeches From the Lakes of Northeastern Wisconsin. *Trans. Wisconsin Acad. Sci.* 26:437 (1931).

Aquatic Insects

23. HUNGERFORD, H. B. The Biology and Ecology of Aquatic and Semiaquatic Hemiptera. *Univ. Kansas Sci. Bull.* 11:3 (1919).

24. NEEDHAM, J. G. Burrowing Mayflies of Our Larger Lakes and Streams. *Bull. US Fish.* 36:267 (1920).

25. BRITTON, W. E., ET AL. Guide to the Insects of Connecticut. Part IV. The Hemiptera or Sucking Insects of Connecticut. *Conn. State Geol. & Nat. Hist. Survey Bull.* 34:807 (1923).

26. NEEDHAM, J. G. & CLAASSEN, P. W. *A Monograph of the Plecoptera or Stoneflies of America North of Mexico.* Thomas Say Foundation Publications, Lafayette, Ind. (1925). Vol. 2, p. 397.

27. GARMAN, P. Guide to the Insects of Connecticut. Part V. The Odonata or Dragonflies of Connecticut. *Conn. State Geol. & Nat. Hist. Survey Bull.* 39:7 (1927).

28. NEEDHAM, J. G. & HEYWOOD, H. B. *A Handbook of the Dragonflies of North America.* C. C. Thomas, Publisher, Springfield, Ill. (1929).

29. CLAASSEN, P. W. *Plecoptera Nymphs of America (North of Mexico).* Thomas Say Foundation Publications, Springfield, Ill. (1931). Vol. 3, p. 199.

30. BETTEN, O. The Caddis Flies or Trichoptera of New York State. *N.Y. State Museum Bull.* No. 292 (1934).

31. JOHANNSEN, O. A. Aquatic Diptera. Part I. Nemocera, Exclusive of Chironomidae and Ceratopogonidae. *Cornell Univ. Expt. Sta. Mem.* No. 164 (1934).

32. FRISON, T. H. The Stoneflies, or Plecoptera, of Illinois. *Bull. Illinois State Nat. Hist. Survey* 20:281 (1935).

33. JOHANNSEN, O. A. Aquatic Diptera. Part II. Orthorrhapha-Brachycera and Cyclorrhapha. *Cornell Univ. Expt. Sta. Mem.* No. 177 (1935).

34. JOHANNSEN, O. A. Aquatic Diptera. Part III. Chironomidae: Subfamilies Tanypodinae, Diamesinae, and Orthocladiinae. *Cornell Univ. Expt. Sta. Mem.* No. 205 (1936).

35. JOHANNSEN, O. A. Aquatic Diptera. Part IV. Chironomidae: Subfamily Chironominae; Part V. Ceratopogonidae. *Cornell Univ. Expt. Sta. Mem.* No. 210 (1937).

36. WRIGHT, M. & PETERSON, A. A Key to the Genera of Anisopterous Dragonfly Nymphs of the United States and Canada. *Ohio J. Sci.* 44:151 (1944).

37. ROSS, H. H. The Caddis Flies, or Trichoptera, of Illinois. *Illinois State Nat. Hist. Survey Bull.* 23:Art. 1 (1944).

38. Townes, H. K., Jr. The Nearctic Species of *Tendipedini*. *Am. Midland Naturalist* 34, No. 1 (1945).
39. Berner, L. *The Mayflies of Florida*. Univ. of Florida Press, Gainesville (1950).
40. Nicholson, H. P. & Mickel, C. E. The Black Flies of Minnesota (Simuliidae). *Minn. Univ. Agr. Expt. Sta. Tech. Bull.* No. 192 (1950).
41. Maynard, E. A. *Collembola or Springtail Insects of New York State*. Comstock Publishing Associates, Ithaca, N.Y. (1951).
42. Johannsen, O. A., et al. Guide to the Insects of Connecticut. Part VI. The Diptera or True Flies. Fifth Fascicle: Midges and Gnats. *Conn. State Geol. & Nat. Hist. Survey Bull.* 80:255 (1952).
43. Harden, F. H. & Mickel, C. E. The Stoneflies of Minnesota (Plecoptera). *Minn. Univ. Agr. Expt. Sta. Tech. Bull.* No. 201 (1952).
44. Usinger, R. L., et al. *Aquatic Insects of California, With Keys to North American Genera and California Species*. Univ. of California Press, Berkeley (1956).

Crustacea

45. Herrick, C. L. & Turner, C. H. *Synopsis of the Entomostraca of Minnesota*. 2nd Rept. of State Zoologist, Minn. Geol. & Nat. Hist. Survey (1895).
46. Weckel, A. L. The Fresh-Water Amphipoda of North America. *Proc. US Natl. Museum* 32:25 (1907).
47. Marsh, C. D. Distribution and Key of the North American Copepods of the Genus Diaptomus. *Proc. US Natl. Museum* 75:Art. 15 (1918).
48. Wilson, C. B. The Copepoda of the Woods Hole Region, Massachusetts. *US Natl. Museum Bull.* No. 158 (1932).
49. Van Name, W. G. The American Land and Fresh-Water Isopod Crustacea. *Bull. Am. Museum Nat. Hist.* 71:1 (1936).

50. Van Name, W. G. A Supplement to the American Land and Fresh-Water Isopod Crustacea. *Bull. Am. Museum Nat. Hist.* 77:109 (1940).
51. Van Name, W. G. A Second Supplement to the American Land and Fresh-Water Isopod Crustacea. *Bull. Am. Museum Nat. Hist.* 81:299 (1942).
52. Hoff, C. C. The Ostracods of Illinois. *Illinois Biol. Monographs* 19:1 (1942).

Mites

53. Marshall, R. Canadian Hydracarina. *Univ. Toronto Studies, Publ. Ontario Fish Research Lab.* No. 39 (1929).
54. Marshall, R. Preliminary List of the Hydracarina of Wisconsin. Parts I–III. The Red Mites. *Trans. Wisconsin Acad. Sci.* 26:311 (1931); 27:339 (1932); 28:37 (1933).
55. Baker, E. W. & Wharton, G. W. *An Introduction to Acarology*. Macmillan Co., New York (1952).

Mollusca

56. Surber, T. *Identification of the Glochidia of Fresh-Water Mussels*. Appendix V to Rept. of US Commissioner of Fisheries for 1914 (1915).
57. Baker, F. C. The Fresh-Water Mollusca of Wisconsin. Parts I and II. *Wisconsin Geol. & Nat. Hist. Survey Bull.* No. 70 (1928).

Protozoa

58. Kahl, A. *Wimpertiere oder Ciliata* [Vol. 1 of F. Dahl's *Die Tierwelt Deutschlands*] (1930–1935).
59. Calkins, G. N. *Biology of the Protozoa*. Philadelphia (2nd ed., 1933).
60. Walton, L. B. A Review of the Described Species of the Order Euglenoidina Block, Class Flagellata (Protozoa) with Particular Reference to Those Found in the City Water Supplies and in Other Localities of Ohio. *Ohio Biol. Survey* 1:343 (1945).
61. Kudo, R. R. *Protozoology*. C. C. Thomas, Springfield, Ill. (1946).
62. Hall, R. P. *Protozoology*. Prentice-Hall, New York (1953).

Some Common Aquatic Organisms

Index to Keys of Plates I–XXXIX

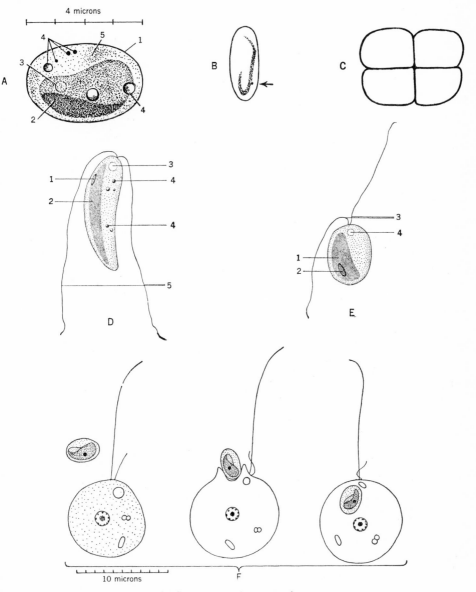

I. Common microorganisms

A—*Vegetative cell of* Chlorella vulgaris *showing typical structures: (1) cell wall; (2) chloroplast; (3) nucleus; (4) inclusions; (5) cytoplasm*
B—*Cross section of cell*

C—*Cell after dividing twice*
D—*Reproductive cell of green alga, illustrating similarity to (E), a green flagellate: (1) stigma; (2) chloroplast; (3) vacuole; (4) oil droplet; (5) flagella*

E—Chlamydomonas: *(1) chloroplast; (2) stigma; (3) flagella; (4) vacuole*
F—*Colorless flagellate,* Oicomonas, *ingesting* Chlorella *alga*

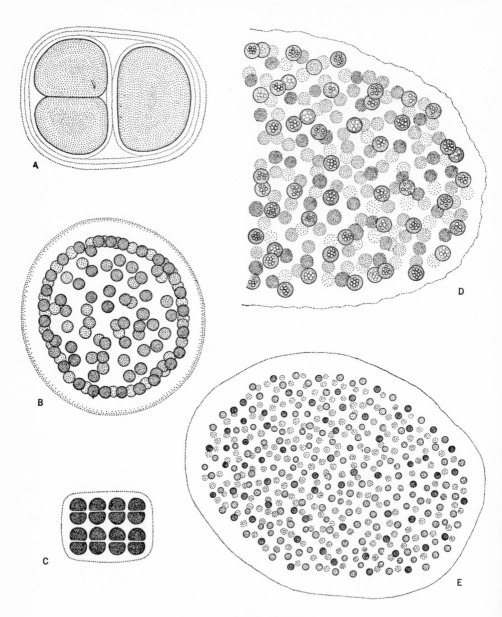

II. Common blue-green algae

A—Chroococcus turgidus   *C*—Merismopedia glauca   *E*—Microcystis incerta
B—Coelosphaerium kutzingi-   *D*—Microcystis aeruginosa
anum

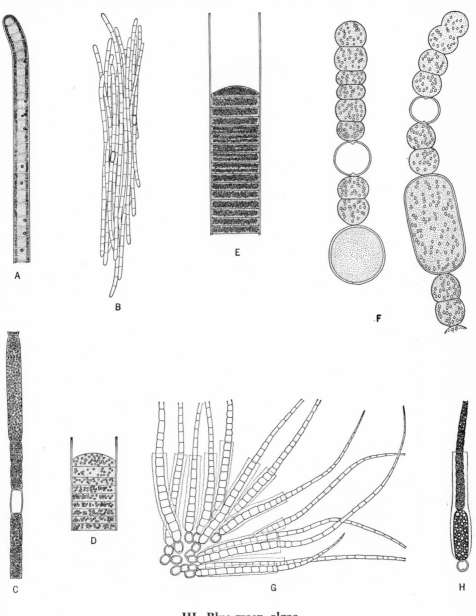

III. Blue-green algae

A—Oscillatoria coprophila
B—Aphanizomenon flos-aquae, *aggregates or filaments*

C—Aphanizomenon flos-aquae, *detail*
D—Lyngbya birgei
E—Lyngbya sp.
F—Anabaena planctonica

G—Gleotrichia echinulata, *portion of colony*
H—Gleotrichia echinulata, *detail*

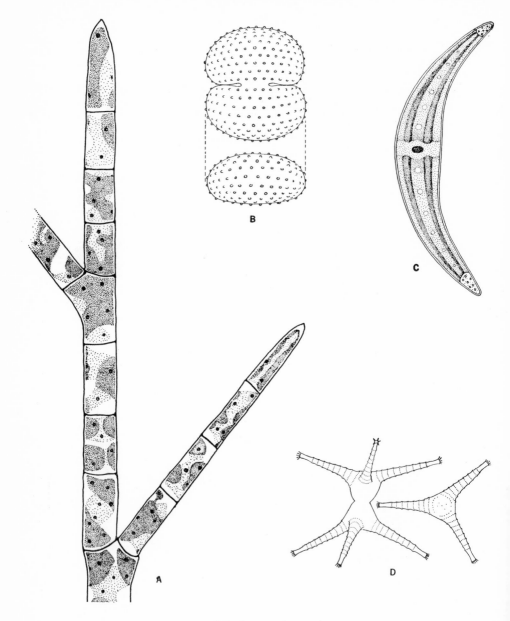

IV. Green algae

A—Cladophora, *fragment*   C—Closterium moniliferum   D—Staurastrum curvatum
B—Cosmarium reniforme   var. paradoxum

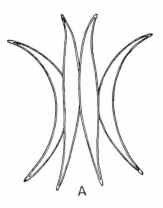

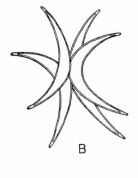

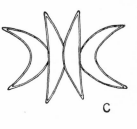

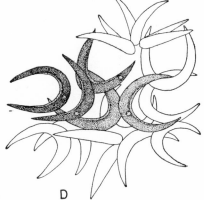

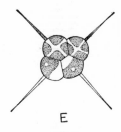

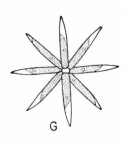

V. Green algae

A—Scenedesmus acuminatus
B—Scenedesmus acuminatus
C—Scenedesmus dimorphus

D—Selenastrum gracile
E—Tetrastrum elegans

F—Crucigenia tetrapedia
G—Actinastrum gracilimum
H—Ankistrodesmus falcatus

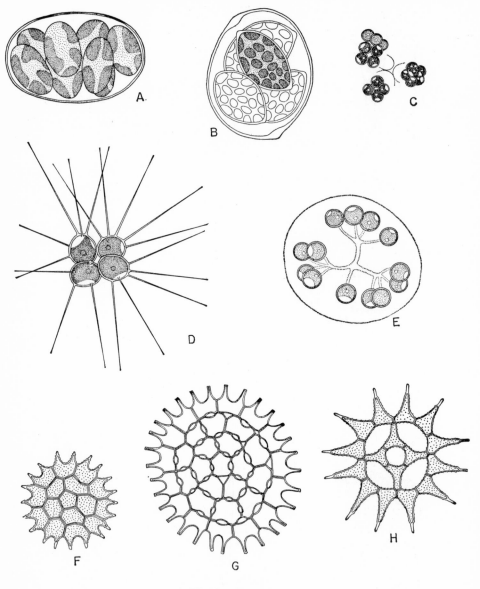

VI. Green algae

A—Oocystis Borgei
B—Oocystis Eremosphaeria
C—Westella botryoides

D—Micractinium pusillum
E—Dictyosphaerium pulchel-
lum

F—Pediastrum Boryanum
G—Pediastrum duplex
H—Pediastrum simplex

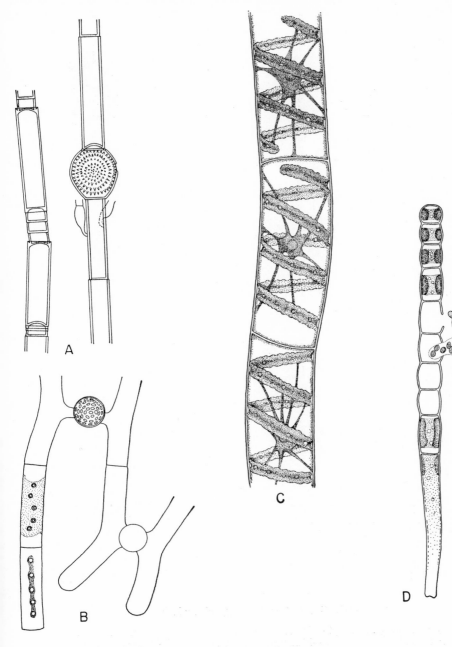

VII. Green algae

A—Oedogonium echinospermum
B—Mougeotia nummuloides

C—Spirogyra porticalis
D—Ulothrix zonata

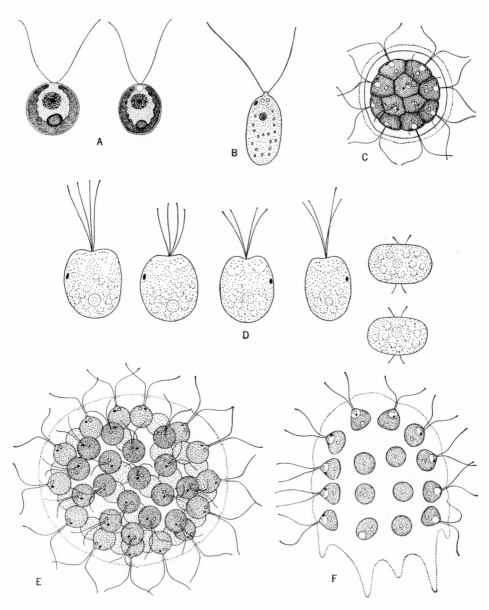

VIII. Green flagellates (Volvocales)

A—Chlamydomonas globosa C—Pandorina morum   E—Eudorina elegans
B—Polytoma uvella   D—Platymonas elliptica F—Platydorina caudata

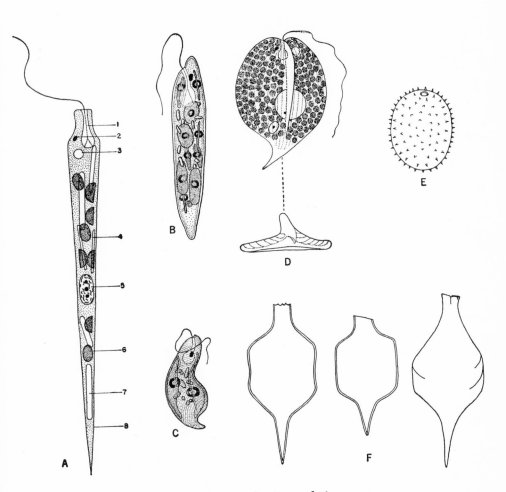

IX. *Euglena* and green relatives

A—Euglena acus: *(1) gul-let-reservoir; (2) stigma; (3) contractile vacuole; (4) paramylum plate; (5) nucleus; (6) chloroplast;*
(7) paramylum plate; (8) cell membrane
B—Euglena gracilis
C—Euglena pisciformis
D—Phacus pleuronectes
E—Trachelomonas hispida, *shell*
F—Strombomonas girardi-ana, *shells*

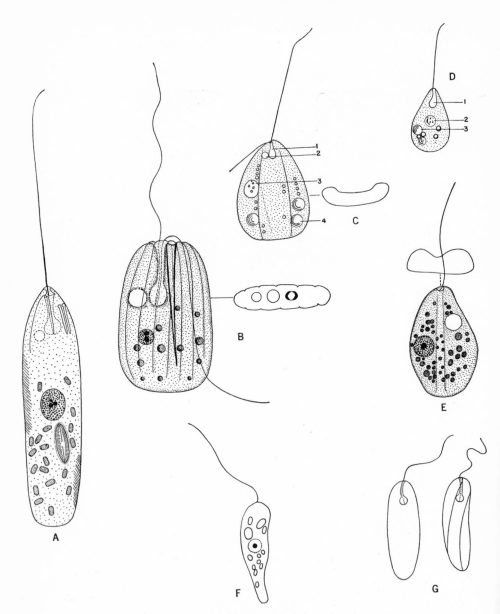

X. Colorless euglenids

A—Peranema trichophorum
B—Entosiphon ovata
C—Notosolenus apocamptus:
*(1) gullet-reservoir; (2)
contractile vacuole; (3)
nucleus; (4) paramylum*

D—Scytomonas pusilla: *(1)
gullet-reservoir; (2) nu-
cleus; (3) paramylum*
E—Petalomonas mediocanel-
lata

F—Astasia clava
G—Rhabdomonas incurva

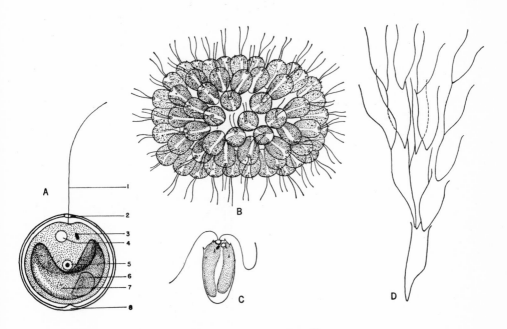

XI. Brown or yellow flagellates

A—Chrysococcus rufescens: *(1) flagellum; (2) pore-shell; (3) stigma; (4) contractile vacuole; (5) nu-* *cleus; (6) volutin granule; (7) chromatophore; (8) thickening in shell*
B—Synura uvella, *colony*

C—Synura uvella, *cell*
D—Dinobryon sertularia, *empty shells, arboroid colony*

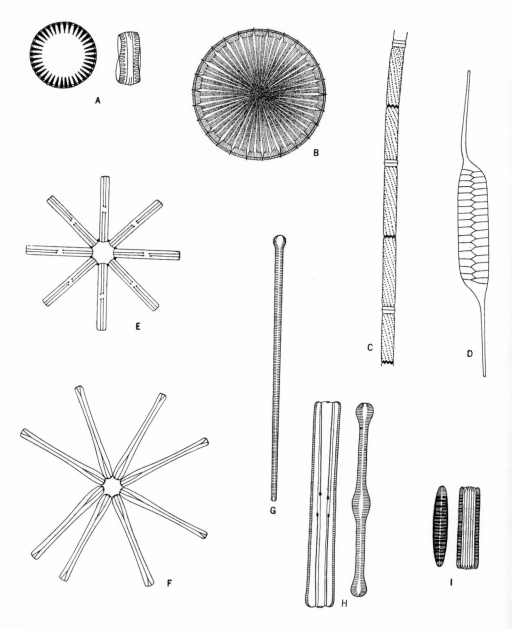

XII. Diatoms

A—Cyclotella meneghiana
B—Stephanodiscus niagarae
C—Melosira granulata var. angustissima

D—Rhizosolenia eriensis
E—Tabellaria fenestrata var. asterionelloides
F—Asterionella formosa, *colony*

G—Asterionella formosa, *cell*
H—Tabellaria fenestrata
I—Diatoma hiemale

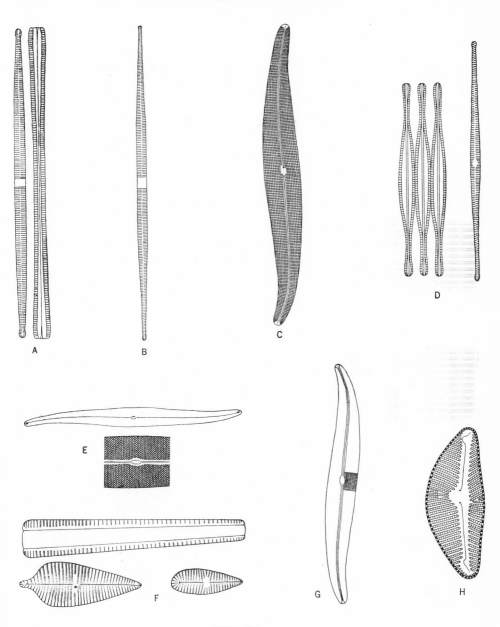

XIII. Diatoms

A—Synedra ulna
B—Synedra acus
C—Gyrosigma acuminatum

D—Fragilaria crotonensis
E—Pleurosigma delicatulum
F—Gomphonema olivaceum

G—Gyrosigma kutzingii
H—Cymbella prostrata

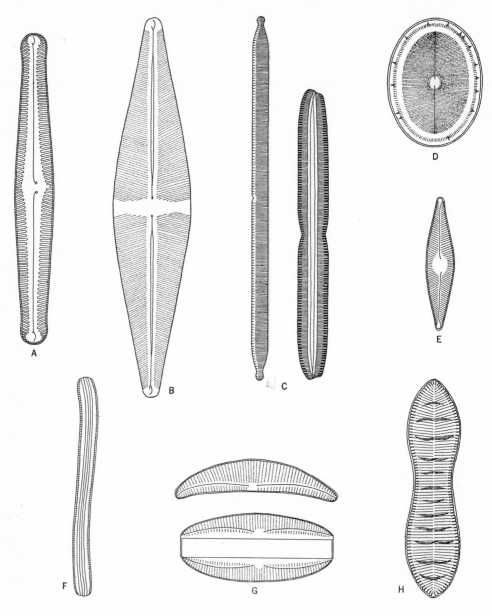

XIV. Diatoms

A—Pinnularia gibba   C—Nitzschia linearis   F—Nitzschia sigmoidea
B—Stauroneis phoenicen-   D—Cocconeis placentula   G—Amphora ovalis
   teron   E—Navicula rhynchocephala   H—Cymatopleura solea

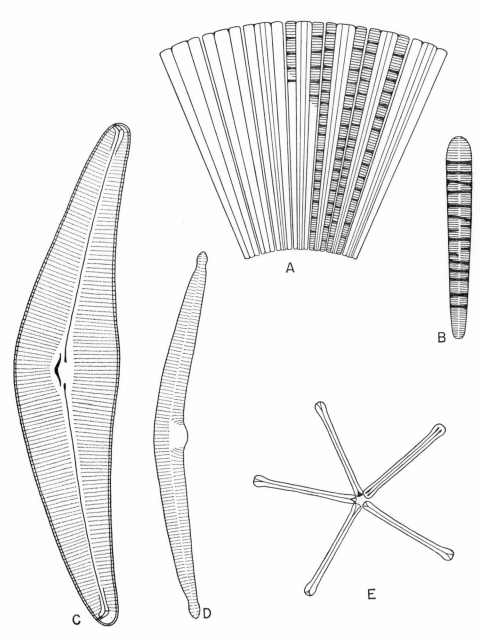

XV. Diatoms

A—Meridion circulare, *valve view*
B—Meridion circulare, *girdle view*
C—Cymbella lanceolata

D—Ceratoneis arcus
E—Asterionella gracillima

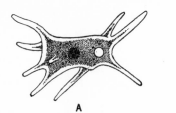

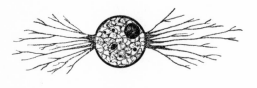

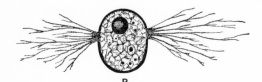

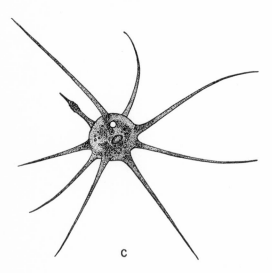

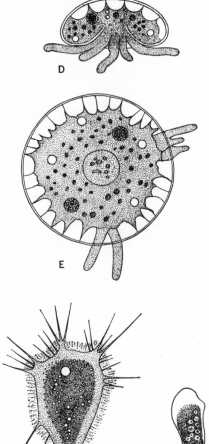

XVI. Amoebas

A—Amoeba vespertilio	*D*—Arcella vulgaris	*F*—Nuclearia delicatula
B—Diplophrys archeri	*E*—Arcella discoides	*G*—Vahlkampfia limax
C—Amoeba radiosa		

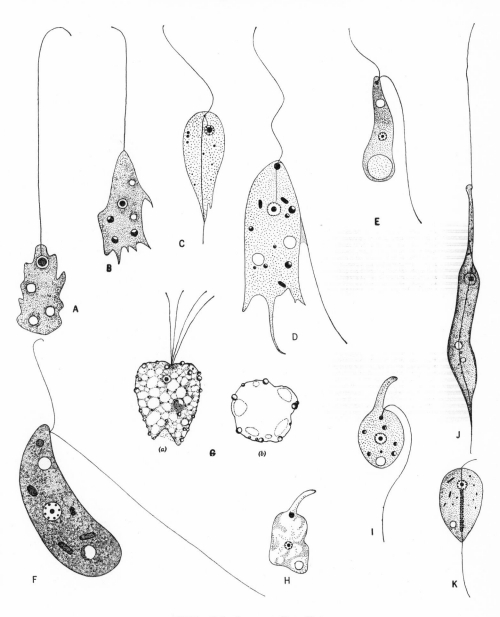

XVII. Colorless zooflagellates

A—Mastigamoeba reptans
B—Mastigella simplex
C—Cercomastix parva
D—Cercobodo agilis
E—Spiromonas angusta

F—Bodo caudatus
G—Collodictyon triciliatum:
   *(a) habit sketch; (b) cross
   section*

H—Amastigomonas de-
   bruynei
I—Rhyncomonas nasuta
J—Phanerobia pelophila
K—Helkesimastix faeciola

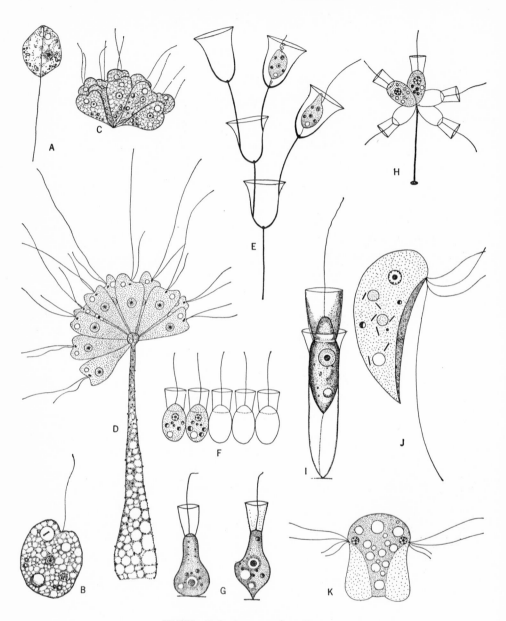

XVIII. Colorless zooflagellates

A—Clautriavia parva
B—Oicomonas termo
C—Oicomonas socialis
D—Anthophysa vegetans

E—Poteriodendron petio-
   latum
F—Desmarella moniliformis
G—Monosiga ovata

H—Codonosiga botrytis
I—Salpingoeca vaginicola
J—Tetramitus pyriformis
K—Trepomonas rotans

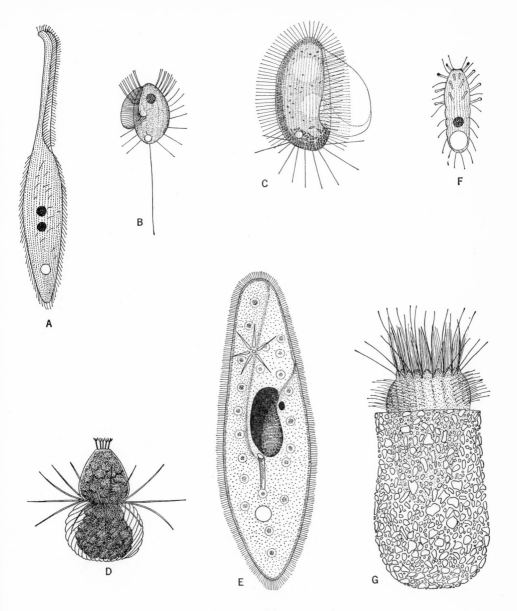

XIX. Ciliates

A—Lionotus sp.
B—Cyclidium glaucoma
C—Pleuronema marinum

D—Mesodinium rubra
E—Paramecium caudatum

F—Enchelyomorpha vermi-
    cularis
G—Codonella cratera

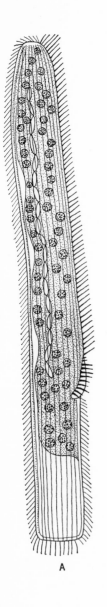
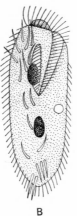
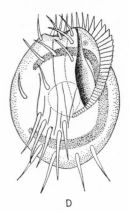

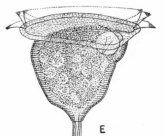
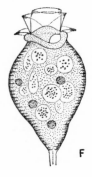

XX. Ciliates

A—Spirostomum ambiguum   C—Stylonichia mytilus   E—Vorticella campanula
B—Oxytrichia bifaria   D—Euplotes patella   F—Vorticella microstoma

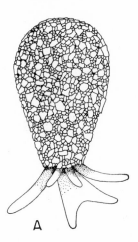

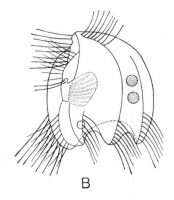

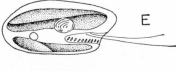

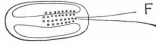

XXI. Common microorganisms

A—Difflugia sp.
B—Epalxis sp.
C—Tintinnidium sp.
D—Tintinnidium fluviatile

E—Cryptomonas erosa, *lateral view*
F—Cryptomonas erosa, *ventral view*

G—Glenodinium foliaceum
H—Gymnodinium sp.

A

B

C

D

E

F

G

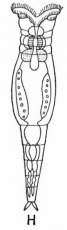
H

I

J

K

L

M

N

XXII. Rotifers

A—Trichotria tetractis
B—Scaridium longicaudum
C—Monommata grandis
D—Squatinella mutica
E—Notommata copeus

F—Epiphanes senta
G—Rotaria citrinus
H—Philodina roseola
I—Euchlanis dilata

J—Pleurotrocha petromyzon
K—Adineta vaga
L—Proales sp.
M—Taphrocampta annulosa
N—Dicranophorus forcipatus

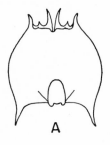

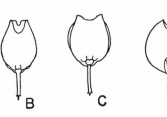

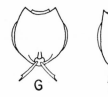

XXIII. Rotifers

A—Brachionus quadridentata
B—Monostyla bulla
C—Monostyla lunaris
D—Lepadella ovalis
E—Colurella obtusa
F—Brachionus angularis

G—Lecane luna
H—Lecane ohioensis
I—Platyias quadricornis
J—Platyias patulus
K—Kellicottia longispina
L—Keratella quadrata

M—Keratella cochlearis
N—Ploesoma lenticulare
O—Notholca acuminata
P—Ploesoma   lenticulare
   (lorica)

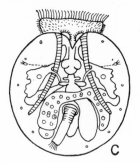

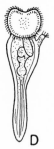

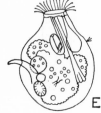

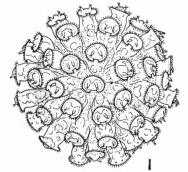

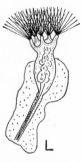

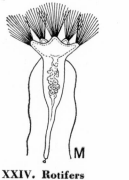

XXIV. Rotifers

A—Cephalodella auriculata
B—Mytilina mucronata
C—Testudinella patina
D—Sinantherina sp.
E—Gastropus stylifer
F—Conochiloides dossuarius

G—Trichocerca multicrinis
H—Trichocerca sp.
I—Conochilus hippocrepis, colony
J—Conochilus unicornis, colony

K—Conochilus unicornis, frontal view of corona
L—Floscularia sp.
M—Collotheca
N—Microcodon clavus

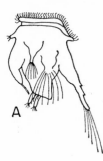
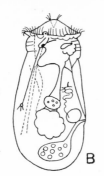
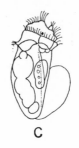
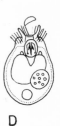

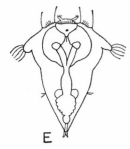

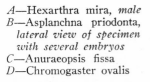

XXV. Rotifers

A—Hexarthra mira, *male*
B—Asplanchna priodonta, *lateral view of specimen with several embryos*
C—Anuraeopsis fissa
D—Chromogaster ovalis

E—Synchaeta pectinata
F—Synchaeta tremula
G—Pompholyx sulcata, *dorsal view of specimen carrying two eggs*

H—Ascomorpha ecaudis
I—Filinia longiseta
J—Polyarthra vulgaris
K—Polyarthra euryptera

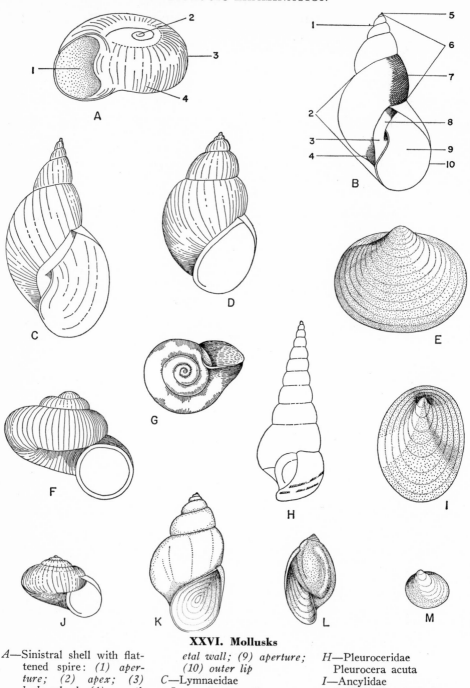

XXVI. Mollusks

A—Sinistral shell with flattened spire: *(1) aper-
   ture; (2) apex; (3)
   body whorl; (4) growth
   lines*
B—Dextral shell with elon-
   gated spire: *(1) suture;
   (2) body whorl; (3)
   inner lip; (4) umbilical
   chink; (5) apex; (6)
   spire; (7) spiral and
   growth lines; (8) pari-*
*etal wall; (9) aperture;
   (10) outer lip*
C—Lymnaeidae
   Lymnaea stagnalis
D—Viviparidae
   Campeloma decisum
E—Sphaeriidae
   Sphaerium corneum
F—Valvatidae
   Valvata sincera
G—Planorbidae
   Helisoma campanulatum
H—Pleuroceridae
   Pleurocera acuta
I—Ancylidae
   Ancylastrum fluviatile
J—Amnicolidae
   Cochliopa riograndensis
K—Amnicolidae
   Bithinia tentaculata
L—Physidae
   Physa fontinalis
M—Sphaeriidae
   Pisidium sp.

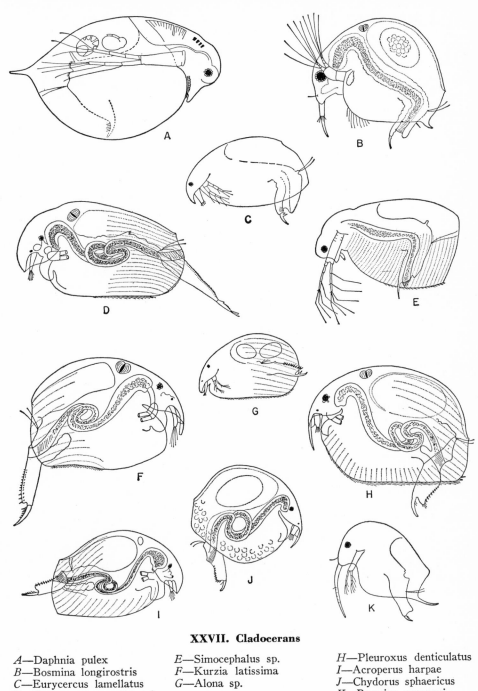

XXVII. Cladocerans

A—Daphnia pulex
B—Bosmina longirostris
C—Eurycercus lamellatus
D—Camptocercus rectirostris

E—Simocephalus sp.
F—Kurzia latissima
G—Alona sp.

H—Pleuroxus denticulatus
I—Acroperus harpae
J—Chydorus sphaericus
K—Bosmina coregoni

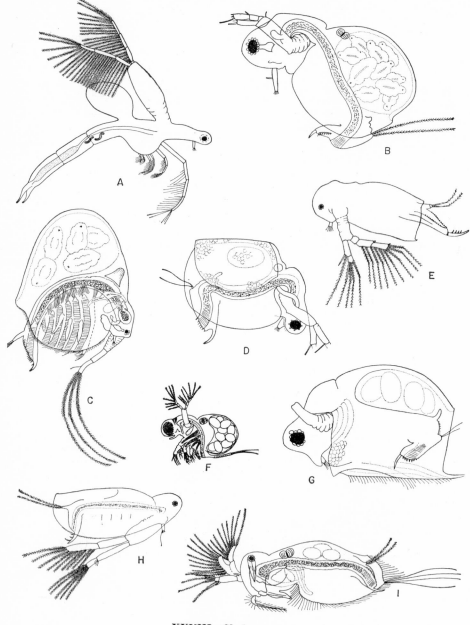

XXVIII. Cladocerans

A—Leptodora kindtii
B—Moina brachiata
C—Holopedium gibberum
D—Ceriodaphnia reticulata

E—Sida crystallina
F—Polyphemus pediculus
G—Scapholeberis sp.

H—Diaphanosoma brachyurum
I—Latona setifera

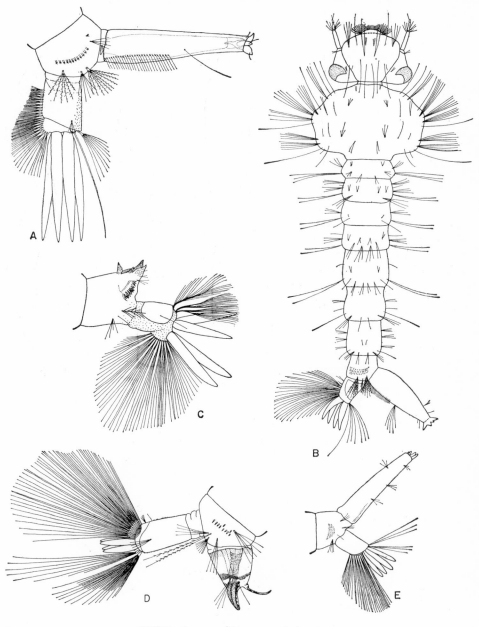

XXIX. Aquatic Diptera (Culicidae)

A—Psorophora ciliata   *C*—Anopheles sp.   *D*—Mansonia perturbans
B—Aedes stimulans   *E*—Culex sp.

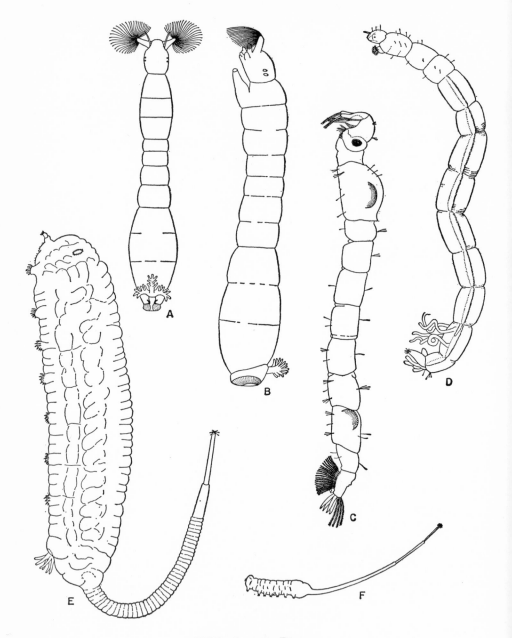

XXX. Aquatic Diptera

A—Simuliidae
 Simulium venustum, *dorsal*
 view, 3–8 mm
B—S. venustum, *lateral view*

C—Culicidae
 Chaoborus sp., *9–10 mm*
D—Chironomidae
 Chironomus sp., *2–25 mm*

E—Syrphidae
 Eristalis sp., *18 mm*
F—Eristalis sp.

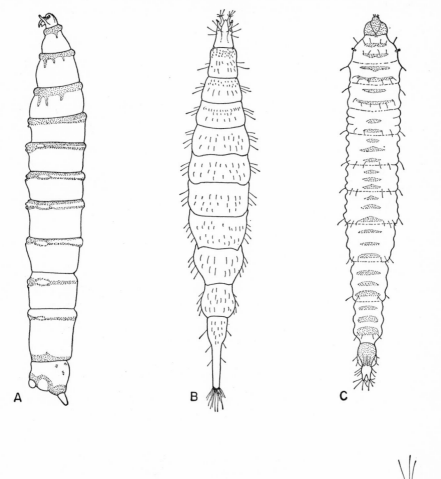

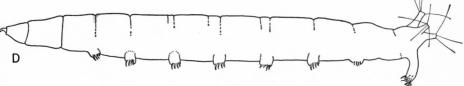

XXXI. Aquatic Diptera

A—Tabanidae
 Tabanus sp., *35 mm*
B—Stratiomyidae
 Stratiomyia sp., *40 mm*

C—Psychodidae
 Psychoda sp., *5 mm*
D—Rhagionidae, *8 mm*

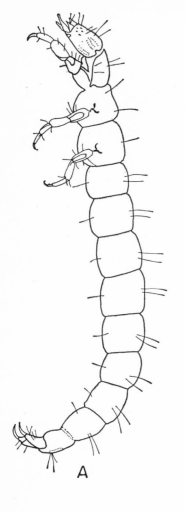

A

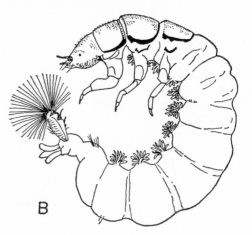

B

C

D

XXXII. Tricoptera (caddisflies)

A—Rhyacophilidae
    Rhyacophila sp.
B—Hydropsychidae
    Hydropsyche simulans

C—Leptoceridae,
    case of Oecetis cinerascens
D—Leptoceridae
    Triaenodes tarda

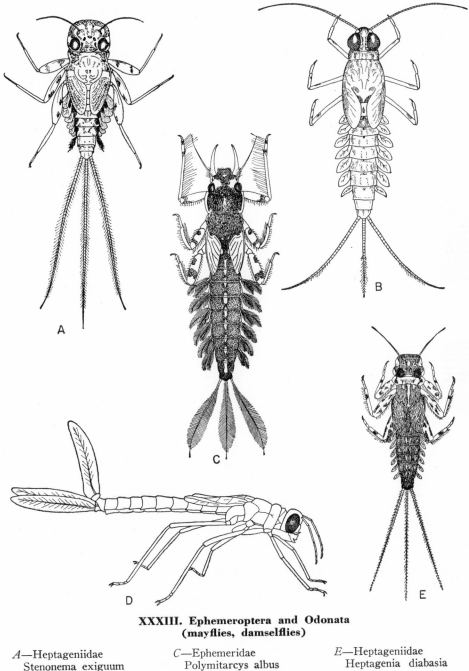

**XXXIII. Ephemeroptera and Odonata
(mayflies, damselflies)**

A—Heptageniidae
  Stenonema exiguum
B—Baetidae
  Baetis spiethi

C—Ephemeridae
  Polymitarcys albus
D—Coenagrionidae
  Lestes stultus

E—Heptageniidae
  Heptagenia diabasia

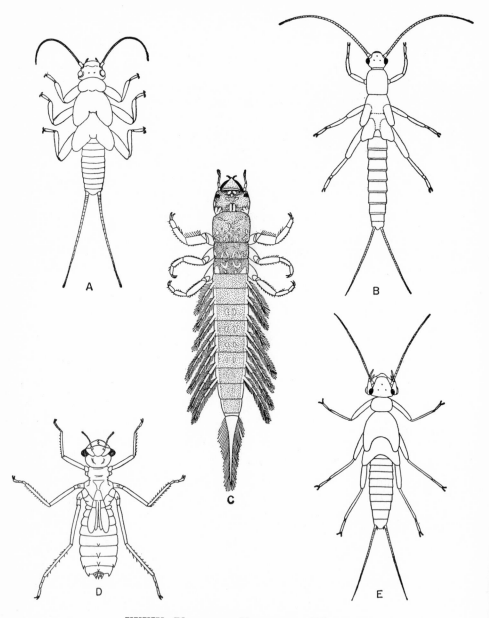

XXXIV. Plecoptera, Neuroptera, Odonata
(stoneflies, alderflies, dragonflies)

A—Perlidae
  Perlesta placida
B—Nemouridae
  Allocapnia vivipara

C—Sialidae
  Sialis luteria
D—Libellulidae
  Helocordulia uhleri

E—Perlodidae
  Isogenus modesta

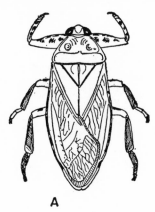

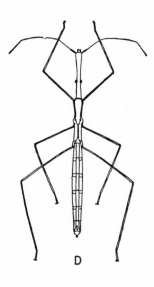

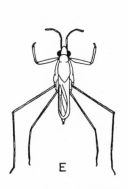

XXXV. Aquatic Hemiptera and Coleoptera

A—Belostomatidae
   Lethocerus americanus
B—Notonectidae
   Notonecta unifasciata

C—Corixidae
   Sigara mckinstryi
D—Hydrometridae
   Hydrometra martini

E—Gerridae
   Gerris marginatus
F—Dytiscidae
   Dytiscus sp., *larva*

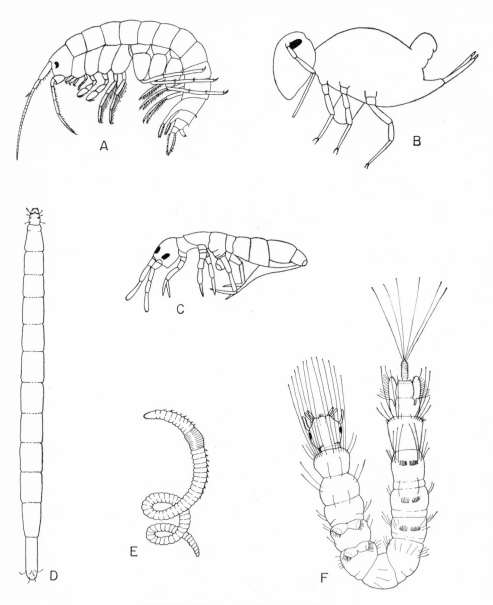

XXXVI. Other aquatic invertebrates

A—Gammaridae
  Gammarus sp., *to 25 mm*
B—Sminthuridae
  Bourletiella sp., *0.5–2.2 mm*
C—Entomobryidae
  Orchesella sp., *1–2 mm*

D—Ceratopogonidae
  Culicoides sp., *3–4 mm*
E—Tubificidae
  Tubifex tubifex, *30–100 mm*
F—Dixidae
  Dixa sp., *4–8 mm*

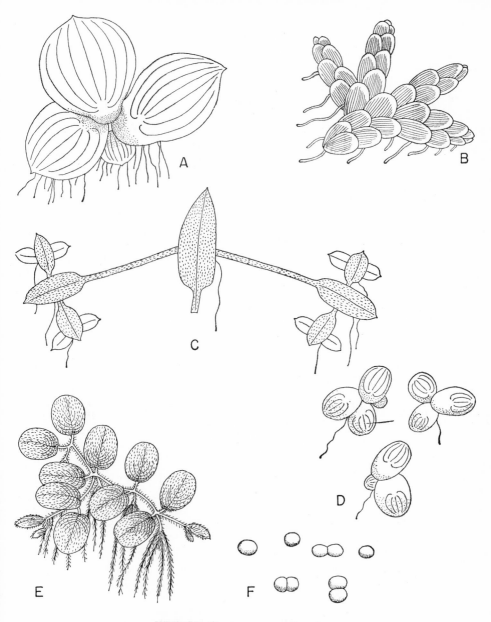

XXXVII. Common aquatic plants

A—Spirodella polyrhiza (Great Duckweed)
B—Azolla caroliniana (Water-velvet)
C—Lemna trisulca (Star Duckweed)

D—Lemna minor (**Lesser Duckweed**)
E—Salvinia rotundifolia (Water-fern)
F—Wolffia columbiana (Watermeal)

XXXVIII. Common aquatic plants

A—Utricularia sp. (Bladderwort)
B—Utricularia, *detail of bladders*
C—Ceratophyllum demersum (Coontail, Hornwort)

D—Ceratophyllum demersum, *detail of leaf*
E—Myriophyllum heterophyllum (Water Milfoil)

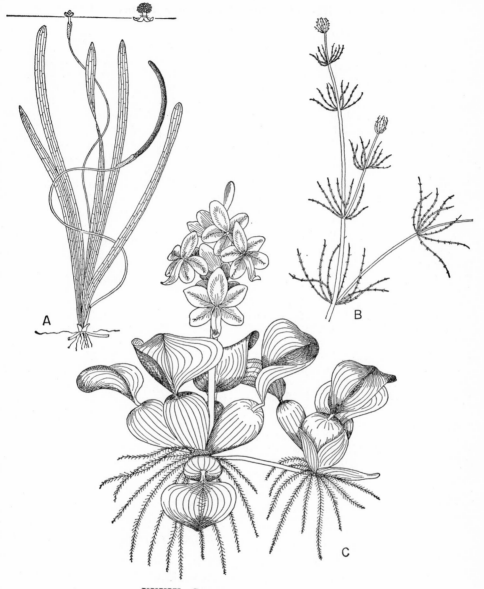

XXXIX. Common aquatic plants

A—Vallisneria americana (Eelgrass, Wild Celery)
B—Chara vulgaris (Stonewort, Muskgrass)
C—Eichornia crassipes (Water Hyacinth)

Index to Algae Illustrated on Color Plates A–F

Recent Changes in Names of Algae

Old Name	New Name	Old Name	New Name
Aphanocapsa	Anacystis	Gloeocapsa	Anacystis
Aphanothece	Coccochloris	Gloeothece	Coccochloris
Chamaesiphon	Entophysalis	Merismopedia	Agmenellum
Chantransia	Audouinella	Microcystis	Anacystis
Chlamydobotrys	Pyrobotrys	Odontidium	Diatoma
Chroococcus	Anacystis	Polycystis	Anacystis
Clathroycystis	Anacystis	Protococcus	Phytoconis
Coelosphaerium	Gomphosphaeria	Sphaerella	Haematococcus
Encyonema	Cymbella	Synechococcus	Coccochloris

Key for Identification of Algae
Illustrated on Color Plates A–F

(By C. Mervin Palmer)

Beginning with "1a" and "1b", choose one of the two contrasting statements and follow this procedure with the "a" and "b" statements of the number given at the end of the chosen statement. Continue until the name of the alga is given instead of another key number. (Where recent changes in names of algae have been made, the new name is given followed by the old name in parentheses.)

1a. Plastid (separate color body) absent; complete protoplast pigmented; generally blue-green; iodine starch test * negative .... (blue-green algae)   4

1b. Plastid or plastids present; parts of protoplast free of some or all pigments; generally green, brown, red, etc., but not blue-green; iodine starch test * positive or negative   2

2a. Cell wall permanently rigid (never showing evidence of collapse), and with regular pattern of fine markings (striations, etc.) ; plastids brown to green; iodine starch test * negative; flagella absent; wall of two essentially similar halves, one placed over the other as a cover .... (diatoms)   24

2b. Cell wall, if present, capable of sagging, wrinkling, bulging, or rigidity, depending on existing turgor pressure of cell protoplast; regular pattern of fine markings on wall generally absent; plastids green, red, brown, etc.; iodine starch test * positive or negative; flagella present or absent; cell wall continuous and generally not of two parts   3

3a. Cell or colony motile; flagella present (often not readily visible) ; anterior and posterior ends of cell different from one another in shape and contents (flagellate algae)   42

3b. Non-motile; true flagella absent; ends of cells often not differentiated ....
.... (green algae and associated forms)   63

Blue-Green Algae

4a. Cells in filaments (or much elongated to form a thread)   5

4b. Cells not in (or as) filaments   18

5a. Heterocysts present   6

5b. Heterocysts absent   12

6a. Heterocyst located at one end of filament   7

6b. Heterocysts at various locations in filment   9

7a. Filaments radially arranged in a gelatinous bead .... *Rivularia*

7b. Filaments isolated or irregularly grouped   8

8a. Filament gradually narrowed to one end .... *Calothrix*

8b. Filament not gradually narrowed to one end .... *Cylindrospermum*

9a. Filament with occasional (false) branches .... *Tolypothrix*

9b. Filament unbranched   10

---

* Add one drop Lugol's (iodine) solution, diluted 1-1 with distilled water. In about 1 min, if positive, starch is stained blue and, later, black. Other structures (such as nucleus, plastids, cell wall) may also stain, but turn brown to yellow.

10a. Cross-walls in filament much closer together than width of filament ......*Nodularia*

10b. Cross-walls in filament at least as far apart as width of filament   11

11a. Filaments normally in tight parallel clusters; heterocysts and spores cylindric to long oval ....*Aphanizomenon*

11b. Filaments not in tight parallel clusters; heterocysts and spores often round to oval ....*Anabaena*

12a. Filament or elongated cell attached at one end and with one or more round cells (spores) at the other end ....*Entophysalis (Chamaesiphon)*

12b. Filament generally not attached at one end; no terminal spores present   13

13a. Filament with regular spiral form throughout ....*Arthrospira*

13b. Filament not spiral or with spiral form limited to a portion of filament   14

14a. Cells more spherical than cylindric in form ....*Anabaena*

14b. Cells more cylindric than spherical in form   15

15a. Filaments loosely aggregated or not in clusters   16

15b. Filaments tightly aggregated and surrounded by a common gelatinous secretion that may be invisible   17

16a. Filament surrounded by wall-like sheath that frequently extends beyond the ends of the filament of cells; filament generally without movement ....*Lyngbya*

16b. Filament not surrounded by a wall-like sheath; filament commonly shows movement ....*Oscillatoria*

17a. Filaments arranged in a tight, essentially parallel bundle ....*Microcoleus*

17b. Filaments arranged in irregular fashion, often forming a mat ....*Phormidium*

18a. Cells in a regular pattern of parallel rows, forming a plate ....
....*Agmenellum (Merismopedia)*

18b. Cells not regularly arranged to form a plate   19

19a. Cells regularly arranged near surface of a spherical gelatinous bead   20

19b. Gelatinous bead, if present, not spherical   21

20a. Cells ovate to heart-shaped; connected to center of bead by colorless stalks ....
....*Gomphosphaeria*

20b. Cells round; without gelatinous stalks ....*Gomphosphaeria (Coelosphaerium type)*

21a. Cells cylindric-oval ....*Coccochloris (Aphanothece)*

21b. Cells spherical   22

22a. Two or more distinct layers of gelatinous sheath around each cell or cell cluster
....*Anacystis (Gloeocapsa)*

22b. Gelatinous sheath around cells not distinctly layered   23

23a. Cells isolated or in colonies of 2 to 32 cells ....*Anacystis (Chroococcus)*

23b. Cells in colonies composed of many cells ......*Anacystis (Microcystis, Polycystis)*

Diatoms

24a. Front (valve) view circular in outline; markings radial in arrangement ......
....(centric diatoms)   26

24b. Front (valve) view elongate, not circular; transverse markings in one or two longitudinal rows ....(pennate diatoms)   4

25a. Cells in persistent filaments with valve faces in contact; therefore, cells commonly seen in side (girdle) view ....*Melosira*

25b. Cells isolated or in fragile filaments, often seen in front (valve) view   27

Flagellate Algae

Green Algae and Associated Forms

63a. Cells joined together to form a net ....*Hydrodictyon*

63b. Cells not forming a net 64

64a. Cells attached side by side to form a ribbon one cell wide and thick; number of cells commonly 2, 4, or 8 ....*Scenedesmus*

64b. Cells not attached side by side 65

65a. Cells isolated or in nonfilamentous or thread-like thalli 66

65b. Cells in filaments or other tubular or thread-like thalli 83

66a. Cells isolated and narrowest at the center due to incomplete fissure ...... (desmids) 67

66b. Cells isolated or in clusters but without central fissure 69

67a. Each half of cell with three spinelike or pointed, knobular extensions .....*Staurastrum*

67b. Cell margin with no such extensions 68

68a. Margin with rounded lobes ....*Euastrum*

68b. Margin with sharp-pointed teeth ....*Micrasterias*

69a. Cells elongate 70

69b. Cells round to oval or angular 72

70a. Cells radiating from a central point ....*Actinastrum*

70b. Cells isolated or in irregular clusters 71

71a. All cells arcuate; with two plastids ....*Closterium*

71b. Cells straight or variously bent or twisted; with one plastid ....*Ankistrodesmus*

72a. Cells regularly arranged in a tight, flat, colony ....*Pediastrum*

72b. Cells not in a tight, flat, regular colony 73

73a. Cells angular ....*Tetraedron*

73b. Cells round to oval 74

74a. Cells with long, sharp spines ....*Micractinium*

74b. Long, sharp spines absent 75

75a. Colony of definite, regular form, round to oval 76

75b. Colony, if present, not a definite oval or sphere; or cells may be isolated 78

76a. Colony a tight sphere of cells ....*Coelastrum*

76b. Colony a loose sphere of cells enclosed by a common membrane 77

77a. Cells round ....*Spaerocystis*

77b. Cells oval ....*Oocytis*

78a. Oval cells, enclosed in a somewhat spherical, often organe-colored matrix ....*Botryococcus*

78b. Cells round, isolated or in collorless matrix 79

79a. Adjoining cells with straight, flat walls between their protoplosts 80

79b. Adjoining cells with rounded walls between their protoplasts 81

80a. Cells embedded in a common gelatinous matrix ....*Palmella*

80b. No matrix or sheath outside of cell walls ....*Phytoconis* (*Protococcus*)

81a. Cells loosely arranged in a large gelatinous matrix ....*Tetraspora*

81b. Cells isolated or tightly grouped in a small colony 82

82a. Plastid filling two-thirds or less of cell ....*Chlorella*

82b. Plastid filling three-fourths or more of cell ....*Chlorococcum*

83a. Cells attached end to end in an unbranched filament 84

83b. Thallus branched, or more than one cell wide 91

84a. Plastids in form of one or more marginal, spiral ribbons ....*Spirogyra*
84b. Plastids not in form of spiral ribbons 85

85a. Filaments when breaking, separating through middle of cells 86
85b. Filaments, when breaking, separating irregularly or at ends of cells 87

86a. Starch test positive; cell margin straight; one plastid, granular ....*Microspora*
86b. Starch test negative; cell margin slightly bulging; several plastids ....*Tribonema*

87a. Marginal indentations between cells ....*Desmidium*
87b. No marginal indentations between cells 88

88a. Plastids, two per cell ....*Zygnema*
88b. Plastid, one per cell (sometimes appearing numerous) 89

89a. Some cells with walls having transverse wrinkles near one end; plastid an irregular net ....*Oedogonium*
89b. No apical wrinkles in wall; plastid not porous 90

90a. Plastid a flat or twisted axial ribbon ....*Mougeotia*
90b. Plastid an arcuate marginal band ....*Ulothrix*

91a. Thallus a flat plate of cells ....*Hildenbrandia*
91b. Thallus otherwise 92

92a. Thallus a long tube without cross-walls ....*Vaucheria*
92b. Thallus otherwise 93

93a. Thallus a leathery strand with regularly spaced swellings and a continuous surface membrane of cells ....*Lemanea*
93b. Thallus otherwise 94

94a. Branches in whorls (clusters) 95
94b. Branches single or in pairs 97

95a. Thallus embedded in gelatinous matrix ....*Batrachospermum*
95b. Thallus not embedded in gelatinous batrix 96

96a. Main filament one cell thick ....*Nitella*
96b. Main filament three cells thick ....*Chara*

97a. Most of filament surrounded by a layer of cells ....*Compsopogon*
97b. Filament not surrounded by a layer of cells 98

98a. End cell of branches with a rounded or blunt-pointed tip 99
98b. End cell of branches with a sharp-pointed tip 100

99a. Plastid green; starch test positive ....*Cladophora*
99b. Plastids red; starch test negative ....*Audouinella*

100a. Filaments embedded in gelatinous matrix 101
100b. Filaments not embedded in gelatinous matrix 102

101a. Cells of main filament much wider than even the basal cells of branches ....*Draparnaldia*
101b. No abrupt change in width of cells from main filament to branches ....*Chetophora*

102a. Branches very short, with no cross-walls ....*Rhizoclonium*
102b. Branches long, with cross-walls 103

103a. Branches ending in an abrupt spine having a bulbous base ....*Bulbochaete*
103b. Branches gradually reduced in width, ending in a long pointed cell, with or without color ....*Stigeoclonium*

ALGAE IDENTIFICATION

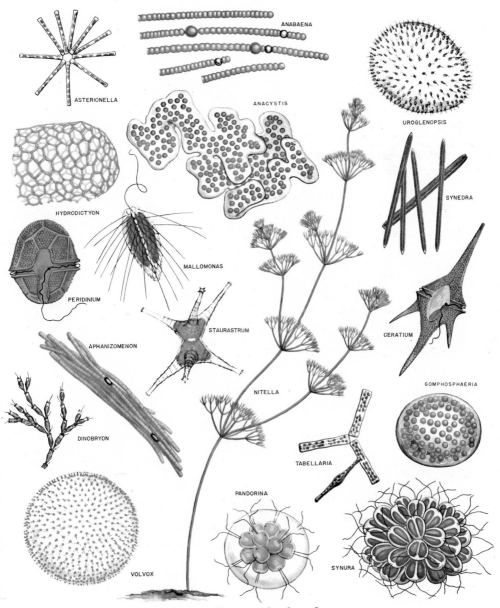

Plate A. Taste and odor algae

IX. BIOLOGIC EXAMINATION

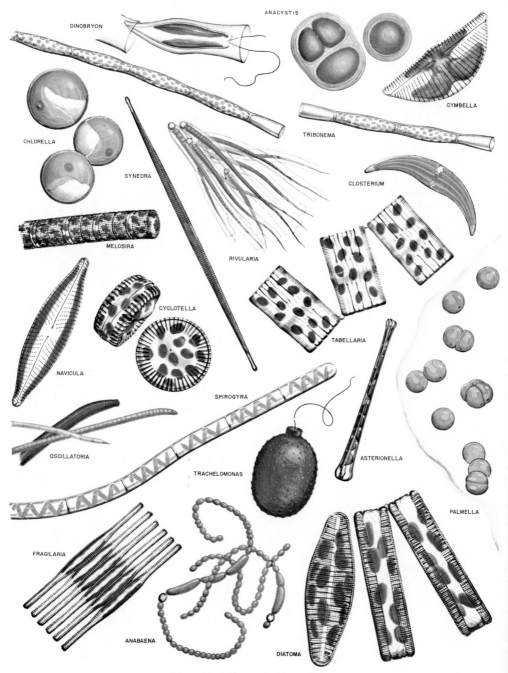

DINOBRYON

ANACYSTIS

CYMBELLA

CHLORELLA

TRIBONEMA

SYNEDRA

CLOSTERIUM

MELOSIRA

RIVULARIA

CYCLOTELLA

TABELLARIA

NAVICULA

SPIROGYRA

OSCILLATORIA

ASTERIONELLA

TRACHELOMONAS

PALMELLA

FRAGILARIA

ANABAENA

DIATOMA

Plate B. Filter clogging algae

ALGAE IDENTIFICATION

PHORMIDIUM

AGMENELLUM

CARTERIA

LEPOCINCLIS

PYROBOTRYS

NITZSCHIA

ANABAENA

EUGLENA

TETRAEDRON

SPIROGYRA

OSCILLATORIA

CHLOROCOCCUM

PHACUS

CHLOROGONIUM

CHLORELLA

GOMPHONEMA

STIGEOCLONIUM

ANACYSTIS

ARTHROSPIRA

CHLAMYDOMONAS

LYNGBYA

Plate C. Polluted water algae

IX. BIOLOGIC EXAMINATION

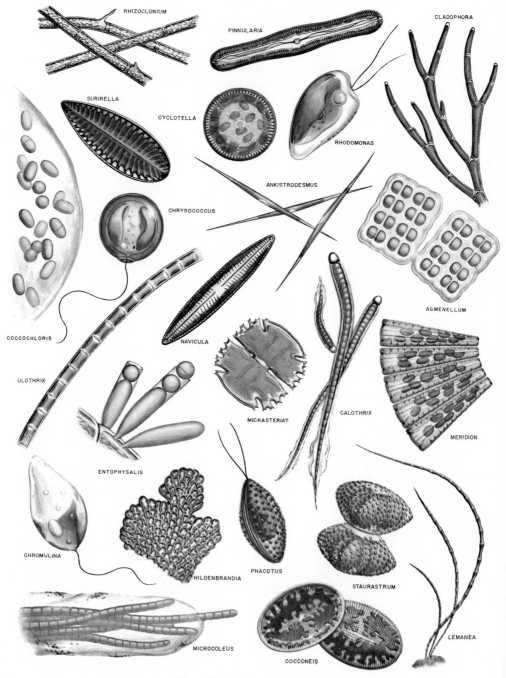

Plate D. Clean water algae

ALGAE IDENTIFICATION

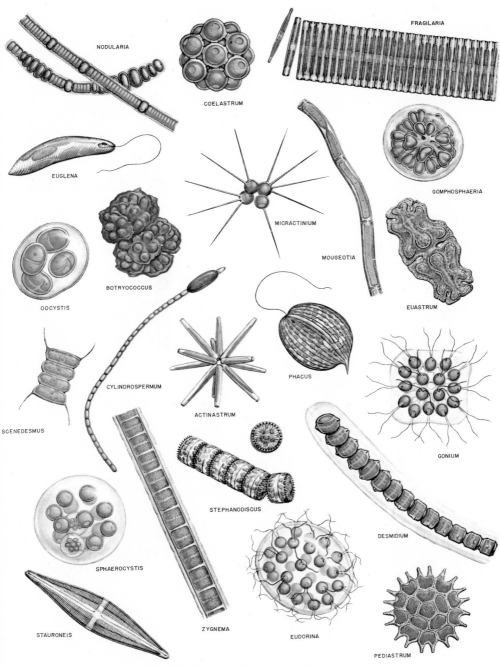

Plate E. Plankton and other surface water algae

IX. BIOLOGIC EXAMINATION

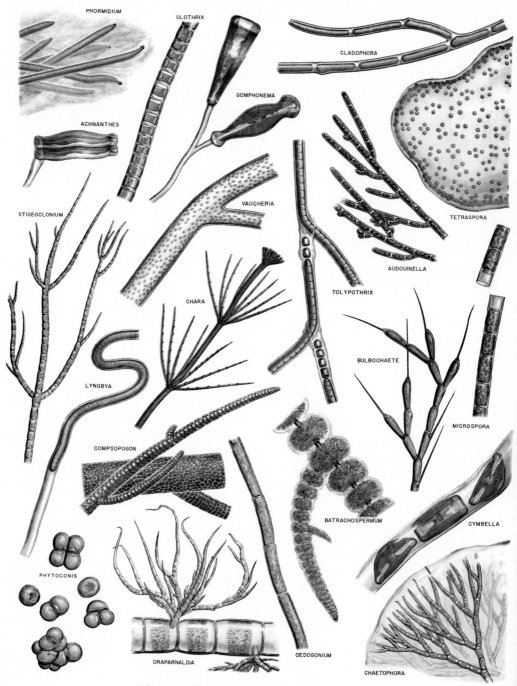

Plate F. Algae growing on reservoir walls

Index

INDEX

A

ABS (*see* Alkyl benzene sulfonate; Surfactants)

Accuracy; definition of, 20
wastewater analyses, WPCF Committee evaluation of, 366
water analyses, Analytical Reference Service, data on, 40

Acetate solution; use of, as buffer, 67, 106, 318, 344
for bromide, 67
pH 4, for chlorine, 106, 377
for radioactive strontium, 344
for zinc, 318

Acetic acid solution;
1+4, for cyanide, 455
1+7, for zinc, 318

Acid; uniform concentrations, 7

Acid solutions; preparation of, common, 8
hydrochloric, 8
nitric, 8
sulfuric, 8

Acid zirconyl-alizarin solution; for fluoride, 141

Acid zirconyl-SPADNS solution; for fluoride, 144

ACIDITY; definition, 46, 367
indicator method for, 367
methods for, in industrial wastewaters, 438
in sludges and muds, 529
in water, 46
in wastewater, 367
potentiometric titration method for, 368

Activated carbon; for organic contaminants, 216

ACTIVATED SLUDGE; tests on, 540
settleability, 541
sludge density index, 542
sludge volume index, 541
suspended matter, 540

ACUTE TOXICITY; bioassay methods for, 545

Agar; for culture media, 581
brain-heart infusion, preparation of, 587
eosine methylene blue, preparation of, 584
plate count, preparation of, 583
Simmon's citrate, preparation of, 587
tryptone glucose extract, preparation of, 583
tryptone glucose yeast, preparation of, 583

Alcoholic sulfuric acid solution; for orthophosphate, 235

ALGAE; index to color illustration of, 732
illustrations of, blue-green, 694, 695
clean water, 742
filter clogging, 740
green, 696, 697, 698, 699
plankton and other surface, 743
polluted water, 741
reservoir wall, 744
taste and odor causing, 739
key for identification of, 733
blue-green, 733
flagellates, 735
green, 737

Alizarin photometric method; for fluoride, 142

Alizarin red solution; for fluoride, 143

Alizarin visual method; for fluoride, 141

Alkali-hypochlorite modification; for dissolved oxygen, 411

Alkali-hypochlorite solution; $2N$, for dissolved oxygen, 411

Alkali-iodide-azide solution; for dissolved oxygen, 407, 414

Alkaline hypobromite method; for total chromium, 126

Alkaline potassium cyanide solution; for lead, 487

Alkaline potassium permanganate solution; for albuminoid nitrogen, 185

Alkaline pyrogallol solution; for methane, 183

ALKALINITY; definition, 48
method for, in industrial wastewaters, 438
in sludges and muds, 530
in water, 48
in wastewater, 369
nomographic determination of, 78
relationship of three forms of, 51

Alkyl benzene sulfonate solution; standard, for surfactants, 297, 299

Alum flocculation modification; for dissolved oxygen, 412

Alum solution; for dissolved oxygen, 412

Aluminon solution; for aluminum, 54

ALUMINUM; method for, 53

Aluminum chloride solution; $6N$, for sulfide, 427

Aluminum hydroxide suspension; for chloride, 86
for nitrate nitrogen, 197
for nitrite nitrogen, 207

DATE DUE

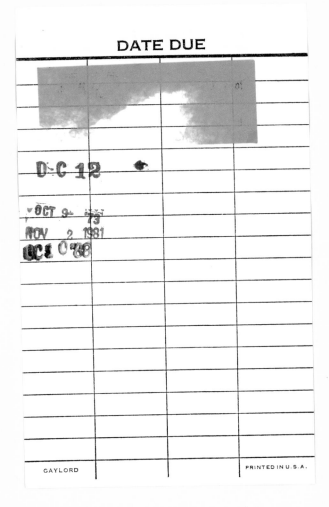